CAELIUS AURELIANUS

On Acute Diseases
and
On Chronic Diseases

CAELIUS AURELIANUS

On Acute Diseases
and
On Chronic Diseases

Edited and Translated by
I. E. DRABKIN

THE UNIVERSITY OF CHICAGO PRESS

THE UNIVERSITY OF CHICAGO PRESS, CHICAGO 37
Cambridge University Press, London, N.W. 1, England
W. J. Gage & Co., Limited, Toronto 2B, Canada

*Copyright 1950 by The University of Chicago. All rights reserved.
Published 1950. Composed and printed by* THE UNIVERSITY OF
CHICAGO PRESS, *Chicago, Illinois, U.S.A.*

8.
C

*The publication of this volume has been aided by a grant from the
Bollingen Foundation, Inc., of New York City*

To

MIRIAM

PREFACE

THE loss of Soranus' treatises on acute and chronic diseases makes Caelius Aurelianus' extant Latin translations of these works an important link in the chain of medical history. They afford us our best insight into the Methodist school of Greek medicine; they preserve—thanks to Soranus' historical interests—considerable material from the now lost works of famous physicians; and they are an important element in the transmission of Greek medicine to the Middle Ages. Apart from their importance for the medical historian, these treatises of Caelius contain much to interest the historian of the Latin language.

A new edition of Caelius' works has long been required. The first editions are not easily obtainable and can at best serve only as a point of departure for the study of the text; the subsequent editions are less rare but are also less dependable. There have been no editions in modern times, largely because the absence of manuscripts and the corrupt state of the text introduced what from one point of view was an insuperable element of uncertainty. But the discovery in 1921 and 1922 of three manuscript leaves from the treatise on *Chronic Diseases* and the more recent discovery of large fragments of Caelius' *Gynaecia*, as well as great philological advances in Greek and Roman medicine, have to a degree reduced this element of uncertainty. Particularly fruitful have been recent critical studies of the Caelian text itself. And so it seems timely to present a new edition that may facilitate further studies by historians of medicine, philosophy, and language.

I am aware that there remain in the text numerous difficulties which I have failed to solve; the notes and translation will help to call attention to these difficulties. But I hope that, by making the material more generally available to students, I shall be contributing to the ultimate solution of many of the problems involved.

I am under great obligation to the Carnegie Foundation, the John Simon Guggenheim Memorial Foundation, and the Bollingen Foundation. The present work was undertaken in 1941 while I held a Carnegie Fellowship in Greek and Roman Science at the Johns Hopkins University; the award of a Guggenheim Fellowship in 1945 enabled

me to complete it. A generous subvention from the Bollingen Foundation has now made possible its publication.

The work owes much to discussions with Professors Henry E. Sigerist, Ludwig Edelstein, and Owsei Temkin, who during my residence at Johns Hopkins were members of the staff of the university's Institute of the History of Medicine. I am also indebted to Drs. Saul Jarcho and Harry Keil, who critically read the entire translation, and to Professor Edelstein, who examined portions of both the text and the translation. These scholars have suggested improvements at many points.

I must also warmly thank the staff of the University of Chicago Press for their efficient and skilful handling of a very difficult assignment.

A major part of the task of preparing the manuscript of this work and seeing it through the press was performed by my wife, Miriam. At every stage of the work I have had the benefit of her expert knowledge and her wise counsel and criticism. In dedicating the book to her I can only attest, not adequately express, my feeling of gratitude.

I. E. DRABKIN

NEW YORK
April 1950

TABLE OF CONTENTS

INTRODUCTION

SORANUS of Ephesus, who studied medicine at Alexandria and practiced at Rome in the time of Trajan and Hadrian, is best known in modern times as the author of the extant *Gynaecia*, a treatise on obstetrics, gynecology, and pediatrics. This work in four books, two portions—on fractures and on bandages—of a surgical treatise, a brief life of Hippocrates (of questioned authenticity), and some fragments preserved in the works of others are, in fact, all the writings of Soranus that we still have in Greek. Yet Soranus was a prolific author, who wrote not only on practically every phase of medical theory and practice but also on philosophical and philological subjects. His reputation as the greatest of the Methodist physicians persisted long after his own time. Indeed, in the three or four centuries after Galen, when literary contributions in the field of medicine were no longer characterized by originality, Soranus' works, in common with Hippocratic and Galenic writings, were among those most widely excerpted and translated. The translations and abridgments produced in those times formed an important element in the transmission of Greek medicine to the Middle Ages.

The foremost of Soranus' translators was Caelius Aurelianus, who prepared Latin versions of a whole series of his works. Little is known about Caelius apart from his writings. He was of African birth and, like Soranus, was a member of the Methodist Sect. He probably lived in the fifth century, though the date cannot be objectively demonstrated and is based chiefly on considerations of style.

Of Caelius' writings, apart from two considerable fragments of a medical catechism (see V. Rose, *Anecdota Graeca et Graecolatina*, II, 163–240) and substantial portions of a translation of Soranus' *Gynaecia*, we are fortunate to possess in fairly complete form Caelius' versions of two great works of Soranus on diseases and their treatment, the *Acute Diseases* (three books) and the *Chronic Diseases* (five books). These two treatises form the subject matter of the present edition.

In these two treatises the various diseases are taken up in an order

which, roughly speaking, proceeds *a capite ad calcem*. The scope of the discussion varies widely, some diseases being dismissed in a few paragraphs, while others are treated in great detail. But a typical account of a disease includes (1) the etymology of the name of the disease, (2) the definition of the disease, (3) the symptoms, (4) the method of distinguishing other similar diseases, (5) the part affected, (6) the treatment as practiced by the Methodists, and (7) the treatment as practiced by others, with a refutation thereof. It may be mentioned in passing that this last division is responsible for no small share of the importance of our text; for a considerable part of what we know about certain Greek medical authors whose works are lost, e.g., Diocles, Praxagoras, Asclepiades, Heraclides of Tarentum, Themison, and Thessalus, is to be found in Caelius' account of their treatment of various diseases.

The history of the text of our treatises can be briefly told. Apart from a dubious reference in Cassiodorus (*Inst*. i. 31. 2), virtually the only direct mention of Caelius before the first printed editions occurs in certain library catalogues, notably two ninth-century catalogues of the monastery of Lorsch. These catalogues indicate that the library possessed Caelius' treatise on chronic diseases, in addition to three books of his *Medicinales responsiones*.

The first printed editions appeared in the sixteenth century. The treatise on chronic diseases was first edited, along with portions of a Latin version of Oribasius, by Johannes Sichart in 1529 at the press of Heinrich Petri in Basle; the treatise on acute diseases was first edited by Winter (Joannes Guinterius) von Andernach in 1533 at the press of Simon de Colines in Paris. In each case a single manuscript seems to have been used for the edition, and in each case the manuscript disappeared after the publication of the work.

In 1921 and 1922 three leaves of the manuscript used by Sichart were discovered in a library at Zwickau. It appears to be a ninth-century manuscript and may have been the very one referred to in the Lorsch catalogues mentioned above.

Comparison of these manuscript leaves with Sichart's text indicates that his edition is generally faithful and dependable. His deviations from the manuscript are confined almost exclusively to correcting obvious errors of the scribe and, what from our point of view is regrettable, substituting the standard orthography of the sixteenth century for that found in the manuscript.[1] But the text as such has

---

1. See p. xxii and the *apparatus criticus* at *Chr.* v. 77–91, 122–28.

been very little altered by the editor, and this accords with Sichart's reputation for care and conservatism as an editor.[2] Occasional marginal notes suggest alternative readings or indicate lacunae[3] or corruptions, though most of Sichart's marginalia merely call attention to proper names or special remedies or to Greek words and have no value for the text itself.

As for Winter's edition of the *Acute Diseases*, while no collation with a manuscript is possible, there is evidence both in the text itself and in a comparison with Sichart's work to support the conclusion that there was no extensive rewriting by the editor. We may take at face value Winter's statement at the beginning of his Preface that he had corrected the text of Caelius 'leviter . . . potius quam severe.' There are no marginal notes in Winter's edition; at rare intervals an asterisk is used to mark passages obviously corrupt.

There have been many subsequent editions of these works, as follows:

1. An edition of the *Chronic Diseases*, practically a reprint of Sichart's text, in the Aldine Collection, *Medici antiqui omnes* (Venice, 1547).

2. An anonymous edition of both treatises at the press of G. Rouille in Lyons (1567; reprinted 1569). This edition, though based on the first editions of Sichart and Winter, has numerous changes, some of them sound, but most of them quite unnecessary. There are also marginal notes containing, among other things, alternative readings, glosses, and comments of such unequal value that they can hardly be the work of a single hand. They range from absolutely certain corrections to the most bizarre misinterpretations. The claim made on the title-page and in the introductory letter that manuscripts were consulted in the preparation of this edition is demonstrably false.[4]

2. See Paul Lehmann, 'Johannes Sichardus,' *Quellen u. Unters. z. lat. Philol. d. Mittelalt.*, IV, 1 (Munich, 1911). Sichart (*ca.* 1499–1552) was a prolific editor, but Caelius' *Chronic Diseases* and the Latin Oribasius appearing in the same volume are the only medical treatises that he published. In editing Caelius, he tells us that he had the help of Ioannes Cornarius, the noted physician and philologist. It may have been Cornarius who brought the manuscript from Basle to Zwickau, where the fragments were found (see Ilberg [1921], p. 824).

3. There is a considerable number of lacunae in the treatise on chronic diseases. The appearance of some half-dozen of them at substantially equal intervals in the text led Schmid (*RPh*, p. 156) to suspect a mutilation in a predecessor of MS L (see also Ilberg, 'Vorläufiges,' pp. 8–9).

4. See Amman's edition, Preface, p. 7; Schmid, pp. 27–35. To put the case briefly, all the lacunae (and no others) found in the first editions are present in the Lyons edition. If the latter did use manuscripts, these manuscripts would have had to be the same as those used by the first editions, or else would have had to belong to the same family. But when we turn to the part of the text covered by L (the manuscript used by Sichart), we find that the Lyons edition

3. An edition of both treatises by Johannes Conrad Amman (Amsterdam, 1709; reprinted with minor changes in 1722 and 1755, and at Venice in 1757), based on the Lyons edition but corrected in many passages by recourse to the first editions of Sichart and Winter and occasionally by original conjectures. Amman reproduces a considerable portion of the marginal notes of the Lyons edition and adds some of his own. Amman's edition also contains the notes of T. J. Almeloveen, about half of which are reprinted from the works of Caspar Barth and Theodor Reinesius. There are also useful indexes prepared by Almeloveen.

4. An edition of both treatises by Albrecht von Haller (Lausanne, 1774; reprinted 1787), based on the text of Amman, with a few original corrections; the marginal notes are excerpted from Amman and Reinesius.

5. An edition of the *Acute Diseases* by C. Delattre (Paris, 1826), based on the text of Amman and corrected occasionally by recourse to the first editions and the Lyons edition; the notes are, for the most part, those of Amman and Almeloveen.

From this review it is clear that, in editing the treatises of Caelius, the first editions, together with the three manuscript leaves, must form the basis. All deviations from the text of the first editions that may be found in any of the subsequent editions are merely conjectural emendations. This is not to deny the value of some of these alterations, but we must always remember that they are conjectures.

Apart from the two treatises themselves, valuable aids in the determination of textual problems in Caelius are the fragments of the *Gynaecia* and the *Medicinales responsiones*, the Greek of Soranus' extant works,[5] and the usage of other Latin translators of Greek medical works, notably Cassius Felix and Theodore Priscian. In fact, Caelius is generally assigned to the fifth century on the basis of a comparison of his Latinity with that of Cassius Felix, whose work is known to have been written in the middle of that century.

---

departs from the manuscript precisely where the first edition does (and nowhere else), and this despite the fact that the text might have been improved at many points by following the manuscript rather than the first edition. None of the other editions, after the first, claims to be based on manuscripts.

5. Caelius constantly reminds the reader that he is rendering Soranus into Latin; but he obviously makes additions of his own from time to time. And, to judge by the fragments from Caelius' version of the *Gynaecia*, for which comparison may be made with the Greek, some of Soranus' material may also have been omitted by Caelius.

Certain textual questions in Caelius may also be resolved by reference to Isidore of Seville who, in *Origines* iv. 6–8, without mentioning his source, quotes directly from Caelius when giving the etymology of names of diseases. And in a few instances the early medieval glossaries quote Caelius directly.[6] More important for our purposes are the medical writings that go under the name of Aurelius, Esculapius, and Gariopontus (Passionarius Galeni). Though recent study tends to minimize the direct dependence of these writings on Caelius,[7] they are no less valuable for the text and interpretation of particular passages in Caelius; for considerable portions of these texts go back, directly or indirectly, to early Methodist material and, to this extent, they derive ultimately from the same source as Caelius.[7a]

Despite the importance of Caelius' work for the historian of medicine and philosophy and for the student of postclassical Latin, relatively little had been done until quite recently to establish and elucidate the text. The work of Barth in the seventeenth century, of Triller in the eighteenth, and Kühn in the early part of the nineteenth century was in large measure vitiated by the failure of these writers to use the first editions.

The critical editions of Greek and Latin medical works beginning in the second half of the nineteenth century—one thinks in particular of the series of works edited by V. Rose—and culminating in the volumes of the 'Corpus medicorum Graecorum' and 'Corpus medicorum Latinorum' furnished an indispensable aid for the study of Caelius. The articles of Helmreich and the dissertation of Friedel emphasized the importance of the first editions. The discovery of the fragments of the Lorsch manuscript and the articles of Ilberg gave further point to this emphasis. Ilberg's article, 'Vorläufiges zu Caelius Aurelianus,' containing a specimen edition of the portion of the text covered by the manuscript, established the broad principles on which an edition of Caelius should be based. Vietmeier in his dissertation studied Caelius' translation of the technical terms used by Soranus. But the most recent and also the most significant contributions are the criti-

6. See P. Schmid, *Caelius Aurelianus et les glossaires*, pp. 119 ff.

7. I.e., apart from direct quotations of Caelius' *Responsiones*.

7a. C. Daremberg, who edited a Brussels manuscript of the Aurelius chapters in the old *Janus*, II (1847), 468–99 and 690–731, was of the opinion that he was dealing with an abridgment of Caelius Aurelianus. But see Schmid, pp. 42–72. It may well be, to judge from the multiplication of manuscripts containing texts of Aurelius, Esculapius, and Gariopontus (see lists of manuscripts in Schmid, pp. 43–44, 69–72), that the presence of these relatively short practical treatises contributed to the neglect of Caelius in the Middle Ages. The historical and doxographical material which bulks so large in Caelius' work and reflects Soranus' interests is almost entirely absent from the practical handbooks.

cal studies of P. Schmid and G. Bendz. The work of both these men is based on a more penetrating study of the Caelian idiom than had previously been attempted. Of the writings on Caelius which are concerned with problems of medical history rather than with philological problems, the most important is that of Meyer-Steineg on the medical system of the Methodists.

THE METHODIST SCHOOL OF MEDICINE

Methodism arose through opposition to the two great schools that had long held the field, the Dogmatic or Logical school and the Empirical school.

The Dogmatists emphasized theoretical principles; they linked reason with observation to infer the existence of unseen entities and causes; they believed that systematic studies of anatomy and physiology were necessary for the physician. Though there were many varieties of Dogmatism and important differences among the leading Dogmatic physicians, the common characteristic was a belief in a 'science' as well as an 'art' of medicine.

The Empirical school, founded in the middle or the end of the third century B.C., had its philosophic roots in skepticism. It rejected unobservable entities and causes and even minimized the value of systematic anatomical and physiological studies as an aid to the treatment of disease. It particularly opposed the extreme Dogmatists, who, in their emphasis on theory, neglected practical experience. In the search for the right treatment the Empirics relied on observation and experience, including the recorded experience of others, and on similarities among the various cases observed. In general, the actual procedures prescribed by Dogmatists and Empirics were not so very different; but the Dogmatist held that his procedures were based on reason and theory, the Empiric on observation and experience.

The Methodist school developed at about the beginning of the Christian Era. The most important figures in the early development are Themison of Laodicea and Thessalus of Tralles, though the actual circumstances of the founding of the school are uncertain. As with the Empirics, the dominant philosophical viewpoint of the Methodists is skepticism, but it is a less radical skepticism, one which permits the formulation of certain general principles based on the observation of individual cases.

Themison was a pupil of the Dogmatist physician Asclepiades,

who taught at Rome for a considerable part of the first century B.C. In fact, Asclepiades has traditionally been considered the forerunner of Methodism. He held that the body consisted of atoms moving about in pores and that disease consisted essentially in some interference with this normal motion. It was probably from this theory that Themison obtained the clue for the doctrine of 'communities' (κοινότητες, 'general states'), which was to be of prime importance in Methodism. According to this doctrine, the basic types of disease are (1) an excessively dry, tense, and stringent state; (2) an excessively fluid, relaxed, atonic state; and (3) a condition which involves both types of abnormality. Since observable manifestations gave the clue to the 'general state' underlying a particular case, it is not surprising that the Methodists developed symptomatology and differential diagnosis to a high degree of perfection. And they distinguished more sharply than did their predecessors between acute and chronic diseases.

Their treatment of disease is essentially the use of relaxing measures to counteract excessive tension and the use of astringent measures to counteract excessive looseness.

It is impossible to define the precise contributions of Themison and Thessalus in the development of this theory and its applications. We may note, however, that Methodism avoids the humoral pathology so prominent in Hippocratic medicine and in the systems of most Dogmatic physicians. The atomist Asclepiades was one of the first to diverge from a strictly humoral pathology in the direction of a solidist pathology. Again, Asclepiades avoided the use of multitudes of drugs, opposing a trend that was particularly prominent among Empiric physicians. In this he had some influence on the Methodists. His emphasis on massage, exercise, bathing, and the use of wine and, in general, his preference for a treatment that was quick, safe, and pleasant also influenced the Methodists.

Themison may have lived as long as the first or second decade of the first century after Christ. In his later years he diverged from the sect of Asclepiades in the direction of Methodism. Some have considered him the founder of Methodism, though others accord this distinction to Thessalus of Tralles, who practiced and taught at Rome in the time of Nero. At any rate, to judge from the criticism that it evoked, Thessalus' system of medicine based on the doctrine of 'communities' was more radical than that of his predecessors or successors. And, in his uncompromising opposition to all other sects,

Thessalus showed little of the eclectic tendency that characterized many of the later Methodists and Roman medicine generally. Thessalus probably contributed greatly to the Methodist system of restorative and metasyncritic treatments used in the intervals of remission in chronic diseases (see p. xx). Certain additions to Themison's doctrine of 'communities' may also be due to Thessalus.

After Thessalus the leading Methodist physician was Soranus of Ephesus. His system of medicine, less radical than that of Thessalus, can best be studied in the treatises of Caelius Aurelianus. While studies of anatomy, physiology, and etiology are represented as having little or no practical usefulness for therapy, there is nonetheless a theoretical interest in these branches. Treatments of non-Methodist physicians are freely adopted. And the good sense of a wise and humane physician rises above the limitations of narrow sectarianism. There is none of the sensational radicalism which later critics rightly or wrongly ascribed to Thessalus. Galen, who is contemptuous of Thessalus, holds Soranus in high regard. We have already noted Soranus' broad philosophical and historical interests, which serve to distinguish his treatises on acute and chronic diseases from mere handbooks of medical practice.

Some ten or twelve other Methodist physicians are known, but they are of much less importance. Methodism continued to exercise considerable influence directly or indirectly for several centuries, thanks largely to the works of Soranus and to the eclectic spirit of later Roman medicine. But it was the Galenic system of medicine that in time became dominant. The teleological basis of that system was more congenial to the Middle Ages than the skeptical viewpoint on which Methodism was based.[8]

NOTES ON THE TRANSLATION

One who attempts a translation of Caelius soon finds that at many points a literal rendering will fail to reveal the underlying sense. That is why I have frequently had to resort to paraphrase and annotation. In addition, a few points may be separately noted here.

8. Apart from the writings of Soranus (and Caelius), most of our information about Methodism comes from the historical preface of Celsus and certain Galenic works. For further study consult R. Fuchs in Neuburger-Pagel, *Handbuch d. Gesch. d. Medizin*, I, 328, and the relevant articles in *Real-Encyclopädie*, especially Edelstein on 'Methodiker' (in Suppl. VI), Kind on 'Soranos,' Deichgräber on 'Themison,' and Diller on 'Thessalos'; also on the medical side the monograph of Meyer-Steineg and on matters of terminology the dissertation of Vietmeier. T. Clifford Allbutt, *Greek Medicine in Rome* (London, 1921), may also be consulted.

1. At the risk of emphasizing the obvious, it should be pointed out that the names of diseases in Caelius or in any other ancient author must not be read with modern connotations. Though we may render the terms *lethargia, cholera, morbus cardiacus, mania,* etc., as 'lethargy,' 'cholera,' 'the cardiac disease,' and 'mania,' the determination of the disease or diseases denoted by each of these terms is a problem for the medical historian, which a mere similarity of names should not be permitted to obscure.

2. There are various technical terms in the system of the Methodists that may be briefly noted here. Whatever formula is adopted in translating them, the important thing is that they be read as technical terms with all their connotations as such. We have noted that the Methodists viewed disease as indicative of an abnormal bodily state, and posited basic types of disease ('communities'), depending on the kind of abnormality. An excessively stringent, tense, or dry state required a relaxing treatment; an excessively loose, relaxed, aton c, or fluid state required an astringent treatment. For the stringentistate Caelius uses the term *strictura* (translating στέγνωσις). I have usually rendered this 'state of stricture.' For the relaxed state Caelius generally uses *solutio* (translating ῥύσις). I have rendered this 'state of looseness.' For the condition which involves both kinds of abnormality together, Caelius uses *complexio* (translating ἐπιπλοκή). For this I use the expression 'mixed state.' The terms *status strictus, status laxus,* and *status mixtus,* frequently used at a later time, are not found in Caelius.

Of considerable importance in our treatises are the various stages of disease. I list some of the terms, together with corresponding terms used in Greek:

initium	ἀρχή, ἀφορμή	'beginning'
augmentum	αὔξησις, ἐπίδοσις	'increasing phase'
status	ἀκμή	'highest stage'
declinatio	ἄνεσις, παρακμή	'decline'

Superpositio (ἐπίθεσις) is generally used by Caelius for the active phase, i.e., the attack, in a chronic disease; *lenimentum* or *dimissio* (διάλειμμα, ἄνεσις) for the interval of remission.

In many diseases each of the stages—increasing phase, highest stage, and decline—is itself marked by attacks of varying intensity, and each of these component attacks has its own beginning, increasing phase, highest stage, and decline. In these attacks an important element of time is the *diatritus* (διάτριτος), which I have rendered

'(end of a) three-day period,' though more exactly, by our method of counting, it represented the termination of a period of two full days.

A few technical terms may also be noted in connection with the Methodist treatment of chronic diseases. When an attack has declined, the treatment in the interval of remission is divided into two parts: (a) A treatment designed to restore the patient's strength. This treatment is called κύκλος ἀναληπτικός or merely ἀνάληψις, terms which Caelius translates by *cyclus resumptivus* and *resumptio*, i.e., 'the restorative cycle' or 'restorative treatment.' It generally includes rest, passive and active exercise, vocal exercise, anointing and massage, and a series of dietary changes leading to a normal regimen. (b) A treatment designed to alter the bodily state so that the disease itself may be overcome. This treatment is called 'metasyncrisis' or 'the metasyncritic cycle' (Latin *recorporatio, cyclus recorporativus*). It may include drastic dietary measures, violent purges, vomitives, and sternutatories, various kinds of irritant plasters, rubefacients, and ointments, vigorous cupping, sun-bathing and more intense applications of heat, massage, various kinds of exercise and bathing, the use of mineral waters, as well as such milder measures as travel and cruising and mental diversion generally. There is a good account of these treatments in *Chr.* i. 17–44.

3. The identification of the substances used in ancient medicaments is often quite uncertain. For inorganic substances considerable help is afforded by K. C. Bailey, *The Elder Pliny's Chapters on Chemical Subjects* (2 vols.; London, 1929, 1932). I have adopted Bailey's practice of leaving the terms *nitrum* and *aphronitrum* untranslated. 'Soda,' though preferable to 'nitre' as a translation of *nitrum*, is not entirely satisfactory. In translating Caelius, and ancient medical works generally, there is often difficulty in the identification of plants. The same name was frequently used to denote different varieties. In some cases, perhaps too seldom, I have left the Greek or Latin name untranslated, e.g., *strychnos* (*uva lupina*), *thapsia*. For *bulbi* (βολβοί) I use the general term 'bulbs' rather than the name of a particular variety (see Liddell-Scott-Jones and *Real-Encyclopädie*, s.v. βολβός).

The names of certain types of medicaments require more or less arbitrary designation. For example, following Adams in his translation of Paul of Aegina, I render *acopa* 'restorative ointments' and *malagmata* 'emollient plasters'; for *dropaces* I employ the term 'pitch plasters' (Adams: 'calefacient plasters'). But the properties of each

drug should be examined on the basis of its ingredients rather than prejudged by the generic designation.

The lists of ancient foods and drugs, with modern identifications, given by W. G. Spencer in the appendixes of his edition of Celsus ('Loeb Classical Library') are very helpful. On some points there is still uncertainty, e.g., on the identification of the various cereals, where the reader may compare N. Jasny, *The Wheats of Classical Antiquity* (Baltimore, 1944).

4. Caelius uses relatively few terms to designate weights and measures. They include both Roman words and Latinized forms of the Greek words used by Soranus. Note the following for the liquid measure of capacity. Standards varied greatly in antiquity, and modern equivalents are here indicated only as rough approximations.

> *cochleare*, 'spoonful,' about $\frac{1}{48}$ pint (4 *cochlearia* = 1 *cyathus*)
> *cyathus*, about $\frac{1}{12}$ pint (6 *cyathi* = 1 *hemina*)
> *acetabulum*, about $\frac{1}{8}$ pint (6 *cochlearia* = 1 *acetabulum*)
> *hemina* or *cotyla*, about $\frac{1}{2}$ pint (2 *heminae* = 1 *sextarius*)
> *sextarius*, about 1 pint

The standards of weight were generally the obol (*obolus*) and drachm (*drachma*). There were 6 obols to the drachm, the latter weighing about $\frac{1}{7}$ ounce avoirdupois. Occasionally the Roman terms *uncia* and *libra* were used. There were 12 *unciae* to the *libra*, the *uncia* being about 1 ounce avoirdupois, and the *libra* about $\frac{3}{4}$ pound avoirdupois.

Caelius occasionally uses *digitus* (δάκτυλος) as a measure of length. It was equal to about $\frac{3}{4}$ inch.

NOTES ON THE TEXT

In establishing the text, the first editions are used as a basis, *G* for the *Acute Diseases*, *S* for the *Chronic Diseases*. Brackets ([ ]) indicate matter to be omitted from the text of the first edition;[9] broken brackets (⟨ ⟩), matter to be added to the text of the first edition. But where the manuscript (L) is available (*Chr.* v. 77–91, 122–28), it will serve as the basis instead of *S*. The paragraph numbers of the Amman edition are retained.

Apart from minor changes in spelling noted below and the correction of obvious misprints, indication is made, either by brackets in the text or by notes in the *apparatus criticus*, wherever the text adopted diverges from that of the first edition. The adopted reading

9. In the translation, however, such brackets indicate material added as an aid to the interpretation of the text.

is ascribed to its first proposer, so far as ascertainable; where no ascription is made, the present editor is to be considered responsible for the change.[10]

The *apparatus criticus* also includes readings (especially of *R, Rm, A, Am*) which, though not adopted for the text, may possibly be correct or may have given the clue to a correct reading. But no attempt has been made to record all the variants, since by far the greater number throw no light at all on the text of Caelius.

In matters of orthography I have generally adhered to the first editions, even where these editions show inconsistencies within themselves and with each other. But the manuscript leaves (L) have influenced me to write *tamquam, quamquam, numquam, circum-*, etc., throughout both works for *tanquam, quanquam, nunquam, circun-*, etc., of the first editions. I have not thought it advisable, however, to make a general revision of the first editions on matters of assimilation. Both the manuscript and the first editions show great variation and inconsistency in this regard, though it should be pointed out that the manuscript has many forms like *adpetenda, adficiens, inruit*, and *inmodico*, which were changed by *S*.

The manuscript has led me to write *sucus, femina, cetera, inicio, ilico*, etc., throughout both works for *succus, foemina, caetera, iniicio, illico*, etc., of the first editions. But I have purposely avoided making any thorough revision of the spelling on the basis of L, not only because of the restricted compass of L and its own inconsistencies, but because its orthography can be of little help at best in determining Caelius' usage.

The reader, then, will find in the parts where L is the basis such spellings as *strutii, gonorria, venerius, diafragmate, sumsit*, and *quiliacis*, to give but a few examples, while *struthii, gonorrhoea, venereus, diaphragmate, sumpsit*, and *coeliacis* are kept throughout the rest of the book; but it seemed less objectionable to admit such disparity than to make a wholesale revision on the basis of the slight evidence of L.

I have made certain minor changes in spelling without mention in the *apparatus*. For example, I have written *hiems, sincerus, meracus*,

10. Because of the war the publications of Schmid, Bendz, and Hagendahl did not reach me until the present edition was virtually complete. Where I now find that my conjectures had been anticipated by these writers, I have given them the full credit. I find, too, that some (approximately one-fifth) of the emendations I proposed in an article, 'Notes on the Text of Caelius Aurelianus,' *Trans. Amer. Philol. Assoc.*, LXXVI (1945), 299–320, had been arrived at by Schmid and Bendz in publications which reached me only after the appearance of my article. I have in the present edition acknowledged their priority in such cases.

pernicies, lacrimatio, maestitudo, faenugraecum, haedinus, feniculum, opportunus, coacervatim, cum, cotidie, locutio, etc., for *hyems, syncerus, meratus, pernities, lachrymatio, moestitudo, foenugraecum, hoedinus, foeniculum, oportunus, coadcervatim, quum, quotidie, loquutio*, etc., of the first editions. But where L is the basis (*Chr.* v. 77–91, 122–28) I have set out the variants quite fully, to show both the spelling in the manuscript and the type of change made by the editors.

The endings of Greek words have generally been left as found in the first editions, even where these editions have such forms as *manian* and *maniam* side by side. And in other respects, rather than impose an arbitrary consistency, I have left unaltered such forms as *tracantum, dragantum,* and *dracantum, cotoneo* and *cydonio, obtrusio* and *obstrusio, diffiniens* and *definiens,* etc., wherever they occurred.

I have also retained the spellings *his* and *hi* in cases where for an earlier author one would be inclined to alter to *is* and *i* (or *iis* and *ii*). G has *his* and *hi* in these cases; S, *hiis* and *hii;* L, *his* (the nom. pl. does not occur in L). Rose alters to *is* and *ii* in editing Caelius' contemporaries, and Ilberg presumably would perform the alteration in the case of Caelius (see the portion edited in 'Vorläufiges'). Indeed, such evidence as the corruption of *viis* to *in his* (*Ac.* i. 18; i. 119; ii. 175; cf. *parvus,* i. 47) may possibly indicate that the spelling with *h* was not Caelius'. But, since there is doubt, I have declined to make the alteration.

In view of what must have been the frequent confusion of *e* and *i* in the manuscripts underlying the first editions, it is often difficult to tell whether we are dealing with a future or a present in such forms as *extendet,* and doubly difficult to know how to treat a form like *accedet.* But, so far as the text is concerned, I have retained the forms of the first edition wherever it was possible to do so. I have not followed the Lyons edition (*R*) in the scores of cases where it changes *fiet* of the first edition to *fit.*

With some hesitation I have kept *scarificatio, scarifico,* and the corresponding inflectional forms, though Ilberg would alter to *scarifatio* (*scarefatio*) and *scarifo,* and so presumably would Rose if he were editing our text.

One evidence of the general reliability of the first editions is the substantially complete agreement between them in matters of language and style (though there is no reason to suppose that Winter was familiar with the work of Sichart). Both of them reproduce Caelius' unusual type of Latin, and, rather than rewrite the text,

they leave obscure and even palpably corrupt passages uncorrected. But there are a few differences in vocabulary which are worth noting. The word for the pleural membrane is *hypezocos* (=ὑπεζωκώς) in *G* and *hypozygos* (=ὑπόζυγος) in *S*. Among other ancient writers, only the first form is attested. Is *S* guilty of an error here, as he was in substituting *onirogonos* for *onirogmos* (see *Chr.* v. 80 ff.)? There is a similar lack of agreement on the word for jaw muscles, *siagonitae* in *G* (=σιαγονῖται, as often in other authors), but *siagones* in *S* (= σιαγόνες, the word commonly used in other authors for the jaws themselves). Less striking perhaps but no less interesting is the fact that time and again *S* has *ac* in the sort of context where *G* invariably has *at*. This disparity indicates a confusion somewhere in the tradition, but it would be rash to resort to wholesale revision; I have generally preferred to keep the readings of the editions, with an occasional note where the alternative reading seemed particularly apposite.

The names of drugs compounded with *dia-* offer some difficulty. Where the Greek genitive plural was originally involved, e.g., *diatessaron, diachylon, diacodion, diaspermaton*, there is only the question whether to write as one word or two. Where the genitive singular in *-ou* was originally involved, the words in time came to be considered as regular neuters. The confusion in spelling and pronunciation between *u* and *ū* (= *um*) was probably a factor in the change (note the diversity of spelling in the inscriptions, e.g., *CIL*, XIII. 3. 2, No. 10021, and p. 604). In our first editions we find the forms *diaglaucium, diamelilotum, diasamsucum*, and the like. In such cases I have, with some hesitation, preferred the forms *diaglauciu, diamelilotu, diasamsucu*, etc. There is some evidence, e.g., in Cassius Felix, that in the fifth century the genitive in these cases was still felt as such. This seems to be the case with other genitive singular endings, e.g., in *diascammonias*. Perhaps for this reason *dia* should be written separately (so generally Rose in his editions), but I have elected to keep the compounded forms.

SELECTED BIBLIOGRAPHY

Unless otherwise stated, Soranus *Gynaecia* is cited by page and line of the edition of J. Ilberg in the 'Corpus medicorum Graecorum' (Leipzig, 1927); Caelius Aurelianus *Gynaecia* by book and paragraph in the edition of M. F. and I. E. Drabkin. The fragments of Caelius Aurelianus *Medicinales responsiones* are cited from the edition of

Rose, *Anecdota Graeca et Graecolatina*, Vol. II (*Salut. praec.* = *Salutaria praecepta; Diaet. pass.* = *De speciali significatione diaeteticarum passionum*). Aurelius is cited in the edition of C. Daremberg, *Janus*, Vol. II (1847). *Ac.* and *Chr.* are used as abbreviations for Caelius' treatises on acute diseases and chronic diseases, respectively.[11]

Certain works are cited merely by the name of their author, viz., Almeloveen, Barth, Bendz, Deichgräber, Friedel, Hagendahl, Helmreich, Kühn, Reinesius, Schmid, Vietmeier, and Wellmann. These works are included with others in the following selected bibliography.

VAN ALMELOVEEN, T. J. Notes and indexes to Caelius Aurelianus in Amman's edition (see above, p. xiv).

ALTHOFF, KLAUS. *Caelius Aurelianus, Ueber die akuten Krankheiten. 3. Buch.* Diss. Greifswald, 1940.

BARTH, CASPAR. *Adversariorum commentariorum libri LX.* Frankfort, 1624.

BENDZ, GERHARD. 'Caeliana: Textkritische und sprachliche Studien zu Caelius Aurelianus,' *Lunds Univ. Årssk.*, N.F., avd. 1. Vol. XXXVIII, No. 4 (1943). (Cited as 'Bendz' without title.)

———. 'Zu Caelius Aurelianus,' *Eranos*, XLI (1943), 65–76. (Cited as 'Bendz *Eran* 41.')

———. 'Some Critical Latin Word Studies,' *ibid.*, XLIII (1945), 36–57. (Cited as 'Bendz *Eran* 43.')

DEICHGRÄBER, KARL. *Die griechische Empirikerschule.* Berlin, 1930.

DIELS, HERMANN. *Anonymi Londinensis ex Aristotelis iatricis Menoniis et aliis medicis eclogae.* Berlin, 1893. (Cited as '*Anon. Lond.*')

DRABKIN, I. E. 'Notes on the Text of Caelius Aurelianus,' *Trans. Amer. Philol. Assoc.*, LXXVI (1945), 299–320.

DRABKIN, M. F. and I. E. *Caelius Aurelianus, Gynaecia.*

FRIEDEL, VICTOR H. *De scriptis Caelii Aureliani.* Diss. Bonn. Bischofsweiler, 1892.

FUCHS, ROBERT. 'Aus Themisons Werk über die acuten und chronischen Krankheiten,' *Rhein. Mus.*, LVIII (1903), 67–114. (Cited as '*Anon. Paris.*')

HAGENDAHL, HARALD. 'Notes critiques sur le texte de Caelius Aurelianus,' *Eranos*, XLIII (1945), 243–62.

HELMREICH, GEORG. 'Zu Caelius Aurelianus,' *Arch. f. lat. Lexik.*, XII (1902), 173–86, 309–36.

ILBERG, JOHANNES. 'Aus einer verlorenen Handschrift der Tardae passiones des Caelius Aurelianus,' *Sitzungsber. d. Preuss. Akad. d. Wiss.*, 1921, pp. 819–29. (Cited as 'Ilberg [1921]' without title.)

———. 'Ein weiteres Blatt der Lorscher Handschrift des Caelius Aurelianus,' *ibid.*, 1922, pp. 282–84.

———. 'Vorläufiges zu Caelius Aurelianus,' *Sächs. Akad. d. Wiss.*, phil.-hist. Kl., 1925 (see the review by R. Fuchs, *Philol. Wochenschrift*, XLVI [1926], 822–27). (Cited as 'Ilberg, 'Vorläufiges.' ')

JUNGMAIR, LEO FRANZ. *Caelius Aurelianus Über die schnellen oder akuten Krankheiten.* A German translation of *Acute Diseases*, Book I. Diss. Düsseldorf, 1939.

11. Though *Celeres passiones* and *Tardae passiones* are the names by which Caelius seems to have preferred to designate his works— Soranus' title was περὶ ὀξέων καὶ χρονίων παθῶν—the adaptability of the abbreviations *Ac.* and *Chr.* to both English and Latin dictated their choice here.

KIND, ERNEST. Art. 'Soranos' in *Real-Encyclopädie d. class. Altertum.*

KÜHN, CARL GOTTLOB. *Opuscula academica medica et philologica*, II, 1–190. Leipzig, 1828.

MEYER-STEINEG, THEODOR. *Das medizinische System der Methodiker: Eine Vorstudie zu Caelius Aurelianus "De morbis acutis et chronicis."* 'Jen. medizin.-hist. Beitr.,' Nos. 7/8. Jena, 1916.

REINESIUS, THOMAS. *Variarum lectionum libri III priores.* Altenburg, 1640.

ROSE, VALENTIN. 'Aus den Medicinales responsiones des Caelius Aurelianus,' *Anecdota Graeca et Graecolatina*, Vol. II. Berlin, 1870.

SCHMID, PIERRE. *Contributions à la critique du texte de Caelius Aurelianus* Diss. Neuchâtel, 1942. (Cited as 'Schmid' without title.)

———. 'Notes relatives aux livres 2 et 3 des *Maladies aiguës* de Caelius Aurelianus,' *Mnemosyne*, XI (1943), 133–55. (Cited as 'Schmid Mn.')

———. 'Notes critiques sur le traité des *Maladies chroniques* de Caelius Aurelianus,' *Rev. de Philol.*, XVII (1943), 37–55, 131–56. (Cited as 'Schmid RPh.')

———. 'Caelius Aurelianus et les glossaires,' *Mélanges offerts à M. Max Niedermann*, pp. 119–23. Neuchâtel, 1944.

TRILLER, DANIEL WILHELM. *Clinotechnia medica antiquaria.* Frankfort and Leipzig, 1774.

VIETMEIER, KARL. *Beobachtungen über Caelius Aurelianus als Uebersetzer medizinischer Fachausdrücke verlorener griechischer Schriften des methodischen Arztes Soranos von Ephesos.* Diss. Gütersloh, 1937.

WELLMANN, MAX. *Die Fragmente der sikelischen Ärzte Akron, Philistion und des Diokles von Karystos.* Berlin, 1901. (Cited as 'Wellmann' without title.)

———. 'A. Cornelius Celsus: Eine Quellenuntersuchung,' *Philol. Unters.*, Vol. XXIII. Berlin, 1913. (Cited as 'Wellmann, Celsus.')

ABBREVIATIONS USED IN THE *Apparatus criticus*

L—Fragments of MS now at Zwickau containing *Chr.* v. 77–91 and 122–28.

S—*Caelii Aureliani Siccensis tardarum passionum libri V.* Edited by J. Sichardus. Basle, 1529.

G—*Caelii Aureliani Methodici Siccensis liber celerum vel acutarum passionum.* Edited by J. Guinterius Andernacus. Paris, 1533.

R—*Caelii Aureliani De acutis morbis libri III. De diuturnis libri V.* Lyons: Apud G. Rovillium, 1567. Entries on the page of errata are incorporated in the text of R.

A—*Caelii Aureliani Siccensis De morbis acutis et chronicis libri VIII.* Edited by J. C. Amman. Amsterdam, 1709. (If other printings of this edition are referred to, they will be specially indicated.) Notes and indexes by T. J. Almeloveen.

Sm, Rm, Am—the marginal notes in the editions S, R, and A, respectively.

edd.—the consensus of SRA in the case of the *Chronic Diseases*, and of GRA in the case of the *Acute Diseases*.

TREATISE ON ACUTE DISEASES

CAELII AURELIANI
Methodici Siccensis
CELERUM VEL ACUTARUM PASSIONUM

CAPITA PRIMI LIBRI

CAPITA LIBRI SECUNDI

CAELIUS AURELIANUS
Methodist Physician of Sicca
ON SWIFT OR ACUTE DISEASES

iii

CAPITA LIBRI TERTII

BOOK III

TREATISE ON ACUTE DISEASES

LIBER PRIMUS
(*PRAEFATIO*)

1   Aiunt Ippallum pythagoricum philosophum interrogatum quid ageret, respondisse 'nondum nihil: nondum quidem mihi invidetur.' si igitur proficientium testis est invidia, quae nobis olim comes est, magna gerimus in his quae gerimus. placet itaque, Bellice discipulorum summe, Celerum passionum libros scribere quos tibi utiles magis quam necessa-

2 rios fore confido. utiles inquam, ut si qua forte a Graecis obscure dicta sunt, revelentur; non inquam[1] necessarios, haec enim necessario in quo sunt posita me tradente legisti. nam Interrogationum ac responsionum libros quibus omnem medicinam breviter dixi iamdudum ad Lucretium nostrum perscriptos aptissime destinavi. is enim ut nosti ex omni parte Graecarum scientia praeditus est literarum.

3   principio te scire volo omnium celerum passionum aliquas esse cum febribus, aliquas sine febribus. quarum necessario cum febribus sunt plurimae, ut phrenitis, lethargia, pleuritis, peripneumonia; sine febribus autem synanche, cholera, et id genus, sicut ex consequentibus docebimus. sed exordium sumemus ab his quae cum febribus esse noscuntur, siquidem febres sunt acutis magis comites passionibus, in quibus est phrenitis praeponenda.

4   nomen igitur sumpsit a difficultate mentis, sicuti et dysenteria et dysuria quod urinam vel ventrem impediant: phrenas enim graece[2] mentes vocaverunt, quarum[3] ut supra diximus impedimentum phrenitica ingerit passio. nam Demetrius Erophilum sequens, libro sexto quem De passionibus scripsit, hanc diffiniens

---

[1] non inquam *Buecheler, Kleine Schriften II. 190*: nonnunquam G

[2] Graeci *Delattre; cf. Ac. ii. 83, iii. 3*

[3] quarum *Rm*: quare G

2

BOOK I
(*PREFACE*)

1   IT IS said that the Pythagorean philosopher Hippasus, when asked what he had accomplished, replied: 'Nothing as yet; at any rate, I am not yet an object of envy.' If, then, envy is evidence of accomplishment, my achievements in my own field may be considered noteworthy, since they have long been an object of envy. And so, Bellicus, best of my pupils, I propose to write a treatise on acute diseases, and I trust you will find it
2   useful, even though not absolutely essential. Useful, I mean, in clarifying what may not have been clearly written by the Greeks; but not absolutely essential, for you have already had to read this material, under my instruction, in the original Greek.[1] As for my treatise *Questions and Answers*, which I wrote some time ago, briefly covering the whole field of medicine, I very appropriately dedicated that work to my friend Lucretius; for, as you know, he is thoroughly versed in Greek.
3   At the outset I would have you understand that of all acute diseases some occur with fever and others without fever. Those that always occur with fever are very numerous, e.g., phrenitis, lethargy, pleurisy, and pneumonia. On the other hand, synanche, cholera, and diseases of that type are not accompanied by fever, as we shall show hereafter. But we shall begin with those diseases that are known to occur with fever, for fever is more apt to accompany acute diseases. And among these diseases phrenitis is to be taken up first.
4   Phrenitis derives its name from the fact that it involves a mental affliction, just as dysentery and dysuria are so called because they involve interference with the bowels or the urine. For the Greek word for mind is *phrēn*, and, as we have said, it is a disturbance of the mind that is produced by the disease phrenitis. Thus in Book VI of his work *On Diseases*, Demetrius, following Herophilus,[2] defines phrenitis as a violent attack of madness (*de-*

---

1. The sentence is obscure and may possibly refer to Bellicus' use of a previous (original?) copy of Caelius' translation of Soranus.
2. Or merely 'Demetrius the follower of Herophilus.'

3

delirationem dixit vehementem cum alienatione atque ⟨frequentius[4] cum⟩ febre, et in interfectionem celerem, aliquando[5] et in sanitatem.

5   sed neque a deliratione vehementi alienationem differre quisquam existimet; neque[6] sane passionem frequentius cum febribus, sed iugiter ac necessario numquam sine febribus esse accepimus. dehinc ultra disciplinam elatus longa hoc diffinitione explicasse perspicitur, adiciendo cito interficientem esse passionem vel in sanitatem celerem. erat facile acutam vel celerem passionem dicere quod in utramque partem ocius feratur, et esset hoc diffinitioni sufficiens.

6   Asclepiades primo libro De celeribus scribens passionibus phrenitis, inquit, est corpusculorum[7] statio sive obtrusio in cerebri membranis frequenter sine sensu,[8] cum alienatione et febribus. hanc ipse explanans[9] diffinitionem 'cum febribus' dixisse inquit, siquidem sine his etiam mente alienantur vel qui papaver aut mandragoram aut altercum biberint, aut immensa ira aut nimio timore commoti vel maestitia etiam compressi aut epileptica agitati passione. 'sine consensu,' inquit diffiniens, ne etiam pleuriticum vel peripneumonicum phreniticum putaremus, qui in statu passionis septima vel octava die saepe mentis erroribus agitantur.

7   eius sectatores quidam residuam partem diffinitionis disserentes stationem corpusculorum vel obtrusionem aiunt eum dixisse 'secundum membranas cerebri,' siquidem sint etiam medullarum spinae membranae in quibus cum fuerit obtrusio non ingerit phrenitim. pluraliter autem usum dicunt ut 'membranas' diceret, siquidem sive per multas sive per omnes id eveniat: etenim si singulariter poneret, negaret esse in multis, sed quisquis hunc sequeretur unius esse membranae causam putaret.

4 ⟨frequentius⟩ *Bendz 77*

5 aliquando *transposuit Schmid 75 post* atque (*lineae praecedentis*)

6 neque *Bendz 77*: quam *G*: hanc *R* (*non addito post* passionem)

7 corpusculorum ⟨parvorum⟩ *Wellmann, coll. Ac. i. 119* (*Celsus 106, n. 1*)

8 consensu *Rm, ut ad fin. huius paragraphi, sed cf. Ac. i. 7, 15, 17*

9 explanans *Almeloveen, coll. Ac. i. 16*: explorans *G*

liratio) accompanied by loss of reason (*alienatio*) and frequently by fever, and swiftly leading either to death or at times to restoration of health.

5   But no one can hold that loss of reason (*alienatio*) is essentially different from madness (*deliratio*). Again, we know definitely that phrenitis occurs with fever, not merely frequently but always, and that it never can occur without fever. Furthermore, in making his definition long by adding an explanation that the disease leads to swift death or swift recovery, Demetrius obviously exceeded the proper bounds. For he could easily have called it an acute (swift) disease, because in either case it terminates swiftly, and this would have been sufficient for the definition.

6   Asclepiades in Book I of his *Acute Diseases* says that phrenitis is a stoppage or obstruction of the corpuscles in the membranes of the brain frequently without any feeling [of pain][3] and accompanied by loss of reason and by fever. In explaining this definition, he asserts that the phrase 'accompanied by fever' is included because loss of reason may also occur without fever, e.g., in cases of people who have drunk poppy juice, mandragora, or henbane, or were under the influence of profound anger or great fear or grief, or were shaken by an epileptic seizure. And again, he says that the phrase 'without any feeling [of pain]' is included in the definition so that we may not regard as suffering from phrenitis the patient with pleurisy or pneumonia who, at the highest stage of the disease, on the seventh or eighth day, often suffers mental aberration.

7   Certain followers of Asclepiades, discussing the rest of the definition, declare that he spoke of a stoppage or obstruction of corpuscles 'in the membranes of the brain,' since there are also membranes of the spinal cord in which such stoppage does not give rise to phrenitis. And they say that Asclepiades used 'membranes' in the plural because the disease may occur in several or in all the membranes. If he had used the singular, he would be denying the reference to more than one membrane; and whoever depended on his word would suppose that the cause resided in a single membrane.

3. The reading (*sensu* or *consensu*, translating Greek *pathos* or *sympatheia*) and the precise meaning of the phrase are doubtful. Possibly the meaning is: 'not arising sympathetically from any other affection,' or 'not accompanied by any sympathetic affection.'

'frequenter' autem quod adiecit diffiniens, quidam sequentibus adscripserunt ut sic intelligamus 'frequenter sine consensu,'
siquidem cum sensu[10] atque vehementer fiat aliquando phrenitis.
8 alii vero antecedentibus esse inquiunt iungendum ut sic intelligatur 'frequenter statio vel obtrusio.' quomodo[11] febrem illam
vehementem dixit, cum de causis tractaret, [et][12] quae per stationem vel obtrusionem fuerit, illam vero solubilem atque levem
quae ex turbatione fuerit liquidarum materiarum atque spiritus, sic etiam phreniticae passionis[13] illam dixit esse vehementem
quae statione vel obtrusione fuerit effecta corpusculorum. alii
vero non, inquiunt, quod sine obstrusione fiat aliquando phrenitis, hoc Asclepiadem dixisse accipiamus, sed quia sola ex
vehementi: sunt etiam quaedam in hominibus sanis obstru-
siones.

9   erat igitur melius ut manifestis et consequentibus[14] verbis
intelligendam traderet passionem, et non per occultam atque
dissonantem obtrusionem et quae fortasse neque esse probetur,
sicut libris quos Contra[15] sectas sumus scripturi[16] docebimus.
sed neque oportuit eandem obtrusionem simul phrenitim atque
phreniticae passionis causam vocare, siquidem vis locutionis
nihil aliud designet quam phrenitim esse phreniticae passionis
10 causam. est enim[17] dicere quod secundum Asclepiadem causae
ascriptionum[18] sive partitionum sint, quas Graeci categorias
appellant, non appellationum, quas idem prosegorias vocant.
non enim alienationis aut febrium sed alienandi vel febricitandi
causas nominat; sic etiam phrenitizandi non phreniticae passionis causas dixit. primo ad aliud ex alia re transire vide-
11 bimur, utrumne partitionum aut ascriptionum an appellationum
sint causae: de qua re, cum De passionum causis scribere coeperimus, dicemus.

dehinc paululum progrediens ait:[19] 'quae statio corpusculorum
sive obstrusio in qualibus vel ex qualibus corpusculis fiat, atque

[10] cum sensu] *an* consensu *vel* cum consensu? *v. adn. ad Ac. i. 6*
[11] quomodo ⟨enim⟩ R   [12] *om.* R
[13] phreniticam passionem R
[14] cum sequentibus G: *corr.* R
[15] contra Rm: intra G
[16] sumus scripturi *Friedel 50*: unius scriptoris G
[17] est enim *Schmid 76*: etenim G
[18] causae ascriptionum *Friedel 28*: causa ea scriptionum G
[19] at G: ⟨ait⟩ at R

The word 'frequently' in the definition is connected by some with what follows, so that we have 'frequently without any feeling [of pain],' for sometimes phrenitis *is* accompanied by violent
8 pain. But others say that 'frequently' is to be taken with what precedes, so that the meaning is '[phrenitis is] frequently a stoppage or obstruction.' [They point out that] in treating of causes, Asclepiades considers fever serious if it takes place by stoppage or obstruction, and less serious and more readily overcome if it takes place through a disturbance of the bodily fluids and the pneuma. In the same way [according to their view] he implies that a case of phrenitis is serious if it results from a stoppage or obstruction of the corpuscles. Others, however, take the view that Asclepiades' language implies not that phrenitis sometimes occurs without such a stoppage but that it occurs only as the result of a severe stoppage. Indeed [they say], some stoppages are present even in healthy bodies.
9 It would therefore have been better for Asclepiades to describe the disease in clear and suitable language and not with reference to an obscure and confusing 'stoppage.' In fact, this stoppage may not even exist, as we shall show in a treatise we are planning to write against the sects. Moreover, Asclepiades should not have referred to the same stoppage both as phrenitis itself and as the cause of phrenitis. For the language of his definition can
10 only mean that phrenitis is the cause of phrenitis. One may say that according to Asclepiades the causes are to be connected with predicables (Greek *categoriae*), not with mere substantives (Greek *prosegoriae*). Thus he here gives the causes not of loss of reason or of fever but of losing the reason or of being feverish, and similarly not of phrenitis but of being phrenitic. [But to go into this discussion now] would be to pass at the outset from our
11 present inquiry to the question whether causes are to be connected with categories, i.e., predicables, or with substantives. And that is a question which we shall discuss at the beginning of our work *On the Causes of Diseases*.[4]

Furthermore, a little later Asclepiades says: 'In Book X of our work we clarified for the first time the nature of the stoppage or obstruction, and the type of corpuscles involved in this stop-

4. The reference is to Soranus' *Aetiologumena*, which is no longer extant, though parts are believed by some to be preserved in *Anonymus Parisinus* and *Anonymus Londinensis*.

etiam quomodo ea quae partibus eveniunt totum commoveant
corpus ac febres generent, primo in his quae decimo[20] scripsimus
enodavimus.' nunc enim febres inquit generent, non febricitare. oportebat autem proprie, non improprie loqui.

12   alii haec defendentes aiunt eum verbis significasse phrenitim
esse passionem ex obtrusione effectam. 'habet consuetudinem
pro effectu causas ponere. denique luem diffiniens, "lues,"
inquit, "est qualitas insueta in his ubi est locis consistentium
animalium, qua ex communi causa facilibus morbis et inter-
fectivis adficiuntur." etiam nunc luis causam pro effectu sumpsisse perspicitur. causa etenim luis est qualitas; lues autem
declivitas in aegritudinem prona atque celeberrima, communi-
13 bus antecedentibus causis. et in aliis vero his utitur saepe
sumptionibus,[21] quas Graeci metalepses appellant, ut exempli
causa dicat densatum liquorem pro partibus liquoris densatis:
partes enim ad totum redigit.' sed neque expiant his maledicta,
sed ostendunt etiam in aliis similibus peccatis adfectum. quaerimus enim non si consuetudinem habuit sumptionis[22] faciendae, sed utrum haec consuetudo recta esse videatur. externa
etenim si fuerit haec a diffinitionibus consuetudo, veniam fortasse merebitur; in diffinitionibus vero non poterit ad veniam
14 pertinere. oportebat enim diffinitive loquentem propriis uti
sermonibus, et non abusivis neque sumptionibus,[23] quae in
contrarium saepe vocentur.

neque nunc obstrusio causa est phreniticae passionis, sicut in
aliis ostendimus, neque causam debuit pro effectu accipere, neque
in membranis consequentem obtrusionem fieri, sed in sensibus,
hoc est in sensualibus viis, quas Graeci aestheteria[24] vocant.

[20] decimo ⟨libro⟩ R
[21] transsumptionibus Rm
[22] transsumptionis Rm
[23] transsumptionibus Rm
[24] αἰσθητήρια A: αἰσθήρια G

5. I.e., if his use of a verbal instead of a noun is to save him from the charge of tautol-
ogy in his definition of phrenitis, he should have been consistent and used the verbal instead of the noun in the passage just quoted.

page, and also how that which takes place in parts of the body can cause a disturbance in the whole body and produce fever.' That is, he there says 'produce fever,' not 'produce a state of being feverish.' But he should have used language strictly, not loosely.[5]

12 Some, however, defend Asclepiades' definition and hold that he means merely that the disease of phrenitis results from a stoppage. 'It is [they say] his custom [in defining a disease] to set forth the cause instead of describing the resultant disease itself. Thus in defining plague[6] he says: "Plague is an unusual condition of living creatures in the particular locality affected, because of which condition they are prone to be visited with deadly diseases arising from a common cause." Here, too, he seems to have set forth the cause of plague instead of describing the resultant disease. For the cause of plague is a condition; but plague itself is an easy slipping into a disease which arises from

13 common antecedent causes and affects large numbers. And in other cases, too, Asclepiades often uses such substitutions of language (Greek *metalēpseis*). He speaks, for example, of a thickened fluid instead of the thickened parts of the fluid, using the whole for the parts.' But his defenders do not by these instances excuse his improper use of language; they merely show that he made similar errors in other connections, too. Now we are interested not in whether he was in the habit of making such substitutions but in whether this habit is proper. And, indeed, if the practice were not used in definitions, it might perhaps be excus-

14 able, but in the case of definitions it is unpardonable. For in giving a definition one should use words in their strict sense, not loosely, and one should not employ substitutions, which are often interpreted wrongly.

Now the stoppage is not the cause of phrenitis, as we have shown elsewhere.[7] Furthermore, Asclepiades should not have mistaken the cause for the actual disease, nor should he have said that the obstruction takes place in membranes. He should rather have said that it takes place in the senses, i.e., in the sensory passages (Greek *aesthētēria*). For Asclepiades holds that,

6. Or pestilential fever. Cf. Celsus iii. 7.

7. The reference is probably to Soranus' *Aetiologumena*.

omnis enim phrenitis[25] alienationem generaliter, communiter
autem alienationis substantiam in sensibus constitutam existi-

15 mavit Asclepiades. denique in Diffinitionum libris alienationem
diffiniens hoc genere explicavit: alienatio est passio in sensibus,
ex qua aliquando maiores intellectus efficiuntur capacitate
sensualium viarum,[26] aliquando vero viae capaciores motibus.
sed hoc intardans, inquit, ac sine febribus furor vocatur, quem
vulgo insaniam dicunt; recens autem atque cum febribus neque
cum sensu[27] phrenitis intelligitur.

si igitur phrenitis passio est in sensu,[28] non recte eam principaliter diffiniens obstrusionem dicit esse in cerebri membranis.

16 addo etiam fieri phrenitim ex consensu perseveranti ac vehementi, sicuti ex aliis antecedentibus causis. oportuit ergo etiam
in eo quod diffiniens adiecit verbum frequentiae[29] servare ordinem, ne dicendi ambiguitatem daret, ex qua eius sectatores
inter se plurimum pugnaverunt.

mentitur etiam apertissime cum suam explanans diffinitionem
dicit quod papaver alienationem facit. soporiferam etenim ingerit pressuram. hoc adeo defendentes quidam eius sectatores

17 aiunt etiam somno fieri alienationem. ipse denique Asclepiades
in primo libro Celerum passionum furiosos inquit facere somnum:
sic etiam '⟨papavera⟩[30] alienationem faciunt.' his nos respondebimus differre pressuram a somno. contra naturam etenim
pressura intelligitur, secundum naturam somnus. papavera
autem pressuram, non somnum faciunt. at si accipiunt etiam
pressuram somnum vocari, quae necessario contra naturam
est, oportebat etiam lethargos dicant alienari, et erit diffinitio
phreniticae passionis lethargiae communis. et in lethargis obtrusio est secundum Asclepiadem in membranis cerebri cum
febribus ac sine sensu.[31] dehinc etiam in furore febricitantium

[25] fort. scrib. omnem enim phrenitim

[26] sensualium viarum *Bendz 78*; sensu aliarum viarum *G*

[27] cum sensu] consensu *Rm* (*v. ad. Ac. i. 6*)

[28] fort. sensibus

[29] 'frequenter' *Schmid 77*

[30] papavera *addidi*: somni *add. Rm*

[31] consensu *R* (*v. ad Ac. i. 6*)

in general, every case of phrenitis involves mental impairment
(*alienatio*), and that the essence of mental impairment is in the
15 senses. In fact, in defining mental impairment in his treatise
On Definitions, Asclepiades explains the term in the following
way: 'Mental impairment is an affection in the senses, and in
this affection sometimes the mental activity is too great for the
capacity of the sensory passages; but in other cases the passages
are too large for the motions [of the corpuscles]. When this disease is chronic and without fever, it is called *furor* or, commonly,
insania;[8] but a recent [i.e., acute] case with fever and without
any feeling [of pain] is called phrenitis.'

Now, if phrenitis is a disease in the senses, Asclepiades is
wrong in defining it in the first instance as an obstruction in the
16 membranes of the brain. I may add that phrenitis may also take
place as a result of a persistent and severe affection, as well as
from other antecedent causes. Consequently, in adding the
word 'frequently' to his definition of the disease, Asclepiades
should have watched the order of words, to avoid the ambiguity
which occasioned such disagreement among his followers.[9]

Moreover, he is clearly mistaken when, in explaining his definition, he says that the drinking of poppy juice causes mental
derangement.[10] It does, to be sure, bring about a profound stupor
resembling sleep. But some of the followers of Asclepiades actually seek to defend his statement by arguing that the mind is
17 unbalanced during sleep. In fact, Asclepiades himself in Book I
of his *Acute Diseases* declares that sleep unbalances the mind;
hence the statement that poppy juice causes mental derangement. Our answer to this is that stupor differs from sleep; for
stupor is considered as something abnormal, sleep as something
normal. And poppy juice produces stupor, not sleep. Now if they
[the defenders of Asclepiades] agree that stupor, which is always
unnatural, may be called sleep, they ought to say that persons
with lethargy also suffer mental derangement. And their definition of phrenitis and lethargy will then be the same. In fact, according to Asclepiades, lethargy, too, involves a stoppage in the
membranes of the brain, with fever and without any feeling [of
pain]. Furthermore, the definition of mania accompanied by fe-

8. Greek *mania*.

9. Cf. *Ac.* i. 6–8.   10. Cf. *ibid.* i. 6.

communis erit diffinitio. in his enim ut[32] ipse ait obtrusionem
in membranis cerebri frequenter sine ⟨consensu, cum⟩[33] febribus atque [cum][34] alienatione effectam.

18   huic occurrentes quidam aiunt quod inquit 'cum febribus'
duo significare: unum quod tardantem cum membranarum obtrusione longi scilicet temporis febrem significet, et non ex ipsa
sumpserit[35] exordium; aliud cum febribus quidem, sed ex causa
obtrusionis membranarum, ⟨quod, inquiunt, debemus diffinitione explicatum accipere. etenim furore febricitantium non
ex obstrusione membranarum⟩[36] febres oriuntur parvae atque
mitiusculae:[37] in viis enim minutissimis[38] fiunt plagae sive percussus[39] atque adfricationes quae corpori minime accendere fer-
19   vorem possint. sed etiam nunc confitentur confusum dictum,
si ex hoc duo significat, alterum ex his verum, alterum falsum.
dehinc febres fieri in phreniticis ex obstrusione membranarum
solitum accipiamus, eorum tamen dictis repugnans. additur
enim alienatio cum[40] febribus, denique etiam obstrusio ex qua
alienatio fiet: quod igitur secundo sequitur, causa prioris esse
non potest.

addo etiam febres quae per totum corpus, causam earum ex
obtrusione membranarum factam, quo[41] totum corpus accenda-
20   tur, ratione carere. etenim in epilepticis, quibus etiam raptus
omnium membrorum ex cerebri membranis atque maiorum
⟨corpusculorum⟩[42] causa secundum Asclepiadem descendit
(quapropter etiam phlebotomiam probat adhibendam), oportebat magis ac vehementius febrem accendi, siquidem maiora

[32] et Schmid 79, sed v. Bendz 66: om. R

[33] suppl. Schmid 78, coll. Ac. i. 6: fort. ⟨sensu, cum⟩

[34] secl. Schmid 79

[35] sumpserit Rm: soluerit G

[36] ⟨quod ... membranarum⟩ huc ex Ac. i. 25 transposuit Schmid 80

[37] immitiusculae G: corr. R

[38] in viis etenim (enim Bendz 79) minutissimis Schmid 81; cf. etiam Ac. i. 119, ii. 175:
in his et imminutissimis G

[39] percussa G: corr. Rm

[40] cum om. R

[41] qua R

[42] maiorum ⟨corpusculorum⟩ Schmid 84, coll. Ac. i. 119: maiore G (retin. Bendz
79)

ver will also be the same [as that of phrenitis]; for in these cases
Asclepiades himself speaks of a stoppage in the membranes of
the brain, frequently without any feeling [of pain] but with fever
and with loss of reason.

18 In opposition to this argument, some say that his phrase 'with
fever' has two different meanings: one, that there is a chronic
fever, i.e., one of long duration, accompanied by an obstruction
in the membranes, but not arising from such an obstruction; or,
secondly, that there is a fever but that it arises by reason of a
stoppage in the membranes [of the brain]. And [according to the
supporters of Asclepiades] it is in the latter sense that we ought
to understand his definition of phrenitis. On the other hand
[they say], in mania accompanied by fever the small mild fevers
that arise do not proceed from a stoppage in the membranes [of
the brain]; they proceed rather from impacts, blows, and friction in the smallest passages, blows which could hardly kindle
19 much heat in the body. But by their very argument the supporters of Asclepiades admit that his expression is unclear, if it
can have two meanings, one true and the other false. Again, even
if we were to admit that fever usually occurs in phrenitis by
reason of an obstruction in the membranes, such a view still
contradicts what the supporters of Asclepiades say. For 'loss of
reason with fever' is contained [in Asclepiades' definition], and
so also is the obstruction from which the loss of reason arises.
But that which follows cannot be a cause of what precedes.[11]

I may add, with reference to the fever throughout the whole
body, that it is illogical to say that the cause of it and of the consequent kindling of the whole body can be an obstruction in the
20 membranes [of the brain]. For in epilepsy the seizure of all the
limbs comes, according to Asclepiades, from the membranes of
the brain and is due to the larger corpuscles. (In fact, for this
reason he recommends venesection in these cases.) But on his
theory there is even more reason why an intense fever should be
kindled in epilepsy. For the larger corpuscles in the larger pas-

11. The point may be that Asclepiades' definition does not make *obtrusio* prior in
time to *alienatio* and *febres*, which it should if *obtrusio* is the cause of *alienatio* and *febres*.
(Caelius seems to imply here that the definition actually makes *obtrusio* subsequent, but
this is not supported, at least not by *Ac.* i. 6.)

The text, however, is uncertain and the interpretation very doubtful. If *cum* be
bracketed (so *R*), the meaning may be: 'For if [as they say] loss of reason follows fever,
so also must the obstruction from which the loss of reason arises. But that which follows
cannot be a cause of what precedes.'

corpuscula maioribus viis constituta[43] maiores faciant plagas sive percussiones et adfricationes.

in libris denique Diffinitionum phrenitim inquit esse alienationem repentinam cum febribus. sed etiam novus furor, quem insaniam vocant, saepe movetur cum febribus.

21 nos igitur manifeste atque breviter, quantum res patiuntur, intelligentiam sive diffinitionem passionis trademus, dicentes phrenitim esse alienationem mentis celerem cum febri acuta atque manuum vano errore, ut aliquid suis digitis attrectare videantur, quod Graeci crocydismon sive carphologian vocant, et parvo pulsu ac denso.

22 ## I. UTRUMNE SINT SIGNA PHRENITICAE FUTURAE PASSIONIS

Dehinc quaerendum utrumne sint signa phreniticae futurae passionis. Nam multi sectarum principes, inter quos fuit et Asclepiades, signa futurae passionis posuerunt. at Thessalus et eius sectatores id posse fieri negant, dicentes quia si[1] futurae phreniticae passionis signa vera atque necessaria fuissent, oportebat [autem][2] omnes in iisdem constitutos necessario esse phreniticos. nunc vero quidam cum his afficerentur signis in phreniticam passionem non venerunt. secundo oportebat etiam aliarum passionum futurarum esse signa. nullius autem futurae passionis signa esse perspicimus, neque igitur phreniticae

23 passionis esse posse signa credamus. sed neque praestantius quicquam antecedentium causarum, ut adustio, cruditas, vinolentia, atque exercitium post cibum, vel mansio sive somnus in speluncis confertur, aut nova politura in muris parietis[3] cubiculorum. haec alias quoque passiones ingerunt generaliter, ut lethargiam, apoplexiam, epilepsiam. neque multos tempore certo specialiter phreniticam incurrere passionem, ut autumno vel alio quolibet, firmum esse credamus. incertum est enim, siquidem non omnes phrenitici efficiantur, sed alii diversis

24 afficiantur passionibus. neque etiam vigilare, ac iugiter cum

---

[43] viis constituta *conieci*: viis statione facta *coniecit Schmid 85*: mista (mixta *Delattre, Wellmann, Neue Jahrb. 21. 695, n. 7, Bendz 80*) cum toto G

[1] si *R*: non G   [2] *om. R*

[3] pariete *Almeloveen* (*secluso* muris): ⟨et⟩ parietibus *Rm* (*retento* muris): *fort.* parietis (*abl.*) *vel* parietibus (*secl.* muris)

sages produce more powerful blows or impacts and more extensive friction.

Finally, in his work *On Definitions* Asclepiades declares that
phrenitis is a sudden mental derangement accompanied by
fever. But the first onset of mania or insanity, as it is called,
also frequently occurs with fever.

21   We shall now set forth our own understanding or definition of
phrenitis clearly and as briefly as the facts permit. We say that
phrenitis is an acute mental derangement accompanied by acute
fever, a futile groping of the hands, seemingly in the effort to
grasp something with the fingers (Greek *crocydismos* or *carphologia*), and a small, thick[12] pulse.

22   I. ARE THERE SIGNS OF THE COMING
                   OF PHRENITIS?

W E MUST now inquire whether there are signs of the coming
    of phrenitis. Many leaders of sects, e.g., Asclepiades, have
asserted that there are such indications. But Thessalus and his
followers deny this, and reason as follows: 'If there were sure
and inevitable indications of the future onset of phrenitis, all
who manifested such signs would necessarily become phrenitics.
But some of those who show these symptoms do not incur phrenitis. Again, we should expect that there would be indications
of the future onset of other diseases, too. But this is the case
23 with no other disease. There is consequently no reason for us to
suppose that there are indications of a future onset of phrenitis.
And, in fact, no antecedent cause can be specifically adduced in
this connection, such as exposure to heat,[1] indigestion, excessive
drinking of wine, exercise after eating, living or sleeping in caves
or in rooms in which the walls have been freshly plastered. These
circumstances may in general produce other diseases, too, such
as lethargy, apoplexy, and epilepsy. And let us not take it as
established that a great many people are specifically affected by
phrenitis at a particular season, like autumn or any other. Since
not all are seized with phrenitis but some with one disease and
24 others with another, we can draw no conclusion. Indeed, neither

12. I.e., rapid. Cf. 34. But *densus, creber*, and *celer*, as applied to the pulse, do not always seem to have been regarded as equivalent terms. Cf. Rose, *Anecdota Graeca*, II, 278.

1. The reference is to heatstroke or sunstroke (cf. *encauseos*, Cass. Fel., p. 154. 4). So
also *Ac.* i. 33, 103.

dolore urinam[4] reddere parvum vel plurimum,[5] atque gravedine[6]
vel dolore capitis vel occipitis vel clunium affici aut oculorum
rubore.[7] haec enim signa communia sunt passionum quae
vexata membrana cerebri fiunt atque male laborantium aegrorum, non necessario omnium ac semper phreniticorum. dehinc
audacia sine ratione vel econtrario securitas et hilaritas non
futuram sed praesentem alienationem designant.

25   haec expugnantes Asclepiadis sectatores contra primum responderunt: quamquam, inquiunt, signis futurae passionis aegri
afficiantur, ratione tamen certa non in ipsam plerumque veniunt, siquidem imminentem passionem cohibeat medicinalis
vera curatio, [quod inquiunt debemus diffinitione explicatum
accipere etenim furore febricitantium non ex obstrusione mem-
branarum][8] quae non sinat initium sumere. non igitur negant
26 signa fuisse futurae passionis. dehinc signorum quaedam inquiunt secundum Asclepiadem esse necessaria, ut cordis vulneratio mortis signum, quaedam non necessaria, sed frequenter
futura significantia, sicut membranae capitis vulneratio mori-
turum vulneratum significat. frequenter enim hoc, non iugiter
ac necessario contingit; et futurae[9] igitur phreniticae passionis
signa frequentiam[10] non necessitatem futurorum designant.[11]
quapropter manet genus futurae phreniticae passionis in signis,
quamquam ⟨non⟩[12] necessario in eam veniant aegrotantes.

contra secunda vero haec probaverimus et de singulis scri-
27 bentes docebimus. dehinc potest etiam soli phreniticae passioni hoc privatum inveniri: ut enim ab aliis passionibus differt,
sic etiam cum nondum est, differre. ceteris respondentes aiunt
antecedentes causas, quas procatarcticas[13] appellant, singulares
quidem non esse futurae passionis signa, neque rem sine tempore neque concurrentia, ut forte oculorum sanguinolentia vel

⁴ urinae *Rm*   ⁵ *fort.* parvam vel plurimam

⁶ gravedinem *G: corr. R*

⁷ certa signa sunt *add. Rm*

⁸ quod . . . membranarum *hinc ad Ac. i. 18 transposuit Schmid 80*

⁹ futura *G: corr. A*

¹⁰ frequentia *G: corr. Rm*

¹¹ designantia *G: corr. Schmid 85*

¹² *add. R*   ¹³ procataracticas *G: corr. A*

2. It is also possible that 'we' refers to Caelius (Soranus).

wakefulness, nor the continual passing of urine in small or large amounts with pain, nor the sensation of heaviness or pain in the head, the occiput, or the loins, nor redness of the eyes [is a sure sign]. For these are general indications of diseases which involve an affection of the membrane of the brain, and of patients who are seriously sick, but not necessarily all such patients and not in every case those suffering from phrenitis. And, again, irrational boldness or, on the other hand, carefreeness and giddiness indicate not a future but a present aberration.'

25   In refutation of the first of these points the followers of Asclepiades argue as follows: 'Though patients may show signs of a coming of disease, they often avoid it for the good reason that an effective medical treatment inhibits the threatening disease and prevents it from getting started. That is no reason for deny-
26 ing that there are indications of the coming of the disease.' They then proceed as follows: 'According to Asclepiades, certain indications point to inevitable consequences. For example, a wound of the heart is a sure sign of death. But certain other signs, while they do not indicate inevitable consequences, indicate what will frequently follow. Thus injury to the membrane of the head generally indicates that the victim will die, but this is a frequent result, not an invariable and inevitable result. And so in the case of phrenitis the signs that point to a coming attack indicate only what is probable, not what is inevitable. That is, while there are signs of the coming of phrenitis, patients manifesting such signs do not necessarily incur the disease.

'And against the subsequent arguments [of Thessalus and his followers], we² may set forth the following considerations, giving
27 the details in the course of our exposition. It is quite possible that this matter [of "signs of a coming disease"] is something peculiar only to phrenitis.³ For just as this disease [when it is present] differs from all others, so it may also differ before it is actually present. And as to the other arguments, it is true that the antecedent causes (Greek *procatarcticae*), taken one by one,⁴ cannot be considered signs of the coming of the disease, nor can anything undefined in time be so considered; and the same is true of the concomitant symptoms, e.g., bloodshot eyes or heavi-

3. This is in answer to the argument that no such signs have been found for any other disease (22, above).

4. The phrase may possibly mean 'even though specific.'

capitis gravedo, sed in unum coacervata atque concurrentia.
28 audacia vero sine ratione[14] atque hilaritas certa significatione
dicta sunt[15] signa futurae phreniticae passionis, sicuti et[16] in
externis quamquam praesentia[17] parvitate iam latentia pro futuris accipimus. igitur Thessalus primo libro Diaetetico praecepit phlebotomari in stricturam magnam venturos, atque hos
ita designat iugiter febricitantes et usque ad dimissionis tempus
submerso pulsu affectos, frequenter vel cum dolore urinam red-
dentes: cum haec praesentis iam sint vehementiae signa, non
futurae.

29   ex ea enim significatione futuram dicunt intelligi phrenitim,
quae non naturalis est, sed multorum placitis est firmata. dehinc praesentis passionis signa necessaria esse confitentur.
aiunt enim quaedam esse quae futura denuntient, quaedam quae
saepe futura, quorum secunda futurae phreniticae passionis
esse dicunt, siquidem non necessario sequatur. quod[18] enim[19]
est repugnans. omne etenim signum ad eam rem quam signifi-
caverit intelligitur, est enim ex his quae ad aliquid intelliguntur.
quomodo igitur signum vocari potest, cum[20] non solum praesens
non est quod ostenderit, verum etiam in quibusdam neque
erit?

30   secundum nos itaque declivitatis atque pronae aegritudinis in
phrenitim ⟨signa⟩ recte nuncupantur,[21] ut labiles in passionem
aegros pronuntiemus, quos Graeci eunosus[22] totius appellatione
vocant. ipsius enim verbi qualitas sive veritas excussa designat aliquid esse quo res ferantur nec tamen necessario venturae.
signa igitur res ipsa semper praesens quae significatur ostendit,
qua saepe etiam futura noscuntur. alia vero esse signa declivitatis in phrenitim, alia in lethargiam atque ceteras passiones, ex his reddere coeperimus cum sua suis manifestabimus.

[14] sinceratione G: corr. R

[15] dicta sunt Schmid 85: dictans G

[16] fort. enim

[17] fort. praesentia quamquam vel quaedam praesentia

[18] quid edd.

[19] fort. tamen vel autem

[20] cuius edd.

[21] ⟨signa⟩ recte nuncupantur scripsi: ⟨signum R⟩ recte nuncupatur G

[22] ἐυνόσους G: ἐπινόσους A, sed cf. εὐπαθής

ness of the head, symptoms which appear all together and ac-
28 company the disease. But unreasoning boldness and giddiness
have been surely identified as signs of the coming of phrenitis.
And, as in the case of external disorders, we consider as future
conditions certain present conditions, though they are still unseen because of their smallness. Thus Thessalus himself in Book
I of his work *On Regimen* prescribes venesection for those who
are about to pass into a severe state of stricture. In this class he
places those who have continuous fever and a low pulse until
the time of remission, and pass urine frequently or with pain.'
Actually, however, these conditions indicate a serious disorder
that is present and not in the future.

29   Now they [the followers of Asclepiades] assert that from this
set of signs the coming of phrenitis may be expected. This, however, is not a necessary consequence but is based merely on widespread opinion. Moreover, they really admit that signs are necessarily connected with some present disorder. To be sure, they
hold that certain signs indicate what is to be, that certain other
signs indicate what is *likely* to be, and that to this second group
of signs belong the signs of the coming of phrenitis, since phrenitis does not inevitably follow. But such a view is illogical. For
every sign is to be understood with respect to what is signified,
since a sign belongs to those things which are understood in rela-
tion to something else. How, then, can anything be called a sign
if the thing signified not only is not present but in certain cases
will never come about?

30   And so in our opinion, it is right to speak of signs of a [present]
condition that is apt to pass into phrenitis.[5] Hence we may speak
of patients who are slipping into the disease, persons whom the
Greeks include in the general term *eunosoe*. This word by its
very nature and its fundamental meaning indicates that there
is a state to which things are tending, though they need not arrive at that state. And so the present condition, which is what is
indicated in each case, produces signs, and from this present
condition the future, too, is often revealed. Now the signs which
indicate that a patient is on the verge of phrenitis are different
from those which indicate that he is on the verge of lethargy or
some other disease, as we shall undertake to show hereafter
when we distinguish each disease by its own signs.

5. But it is not right to speak of 'signs of future phrenitis.'

31 II. QUAE SEQUUNTUR EOS QUI IN PHRENITICAM
        PASSIONEM PRONI INTELLIGANTUR, QUOS
                  LABILES DIXIMUS

IN PHRENITICAM igitur passionem pronos vel declives sequitur
    febris acuta atque difficile ad superficiem corporis ascendens,
pulsus humilior densior, vultus subinflatus sive plenus, sanguinis per nares destillatio, vigiliae iuges aut turbatus somnus
et insomnia[1] turbulenta, mentis sollicitudo ac gravitas[2] sine ratione, frequens tergorum conversio[3] iacendi cum capitis assidua
commutatione, aliquando etiam sine causa hilaritas, oculorum
rubor cum levi lacrimatione, et circumiectio manuum sine ullo
capitis dolore, articulorum frigus sine tremore, urinae abun-
32 dantia flavae aquatae tenuis et paulatim exclusae, aliquibus
etiam sonitus capitis atque aurium tinnitus, dolor quoque
capitis repentino[4] quiescens[5] nulla ex manifesta ratione, praecordiorum etiam tensio, visus attentus vel frequenter palpebrans.

   quidam medici ex quibus sunt Asclepiadis sectatores, etiam
attendunt aeris qualitatem, quam Graeci catastema vocant, et
tempus et antecedentes causas et naturam et aetatem. aeris inquiunt habitum[6] ne concalescat,[7] quod eius causa[8] plurimos
afficiat [ut saepe oculorum lippitudines vel ulcera];[9] tempus
autem, ut aestatis finem vel autumnum, in his enim aiunt hanc
33 frequentare passionem; antecedentes inquiunt causas, ut vinolentiam vel vigilias ac iuges adustiones; naturam inquiunt[10]
aegrotantis, ut si fuerit mente mobilis atque iracundus, vel in
disciplinis literarum exercitatus, aut capite debilitato et facile
inflationem sentienti, vel si quoties aegritudine afficitur facile
alienatione vexetur; aetatem inquiunt si iuvenis. omnia quidem
sunt providenda: non enim ex uno vel duobus sed ex multis concurrentibus significatio firmatur. unum etenim quiddam etiam
ad aliud quiddam commune est: at vero in unum conveniens
multorum concursus discretionum facit intelligentiam pro-
minere.

    [1] insania *edd.*: *corr. Bendz 80*   [2] gravitas *scripsi*: pravitas *edd.*
    [3] conversio *Bendz 80*: est versio G: inversio *Rm*
    [4] repentino *Schmid 86, coll. Ac. ii. 9*: repente non G   [5] quiescens *Rm*: quiescit G
    [6] habitu G: *corr. Rm*   [7] concalescat *conieci*: quis (is *R*) calescat G
    [8] eius causa] eius causis (= καῦσις) *R*: eius cauma (= καῦμα) *vel* eius causos (= καῦσος)
coni. Helmreich 310: *fort.* ea causa *vel* encausis
    [9] *seclusi*   [10] inquit G: *corr. Rm*

31 ## II. THE SYMPTOMS OF PERSONS ON THE VERGE OF PHRENITIS, WHOM WE HAVE CALLED 'SLIPPING INTO THE DISEASE'

THOSE who are on the verge of phrenitis or are slipping into the disease show the following signs: an acute fever hardly rising to the surface of the body, pulse low and thick, face somewhat puffed up or full, dripping of blood from the nostrils, continual sleeplessness or troubled sleep with confused dreams, unreasonable worry and concern, frequent turning of the back while lying, and continual changing of position of the head; at times there is also giddiness without reason, redness of the eyes with slight tearing, tossing about of the arms, absence of pain in the head, coldness of the limbs without trembling, abundance of urine, light-colored, watery, thin, and discharged a 32 little at a time. In some cases there is also a sensation of noise in the head and ringing in the ears; also pains in the head suddenly abating for no obvious reason, precordial[1] tension, and fixity of gaze or frequent blinking.

Some physicians, among them Asclepiades and his followers, also consider in this connection the weather (Greek *catastēma*), the season, the antecedent causes, the nature of the patient, and his age. They speak of the weather and the danger of its becoming very hot, for that causes many cases [of this disease]. They speak of the season, too, especially the end of summer or autumn, for they say that this disease is frequent at those times. 33 They speak of antecedent causes, like excessive drinking of wine, lack of sleep, and exposure to heat. They speak of the nature of the patient, e.g., if he is of inconstant temperament and easily angered, or much devoted to reading, or if his head is weak and prone to feel congestion, or if he is easily subject to mental aberration whenever he suffers from illness. They consider his age, if he is young. All the circumstances must be taken into account, for the indication of phrenitis is confirmed not by one or two signs but by the concurrence of many, since each one by itself is found in other diseases, too, but the concurrence of many signs makes possible a clear differentiation between this and the other diseases.

1. Caelius uses *praecordia* to translate Greek *hypochondria*. The term 'precordial region' thus somewhat loosely designates the hypochondriac and gastric regions.

34   III. QUOMODO INTELLIGITUR PHRENITIS

INTELLIGIMUS phrenitim ex toto signorum concursu. unum
etenim singulare quicquam, ut est alienatio vel febricula,
non designat phreniticum; sed si multa concurrerint quae nihil
aliud quam passionem designent, ut sit significatio quae, ut
supra diximus, ex multis confecta unum faciat signum et significans eius rei quam demonstrat. quare, ut dixi, intelligimus
phrenitim ex concurrenti febre acuta et alienatione et pulsu
parvo atque crebro, attestante carphologia et crocidismo: ex his
enim intelligitur passionis genus.

35   magnitudinis vero atque proprietatis differentiam plurima
atque alia sunt quae designant, a Graecis symptomata appellata, ut febres[1] continuae vel hemitritaeae[2] [esse][3] vel inaequales,
atque ⟨ad⟩[4] superficiem corporis difficile ascendentes, alienatio
intra diatriti[5] vel post diatriti[5] tempus, iugis aut intercapedinata,
cum risu tacito aut cum cachinno et cantilena vel certe maestitudine, silentio vel murmure aut vagitu aut levi secum sua ipse[6]
mussitatione vel mentis indignatione, ut in furore exiliens difficile teneatur, atque omnibus iracundus sit et exclamet vel sese
percutiat aut suam vestem atque propinquantium scindat aut
metu se abscondendum existimet aut lacrimetur, atque secum
loquentibus non respondeat, cum loquatur tamquam[7] visis, et
non solum ⟨non⟩ visis,[8] sed etiam mortuis, et neque potum
36   postulet neque cibum, aut acceptum vehementer invadat et
immasticatum transvoret, aut[9] masticet neque transvoret sed
in ore contineat, et post paululum proiciat; lucem quoque aut
tenebras fugiat, adsint etiam vigiliae iuges aut parvus et turbulentus somnus, oculi sanguinolenti cum tensione venarum suarum, et fixo visu atque sine ulla palpebratione aut multum
mobili et cum iugi palpebratione, aliquando etiam manuum ante
oculos praemissione[10] quasi aliquid apprehendere vel detrahere
volentium, quod aut inhaesisse oculis aut antevolare aegro-
37   tanti videatur; vultus etiam quibusdam collectus atque conductus, genarum rubor perseverans aut per intervalla in pal-
lorem mutatus, capitis siccitas quae statim ebibat fomenti li-

[1] febris G: corr. Rm   [2] hemitritaeas G: corr. Rm   [3] om. R
[4] atque ⟨ad⟩ scripsi, coll. Ac. i. 31: adque A
[5] diatria G: diatritaeum Rm: corr. Bendz 81
[6] ipsius Rm   [7] nunquam Rm
[8] solum ⟨non⟩ visis R: solum vivis Hagendahl 246   [9] aut A: atque G   [10] praemissio R

III. HOW TO RECOGNIZE PHRENITIS

34

W̲E̲ ̲R̲E̲C̲O̲G̲N̲I̲Z̲E̲ phrenitis from the combination of all the signs. For any single sign, e.g., mental derangement or fever, does not indicate phrenitis; but the case is otherwise if many signs concur which together can indicate only this disease. In this case an indication is obtained, as we have said, from many circumstances, and constitutes a single sign indicative of the situation. We therefore recognize phrenitis, as I have said,[1] from the combination of acute fever, mental derangement, small and rapid pulse, and the plucking at straws and hairs. For it is on the basis of these signs that the kind of disease is recognized.

35 But there are many other signs (Greek *symptōmata*) that indicate differences in severity and in special features of the disease, e.g., unremitting or semitertian or irregular fevers, fevers hardly reaching the surface of the body; mental aberration before the end of the three-day period or after that period, either continuous or interrupted, quiet or loud laughter, singing or a state of sadness, silence, murmuring, crying, or a barely audible muttering to one's self; or such a state of anger that the patient jumps up in a rage and can scarcely be held back, is wrathful at everyone, shouts, beats himself or tears his own clothing and that of his neighbors, or seeks to hide in fear, or weeps, or fails to answer those who speak to him, while he speaks not only with those who are not present but with the dead, as if they

36 were in his presence; and asks for neither food nor drink, or when he does take food falls violently upon it and gulps it down unchewed, or else chews it but does not swallow it, keeping it in his mouth and after a while spitting it out. And he shuns light or darkness, experiences continuous sleeplessness or short troubled sleep; his eyes are bloodshot, the blood vessels being distended; his gaze is fixed without any blinking, or else keeps wandering about with constant blinking; sometimes he puts his hands before his eyes as if seeking to catch or remove some object which he thinks has become stuck in his eye or is flying in

37 front of him. In some cases the face is contracted and drawn; there is redness of the cheeks, either persisting or changing at intervals to pallor, a dryness of the head so that the moisture of

1. *Ac.* i. 21.

quorem, dentium stridor, guttae sanguinis levissimae per nares,
capitis frequens alienatio,[11] cum aurium intentione, ut aliquid
audire videatur, indecens iacendi positio, pedum quoque iugis
ex alto submissio, corporis vacua fortitudo, articulorum iugis
torpor, raptus etiam vel attractio cooperimentorum a pedibus
ad superiora, ventris fluor, urinae aquatae vel felleae cum nube-
38 culis portentuosis; ultimo quibusdam etiam vultus mortuosus,
aliis cum collo subinflatus,[12] manuum tremor, pulsus creberrimus
atque submersus et tremulus et imbecillis, aliquando etiam deficiens et in similitudinem oleo defecti luminis marcescens, praecordiorum vehemens tensio atque ad superiora adductio, singultus, linguae impedimentum atque locutionis inapprehensibilis
articulatio; dehinc quibusdam diaphoresis, quibusdam spasmus,
aut pressura quae lethargicam passionem attestantibus ceteris
denuntiet. [hoc pulsus inducit celeres multos aut parvos saltus,
in magnitudinem erectio quae sit aetati aegrotantis[13] incongrua,
atque subinanis][14] relevatis autem atque ad sedem[15] pergentibus
omnia supradicta minuuntur.

39   gravius autem ac perniciose affici dicimus eos quos ut supradictos[16] plurima atque varia fuerint secuta et iugiter[17] et sine
ulla indulgentia[18] laxamenti. peius autem[19] laborare dicimus
eos qui post primam diatriton fuerint hac affecti passione,
quam qui ante ipsam. etenim praesauciatis viribus quicquid
adhibetur grave atque indignum[20] adiutorium, vel phlebotomia[21]
40 quae principaliter temporis causa adhiberi prohibetur. exitia-
liter etiam affici dicimus eos qui asperrimi atque audaces fuerint
aegrotantes (insanitivi[22] etenim etiam sani si[23] iracundi esse
perspiciuntur), nec non etiam qui subridere videntur et stridore
dentium aut singultu affici. his etiam[24] spasmus imminere significatur. gravius etiam si mutabiles fuerint colore et tremuli et
stertentes aut fastidiosi per omnia.

[11] acclinatio *Rm*: *fort.* inclinatio *vel* declinatio   [12] *an* subinflato?
[13] quae sit aetati aegrotantis *Schmid 88, coll. Ac. ii. 3, 11*: quaesita et aegrotanti *G*
[14] *seclusi*
[15] salutem *Triller ap. Kühn 25*: sanitatem *Rm*
[16] ut supradictos] supradictorum *Bendz Eran 43. 54*: ex supradictis *Hagendahl ibid.*
[17] iugiter *Rm*: iugi *G*   [19] etiam *Bendz Eran 43. 54*
[18] indulgia *G*: *corr. Rm*   [20] indignum ⟨est⟩ *R*
[21] phlebotomia *Rm*: phlebotomiae *Bendz Eran 43. 54*: phlebotomice *G*
[22] insontine *G*: insanitive *Bendz Eran 43. 56*: *cf. Sor. Gyn., p. 68. 17*
[23] sani si *conieci*: sanis *G*: sani *Rm*   [24] *fort.* enim

a fomentation is quickly absorbed, gnashing of the teeth, slight bleeding from the nostrils, frequent change of position of the head, with a straining of the ears so that the patient seems to be listening to something; unseemly position in lying, constant raising of the feet from below, useless bodily strength,[2] continual numbness of the extremities, pulling or drawing of the bedclothes from the feet upward, flux of the bowels, urine that is

38 watery or bilious with unnatural cloudy patches; finally, in some cases a deathlike face, in others face and neck somewhat puffed up; trembling of the hands; very rapid pulse, submerged, quivering, feeble, sometimes even failing, and fading away like a lamp that has run out of oil; pronounced tension and drawing up of the precordia, hiccoughs, and an impediment of the tongue, rendering speech unintelligible. Then in some cases there occurs colliquative sweating, in others convulsion, or so profound a stupor as to indicate, in conjunction with the other symptoms, the imminence of lethargy.[3] But when the condition of the patient is relieved and he is on his way to recovery, all these symptoms are reduced.

39 We hold that those patients are gravely and dangerously affected who show many varied symptoms, as described above, continually and without any remission or alleviation. And we say that those who are affected by phrenitis[4] after the first three-day period [of their illness] are more seriously ill than those who are affected before the end of that period. For, since the patient's strength has already been impaired, whatever remedy is employed is apt to be a dangerous and improper remedy, even venesection, which, chiefly because of this element of time, can-

40 not be permitted. Furthermore, we hold that patients who are fierce and violent are most dangerously ill. (In fact, even people in health who are given to fits of anger are, in a sense, mad.) The same is true of those patients who smile to themselves, gnash their teeth, or have hiccoughs. This is an indication that convulsion threatens them. The case is also serious if the patient's complexion changes, and he trembles, snores, or shows distaste for everything.

2. The meaning is doubtful. Cf. *Chr.* i. 152, 154; *Ac.* i. 101.

3. I have omitted the sentence that follows in the text; it may originally have been a gloss on *ceteris*. To be sure 'a pulse abnormally large for the patient's age and somewhat empty' is an indication of a change from phrenitis to lethargy (see *Ac.* ii. 3 and 11). But the phrase *hoc . . . saltus* seems to be corrupt.

4. I.e., by the specific symptoms of phrenitis, e.g., mental derangement. Cf. *Ac.* i. 35.

aliarum vero principes sectarum iuxta aetatis differentiam
gravius affici dicunt iuvenes a ceteris aetatibus, iuxta sexum et
naturam viros a feminis,[25] quomodo etiam sapere plus est in
41 iuvenibus atque maribus:[26] maius enim fit malum firmitate re-
liqua adiutum. dehinc etiam illos qui natura fuerint tristes et
in passione cum ridiculo deliraverint, aut rursum hilares natura atque cachinnosi cum iracundia et maestitudine, aegrotantes gravius affici dicunt, siquidem nulla vestigia ex his quae
sanitati fuerint consueta remansisse videantur.

nos vero dicimus communiter graviter laborare quos passionis
adficit magnitudo. illud enim semper in aegritudine magis afficit[27] quod a natura plurimum recesserit.

42   IV. QUAE SUNT HUIC SIMILES PASSIONES ET
              QUOMODO DISCERNUNTUR

SIMILES sunt atque vicinae phreniticae passioni ex ipsa alienatione furor, quam vulgo insaniam vocant, melancholia,
pleuritis, atque peripneumonia, quae saepissime accessionis
tempore alienationem faciunt, item mentis alienatio in his qui
mandragoram aut altercum biberint. internoscuntur autem
furentes atque melancholici a phreniticis, siquidem alienatio
sine febricula atque crocidismo vel carphologia esse videatur;
dehinc tardae[1] saepissime atque sine passione. item melancholia fellis nigri vomitum faciat,[2] stomacho patiente aut plus a
43 ceteris corporis partibus aegrotante. praestantius autem odisse
homines facit, atque vultus colorem plumbeum.

item ut[3] pleuritis et peripneumonia et omnes passiones quae
ex dolore accessionis tempore alienationem faciunt, internoscuntur hoc modo, primo quod cum dolores asperantur, extendi-

---

[25] a foeminis *Schmid 88*: ac foeminas G
[26] maribus *Schmid 89*: maioribus G (*retin. Bendz 30*)
[27] *fort.* afficitur
[1] tarde G
[2] facit R
[3] ut *om.* R: *fort.* et

---

5. Cf. *Chr.* iv. 136. And, on this analogy, phrenitis, which affects the mind, is more
severe in cases where normally the mind is more vigorous.

Now the leaders of other sects say that the gravity of the affliction varies with age, young people being more seriously affected than those of other ages, and also with sex and nature, men being more seriously affected than women, since the mind is
41 more vigorous in young people and in men. For a disease is more severe [they say] when there is general strength to support it.[5] Again, they say that those patients are more seriously affected who are naturally sad but in the course of the disease rave with laughter, or, again, those who are naturally lively and given to loud laughter but in the course of the disease are angry and dejected. For in such cases there seem to be no traces left of the qualities which the patients showed in health.

But we Methodists take a general view, viz., that the disease is grave when it occurs in potent form. For in every case the greater the abnormality produced by a disease, the more serious is the disease.

42   IV. DISEASES RESEMBLING PHRENITIS AND HOW THEY ARE DISTINGUISHED FROM IT

SIMILAR and kindred to phrenitis in respect to loss of reason are mania (i.e., *furor*, commonly called *insania*), melancholy, pleurisy, and pneumonia. These diseases in periods of exacerbation very often produce mental aberration. Also resembling phrenitis is loss of reason due to the drinking of mandragora or henbane. Now mania and melancholy may be distinguished from phrenitis; for in mania and melancholy the mental derangement is not found to be accompanied by any fever[1] or by plucking at bits of wool and straw. And generally mania and melancholy are chronic diseases and without pain. Furthermore, melancholy is accompanied by the vomiting of black bile, for the esophagus is affected or, at any rate, more particularly affected than the other
43 parts of the body. Melancholy causes the patient to entertain a strong dislike for people; it produces a leaden complexion.

And not only pleurisy and pneumonia but all the diseases that cause loss of reason because of the pain at the time of an attack may best be distinguished from phrenitis in the following way. When the pains in these diseases become intense, the mental de-

1. But cf. *Ac.* i. 45.

tur atque consurgit alienatio, et eorum indulgentia minuitur,
quippe levis atque solubilis deliratio. nam phreniticorum si
ex consensu fuerit facta, tamen et non semper accessionibus
aucta aut demissionibus minuta, sed magis intardans atque
perseverans perspicitur.

44   si vero poto malo medicamine vel alterco alienentur, discernuntur secundum interrogationem praecedentium causarum.[4]
sed quia etiam de medicamine poto potest phrenitis evenire
(non enim praeordinatae atque fixae sunt necessario eius antecedentes causae), ad[5] interrogationem praecedentium causarum
aeger credibilis esse non potest, item externi, hoc est ab aegro
alieni, antecedentia nescire possunt, potius[6] differentiam accipimus, ut si non febricitat, hoc sit signum internoscendarum
causarum, si autem febricitat, crocidismus atque carphologia et
densitas pulsus absint. his enim qui mandragoram vel altercum biberint rarus est pulsus.

45   V. QUOMODO DISCERNIMUS A PHRENITICIS EOS
          QUI FURORE FEBRICITANT

QUOMODO furentes sive insanos a phreniticis sola febrium sin-
    ceritate omnes sectarum principes discreverunt,[1] et saepe
etiam febris ex aliis causis his passionibus incidit, oportebat hos
etiam cum febribus furore delirantes a phreniticis discernere:
non quidem mutandae curationis causa, omnes etenim passiones
celeres supradictae atque tardae, sed in superpositione[2] constitutae, quam Graeci epithesim vocant, laxativa atque mitigativa indigent curatione, sed ad demonstrationem quo probe-
46 mus[3] etiam specialium uti discretione haec posuimus. est autem utilissimum etiam localibus adiutoriis ut patientibus locis

    [4] praecedentes causae *edd.*

    [5] *fort.* ⟨et⟩ ad

    [6] potius *Rm*: totius *G*: *an* tutius?

    [1] decreverunt *G*: secreverunt *Rm*

    [2] insuper positione *edd.*: *corr.* Kühn 26

    [3] possemus *Rm*

    2. Or reading *praecedentes causae*: 'such antecedent causes are discerned by ques-
tioning.'

rangement is aggravated and increased; but when the pains are mitigated, the derangement is lessened, for it is not serious and is easily cleared up. But the loss of reason in phrenitis, even if it does occur with concomitant pain, still is not always increased in attacks or decreased in remissions but is found to be more abiding and persistent.

44   If, on the other hand, loss of reason follows the drinking of a poisonous drug like henbane, the diagnosis is made by questioning about the antecedent circumstances.[2] But phrenitis, too, may result from the drinking of a drug, for the antecedent causes of phrenitis are not immutably fixed and perfectly regular. Moreover, the patient's answers to questions about antecedent causes may not be reliable, and outsiders, i.e., strangers to the patient, may be unfamiliar with the previous circumstances. In such cases we prefer to obtain a diagnosis as follows. If the patient has no fever, it is a sign that the disease is to be distinguished [from phrenitis]; the same is true even if he has fever but does not pluck at wool and straw and if his pulse is not rapid. For those who have drunk mandragora or henbane have a slow pulse.

45   ## V. HOW TO DISTINGUISH BETWEEN CASES OF MANIA IN WHICH FEVER IS PRESENT AND PHRENITIS

ALL the leading physicians of the various sects have distinguished cases of mania from those of phrenitis by the mere absence of fever. Yet fever from other causes often supervenes in mania or insanity. It has therefore become necessary to distinguish between cases of mania where fever is present and phrenitis; not, however, for the purpose of changing the general treatment (for all the aforesaid acute diseases, as well as chronic diseases, provided that they are at the stage of an attack [Greek *epithesis*], require a relaxing and soothing treatment), but rather to show how we should distinguish specific diseases [of

46 the same general character].[1] Moreover, it is very useful to apply local remedies as a treatment for the parts affected or at

1. I.e., all these diseases basically involve *strictura*, yet they are different diseases. *Specialium*, however, may refer not to diseases but to remedies.

vel plus patientibus curationem adhibeamus. nam phreniticis
atque furiosis caput magis, melancholicis stomachus patitur.

igitur non febricitare furiosos percunctatum[4] non est sive uni-
versale, quod Graeci catholicon vocant, sed est discrepatione
partile, siquidem, ut diximus, quidam febribus afficiantur, sed
phrenitici acutis vel celeribus, furiosi vero tardis, quamquam
sit etiam hoc insufficiens discretioni, propter eos qui repentino
furore agitati febricitant.

47 remanet ut ordine accidentium discretionem faciamus. praecedit enim febrem in furiosis alienatio, in phreniticis vero febricula alienationem. sed quia aliquando potest furentum alienatio concurrens febriculae latere, aut ordinis aut interroga-
tionis, ut supra diximus, causa, siquidem ab aegro narrari non
possit, advertamus in phreniticis parvum atque crebrum esse
pulsum necessario, in furiosis vero maiorem. sed quia initii vel
augmenti accessionis febrium parvus[5] atque creber pulsus esse
potest, declinationis autem atque indulgentiae[6] maior, illud advertere debemus, quia in phreniticis etiam tunc parvus atque
densus perseverat, ut discretionem magis ex pulsu faciamus,

48 quamquam etiam ipsa infirmetur saepe febrium nequitia, quae
ut in aliis passionibus sic etiam in furiosis pulsum parvum atque
densum servat. ita discerni vel internosci potest, cum neque
crocidismum in aegrotantibus viderimus, quod est ex operimentis fimbriarum veluti decerptio, neque carphologiam, quae
est festucarum levium a parietibus veluti detractio, quam
necesse est phreniticos facere. quae denique si furiosis advenerint in febribus constitutis, in phreniticam passionem ex insania
venisse pronuntiamus: tamquam rursum ex phrenitica passione,
cedentibus[7] propriis signis, hoc est supradictis, in furorem
transeant,[8] non aliter quam si etiam aliis adtestantibus[9] signis
in lethargiam veniant, vel certe relevati ex lethargia in phreniticam redeant.

---

[4] *an* percuntativum? *Cf. Chr. iv. 114*

[5] parvus *Bendz 82*: par in his G: *an leg.* parvus in his (*sc.* furiosis)?

[6] indigentiae G: *corr. Rm*

[7] et phrenitica passio recedentibus G: *corr. Bendz Eran 41. 76 (qui etiam* passione
recedentibus *conicit)*

[8] transeat R (et . . . passio *retentis*)

[9] adtestantibus *Schmid Mn 134*: id testantibus G

any rate those more seriously affected; and in phrenitis and
mania the head is chiefly affected, in melancholy the esophagus.[2]

Now the statement that persons suffering from mania do not
have fever is not a universal or general truth (Greek *catholicon*);
it is true in some cases and not in others; for, as we have said,
some do have fever. In phrenitis, however, the fever is acute or
swift, and in mania slow (chronic). But this, too, is an insufficient ground for distinction, because of the cases where patients
are seized in an acute attack of mania with fever.

47   Hence we must distinguish the diseases on the basis of the
order of the symptoms. Thus in mania[3] the loss of reason precedes the fever, but in phrenitis the fever precedes the loss of
reason. But, since in mania the loss of reason may sometimes
be accompanied by fever and the order of occurrence may be
unknown and the facts unobtainable by the type of questioning
described above, because of the patient's inability to give an
account, we must then recall that in phrenitis the pulse is always small and rapid, but it is larger in mania. But [in mania],
either at the outset of the disease or in the increasing phase of
an attack, the pulse may be small and rapid, while when there
is a decline or remission the pulse is larger; we must therefore
note that in phrenitis, even in such a remission, the pulse continues small and rapid. Hence we may distinguish the diseases
better by the pulse, though even this distinction may be upset
48 by stubborn fevers which in cases of mania, as in other diseases,
may keep the pulse small and rapid. In that event the diseases
may be discerned or distinguished by the fact that in mania we
find neither *crocydismos*, a sort of plucking of threads from the
covers, nor *carphologia*, a sort of picking of small pieces of straw
from the walls; but sufferers from phrenitis always show these
symptoms. And if these symptoms *do* appear in [what was] a
case of mania accompanied by fever, we say that the case has
passed from mania to phrenitis, just as, on the other hand, cases
may pass from phrenitis into mania with the disappearance of
the symptoms of phrenitis described above. In the same way, if
other signs are present, cases of phrenitis may pass into lethargy,
and, indeed, these patients may be relieved of their lethargy and
return to phrenitis.

2. Or the cardia. Cf. *Chr.* i. 182–83.
3. I.e., mania accompanied by fever.

49 ## VI. QUOMODO DISCERNIMUS DORMIENTES PHRENITICOS AB HIS QUI IN LETHARGI-CAM DEVENIUNT PASSIONEM

Quomodo phrenitici aliqui augmento passionis in lethargiam, aliqui declinatione in somnos devenerint, et cum aspectu commune[1] quod utrique non sentiunt, atque multos inexercitos medicos errore fefellerint,[2] ut dormientes tamquam depressos excitarent, aut oppressos tamquam dormientes sine adiutorio passioni traditos reliquissent, utilem ducimus eorum discretionem faciendam.

discernuntur igitur colore, charactere, respiratione, pulsu, 50 tactu, schemate iacendi, febrium magnitudine. colore inquam, dormientium enim mundum corpus atque floscule[3] vividum et naturali habitudine plenum, oppressorum vero in lethargia passione pallens vel plumbeum vel quolibet alio[4] colore affectum invenitur. character autem dormientium hilaris, lethargicorum tristis invenitur. item spiratio dormientium ordinata, lethargicorum tarda esse probatur. pulsu etiam discretionem facimus, quod quamquam utrique subinflatus atque maior, tamen cum inanitate in lethargis, cum plenitudine dormientibus invenitur. tactu autem lethargis etiam praecordia distenduntur plurimum, et totum corpus durius fiet ob nimiam stricturam; dormientibus vero econtrario, quia strictura minuitur, etiam praecordia re-51 laxantur et totius corporis tactus mollior efficitur. schemate iacendi discretio fiet, siquidem lethargi a capite lecti ad pedum loca labantur et incomposito vel indisposito iaceant corpore; dormientes vero congrua naturae positione cernantur. magnitudine inquam febrium, dormientium enim minor ac lenior, lethargorum maior atque aspera febricula invenitur. quapropter observanda sunt etiam tempora. si enim in declina-

[1] an communi?
[2] fefellerint R: fefellerunt G
[3] floride Rm
[4] alieno Rm

49   VI. HOW TO DISTINGUISH BETWEEN PATIENTS
WITH PHRENITIS WHO ARE ASLEEP AND
THOSE WHO ARE PASSING INTO LETHARGY

S OME patients with phrenitis pass into lethargy as their disease
increases, and others drop into sleep as the disease wanes;
and both cases present a similar appearance because in neither
is there any consciousness. Hence many inexperienced doctors
have been deceived. Thinking that those who were merely sleeping were suffering from lethargy, they have roused them; and,
on the other hand, thinking that those who were really suffering
from lethargy were merely sleeping, they have abandoned them
to the disease without any treatment. We therefore believe it
useful to give the means of distinguishing these two states.

The distinctive features are the complexion, expression, respiration, pulse, reaction to touch, position in bed, and degree of
50 fever. I mention complexion because in the case of those sleeping
the body has a clean appearance, a blooming freshness, and
complete naturalness, while in those sunk in lethargy it is found
to be pale, or the color of lead, or some other color. Again, the
expression of those who are asleep is cheerful, of those who have
lethargy sad. And the respiration of the sleeping is found to be
regular,[1] of those who have lethargy slow. We also distinguish
by the pulse; for, though in both cases the pulse is somewhat
inflated and large, yet it has an emptiness in lethargy, and a
fulness in those who are merely sleeping. Moreover, in lethargy
the precordial region is very tense to the touch and the whole
body hard because of the strong state of stricture. But, contrariwise, in the case of those who are merely asleep, since the state
of stricture is lessened, the precordial region is relaxed and the
51 whole body is softer to the touch. The position in bed will also
serve as a criterion, for those who are suffering from lethargy
slip from the head of the bed toward the foot and lie in a confused and disordered position, while those who are merely sleeping are found to assume a natural position. As for the degree of
fever, those merely sleeping have a lesser and milder fever, those
suffering from lethargy a greater and harsher fever. And we
must also have regard for the element of time. For if the patient

1. And, it is implied, of normal rate.

tione passionis et in dimissione vel declinatione accessionis
sensus aegrotantium quieverint, intelligimus somnum; si vero
in augmento passionis vel accessionis et magis in eius initio vel
augmento id acciderit, lethargum pronuntiamus.

52   VII. QUAE SINT DIFFERENTIAE
PHRENITICAE PASSIONIS

DIFFERENTIAS phreniticae passionis quidam ex accidentium
proprietate faciendas existimant. aiunt denique aliam
esse alienationem cum risu atque puerili saltatione, aliam cum
maerore atque exclamatione vel silentio aut timore. nos vero
aliam dicimus esse ex strictura, aliam ex complexione stricturae
atque solutionis. est enim verum ita discernere, ut non accidentium diversitas passionis differentias ostendat, sed generalis
quaedam ac necessaria designatio, quae fiet ut supra diximus
ex principalibus passionibus, unde etiam curationum ratio sumatur.

53   VIII. QUIS LOCUS IN PHRENITICIS PATITUR

QUAESITUM etiam quis locus in phreniticis patitur, et magis
a principibus aliarum sectarum, ut secundum differentiam
patientis loci curationes adhiberent et localia locis adiutoria
compararent.[1] nos autem sive locorum sive vicinitatis eorum
causa generalem curationem non mutamus. non est enim sub
eodem genere iacens locorum necessaria differentia.
aliqui igitur cerebrum pati dixerunt, alii eius fundum sive
basin, quam nos sessionem dicere poterimus, alii membranas,
alii et cerebrum et eius membranas, alii cor, alii cordis summita-
54 tem, alii membranam quae cor circumtegit, alii arteriarum eam
quam Graeci aorten[2] appellant, alii venam crassam, quam iidem
phleba pachian[3] vocaverunt, alii diaphragma. et quid ultra
tendimus quod facile explicare possumus, si id quod senserunt

[1] compararent R: comparent G

[2] ἀόρτην G

[3] φλέβα παχεῖαν G

has lost consciousness in the declining phase of the disease and
during the remission or abatement of an attack, we recognize
that it is merely sleep; but if this happens in the period of increase of the disease or of an attack, and particularly at or near
the beginning of such an attack, we conclude that it is lethargy.

52   VII. THE DIFFERENT TYPES OF PHRENITIS

S OME say that different types of phrenitis must be distinguished by the symptoms peculiar to them. Thus they say
that in one type the loss of reason is manifested by laughter and
childish dancing, in another type by sadness, crying out, silence,
or fear. But we hold that there are two types, one involving a
state of stricture, the other a combination of stricture and looseness. For it is proper to make distinctions in such a way that
different types of a disease are shown not by differences in
symptoms but by a general and invariable indication. Such an
indication will be obtained, as we have said above, from the
leading types of disease, and it is on this indication that our
system of treatment also depends.

53   VIII. THE LOCUS OF THE AFFECTION
                    IN PHRENITIS

W HAT part [of the body] is affected in phrenitis? This question has been raised particularly by leaders of other sects
so that they may apply their treatments according to the different parts affected and prepare local remedies for the places in
question. We, however, do not alter our general therapy on the
basis of these places or the regions about them. For in a given
general type of disease a difference in the parts affected is not
an essential difference.

Now some say that the brain is affected, others its fundus or
base, which we may translate *sessio* ['seat'], others its membranes, others both the brain and its membranes, others the
heart, others the apex of the heart, others the membrane which
54 incloses the heart, others the artery which the Greeks call *aortē*,
others the thick vein (Greek *phleps pacheia*), others the diaphragm. But why continue in this way when we can easily
clarify the matter by stating what these writers really had in

dixerimus? nam singuli eum locum in phreniticis pati dixerunt
in quo animae regimen esse suspicati sunt. denique singulorum
iudicium atque assertionem pertractantes expugnabimus libris
quos De passionum causis scribemus.

55 nos igitur communiter totum corpus pati accipimus, etenim
totum febre iactatur. implet denique phreniticorum significationem[4] febrium signum quapropter totum corpus curamus.
sed plus pati dicimus caput, etenim antecedentia demonstrant
signa, ut eius gravedo, tensio, dolor, sonitus, aurium tinnitus,
siccitas, atque sensuum impedimentum, et cetera quae iam passionis praesentis esse signa noscuntur, singuli sensus suo careant[5]
apprehensionis officio, palpebra dura, oculi sanguinolenti ac
prominentes, genarum rubor, venarum extensio, vultus inflatio ac plenitudo, linguae asperitas.

56 eos vero qui nos ex naturali tractatu, quam Graeci physiolo-
giam, patientem locum apprehendere dixerunt, siquidem praenoscentes animae regalia in capite constituta, exinde mentis
alienationem fieri acceperimus, ita expugnamus ut primo regale
locum incertum[6] remanserit. sed nos varietas atque multitudo
accidentium in capite signorum plus a cetero corpore docuit
⟨id⟩[7] pati.

57 sed aiunt faciem magis plurimis signis affici, et propterea
huic esse adhibenda adiutoria. 'nunc vero cucurbitam occipitio
apponitis, siquidem[8] per apertionem, quam Graeci anatomiam,
didiceritis sensuales vias inde sumere exordium.' hic rursum
similiter eos peccare perspicimus. etenim faciem curamus cataplasmate atque vaporatione, atque occipitium tamquam dolens
et extentum apposita cucurbita scarificamus, sicut etiam alias
partes atque praecordia, si in tumore fuerint constituta.

explicata varia[9] passionis apprehensione ad eius curationem
transeamus.

---

[4] significatione *edd.*

[5] carentes *Rm*

[6] incertum *Triller ap. Kühn 30*: maternum *G*: internum *R*

[7] ⟨id⟩ *R*

[8] si quidem *G*: quasi quidem *Rm*

[9] varia *A*: variae *G*

mind? For in every case they hold that the part affected in phrenitis is that in which they suspect the ruling part of the soul[1] to be situated. In my work *On the Causes of Diseases* I shall examine and refute their several conclusions and declarations.

55   Now we hold that in phrenitis there is a general affection of the whole body, for the whole body is shaken by fever. And fever is one of the signs that make up the general indication of phrenitis, and for that reason we treat the whole body. We do hold, however, that the head is more particularly affected, as the antecedent symptoms indicate, e.g., its heaviness, tension, and pain, head noises, ringing in the ears, dryness, and impairment of the senses; and the other symptoms which are found when the disease is already present, viz., the loss of function by each of the senses, eyelids stiff, eyes bloodshot and bulging out, cheeks red, veins distended, face puffed up and full, and tongue rough.

56   But there are those who argue as follows: 'We determine the part affected on the basis of the theory of nature (Greek *physiologia*), for we know in advance that the ruling part of the soul is located in the head, and conclude that that must be the source of mental derangement.' Our answer to them is that, to begin with, the place of this ruling part is uncertain.[2] But the number and variety of symptoms occurring in the head have shown us that this organ is more particularly affected than the rest of the body.

57   Now they answer that the face is even more intensely affected and shows the most symptoms and that therefore the remedies should be applied to it. 'But you,' they say to us, 'apply cupping to the occiput, since you have learned by dissection (Greek *anatomia*) that the channels of the senses originate there.' But here again, as before, these physicians are mistaken. For we do treat the face with poultices and hot applications; and as for the occiput it is because it is painful and swollen that we use cupping and scarification, just as we also treat other parts, e.g., the precordia, if inflamed.

Having taken up the various matters concerned with the recognition of the disease, let us now pass to its treatment.

1. I.e., the reason. With this whole paragraph cf. *Anon. Paris.*, pp. 69–70.
2. The text is doubtful.

58 ## IX. QUOMODO CURANDI SUNT PHRENITICI

Quomodo curationibus principio locus aptandus est, iacere oportet phreniticos in loco omni ex parte devio ne aliqua transeuntium voce pulsentur, fenestris etiam altioribus luminato: saepe enim in passione constituti alienationis causa sese praecipitantes latuerunt. dehinc ob obscurationis[1] proprietatem strictura laborantes in lucido[2] atque tepido et amplo mediocriter locamus. etenim ultra modum fervens naturaliter febricula caput incendit; et rursum frigidus constringit atque corporis auget densitatem; item nimium lucidus membranam

59 percutiet cerebri immodici splendoris causa; parvus etiam si fuerit atque humilis tecto,[3] suffocabilis erit aeris paupertate.

sit etiam sine ullo picturae figmento, ne visa aegri ex picturis mente accipientes, quae Graeci phantasmata vocaverunt, plus asperentur aut in risum solvantur, maxime cum ratione careat multorum ingressum aut frequentiam prohibere, et pictura occasionem lacerandae mentis acquirere, cum iugi visu falsa coguntur pro veris accipere. hinc etiam splendidi colores parietum sive straminum vel operimentorum prohibendi: resultantes enim, ut ita dixerim, percutient visum.

60 solutione autem optinenti laborantes econtrario iacere oportet loco medie obscuro atque refrigeranti. neque enim nimium frigidus neque obscurus passionis mitigare celeritatem potest. stramenta etiam omnibus mollia atque operimenta conveniunt, sed tenuia solutione laborantibus, corpulenta vero atque calida strictura affectis. sic[4] etiam lectus omni ex parte firme locatus, ut cum fuerint impatienter iactati vel necessitate cogente devincti[5] immobilis perseveret: foribus etiam atque fenestra aversi ne ingressu hominum asperentur.

---

[1] *fort.* curationis
[2] *fort.* in ⟨loco⟩ lucido
[3] humili tecto *R*: *fort.* humilis tecti
[4] sit *A*
[5] devincti *Rm*: devicti *G*

58 ## IX. THE TREATMENT OF PHRENITIS

THE first step in all treatments is to have the patient in a proper place. Thus in phrenitis the patient should lie in a place completely sequestered, so that he may not be disturbed by the voices of passers-by. The place should be lighted through high windows; for it often happens in this disease that unguarded patients in their madness jump out [of windows]. Again, because of the properties of darkness,[1] in cases involving a state of stricture place the patient in a moderately light, warm, and spacious room. For a place that is excessively hot tends by its very nature to inflame the head with fever, while a cold place constricts and increases the condensation of the body. Likewise, too much light will harm the membrane of the brain by its ex-
59 cessive brightness. And if the place is small and the ceiling low, it will be stifling because of lack of air.

There should be no paintings in the room, lest they cause the patient to experience apparitions (Greek *phantasmata*) and to become more excited or burst into laughter. And it is most unreasonable, on the one hand, to keep many people from visiting or gathering near the patient and, on the other, to make possible further injury to the patient's mind through paintings. For, by continually gazing at paintings, he is led astray as to what is real. Similarly avoid bright colors on walls, spreads, or covers, since these colors will jump out, as it were, and strike the vision.
60 On the contrary, in cases where a state of looseness prevails, the patient ought to lie in a moderately dark and cool place; for excessive darkness and cold cannot lessen the acuteness of the disease. Furthermore, soft bedding and covers are suitable for all cases, thin for those suffering[2] from a state of looseness, and heavy and warm for those suffering from a state of stricture. And the bed should be firmly fixed in place on all sides so that it will remain stationary when the patient tosses about restlessly, or of necessity has to be confined by bonds. And he should face away from the door and window to avoid being excited by the passing of people.

1. Darkness has an astringent, and light a relaxing, property, according to the Methodists. On the Methodist treatment of phrenitis see also *Anon. Paris.*, pp. 71-73.

2. I.e., predominantly. It must be remembered that, according to the Methodists, the basic state in phrenitis is *strictura*, though *solutio* is sometimes present and even dominant (cf. *Ac.* i. 52).

61   at si etiam alienatio fuerit principali passioni contraria, ut
strictura laborantes lucem odisse faciat, solutione laborantes
tenebras, oportet aliis oculos contegi, aliis tenue atque blandum
lumen immittere lucernae aut lucis aetheriae, sed arguto usu
machinatum, quo velut[6] per quandam cavernam aegrotantis
vultum perfundat et nullas tangat alias corporis partes. sic
etiam mitigabitur alienationis augmentum, et adiutorium passioni aptum congrue servabit qualitatis effectum. laxat enim,
ut supra diximus, lux colore quo[7] videtur, sed consequenter
necessario suae tenuitatis causa manet cetero circumfusa corpori
62 tametsi non videatur. similiter etiam obscuritas vel tenebrae,
si fuerint aegrotantibus odiosa et curationi necessaria, erunt
artis astutia componenda.[8]

sed si ita fuerint alienatione commoti qua obscurari totum vel
luminari velint, erit coniciendum ut quibus obscurum aerem
fecerimus calidum tamen faciamus, quibus autem lucidum,
econtrario vero frigidum faciamus, ut et congruam passioni
servemus qualitatem et eorum furorem mitigando non aspe-
63 remus. si vero nihil aegrotantes prava cupiditate[9] turbaverit,
servabit lucem strictura, obscuritas solutione laborantibus adhibenda.[10] vel quomodo turbatio atque motus et iactatio corporis
celeritatem asperat passionis, erit aliquando mitigandi furoris
causa aegrorum voluntati serviendum. stringitur enim magis
solutio vel strictura laxatur, si gravioribus aversis parva contrarietate vexantes[11] strictura laborantibus obscurum, sive solutione laborantibus lucidum adhibendum iudicamus locum.

[6] velim G: corr. R   [7] cum Rm
[8] odiosae et c. necessariae, e.a.a. componendae R
[9] cupiditas Rm
[10] si vero . . . laborantibus adhibenda fort. transp. post iudicamus locum (63 fin.)
[11] vexentur G: vexentur ⟨sive⟩ R

3. On color as an essential of visibility, see, e.g., Aristotle De anima ii. 7.

4. As in the case where the patient's eyes are covered. In the other case the light is
not permitted to surround the patient's body.

61   But if the mental derangement acts in a way contrary to the
dominant state, so that it causes those suffering from a state of
stricture to shun the light and those suffering from a state of
looseness to shun darkness, cover the patient's eyes in the former
case, and in the latter case admit a small amount of soft light.
This light may be lamplight or daylight but should be skilfully
arranged, so that by the use of a small aperture it will cover only
the patient's face, without touching any other parts of his body.
In this way the spread of mental derangement will be allayed,
and at the same time a remedy appropriate to the disease will
have its proper and natural effect. For, as we have indicated
above, light is a relaxing agent by reason of the color by which
it is seen;[3] but of necessity because of its fineness it completely
62   envelops the rest of the body even though unseen.[4] Similarly,
shade or darkness, if distasteful to patients but necessary to
their treatment, will have to be arranged with skill and adroit-
ness.
      But if the patients are so completely deranged that they want
to be in complete darkness or in bright light, we shall have to
see to it that in the cases where we make the air dark we also
make it warm, but in the cases where we make the air bright we
also make it cold.[5] In this way we may adhere to the type of
treatment required by the disease and at the same time soothe
63   the madness of the patients and avoid exciting them. If, however, no such perverse desire troubles the patients, keep those
who are suffering from a state of stricture in the light, but prescribe darkness for those suffering from a state of looseness. But,
since excitement, motion, and tossing of the body heighten the
acuteness of a disease, we must on occasion yield to the desires[6]
of the patients for the sake of soothing their madness. For a state
of looseness is checked and a state of stricture relaxed more successfully if we go counter [to the basic treatment] in minor matters, but not in the major procedures, and decide to use a dark
room in cases involving a state of stricture or a light room in
cases involving a state of looseness.

      5. Counterbalancing measures. Darkness is astringent, and warmth relaxing; light is
relaxing, and cold astringent, according to the Methodists.

      6. This seems to refer again to the cases in which the patient with *strictura* desires
darkness, etc. It may be that the sentence now at the beginning of 63 belongs at the end.

64   dehinc si strictura obtinuerit, convenit aegrum usque ad accessiónis declinationem vigilare, tunc somno dimitti. at si longa fuerit accessio, etiam ante dimissionem somnus poterit adhiberi. maior enim ab intemporali somno vigiliarum est vexatio, siquidem etiam vires aegrotantis insumat.[12] dehinc iudicio nostro abstineri vel tolli non potest, somni autem intemporalitas si fuerit interrumpenda, excitare dormientem poterimus atque soporis oppressionem prohibere. delirationes vero aegrotantium usu dextero atque artificio servientes[13] accipere et tolerare debebunt, ut aliis assentiant, alias vero[14] consentientes redarguant, ne frequenti correctione asperos faciant aegrotantes. denique si quos sanitatis tempore invisos habuerunt intrare prohibemus, ne his visis asperentur; eos vero quos
65 metu aut verecundia coluerunt per intervalla intrare permittimus, parit enim frequentia contemptum.

at si exilire de lecto viderimus nimietate furoris, melius erit plurimis uti ad remedium ministris, sed qui possint lenitate retinere, ut etiam laxamentum stricturae praebeamus. vel si defuerint[15] qui ut supra diximus teneant, aut ipsorum visu commoti fuerint aegrotantes, ligationibus utimur, sed praetectis lana aut veste locis quos vinculis nectimus, ne maior utilitate quiescendi imprimatur vexatio. ligationibus etenim immodice constricta necessario tumescunt: propterea omnis in peius extenditur passio.

66   si linguae atque totius oris siccitas fuerit, oportet spongia tenera, aqua calida infusa atque mediocriter expressa, sensim universa quae siccaverunt humectare, non sine cautione: adiunctos enim saepe digitos spongiae[16] alienatione coacti aegri momorderunt. quapropter si fieri poterit, cogendi sunt ut exerant linguam, atque ita supradicta faciamus.

declinante accessione, hoc est cum e visceribus reclusus fervor ad superficiem corporis atque articulos venerit aegrotantis, pulsus quoque densitas et humilitas in amplitudinem atque rari-

---

[12] aegrotantes insinuat G: corr. Friedel 31, n. 3

[13] ferventes G: corr. R

[14] vero ⟨non⟩ Hagendahl 247

[15] defuerint Rm: fuerint G

[16] spongia G: corr. R

64   Now if a state of stricture predominates, it is well for the patient to be kept awake until the attack begins to decline and then
to be allowed to sleep. But if the attack is long, sleep may be
permitted even before the remission. For the harm of wakefulness is greater than that of untimely sleep, since wakefulness
robs the patient of his strength. Moreover, the harmful effects
of wakefulness cannot be prevented or terminated at our pleasure, whereas, if we have to interrupt an untimely sleep, we can
arouse the sleeper and forestall the oppressive effect of the sleep.
The attendants will have to endure the crazy whims of the patient and deal skilfully and ingeniously with them, agreeing to
some and rejecting others, sympathetically, however, to avoid
exciting him by frequent opposition. And do not permit people
who were disliked by the patient before he became ill to enter
the sickroom, for his condition would be aggravated by seeing
65   them. But permit people who are regarded by the patient with
awe or veneration to enter, yet only at intervals, for 'familiarity
breeds contempt.'
      Now if the patient is seen trying to jump out of bed in a fit
of insanity, it will be better to use the aid of a large number of
servants who can hold him back gently, so that relaxing treatment may still be applied to the case which involves a state of
stricture. If, however, there are not the servants to hold the patient back in this way or if the patient is aroused by the sight of
the servants, use bonds. But use wool or clothing to protect the
places where the ropes are tied, lest the harm done the patients
be greater than the advantage gained in keeping them quiet.
For those parts which are very tightly constricted by bonds
always become swollen and such swelling aggravates every
disease.
66   If there is dryness of the tongue and the whole mouth, take a
soft sponge, dip it in warm water, squeeze it somewhat, and
gently moisten all the parts that are dry. But this must be done
with caution, for patients under the compulsion of mental derangement have often bitten the fingers holding the sponge. The
patient must therefore be induced, if possible, to thrust out his
tongue; we may then proceed as described.
      When the attack declines, i.e., when the heat released from
the viscera comes to the surface of the body and the limbs of
the patient and the pulse changes from thick and small to large

tatem venerit, oportet pubetenus, hoc est inter umbilicum et
pectinem, quod Graeci etron[17] appellant, lanas oleo calido ex-
67 pressas apponere: quae omnia etiam vicina contegant, ut in-
guina atque vesicae partes vel si qua ventrem contegant. fovendum caput oleo dulci atque calido, dehinc alienatione perseverante etiam calida cum oleo mixta, quod Graeci vocant hydrelaeon. paulo etenim vehementius hoc genus fomenti operatur, si ut supra diximus oleo aqua calida misceatur, vel faenugraeci aut lini seminis sucus. sed haec singula sine ullo esse
odore debent atque nullo fumi afflatu vexata,[18] ne caput impleant et alienationem exasperent.

68   at si adiuncta fuerit stricturae solutio, ut aut venter fluens aut
sudores esse videantur, caput supradicto modo atque fomentis
supradictis curabimus: etenim alienatio tumore membranarum
cerebri fiet. medias vero partes frigido ac viridi curabimus oleo.
si autem plurima atque superans fuerit, et occulte in diaphoresim venire posse aegrotantes viderimus, tunc etiam caput dulci
quidem sed frigido oleo fomentamus: etenim frigus diaphoresim,
dulcedo stricturam temperat. detergendus etiam erit saepissime
sudor, qui per vultum atque thoracem emicuerit, spongia molli.

69 at si plus fuerit extentus ut integros solvi videamus, etiam flabris
utimur, non quidem sine respectu alienationis. etenim si con-
stricturam ea curatione mitigari videamus, audacius id facere
perseverabimus. si autem asperari senserimus, erunt minuenda quae gerimus, conicientes non tantum solutionem constringi adiutoriis quantum alienatio[19] augetur. namque necessario requies congrua solutioni atque noxius motus accipitur.

declinante accessione os colluere iubemus aegrotantem ex aqua
calida, vel si impatienter siti iactatur dabimus ei potum: sed

[17] ἧτρον (sic) G

[18] vexativa coni. Bendz Eran 43. 56

[19] alienatione G: corr. R

7. In general, we may think of 'thick' and 'rare' as equivalent to 'rapid' and 'slow,'
respectively. But see *Ac.* i. 21 n.

and rare,[7] pieces of wool wrung out of warm olive oil should be
applied to the hypogastrium, i.e., between the umbilicus and the
67 pecten, a region which the Greeks call *ētron*. These applications
should also cover all the neighboring regions, including the
groins, the region of the bladder, and the abdomen. Foment the
head with warm sweet olive oil. And if the aberration persists,
also use warm water mixed with olive oil (Greek *hydrelaeon*).
For this type of fomentation acts more strongly if warm water,
as we have just said, or the juice of fenugreek seed or flaxseed is
mixed with the oil. But each of these ingredients must be odorless and untainted by any breath of vapor, to avoid filling the
patient's head and aggravating his derangement.

68   But if a state of looseness is combined with the state of stricture, so that loose bowels and sweating occur, treat the head in
the manner described, using the previously mentioned fomentations, for the loss of reason is still due to inflammation of the
membranes of the brain. But treat the middle parts with cold
green olive oil. If, however, the state of looseness is very general
and predominant and it is evident that the patient may lapse
into colliquative sweats, still foment the head with sweet olive
oil, but let the oil be cold. For the cold counteracts the sweating,
while the sweetness relieves the stricture. And using a soft
sponge, keep wiping away the sweat which breaks out at the
69 head and chest. But if the colliquescence is even more general,
so that the whole body is seen to be in a state of dissolution, use
fans, always, however, with due regard for the patient's mental
derangement.[8] Thus if the state of stricture is found to be relieved by this treatment, continue the procedure even more
vigorously. But if the condition is found to be aggravated, this
treatment will have to be curtailed, for we may then infer that
the treatment is not overcoming the state of dissolution as
much as it is aggravating the mental derangement. Indeed, rest
is always considered good for a state of looseness and movement
harmful.

As the attack abates, have the patient wash his mouth with
warm water, or if he tosses about, beset by unbearable thirst,
permit him to drink the water. Let him take a large quantity if
he is suffering from a state of stricture alone, for the water will

8. Which requires relaxing and not astringent treatment.

strictura sola laboranti plurimum, ut densitas irrigetur; solutione laboranti parvum, vel si plurima cogit solutio, etiam frigidum.

70   X. DE PHLEBOTOMIA¹

At si sola atque vehemens strictura aegros in phreniticam extemplo passionem perduxerit, designat adhibendam esse phlebotomiam, permittentibus viribus: atque si passio cogit, intra diatriton; si minus, in ipsa prima diatrito, ultra numquam. vexantur enim in eiusmodi aegritudinibus corporis vires. phlebotomandi autem disciplinam vel magnitudini passionis moderationem faciendi congruam, libris quos De specialibus adiutoriis scripturi sumus, docebimus, principaliter monentes ne usque ad animi defectum, quem Graeci lipothymian vocant, adiutorium

71 tendere nitamur. timendum enim hoc saepe est accidens, quod Graeci symptoma vocant, quamquam in omnibus passionibus, siquidem sit mortuosum, plus tamen in phreniticis afficitur² male praetacta nervositas. dehinc post phlebotomiam caput similiter fovemus, atque occipitio lanas oleo calido ac dulci madidas apponimus, similiter etiam vertebris, quas Graeci ischia³ vocant, praecordiis etiam atque pectini.⁴ haec enim necessario in phreniticis passioni consentiunt.

72   at si intra diatritum, ut supra diximus, phlebotomia fuerit adhibita, post paululum os colluere aqua calida aegrotantes facimus. potum quoque dabimus, dehinc dormire permittimus. sin vero in ipsa diatrito phlebotomia adhibita, cum adiutorii⁵ motus quieverit, oleo aegrotantium corpus perungendum erit atque a ministris facies lavanda, ut alienatio nullo novorum vultu asperetur (noti enim usu prudentes delirationes accipiunt⁶ non resistendo), praesentibus etiam his quibus, ut supra docuimus, aegrotantes verecundiam debent.

---

¹ *inscriptio capitis vix genuina videtur*

² *fort. interpung. post* phreniticis *et scrib.* afficitur ⟨enim⟩ *vel sim.*

³ *ἰσχία G*

⁴ pectori *Triller ap. Kühn 42*

⁵ adiutorio *G: corr. Schmid 90*

⁶ accipiunt *Hagendahl 247, coll. Ac. i. 64, 80*: faciunt *G: fort.* patiuntur *vel* capiunt

help overcome the congestion. But let him take only a little if he
is also suffering from a state of looseness.[9] And if the state of
looseness is so extensive as to require it, the little water taken
should be cold.

70

X. VENESECTION

B UT if a powerful state of stricture alone has suddenly brought
the patient to phrenitis, the use of venesection is indicated,
the strength of the patient permitting. If the case requires it,
venesection should be performed before the end of the first
three-day period; otherwise at the very end of that period, but
never later, for the body's strength is impaired in diseases
of this kind. In a treatise I am planning to write *On Special
Remedies* I shall take up the whole subject of venesection and
the method of adapting it to the severity of the disease. My chief
warning is that we should not try to use this remedy to a point
71 where there is fainting (Greek *lipothymia*). For this occurrence
(Greek *symptōma*) is indeed cause for alarm; and though this is
the case in every disease, since fainting is a dangerous sign, it is
particularly so in phrenitis, for the patient's nerves and sinews
have been attacked and are seriously affected. After venesection,
foment the head, as before, and apply wool soaked in warm
sweet olive oil to the occiput, and also to the hip joints (Greek
ischia), the precordia, and the pecten, for these parts are always
sympathetically affected in phrenitis.

72   Now in the cases referred to above, where venesection is performed before the end of the three-day period, wait only a short
while and then have the patient wash his mouth with warm
water, give him some to drink, and then permit him to sleep.
But in cases where venesection is performed at the end of the
three-day period, as soon as the disturbance caused by this procedure has abated, have the body of the patient anointed with
oil and his face washed by his own servants so that his mental
derangement should not be further aggravated by the sight of
new faces. For persons familiar with the patient become prudent
through experience and accept the aberrations without resisting
them. And, as we have said, persons to whom the patient owes
respect should also be present.

9. I.e., in conjunction with the *strictura* that is always present in this disease.

73   cibum dabimus simplicem digestibilem parvum laxativum,
ut est alica⁷ calida aqua aut mulsa decocta, vel panis ex aqua
calida, aut alica supra dicta sorbilis facta, vel ex melle atque
oleo et anetho et sale paucissimo praecocta. solutione autem
laborantibus pultem dabimus atque panem et ova hapala.⁸ dehinc omnes somno dimittimus, vel si minime dormire potuerint,
quiescere tamen iubemus: non enim minus somnus cibo reficit
74 opportunus. dehinc alia die a cibo abstinemus, fomento atque
potu utentes.

secunda vero diatrito si venter suum non agnoverit officium,
clysterem adhibebimus ex aqua et oleo calido, vel decoctione
faenugraeci aut lini seminis cum oleo. etenim intestinorum
siccitas rigatur, et aliena quae retinebantur excludentur, et acrimonia quae ex ipsis nascens exalatione⁹ quadam capitis tumentia
asperabat¹⁰ detrahetur, atque ipsum caput localibus adiutoriis
75 melius praeparatur. tum post iniectionem¹¹ medias partes cataplasmate curamus ex faenugraeci et lini seminibus admixto
polline, quod Graeci macton vocant, et est omnibus usitatum.
dehinc simili supra dicto cibo utemur.

alia vero diatrito caput detondemus: etenim detractis capillis
partes reflantur, plurima gravatione liberatae. tunc post tonsuram lanis oleo calido expressis caput tegemus.

76   XI. DE CUCURBITA¹

ALIA dehinc diatrito rasis partibus cucurbitam apponimus
occipitio mitiganter, atque sub ipsa fronte sanguisugas
facimus inhaerere quatuor vel quinque, ut non ex una parte detractio fieri sanguinis videatur, sed veluti circulatim,² ⟨ut⟩³ totum spiret atque relevetur⁴ caput. at si plurimum laxamentum
facere voluerimus, totum caput rademus et per circulum plurimas cucurbitas affigimus, alteram occipitio, alteram medio capitis, quod Graeci bregma vocant, alias duas superius a temporibus, sed neque cum multa flamma neque multo tempore im-

---

⁷ *fort. scrib.* alica ⟨ex⟩   ⁹ ex alienatione *G: corr. Schmid 93* (exh-)
⁸ ἀπαλὰ *G*   ¹⁰ aspernabat *G: corr. R*
¹¹ iniectionem *Triller ap. Kühn 43*: intellectionem *G*: interiectionem *Schmid 94*
¹ *vid. cap. X*
² circulatim *Helmreich 316*: circulatis *G*: circularis *R*
³ ⟨ut⟩ *R*   ⁴ reveletur *G: corr. R*

73 Prescribe a small amount of simple, digestible, and laxative
food, such as spelt groats in warm water or boiled down with
hydromel, or else bread moistened in warm water, or spelt groats
prepared as a gruel, e.g., cooked with honey, olive oil, dill, and a
very little salt. But in cases involving a state of looseness prescribe a thick porridge, bread, and soft eggs. Then in all cases let
the patients sleep—for timely sleep refreshes no less than food—
74 or if they are unable to sleep have them remain quiet. Then on
the next day keep them from food, prescribing fomentations
and drink.

   At the end of the second three-day period, if the bowels do not
perform their function, administer a clyster of water and warm
olive oil or a decoction of fenugreek seed or flaxseed with olive
oil. Thus the dry bowels will be moistened, and the fecal matter
which was being retained will be expelled. And the pungent
vapor that arose as an exhalation from this matter and aggravated the inflammation of the head will be removed. And the
75 head itself will be better prepared for local remedies. Then after
the clyster treat the middle parts with a poultice of fenugreek
seed and flaxseed, with the addition of flour, a poultice which the
Greeks call *macton* ['kneaded'] and is used by all. Then give food
similar to that described above.

   And at the end of the third three-day period clip the hair from
the patient's head, for when the hair is removed the parts
breathe freely again, unencumbered by the excessive weight.
Then after the cutting of the hair cover the head with wool
wrung out of warm olive oil.

76   XI. CUPPING

THEN at the end of the fourth three-day period shave the
region of the occiput and apply mild cupping there. Also
apply four or five leeches to the forehead, so that the withdrawal
of blood may not be made from only one region but in a kind of
circle, and the whole head may breathe and be refreshed. But if
it is desired to produce the greatest measure of relief from the
state of stricture, shave the whole head and apply a large number of cups in a circle, one to the occiput, one at the middle of
the head (Greek *bregma*), and two others above the temples.
But do not use much flame or permit the cups to remain on for

morari. arentes enim atque siccatae facile conmovent, caput
implent, ac mentis faciunt alienationem augeri.

77   ita detractis cucurbitis si partes erubuisse viderimus, leniter
scarificamus; si minus,[5] mitiganter[6] vaporantes spongiis sed non[7]
nimis calidis[8] relaxamus.[9]   vapore etenim nimio tamquam
frixantes densamus. quapropter ut supra diximus post iugem
atque temperatam vaporationem, ubi partes rubuisse viderimus,
scarificamus. post namque etiam vaporatio ante cucurbitae
appositionem adhiberi debet, ne plurimum infixa immoretur et
inde partes radi videantur. suppositis[10] ergo cucurbitis, cum sufficientem locorum verticem factum viderimus, scarificamus. sic[11]
enim non solum cucurbitae quassatio mitigatur, sed etiam fluoris
78 sanguinis facilitas fiet. explicita scarificatione, rursum cucurbitas
imponimus ut sanguinis detractio fiat, sed eo tempore capiti atque collo et vicinis partibus leves erunt cucurbitae apponendae,
quo in laxamentum consentiant. at si in praecordiis tumor fuerit,
erunt ipsa prius scarificanda, sic etiam et vesicae partes vel vicinae eius.

tunc in alia diatrito caput, dehinc clunes: etenim[12] simul scari-
ficare noxium atque vexabile est. erit enim eiusdem temporis
multas per partes effecta sanguinis detractio phlebotomiae,[13]
79 quae necessario vires absumat. quapropter partiatim erit adhibenda cucurbita, ut exempli causa nunc praecordiis atque pubetenus praerasa capillatura, nunc capiti, nunc clunibus ac verte-
brotenus, quod Graeci ischion[14] vocant, ceteris quoque partibus
fomento curatis ac decoctionibus supradictis et cataplasmatibus
relaxatis, atque ita levibus[15] cucurbitarum raptibus utemur,
quas[16] Graeci abusive[17] cufas[18] vocant, praefricatis partibus

[5] si minus] *fort.* sed prius *vel sim.*

[6] mitigamus *edd.*

[7] sed non *scripsi*: sine *G*: non *R*

[8] calidis ⟨ac⟩ *R*

[9] relaxantes *R*

[10] depositis *Rm*

[11] si *G*: *corr. Rm*

[12] etiam *G*: nam *R*

[13] *an* phlebotomia?

[14] ἰσχιον *G*

[15] levibus *Almeloveen*: lenibus *G*

[16] quas *Almeloveen*: quos *G*

[17] ab usu *Triller ap. Kühn 48*

[18] cufar *G*: *corr. A (litteris Graecis)*

a long time. For these dry cups have a strong and ready action; they congest the head and aggravate mental disturbance.

77   If, on removing the cups, it is found that the parts have become red, scarify them moderately; otherwise warm them gently with sponges that are not too hot, and thus relax them. But if the heat is excessive, the effect will be to roast the parts, as it were, and harden them. And so when we see, after the continual application of moderate heat, that the parts have become red, we scarify them, as I have said.[1] And then, before the cup is [again] applied, the parts should be warmed, so that the cup will not have to remain attached for very long and thus cause injury to the parts. And so, after the cups have been applied, when you see that the parts have developed a sufficient swelling, scarify them. For in this way not only is the shock involved in cupping
78 mitigated, but the flow of blood is facilitated. And when scarification has been performed, again affix the cups so that blood may be withdrawn. But at that time mild cupping should be applied to the head, neck, and neighboring parts, so that these parts may also experience relaxation. But if there is an inflammation in the precordia, this region will first have to be scarified, as will also the region of the bladder and the surrounding parts.

Then, at the end of the next [i.e., the fifth] three-day period, treat the head in the same way and after that the loins, for the scarification [of these parts] at the same time would be harmful and irritating. Indeed, the drawing of blood at the same time from many parts is the function of venesection, which always
79 consumes the strength. And so cupping will have to be performed part by part, being applied at one time, for example, to the precordial and pubic regions (the hair being first shaved off), at another time to the head, at still another time to the loins and the region of the hip joint (Greek *ischion*). Also foment the other parts and soothe them with the decoctions and poultices described above. And then make use of cups of mild action which the Greeks loosely[2] call *cuphae* ['light']. But first massage the

1. This is not what was said above and is an indication that the text beginning with *si minus* may be corrupt.

2. I.e., with transferred epithet (καταχρηστικῶς). The term 'light' is applied to the instrument itself instead of to its action (*levibus raptibus*) or to the mode of application (*Chr.* v. 74; cf. Cass. Fel., p. 170. 21). 'Light' cups often denote cups employed without scarification (cf. Soranus *Gyn.*, p. 101. 3).

80 adtractatione[19] manuum. at si vires illaesae aut minus laesae
fuerint post detractionem sanguinis factam, spongias expressas
ex aqua calida partibus applicamus, vel oleo calido mediocriter
fovemus. tunc totum corpus perunctione[20] curamus his operan-
tibus magis qui aegro serviendo iam noti sunt, ne mentis alienatio asperetur. etenim eorum facile accipiunt atque redarguunt
delirationem, praesentibus ut saepe diximus his quibus verecundiam aegrotantes debent.

post perunctionem factam, ut supra diximus, cibum dabimus.
81 at si accipere congrua noluerint, vel contraria voluerint, erunt
fallendi. facile enim id fieri potest, siquidem etiam mentis
aegritudine afficiantur. dabimus ergo congrua fingentes ea
quae ipsi petebant. at si minime consenserint, erit confictionis[21]
argumentatio adhibenda, ut si exempli causa vinum accipere
cupiunt, mulsum demus; vel si ptisanae sucum petierint, alicam
demus vel ex milio in similitudinem ptisanae confectam,[22] cum
possint, si ex aliqua parte sapuerint, hortationibus aut metu
compesci. si neque hoc fieri potuerit, dabimus ea quae non satis
aliena sint ab his quae rationi conveniunt, ut olus aut ptisana.[23]
82 dabit enim quiddam laxamenti atque indulgentiae asperitatibus
animorum concupita oblatio, et non omnino sine cibo atque
nutrimento perseverabunt. vinum vero omnino negamus tamquam repugnans et nihil a veneno differens. etenim datum statim furorem exasperat atque in nimiam magnitudinem tollit.

post refectionem itaque erunt somno dimittendi, vel quod est
vicinum somno requies adhibenda; atque usque ad totius passionis statum alterna vel per intervalla cibi refectio, hoc est interposita diei unius ieiunitate, permittentibus quidem viribus.
sed ea die qua cibum non dederimus, erit cataplasmatibus
utendum congruis atque iugibus usque ad medium tempus dimissionis.

83 at si porrecta in dies numerosior[24] erit aegritudo et statum in-
firmitas acceperit, convenit ut declinatione, augmento vel impetu

---

[19] ad tractationem G: corr. Schmid 94 (att-): cf. adtrectatione Ac. ii. 207, sed attractare G, Ac. i. 88, attractentur Cael. Aur. Gyn. i. 95

[20] per unctionem G: corr. Schmid 95

[21] confictionis R: confectionis G

[22] confectum edd. (sc. sucum)

[23] ptisanam R   [24] numerosiores Rm

o parts manually. If, however, after the withdrawal of blood has been accomplished, the patient's strength is unimpaired or little impaired, apply sponges wrung out of hot water to these parts or foment them moderately with warm olive oil. Then have the whole body anointed, using for this task persons who are already known to the patient through previous service, to avoid aggravating his disturbed mental state. For these servants readily accept the patient's dotage and minimize it. But, as we have often said, some persons should also be present to whom the patient owes respect.

After having the patient anointed, as described, give him food.

31 But if he refuses to take suitable food or prefers unsuitable, he will have to be deceived. But this will be easy, since his mind is also affected. Thus give him the suitable food, pretending it is what he himself asked for. But if he does not yield, you will have to win him over by counterfeiting the food.[3] For example, if he wants wine, give him mead; if he asks for barley water, give him spelt water prepared, say, with millet to seem like barley water. And if he has some measure of sanity, he can be controlled by exhortation or fear. But if this, too, fails, give him food which is not very different from that which reason requires, e.g., vege-

32 tables or pearl barley. In fact, the serving of what the patient desires will in itself mitigate in some measure and relieve his mental derangement; at the same time, he will not continue entirely without food and nourishment. But we forbid wine absolutely, as harmful and no different from poison. For, as soon as it is taken, it excites the patient's madness and greatly aggravates it.

Now when he has taken food, let him sleep or, what is next to sleep, rest. And until the disease reaches its highest stage, the giving of food should be alternated with intervals of fasting, these intervals lasting one day, provided that the strength of the patient permits. But on the day on which we do not give food we shall have continually to apply suitable poultices, down to the mid-period of the remission.

33 But if the illness continues from day to day and is of considerable duration and the patient's infirmity reaches its highest stage, it is advisable during the period of decline, when the increase or force of the disease has been spent, to prescribe passive

3. Cf. Aurelius, p. 726. 19 ff. Perhaps: 'win him over by deceit.'

passionis transacto, motum gestationis adhibeamus, si vires
patiuntur, in domo suspenso lecto, si aer loci bonus atque mun-
dus fuerit. etenim si motus vel gestatio somnum ruperit,
rursum addormiunt atque difficile expergiscuntur perseverante
iugi motu. at si hoc fieri non potuerit, in vicina porticu gestatio
adhibenda, ita ut sella baiulatoria vel quolibet sessorio leniter
84 atque mediocriter moveantur. similiter enim etiam si fuerint
experrecti, non statim erit gestatio incidenda. nam repentina
statio atque interrupti motus in praeteritas vigilias revocant
aegrotantes. non enim dimissio accessionis sed totius passionis
declinatio nunc curationem poscit. quapropter oportet aegros
perseveranter movere, sed leniter atque sensim et sine ulla nimietate.

at si solutio magis inerat passioni, non erit gestatio adhibenda.
tenuat enim atque dirarat motus; dehinc cum solutio provocatur
etiam vigiliae necessario augentur. in dimissione vero accessionis, quam Graeci anesin vocant, perseverandum est localibus
adiutoriis[25] cucurbitae appositione, sed non adhuc adiungenda
85 scarificatio. bonum est enim corporibus sua servare ne latenter
effusione frequente[26] aegrotantes in diaphoresin veniant.

at si aliquo in loco vehemens dolor emerserit, sola erit scarificatione curandus. tunc consequentibus atque congruis vaporationibus et fomentis et cataplasmatibus et perunctione[27]
utendum et cibo, cum temporis opportunitatem viderimus, quae
probatur signis quae De febribus scribentes docebimus. generaliter autem omnium passionum strictura laborantes minus cibamus, convenit enim cibi parvitas densitati, siquidem corpora
minus exhalent; utque[28] econtrario solutioni plurimus convenit
cibus, siquidem celerius insumatur plurimae exalationis causa.
86   at si vires aegrotantis fuerint dissolutae, et febres non ita
acres sed tunc spem veluti declinationis[29] ostentent,[30] aspicienda
erit imbecillitas virium. dandus cibus et si necessitas coegerit[31]
etiam vinum, sed omnino parvum, ad relevandas corporis vires.

[25] adiutoriis ⟨et⟩ (*fort. suppl.* ⟨vel⟩) R

[26] frequenter G: frequenti R (*sed cf. 94*)

[27] punctione G: *corr. Helmreich 316*

[28] *fort. erat* atque: *sic Hagendahl 248; cf. Bendz 47*

[29] declinationes G: *corr. Rm*

[30] ostendent *Bendz 84*

[31] coegerit *Reinesius* (*v. Kühn 50*): caeperit G: coeperit R

exercise, if the patient's strength permits. This exercise may be taken in a hammock in the patient's house, provided that the air of the place is good and wholesome. And even if the exercise breaks into his sleep, he falls asleep again and can hardly be awakened so long as the motion continues unbroken. But if it cannot be arranged [in the house], the treatment should be given in a neighboring portico, in a sedan chair or any other type of 84 chair, with gentle and moderate movements. And even if the patient wakes up, the motion must not be stopped at once; for a sudden halt and interruption of the movements will cause him to resume his former sleeplessness. And at this stage it is no longer the remission of the attack but the decline of the whole disease that is the object of the treatment. Hence we must continue this movement of the patient, but gently, gradually, and without excess.

If, however, a state of looseness was an important element in the disease, then passive exercise must not be employed. For motion causes dilation and rarefaction. Again, when a state of looseness is involved, sleeplessness is inevitably increased. But when there is a remission in an attack (Greek *anesis*), continue with the local remedies by applying cups, but no longer use 85 scarification in this connection. For it is a good thing for bodies to preserve their substance; otherwise, patients may quietly lapse into diaphoresis, with the frequent outpouring of matter.

But if extreme pain arises at any point, the only treatment is scarification. In addition, employ fitting and appropriate applications of warmth, fomentations, poultices, and anointings. And prescribe food when the occasion is seen to be opportune. This opportuneness is confirmed by signs that we shall describe in our book *On Fevers*. In general, however, give less food to those suffering from a state of stricture in diseases of all kinds; for a small amount of food is appropriate in cases of congestion, since bodies in that state breathe less readily. On the contrary, a great deal of food is good for a state of looseness, the food being more readily used up because of the body's unimpeded respiration.

86   But if the patient's strength has melted away and, from the fact that his fever is not so acute, there is some hope that the disease is in its decline, have regard for the patient's weakness and give him food and even wine, if necessary, though only a

in his enim sane magis erit consideranda liquidarum emissio materiarum atque corporis defluxio et cutis veluti ruginosa[32] vel sulcata pannositas, quam Graeci rhacosin vocant. etenim humilitas atque densitas pulsus plurimos fecit[33] errare, ut putarent virium solutionem, atque ita importune vinum dantes insupera-

87 biles mentis alienationes fecerunt excitari. quapropter oportet etiam cum aliis pulsum considerare, non solum si densus atque humilis est (hoc enim etiam non solutis viribus saepe occurrit), sed si etiam imbecillis, et in comparatione multarum effusionum[34] semper ac magis densatur atque humilis et tremulus efficitur. cordis enim[35] motus tarditate quadam defecti spiritu motu torpescit, ut post factum saltum ad semet ex residuo corpore praerogatum spiritum trahat, difficulter[36] alium faciat saltum, siquidem non possit spiritus usque ad articulorum finem

88 vel omnium membrorum pervenire summitatem. his denique accedit tremor sed non a tempore quo corpora requiescunt, sed cum aliquis sua membra attractare[37] tentaverit. etenim cessante officio atque nisu[38] aegrotantis tremor si fuerit, solitus[39] atque e natura vel sanitatis[40] tempore intelligitur iam fuisse.

providendum itaque quia in ista aegritudinis qualitate incauta vini dandi consuetudo, protervitas[41] ut supra memoravimus accusabilis apud inertes, quos idiotas appellant, invenitur, quamquam passionis causa aegrotantes interfecti videantur. quapropter erit primo periculum praedicendum ac deinde vinum dandum.

89 at si virium solutio non fuerit, sed ex sponte profectus in meliorem partem passionis fuerit demonstratus, non ilico praecipue[42] festinandum circa mutandum curationis cursum, nisi triduo fuerit confirmata passionis declinatio. etenim facilis[43] in recursum peiorem atque in augmentum hoc passionis est genus, etiamsi parva occasio impulerit causae.[44] quapropter

---

[32] rugosa *Rm*

[33] fecit *R:* facit *G*

[34] effusione *G: corr. Rm*

[35] enim *Rm:* etiam *G*   [40] sanitas *G: corr. Rm*

[36] ⟨et⟩ difficulter *R*   [41] propter vitas *G: corr. Rm*

[37] attrectare *R: cf. adn. ad Ac. i. 79*   [42] praecipitanter *Triller ap. Kühn 55*

[38] visu *G:* usu *Rm*   [43] facilius (*vel* facile) *Triller ap. Kühn 55*

[39] solutus *G: corr. Hagendahl 249*   [44] causam *Triller ap. Kühn 56*

little, to restore his bodily strength. In such cases pay particular attention to the emission of fluids and the body's loss of substance, and to wrinkles, furrows, and raggedness of the skin (Greek *rhacōsis*). For many physicians have been deceived by a low, thick pulse into thinking that the patient's strength has collapsed. They have consequently given wine at the wrong time 87 and have caused insuperable mental derangement. We must, of course, consider the pulse along with the other signs, observing not only whether it is low and thick (for this often occurs even when the strength is not exhausted) but also whether it is weak and whether, in proportion to the extent of the bodily losses, it constantly becomes more dense, submerged, and quivering. For the motion of the heart deprived of pneuma is affected by sluggishness, as it were, and becomes languid; thus, after making a beat, the heart tries to draw to itself from the rest of the body the pneuma that had been previously distributed and makes another beat only with difficulty, since the pneuma cannot reach to the ends of the limbs or to the extremities of any of 88 the parts. The result is that there is a tremor at these extremities, not at the time when the body is at rest but when one tries to draw up one's limbs.[4] But if the tremor also occurs in the absence of any exercise or exertion, we may conclude that it was usual and natural even when the patient was healthy.

And note that in this type of illness the dangerous custom of prescribing wine, a practice evidencing reprehensible wantonness, as we have said,[5] is often found among laymen (Greek *idiōtae*). Yet, because of the nature of the disease, patients [so treated] are found to have been killed.[6] Therefore [when wine is necessary], the danger should first be made clear,[7] and then the wine given.

89 But if there is no collapse of strength and the patient seems to have improved spontaneously, do not on that account rush headlong to change the course of treatment. The decline of the disease must first be confirmed by a three-day period; for it is the nature of this disease that patients easily suffer setbacks and

4. Or possibly 'rub' or 'exercise.' The text and meaning of this and the following sentence are uncertain.

5. Cf. *Ac.* i. 82.

6. Possibly the meaning is: 'And the deaths in these cases appear to be due to the disease,' *sc.* 'though actually the wine was the cause.'

7. I.e., to the kinsmen of the patient.

etiam tunc propter difficultatem passionis cautius erunt omnia agenda.

atque primum capiti vel magis patientibus locis cerotum
90 apponendum ex oleo dulci confectum. at si reliquiae fuerint in tumoribus viscerum, cataplasmatibus erunt perseverantius relaxandae, vel pinguibus palmulis, siquidem non praesentis temporis sed etiam sequentis habeant relaxandi virtutem. tunc etiam convenit caput fomentis curare frequentius, sed cauta diligentia ne qua pars frigore tangatur. nam lata spongia erit supponenda gutturi atque mento, dehinc paulo prominentius a
91 lecto producendus aeger atque paululum inclinandus; tunc supponenda scaphula alta aqua calida plena, deinde duo adhibendi qui foveant alterno officio ne ullo tempore fomentum frigescere faciat caput. per intervalla denique erit etiam oleo perfundendum et manibus leniter defricandum, sed non impressis; tunc expressa spongia detergendum, et ultra quae humectata sunt forte pannis calidis detergenda atque lana calida contegenda.[45] tunc residuum corpus oleo perungendum molli quidem tactu ma-
92 nuum. procedente declinatione solitum nobis est uti etiam fomento a genibus ad inferiora. tunc comparatione profectus cibi augenda humanitas. primo enim oportet ac sufficit varietatem de simplicibus facere, dando pultem aut sorbilem cibum, ova atque panem vel elutam alicam, et non alternis sed cotidianis diebus. et plurimum comparatione praeteriti temporis illorum dierum quibus parvum dare solebamus; simpliciorem vero et tenuem atque parvum illis diebus quibus nihil dare solebamus.
93   confirmata atque plurimum proficiente declinatione, erunt addenda[46] etiam mediae materiae pulmenta, quod[47] Graeci mesen hylen[48] appellant, ut pisces saxatiles, cerebrum, olera, sed non acria, ut betam, malvam.[49] tunc etiam ex deposito, ut salsum, olivas,[50] haec enim quae[51] de cellario proferuntur (Graeci[52] apothecion[53] vocaverunt). oportet etiam advertere ut quando damus multum, minoris sit nutrimenti, aut quando parvum, maioris sit nutrimenti, sicut Responsionum libris resumptivum

---

[45] contegenda *Rm*: est tergenda *G* (*cf.* est versio *G, Ac. i. 31*)

[46] addendae *G: corr. A*

[47] quam *Delattre* (*cf. Ac. i. 95*)

[48] μέσην ὕλην *G*

[49] beta, malva *R*

[50] *fort.* olivae

[51] quae *secl. A*

[52] ⟨quod⟩ Graeci *R*

[53] *cf. Ac. iii. 204*

renewal of attacks with little apparent reason. Therefore, even
in the stage of recovery, everything must be done with considerable care because of the difficulty of dealing with the disease.

90   In the first place, apply a cerate made with sweet olive oil to
the head, that is, to the parts chiefly affected. And if there is
any residual inflammation in the viscera, soothe it by the constant application of poultices, such as those made with juicy
dates, since their relaxing property is not merely temporary but
lasting. And then foment the head frequently, but take care
that no part is chilled. Thus place a broad sponge under the
throat and chin, and raise the patient's head somewhat from
91   the bed and have him bend forward a little. Then have a deep
bowl filled with hot water placed near by, and let two servants
alternate in applying the fomentation, so that the head will not
become chilled at any time. Then at intervals pour olive oil on
the head and gently rub it with the hands without applying
pressure. After that wring out a sponge and wipe the head and
also wipe with warm cloths any other parts that may have become wet. Cover these parts with warm wool. Then anoint the
92   rest of the body with oil, using gentle manual application. As the
disease continues to decline, we generally foment also the parts
from the knees downward. And then the patient's diet should be
increased in proportion to the degree of recovery. First it is
necessary and sufficient to obtain variety from simple foods,
such as porridge, gruel, eggs, bread, and washed spelt groats.
This type of food should now be given not on alternate days but
every day. On those days on which we formerly gave a small
amount of food[8] we should now give a comparatively large
amount. And on the days on which we formerly gave nothing
we should now give a small quantity of light, simple food.
93   As the decline in the disease becomes assured and continues
to proceed, add foods of the middle class[9] (Greek *mesē hylē*),
such as rockfish, brain, and nonacrid vegetables like beets and
mallows. And later give the patient preserved food, including
pickled fare and olives, that is, food brought from the larder
(Greek *apothēcion*). And see to it that the food is less nourishing
when given in large quantity and more nourishing when given
in small quantity, as I indicated in the work entitled *Answers* in

8. Cf. *Ac.* i. 82.
9. In general, bland food: see Celsus ii. 18.

94 cyclum[54] scribentes docuimus. semper autem tantus[55] dandus
est cibus ut intra dimissionis medietatem digeratur, et nihil
superfluum sequens inveniat accessio. augendi sunt igitur cibi
pro virium quantitate. denique si se corporis fortitudo attollere coeperit, dabimus etiam volantum carnes, ut turdos vel
pullos gallinarum et columbinorum, tunc etiam porcinam carnem atque crura porcina, quae Graeci acrocolia vocaverunt, vel
quae motu frequente exercentur in iisdem animalibus. dabimus
etiam haedinam carnem resumptis viribus.

95   ut omnes supradictos cibos facile accipere ac digerere possit
aegrotans, ordinem cibi componimus ut primo demus ea quae
sunt mediae materiae, quam Graeci mesen hylen vocant, ut
pultes, pisces, cerebrum, alica,[56] sed quae[57] non percutiant, ut
ficus vel ex melle, aut mulsum coctum, malum vel celsa; tunc
deinde volantia, sed non pinguia neque cibis nutribilibus ades-
cata ob acquirendam pinguedinem, sed mediocriter carnosa;
ultimo porcinam atque haedinam.

96   proficiente curatione addenda erit gestatio quae in domo vel
in porticibus fiat, sed haec quoque erit sensim augenda: similiter
etiam et corporis unctio atque defricatio. cibus supradictus
nunc quantitate nunc qualitate erit augendus. tunc lavacrum
adhibendum; et in abstinentia vini permanendum. cum autem
sine ulla inquietudine corpus habitare senserimus, dabimus
vinum splendens leve[58] atque medie acre, non nimii odoris,
temporis mediocris, ut neque vetustum neque satis novum sit.

97 erit praeterea aquatum dandum: metuenda est enim in ista
passione vini datio, siquidem eius in tumore fuisse substantia
videatur. tempore igitur quo vinum damus erit primo aeger
perungendus, tunc idem modus cibi dandus.

cum omnis deinde solicitudo recesserit atque omnia suspecta
circumscripta viderimus et alienatio mentis omni ex parte recesserit, febribus desertis atque viribus resumptis, impavide
omnibus supradictis utendum erit coniunctis, ut gestatione,

98 unctione, lavacro, et vario cibo atque vino. omni autem tem-

---

[54] cyclum *Schmid 96*: quid tunc *G*: cibum *coni. Friedel 35*

[55] tantus *Schmid 97*: utantur *G*

[56] *fort. scrib.* alia

[57] quae ⟨caput⟩ *R*

[58] lene *Rm*

94 the discussion of the restorative cycle. And always prescribe
food in such quantity that it will be completely digested by the
middle of the remission, so that the subsequent attack will find
nothing left over. And increase the quantity of food in proportion to the patient's strength. Then, as the patient's bodily
strength begins to grow, give him the flesh of birds like thrushes,
young chickens, and squabs; and later also pork and pig's
trotters (Greek *acrocōlia*[10]) or the parts which are subjected to
frequent motion in these animals. And when the strength has
been restored, prescribe also kid's flesh.

95   In order that the patient may easily take and digest all these
foods, so arrange their order as first to give those which are of
the middle class (Greek *mesē hylē*), e.g., porridges, fish, brain,
spelt, and foods that do not have a pungent effect, as do figs,
especially with honey, boiled mead, apples, and mulberries.
Then prescribe the flesh of fowls, not those that are naturally
fat or crammed with nutritious food to become fat, but rather
those with a moderate amount of flesh. Finally, prescribe pork
and lamb.

96   As the treatment proceeds successfully, add passive exercise
either in the house or in porticoes, and gradually increase this
exercise, too. Also have the patient's body anointed and
massaged more frequently. And have the diet described above
increased, first in quantity and then in strength. Then prescribe
bathing, but have the patient continue to abstain from wine.
When, however, his body is seen to be free from any disturbance,
prescribe a clear wine, mild and somewhat tart, but with no pronounced odor, and moderately aged, i.e., neither very old nor
97 quite new. Moreover, have the wine mixed with water, for in
this disease there is a risk in giving wine, since the essence of the
disease evidently lies in the inflammation. And at the time
when the wine is given, first anoint the patient and then serve
him the same amount of food [as he has been taking].

    And then when the period of anxiety is all over and all
grounds for suspicion removed, the patient's mental derangement entirely cleared up, his fever gone, and his strength restored, you may without hesitation use all the aforesaid treatments together, the passive exercise, anointing, bathing, varied
98 food, and wine. And during the whole period of recovery take

10. I.e., extremities.

pore resumptionis erit curandum ut ab alienatione mentis reducti sapere cogantur. plerique enim usque ad sanitatis tempus maestitudinem vel iracundiam aut alienationem mentis servaverint.[59] quare oportet eos qui hilaritate afficiebantur severa verborum atque tristi oratione corrigere; sic enim mentis laxata habitudo atque puerilis[60] effrenata bacchatio coercetur: eos vero qui maestitudine atque ira afficiebantur, leni[61] consola-
99 tione atque nunc dictis hilarioribus et iucunditate relevare; etenim taedium vel maestitudo non solum in his sed etiam in aliis passionibus valuit saepe passionem refricare. nam si sani homines plerique anxietate in passiones corporis devenerunt, nimirum etiam qui nondum sunt passione purgati in eandem[62] redeant, cum animae qualitas sua, ut ita dixerim, cubilia quadam vulneratione affecerit.

haec est secundum methodon curatio phreniticae passionis. dehinc aliarum sectarum principes quid ordinaverint prosequamur.

100   XII. AD DIOCLEM

HIPPOCRATES igitur solum nomen videtur tetigisse passionis libro quem De ptisana scripsit, item libro praedictivo quem Prorrheticum appellavit: nam curationem nullam tradidit. sed neque Praxagoras neque Herophilus.

Diocles vero libro quem De febribus scripsit ait oportere phreniticos fortes atque audaces lavacro curari, simili[1] etiam phlebotomare iuvenes fortes atque plurimum sanguinis[2] abundantes vel consuetudine vinolentos, quosdam intra sextum diem,
101 aliquos vero etiam post septimum et octavum. item libro quem De passionibus et earum causis et curationibus scripsit, non solum, inquit, ex brachio sanguis est phreniticis detrahendus, sed etiam de venis quae sub lingua sunt.

quantum ad haec miseris erat melius debilitate potius quam

---

59 servaverunt *R*   62 eadem *G: corr. R*

60 pueris *G: corr. Rm*   1 similiter *R*

61 leni *Rm*: levi *G*   2 sanguine *R*

---

1. The references are to *Regimen in Acute Diseases*, chap. 2, and the early sections of *Prorrhetic* i. Actually, phrenitis is mentioned in many other books of the Hippocratic Corpus as we have it, e.g., in *Prognostic, Epidemiae* i, iii, and vii, *Aphorisms, Coan Pre-*

measures that the patient may be restored from a condition of
mental derangement to a state of complete sanity. For in most
cases patients remain in a state of sadness, anger, or aberration
right up to the return of physical health. It is necessary, therefore, to use grave and serious language to those whose state had
been one of hilarity. For thus the weakened condition of their
mind and their childish and unrestrained raving are brought
under control. But those who are in a state of sadness or anger
must be soothed with gentle encouragement and pleasant and
99 cheerful language. For tedium or sadness often has the effect, not
only in this but in other diseases, of exciting the malady anew.
For if healthy people in many instances incur bodily illnesses
because of a troubled state of mind, it is not surprising that
those who are not yet cured of a disease should suffer a relapse
when their mental state has, so to speak, dealt a wound to their
sickbed.

So much for the treatment of phrenitis according to the
Methodists. Let us now discuss the procedures adopted by the
leaders of other sects.

100   XII. REPLY TO DIOCLES

H IPPOCRATES seems merely to have mentioned the name of
this disease in this work *On the Ptisan* and also in the prognostic book which he called *Prorrhetic*. But he gave no treatment.[1] And neither did Praxagoras, nor Herophilus.

Diocles, however, in his book *On Fevers* says that phrenitics
who are strong and impetuous should be treated with baths. Also
that for young patients who are strong and full-blooded or who
habitually drink much wine venesection should be employed, in
some cases before the sixth day, but in others even after the
101 seventh or eighth day. And in the book which he wrote *On
Diseases and Their Causes and Treatment* he declares that in
phrenitis the blood should be taken not only from the arm but
from the veins under the tongue.

But so far as these measures are concerned, it would be better
for these poor people to be weak than to possess the empty ad-

_____

notions, and *On Hebdomads*. Note also that *On Diseases* iii. 9 and *On Affections*, chap. 10,
contain discussions of the treatment; and that of these two works the former is quoted
on more than one occasion by Caelius (Soranus).

vana corporis fortitudine laborare, ne tantis cladibus errantis
medici vexarentur. etenim audacia et irrationabilis fortitudo
102 peiorantis est passionis, et magis in augmento. perniciosius
autem, cum passio vehementescit vexato tantis turbationibus
aegro, lavacrum adhibere, quod est econtrario[3] utilissimum in
declinatione, etiam non audacibus neque fortibus phreniticis.

dehinc noxius est etiam clyster acrior, quem saepissime probant,[4] atque nihil ab veneficio[5] differens. phlebotomia quoque
iugulatione non differt cum vexatis viribus adhibetur, ut aiunt,
post septimum vel octavum diem. atque ita etiam ex vinolentia
in phreniticam passionem venientes convenit plerumque non
103 phlebotomari, cum forte etiam solutio adfuerit. alios etiam,
hoc est ex aliis causis phreniticos effectos, ut est adustio, saepe
phlebotomari oportet. sed neque parum sanguinis habentes,
quos Graeci oligaemus[6] appellant, ita curandi erunt ut phlebotomi beneficio priventur. et quid ultra? cum enim non
aetates neque cetera quae superfluo[7] posuerunt providenda probemus, sed passionem magis atque eius comitantia considere-
mus. falsa denique ac superstitiosa est etiam ex venis sub lingua
constitutis sanguinis detractio. etenim caput implet et eius
fluor abstineri difficile potest.

104 ## XIII. AD ERASISTRATUM

ERASISTRATUS tertio libro De febribus scribens hoc solum
dixit, quomodo in febrium alienatione vinum convenit cum
melle dari: non ad examen dandi tempora sumpsit. dicit denique multis profuisse et miratur quomodo, nescius temporum
convenisse fortunam. dehinc multam inflationem facere nemo

---

[3] econtrario Rm: econtrarium G (cf. Ac. ii. 51)

[4] probat R

[5] veneficio Rm: officio G

[6] ὀλιγαίμους G

[7] superflua Rm

---

2. Or perhaps 'unaccountable strength' or 'paradoxical strength.'

3. I.e., Diocles and his followers. But the plural may possibly be due to the periph-
rasis οἱ περὶ Διοκλέα = Diocles. For a similar shift to the plural, cf. Ac. i. 105 and Soranus Gyn., p. 122. 19.

vantage of bodily strength; they would then avoid such disastrous treatment at the hands of an ignorant physician. Indeed,
impetuosity and unreasoning [display of] strength[2] are signs that
the disease is becoming worse, particularly so in its increasing
102 phase. And when the disease becomes very intense and the
patient is subjected to violent attacks, it is dangerous to prescribe baths. This treatment, on the contrary, is most advantageous in the decline of the disease and then need not be
limited to strong and impetuous phrenitics.

Again, a sharp clyster, which they[3] often recommend, is
actually harmful and no different from poison. Venesection, too,
is equivalent to murder if it is performed when the patient's
strength is impaired, that is, after the seventh or eighth day,
which is when they prescribe it. And venesection should generally not be used in the case of those who incur phrenitis from excessive drinking of wine, since a state of looseness may also then
103 be present. But venesection should often be used in other cases,
too, that is, in cases of phrenitis arising from other causes, such
as exposure to intense heat. On the other hand, in treating
those who have little blood (Greek *oligaemoe*), we should not altogether deprive them of the advantages of venesection. But
why labor the point? We simply do not agree that the age of the
patients and the other irrelevant criteria which they have laid
down should be taken into account; we hold that the disease and
its symptoms are the prime considerations. Finally, the withdrawal of blood from the veins situated under the tongue is an
error and a superstition, for it congests the head, and the flow of
blood can only with difficulty be controlled.

104   XIII. REPLY TO ERASISTRATUS

IN BOOK III of his work *On Fevers*, Erasistratus declares merely
that in cases of mental derangement with fever wine should
be given with honey; but he does not take up the question of the
time at which it should be given. He goes on to say that wine
has benefited many patients, and he wonders why, not realizing
that a fortunate timing accounted for the success. But there is
no doubt that this treatment causes much flatulence and very

dubitat atque plenissimam ventris commotionem, quippe cum neque dandi quantitatem adiecerit neque alias adiutorii partes manifestandas adverterit.

105   XIV. AD ASCLEPIADEM

A SCLEPIADI responsuri eius primum dogma proponamus, qua voluti[1] apprehensionis falsitate peccatis etiam involvuntur curationum. primordia namque corporis primo constituerat atomos, [secunda][2] corpuscula intellectu sensa sine ulla qualitate solita, atque ex initio comitata, aeternum moventia. quae suo incursu offensa mutuis ictibus in infinita partium fragmenta solvantur magnitudine atque schemate differentia; quae rursum eundo sibi adiecta vel coniuncta omnia faciant sensibilia, vim in semet mutationis habentia, aut per magnitudinem sui, aut per 106 multitudinem, aut per schema, aut per ordinem. nec, inquit, ratione carere videatur[2a] quod nullius faciant qualitatis corpora: aliud enim partes, aliud universitatem sequetur. argentum denique album est, sed eius affricatio nigra; caprinum cornu nigrum, sed eius alba serrago. fieri etiam vias ex complexione corpusculorum intellectu sensas, magnitudine atque schemate differentes, per quas sucorum ductus solito meatu percurrens, si nullo fuerit impedimento retentus, sanitas maneat, impeditus 107 vero statione corpusculorum morbos efficiat. fit autem eorum statio aut magnitudinis aut schematis aut multitudinis aut celerrimi motus causa, aut viarum flexu †conclusione atque squamularum exputo.†[3] varias inquit fieri passiones locorum

[1] veluti Rm

[2] om. R   [2a] videtur R

[3] fort. conclusione corpusculorum effecto vel sim.: atque squamularum conclusione Kühn 64, omisso exputo (squamulae = fragmenta [105])

---

1. If we keep secunda (G) or read secundo, the effect is to distinguish the atoms and corpuscles in the system of Asclepiades. This is probably an incorrect interpretation of Asclepiades, but we cannot be sure that the mistake was made by a post-Caelian corrector and not by Caelius himself. Cf. Soranus Gyn., p. 95. 25.

2. I.e., not perceptible by the senses.

3. Or 'combinations of corpuscles,' which would better suit the argument. But Caelius' language throughout the passage betrays an imperfect understanding of the subject.

4. The word seems to refer loosely both to fragmenta and to corpuscula, but what the fragments are is not stated.

considerable disturbance of the stomach and bowels. And, what is more, Erasistratus does not indicate the quantity of wine to be given, nor does he consider it necessary to make clear the other parts of his treatment.

105   XIV. REPLY TO ASCLEPIADES

BEFORE answering Asclepiades, let us first set forth his basic doctrine, for this doctrine involves him and his followers in misconceptions which lead to mistakes in treating diseases. Now, to begin with, he posits atoms as the first principles of the body, corpuscles[1] apprehended only by the understanding,[2] endowed with none of the customary qualities of things, always found in combinations, and endlessly moving about. When these corpuscles[3] suffer collision in the course of their motion, they split up, under the mutual impact of the blow, into countless fragments differing in size and shape; again, as they[4] move, they form, through attachment or union, all the perceptible bodies. These bodies have within themselves the capacity for change[5] by reason of the size, number, shape, and order [of the con-
106 stituent corpuscles]. And it would not be illogical, says Ascle-piades, to hold that such a result can be produced by corpuscles which in themselves possess none of these qualities. For the properties of a whole are necessarily different from those of its parts. For example, silver is white, but particles rubbed off are black; a goat's horn is black, but particles chipped from it are white. Now out of the union of corpuscles passages varying in size and shape are formed, which may be apprehended only by reason. Through these passages the body's fluids are conducted with a regular motion. So long as this process is not checked by any impediment, the state of health continues; but if the flow is impeded by a blocking of the corpuscles, a state of disease re-
107 sults. Now such a blocking of the corpuscles comes about be-cause of their size, shape, number, or excessive speed of motion, or because of a bending of the passages. . . . Different diseases,

5. Caelius seems to mean that the size, number, shape, and order of the corpuscles determine the varying qualities of the perceptible bodies. The sentence may be in-terpreted 'these corpuscles have within themselves the potentiality for effecting change [in the perceptible bodies which they form] by reason of their size, number, shape, and order.'

aut viarum differentia, et non omnes statione corpusculorum
sed certas, hoc est phrenitim, lethargiam, pleuritim, et febres
vehementes; solubiles vero liquidorum atque spiritus turbatione.
item bulimum magnitudine viarum stomachi atque ventris
fieri sensit; defectionem vero atque corporis fluxam[4] et irregi-
108 bilem laxitatem viarum inquit raritate fieri; item hydropismum
perforatione carnis in parvam formulam viarum quae possit
solita[5] corporis nutrimenta inaquare. item typum cotidianum
maiorum corpusculorum statione fieri asseverat,[6] cito enim inquit ea exantlari atque impleri; tertianum vero minorum statione corpusculorum, item quartanum minutissimorum, difficile enim impleri atque exantlari possunt. febrium ponunt
signum fervorem plurimum atque immutationem pulsus in vehementia, nisi ex aliqua[7] haec manifesta fuerint causa.

109 et neque inquit esse in passionibus statos dies quos crisimos
appellant: etenim non certo aut legitimo tempore aegritudines
solvuntur. vinum iubet febricitantibus dari, sed adiecta discretione; impari denique[8] adhibendum probavit primo clysterem
et iugiter adhibendum. non etiam sitim vehementem donec
pulsus concidat probat: etenim opportunitatem temporis fieri
magis ab artifice posse, quam sua sponte aut deorum nutu venire. appellavit denique illam manificam.[9]

110 item in hemitritaeo[10] clysterem atque vomitum probat circa
vesperam pridie;[11] sed in his qui periodicis typis afficiuntur

[4] *fort.* fluxum

[5] solida *A* (*ed. 1722*)

[6] asseverat *R*: -nt *G* (*cf. 102 n.*)

[7] *fort.* alia

[8] denique ⟨die⟩ *R*

[9] magnificam *G*: *corr. Triller ap. Kühn 66, nisi scrib.* manu factam

[10] in hemitritaeo *scripsi*: in hemitritaea *Kühn 67*: in Samothracia *G*: in semitertiana
Wellmann, Celsus 113, n. 1: vinum Samothracium *Triller (v. Kühn 66): fort. scrib.* in
⟨hemitritaeo vinum⟩ Samothracium

[11] *fort.* prima die

6. Cf. Soranus *Gyn.*, p. 96. 15.

7. So that both processes are concluded in a single day.

continues Asclepiades, arise because of differences in the parts and passages of the body. And not all diseases are caused by stoppage of the corpuscles.[6] Certain ones are so caused, viz., phrenitis, lethargy, pleurisy, and severe fevers; but mild diseases are caused by a disturbance of the bodily fluids and the pneuma. Asclepiades further holds that bulimia is caused by distention of the passages in the esophagus and stomach; that fainting accompanied by uncontrollable bodily flux and atony

108 comes from the expansion of the passages; that dropsy is caused by the boring of a type of small duct in the flesh, capable of turning the usual nutriment of the body into water. And he asserts that the quotidian type of fever is caused by the stoppage of larger corpuscles, for these can quickly be removed and can quickly fill up the space again.[7] But the tertian fever is caused by the stoppage of smaller corpuscles; and the quartan by stoppage of the most minute. For it is only with difficulty that these can fill up the passage and be drawn off again. Asclepiades and his followers take great heat and a change in the strength of the pulse to be a sign of fever unless these symptoms have clearly arisen from some other cause.

109 Asclepiades denies that in diseases there are decisive days (Greek *crisimoe*, 'critical'), for illnesses do not break up at a definite or regular time. He prescribes wine for those suffering from fever, but with the exercise of discretion. And he says that a clyster should first be administered on an odd-numbered day of the disease and regularly continued. He does not approve of withholding drink until the pulse collapses. He holds that the appropriate time for treatment is more likely to be created by the skilful physician than to appear by itself or by the will of the gods. And he calls this creation 'hand made.'[8]

110 In semitertian fevers[9] he administers a clyster and an emetic on the evening before [an attack].[10] But in cases of periodic

8. I.e., artificial as opposed to natural (χειροποίητος in contrast with αὐτοφυής). Cf. *Chr.* ii. 218; *Ac.* ii. 123, iii. 165.

9. The text is uncertain, and the reference may be to Samothracian wine (Triller, Friedel), as later in this paragraph, or to cases occurring in Samothrace (G). As for the latter reading, note that Asclepiades in particular differentiated his treatment according to the various regions. Cf. *Ac.* i. 139, ii. 129 ff.

10. The meaning of *pridie*, if, indeed, that is the right reading, is uncertain; and the text throughout the sentence is doubtful.

vomitum praeponit clysteri. item lue aegrotantibus vomitum
et lavacrum probat; typicis vero clysterem et vomitum et vinum Samothracium atque salsum bibendum inquit, primo
usque ad tres quartas sextarii, et superbibendam partem sextarii.
item tempus dandi cibi non dimissione perfecta sed accessionis
declinatione dicit. et quosdam prima die, quosdam secunda,
quosdam tertia, quosdam quarta vel quinta aut septima cibari
111 iubet. phlebotomat eos qui cum dolore fuerint aegrotantes,
alios omnes prohibet phlebotomari, et magis specialiter phreniticos, adiciens etiam non esse tondendos, loci quoque obscuritatem recusans. item cardiacos vehementioribus clysteribus
curat, et cum levi fuerint indulgentia relevati, reficit vino et
cibo. in synanchicis vero ut supradictis[12] etiam utitur pharingo-
tomia, hoc est cannae sive gutturis ob respirationem divisura.
item hydropibus paracentesin probat qua, inquit, si forte plus
modo fuerit facta humoris detractio, erunt aegri aqua calida re-
112 plendi tantum quantum plus videbamur abstulisse. huic sane
adiutorio[13] detractionem sanguinis ex talo factam, hoc est ex
eius vena interiore, similiter mederi dicit. et non esse activas
atque operantes causas aegritudinum in liquidis constitutas,
quas synecticas vocant, sed esse antecedentes, quas Graeci procatarcticas appellant. item plenitudinem plerasque passiones
adiuvare dicit.

laudat etiam in Salutaribus praeceptis vitae varietatem, atque
vehementer utile dicit aquam bibere et frigida lavari, quam
113 psychrolusiam appellant, et frigidam bibere. item habitudinem
athleticam negat esse tutam. et neque ullam digestionem in
nobis esse, sed solutionem ciborum in ventre fieri crudam et per
singulas particulas corporis ire, ut per omnes tenuis vias[14] penetrare videatur, quod appellavit leptomeres, sed nos intelligimus
spiritum. et neque inquit ferventis qualitatis neque frigidae

[12] ut supradictis] cucurbitis *Wellmann, Celsus 90*   [13] morbo *Rm*
[14] vias *Haller*: visa *G*

---

11. In addition to the sense in which the word 'pharynx' is now used, Greek medical
writers sometimes use the same word to denote the windpipe, especially its upper part.
Thus the operation of laryngotomy or tracheotomy is here referred to.

12. Or 'predisposing.'

13. An overabundance of blood, causing suffusion into the arteries from the veins,
was, according to Erasistratus, a cause of febrile diseases. 'Plethora' here probably refers
to such suffusion.

fevers he prescribes the emetic before the clyster. Again, for
those suffering from pestilential fever he prescribes vomitives
and baths; and in periodic fevers clysters, emetics, and wine of
Samothrace, which he has the patient drink salted, first as much
as three-quarters of a sextarius and, later on, another half-
sextarius. And he declares that the proper time to begin giving
the patient food is not when the remission is complete but when
the attack beings to abate. He has some of his patients fed on
the first, and others on the second, third, fourth, fifth, or seventh
11 day. He performs venesection on those whose illness is accompanied by pain; but he bars this treatment for all others, and especially for phrenitics, adding that their hair should not be cut
and that they should not be kept in a dark place. He treats those
suffering from the cardiac disease with strong clysters, and, after
they have been relieved by gentle care, he restores their strength
with wine and food. In cases of synanche, in addition to using
the above treatments, he also performs pharyngotomy,[11] i.e., an
incision of the windpipe to facilitate breathing. In dropsy he
recommends paracentesis, saying that if the withdrawal of fluid
in this treatment happens to exceed the proper limit, the patient
should be replenished with warm water to the extent of the
112 excessive withdrawal. He also says that the withdrawal of blood
from the heel, i.e., from its interior vein, will similarly remedy
excesses in this treatment. Asclepiades holds that the humors
are not the seat of the immediate and efficient causes of diseases
(Greek *synecticae*), but of the antecedent[12] causes (Greek *procatarcticae*); and that plethora[13] is a contributing factor in most
diseases.

In his *Rules of Health* he recommends variation of the mode of
life and considers very helpful the drinking of water, and especially of cold water, and bathing in cold water (Greek *psy-
113 chrolusia*). He says that the athletic constitution is not safe. He
holds that there is no digestion [i.e., coction] of food in our bodies
but that the food is broken down in the belly undigested and
passes through the several parts of the body, evidently penetrating all the fine passages. Asclepiades calls the substance *leptomeres* ['consisting of fine parts'], but we use the term *spiritus*
[*pneuma*, 'breath']. This substance has, in his judgment,
neither a hot nor a cold character, because of its extreme thin-

esse, nimiae suae tenuitatis causa, neque alium quemlibet sensum tactus habere, sed per vias receptaculorum nutrimenti nunc arteriam, nunc nervum vel venam vel carnem fieri.

item transvorationis primam partem dicit extentione fieri faucium, secundam viarum tenuitate quae ad ventrem ducunt.

114 item orexim, quam nos appetentiam dicere poterimus, eam quae cibum appetit, viarum maiorum[15] patefactione[16] fieri dicit in stomacho atque ventre; eam autem quae potum appetit parvarum viarum causa fieri dicit. praeterea excrementa ventris (Graeci scybala dicunt) negat aliena esse natura, siquidem etiam ex ipsis corpora augeantur: quaedam denique, inquit, animalia ex ipsis solummodo nutriunt.[17]

115 somnum enim etiam fieri spiritus sensibilis crassificatione asseverat. deinde regnum animae aliqua in parte corporis constitutum negat, etenim nihil aliud esse dicit animam quam sensuum omnium coetum;[18] intellectum autem occultarum vel latentium rerum per solubilem fieri motum sensuum, qui ab accidentibus sensibilibus[19] atque antecedenti[20] perspectione[21] perficitur; memoriam vero alterno eorum exercitio dicit. omnia praeterea fieri necessitate, et nihil sine causa, et neque naturam aliud esse quam corpus vel eius motum. deinde, inquit, non solum prodest sed etiam nocet.

hoc est Asclepiadis dogma. nunc quemadmodum phreniticos curaverit prosequemur.

116   XV. ITEM AD ASCLEPIADEM
                 [PHRENITICOS CURANS][1]

PHRENITICOS curans primo libro Celerum vel acutarum passionum[2] expugnat eos qui contraria posuerunt adhibenda; secundo quomodo declinanda vel avertenda sit phrenitis;[3]

---

[15] maiore G: corr. Gumpert (v. Kühn 68)

[16] patefactione Rm: perfectione G

[17] nutriuntur Rm

[18] centrum Triller (v. Kühn 69)   [19] sensilibus edd.

[20] antecedentis Wellmann, Neue Jahrb. 21. 699

[21] perceptione Triller (v. Kühn 69)

[1] secl. Helmreich 314: phreniticos curantem A

[2] passionum ⟨primo⟩ Schmid 101   [3] phrenitis ⟨docet⟩ R

ness, nor does it have any other tangible quality; but, as it passes through the channels in the parts which receive nutriment, it is made now into artery, now into sinew, vein, or flesh.

Asclepiades says that the first part of the act of swallowing is accomplished by a stretching of the fauces, and the second by 114 the fine passages leading to the stomach. The desire for food (Greek *orexis*, which we may translate *appetentia*) is the result of dilation of the larger passages in the esophagus and stomach; while the desire for drink is due to the small passages.[14] Again, he denies that the excrements of the bowels (Greek *scybala*) are of a character foreign to the body, for bodies are, in fact, nourished by them. That is, certain animals find their nutriment solely in this excrement.

115 He holds that sleep results from a thickening of the perceptive pneuma; and he denies that the ruling part of the soul is situated in a definite part of the body. In fact, the soul, he says, is nothing but the combination of all the senses; and the apprehension of imperceptible or unseen things takes place through the swift motion of the senses, this act of apprehension being fulfilled with the help of perceptible objects and previous acts of perception. He considers memory the result of the exercise of perception and apprehension in turn. And he declares that all things happen by necessity, that there is nothing without a cause, and that nature is nothing but body and its motion. And so nature not only helps but also harms.

Such is the doctrine of Asclepiades. We shall now consider his method of treating phrenitis.

116   XV. REPLY TO ASCLEPIADES (*Continued*)

IN BOOK I of his work *On Swift* (i.e., acute) *Diseases*, Asclepiades takes up the treatment of phrenitis and refutes those who prescribe contrary[1] measures; secondly, he indicates how

14. I.e., to the dilation of the small passages? The meaning is uncertain; with the reading of *Rm* it would appear that hunger and thirst are due to the dilation and contraction, respectively, of the passages.

1. I.e., measures inconsistent with one another and contradictory. But the reference may be to measures mistakenly believed by their proponents to be 'contrary' measures in the sense of the maxim *contraria contrariis curantur*. There is still another possibility; for, when the customary rational remedies in any disease proved to be of no avail, some physicians used remedies just the opposite of these. It may be in this sense that the term 'contrary' is here employed (see, e.g., Celsus iii. 9. 2; vi. 6. 8E). The term would then generally include such drastic measures as are noted immediately below.

tertio quomodo curanda cum fuerit. contradicens igitur primo
incusat[4] clysteres atque irim bibendam et acetum cum melle et
ex sinapi apophlegmatismum et tonsuram, siquidem horta-
mento quodam liquidorum[5] faciat ad caput ascensum, et in
constrictionem[6] atque tensionem cerebri membranam cogat.
117 accurrit enim incisurae capillorum materies, et pori denique et
capilli post tonsuram crassescunt atque fortiores fiunt. quapropter etiam sani[7] homines si post cibum totonderint, tussicula
118 atque catarrho vel lippitudine vexantur. dehinc si lanis caput
post tonsuram tegere curamus, quanto melius si naturali tegmine capillorum lateat obtectum? improbat etiam in obscuro
loco iacere aegrotantes. in luce enim, inquit, mentis sive intelligentiae visa debilia atque parva efficiuntur cum sensualibus
visis arguuntur, sicut nocturni luminis ac funalium flamma sub
aetheria luce constituta visi potioris oppressione languescit.
in obscuro autem econtrario vehementiora atque maiora fieri
mentis atque intelligentiae visa asseverat, cum nullis sensualibus visis arguuntur quiescentibus sensibus. denique tamquam
praesentia vel vera fiunt sicuti somniantum; etiam tunc enim
119 silentibus sensibus solius mentis visa operantur, ac deinde cum
nullis adhuc sensualibus visis avocantur,[9] tamquam praesentium
non praesentium visa sequuntur.

phlebotomiam etiam nihil inquit iugulatione differre in phreniticis, siquidem sit cum dolore aegrotantibus congrua: nam
dolor maiorum corpusculorum statione fiet, quae sola phlebotomia exantlari posse noscuntur. phrenitici igitur nullo dolore
vexantur, siquidem angustis in viis[10] parvorum facta videatur
statio, et propterea phlebotomati animi defectu atque corporis
frigido torpore afficiantur aut vocis amputationem aut mentis
alienationem sustineant. detracta enim materie passionum
causa remanente, crassificari contingit atque corporis facere al-

---

[4] incusat *A*: in causa *G*: recusat *R, coll. Ac. i. 120*

[5] liquidorum *Bendz 86*: liquidior *G*: liquor *Helmreich 315*

[6] constructionem *G*: *corr. A*

[7] etiam sani *Schmid 98*: etiamsi *G*: etiam, si *Friedel 29*

[9] visis avocantur *Schmid 100*: incisa vocantur *G*

[10] angustis in viis *Schmid 82*: angustiis in his *G*

phrenitis is to be prevented and avoided and, thirdly, how it is to be treated if it does occur. In his refutation he first criticizes clysters, the drinking of iris and of oxymel, and the use of mustard to promote the discharge of phlegm. He also criticizes the cutting of the hair; for by a kind of stimulation this causes the [bodily] fluids to rise to the head and produces constriction

117 and tension of the membrane of the brain. Matter is attracted by the cutting of the hair, and the pores and hair grow thick after the cutting and become stronger.[2] Thus even healthy persons who cut their hair just after eating are sometimes affected

118 by cough, catarrh, or inflammation of the eyes. And if we have to be careful to cover the head with wool after the haircut, how much better if the head had remained protected by its natural covering? Asclepiades also criticizes the practice of having the patient lie in a dark place. For in the light, he says, the visions of the mind or imagination become weakened and diminished, being overpowered by the images actually perceived, just as the flame of a night lamp or torch is weak in the daylight, being overwhelmed by this more powerful object of sight.[3] In the dark, on the other hand, the visions of the mind or imagination, he says, become larger and more powerful, not being overpowered by images actually perceived, since the senses are at rest. These visions of the mind become, in a sense, actual and real, like the visions in dreams; for in dreams, too, the senses are at rest and

119 it is the visions of the mind alone that have effect. And these mental images are not diverted by any actual sense-perceptions and therefore strike the patient as visions of real objects, though they are not real.

Venesection, says Asclepiades, is equivalent to murder in cases of phrenitis, since it is a suitable treatment only in illnesses involving pain. For pain arises from the blocking of the larger corpuscles, which, it is known, can be drawn off only by venesection. But phrenitics [he says] are not affected by any pain, for in their case the small corpuscles are blocked in the narrow pores. For that reason phrenitics who are subjected to venesection experience fainting and a chill numbness of the body, or loss of voice, or loss of reason. For whenever matter is withdrawn but the cause of a disease remains, a thickening results, and a cold-

2. Stiffer?

3. I.e., the daylight. Or reading *vis*, 'by this more powerful force.'

gorem; tunc ad cerebri membranam spiritum vel fervorem ferri,
et[11] statione corpusculorum geminata quoque alienatione.

120   et recte quidem clysteres atque irim et mulsum ex aceto et
⟨ex⟩[12] sinapi apophlegmatismum recusat, sed se ipse quoque
impugnans sicuti in consequentibus docebimus. item tonsuram
atque obscurum locum et phlebotomiam non recte prohibere
voluit. nocentur enim quidam non tonsurae causa sed intempo-
ralitatis eiusdem: denique etiam sanos post cibum tondentes
nocere[13] manifestum est, ante cibum vero opportunitatis causa
relevari. dehinc etiamsi vi sua prodesse tonsuram negat,
oportuit tamen eam adhiberi propter usum localium adiutoriorum, sine qua necessario adhiberi non possunt, sicut superius
docuimus.

121   aeris vero qualitas non occulta causa sed manifesto passionis
indicio erit iudicanda. secundum passionem igitur quomodo
videmus alios strictura, alios solutione magis affici, convenit
ut pro differentia his lucidus, illis obscurus sit adhibendus. nam
crassitudine ac frigore constringens aer redarguit corporis defluxiones, quas Graeci aporrhoeas vocant. at si, ut nuper docuimus, proprietatem accidentium servaverimus, quomodo quidam lucem fugiunt vel oderunt, alii tenebras, convenit ut alios
obscuro, alios lucido esse faciamus loco. quid dicam quomodo
pleraque aegris aliter sunt quam videntur? ex visis namque veris
ducentes quidam mentis errorem, falsitate magis afficiuntur.

122 sic denique Hercules filiorum et coniugis inimicos visibus vultus
accepit; Orestes etiam Electrae furiales vultus expavit. non
omnes igitur lucido in loco iacere concordat, sicut latius Adiutoriorum libro explicamus.[14]

[11] et fort. secl.

[12] ⟨ex⟩ R (cf. Ac. i. 116, sed contra Bendz 24)

[13] noceri Rm, fort. recte

[14] an explicabimus?

4. See Ac. i. 61 ff.

5. Referring to the argument in 118–19.

6. Cf. Euripides Heracles 970 ff.; Orestes 264.

7. I.e., it would be better for those whose delusions are based on what they see not
to see anything.

ness is produced in the body; then pneuma and heat are carried
to the membrane of the brain, and with the blocking of the corpuscles the mental derangement is aggravated.

120   Now Asclepiades is right in rejecting clysters, iris, oxymel,
and the use of mustard to promote the discharge of phlegm, but
thereby he contradicts himself, as we shall show in what follows.
And he errs in his desire to bar the cutting of hair, the use of a
dark room for the patient, and venesection. Some patients, to be
sure, are harmed, not because the hair is cut, but because it is cut
at the wrong time. Thus it is well known that even healthy persons are harmed if their hair is cut just after they have taken
food; but if this cutting is done before they take food, they are
relieved because the time is suitable. Again, even if Asclepiades
is right in denying that the cutting of the hair is advantageous
in and of itself, it must still be performed in order to use local
remedies which cannot otherwise be applied, as we have indicated above.

121   And the type of air [suitable for patients] will have to be de-
cided not by some obscure reasoning but by the obvious signs of
the disease. And since, with reference to the disease, we see that
in some cases a state of stricture predominates and in others a
state of looseness, we must, in view of this difference, use light
for the former cases and darkness for the latter. For that air
which, by reason of its thickness and chill, has an astringent
effect represses discharges from the body (Greek *aporrhoeae*).
But even if, as indicated above,[4] we have regard to the nature
of the symptoms, since some patients avoid and dislike light,
and others darkness, we should have to put the former in a dark
place and the latter in a bright place. And it goes without saying
that to the sick many things appear different from what they
really are;[5] in fact, some patients are victims of illusion, though
122 their error arises from an actual visual image. Thus Hercules,
when he looked upon his sons and wife, saw the faces of his
enemies, and Orestes was terrified by the countenance of
Electra, whom he mistook for a Fury.[6] It is not proper, therefore,
for all patients to lie in a bright room,[7] as we explain at greater
length in our book *On Remedies*.[8]

8. If this is the work *On Remedies* often mentioned by Caelius as part of the *Responsiones*, *explicabimus* should probably be read: 'as we *shall* explain.' But see Friedel, p. 45.

est etiam vehementer noxium phlebotomiae utilissimum adiutorium prohibere, quippe cum videamus in ipso usu saepe
passionem fecisse compendium. etenim defectio vocis atque
algor sequentur eos qui incongrue fuerint phlebotomati, con-
123 iuncta scilicet solutione, aut intemporaliter aut immodice. vanum est etiam quia non dolent phlebotomiam prohibere, tamquam maiorum corpusculorum congruam detractioni, quorum
obtrusione dolores efficiuntur. primo enim paralyticos et peripneumonicos et apoplectos congrue phlebotomamus cum nullis
doloribus afficiantur. secundo etiam phrenitici dolent, sed
eorum mens, quia iudicio caret, nescit queri quod doleat. videmus namque eos sese mordere aut urere aut pungere, et naturale non est nullo dolore cogente fieri[15] existimare. dehinc maiorum corpusculorum detractionem etiam minorum necessario
sequitur. at phrenitici non solum alienantur, sed febricitant:
124 ita febres secundum Asclepiadem maiorum corpusculorum
statione fiunt. si igitur propter alienationem non convenit,
propter febres tamen convenit adhibere phlebotomiam (sic
etiam sanguis maiorum corpusculorum materia). sed non
solum ⟨sanguinem⟩[16] detrahit phlebotomia verum etiam spiritum et fervorem, quae ut dicit parvorum sunt corpusculorum
materiae. convenit igitur secundum ipsum phreniticos phlebotomari, ut detractione minorum corpusculorum alienatio
mentis, maiorum febres auferantur. apparet itaque neque secundum se consequenter Asclepiadem phlebotomiam prohibere.
125   proinde praecavens vel avertens mentis alienationem, iubet
addisci quae sit accessionis ac dimissionis dies; tunc graviori die
cibum dari paucissimum, atque expectato febrium statu dari
ptisanam vel ordeum aut alicam aut cum beta lenticulam vel
his quicquam simile, coniciens solam ex his dandi novitatem

---

[15] ⟨haec⟩ fieri R: an quae *pro* et *praecedente?*
[16] *addidi*

---

9. Or perhaps 'is the source of the larger corpuscles.'

10. Or perhaps 'are the sources of the smaller corpuscles.'

It is also quite wrong to forbid venesection, which is a most valuable remedy. Indeed, we often see cases benefited by its use; for loss of voice and chill are consequences only of its improper use, e.g., in cases where a state of looseness is also involved or when blood is let at the wrong time or in excessive amount. It is also wrong to bar venesection on the theory that no pain is here involved and that venesection is useful only for the withdrawal of the larger corpuscles, the obstruction of which produces pains. For, in the first place, we are successful in our use of venesection in cases of paralysis, pneumonia, and apoplexy, though these patients suffer no pain. And, in the second place, phrenitics do suffer pain, but their mind, being deprived of its reason, is unable to complain of the pain. We see them bite, burn, or prick themselves, and it is unnatural to suppose that this takes place except because of some compelling pain. Thirdly, the withdrawal of the smaller corpuscles is a necessary consequence of the withdrawal of the larger. Now phrenitics suffer not only from loss of reason but from fever; and, according to Asclepiades, fever results from a blocking of the larger corpuscles. And so, even if venesection is not an effective remedy for the loss of reason, it is for the fever. For the blood is a substance composed of large corpuscles.[9] But venesection removes not only the blood proper; it also removes pneuma and heat, and these, Asclepiades says, are substances composed of small corpuscles.[10] Thus on his own principles venesection is proper in cases of phrenitis, in order that the mental disturbance may be relieved by the withdrawal of the smaller corpuscles, and the fever by the withdrawal of the larger. It is evident, therefore, that Asclepiades' opposition to venesection is not consistent with his own principles.

In discussing the prevention and avoidance of mental derangement,[11] Asclepiades bids us observe what the days of attack and remission are. Then on the [first] day of an attack he orders that a very small amount of food be given, and, while awaiting the highest stage of the feverish attack, he has the patient take pearl barley, unpeeled barley, spelt groats, lentils with beets,[12] or something similar. His thought is that the mere

123

124

125

11. I.e., how to prevent a fever from passing into phrenitis. Cf. 116.

12. From what follows it seems that all these are to be given in the form of gruels.

prodesse, nec habendum iudicium quid istorum debeamus
offerre, sed potestati aegrotantium dimittendum quid velint
eligere; alia die si febricula perseveraverit, exantlare obtrusiones
et requiem corporis adhibere aquam dantes potandam, non plus
quam bis in die usque ad heminam vel duas, et hunc modum
126 etiam nocte servare. sic rursum secunda die, transacto accessionis augmento, dandum quiddam de praescriptis sorbilibus;
atque alia die declinante febricula uti sorbili cibo, perseverante
vero rursum abstinere, †et praeterito similem tertium imitari
diem.†[17] tunc septima audere iam pane atque piscibus et vino
uti. solvitur, inquit, enim passio tertia saepe periodo.

ad haec respondemus quia etiam si sua sponte passio intra
septimum diem solvi potuerat, non solvetur iniquae curationis
causa. etenim neque de somno neque de vigiliis neque de capitis
fomento vel ceteris quae ad diligentiam pertinent curationis
quicquam videmus ordinatum. solis ex tribus medelam credidit
adhibendam, potu, cibo, clystere, et hoc tamquam de experi-
127 mento. nam cibus, ut voluit, ante dimissionem dandus, transacto mox accessionis statu, turbatis adhuc liquidis atque spiritu, quo febres duplicentur et alienatio mentis ardescat. et
non solum intemporaliter verum etiam incongrue: stringit enim
ordeum et lenticula, relaxat ptisana et alica. et non possunt
contrariae qualitatis species iisdem passionibus adhiberi nulla
discretione servata. dicimus etiam curiosum genus pulmenti
atque congestum et primae oblationi contrarium esse betam
cum lenticula, quod appellavit seutlophacen;[18] item ptisanam.
128   contrarius etiam clyster atque noxius perspicitur omnibus quidem propter intestinorum mordicationem et cetera, magis tamen
solutionem. ipse denique accusans utentes[19] ait continuationem

---

[17] *locus obscurus; cf. 129*

[18] teutlophacen *R*

[19] utentes *Rm*: urentes *G*

---

13. By a clyster; see 129.

variety of choice in this prescription is advantageous and that
we should not decide which of these foods to offer the patients
but leave it to them to choose what they want. The next day, if
the fever persists, he draws off the obstructing matter,[13] has the
patient rest, and prescribes the drinking of water, but no more
than twice during the day, one or two heminae in amount, and
26 the same at night. But the following day, when the increasing
phase of the attack is past, he prescribes one of the gruels just
mentioned. And on the next day, if the fever abates, he prescribes soft food; but if the fever persists, he has the patient
again abstain from food. . . .[14] Then on the seventh day he prescribes bread, fish, and wine. For, says he, the disease generally
breaks up by the end of the third period.[15]

To all this our answer is that, though the disease might have
broken up spontaneously before the seventh day, this faulty
treatment will prevent its breaking up. And, in fact, we find no
prescription of Asclepiades dealing with sleeping or remaining
awake or fomentations of the head or the other elements of
medical treatment. Asclepiades believes in a treatment consisting merely of three elements—drink, food, and the clyster,
27 and these evidently on an empirical basis. Thus he prescribes
the giving of food before the remission, when the highest stage
of the attack has just passed but the humors and pneuma are
still confused, a condition in which fever increases and mental
derangement grows more intense. And the prescription is not
only untimely but also inconsistent. For barley and lentils have
a binding effect, while pearl barley and spelt groats are laxative,
and substances of contrary qualities should not be employed indiscriminately in the same disease. Moreover, we consider beet
with lentils (called *seutlophacē* by Asclepiades) a highly flavored
type of dish, heavy, and not suitable as a first offering for the
patient. So also is pearl barley unsuitable.

28   Now the clyster, too, is obviously harmful and injurious to all
patients on account of its griping effect upon the bowels and for
other reasons, particularly the flux which it causes. And Asclepiades himself, in opposition to those who use clysters, says that

14. The text is uncertain; from 129 it would seem that there was originally some
reference either to the resumption of food after the fever or to the use of the clyster again.

15. I.e., the third three-day period, including the fifth day (in part), the sixth day,
and the seventh day (in part). First period: days 1-3; second period: days 3-5.

clysterum incendium atque sitim facere: inusta enim intestina
melle atque ceterarum specierum mordicatione movent fervorem plurimum, qui per alta quadam continuitate viarum membranae cerebri influat. cuncta etenim, inquit, quae sunt in alto
corporis constituta sese occulta vicinitate contingunt, quorum
129 in numero membranam cerebri ponimus. revocat etiam et grave
passionis[20] atque perniciosum malum, nihil enim in ipsa gravius
quam ventris est fluor. quod igitur crescit peiorante passione,
hoc perhibet fieri clysterum provocatione.

denique quae culpans alios dixerit in ipsum convertenda
utentem clystere. non enim dici potest solam frequentiam
iniectionis accusasse, genus autem innoxium iudicasse, cum manifeste propter acrimoniam clysteres noxii iudicentur, et magis
etiam si usu frequenti atque copia peccaverint adhibentes. quid
dicam quod neque semel Asclepiades clysterem iusserit adhiberi, cum secundo una[21] die dixerit innovandum, dicens perseverante rursum cibo abstinendum, †et innovandum tertio praeterita
die[22] quo clyster fuerit adhibitus. †[23]

130   est etiam vanum sine disciplina temporis potum ordinare;
ait enim bis dandum in singulos dies. mitto non omnibus aegris
eundem modum competere strictura atque solutione laborantibus. at iste duas heminas omnibus iussit dari, sed etiam vinum
atque varium cibum septima die offerendum dixit, non declinationem passionis sed numerum dierum advertens, tamquam
tunc necessario solvi passionem existimans, quod est iuri vel
legibus simile.

131   dehinc explicita passionis avertendae[24] praecautione praesentis, hoc est iam effectae, curationem[25] ordinavit, cuius du-

[20] passioni R   [22] die ⟨a⟩ R

[21] una om. R   [23] cf. 126

[24] advertendae G: corr. R

[25] hoc etiam effecta curatione G: corr. Schmid 100

a succession of clysters produces a burning sensation and dryness. He points out that the bowels, inflamed by the honey and by the griping effects of the other substances, give rise to an intense heat which passes upward from the lower parts to the membrane of the brain through passages that are somehow connected. For all the internal parts of the body, he says, are joined by imperceptible connections; and among these internal

29 parts is the membrane of the brain. Now the clyster brings back a grave and deadly danger in this disease, for there is nothing more dangerous in phrenitis than flux of the bowels. Thus Asclepiades shows that the use of clysters promotes the very effects which would naturally be caused by an aggravation of the disease.

And so his arguments in opposition to others may be turned against himself in so far as he makes use of the clyster. And it cannot be said that he objected merely to the frequency of clysters and considered the type of treatment as such harmless. The obvious fact is that clysters are considered harmful because of their sharpness, and the harm is only greater if they are used frequently and in excessive amount. Now I need not point out that Asclepiades prescribes the administering of a clyster, and not merely once. For he says that the treatment should be given twice in one day,[16] that if [the fever] persists, no food should be taken. . . .

30 It is also wrong to prescribe drink [as Asclepiades does] without any sound indication of the time element. For he says [merely] that it should be given twice each day. Now I need not point out that the same quantity of drink is not suitable for all patients, i.e., those suffering from a state of stricture as well as those suffering from a state of looseness. Yet Asclepiades prescribes two heminae of water for all. And, what is more, he prescribes wine and varied food on the seventh day, directing his attention not to the actual decline of the disease but to the number of days, apparently on the assumption that the disease must necessarily be broken up at that time. But such a prescription sounds more like a judicial or legislative decree.

31 Then, having concluded his explanation of measures for preventing phrenitis, he sets forth the treatment of the disease when it is present, that is, already in existence. There are, he

16. But cf. 125.

plicem dicit differentiam: unam meticulosam ac multis phreniticis aptandam, aliam vehementem atque periculosam, quam
philoparabolon appellavit.

quarum primam ordinans, si, inquit, eum qui non sit ab alio
curatus acceperunt, et propterea nullo sit tentatus adiutorio,
odoramentis utemur, hoc ⟨est⟩[26] castoreo, peucedano, ruta, et
aceto, vel ex his infuso liquore, et clystere detrahendae obtru-
132 sionis causa. sin vero ab aliquo medico fuerat ante curatus,
erit, inquit, omnis unctio atque cataplasma vel odoramentum
prohibendum statim primo ingressu, et ad lucem ex umbra trans-
mutandus aegrotans, sternutamentum etiam adhibendum, mulsum aestate quater, hieme bis in die, dimidia hemina in singulis
potionibus, sed praecocto melle ne venter humidus aut fluidus
fiat. tunc veniente nocte primo ad domicilium mediocre sece-
dendum atque plurimus vel apertus aer fugiendus. dehinc si
aliqua fuerit accessio vel articulorum stupor, his transactis,
dandum quidquam de praescriptis sorbilibus necessario. si
autem aequalia permanserint febrium signa, statim vespertino
133 tempore oleo totum corpus perungentes, caput etiam atque
collum rosaceo, dabimus sorbilem cibum. tunc ad largiendum
requiem vel somnum sufficiens erit motus baiulatoria sessione
adhibitus; mox aegros mites ac delicatos facit. aliqui denique
phreniticorum dirarato corpore motus causa deficiunt: quapropter nocte magis atque post cibum gestationem convenit
adhibere. haec est secundum Asclepiadem meticulosa[27] atque
cauta differentia curationis.

134 huic extemplo respondemus quia nulla est meticulosa[27] differentia curationis arte formata sed est potius tuta; neque etiam
vehemens, quam secundam posuit periculosam ac metuendam,
vocanda est enim artis iudicio probata necessario magis quam

---

[26] ⟨est⟩ A

[27] meticulosa *scripsi*: metu periculosa G

says, two different methods of treatment, one cautious and
suitable in many cases of phrenitis, the other violent and
dangerous, *philoparabolos*, as he calls it.

In describing the former of these methods he first considers
patients who have not been previously treated by another
physician and have therefore not been tampered with by any
other treatment. In these cases he uses aromatic substances,
such as castor, sulphurwort, rue, and vinegar, or an infusion of
these substances, and also a clyster for the purpose of removing

32 the obstructing matter. If, however, a patient has been previously treated by some other physician, all ointments, poultices, and
aromatic substances should be stopped immediately upon our
entrance into the case, the patient transferred from a dark to a
bright place, a sternutatory administered, and honey drink
prescribed, four times a day in summer and twice a day in winter, half a hemina in each drink, with the honey cooked in advance so that the bowels do not become moist or fluid. And,
as evening approaches, Asclepiades has us first remove the
patient to a rather small room, avoiding an excess of fresh air.
Then, when this has been done, if there is any increase in fever
or numbness of the limbs, we must, he says, give the patient one

133 of the gruels mentioned above.[17] But if the signs of fever continue without increase or decrease, we must, while it is still
evening, anoint the patient's whole body with olive oil, and his
head and neck with rose oil, and give him gruel-like food. Then,
in order to promote rest or sleep, passive exercise in a sedan
chair will be adequate, for it quickly relaxes and calms the
patient. In fact, in some cases of phrenitis the patient faints
when the motion causes excessive dilation of the body; and for
that reason this passive exercise should be employed preferably
at night and after a meal. Such is Asclepiades' cautious and cir-
cumspect type of treatment.

134   In answer to him let us state at the outset that no variety of
treatment which is a product of medical skill should be called
'cautious'; 'safe' is a preferable designation. Furthermore, the
second treatment which he sets forth as involving danger and
hazard is not a 'violent' treatment [if it is a product of medical
skill]. For in that case, rather than call it by that name, we
should consider it a necessary measure approved by professional

17. Cf. 125.

supradicto est vocabulo nuncupanda. at si vere fuerit illa
quam putat tuta, quomodo non omnibus sed multis erit phreniticis congrua? aut cur non manifestavit quibus sit incongrua?
135 quid dicam quia ipsa quoque quam putat tutam passione[28]
peior esse perspicitur? primo etenim invidiose iubet siqua ante
ipsum medicus adhibuit repudianda; at si non adhibuerit, tunc
probanda, tamquam legitimum putans ut haec aliis adhibenti-
bus noceant, ipso medeantur. dehinc neque quibus utendum
sit his prohibitis dixit, ut oporteat phreniticum sine ullo adiutorio derelinqui.

est etiam vehementer noxium aceto uti atque peucedano et
ruta et castoreo. premunt haec enim et vertigines ingerunt
136 et ob acrimoniam sui tumentes dissecant membranas; hinc
etiam alienationem geminant aut pressuram ingerunt vehementem. horum testis ipse est Asclepiades. accusans enim
eos qui rutam probaverunt adhibendam, vitandas inquit primo
gravabiles virtutes, siquidem ascensu quodam inspirationis caput invadant, et magnas menti occasiones alienationis subi-
ciant. propterea[29] paulo superius in eodem libro ait ipsum caput
obsidere non sinunt hi qui curantes[30] cataplasmatibus ex[31]
aceto et polline, et confectis fomentis ex multiformi materia
137 abluendum existimant: similiter ungentes non solum caput sed
etiam faciem atque collum, quae omnia non difficulter naris
implent[32] odoris acerrimi atque gravabilis. nobis denique saepe
contigit ingredientibus ad aegros quibus haec fuerant adhibita
vertiginem pati.

quid nunc, Asclepiades, gravius olens habuisti castoreo?
quid gravabilius ab his quae adhibenda confirmas? cataplasma[33] vero ex pollinibus et aceto fuit cataplasma remoto
aceto per se efficax, laxativum est enim. sed[34] acetum tibi re-

[28] passionem G: corr. Schmid 102

[29] praeterea R

[30] curant R

[31] ex Schmid Mn 147: et edd.

[32] implendae G: corr. Rm

[33] cataplasmata G: corr. R

[34] sed A: si G

judgment. Again, if the other treatment is really, as he thinks, safe, why is it not suitable in all cases of phrenitis but only in a considerable number? And why did he not indicate those for
35 whom it would be unsuitable? I need not point out that the treatment which he considers safe is obviously worse than the disease itself. In the first place, he invidiously insists on rejecting every treatment that any other physician had applied before him. He approves only of measures not used by others, apparently considering it ordained that these procedures will be harmful if applied by others, but salutary if applied by himself. Again, after rejecting the treatments used by others, he does not tell us what measures we should use, so that it becomes necessary to leave the phrenitic without any remedy.

Moreover, the use of vinegar, sulphurwort, rue, and castor is extremely harmful, for these substances produce an oppressive feeling and cause dizziness and, because of their pungency, dam-
36 age the inflamed membranes. They therefore also aggravate the mental derangement or cause a profound stupor. Asclepiades himself attests this. For in opposition to those who approve of the use of rue he says, in the first place, that drugs having pungent qualities should be avoided, on the ground that, as they ascend with the breath, they attack the head and bring about great mental disturbance. For the same reason, a little earlier in the same book he writes that those who treat the head with poultices made with vinegar and flour do not permit it to obtain rest; and that the same is true of those who recommend washing the head with fomentations made of many diverse sub-
37 stances. A similar error, he says, is made by those who anoint not only the head but also the face and neck, from all of which parts the nostrils are readily filled with a sharp and oppressive odor. In fact, says he, when we visit patients who have been given this treatment, we often find ourselves becoming dizzy.

But, come now, Asclepiades, what more pungent substance have you ever handled than castor? What more oppressive drug than those which you yourself recommend [in the treatment of phrenitis]? And with regard to the poultice made with flour and vinegar, the removal of the vinegar would not impair the intrinsic effectiveness of the poultice, for the latter has a relaxing quality. But it is the vinegar that involves you in inconsistency;

pugnat: ipso enim caput foveri iussisti. clysteris vero culpam
superius probavimus.

138　　est etiam iners omnes aegros, ut voluit, ex tenebris ad lucem
transferre, cum quidam tenebris curari magis videantur, sicut
superius demonstravimus. vexat etiam ptarmicum quod credidit adhibendum: acre est enim atque ignitum, ut piper,
struthium, et album helleborum, quibus tumentes membranae
ex eorum acrimonia in asperitatem surgunt, et agitatione
sternutamenti³⁵ extentae provocantur. denique ⟨si⟩³⁶ statio
corpusculorum causa est phreniticae passionis, ut putat, vehementius eam his rebus excitari suspicandum est, cum ad sternutamenti motum materia concurrit.

139　　omnino denique sic curationes suas confundit ut quae etiam
ipse ordinavit excludat, cum sibi quadam comparatione fuerint
opposita. ait denique maiora adiutoria vitanda, siquidem nocere magis quam prodesse videantur. sed quid tandem levioribus laceramus, si fomentis atque unguentis et cataplasmatibus
et odoramentis ⟨prohibitis⟩, [et]³⁷ sternutamentis aegros affici-
endos credidit? quibus apparet eum contra semet tulisse sententias.

　　caret etiam artis auxilio quod pro temporum³⁸ aere atque
loco ordinanda adiutoria putat, et non pro passionis tempore.

140　　dehinc non oportet solum considerare quoties potum demus,
verum etiam quando. etenim accessionis tempore limpida quoque aqua febrium facit incendium. mulsum vero dandum dicit
sublevandi pulsus causa, nescius quomodo proprium phreniticae passionis inesse parvum atque humilem pulsum, ut lethargo maiorem ac tardum. oportuit igitur passionem destrui,
non pulsum optari maiorem, qui saepe peiorando consurgit,

³⁵ sternutamenta G: corr. Schmid 90: ⟨ob⟩ sternutamenta R
³⁶ ⟨si⟩ R
³⁷ ⟨prohibitis⟩, [et] Schmid 105
³⁸ tempore Rm

18. Cf. 131, where presumably the aromatic substances were used as fomentations.

for you yourself prescribe fomentation of the head with vinegar.[18] And as for the clyster, we have already shown its danger.

38   It is also unsound to transfer all patients, as Asclepiades prescribes, from dark to light places, for some seem to be helped
more by darkness, as we have shown above. And the sternutatory which he recommends is actually harmful. For it is a sharp
and burning substance, e.g., pepper, soapwort, or white hellebore; and by its sharpness the inflamed membranes are irritated
and in the agitation of sneezing are stretched and excited. Again,
if a stoppage of the corpuscles is the cause of phrenitis, as he believes, we should suspect that the stoppage would be greatly aggravated by this treatment, for the gathering of matter accompanies the action of the sternutative.

39   In fact, Asclepiades so confuses his treatments as to bar the
very things he prescribes,[19] since comparison will show that in
these prescriptions he is self-contradictory. And he advises the
avoidance[20] of major remedies, since they seem to him to be
doing more harm than good. But why criticize him on less important grounds, when, on the one hand, he bars the use of
fomentations, ointments, poultices, and aromatics[21] and, on the
other hand, treats the patient with sternutatories? In this he
clearly contradicts himself.

Moreover, Asclepiades goes counter to the principles of
medical art in holding that treatments should be regulated by
considerations of season and place and not by the time element
of the disease.

40   Again, it is necessary to consider not only how often we
should give drink but at what time. Thus, at the time of an
attack, even pure water causes a violent fever. Now Asclepiades says that honey-drink should be given in order to
strengthen the pulse, not knowing that a small, submerged
pulse is merely a characteristic of phrenitis, just as a large, slow
pulse is a characteristic of lethargy. He should therefore have
sought to overcome the disease and not merely to obtain a
larger pulse, which often comes when the patient grows worse,

19. On the other hand, the meaning may be that his treatments when brought together are in mutual opposition and that the therapeutic effect is consequently destroyed.

20. I.e., for patients previously treated by another physician. Cf. 132, 136.

21. Cf. 132.

quando ex phrenitico in lethargum venerit. ita quoties potum demus autumno vel verno tempore non docuit.

141   dehinc clystere utens mellis metuit admixtionem; ne ventrem, inquit, fluidum faciat, decoquendum iussit. et[39] clysterem non timuit ne ventrem commoveret.

falsum est etiam, cum continua atque iugis fuerit passio, circa vesperum cibum dare, siquidem etiam secundum ipsum Asclepiadem releventur omnes lucis initio, vespero accessiones augeantur. natura, inquit, vesperum ob aeris crassitudinem densata inflat corpora atque initium generat accessionis; omnibus denique pulsus levatur statim ex medio die initium sumens. omnino igitur ratione caret vesperum cibo tempus eligere, quo

142 etiam secundum Asclepiadem accessiones augentur. grave est etiam oleo rosaceo tumentia frigerare atque constringere, et ex odore vertiginem facere atque pressuram, et inchoante accessione aegros ad alium transmutare locum, quando magis eos oportebat quiescere. sed neque cotidie cibo nutrire est ut putat necessarium, et magis si nulla fuerit solutio coniuncta, solo tumore constrictis corporibus, quo ferre non possint cotidianam cibi sumptionem.

noxium est etiam omnes gestatione agitare. in his enim qui solutione et constrictione vexantur magis extenditur passio. et horum testis Asclepiades est primus, etenim ait vias apertiores

143 fieri gestatione. denique defectio atque diaphoresis sequitur eos qui incongrue gestatione fuerint moti, quod quidem nescius qua causa fiat, tamquam remedium quaerens vexationi gestationis, nocte gestari atque post cibum aegros aestimavit, scilicet ut non solum incongruo adiutorio, verum etiam inordinato homines noceantur. neque enim sanis utilis gestatio post cibum.

inertem etiam perspicimus diaetam quod ait quibusdam esse

[39] *fort.* at

as when he passes from phrenitis into lethargy. And Asclepiades
does not indicate how often we should give drink in the autumn
or in the spring.

41   Again, in his use of the clyster he fears the admixture of
honey, which he orders boiled down[22] to avoid making the bowels
loose, as he says. But he does not fear the agitation of the bowels
by the clyster.

It is also wrong, in a continuous and unbroken disease, to
give food around evening; for, even according to Asclepiades
himself, all patients are relieved at dawn but suffer renewed attacks in the evening. Evening, he says, with its dense air
naturally congests bodies already constricted and causes the
onset of an attack. And in all these cases the pulse becomes
stronger, beginning at midday. It is therefore quite unreasonable
to decide to give food in the evening, when, according to Ascle-
42 piades himself, the attacks are aggravated. It is also dangerous
to cool and contract the inflamed parts with rose oil, or to produce dizziness and stupor with aromatic substances, or to transfer the patients to another place at the beginning of an attack
when it is better for them to be quiet. And it is not necessary, as
Asclepiades thinks, to give food every day, particularly if no
state of looseness is involved but only a state of stricture with
inflammation, so that the body is not able to take food daily.

And it is wrong to prescribe passive exercise for all patients.
For in the case of those who suffer from a mixed condition of
looseness and stricture the disease is aggravated [by such ex-
ercise]. And Asclepiades himself is our chief witness to this fact.
For he tells us that the pores become wider because of the
43 motion. And as a consequence those who are wrongly subjected
to it suffer fainting and colliquative sweating. But Asclepiades,
not knowing why this happens, apparently seeks to overcome
the harmful effects of passive exercise and orders the treatment
to be administered to the patients at night and after eating, no
doubt so that they may suffer from a treatment that is not only
ill-suited to them but poorly regulated. For even in the case of
healthy persons such exercise after eating is not good.

We also consider this [first] method of treatment unsound, for
the reason that, though Asclepiades tells us that it is unsuitable

22. The reference in 132 is to honey for drinking.

contrariam nec tamen docuit quibus: si enim quos nocet nes-
cierimus, necessario etiam quos relevet nescire consequitur.

144 tradens etiam periculosam sive temerariam,[40] quam philoparabolon appellavit, ita composuit curationem. in alia[41] inquit habere similia praedictae [passioni],[42] solum quod vinum
pro melle circa vesperam, non nisi omnino coegerit passio,
damus, si minus primo ingressu statim. atque plurimum et extentum, hoc est meracum, et salsum dabimus vinum, quod appellavit tethalassomenon. etenim, inquit, quae primo imbecilla
atque tarda de sorbilibus et mulso[43] dederunt aegro commoda,

145 omnia ex vino celerius atque coacervatim implentur. etenim
fervor plurimus accedit et pulsus erectio, et roscida sudatio
mitigatur, tamquam ex cautere per totum corpus vino concurrente atque inurente sensum.

scientia haec est vehementior quam dicit curatio, pro mulso[43]
habens vinum, ut ceteris peccatis manentibus in odoribus et
fomentis et sternutamentis et iacendi loco et gestatione omnibus ordinata, graviorem ex vino vexationem adiecerit. in quibus neque mulsum recte secundum ipsum ordinatum esse perspi-

146 cimus. dat enim vinum et incongrue et intemporaliter et immodice.

incongrue inquam, quoniam salsum et propterea acre: quando
decoqui mel iubet[44] ne venter veniat in fluorem, atque ab aliis
ordinatum clysterem removet, et tamquam in commemorationem ducentem gravem phreniticis vexationem, hoc est fluorem ventris, cum magis salsum vinum id facile possit efficere, et
per acrimoniam febres atque tumens corpus incendere.

intemporaliter autem, quomodo circa vesperam quando se-

---

[40] temeram G: corr. R

[41] aliis Rm   [42] seclusi

[43] mulsa edd., quae est correctio scribae, ut videtur, perperam 'mulsum' valere οἰνόμελι
non μελίκρατον iudicantis. Cf. 132, 140, 145 fin.

[44] decoqui mel iubet scripsi: denique mel iubet G: denique mel ⟨coqui⟩ iubet R

for certain patients,[23] he does not tell us for whom. And if we do
not know whom it harms, it follows necessarily that we do not
know whom it helps.

44   In setting forth the dangerous or daring treatment, which he
calls *philoparabolos*, Asclepiades describes it as follows. 'In other
respects,' he says, 'it is similar to the aforesaid [i.e., the cau-
tious] treatment, except that if the case clearly calls for it, we
give wine instead of honey in the evening or else immediately
upon our entrance into the case: and we give a copious amount
of strong (i.e., undiluted) wine mixed with brine[24] (*tethalassōmenos*). For all the help previously given the patient slowly and
in small measure by gruels and honey-drink is now given more
45 swiftly and in full measure by the wine. For a considerable
amount of heat comes to the body, and there is a strengthening
of the pulse, while the dewlike perspiration is relieved, just as if
the wine coursed through the whole body from a cautery and
burned into the sensory channels.'

On the basis of all knowledge, this treatment is even more
violent than he says, for it substitutes wine for the honey-drink.
And, since the other faults remain, viz., the use of aromatic
substances, fomentations, sternutatories, errors in placing the
patient's bed, and the prescription of passive exercise for all patients, the effect of using wine is simply to increase the patient's
hardship. That is, in these cases we see that Asclepiades does not
prescribe a honey-drink, which would at least have been con-
46 sistent with his own principles; he gives the patient wine, and
the prescription is inconsistent, untimely, and excessive.

It is inconsistent, I say, because the wine is mixed with brine
and for that reason sharp. Yet Asclepiades has honey boiled
down to avoid a flux of the bowels[25] and rejects the use of a
clyster as prescribed by others, on the ground that in cases of
phrenitis it causes a recurrence of severe agitation, that is, flux
of the bowels, though the salted wine [which he prescribes] can
produce this same result much more readily and by its sharpness can aggravate fever and inflammation of the body.

Asclepiades' prescription of wine is ill-timed because the wine
is to be taken either about evening, when, according to Ascle-

23. Cf. 131.
24. Or perhaps 'with salt.'
25. 132, above.

147 cundum ipsum fiet accessio, vel certe statim ut ait primo ingressu, tamquam secum opportunitatem dandi attulerit vini.

item immodice dare probatur, quomodo multum[45] atque meracum, et propterea ignis in modum vexare perspicitur, ut vere
ipsum videatur cauteris esse virtute, quae nervos incurrens
atque penetrans infestae iamdudum febriculae coniuncta, etiam
illud quo sapimus,[46] et[47] alienationem geminet mentis aut spasmum faciat aegrotanti: asserens[48] etiam quod hi qui non multum[49] neque meracum accipere voluerint noceantur, siquidem
148 minus inebriare contingat. erat enim conveniens omni phrenitico qui ab eo curatur hanc adhibere propriam alienationem
mentis, aut omnino vinum accipere noluisse,[50] quippe cum Asclepiades ex vino frequenter phreniticos fieri fateatur atque similes
ebriis inveniri. quomodo igitur credi potest eosdem multo vino
accepto atque meraco relevari, quibus alienatio ex vino facta
perspicitur, quae necessario in capite simili semper vexatione
operatur?

149 in his nos credulitate occupari existimat, ut tamquam ebrios
plurimum vinum in altum somnum demergit, non aliter etiam
phreniticos vinolentia in somnum venire posse putemus, multo[51]
atque meraco potu affectos. haec enim vere ipsorum aliquis
dicere potest, sed contra erit advertendum nullam esse similitudinem vinolentiae phreniticae passionis. in ebriis enim alienatio ex multitudine poti vini facta perspicitur, quae reflata tempo-
ralem citius alienationem solvit. in phreniticis vero ex tumore
alienatio fiet. quo considerandum est quia vinum in his reflari
150 minime potest propter difficultatem viarum, quae sunt ex morbo

---

[45] multum *scripsi, coll. 148*: mulsum *edd.*
[46] sapimus ⟨offendit⟩ *R*
[47] et *fort. secl.*
[48] asserens *R*: afferens *G*
[49] mulsum *edd.*
[50] noluisset *edd.*　　　　　　　　　[51] mulso *edd.*

47 piades himself, the disease becomes more active, or else it is to
be taken immediately, as he says, upon our very entrance into
the case, as if that entrance must coincide with the proper time
for administering wine.

And Asclepiades' prescription of wine is excessive, for he prescribes undiluted wine and in copious amount. As a consequence,
the wine acts like fire in attacking the patient and actually seems
to have the nature of a cautery. This fiery quality attacks the
nerves and sinews and penetrates them, accompanied from the
beginning by a dangerous fever, and also strikes the mind, aggravating the mental disturbance or causing convulsion in the
patient. And Asclepiades adds that those who refuse to take a
large amount of undiluted wine are harmed because they are

48 not likely to become drunk. Indeed, it would seem to follow
that, in every case of phrenitis treated by Asclepiades, the
patient either showed this characteristic aggravation of the mental disturbance or was one of those who refused altogether
to take wine. For Asclepiades admits that phrenitis frequently
comes from drinking and that those suffering from the disease
are often found to resemble inebriates. How, then, can he suppose that the same persons are relieved of the disease by the
drinking of a large amount of wine, and that undiluted, if he
holds that they lose their reason as a result of drinking? For loss
of reason in all cases manifests itself by a similar type of mental disturbance.[26]

49   Now in this matter Asclepiades seeks to impose upon our
credulity. He would actually have us believe that just as those
who drink a great amount of wine are plunged into a deep sleep,
so also phrenitics can pass [from the disease] into sleep through
drunkenness caused by the copious drinking of undiluted wine.
In fact, one of his followers is able to say just this; but we must,
nevertheless, observe that phrenitis is not at all like drunkenness. For in the case of those who are drunk the loss of reason
obviously results from the drinking of a great deal of wine and
is only temporary, being quickly ended when the wine passes off.
In phrenitis, however, loss of reason results from an inflammation. Hence it must be noted that in these cases because of the

50 stoppage of the pores the wine cannot be passed off. These pores

26. The point seems to be that there are not two types of aberration, one caused by
wine, the other removed by wine.

adeo densatae ut neque naturalia, quae per sensuales vias excludi consueverunt, reddantur, neque accepta per cibos im-
partiri corpori facile videantur, vel per tenues vias digestione
soluta propriari[52] atque ad sua destinata pervenire, sed manentia
statione insueta novo turbore corpus afficiant, atque tumentia
exagitent, mentem quoque turbent, vel receptacula quaeque
percutiant, tempore quo etiam ille spiritus qui naturalis[53] ac
tenuis est angustatos suos ambitus pungat ac dolores corporis
efficiat.

mitto etiam quomodo si, ut volunt, ebriis similes phreniticos
accipimus, non oportuit ebrium inebriando curare, nullus enim
151 vinolentus bibendo in sobrium venit. nam magis econtrario qui
perseverando potaverunt multo poto multum mentis alienationem auxerunt, aut in spasmum aut in vigilias incurabiles devenerunt. adiuvant etiam vexationem vinolentiae gravabilia
odoramenta atque fomenta, quibus denique fortes ac recte valentes in conviviis incautius usi multa se gravatione vexarunt.

ait etiam vinum in cauteris similitudinem abstinere sudorem,
cum idem dicat mitigari alienationem accepto vino, cum se
plurimi ac per totum corpus sudores effuderint, ut secundum
ipsum id sit intelligendum quod nunc abstineat vinum sudores,
152 nunc faciat. libro denique quem De communibus adiutoriis
scripsit utriusque virtutis vinum dixit. sicut enim, ait, coagula
densant atque extenuant lactis naturam, cum caseus ex lacte
crassescat et materia exinde tenuior ac magis liquida fiat, quam
Graeci oron[54] appellant, atque haec contraria eadem virtute
suffecta separantur, non aliter et vinum vi quadam suae per-
cussionis plurimam nutrimenti partem densare accepimus, atque
in se cogere, plurimam vero resolvere ac dirarare et tenuem
facere.

[52] appropriari *Schmid RPh 132* (*cf. Triller Clinotechnia 127*)
[53] *fort.* natura levis   [54] ὀῤῥὸν *edd.*

are so constricted by the disease that the natural fluids, which are normally secreted over the sensory channels, do not flow out; and the substances taken in by way of food apparently cannot be readily distributed to the body, i.e., they cannot be reduced by digestion, apportioned [to the several parts of the body], and brought to their respective goals over the narrow passages. On the contrary, unable to move because of the abnormal stoppage, they bring a new disturbance to the body, irritate the inflamed parts, agitate the mind, and strike at all its recesses at the very time when the thin, natural pneuma pierces its constricted orbit and causes bodily pains.

I need not point out that even if we consider phrenitics to be like intoxicated persons, as Asclepiades and his followers would have us do, we should still not treat one who is drunk by adding to his drunkenness. No drunken person has ever become sober 51 by drinking. On the contrary, those who continue to drink greatly aggravate their mental derangement by their excessive drinking or fall into convulsions or incurable sleeplessness. Moreover, the distress caused by drinking the wine is increased by pungent aromatics and fomentations; in fact, even when strong and vigorous men make careless use of these in drinking parties, they bring an oppressive heaviness upon themselves.

Asclepiades also says that, like a cautery, wine represses sweating; but he also tells us that the taking of wine relieves the mental derangement as profuse sweats pour out over the whole body. That is, according to Asclepiades, we must take it that 52 wine sometimes represses and sometimes causes sweating. In fact, in the book he wrote *On Common Remedies* Asclepiades declares that wine has both these qualities. He compares the action of wine with that of rennet. Rennet, he tells us, both thickens and rarefies milk, cheese being formed from the milk by a thickening process, while the remaining matter (Greek *oros*, 'whey') thereby becomes thinner and more liquid. That is, these two contrasting products are separated out under the influence of the same agent. He holds that in the same way we know that wine by virtue of its penetrating quality causes a condensation and coagulation of a large part of our nourishment and, at the same time, a dissolving, thinning-out, and rarefaction of another large part.

quibus probatur repugnantia ex iisdem promittere et frigido
153 exemplo denique errare. sed neque discretionibus generalibus
vini coniectura convenit, falsis exemplis immissa. in his denique adhuc constitutus demonstrationibus vanis involvitur,
dicendo vini tutam[55] potationem in passionibus tardis magis
quam in celeribus vel acutis, et in his qui dimissionibus relevantur magis quam in his qui continuatione vexantur, et senibus
magis quam in[56] iuvenibus, et praepurgatis clystere vel sitientibus magis quam plenis cibo, et inchoantibus ac deficientibus
febribus magis quam summa tenentibus, et post accessionem
potius quam ante ipsam.

154   nunc autem curans phreniticos ordine quodam usque ad finem
servato, sicut in nutriendis virginibus,[57] vinum dari constituit
in celeri passione atque continua, et omnibus nihil sane considerans sed statim primo ingressu ac frequentius in statu passionis: tunc enim, inquit, vehementius alienantur aegrotantes.
praeterea et in vehementia accessionis intelligitur dare cum vespero tempore dandum iubet.

haec sunt quibus neque sibi conveniens phreniticorum curationem ordinasse probatur, quamquam plurima quae dici po-
tuerant infinita consideratione taceantur.

155   XVI. AD THEMISONEM

Quomodo Themison scribens Celerum passionum curationes
     antiquorum peccatis assentiens quaedam incondita dereli-
quit (nam necdum purgaverat suam sectam, et ob hoc phreniticorum ordinans curationem quibusdam erroribus implicatur),
ipsius quoque inspicienda sunt singula.

55 tutam *Rm*: tritam *G*

56 in *secl. Schmid Mn 135*   57 viribus *Triller ap. Kühn 77*

Thus we see that Asclepiades, led astray by a poor comparison, actually holds that opposite effects may arise from identical
§ 53 conditions. But his guess does not accord with the general characteristics of wine and is based on false analogies. Depending on these analogies, he becomes involved in futile arguments, holding that the drinking of wine is safer in chronic than it is in swift (i.e., acute) diseases, in cases which are relieved by remissions rather than in those in which the attack is unremitting, in old people rather than in young, when the patients have been purged with a clyster and are dry rather than when they are replete with food, when the fever is beginning or declining rather than when it is at its height, and after an attack rather than before one.

§ 54 But in his treatment of phrenitis Asclepiades adheres throughout to his definite prescription, as in dealing with the diet of maidens.[27] Thus in this acute and unremitting[28] disease he orders wine to be given to all patients,[29] without further consideration, at the very outset of the treatment, and even more frequently at the highest stage of the disease. For it is then, he says, that the patients' minds are more violently disturbed. In fact, we may say that he prescribes wine when the attack is most violent, for he orders it to be given in the evening.

So much for the proof that Asclepiades' treatment of phrenitis is inconsistent with his own statements, though we leave our consideration of the matter unfinished and pass over in silence many things which might have been said.

§ 55 ## XVI. REPLY TO THEMISON

IN HIS work *On the Treatment of Acute Diseases* Themison repeated errors of the ancients and left certain matters confused. (For he had not yet purged his sect,[1] and therefore in his rules for the treatment of phrenitis he is involved in certain errors.) For this reason we must consider various details of his work, too.

27. The meaning here is doubtful. The reference may possibly be to such cases of mental disorder as are described in the Hippocratic περὶ παρθενίων. If *viribus* be read, the meaning may be 'as in dealing with diet in [ordinary] convalescence.'

28. I.e., in the sense in which chronic diseases show remissions.

29. I.e., to all who require the second or hazardous treatment.

1. I.e., freed its teaching of error.

primo igitur ex prima diatrito nutriendos dicit, nullis etiam
cogentibus causis, quod est improprium tempori. dehinc dat
sorbilia, ita cucurbitam,[1] aut solum mulsum, aut pomorum
quaedam. quomodo nunc dissimilitudo virtutis ciborum docet,
156 errorem facile eius perspicimus. etenim sorbilia quae posuit
suci sunt melioris, cucurbita vero cito corrumpitur, poma quoque suci maligni ac facile acescentis esse noscuntur, etiamsi sani
fuerint accipientes: quibus[2] denique medio cibo uti debere Salutaribus praeceptis docuimus. ubi autem viscera tument et
altiora febribus inuruntur, multo facilius acescere poma probamus.

prohibet sane in fomentis peucedanum, castoreum, rutam;
157 sed aceto rosaceo admixto[3] hiberno tempore, aestate vero aqua
admixta rosaceo initio passionis caput foveri iubet, non coniciens[4] quomodo ob magnitudinem transcenso initio extemplo
passio[5] sumit augmentum. dehinc etiam si initium habere potuerit, quod est difficile, erat melius constrictivis uti lenioribus,
ut oleo hispano atque novo. etenim acetum et rosaceum percutit et implet caput. quod autem refrigerantis ac densantis virtutis est, crescente strictura incongruum esse perspicitur. ita
iuxta differentiam temporum hiemis vel aestatis fomenti mutare qualitatem nullius est rationis.

158 item duobus diebus vel tribus transactis, etiam hederae foliis
vel suco, aut serpilli aut mentae vel cuiusquam similis virtutis
simplicium ac non vehementium specierum cum oleo atque aceto per intervalla fovendos dicit, etiam nunc non iuxta sectae
rigorem. neque enim ad numerum dierum oportet fomenta ordinare, cum debeamus magis passionem vel[6] tempus attendere; et

---

[1] cucurbita *G*: *corr. R*   [2] quos *Rm*

[3] admixto *Haller*: admixta *G*: *del. Kühn 83*

[4] coniciens *Hagendahl 250*: continens *G*

[5] passionis *G*: *corr. Rm (nisi fort.* passionis ⟨vis⟩: *cf. Hagendahl 251)*

[6] vel (= ἤ)] quam *R*

Now, in the first place, he prescribes nourishment for the patients from the [end of the] first three-day period on, even in the absence of any compelling reasons.[2] But this procedure is ill-timed. Again, he prescribes gruels, gourd, plain honey-drink, or certain fruits. But we can readily see his mistake from the diverse properties of these foods. The gruels that he prescribes are of good juice,[3] but the gourd spoils quickly. Fruits are also known to be of bad juice and easily turn sour, even when eaten by healthy persons. In fact, they should then be eaten only in the course of a meal, as we have indicated in our *Precepts on Health*. But when the viscera are inflamed and the deeper parts of the body burn with fever, fruits, as we know, turn sour much more quickly.

Themison, to be sure, bars the use of sulphurwort, castor, and rue in fomentations. But he does prescribe that in the winter the head be fomented at the beginning of the disease with vinegar to which rose oil is added, and in the summer with rose oil to which water is added. He does not grasp the fact that after its onset the disease, by reason of its seriousness, immediately grows more intense. Again, even if he could catch the disease at the beginning, which is rarely possible, it would have been better to use milder astringents, such as new Spanish oil. For the mixture of vinegar and rose oil pervades and congests the head. And that which has a cooling and condensing property is obviously unsuitable while the state of stricture is increasing. Moreover, it is unreasonable to change the nature of the fomentation on the basis of the seasonal differences of winter and summer.

Themison goes on to say that after two or three days have passed the patient should be fomented at intervals. For this purpose he recommends leaves or juice of ivy, thyme, mint, or any other simple but not powerful drug of similar properties, in olive oil and vinegar. Yet even in this prescription Themison is not strictly in accord with our sect. For fomentations should not be prescribed according to a schedule of days; the disease rather than the time should be the prime consideration. And we should not apply astringents to inflammations or use substances of

2. Cf. 160.

3. εὔχυλος. Cf. Celsus ii. 19. 21. The term is roughly equivalent to 'easily digestible.'

neque constrictiva tumoribus atque gravabilia aegrotantibus adhibere. nam hedera cum bibitur, mentis errorem inducit.

159   cadit etiam cum in accessione thoracem putat unguendum et in his qui forte[7] ardorem sentiunt rosaceo fovendum. hoc etenim cum virtutis sit densativae constringit tumentia et ardorem geminat. omne etiam unguentum accessionis tempore et magis in augmento febrium incendium facit ex superficie corporis ad altiora perduci.

peccat enim[8] et in reprobandis odoramentis non docendo quae illa sint; ac quot diebus abstinemus aegrotos unguentum adhibendo, quod est laboriosum nisi etiam cibus fuerit datus. oportet enim neque cibari non antecedente perunctione, neque perungi nisi cibus fuerit consecutus. sed etiam post unctionem aqua frigida faciem fomentat, constringens rursum tumentia 160 [phreniticis strictura caput afficit].[9] omni[10] etenim phrenitico strictura caput affici nemo negat.

item inaniter putat ex tertia die qua mente alienari coeperunt, nulla accessionum discretione cogente, cotidie cibum dari. at si alternis diebus fuerit occurrens accessio, alternandum etiam nutrimentum: oportuit enim, nisi[11] declinato solutionis metus occurrerit atque cotidianis diebus accessiones[12] fuerint effectae, omnibus cibum alternis dari. nam non potest corpus diurnis accessionibus gravatum suis partibus applicare nutrimenta quae sumpserit.

161   sed hic gravius peccans ait adiuvare etiam lavacrum, quamquam sit adhuc passio in gradu constituta, tribus tamen vel quatuor diebus transactis quo mentis alienatio irruisse videtur. quomodo igitur conveniens lavacrum passioni probatur, cum necdum cotidianis diebus cibum dare videatur? quippe cum adhuc passio suae magnitudinis teneat summitatem, et propterea miti-

[7] fortem *Rm*

[8] etiam *Rm*

[9] *seclusi*

[10] omnis *G: corr. R*

[11] sive *G: corr. A*

[12] accessionis *G: corr. R*

4. The point seems to be that in these (exceptional) cases the burden of distribution must be eased by giving a smaller amount of food each day rather than a larger amount on alternate days. But the text and interpretation are not quite certain.

pungent odor for the patients. And, in fact, the drinking of ivy produces a mental disturbance.

Themison also errs in holding that during an attack the chest should be anointed and, in the case of those who have a burning 159 sensation, fomented with rose oil. For, since this substance has an astringent property, it constricts the inflamed parts and aggravates the burning sensation. And all anointing at the time of an attack, and particularly during the increasing phase, causes burning fevers to pass from the surface of the body to the deeper parts.

In disapproving of the use of strong-smelling substances, Themison errs in not indicating just which substances he means. He also errs in prescribing daily anointing during the period in which the patient is kept without food, though anointing causes distress unless food is also given. For the patient should not be fed without a previous anointing or anointed unless food is to follow. Moreover, after the anointing Themison prescribes an application of cold water to the face, again constricting the in- 160 flamed parts; for no one will deny that in all cases of phrenitis the head suffers from a state of stricture.

Themison also holds the mistaken opinion that, beginning with the third day from the time when the patient first shows loss of reason, food should be given him every day; he makes no distinction based on the nature of the attacks. But if the attacks come on alternate days, nourishment should also be given on alternate days. In fact, food should be given on alternate days in all cases except those in which there is fear of extreme atony in the declining phase of the disease, and in which the attacks run their complete course each day. For when the body is distressed by daily attacks, it cannot distribute to the several parts the nourishment it has taken.[4]

161   But Themison makes an even more serious error in holding that bathing is advantageous, even when the disease is still on the increase, three or four days from the time the patient first shows mental derangement. Indeed, how can it be said that bathing is helpful at a stage in the disease when it is clearly not yet proper to give food every day? For the disease is still at the height of its strength, and for this reason a soothing treat-

gativa sit curatio magis quam turbatio ex lavacri commotione
162 adhibenda. mitto quod aeger ad haec magis moveatur alienatione mentis nec ullo assensu nostro pareat imperio, siquidem
ferali mente omnia quaeque[13] accipiat ac[14] recuset.

item iubet lavantes solium primo descendere, tunc ascendentes solium fricari[15] plurimum, et rursum descendere, quod
est laboriosum. sufficiebat enim defricatos tunc solum[16] descendere, cum se modico senserint sudore vexatos. at iste post lavacrum oleo rosaceo caput fovet, quo gravius odore impletum
aegrotantes afficiat.

163 est autem incongruum atque inconsequens[17] laxata, ut putat,
lavacro corpora oleo rosaceo fomentare, cum sit frigidae atque
constrictivae virtutis et propterea corporis efficiat densitatem.
non enim eius frigus erit aquae frigidae comparandum, cum
aqua frigida ob extinguendum fervorem veluti cocti corporis adhibeatur; rosaceum vero perseveratione quadam simili atque
eadem vexatione iugi frigore et odore percussibili caput afficiat.

164 vinum etiam dandum declinationis ordinavit tempore, cum
neque omnibus hoc sit adhibendum sed solis illis qui simplici
aegritudine afficiuntur. dehinc non in omnibus prohibuit vinum salsum, sed in his qui sunt insueti, nescius quia consueti
vexantur, siquidem sit natura noxium febricitantibus vinum.
consuetudo autem nihil aliud prodesse, quam ut non plurimum
corpora noceantur, potest. nos vero oportet consuetudinem rerum utilium facere, noxiarum fugere.

dat etiam vinum plurimum: heminam etenim vel tres dimi-
165 dias iubet ante cibum, si fuerit sitis nimia consecuta. quod est,
ut sentio, sine ulla ratione. in gravi enim ac periculosa aegritudine, nudis et sitientibus visceribus, ingrediens vinum facile
concurrit ad nervos, atque mentis iudicium tollit, cum non

---

[13] quaeque *Triller ap. Kühn 85*: quoque *G*

[14] aut *Triller ibid.*

[15] fricari *R*: fricare *G*

[16] *fort.* solium *Bendz 38*

[17] atque consequens *G*: *corr. Bendz 88*: neque consequens *Rm*

ment should be given rather than a bath, with the disturbance
162 and excitement that it involves. I need not point out that, in
addition, the bath aggravates the patient's mental derangement
so that he fails to co-operate with us in following our instructions
and accepts or refuses everything in the manner of a brute.

Again, Themison instructs those bathing first to descend into
the tub, then to come up and have a thorough rubbing, and then
to descend again—a wearisome procedure. It would have sufficed if they first had their rubdown and only then descended
into the bath, when they felt affected by mild sweating. After
the bath Themison has the patient's head fomented with rose
oil. The result is that it is pervaded with the scent, and the
condition of the patient is aggravated.

163   Moreover, it is improper and illogical to relax the body, as
Themison suggests, with bathing, and then to foment it with
rose oil, for the oil has a chilling and astringent quality and for
that reason causes a condensation of the body. And the cold
property of the oil is not to be compared with that of cold water;
for cold water is used to quench the heat, for example, of a substance that has been cooked, while rose oil by its continuous
coolness and penetrating odor attacks the head with a constant
action and uninterrupted siege.

164   Themison also prescribes wine during the declining phase of
the disease. We hold, however, that wine should not be given to
all but only to those who are suffering from the disease in simple
form. Again, he does not bar salted[5] wine in all cases but only
when the patient is not accustomed to it. He does not realize
that those who are used to it are also adversely affected. For by
its nature wine is harmful in cases of fever. Those who are accustomed to it merely have the advantage that their bodies may
not be harmed very much. But we ought to get people used to
helpful, not to harmful, things.

Now Themison prescribes a considerable amount of wine. He
has the patient take a hemina before his food, or even one and a
half heminae, if there is great thirst. This prescription, I think,
165 is quite without reason. For in a severe and dangerous disease,
when the vital organs are bereft [of their juices] and parched,
wine on entering the body quickly passes to the nerves and
sinews and robs the mind of reason, since there has been no

5. Cf. 144.

habuerit praemissum cibum, quem incurrens quadam tarditate
moretur.

proficientibus igitur aegris perseverandum inquit in utendo
vino; si vero profectus cessaverit, tribus vel quatuor diebus
aquam dabimus usum vini differentes: rursum dierum numerum
et non passionis considerans[18] motum. quapropter etiamsi post
tres dies difficultas adhuc declinationis obstiterit, non oportet
ad usum vini descendere. etenim sollicitae passiones his im-
pulsibus[19] facile ad augmenta recurrunt.

haec nunc[20] Themison phreniticis curandis ordinavit, sed post
ex methodica secta multa bona contulit medicinae.

166   XVII. AD HERACLIDEM

EMPIRICORUM sufficit soli Heraclidi Tarentino respondere: etenim[1] eorum[2] posterior, atque omnium probabilior apud
suos invenitur. idem namque primo libro Curationum de internis passionibus varias curationum differentias scribit pro
suspicionibus causarum. nam primum phreniticum iacere iubet
loco obscuro, siquidem luce, inquit, eorum mens asperatur, cum
plerosque magis videamus tenebris asperari, atque luce eos qui
adiuncta solutione afficiuntur, adeo ut si paulo vehementior
fuerit, diaphoreticam faciat solutionem.

167   item iubet ventrem clystere deduci, tunc phlebotomiam adhiberi, atque alia die rursum usum innovari clysteris, non advertens quomodo tumentibus praecordiis atque extentis vel
adductis simul cum visceribus, periculosum est quicquam acre
vel quod commoveat immitere, quo retento tumor magis augeatur. dehinc turbulentum atque vexabile et per omnia contrarium esse perspicitur eadem die clysterem atque phlebotomum

[18] considerantes G: corr. Schmid 106

[19] in pulsibus G: corr. Rm

[20] tunc Triller ap. Kühn 85

[1] fort. est enim Deichgräber

[2] (nemine) eorum Schulze (vid. Gomperz, Die Apologie der Heilkunst², p. 155), Wellmann, Celsus 39: fort. pro posterior scrib. prior vel primus (cf. Ac. ii. 2)

1. Some such qualification is necessary if the text is retained.

previous intake of food into which the wine might flow with a consequent slowing-down of its passage.

As the patients improve, says Themison, we must continue to use wine, but if the improvement ceases we must prescribe water for three or four days and postpone the use of wine. Here, too, he is concerned with the number of days and not with the course of the disease. In our judgment, even if after three days the difficulty of bringing the disease into its declining phase still persists, we should not resort to the use of wine. For diseases are aroused by these stimulants and easily revert to their active state.

Such, then, are Themison's instructions for the treatment of phrenitis. Later, however, as a member of the Methodist Sect he made many valuable contributions to medicine.

166

XVII. REPLY TO HERACLIDES

HERACLIDES of Tarentum is the only one of the Empirics whom we need answer. For he is their last [great][1] leader and is the best of them all. Now in Book I of his work *On the Treatment of Internal Diseases* he sets forth various types of treatment corresponding to his various guesses as to the causes.[2] To begin with, he says that in phrenitis the patient should lie in a dark place, since the mind is excited by light. Now, actually, we find that most patients are more excited by darkness and that light has an adverse effect only on those who suffer from so severe a state of looseness in addition [to the state of stricture] that, if the state of looseness is aggravated even a little,[3] colliquative sweats ensue.

167   Heraclides also prescribes a clyster for the bowels, to be followed by venesection, and on the next day another clyster. In this he fails to observe that, when the precordial region and the viscera are inflamed and distended or drawn, it is dangerous to inject any sharp substance or one that would cause irritation and, by being retained, increase the inflammation. Again, it is obvious that to administer a clyster and perform venesection on

---

2. Cf. 179. The second type of treatment is for phrenitis caused by indigestion. The cause of phrenitis in which the first type of treatment is used is not specifically mentioned. There may be a lacuna, however, after *nam primum*.

3. Or possibly: 'if the light is a little too intense.'

adhibere, quippe cum neque tempus utendi dixerit, neque qui
sunt phlebotomandi discreverit. etenim eos qui solutione afficiuntur nocet ut gladius. extendit peccatum dicendo oportere
cotidie adhiberi clysterem, ut neque quiescendi aliquod tempus
occurrat, et cibo non nutriatur, viribus[3] privet iniectio.

168   tradens etiam localia[4] adiutoria, caput fovet decoctionibus
lauri, tunc novacula radit, et ex eodem liquore vaporat, post
rosaceo oleo caput atque nares iubet ungi, percutiens tumentia
ante declinationem ex fomentis supradictis, implens etiam caput
ex odore lauri, atque gravedines ac vertigines efficiens, similiter
et ex oleo roseo constringens simul ac frigidans cerebri membranam. imponit praeterea cataplasma ex polline et aqua mulsa,
admiscens iris illyricae decimam partem et lentiscini olei et aro-
matici calami. quae omnia ignea atque percutientia odoris causa
esse perspiciuntur, et oportebat tumentia congruis relaxare
virtutibus. item iubet post haec medicaminibus ungi caput et
169 nares hoc genere confectis: peucedani, castorei, opii, ut in libro
quem Nicolaum vocat, olei amygdali amari pondus supra scriptum, sed praetriti cum aceti sextariis duobus et olei irini unciis
tribus, quorum usus ita, inquit, erit adhibendus ut praecale-
facta apponantur. ex quibus gravatio capitis atque commutatio
nascetur, ut statim alienatio in pressuram transeat, cum tantis
perniciosissimis malis aegrotantis caput obsidetur.

170   Empiricos laudat.[5] mirandum sane unde haec ei[6] venisse suspicio potuerit ut discrepantium commixtio unam facere virtutem

---

[3] ⟨et⟩ viribus R
[4] loca alia G: corr. Rm
[5] Empiricos laudat fort. secl.   [6] eis Deichgräber

the same day causes the patient disturbance and distress, and
is inadvisable on all grounds. And Heraclides does not indicate
the time for using these procedures, nor does he specify those
upon whom venesection should be performed. Now for those
who suffer from a state of looseness the lancet is as harmful as a
sword. Heraclides goes even further astray in holding that a
clyster should be given every day, for then there is no time for
rest, the food confers no nourishment, and the body is robbed
of its strength by the injection.

68   Again, in discussing local remedies he recommends fomenting
the head with decoctions of laurel, then shaving it with a razor
and steaming it with the same fluid. Afterward he has the head
and nostrils anointed with rose oil. Thus he irritates the inflamed parts with these fomentations before the declining phase
of the disease, congests the head with the scent of laurel, and
causes a feeling of heaviness and dizziness. In the same way by
the use of rose oil he produces constriction in the membrane of
the brain while cooling it. In addition, he applies a poultice
made of flour and hydromel, with the addition of a tenth part of
Illyrian iris, mastic oil, and sweet flag. But all these substances
obviously burn and sting with their heavy scent. He should
rather have softened the inflamed parts with substances of
suitable properties. After the aforesaid treatments Heraclides
directs that the head and nostrils be anointed with drugs com-
169 pounded as follows: sulphurwort, castor, and poppy juice, as
prescribed in the book entitled *Nicolaus*, and the aforementioned weight[4] of bitter almond oil, all previously rubbed down
in two sextarii of vinegar and three ounces of iris oil. This compound, says Heraclides, should be heated before being applied.
The effect of these ingredients, however, is a heaviness of the
head and also a sudden change from a condition of mental
aberration to one of stupor as the patient's head is overwhelmed
by so many damaging ills.

170   Heraclides extols[5] the Empiric physicians. But we must indeed
wonder whence the notion could have come to him that the mix-

4. Caelius (Soranus) is quoting directly from Heraclides' *Treatment of Internal
Diseases*. Kühn (p. 171) refers the phrase to *decimam partem* (168) but this does not
seem possible.

5. Or perhaps 'cites' (as authorities?). The meaning is doubtful. Possibly the sentence was originally a marginal note to *illis* (or earlier to *eis*, if that is the correct reading). But the text may be corrupt, with *Empiricos* (-*us*) properly referring to Heraclides.

posse putaretur, vel quae illis natura vel fortuna fuerit magistra, quas saepe suis inventionibus duces fuisse testantur, vel certe quomodo discrepantis[7] historiae in ista medicaminis confectione iudicium tacuerunt.[8] sed si hoc experimentum dixerint, apertissime delirabunt, ut laborans empirica[9] ad occultarum confugiat apprehensionem causarum.

171   item iubet nocte caput vaporari, si facultas fuerit, papaveris decoctione atque serpylli, non adiciens usus causam neque rationem qua sit hoc circa vesperam faciendum, cum tunc maxime phreniticis asperius tempus occurrat. vaporatio autem caput exagitat, et tunc magis in requie fuerat habendus aegrotans. sed intelligimus eum in ista fuisse rerum diversitate coactum, cum solas vigilias aegrotantis attendit, somnum quibuscumque ambi-

172 tionibus adhibendum existimare.[10] quin etiam potandos dicit aegrotantes antidotum[11] diacodion cum mulsi sextario, vel seminali medicamine poto, quod diaspermaton vocant, aut tussiculari, quod bechicum appellant: cum magis opium, hoc est papaveris lacrima, densitatem faciat; item seminalis potio acrimoniae causa incendium faciat viscerum, atque haec omnia gravando pressuram magis quam somnum facere videantur. somnus enim laxatis fiet corporibus indulgentia naturali; pressura vero densatis adversitate morborum. igitur praescripto medicamine negligens tumentia contrariis stricturam geminat rebus [non similibus],[12] quomodo cum causa impeditionis somni, hoc est strictura, augetur, in lethargicam passionem aegrotantes veniunt, vel certe maiores vigilias.

---

[7] discrepantes *A*

[8] latuerunt *Bendz 86*

[9] *an* empirice?

[10] existimare *R*: existimat *G*

[11] antidoto *R*   [12] *seclusi*

---

6. An ironical allusion to ἡ κρίσις τῆς ἱστορίας of the Empirics. Cf. Deichgräber, pp. 126–28, 298–301. If *discrepantes* (*A*) and *latuerunt* (Bendz) be read, the meaning would be: 'that the conflicting accounts . . . escaped their critique.'

ture of incompatible substances was able to produce a substance with a single property; or what sort of nature or chance instructed these Empiricists, for they keep asserting that nature and chance were their guides in their discoveries. And surely [we must wonder] that they suppressed their critique of the conflicting accounts of the preparation of this remedy.[6] But if they say that their procedure is a matter of experience, they will be so obviously in error that their empiricism will have to resort in distress to an attempt to grasp hidden causes.[7]

71   Heraclides also prescribes the use of a decoction of poppy and thyme to warm the patient's head at night, if it is possible. But he does not give us the reason for this treatment, or for administering it during the evening, which is a particularly trying time for patients with phrenitis. Moreover, the hot application agitates the head, and in any case it would have been better to keep the patient quiet in the evening. It is our belief that Heraclides, despite the variety of circumstances, centered his attention solely on the sleeplessness of the patients and was led to the conclusion that sleep should be induced by every possible
72 means. In fact, he says that the patients should drink the drug made from poppy heads (*dia cōdiōn*) with a sextarius of mead, or the drug of seeds (Greek *dia spermatōn*), or a cough remedy (Greek *bēchicon*). The truth, however, is that opium, or poppy juice, has an astringent effect. Again, the potion made from seeds inflames the viscera by its harshness; and all these drugs by their oppressive action are evidently more likely to produce stupor than sleep. For sleep comes when bodies are relaxed by the gentle action of nature; stupor when they are constricted by the hostile action of diseases. And so, by using this type of drug without regard to the inflammation, Heraclides aggravates the state of stricture by contrary measures.[8] Thus, as the cause of the lack of sleep, namely, this very state of stricture, is augmented, the patient passes into the disease of lethargy or at least into a more serious condition of sleeplessness.

7. Or perhaps: 'so that Heraclides, beset by his Empirical doctrines, has to take refuge by trying to grasp hidden causes.'

8. Either in the sense of 'conflicting,' 'inconsistent,' 'harmful,' or in the sense indicated in 116, n. 1. In either case *non similibus* seems to have been a marginal note on *contrariis*.

173   item eodem libro accusans utentes medicaminibus ex castoreo
atque aceto et spondylio confectis et cataplasmatibus ex aceto,
siquidem sint acria, ipse quoque nihil minus peccare videtur
adhibens gravabiliora atque acriora. etenim dicere quomodo
non ad solvendam passionem sed servandi aegroti causa haec
adhibuit, est omnino inertiae. nam primo quibus passio levigatur, his etiam aeger servatur; secundo quibus laborans retinetur in vita, iisdem etiam passio relevatur; tertio cum non
parvo periculo ex vigiliis afficiantur, maius tamen ex pressura
Heraclides facere perspicitur. nam somnum fecisset gravabili-
bus utens medicaminibus, cum sit semper, ut in utilibus maius,
sic in adversis levius eligendum.

174   sed, inquit, ut vinum mediocriter datum nutribile ac salutare
probatur, plurimum vero atque immodice datum capitis gravedinem atque mentis errorem facit, sic etiam medicamen supradictum moderatione accedente somnos faciles facit remota gravedine. est autem exemplum dissimile. horum etenim medicaminum etiam si parvum quidquam fuerit datum, gravedinem
facit, si plurimum, mortem. nam quia gravatio magis quam
somnus efficitur facile perspicere poterimus. etenim de somno
coloris melioris efficitur corpus, fortitudine quoque acquisita;
ex medicaminis vero pressura, pallor atque debilitas et gravatio
corporis nimia sequetur. dehinc omnis somnus in corpore spira-
bili atque indulgentia laxato nascetur.

175   medicamina vero quae ob vigiliarum mitigationem dantur
magis accessionis tempore offerenda dicuntur. tum enim vehementer aegri vigilare noscuntur, cum sit impossibile turbore
corpus impletum somni tunc indulgentia temperari, cum haec
commoda[13] medicamenta etiam sponte ventura[14] corrumpant,
incendant[15] etiam altiora, et praesentem augeant accessionem.

176 neque enim etiam cibos consuetos atque qualitate convenientes[16]

---

[13] incommoda R, *fort. recte*

[14] venturam R (*sc.* indulgentiam): *fort.* venturum (*sc.* somnum)

[15] corrumpat, incendat (*et mox* augeat) G: *corr.* R

[16] qualitate convenientes *A*: qualitatem conveniens G: qualitatem convenientem *Rm*

173   In fact, Heraclides in the same book criticizes those who use drugs made with castor, vinegar, and spondylium and poultices made with vinegar, because he considers these drugs acrid; but he himself seems to be no less in error, for he uses drugs that are even more oppressive and acrid. And to say that he prescribes this treatment for the purpose not of breaking down the disease but of saving the patient is utter foolishness. For, in the first place, the patient is saved by the very means by which the disease is relieved; secondly, the disease is relieved by the very means by which the patient is kept alive; and, thirdly, though sleeplessness [in cases of phrenitis] involves no little danger, it would seem that Heraclides increases the danger by imposing stupor. That is, he would try to produce sleep by using oppressive drugs, though one should always choose the lesser evil, just as one should always choose the greater good.

174   But, says Heraclides, just as wine in moderation is nutritious and healthful, yet in excess causes heaviness of the head and mental aberration, so the type of drug referred to above,[9] if given in moderation, produces gentle sleep without oppressiveness. But the analogy of wine is quite inappropriate. For in the case of these drugs, if even a small quantity is given, it produces a feeling of heaviness; a large quantity causes death. And we can easily observe that stupor rather than sleep is produced. For in the case of sleep the body acquires a better color and also gains strength; but pronounced pallor, weakness, and languor of the body are the consequences of stupor induced by a drug. Again, sleep can come only to a body that can breathe and is gently relaxed.

175   Now the Empirics say that the drugs they give to overcome sleeplessness should be given preferably at the time of an attack. Their reason is that at that time the patient is obviously widest awake, since his body is wracked by confusion and cannot be calmed by gentle sleep. But even if these benefits [of sleep] come spontaneously, the drugs vitiate them,[10] cause inflammation of the interior parts of the body, and aggravate the actual attack.

176   Indeed, at the time of an attack one should not give the patient the food he is accustomed to, even if it has suitable properties;

9. 169.

10. Or reading *venturam* (R) or *venturum*: 'But in fact these fine drugs vitiate sleep even if it does come spontaneously.' ('These harmful drugs *etc.*,' R.)

accessionis tempore offerre, vel quod multo levius est aquam,
⟨quae⟩[17] corrumpi posse negatur, ut ⟨non⟩ cuiquam credendum[18]
sit supradicta medicamina isto praesertim tempore digestionis
officio superari.

ait praeterea succumbente passione dandum iuscellum[19] simplex gallinaceum, vel sucum ptisanae, ordei, vel orizae, ac deinde per profectum ad usum panis accedere levi ex farina confecti, et gobionum piscium pulmentum, secundo carnis gallina-
ceae ac leporis: quae non recte quisquam etiam declinationis
177 tempore ob reficiendum corpus prima dari permittat. quae
quidem declinatio forsitan nec futura sit his malignis aegrotanti
atque tantis affecto, et nulla mitigatione tolerato, neque oris
collutione neque potu neque cibo. mitto etiam quia si dimissio
fuerit facta, non necessario tempus accipit praefinitum: etenim
nunc decima nunc duodecima die vel ultra saepius occurrit.
quapropter tantis diebus innutritum aegrotantem relinquere
non solum noxium, verum etiam impossibile esse perspicitur.
dehinc gallinarum iuscellum[20] facile corrumpitur, et est digestione difficilis hordei atque ptisanae sucus; oriza vero quod strin-
178 gat nulli dubium est. atque ita panis quantitatem augere nos
quoque admittimus. pisces autem gobiones dare prohibemus.
etenim locum in passionibus celerrimis vel acutis acrior cibatio,
quam drimyphagian[21] vocant, non habet. item dari iubet * *[22]
atque varios cibos, et neque lavandam faciem, neque aliam
congruam corporis diligentiam ordinandam vidit, sine qua minime digestio fieri potest non solum variae cibationis, verum
etiam simplicis, nisi corpori perunctionibus atque alia diligentia
179 recreatio[23] fuerit illata. haec est secundum Heraclidem curationis prima phreniticorum differentia.

illis vero qui cruditate phrenitici fuerint effecti, ita curationem
ordinavit ut supradicta similiter adhibeantur. cataplasma vero
non prius quam clyster antecesserit adhiberi iubet. etenim
perniciosum est, inquit, pleno corpori haec adhibere, siquidem
ad caput rapta materia in salutis periculum praecipitet aegro-

---

[17] aquam ⟨quae⟩ R: aqua G, fort. retin.

[18] ⟨non⟩ cuiquam credendum scripsi: cuiquam ⟨minime⟩ credendum R

[19] viscellum edd. (v. Kühn 172–74)　　　　　　[20] viscellum edd.

[21] drimyphagian Schmid 107: polyphagian edd.

[22] ⟨leporem⟩ suppl. R: an suppl. ⟨vinum⟩?　　　　[23] recreatio Rm: recreato G

one should not even give water, which is much easier to manage and, it is said, cannot spoil. We must therefore not believe that, at that time in particular, the drugs mentioned above can be controlled by the digestive process.

Again, Heraclides says that, as the disease subsides, a simple chicken broth should be given or a gruel of pearl barley, unpeeled barley, or rice; and as the patient makes progress he may begin to have bread made of a light flour, and gudgeon fish sauce and, thereafter, some meat of poultry or hare. But it would be wrong for anyone to prescribe these as the first foods for repairing the body, even during the actual decline of the disease. And this decline may, in fact, never come, if the patient is beset by so many harmful drugs and receives no refreshing relief, mouth wash, drink, or food. I need not point out the further fact that, even if the decline does come, it does not necessarily come at a predetermined time. For it sometimes occurs on the tenth day, sometimes on the twelfth, and frequently even later. Now to leave the patient so many days without nourishment is obviously not only harmful but impossible. Furthermore, chicken broth easily decomposes, the gruels of unpeeled barley and pearl barley are hard to digest, and rice is admittedly binding. And though we, too, allow the patient more bread [as he improves], we do not permit gudgeon fish to be given; for acrid food (Greek *drimyphagia*) has no place in swift or acute diseases. What is more, Heraclides prescribes . . . and varied food without observing that he should also prescribe washing of the face and other suitable treatments for the body. Otherwise there can be no digestion, not merely of varied food but even of simple food; that is, the body should first be refreshed by anointing and other suitable treatments. So much for what Heraclides calls his first type of treatment in phrenitis.

In the case of those, however, who incur phrenitis through indigestion, he so regulates the treatment that the same procedures are similarly carried out, but the application of a poultice is not permitted until a clyster has been administered. For it is disastrous, he says, to apply poultices to a body that is replete, since the carrying of matter to the head quickly en-

tantem. atque ita prohibendam dicit phlebotomiam, adhibendam vero corporis purgationem poto medicamine quod appellat
diascammonias, hoc est quod ex diagridio[24] conficitur.

180   quibus apparet hunc suae sectae peccata custodire, ut ea quae
Empirici servabilia vocaverunt etiam nunc adhibenda existimet, adiciens etiam peiora prohibendo phlebotomiam, quae simplici atque innoxio laxamento nullis obstantibus adhibita facile
laxato corpore passionem posset auferre. cuius in vicem no-
centissimam adhibendam purgationem iudicavit scammoniae,
quae est gravior cruditate quam ipse metuens in contraria venit
argumenta curationis. etenim ex hac corporis purgatione sive
liquidarum detractione materiarum corpus confluere manifestum est, atque eius solida quadam dimissione lentescere, et in
liquida migrando deperire.

181   mitto quod neque suae sectae servaverit morem quae numquam vasculorum corporis materias attenderit, siquidem sint
non solum occultae, verum etiam Empiricorum iudicio falsissimae. etenim existimare quod discendae passionis causa sucorum nominaverit cruditatem potuimus, nisi etiam curationis
ordinem ipsum intuens discessisset adeo ut etiam scammoniam
bibendam credidisset. quaerendum etiam ubi esse cruditatem
suspicetur quam[25] scammonia putaret detrahendam. in intestinis? sed sic fuerat melius atque facilius eam clystere purgare.
an in capite? an vero in toto corpore? sed cum haec incerta
dimiserit, videtur iudicium sui operis medicamini dimisisse, ut
tamquam sentiens animal operetur, separando a naturalibus
aliena, hoc est cruditate corrupta, atque[26] sola detrahere.[27]

²⁴ diagredio *edd*.

²⁵ quam *R*: ubi *G*

²⁶ eaque *Triller ap. Kühn 175*   ²⁷ detrahat *Rm*

dangers the life of the patient. Heraclides also bars venesection [in these cases] but orders a potion of a drug from scammony juice (Greek *dia scammōnias*) as a purge for the body.

80   Hence it appears that he observes the errors of his sect, evidently believing that what the Empirics term 'observable'[11] should in this case be employed. But he contributes even worse errors by rejecting venesection. For venesection, if performed when there are no unfavorable conditions, can easily dispel the disease, since the body is relaxed by the simple and harmless relief which this treatment affords. But in its place Heraclides advocates the use of a most harmful purge, scammony. This purge is actually worse than the indigestion that prompted him in fear to prescribe contrary[12] therapeutic measures. For, as a result of this purging of the body or removing of matter in liquid form, the body itself obviously liquefies; that is, its solid matter grows soft by a sort of melting process and as it passes into a liquid form is lost.

81   It is unnecessary to point out that Heraclides does not observe the customary teaching of his sect, which has never given consideration to the substances contained in the vessels of the body, since these substances are not only concealed from view but, in the judgment of the Empirics, not even existent.[13] We might, indeed, have supposed that it was to an unconcocted state of the humors that Heraclides referred in characterizing this form of the disease had he not gone so far as to hold that scammony should be taken by way of treatment. And we must ask where he supposes the undigested matter is which he thinks must be gotten rid of with scammony. In the bowels? But in that case it would have been better and easier to clear out this matter with a clyster. Or in the head, or, indeed, in the whole body? In failing to answer these questions he seems to have left the judgment of his work to the drug itself, in the hope that it would act like a conscious being, separating out from the normal parts of the body the foreign substances, i.e., those that have decomcomposed by not being digested, and removing these alone.

11. *servabilia* = τηρητικά, a reference to τήρησις, 'observation,' of Empiric philosophy. But the meaning of our passage is uncertain, and the attempt to explain it on the basis of word play with *custodire* may be mistaken.

12. Probably the sense of 'harmful' is also involved here.

13. I.e., Heraclides seems to embrace a humoral pathology, but his therapy is not consistent with such a pathology.

182   tertiam inde curationis scribit differentiam qua iubet, si totum corpus non fuerit multo sanguine gravatum sed solae capitis partes videantur impletae, ex vena frontis detractionem fieri:
cum neque passionis esse causam sanguinem videamus, neque
ex patientibus locis detractio aliquid medeatur. etenim magis
patientes adimplet partes primo ex antecedenti fasciolae constrictione, secundo ipsius coactae materiae concursu.

illos vero quos corruptione, inquit, in passionem venisse viderimus, clystere purgandos, aquam dantes largius bibendam,
aliquando etiam mulsum[28] vinum chium aut rhodium, sed primo
183 aquatum secundo etiam meracum. hic etiam rursum suae sectae
rigorem contempsit, suspicionibus in errorem deductus, liquidarum materiarum corrupta temperare festinans, et ita iugiter
ut incurabilem faciat manere passionem. dat etiam sine tempore vinum.

et quid pluribus? ita curandi diligentiam permisit[29] ut varia
mobilitate videatur esse confusus. quorum omnium meminisse
decet sed solam supradictorum probare rationem.[30]

haec sunt quae de phrenitica passione credidimus ordinanda.
nunc de ceteris celeribus vel acutis cum febricula passionibus
sequenti docebimus libro.

[28] mulsum ⟨aut⟩ R
[29] praetermisit A
[30] sola supradictorum probari ratione G: corr. R

82   Heraclides then sets forth the third type of treatment, in which he prescribes that if the whole body is not weighed down with excess blood, but only parts of the head seem congested, blood should be withdrawn from the vein of the forehead. But it is obvious that blood is not the cause of the disease, and its withdrawal from the affected parts does not help any; indeed, it is especially the affected parts that the blood continues to congest, first, because of the previous constriction of the bandage and, secondly, under the pressure of the resulting flow of matter [to the place of venesection].

And in the case of those who we find have fallen into the disease through decomposition [of the humors], Heraclides prescribes that they be purged with a clyster and given much water to drink and sometimes Chian or Rhodian honey-wine, at first

83 mixed with water, but later undiluted. Herein again led into error by his guesses, he departs from the strict teaching of his sect. He makes haste to overcome the decomposed state of the humors, but with such persistence that he renders the disease incurable. And his prescription of wine is made without any indication of time.

But why say more? He sets forth the account of his treatment in such a way that he seems to be shifting about in constant confusion. Though it is proper for us to bear in mind all that he says, as set forth above, we must approve only the part supported by reason.

This concludes our account of the disease of phrenitis. We shall in the next book deal with the other swift or acute diseases accompanied by fever.

LIBER SECUNDUS

I. DE LETHARGO

CELERUM cum febricula passionum primam superiore libro tradidimus phrenitim; nunc lethargicam cum ceteris ordinamus. vocatur lethargus a consequenti passionis oblivione: Graeci enim lethen oblivionem vocaverunt, argiam vacationem, quam corpori atque animae ingerit vis supradictae passionis. et est comparatione[1] gravior phrenitica,[2] non aliter quam negatus in toto visus ab ex parte impedito, vel silentium ab impedita locutione, aut surditas ab auditus falsitate, vel hebetudo sensuum a difficultate.

2 denique vehementi strictura phrenitici saepissime in lethargiam venerunt, utque[3] declinante lethargia aliquando econtrario lethargi in phrenitim deciderunt: quorum[4] rarius[5] ex supradictis posteriora[6] contingunt, siquidem facile periclitantes passionis magnitudine in peiorem deveniant, difficile autem in periculis bona locum accipiant. quapropter Asclepiadi credendum non est dicenti pulsum atque respirationem humaniorem lethargis quam phreniticis esse, siquidem habeat magnitudinem et per-
3 cussum fortiorem, tamquam iugi somno dormientium. sed neque iste somnus est impeditis omnibus naturalis actionis[7] officiis, sed est oppressio quae nihil resumat aegrotantem ac potius demergat. neque etiam pulsus fortis sed magis debilis percussus invenitur atque piger ac inanis. quod autem in inflationem[8] erectus videtur, non fortitudinis causa sed passionis nequitia id efficitur. denique in his quibus ob phreniticam passionem parvus est pulsus, saepe peiorante morbo atque in lethargiam transeunte, pulsus in magnitudinem erigitur ob spe-

---

[1] comparatio G: *corr. R*

[2] phrenitice G: phrenetide R (-it- *A*)

[3] *fort.* atque (*cf. adn. ad Ac. i. 85*)

[4] quorum ⟨haud⟩ (*melius* ⟨non⟩) R (*retento* prima)

[5] gravius *Hagendahl 253* (*retento* prima)

[6] posteriora *Bendz 87*: prima G

[7] actionis R: accessionis G   [8] in inflatione G: inflatione R (*om.* in)

BOOK II

I. LETHARGY

AMONG the acute diseases accompanied by fever, we dealt first with phrenitis in the preceding book. We shall now discuss lethargy and the others. Lethargy receives its name from the loss of memory which the disease involves. For the Greek word for forgetfulness is *lēthē* and for idleness *argia*, and these are the characteristics forced upon the body and soul by the power of this disease. And it is a more serious disease than phrenitis, just as is complete loss of vision compared to partial impairment, complete speechlessness compared to an impediment in speech, total deafness compared to mere lapses in hearing, or a general blunting of the senses compared to mere difficulty in using them.[1]

2   Again, patients with phrenitis often pass into lethargy because of the extreme state of stricture; contrariwise, those with lethargy sometimes pass into phrenitis as the lethargy wanes. Of these two cases of change the latter, as we have said, takes place rarely. For those who are exposed to danger through the seriousness of their disease may easily pass into a worse one. But it is only rarely that a change for the better takes place in the midst of danger. Therefore, we must not believe Asclepiades when he says that the pulse and respiration in lethargy are more normal than in phrenitis, being fuller and having a stronger

3 thrust in lethargy, as in an uninterrupted natural sleep. The fact is that lethargy is not sleep with a hindrance of all the functions of normal activity; it is a state of torpor which does not refresh the patient but rather depresses him. And actually the pulse is not strong but is generally found to have a weak beat and to be sluggish and empty.[2] That it seems puffed up is due not to its strength but to the malignant character of the disease. And, in fact, in cases where the pulse is small because of phrenitis, as the disease grows worse and passes into lethargy the

1. The comparisons refer to the attributes of lethargy as against those of phrenitis.
2. Cf. *Ac.* i. 50.

cialem proprietatem passionis, non proficientium virium causa,
quippe cum generaliter strictura peiorante omnia deterius roborentur.

4   sed hanc plerique diffinientes passionem aiunt lethargiam esse
delirationem cum febribus acutis ad perniciem ducentibus: et[9]
erat non delirationem sed pressuram dicere.   Demetrius autem
Herophilus[10] passionem inquit acutam[11] cum pressura et obstrusione sensuum ⟨frequenter⟩[12] cum febribus. in qua diffinitione
ambiguum est quo[13] sit accipiendum 'frequenter,' utrumne antecedenti serviat orationi, ut intelligamus 'frequenter cum difficultate sensuum,' an consequenti sit orationi iungendum, ut
intelligamus 'frequenter cum febribus,' an vero utrique serviat
parti. quo invenimus nihil recte esse diffinitum: semper enim
cum difficultate sensuum atque febribus haec intelligitur passio.

5   Asclepiades hanc passionem non definivit, sed Alexander
Laodicensis ex Asia secundum ipsum ait lethargum esse subitam
vel recentem ⟨alienationem⟩[14] cum febribus et pressura atque
sensuum iugi difficultate. sed esse videmus plerumque etiam
cum dimissionibus lethargiam; et pressuram id ipsum esse perspicimus quod est sensuum difficultas, quamquam hanc graviorem putaverint[15] pressuram. nec sane debuit in diffinitione
magnitudinis differentias ponere, sed passionis genus quem-
6 admodum intelligatur manifestare.   nonne etiam complexionem magis phreniticae passionis cum lethargia dedisse videtur?
denique alienatio subita ac recens[16] cum febribus acutis phreniticae est passionis; pressura vero cum febribus lethargiae.

Athenaeus Tarsensis furorem inquit mentis cum maestitudine, siquidem Asclepiades in primo libro Celerum passionum
dixerit phreniticis alienationem cum turbore effici, in lethargis
cum somno atque tristitia. alii alienationem cum maestitudine
et iugi somno esse lethargiam dixerunt: etenim non habent men-

[9] *fort.* at

[10] Herophilius *A*: sed *cf. Ac. ii. 141, 147, et lectiones cod. Paris. Sor. Gyn., p. 122. 5,
129. 4, 131. 8, al.*

[11] acutum *G: corr. R*

[12] *suppl. R*

[13] quo *R*: quod *G*: quid *Helmreich 317*

[14] *suppl. Rm*

[15] *fort.* putaverit (*sc.* Alexander)

[16] ac recens *Bendz 89*: acrescens *G*

pulse is often increased in size. This change is due to a specific characteristic of the disease of lethargy, not to any improvement in the patient's strength. For, in general, as a state of stricture becomes worse, all the symptoms indicative of disease become stronger.

4   In defining the disease of lethargy, many say that it is loss of reason with acute fever leading to death. But one should speak of stupor, not of loss of reason. Demetrius the Herophilean calls lethargy an acute disease involving stupor and an impairment of the senses frequently with fever. In this definition it is not clear how the word 'frequently' is to be taken. Is it to be joined with the preceding words, so that we take 'frequently' with 'impairment of the senses'; or is it to be joined with the following words, so that we take 'frequently' with 'fever'; or, indeed, does it go with both parts? But the description is in any case inaccurate. For this disease is *always* observed to involve an affliction of the senses and also fever.

5   Asclepiades does not define this disease,[3] but Alexander of Laodicea in Asia Minor declares, on the authority of Asclepiades, that lethargy is a sudden loss of reason, i.e., one of recent origin, with fever and stupor and unremitting impairment of the senses. But we find in many cases that lethargy also occurs with remissions; and the stupor is obviously the same thing as the impairment of the senses, though they [the followers of Asclepiades] take this impairment to be a more serious form of stupor. And surely in his definition Alexander should not have indicated differences in severity but should have shown how
6 the generic nature of the disease was to be defined. Again, does he not seem rather to have described a combination of phrenitis and lethargy? For 'a sudden (i.e., recently occurring) loss of reason with acute fever' is indicative of phrenitis. Stupor with fever, on the other hand, is the mark of lethargy.

Athenaeus of Tarsus defines lethargy as mania together with depression, on the basis of a statement of Asclepiades, in Book I of his work *On Acute Diseases*, that in phrenitis loss of reason occurs with violent turmoil, but in lethargy with sleep and depression. Others have said that lethargy is loss of reason with depression and uninterrupted sleep, on the ground that the mind

---

3. I.e., formally in his writings. But such a qualification is unnecessary if *ipsum* in the next sentence refers to Alexander, not Asclepiades.

tem in furorem extentam, ut Athenaeus ait, sed sola in alienatione constitutam, ut Asclepiades.

7   sed etiam nunc traditiones caducas simul advertendas existimo ex his quae supra memoravimus. non enim somnus in
lethargis esse advertitur: ceterum nullum periculum sequeretur,
neque etiam accessionis tempore magis aegros afficeret. item
neque iugis in omnibus est pressura, sed etiam plerumque dimissionis intercapedine levigatur. at si cum febribus esse non
adiungerent, ut Asclepiades fecit, communis esset cum epilepsia
diffinitio.

Leonides autem episyntheticus lethargus, inquit, est obtrusio[17]
secundum vias membranarum, cum furore mentis atque febre
8 et maestitudine ac pressura et pulsu magno. sed neque causam
oportuit dicere, quae sit occulta atque apud veteres discrepans
et iniudicata, cum passionem manifestare fuerit necessarium:
neque etiam maestitudinem vel tristitiam atque mentis furorem,
etenim pressura[18] in semet maestitudinem atque furorem continet.

item Menemachus pressuram inquit celerrimam vel acutam
cum acutis febribus et non semper iugibus. Soranus vero, cuius
haec sunt quae latinizanda suscepimus, pressuram inquit celerem esse vel acutam, cum acutis febribus et pulsu magno ac
tardo atque inani. frequentare inquit in senibus, siquidem apti-
or sit sensuum difficultati atque demersioni ipsa quoque se-
nectus.

9   II. QUAE SEQUUNTUR EOS QUI IN LETHAR-
GIAM VENIRE POSSE NOSCUNTUR

SEQUUNTUR eos qui in lethargiam faciles ac proni esse videntur
aliqua communia ex his quae etiam in[1] phrenitim fore denuntiant;[2] aliqua propria quae etiam causa[3] communi tamquam

[17] obtrusio Rm: lethargia G

[18] pressuram G: corr. R

[1] in om. R

[2] denuntiat G: corr. R

[3] ⟨in⟩ causa R: an secl. quae etiam causa communi tamquam propria?

of the patient does not pass into a state of mania, as Athenaeus holds, but remains merely in a state of aberration, as Asclepiades holds.

7   But I think that, on the basis of what has been said above, we may view all these accounts of lethargy as insufficient. For it is not natural sleep that we observe in cases of lethargy; indeed [if it were sleep], there would be no danger, nor would lethargy cause the patients greater distress at the time of an attack. Again, the stupor is not in all cases constant but is generally relieved by intervals of remission. Furthermore, where the definers do not add, as Asclepiades does,[4] that lethargy is accompanied by fever, the definition becomes the same as that of epilepsy.

Leonides the Episynthetic declares that lethargy is a stoppage in the pores of the membranes [of the brain], accompanied by
8 madness, fever, depression, stupor, and a large pulse. But he should not have set forth the cause, since it is obscure and a matter of dispute among the ancients, a dispute which is still unsettled. Instead, he should have made clear what the disease is. And it is not necessary to speak of dejection, depression, and madness. For the term 'stupor' contains the notions of dejection and madness.

Menemachus defines lethargy as a swift or acute attack of stupor with acute, though not in all cases continuous, fever. But Soranus, whose work I have in these pages undertaken to translate into Latin, declares that lethargy is a swift or acute attack of stupor with acute fever and a large, slow, and hollow pulse. He adds that it is more common in old people, for impairment of the senses and depression are more characteristic of old age.

9   II. THE SYMPTOMS OF THOSE WHO EVI-
            DENTLY MAY BE ON THE VERGE
                    OF LETHARGY

THOSE who are evidently on the verge of lethargy show some of the same general characteristics that also herald the coming of phrenitis. They also show some specific signs, which we

4. The reference is probably to sec. 5, in which case *ipsum* (5) = *Asclepiadem*, and *fecit* = *adiunxit*. If, however, the reference is to sec. 6, *fecit* = *non adiunxit*.

propria accipimus, ut sunt ea quae in phreniticam venturos passionem designare praescripsimus, ut febres acutae ac vehementes
et saepe continuae ac difficile ad superficiem corporis ascen-
10 dentes, capitis gravedo vel somnus aut dolor vehemens repente
ac sine ratione recedens, tinnitus aurium, vultus inflatio, pallor
tamquam ex vinolentia et maestitudo vel tristitia.

erit praeterea tacitus is qui natura atque sanitatis tempore
fuerat multiloquus, tunc piger ac non sponte initians loquelam
sed alienam prosequens, suarum tacitus querelarum aut non
digna ratione referens, multo etiam veluti somno affectus, nec
quicquam somnians aut eorum quae somniaverit memor,
schema iacendi frequenter supinum contra solitam consuetudinem, oscitatio iugis, extensio crurum tamquam mox e somno ex-
11 pergiscentis, pulsus etiam inaequalis, post aliquantos[4] saltus
ordinatus, aut inordinatus, et pro aetate aut natura maior aut
tardior, aliquando etiam in inanitatem intercapedinatus, quod
denique si in phrenitica passione contigerit, in lethargiam transi-
turos aegrotantes significat. etenim maiorem pulsum fieri,
neque tardum neque inanem sed aetati aegrotantis convenientem, speciem declinantis phreniticae passionis accipimus; certius
etiam quoties circa numerum aequales minoribus maiores saltus
efficiuntur ac velocibus et densis et vehementibus; multo potius
si etiam multo[5] maiores atque celeres fuerint.

4 aliquantos *Helmreich 317*: aliquando *G*: aliquot *R*
5 multi *G*

---

1. I.e., when symptoms indicative of another disease, presumably phrenitis, are also
present. But the meaning of the phrase is doubtful, and, in fact, some confusion in the
discussion of general and specific signs seems to indicate textual corruption. We should
expect a phrase like 'although any one of these symptoms may also be found in other
diseases' (cf. *Ac.* i. 33), but *etiam causa communi*, even with *R*'s insertion of *in*, can
hardly sustain such a meaning.

recognize as specific even where the disease is complicated.[1]
Compare our previous discussion of the signs indicative of the
coming of phrenitis.[2] Now the signs that characterize persons
on the verge of lethargy are acute and violent fever, often unremitting and hardly ever reaching the surface of the body, a feel-
10 ing of heaviness in the head, sleep,[3] sharp pain suddenly disap-
pearing without any obvious reason, ringing in the ears, face
puffed up, pallor like that occasioned by excessive drinking of
wine, and depression or dejection.

In addition, if the patient has been naturally talkative in
health, he is now silent and sluggish, never of his own motion
beginning a discussion, but giving answers; he is silent about his
malady or else says things devoid of reason. He seems to be overcome by a sort of deep sleep; he has no dreams or else is unable
to remember what he has dreamed. He frequently lies on his
back contrary to his usual custom, yawns continually, and
11 stretches his legs, as if about to awake from sleep. The pulse is
unsteady, becoming regular after several beats or remaining irregular; it is larger and slower than normal for the patient's age
and nature and, from time to time, becomes empty. And if such
a pulse occurs in a case of phrenitis, it indicates that the patient
is about to lapse into lethargy. On the other hand, if the pulse
in phrenitis becomes larger without also becoming slow or
empty, and takes on characteristics appropriate to the age of
the patient, we take it as an indication of the decline of phrenitis.
And it is a surer indication [of a decline in phrenitis] if the number of large pulse beats is equal to the number of small beats
[previously found],[4] and if the increase in the size of the pulse
is not offset by loss in speed, thickness,[5] or strength. It is an even
surer sign if there is a large increase in the size of the pulse without loss of speed.[6]

2. *Ac.* i. 31 ff.

3. If the text is sound, this is the outstanding difference between the symptoms
preceding phrenitis and those preceding lethargy.

4. I.e., in a given interval of time.

5. Cf. *Ac.* i. 21 n.

6. Or possibly 'with increase of speed.' If *multi* (G) be retained, the meaning might
be: 'if a large, rapid pulse is maintained.'

12   quidam attenderunt etiam naturam aegrotantis, si salivosus
semper fuit: etenim declives atque faciles istius modi naturae in
pressuram[6] probantur. attendendam etiam consuetudinem
aiunt, utrumne febricitans in pressuram venire ac demergi solebat; aetatem quoque, utrumne sit mediae;[7] et aeris habitum,
utrum multis hanc ingesserit passionem; et anni[8] vel temporum
partem utrum autumni media, tunc enim frequentare istam
passionem probaverunt.

13   III. QUOMODO ⟨INTELLIGITUR LETHARGUS⟩[1]

IAM lethargum intelligere debemus: est enim melius atque
certius sic ut[2] in phreniticis dicere, quam si dicas 'quae sunt
signa lethargi.' unum enim quicquam singulare, ut est pressura
vel febricula, non significat lethargum, sed plurima atque sibi
convenientia, ut concursus multorum signum faciat indicabile
lethargi. lethargus vero sit signo indicatus, ut supra diximus.
    intelligimus lethargum ex obtrusione atque hebetudine sensu-
um, pressura etiam atque febre acuta sive iugi sive demissionibus
14 intercapedinata, pulsu magno tardo inani et inflato. sine his
enim neque esse ⟨neque⟩[3] intelligi lethargus potest. nam
quaedam praeterea alia sequentur multa vel pauca secundum
passionis magnitudinem, vel generalis temporis atque specialis
differentiam. primo igitur sequitur dubia atque somni similis
pressura et demersio, sed quam facile aeger vocatus excutiat;
interrogatus sane non statim sed secundum respondeat; tunc
iussus vel oscitatione persuasus inspectioni linguam exerere,
aut non id faciat aut tarde fieri consentiat; vel cum protulerit
non reducat aut tarde colligat; si quid etiam manu tenuerit,
nescius atque sine voluntate dimittat; et loquens priorum obli-

---

⁶ in pressuram R: impressuram G

⁷ media *Helmreich 318*

⁸ animi G: *corr.* R

¹ *inscriptionem supplevit Friedel 28, coll. Ac. i. 34*: quomodo discernimus lethargos
ab his qui similibus afficiuntur G, *quae inscriptio non huc sed ad caput IV pertinet: an
scribendum* quomodo iam lethargum intelligere debemus? *(i.e., iam praesentem,* τὴν
ἤδη λήθαργον)

² sicut G: *div. Friedel 29: editores alii aliter*

³ *supplevi, coll. 25* quantum intelligitur atque est lethargus

12 Some physicians [in deciding whether lethargy is imminent] consider the patient's nature, noting whether he has always had an excessive flow of saliva. For persons with this characteristic are supposed to be more readily susceptible to lethargy. And these physicians say that we must also consider the patient's habitual reactions, noting whether fever has usually caused him to become sunk in stupor; and that we must also consider the patient's age, particularly if he is of middle age; and also the climate, noting whether the disease is common in the region; and the season of the year and division of the season, in particular if it is mid-autumn. For they hold that the disease is most common at that time.

13 ## III. HOW TO RECOGNIZE LETHARGY

WE MUST now tell how to recognize lethargy. And it is better and more definite to use this phraseology,[1] as we did in the case of phrenitis, than to say 'what are the signs of lethargy?' For any single circumstance, such as stupor or fever, does not definitely point to lethargy; but the union of many mutually corroborative circumstances is required to constitute the picture indicative of lethargy. Let us then, as we have said, recognize the disease of lethargy by this picture.

We recognize a case of lethargy by the impairment and dulness of the senses, stupor, acute fever either continuous or re-
14 mittent, and large, slow, empty, and inflated pulse. For lethargy can neither exist nor be recognized in the absence of these indications. Now, in addition, there are certain other concomitant symptoms, many or few, depending on the severity of the disease and on differences in the general and special circumstances. First, then, there is the sunken stupor, an indeterminate state that resembles sleep. The patient when summoned may easily shake this off, and, on being questioned, make answer, not immediately, to be sure, but after a while. Then if he is ordered or coaxed to open his mouth and put out his tongue for us to examine, he will either not do so or will comply slowly. And if he does put it out, he will not draw it back or will do so slowly. And if he has been holding something in his hand, he will drop it unwittingly and involuntarily. In speaking, he will forget what has

1. I.e., 'how to recognize lethargy.' Cf. *Ac.* i. 34.

15 viscatur, et neque enuntiationis ordinem servet, sed potius in-
    tercidat,[4] exprimere etiam quae loquitur non valeat; nullo cor-
    poris attestante defectu, manus impatienter extendat, attestante
    tremore atque membrorum saltu; nulla etiam siti afficiatur, sed
    frequenti ac reflua saliva ore impleto spuere contendat, tunc
    supra mentum atque stramenta[5] sputa remaneant; ac si urinam
    mittere fuerit admonitus matellam non postulet, vel si peti-
    verit nesciat datam, atque urinam non dimittat nisi fuerit ad-
    monitus; hanc quoque difficulter excludat vel paulatim et tur-
    bulentam; aut[6] plurimam[7] salivam aut exustam et crassiorem,
    aliquando etiam indigestam.

16   crescente passione iacendi schema supinum iuge efficitur,
    color plumbeus vel lividus, vultus ipse conductus atque concur-
    rentibus superciliis caperatus, non aliter quam maestitudine
    sive luctu videmus oppressos, lapsus etiam a superioribus lecti
    partibus ad inferiora, negligenter abiectis cruribus atque con-
    versis, residuo quoque corpore non recte disposito, pulsus maior
    rarus inflatus, respiratio tardior ac maior cum quodam gemitu,
    conductio praecordiorum ad superiora, oppressio sensuum et
    difficilis recordatio, adeo ut nisi[8] puncti vel inclamati[9] fuerint
    non excitentur, sed solum motis labiis leviter atque conductis
17 rursum demergantur; sint etiam obscurae vocis, ac deinde si
    fuerint manu lacessiti aut punctione aliqua adhortati vel titillis,
    non exaudiant; vel si quis eorum manus levaverit ac dimiserit,
    statim concidant, ventris etiam atque urinae officio cessante
    adeo ut plerique ex passione liberati, discussa pressura, urinae
    reddendae impossibilitate moriantur.

        at si passio in peius duxerit aegrotantem, respiratio crassescit
    ita ut hirta[10] videatur; palpebrarum quoque non perfecta con-
18 clusio, oculorum cavitas, linguae ariditas atque asperitas, denti-
    um confixio atque stridor adeo ut si quisquam velit facere eorum
    discretionem non valeat, vel certe semiclauso ore ac dimisso,
    ita ut mentum propendens videatur et neque manu conduci

    ---

    [4] intercedat G: corr. Helmreich 318: intercipiat RA
    [5] stramenti G: corr. R
    [6] fort. ac (at?)
    [7] post plurimam interpunx. edd.
    [8] si Bendz Eran 41. 66
    [9] inclamati Bendz Eran 41. 66: inclinati G: incitati Rm
    [10] hirta scripsi: ista G

15 been said; he will confuse and garble the order of letters and will be unable to pronounce his words. Though the body is not faint, he cannot keep his hands outstretched; his limbs tremble and quiver. He feels no thirst, but his mouth is filled with a copious flow of saliva which he tries to spit out, the sputa remaining on his chin and on the bedclothes. If he is reminded[2] to urinate, he does not ask for a pot, or, if he does, he ignores it when it is given him; and he does not pass urine except when reminded.[3] When he does, it is with difficulty and in small quantities of murky appearance. There is copious[4] saliva, dry and thick or, at times, unconcocted.[5]

16 As the disease increases, the patient tends always to lie on his back, his complexion becomes leaden or livid, his face drawn and wrinkled, eyebrows meeting, as we see in men plunged in sorrow or grief. He slips down from the upper to the lower parts of the bed, his legs haphazardly disposed or crossed, the rest of his body also abnormally placed; pulse large, rare,[6] and puffed up; respiration slow and large and accompanied by sighing; precordia drawn upward; affliction of the senses; and inability to concentrate, so much so that only if he is pricked or called loudly can he be aroused, and even then he merely moves and 17 contracts his lips slightly and sinks again into his stupor. His speech is unintelligible, and even if he is prodded with the hand or spurred on by pricking or tickling, he does not give heed. If we raise his hands and then let them go, they fall at once. The functioning of bowels and bladder breaks down, so that many who are relieved of the disease and shake off their stupor die through inability to pass urine.

Now if the patient's condition grows worse, his respiration thickens so that it is rough, his eyelids no longer close com-18 pletely, his eyes are sunken, tongue dry and rough, teeth firmly closed with such gnashing that they cannot be pried apart even if one tries by force; or else the patient's mouth is half-closed and fallen so that his chin hangs down in front, and the separated [jaws] cannot be closed with the hand; there is a

2. Or perhaps 'minded.'
3. Perhaps 'minded,' i.e., 'voluntarily.' Cf. 18.
4. *Plurimam* should perhaps be construed with *urinam*.
5. I.e., loose and watery.
6. I.e., 'slow.'

separata possint, stridore pectoris attestante; atque immissi
vel destillati ob nutrimentum liquoris difficilis atque interrupta
transvoratio, pallor et saltus inferioris labii, articulorum stupor,
unguium livor, guttur prominens atque extans, pulsus humilis
ac per profectum diminutus, sudores frigidi et glutinosi vultum
secus et collum, plerumque etiam involuntaria urinae vel stercorum emissio, et spasmus, hoc est membrorum conductio.

19   at si ad salutaria signa aeger coeperit recurrere ut passio minui videatur, omnia supra dicta leviora efficiuntur. et quidam
profecto in sanitatem veniunt, reddita scilicet valetudine meliore; aliqui vero alienatione mentis recedente pressura tentantur, tunc etiam pulsus humilior atque densior fiet, aut admoniti
rursum demerguntur ut complexae¹¹ duae passiones videantur;
aliqui denique e lethargo liberati absolutam phrenitim incurrunt
ac deinde ad sanitatem pervenerunt.

20   IV. QUOMODO DISCERNIMUS LETHARGOS AB
HIS QUI SIMILIBUS AFFICIUNTUR¹

Quomodo et defectio animi in febribus veluti sensuum facit
hebetudinem, ita mandragoram vel altercum bibentes opprimuntur gravatione sorbili² sopori simili, item alii lumbricorum adiectione deprimuntur, discernenda cuncta sunt ne
umquam similibus inducti vera putemus.

defectionibus igitur animi densus atque parvus et coacervatim interiens pulsus efficitur. mandragoram vero vel altercum
bibentibus pulsus rarus sed plenior fiet; at³ lethargis inanis et
21 inflatus. item his qui lumbricorum vexatione afficiuntur vel
demerguntur densus et velox et parvus et deficiens pulsus invenitur, et magis tempore dimissionis febris. ex⁴ accessionis
augmento, quantum creditur, non valent ventrem vel stomachum lactare atque fellare; in dimissione vero resumpta⁵ inhae-
rescunt visceribus supradictis, atque ita consensum pressurae

---

¹¹ cum plexae G: corr. R

¹ inscriptionem transposuit Friedel 28 ab capite III editionis Guinterianae: habet hic
quomodo curandi sunt lethargi G

² horribili A: terribili Rm: sed cf. Plaut. Mil. Gl. 818f. (Almeloveen)

³ at A: a G

⁴ et Bendz Eran 41. 76: nam R

⁵ fort. resumpti

wheezing sound in the chest; and when liquid is introduced or made to drip into the mouth for purposes of nourishment, swallowing takes place with difficulty and is soon broken off. The lower lip is pallid and twitches, the limbs are numb, nails livid, neck swollen and bulging out, pulse low and gradually weakening; there are cold and clammy sweats about the face and neck, in many cases involuntary emission of urine and feces, and spasm, i.e., convulsive motion of parts of the body.

19 But if the patient begins to show signs of a return to health and the disease appears to be abating, all the symptoms mentioned above are alleviated. And some patients indeed improve and completely regain their health. But others, though their stupor passes, are beset by loss of reason; their pulse becomes more submerged and rapid. And some of these suffer a relapse and are again sunk in stupor, so that the two diseases[7] seem to be intermingled. But others, after being completely relieved of lethargy, pass into simple phrenitis and thereafter are restored to health.

20 ## IV. HOW TO DISTINGUISH LETHARGY FROM DISEASES OF SIMILAR APPEARANCE

A KIND of blunting of the senses is also produced by fainting spells in cases of fever; and those who drink mandragora or henbane are plunged into a stertorous sleeplike stupor; and a state of stupor may also result from an attack of worms. We must therefore distinguish each of these conditions from lethargy, so that we may never be misled by the similarity into considering them as true cases of lethargy.

Thus in a fainting spell the pulse becomes thick and small and all at once vanishes. And in the case of those who drink mandragora or henbane the pulse becomes rare but full. The pulse in 21 lethargy, however, is hollow and puffed up. Again, persons who are sunk in stupor as the result of an attack of worms are found to have a dense, rapid, small, and failing pulse. This is particularly true during a remission in the fever. For it is thought that during the increasing phase of the attack these worms are not able to suck and draw from the esophagus, stomach, and bowels; but that during a remission they regain their strength and cling to these viscera, producing, as a result, a concomitant

7. I.e., phrenitis and lethargy.

ex antecedentibus faciunt. sed haec diligentius Chronias passiones scribentes, cum de lumbricis dicemus, docebimus.

22   # V. UTRUMNE SINT DIFFERENTIAE
LETHARGORUM[1]

Q UIDAM Asclepiadis sectatores etiam differentias lethargorum
tradunt. alium enim per se dixerunt, alium ex antecedenti
passione ut phreniti, atque ex ipsa venientem esse graviorem;
item alium esse novum atque recentem, alium inveteratum
23 atque tardantem, quod ex numero dierum conici dixerunt; et
alium fieri cruditatis ⟨pleno⟩[2] corpore, alium inani atque passione macerato: sed nullam lethargi velut ad lethargum differentiam tradiderunt. existimabile, non certum, probatum est
liquidorum plentitudinem iudicare.[3]

24   item Mnaseas lethargum alium strictura effici, alium solutione dicit, siquidem somnus nunc densitate nunc laxamento
corporum fiat, atque in aliis abstentas videamus officiorum naturalium egestiones, in aliis vero largius influentes, adeo ut
etiam involuntario exitu stercorum[4] sive urinae fundantur.

item multi nostrorum temporibus atque magnitudine con-
stare lethargi differentias tradiderunt. alium enim magnum,
alium parvum esse dixerunt; et alium initio,[5] alium in augmento,
alium in statu, alium in declinatione, et accessione vel dimissione.

sed omnes illi[6] summae atque generalis passionis differentias
25 tradiderunt, et non specialem lethargi. falsum etiam solutione
lethargum fieri, quantum intelligitur atque est lethargus. etenim involuntariam egestionem dicimus, ⟨ut⟩[7] in infantibus,
non solutionis ratione sed mentis occupatione fieri; nihil denique

---

[1] Ad Dioclem *cap. inscribit* G, *quae inscriptio ad cap. VII pertinet*: Quomodo lethargi
inter se differunt *A*: Quae sint differentiae lethargiae *Friedel 28, coll. Ac. i. 52*

[2] *supplevi*

[3] ⟨lethargum⟩ indicare *Rm*

[4] stercora *Rm*

[5] *fort.* ⟨in⟩ initio

[6] illi *scripsi*: illius *edd.*

[7] dicimus, ⟨ut⟩ *scripsi*: dixerunt G

state of stupor. But we shall discuss this in greater detail when we deal with worms in our treatise *On Chronic Diseases*.[1]

22   ## V. ARE THERE DIFFERENT KINDS
OF LETHARGY?

C ERTAIN followers of Asclepiades assert that there are differ- ent kinds of lethargy. They say that one kind arises by it- self, another in consequence of a previous disease like phrenitis; and that lethargy arising from phrenitis is more serious. Again, they say that one type is of fresh and recent origin, while another is long-standing and chronic, which may, they tell us, be in-
23 ferred from the number of days [that the disease lasts]. And they say that one type arises when the body is overloaded with undi- gested matter, another when the body is empty and wasted by disease. But they do not state any difference in the disease as such, that is, between one case of lethargy and another. It is conceivable, to be sure, but has not been definitely proved, that excess of humors is decisive.

24 Mnaseas declares that one type of lethargy results from a state of stricture, another from a state of looseness, on the ground that sleep sometimes takes place when the body is costive and at other times when it is in a fluid condition; and in some cases, he says, we observe that the normal bodily dis- charges are suppressed, but in other cases there is a copious flow, and in fact urine or feces are even passed involuntarily.

Many of our own sect have held that the types of lethargy may be differentiated with respect to time and intensity. Thus one case, they say, is severe, another mild; and one case is just beginning, another is in its increasing phase, another is at its highest stage, another in its decline, and any of these cases may be at the stage of an attack or a remission.

But all those writers give differences that apply to disease generally, rather than any difference that applies to lethargy in
25 particular. And the notion that lethargy arises from a state of looseness is erroneous, so far as the disease is lethargy and may be recognized as such. For with regard to involuntary excretion, we hold that this takes place, as in young children, not by reason of a state of looseness but because their attention is taken up

1. Cf. *Chr.* iv. 107.

plus quam naturae convenit excludunt, sed solum quod debuit
etiam voluntate deponi. tenues etiam sudores pressura fieri non
solutione intelliguntur, sed neque adiutoriis laxativis, sicut in
Adiutoriorum libris demonstrabimus. quapropter lethargi differentias tradendas esse negamus.

26   VI. QUIS LOCUS IN LETHARGIS PATITUR, ET
        QUOMODO CURANDI SUNT LETHARGI[1]

MALE quidam etiam patientem in lethargo partem caput
       dixerunt. ut enim de phreniticis dictum est, communiter
totum corpus patitur, febricula testante;[2] specialiter vero caput
plus ob multitudinem vexationum quibus afficitur. difficile igitur intra primam diatriton lethargus fieri potest, sed frequenter
post ipsam.

et oportet iacere in loco lucido atque calido mediocriter, in accessione per intervalla leviter excitari suo nomine exclamatum.
etenim iugiter titillatu vel impressione ac punctionibus hoc facere nihil aliud quam stricturam[3] erit asperare ob inquietudinem
27 quassationis. dehinc probabilior atque eligenda[4] erit quassabili
et noxia vigilantia quieta pressura. blando etiam articulorum
fricamento utendum est; est autem accessione[5] iugi fomento caput curandum oleo dulci atque calido; mollibus lanis collum
tegendum, blandioris laxamenti causa locorum capiti vicinanti-
um et ob excipiendum ex fomento si quid e capite fuerit lapsum,
tunc aliquando etiam e lecto[6] ad lectum translatione facta. et
declinante accessione oris collutio adhibenda; terminata vero,
potus dandus. at si febrium continuatio fuerit, primo tempore
lucis erunt media fovenda atque dorsum lanis mollibus circumte-
gendum.
28   si magnitudo passionis exegerit, phlebotomia adhibenda intra
primam diatriton aut in ipsa. dehinc si ante diatriton fuerit

[1] inscriptionem similem praebet R (lethargicis, sint, lethargici, R: corr. Friedel 29,
coll. inscriptione cap. IV apud G): Ad Praxagoram G, quae inscriptio ad cap. VIII pertinet

[2] fort. attestante Schmid Mn 134

[3] strictura G: corr. R

[4] ⟨magis⟩ eligenda R

[5] ⟨in⟩ accessione R

[6] e lecto Rm: elato G

with other things. For they do not evacuate any more than is normal but merely what should have been evacuated voluntarily. And the thin sweats are to be considered as due to the lethargic stupor, not to any state of looseness. And they are not the result of laxative remedies, as we shall show in our treatise *On Remedies*. We therefore deny the existence of different types of lethargy as set forth.[1]

26 ## VI. THE PART AFFECTED IN LETHARGY AND THE TREATMENT OF THE DISEASE

CERTAIN writers have declared that in lethargy the part affected is the head, but they are mistaken. For, as we said of phrenitis, the disease is general throughout the whole body, and this is indicated by the fever. But the head, to be sure, is particularly affected because of the numerous attacks to which it is subjected. And lethargy hardly ever appears before the end of the first three-day period [of an illness], but frequently after that period.

The patient should lie in a room that is bright and moderately warm. During the attack awaken him gently at intervals by calling him aloud by name. For to arouse a patient by continually tickling, shaking, or pricking him simply aggravates the state 27 of stricture, the irritation affording him no rest. Furthermore, a calm state of stupor is better and more desirable than an excited and injurious state of wakefulness. Also massage the limbs gently. Again, at the time of an attack foment the head continually with warm sweet olive oil; and cover the neck with soft wool. The purpose of the latter is to afford soothing relaxation to the parts near the head and also to catch any of the oil that may drip down from the head. Then at times move the patient from one bed to another. During the decline of the attack, his mouth should be washed; and when the attack is all over he should be given something to drink. But if the fever is continuous, foment the middle parts of his body early in the morning and place soft woolen cloths round his back.

28 If the intensity of the disease requires it, perform venesection before the end of the first three-day period or else at its end. If venesection is performed before the end of this period, follow

1. Or, perhaps, 'consider it unnecessary to speak of different types of lethargy.'

adhibita, sola fomentatione utemur atque oris collutione et potu
aqua vel mulso. atque si in ipsa diatrito phlebotomia fuerit
adhibita, paululum differentes perunctionem adhibemus atque
oris collutionem. tunc dabimus sorbilem cibum ob celerem
passionem. si fastidiosus fuerit aegrotans, tamquam sanis
saepe contingit post altum somnum experrectis, vel si transvorationis oblitus aut piger, tamquam sunt sani imminente somno
declives in soporem, erit acceleranda alicuius cibi transvoratio
29 ut corpus relaxetur. nam graviore strictura lethargi phreniticis
afficiuntur.

dehinc post cibum paululum differentes atque articulorum
blanda fricatione utentes, dormire permittimus, atque usque ad
declinationis tempus alternis diebus a cibo abstinemus, permittentibus viribus, solo mulso utentes. si autem vires obstiterint,
etiam his diebus sorbilia mediocriter damus. at si venter non
fuerit solutus, clystere utemur oleo calido et aqua in qua decoctum sit faenugraeci semen admixto aliquando[7] melle. tunc
sicut in phreniticis, tondendum caput atque radendum et ap-
30 posita cucurbita scarificandum et sanguisugis relevandum. at
si media tumeant, simili curatione cucurbitae atque cataplasmatum utemur, tamquam in phreniticis ordinavimus.

attendenda etiam cetera passionum accidentia, quae symptomata Graeci vocaverunt, ut ea quae in corpore frigida fuerint
membra blando tactu manibus continentes levi cum fricatione
vaporemus, sudantia citius detergamus, linguae asperitatem vel
ariditatem spongia infusa aqua calida humectemus. nam saepe
faucium siccitate praefocationis imitamur[8] effectum. tunc oculos lemis obsitos vel lacrimantes spongia vaporabimus, atque ita
dimersos excitamus. calidus etenim tactus habet quoddam resumptionis illatae levamen.

31   at si pressura perseveraverit etiam dimissionis tempore et
propterea cibi dandi difficultas occurrerit, oportet aegrotantem
in pressura excitari donec sentiat; tunc priusquam rursum de-
mergatur distillendum ex cochleari sorbile quiddam faucibus,
atque manu mentum quod laxius propendet sublevandum, ut

---

[7] aliquanto *Schmid Mn 134 (sed cf. Ac. ii. 126)*

[8] siccitas p. imitatur *Rm*: siccitates p. imitantur *A*

it merely with a fomentation, washing of the mouth, and a drink of water or mead. But if venesection is performed at the end of this period, wait a short while, then anoint the patient's body and wash his mouth. Then, because the disease is acute, give him some gruel-like food. If he scorns the food, as happens even to healthy persons when waking from a deep sleep, or if he forgets to swallow or is sluggish, as also happens to healthy persons when they become drowsy and are on the point of falling asleep, he must be prodded into swallowing some food so that his body

29 may be relaxed. For persons with lethargy suffer from a more intense state of stricture than do those with phrenitis.

Now after giving this food, wait a short while, then have the patient's limbs gently massaged, and permit him to fall asleep. Until the time when the disease begins to decline, deny the patient food on alternate days, if his strength permits, giving him [on those days] only mead. But if the state of his strength does not permit of this regimen, give him gruels in modest quantity on these days too. And if his bowels are not loose, use a clyster of warm olive oil and water in which fenugreek seed has been boiled; honey may also be added at times. Then, as in the treatment of phrenitis, cut the patient's hair and shave his head, and apply cupping with scarification; also relieve the head by using

30 leeches. But if the middle parts of the body are inflamed, use cupping and plasters for these parts in a treatment similar to that which we prescribed in cases of phrenitis.

Also attend to the other concomitant signs of disease (Greek *symptōmata*). Thus if any parts of the body are cold, take them gently in your hands and warm them with mild rubbing; and promptly wipe off perspiration. If the tongue is rough or dry, moisten it with a sponge dipped in warm water. For often dryness of the throat produces the same effect as choking. And if the eyes tear or are covered with a viscous discharge, use a sponge to warm them and rouse the patient from his sunken stupor. For the application of warmth has a refreshing and restorative effect.

31   But if the stupor persists even at the time of remission, and it is consequently difficult to give the patient food, rouse him from this stupor until he is conscious. Then, before he is again overcome, let some liquid food drip from a spoon into his mouth and raise his chin, which hangs forward loosely, with your hand

infusa priusquam revocentur transvoratione vorentur. at si
forte mutatio accessionum atque pressurae fuerit facta, quod
quidem raro contingit, ut in continuationibus, cibi tempus oriente luce est aptius. utendum etiam spongiarum vaporationibus
et fomentis capitis atque domestica molli ac pensili gestatione.

32   in declinatione vero certissima varius cibus dandus et lavacrum sine vino adhibendum scilicet. in alia vero diatrito danda
poma, tunc etiam vinum: quorum rationem ex his quae in phreniticorum curatione sunt ordinata accipienda dicimus. tunc
cerotarium scarificatis partibus apponemus. haec est secundum
Methodicos lethargorum curatio.

antiquorum vero Hippocrates et Erasistratus et Herophilus
ad eorum curationem nihil posuerunt. sed Serapion Empiricus,
in primo libro quem⁹ Ad sectas scribit,¹⁰ obscura nimium atque
pauca ordinavit, quorum nihil est dignum enarrare.

33   # VII. AD DIOCLEM¹

DIOCLES, libro quo De passionibus atque causis earum et
curationibus scripsit, prohibet demergi lethargos acutis-
simis utens potionibus, atque iugiter corpus defricat, adhibens
etiam sternutamenta, quae Graeci ptarmica vocaverunt: et
neque manifestans quas vocat acutas potiones, utrum in² qualitate acutas, ut est acetum, an officio usus, ut est celerrima transvoratio. sed utrum elegerit, male dictum est. alterum enim
densat corpus strictura laborans, alterum inflat. item sternutamenta corpus vehementi motu concutiunt, et magis membranas
capitis in tumore constitutas, ⟨quas⟩³ iugiter excitare sine dubio
asperatio passionis est. peccatur etiam gravius sine ullo adiutorio caput relinquendo, in quo secundum ipsum passionis est
causa.

⁹ quae G: corr. Wellmann
¹⁰ fort. scripsit
¹ Dioclem R: Asclepiadem G
² in secl. Schmid Mn 134   ³ supplevi

so that he may swallow what has been poured in before it flows back. But if [in such a case] it should happen that there is an interruption[1] of the attack and of the stupor (though such a remission takes place only rarely, as in unremitting fevers), early morning is then a more suitable time for food. Also warm and foment the head, using sponges; and give the patient mild passive exercise, using a hammock in the house.

32 If the decline of the disease is definitely confirmed, prescribe varied foods and bathing, but no wine, of course. And at the end of the next three-day period serve fruits, and then also wine. The reason for these instructions is to be found in our discussion of the rules for the treatment of phrenitis. Later apply a cerate to the scarified parts. So much for the treatment of lethargy according to the Methodists.

Now, of the ancients, Hippocrates, Erasistratus, and Herophilus say nothing about the treatment of this disease. But Serapion the Empiric in Book I of his treatise *Against the Sects* gives a few rules which are quite unclear and not worth reporting.

33 ## VII. REPLY TO DIOCLES

IN HIS treatise *On Diseases and Their Causes and Treatment* Diocles prescribes the use of very sharp potions as a means of overcoming lethargic stupor;[1] he also prescribes constant rubbing and also sternutatories (Greek *ptarmica*). He does not make clear what he means by 'sharp potions,' whether sharp in quality, like vinegar, or sharp [i.e., swift] in their use, the swallowing of the drug being accomplished so swiftly. But in any case he is in error. For the one kind of sharpness further condenses a body already suffering from a state of stricture; the other kind causes flatulence. And sternutatories by their violent action agitate the body, particularly the inflamed membranes of the head, the constant irritation of which necessarily aggravates the disease. Diocles makes an even more serious mistake in failing to give any treatment for the head, where, in his own opinion, the cause of the disease lies.

1. The meaning of *mutatio* here is uncertain.

1. Wellmann (Diocles Frag. 45) interprets *prohibet demergi* as a prescription against bathing, comparing the Hippocratic *De morbis* ii. 66 (VII. 100 L). This is almost certainly an error.

34   VIII. AD PRAXAGORAM[1]

Praxagoras secundo libro De curationibus in sorbilibus cibis,
hoc est ptisanae sucis, semper inquit aegros oportere[2] servari,
cum non semper hoc conveniat, quando declinationis[3] tempore
oportet varia ciborum resumptione vires reparari, non tunc uti
suco ptisanae, sed ipsa potius. ille enim et corrumpi facilius et
inflare perspicitur. deinde clysterem iubet adhiberi, et non inquit metuendum si remanserit non redditus. erat hoc verae rationis, nisi esset virtutis acrioris; sed quia est acerrimae atque
mordicantis qualitatis iuxta veterum consuetudinem, quomodo
sperandum est non gravius nocere quanto plus fuerit tumentibus
35 partibus immoratus?[4] dat etiam meracum bibere acetum cum
melle et piperis immodica quantitate, vel pro vino absinthium,
dicens latere ignaros vini dationem. et fomentum adhibet pedum.

sed ex his omnibus nihil sperandum est utile, sed magis incendia viscerum vel altiorum et veluti putredines tumentium
membranarum ob nimietatem fervoris. non enim cum acriora
collyria tumentes oculos in dolores atque lacrimas plurimas cogere videamus, membranas quoque cerebri delicatas atque faciles
ad iniuriam ob naturam sui tumentes passionis causa minime
ex supradictis inuri credere potest, cum singula igneae virtutis
esse monstrentur. item meracum inquit, hoc est ultra moderationem temperamenti commixtum, acetum cum melle dari,
36 et appellavit oxymeli. nec tamen manifestavit quid sit ultra
modum temperamenti miscendum,[5] utrumne mel debeat superare an acetum: non enim adiecit aquam quoque miscendam.
dehinc quam similitudinem potest absinthium habere cum vino
ut in eius vicem dandum iusserit, nisi[6] sit et hoc generaliter acre

---

[1] Praxagoram *R*: Themisonem *G*

[2] oporteret *G*: corr. *A*

[3] declinationis *R*: declivis *G*

[4] immoratum *G*: corr. *Rm*

[5] miscendum *A*: mittendum *G*: miscere *Rm*   [6] nisi *scripsi*: cum *edd.*

VIII. REPLY TO PRAXAGORAS

34

PRAXAGORAS in Book II of his work *On Treatments* declares that the patients should be kept at all times on liquid foods, that is to say, pearl barley water. But this is not always suitable; for, when the disease declines, the patient's strength should be repaired with a varied diet of restorative foods, and at that time, therefore, we should not use barley water but rather the pearl barley itself.[1] For we know that barley water spoils easily and causes flatulence. Again, Praxagoras prescribes a clyster, telling us not to be disturbed if it is not returned. Now this would be correct if the clyster did not have acrid properties. But since, in accordance with the practice of the ancients, it has a very sharp and biting quality, how can it be expected not to do serious harm, the longer it remains in the congested parts?

35 Praxagoras also prescribes the drinking of unwatered[2] vinegar with honey and a large quantity of pepper, or, as a substitute for wine,[3] wormwood. He asserts that the inexperienced do not know how to administer wine properly. He also prescribes fomenting the feet.

We should not, however, expect any good to come from any of these remedies, but rather a burning of the viscera or inner organs, and a kind of festering of the inflamed membranes because of the excessive heat [of the remedies]. For when we see that sharp eye-salves bring pain and copious tears to inflamed eyes, we may well conclude that the membranes of the brain, which are naturally tender and prone to injury and already inflamed because of the disease, are very severely burned by Praxagoras' remedies. For each of these remedies can be shown to have a burning quality. And he prescribes a strong mixture of vinegar and honey (Greek *oxymeli*), i.e., a mixture in excess of

36 the regular proportions. But he does not make clear which ingredient of the mixture is to be used in excess of the regular proportions, i.e., whether the honey should predominate or the vinegar; for water does not enter into the mixture. Furthermore, what similarity can there be between wormwood and wine, that he prescribes the former in place of the latter, unless it is that the wormwood is also by nature sharp and binding?

1. Or possibly 'the varied diet.'

2. Cf. 35 *fin.*   3. The reference seems to be to the vinegar. See 36.

atque densabile? vinum vero omnibus ante declinationem
aegritudinis adversum est, et magis lethargis ob nimiam vehementiam passionis. immoderate vero, ut ipse voluit, meracum
etiam sanos demergit. ridendum praeterea quod caput patiens
incuratum relinquendum putat et fomentum pedibus adhibendum, †per venas avertendae materiae traductus.†[7]

37   IX. AD ASCLEPIADEM ET THEMISONEM
            ET HERACLIDEM TARENTINUM[1]

ASCLEPIADES primo libro De acutis passionibus scribens multa
       inquit adhibenda lethargis quae phreniticis sunt ordinata.
nititur etiam iugiter dimersos excitari[2] sternutamentis et odoramentis castorei, rutae et aceti, et spondylio et conidia et agno
herbis, baccis etiam lauri, vel communiter, inquit, omne quod
tenuare atque movere vehementer membranas valeat cerebri.
iubet etiam ea adhiberi quae epilepticis vel matrice praefocatis
adhibuit odoranda, hoc est lanam vel capillos aut cervi cornu
vel galbanum carbonibus imposita, et omnia quae caput gra-
38 vare valent vel iniucunda sunt odoranti. omnium inquit praestantius atque operantius esse sinapi tritum cum aceto admixto,
atque hinc caput cataplasmandum et fricandum[3] manibus,[4]
quod excitet aegrotantem. potum dat bis in die vel ter, et veniente nocte offert tamquam phreniticis vinum, vel eo audacius.
etenim, inquit, accedere ex vino furor in phreniticis potest; in lethargis vero numquam, siquidem sint omnes sensus apprehensi
atque mentis vigor oppressus.

---

[7] per venas ⟨eorum⟩ avertendae materiae traductus ⟨ut fiat⟩ R: *fort.* per venas
avertendae materiae ⟨spe⟩ traductus

[1] *hanc inscriptionem habet* R: Ad Heraclidem G

[2] excitare R

[3] fricandum *conieci, coll. 42*: dandum *edd.*

[4] naribus *Almeloveen*

Moreover, wine is unsuitable for any patient before the declining phase of an illness, and particularly so for persons with
lethargy because of the intensity of that disease. But, given in
very strong proportions, as he prescribes it,[4] it causes even
healthy persons to be overcome. Finally, it is ridiculous to hold,
as Praxagoras does, that the head, which is actually affected,
should be left untreated, but that a fomentation should be applied to the feet. . . .[5]

37   IX. REPLY TO ASCLEPIADES, THEMISON, AND
                 HERACLIDES OF TARENTUM

IN BOOK I of his treatise *On Acute Diseases* Asclepiades asserts
that many of the procedures used in treating phrenitis should
be used in lethargy. And he strives continually to arouse those
who are sunk in stupor, using sternutatories and aromatic preparations of castor, rue, and vinegar, and also with cow-parsnip,
fleabane, and agnus castus, as well as bayberries, or, in general,
anything which may be able to attenuate the membranes of the
brain and set them into violent motion. He also gives the patients the same substances to smell as he uses for epileptics or
those suffering from hysterical suffocation, namely, wool, hair,
deer's horn, or the juice of allheal, placed over burning coals, or
any other substance that can congest the head or is unpleasant
38 to smell. But he considers a mixture of powdered mustard and
vinegar to be the best and most effective of all these substances,
and he prescribes it as a plaster for the head; he also prescribes
it in connection with manual massage[1] as a means of arousing
the patient. He orders drink twice or three times daily, and,
when night comes, gives the patient wine, as he does in the case
of phrenitis, and, in fact, even more confidently. For in phrenitis,
he says, mania may supervene because of the wine; but never in
lethargy, since in that case all the senses are attacked and the
action of the mind is overcome.

4. There has been no previous mention of a prescription of unwatered wine. The
reference may be to the vinegar, and possibly to the wormwood, but in any case the discussion is confused.

5. With *R*'s reading: 'to create a passage through the veins of the feet for matter
to be eliminated.' Or reading ⟨*spe*⟩ *traductus*: 'in the misguided hope of eliminating
matter through the blood vessels.'

1. The text and meaning are doubtful. Cf. 42.

ex quibus apparet peius eum a phreniticis lethargum caeca
curatione vexare. etenim noxium atque perniciosum est iugiter
39 eos excitare, sicut supra diximus; multo autem gravius non
communibus remediis hoc facere sed, ut ille putat, sternutamentis immoderate moventibus atque dissecantibus corpus et
magis cerebri membranam in tumore constitutam. si enim pedes, quamquam sint habitudine fortes, in tumore constituti
parvo deambulationis motu facile vexantur atque ob iniuriam
in augmenta tumoris veniunt, quomodo non membranae cerebri in tumore constitutae atque viarum densitate constrictae
magis posse moveri creduntur? dehinc perseverare magis
sternutamenti usum[5] iubet, ut scilicet ita forte convenire videatur, tamquam in chronicis[6] passionibus, ⟨cum⟩ moderatione[7] interea cessante noxius atque vexabilis esse probetur.
40   extendit[8] etiam peccatum ex[9] castoreo atque aceto et ruta et
spondylio atque agno herbis et lauri baccis et conidia.[10] etenim
acetum acre manifeste probatur et quod valeat membranam
inurendo vexare, cum laxamento non constrictione indigeat;
alia quoque graveolentia et quae pressuram faciant non solum
demersis verum etiam recte valentibus improbantur. haec
peccanter ex epilepticorum curatione atque praefocationis matricis transferenda iussit, cum constet etiam in ipsis adhiberi
non oportere sinapi, etiam si chronicas[11] passiones quadam corporis novatione excludit. acutas autem vel celeres provocans
41 in magnitudinem tollit, omnis enim acrimonia tumoribus incongrua. nam et temporaliter quidem aeger omnis tamquam adus-
tus igne consurget, sed rursum gravius opprimetur.

oportet etiam secundum eius praecepta manente capillatura
aliquod cataplasma apponere, et propterea non parvi temporis
vexatione membranam afficere. nam tonsuram noxiam phreni-

---

[5] ⟨in⟩ sternutamenti usu *R*

[6] *fort.* chroniis *Schmid 8*

[7] ⟨cum⟩ moderatione *A*: commoderatione *R*

[8] extendet *G*: *corr. R*

[9] ⟨odoramentis⟩ ex *R, coll. 37*

[10] conyza *R*

[11] *fort.* chronias *Schmid 8*

But from this it is clear that, by his blind treatment, Asclepiades does even more harm in cases of lethargy than in cases of
phrenitis. For, as we have said above, it is harmful and danger-
39 ous continually to arouse persons with lethargy. But it is even
worse to do this not with the usual remedies but, as he suggests,
with sternutatories, which violently agitate and irritate the
body and particularly the inflamed membrane of the brain. Now
our feet, for example, may normally be very sturdy, but when
inflamed they are easily injured by even a little walking, and
because of this injury their inflammation is aggravated. How,
then, can Asclepiades suppose that the membranes of the brain,
when they are inflamed and their passages are congested and
constricted, will be any more able to escape injury [by his treat-
ment]? Again, he prescribes that the use of sternutatories be
continued for some time, perhaps with the idea that the treatment will then seem suitable, as in the case of chronic diseases.
But meantime the bounds of moderation are exceeded, and the
treatment is obviously irritating and harmful.

40   He adds to his error by the use of castor, vinegar, rue, cow-
parsnip, agnus castus, bayberries, and fleabane. For vinegar is
obviously sharp and apt to injure the membrane of the brain by
its burning action, at a time when this membrane requires relaxing rather than astringent treatment. And the other strong-
smelling substances are also to be rejected, for they would produce stupor not alone in those who are already overcome but
even in the strong and healthy. Asclepiades errs in transferring
[to the treatment of lethargy] these remedies, which were used by
him in the treatment of epilepsy and hysterical suffocation. Yet,
obviously, mustard should not be used in these diseases either,
even if it does help to overcome chronic diseases by promoting a
renewal of the body. In the case of acute or swift diseases, how-
41 ever, mustard causes irritation and aggravation. In fact, any
sharp treatment is harmful in cases of inflammation. For, though
every patient will be awakened [by such treatment] for a period
of time, as if scorched by fire, he will later suffer a more serious
relapse.

And according to the instructions of Asclepiades, we must apply a plaster without removing the hair (though we thereby subject the membrane to prolonged irritation). For Asclepiades
considers the cutting of the hair harmful in phrenitis; and, since

ticis probat; his etiam lethargos similiter curandos existimat.
quo fiet ut etiam in ipsis tonsuram prohibuisse videatur. non
enim in illis materiae post tonsuram ascensus vexabiliter caput
poterit onerare; in lethargis vero id minime facere.

   quae si tamquam vexabilis excludenda est, multo magis sinapi
42 excludendum. adducit enim ad semet materiam, sicut inflatae
atque in ruborem deductae eius appositione partes demonstrant.
namque[12] adductam tenendo cogit et viarum perficit densitatem. dehinc odore penetrando membranas inurit, et tamquam
acre collyrium oculos, sic mentes inflammat. quomodo etiam
fricare[13] manibus sinapi lethargos[14] potest cum sensibus ac mente
capti esse videantur?[15]

   atque ita odoramentorum tempus tacuit et solam materiam
nominavit. hoc quidem etiam de dando potu fecisse perspicitur, dicens quoties detur, temporum tacita disciplina. vinum
etiam lethargis est incongruum nulla declinatione passionis
43 firmata. simile est enim ebrios ac vinolentia madentes vino
oportere uti tamquam congrue superdato, in quibus periculum
spasmi fore nemo sapiens negat. at iste importunius vero
lethargis probandum[16] existimat, sperans vini furorem sub oppressione passionis posse latere: vehementer enim curandum
putat occultare noxia quam prohibere.[17] miseriores igitur lethargis phrenitici[18] iudicandi et experimentorum probationi
subiecti. namque etiam in lethargis demersionis aucta vexatio

   [12] eamque R
   [13] fort. fricari
   [14] an lethargus?
   [15] captus esse videatur G
   [16] praedandum vel praebendum Almeloveen
   [17] prohibere Rm: prohiberi G
   [18] an lethargi phreniticis?

he thinks that lethargy should be treated in the same way as phrenitis, he seems consequently to have forbidden the cutting of hair in cases of lethargy, too. But in phrenitis the rising of matter [to the head] after the cutting of the hair does not constitute a troublesome burden for the head; and in lethargy there is no such burden at all.

Indeed, if haircutting is to be forbidden as irritating, there is
42 much more reason for forbidding the use of mustard. For mustard attracts matter to itself, as is indicated by the swelling and reddening of the parts to which it is applied; it holds this attracted matter, condenses it, and thus completes the stoppage of the pores. Then, permeating the membranes with its odor, it sears them; and just as a sharp eye-salve inflames the eyes, so the mustard inflames the mind. And how can Asclepiades prescribe manual massage with mustard for patients with lethargy, if their senses and mind are evidently impaired?[2]

Furthermore, Asclepiades says nothing about the time for using the aromatic preparations, confining himself merely to naming the substances. And he seems to have done the same thing in his prescriptions of drink, telling us how often it is to be taken but giving us no instructions about the time. But, in any event, wine is unsuitable in cases of lethargy so long as it
43 has not been ascertained that the disease is in its decline. Indeed, Asclepiades' notion is like prescribing wine for those who are already drunk and have had their fill. The theory is that any wine given in addition will be helpful. But no sensible physician will deny that there is danger of convulsion in such cases. Yet Asclepiades insistently prescribes wine for lethargy, believing that the violent action of the drink can be concealed under the oppressive power of the disease. For he supposes that greater pains should be taken to conceal injuries than to prevent them.[3] And so we must conclude that [in the hands of Asclepiades] patients with phrenitis are even more to be pitied than those with lethargy, though both are subjected to treatment entirely on the basis of trial and error. For in his treatment of lethargy the stupor is increased by the drinking of wine, as evidenced by

2. Cf. 38. Here, too, the text and meaning are uncertain. Depending on the readings adopted in the two passages, the reference may be to massage of the head or of the body with mustard, or to rubbing mustard on the patient's hands.

3. Possibly *curandum* is to be understood as a substantive: 'to conceal injuries from the patient rather than prevent them.'

ex vini efficitur potu, siquidem spiratio alta[19] ac conductus corporis atque raptus adveniat et celerrime mortis sequatur effectus.

44   Themison libris Acutarum vel celerum passionum recte cetera ordinavit, sed iubet obscuro in loco haberi lethargos. etenim, inquit, lux apta non est, siquidem moveat atque turbet corpora et non sufficiant spiramenta turbationis[20] commotae congruam exhalationem praebere, quapropter etiam sani in luce dormientes gravantur, quorum maxime hi qui sole[21] dormierunt vexari noscuntur: non advertens quod omnis tenebrosus aer constringit. lethargica autem passio nullo alio magis quam strictura cog-

45 noscitur, quam necesse est augeri ob aeris[22] densitatem. sub sole autem dormientes gravari etiam nos asserimus, sed ob contrarietatem afficientium[23] causarum; lux enim solis atque vapor relaxat, econtrario somnus astringit. dehinc lethargia gravis atque perniciosa esse passio perspicitur; somnus autem naturale est officium. item sol gravat caput; lux autem quam lethargicis adhibemus tectorum sub tegmine nullo vapore lucifici solis augetur, neque splendore radiorum perfusum corpus graviter afficitur aegrotantis.

iubet etiam parva per intervalla eorum faucibus insinuari liquorem, quod praeter tempus faciens ardorem illum cuius causa id adhiberi existimat, augere potius quam minuere vide-

46 tur. at si venter strictus fuerit, aloes iubet dari bibendum[24] triobolum, hoc est dimidiam drachmam, cum aqua ante cibum: prodesse inquit prius quam passio augeatur, siquidem multa quae ad caput ex corpore concurrunt detrahentur. Soranus

---

[19] alta *A*: alia *G*

[20] turbationi *R*

[21] ⟨sub⟩ sole *R, ut infra*

[22] aeris *conieci*: solis *G*

[23] efficientium *Rm, fort. recte*

[24] bibendum *scripsi*: apponendum *G*: appensum *R*

---

4. If our text is sound, the point may be that Asclepiades' patient with phrenitis is more unfortunate because he remains alive and conscious longer. Note that 38, above, is somewhat contradictory, but the whole tone here seems to be ironical.

deep respiration and convulsive seizure of the body, followed by swift death.[4]

4   In his work *On Acute* (i.e., swift) *Diseases* Themison gives some correct rules for the treatment [of lethargy], but prescribes that the patients be kept in a dark place. For he holds that light is not suitable, since it excites and disturbs bodies, with the result that the pores are unable to afford a suitable outlet for the disturbance that has been created; and so even healthy persons who sleep in the light feel weighed down, and those who sleep in the sunlight are known to be especially affected. But Themison does not observe that all darkened air has an astringent effect. And lethargy is pre-eminently marked by a state of stricture, which is inevitably aggravated by any astringent property of

45 the air.[5] As for those who sleep in the sunlight, we agree that they feel weighed down. The reason, however, is that the influences to which they are subjected have opposing tendencies. For the light and warmth of the sun have a relaxing effect; sleep, on the other hand, an astringent effect. Furthermore, lethargy is obviously a serious and dangerous disease, while sleep is a normal function.[6] The sun, to be sure, causes heaviness of the head; but the light we prescribe in cases of lethargy is under a roof and not heated by the source of light, the sun. The patient is not adversely affected by this light, for his body is not bathed in the rays of the bright sunlight.[7]

Themison prescribes that at short intervals liquids be introduced into the mouth of the patient. But in doing this at the wrong time he clearly aggravates rather than relieves that burn-

46 ing heat which led him to propose this treatment. And if the bowels are costive, he prescribes a drink of three obols, that is, half a drachm, of aloes taken with water before eating. He holds that this treatment is helpful before the disease increases in intensity, on the ground that much of what passes from the body to the head is thus drawn off. But Soranus, who restored Meth-

5. If *solis* (G) be retained, the sentence is best taken as a continuation of Themison's argument.

6. The point seems to be that it is improper to draw conclusions about lethargy from an analogy based on normal sleep.

7. This seems a contradiction of 'lux enim solis atque vapor relaxat,' above, but the reference may be to the special effect of the direct rays of the sun on the head.

vero, qui normarum regulis methodum restituit, noxiam esse inquit istius modi potionem: forsitan enim ob nimiam stricturam retineatur, et non solum nihil egerat verum etiam ipsa remaneat. credibile autem ad eius pigmenti in stomacho effectum sensum accurrere materiam ac deinde ad caput recurrere, quod per vias stomacho vicinum,[25] et membranas, ad rapienda quae

47 sunt summa facultate aptissimum ob tumoris fervorem. dehinc gravius augeri peccatum videmus cum ante cibum hoc medicamen dari iubet. adiectus enim cibus necessario corrumpitur, manente adhuc in ore aloe. corruptio autem cibi vexat ea quae se circumplexa sunt. attrahens deinde materiam a capite, attrahit etiam eius nutrimentum. non enim ratione quadam tacita veluti animal sentiens poterit medicamen naturalia[26] relinquere, et ab his quae contra naturam sunt detrahenda[27] separare. nutrimenta igitur propria deperdere dubium non est cum vi medicaminis detrahuntur. post tertium diem sternutamento utitur, cum ipse prohibuerit lucido in loco aegrotos iacere, siquidem moveantur atque turbentur liquida et spiritus. sed utique multo vehementius sternutamenta commovere posse perspicimus.

48   dehinc[28] quatuor, inquit, vel quinque dies declinante accessione, si nihil obstiterit, ultra muros producendus aegrotans et usque ad viginti vel triginta stadia gestatione movendus: quo tempore excitare etiam convenit, atque sternutamento et aceti cum sinapi odoramento uti vel cataplasmatibus, et hoc per totam passionem faciendum probat. sed omnino lucem inquit recusandum[29] tamquam commobilem corporis, cum sit gravior in sinapi vel gestationis motu commotio. iners etiam atque vana intentio dierum numerus atque modus stadiorum circa gestationem adhibendam: addo etiam immodicum motum[30] esse stadiorum triginta periclitanti.

49   quid[31] etiam considerans sinapi probaverit adhibendum ratione caret. utrumne tumorem senserit in membrana? sed

[25] vicinum ⟨est⟩ R
[26] naturalia *Schmid Mn 135*: animalia G: utilia R
[27] ⟨ac⟩ detrahenda R: ⟨atque ideo sola sunt⟩ detrahenda *Bendz Eran 43. 45, coll. Ac. i. 181*
[28] dehinc ⟨post⟩ R   [30] *fort.* modum
[29] recusandam Rm   [31] quid *Am*: quod G

8. Caelius may have read στόματι for στομάχῳ in his copy of Soranus.

odism by his normative standards, declares that a potion of this
sort is harmful. For it may be blocked by the extreme state of
stricture and not only may fail to drive anything out but may
itself remain within. And it is conceivable that matter will gather
in the esophagus when the effect of the drug is felt there, and
pass from there to the membranes of the head (which by way of
the pores is near the esophagus); for the head, because of its intense heat and inflammation, is very apt to attract powerful
47 substances. Furthermore, we may note that Themison adds to
his error in prescribing that this drug be administered before the
patient eats. For any food taken thereafter will surely be spoiled
while the aloes still remains in the mouth.[8] And the spoiled food
attacks everything around it. Again, the drug in attracting matter from the head attracts also that which nourishes the head.
For the drug is not a conscious living being and will not be able,
by any secret rational power, to leave what is normal and to
separate from it what is unnatural and must be drawn off. There
is no doubt, therefore, that the head loses nourishment belonging
to it, the nourishment being drawn off by the power of the drug.
After the third day Themison prescribes a sternutatory, though
he had himself forbidden the patients to lie in a well-lighted
place, on the ground that the bodily humors and the pneuma
would be excited and irritated. But it is obvious that sternutatories can cause far more severe disturbance.

48   Then after four or five days, if the attack has declined and
there is no obstacle, Themison directs that the patient be taken
out of the house and carried as much as twenty or thirty stades.
And he says that at that time it is proper to try to rouse the patient by using a sternutatory, an aromatic preparation of vinegar and mustard, or plasters made with these substances, and
that this procedure should be followed throughout the rest of
the illness. But he is quite opposed to the use of any light, on the
ground that it would irritate the body, though actually the irritation produced by mustard or passive exercise is more severe.
And his concern for the number of days and stades in connection with this passive exercise is futile and of no avail. In any
case, if one does risk the treatment, a distance of thirty stades
is excessive.

49   Again, there is no rational explanation of what he had in mind
in prescribing the use of mustard. Did he suppose that there was

haec acrimonia necessario densatur. an vero sensuum torpen-
tium movendorum causa? sed iamdudum lucem ne commoveat
recusavit.

postea inquit radendum sequenti die, duabus ante accessionem horis, servatis cataplasmatibus[32] pane et alica[33] et oleo rosaceo, et lini semine cum posca, vel polenta cum faenugraeco et
aqua mulsa, usum dissimilium cataplasmatum permiscens.
etenim mulsum atque faenugraecum relaxant atque mitigant
tumentia; oleum vero rosaceum atque acetum vel alica constringunt, et propterea in augmento tumores supertendunt.

50   intemporaliter etiam utitur cataplasmatibus, cum ante duas
horas accessionis venturae adhiberi iubet, et sit eo tempore requies adhibenda. dehinc, inquit, si vehementer fuerit oppressus aegrotans, ut neque dimissionis tempore eum valeamus excitare, si praecordia mollia senserimus atque vocem non ita[34]
obtusam, fricationibus corpus calefaciemus; tunc frigida caput
fomentamus coacervatim atque iugiter et quodam percussu, ut
altius a capite demissa veniant fomenta; tunc ad balnea aegrotantem ducemus ut densitatem frigoris relaxemus.

hoc igitur vexationum perdendae salutis magnitudinem vehe-
51   menter excedit. quod enim passio crescere facit, hoc est torporem sensuum, hoc etiam frigida fomentatio cogit augeri. quo
fiet ut si forte temporaliter quisquam aegrotantium raptu quodam horroris[35] frigidae excitetur, vehementius tamen accessionis tempore opprimatur, sicut et ipse eodem in libro nescius
confitetur. dehinc affectans stationem sensuum emovere fomento frigidae, videndum est utrumne in accessione id fieri eligat aut in dimissione. sed si in augmento, contrarium ⟨et⟩[36]
adversum est etiam naturale lavacrum; sin vero dimissionis
tempore, feriuntur[37] ea quae dimissionis ratione indulgentia
quadam tenues vias agnoverant. praeterea post frigidam allu-

---

[32] cataplasmatibus ⟨ex⟩ R (*sed cf. Bendz 24*)

[33] alica *Rm, coll.* alica *infra*: aqua G

[34] ita *R*: istam G

[35] horroris *conieci* (*fort.* horrore): erroris G: terroris *A*

[36] contrarium ⟨et⟩ R: econtrarium G (*cf. Ac. i. 102, Bendz 45*)

[37] *fort.* referuntur

inflammation in the membrane of the brain? But, by reason of its sharpness, mustard would surely have an astringent effect on this membrane. Or did he use mustard for the purpose of arousing the benumbed senses? But he always forbade light, lest it might arouse the patient.

On the day following the above treatment, two hours before the expected attack, Themison prescribes that the patient's head be shaved and plasters continuously applied, consisting of bread, spelt groats, and rose oil, flaxseed and diluted vinegar, or pearl barley with fenugreek and honey-water. But this prescription combines dissimilar plasters indiscriminately. Thus honey-water and fenugreek have a relaxing and soothing effect on the inflamed parts; but rose oil, vinegar, and spelt are astringent and for that reason increase the tension of the inflamed parts as the attack develops.

50   Furthermore, his use of plasters is ill-timed. He prescribes their application two hours before an attack is expected, a time when the patient should have rest. Themison goes on to say that if the patient is so completely overcome that we cannot rouse him even at the time of remission, and if the precordial region is soft to the touch and the voice not too weak, we should proceed as follows. First warm his body by massage, then make copious and continuous applications of cold water to the head, slapping them on so that they come down upon the head from a higher point; after that bring the patient to the bath so that the condensation produced by the cold may be relaxed.

51   Now these irritations far exceed the damage due to the disease itself. For the very thing which the disease aggravates, i.e., the benumbing of the senses, is also necessarily aggravated by the cold applications. Thus, even if a patient is aroused for a short time by a sort of shock as he shivers under the impact of cold water, he will nevertheless be more severely overcome at the time of the attack, as Themison himself in the same book unwittingly admits. And again we must ask whether Themison, in his effort to overcome the blocking of the senses by an application of cold water, prefers to do this during the attack or during the remission. If during the attack, the fact is that even ordinary bathing is unsuitable and harmful; and if during the remission, the matter that had begun to penetrate the thin pores, thanks to the relaxing effect of the remission, is blocked. More-

tionem[38] balneum sanos quoque incommodat implendo caput.

52 quid igitur prodest frigidae[39] ablutio, quae stationem atque torporem viarum excludere putatur, si necessario magis densitas acquisita aegrotantem opprimere perspicitur?

ita corpuscula quorum statione viarum obstrusionem factam existimat facile utique transire vel resilire possunt, si capacitas exitum dederit, in quam venisse vel ex qua exisse videntur. huic autem rei perficiendae frigida repugnat, densat enim atque conducit vias. fatetur sane neque se hoc uti adiutorio cum sit melius, quamquam nominare quod sit metuat: etenim inimicum et neque ipsius dogmati conveniens esse probatur.

53 Heraclides Tarentinus primo libro De internis passionibus proponens lethargos fieri multitudine cruditatis et crassitudine humoris adhibet clysteres, quibus etiam admiscet aquam in qua etiam centaurium fuerit decoctum vel absinthium. dat etiam bibere castoreum et aquam salsam et epithymum. os aegrotantium distendens sensim haec infundit guttatim, quae in os labuntur decurrentia. caput autem posca fovet in qua fuerit laurus decocta et ruta. rasis[40] quoque capillis ungit castoreo vel spondylio et aceto cum oleo veteri, et ex pollinibus adhibet cataplasma, quod appellamus omen lysin, ex posca et absinthio et nitro, vel cantabro ex aceto, dehinc sinapi cum aceto et fico. et iisdem clysteribus post rasuram capitis utitur.

54 dat etiam et radices masticandas, ex[41] sinapi vel pipere apophlegmatismum provocat. utitur etiam balanis si clystere ventrem movere non valuerit; et omne corpus aceto et oleo perungi iubet; sternutamentis commovet et odoramentis castorei et spondylii ex aceto acri resolutis. sed si ex humorum acrimonia fuerit aegritudo confecta, aquam dulcem potare aegrum

---

[38] *fort.* ablutionem *hic vel* allutio *infra*
[39] *fort.* frigida, *sed cf. Ac. iii. 96* perfusionem frigidae
[40] raris G: *corr.* Rm
[41] ⟨ac⟩ ex R: *fort.* et

over, after applications of cold water a bath causes congestion
2 of the head and brings discomfort even to the healthy. Of what
use, then, is the cold dousing, which is supposed to overcome
stoppage and sluggishness of the pores, if the additional constriction produced by the treatment is found to overwhelm the
patient?

That is, the corpuscles, to whose stoppage Themison ascribes
the blocking of the pores, could easily pass through the pores
and bound back [from impacts] if the width [of the pores] afforded a passage for their coming and going. But the cold water
opposes the carrying-out of this process, for it presses together
and constricts the pores. And Themison indeed admits that he
does not use this treatment when there is a better one available
(though he avoids telling us what that better one may be); for
this treatment is clearly hostile and repugnant to his own
teaching.

3   Heraclides of Tarentum in Book I of his work *On Internal Diseases* asserts that lethargy is caused by a large amount of undigested matter and the thickening of the body fluid. He therefore
prescribes clysters containing water in which centaury or wormwood has been boiled. He also prescribes the drinking of castor,
salt water, and thyme-dodder. He gently pries the patient's
mouth open and drop by drop pours in these liquids, which run
down smoothly into the mouth. In addition, he foments the
head with diluted vinegar containing decoctions of laurel and
rue; and, shaving off the patient's hair, he anoints his head with
castor or cow-parsnip mixed with vinegar and old olive oil. He
also prescribes a plaster of raw flour, which we call *ōmēlysis*,
with diluted vinegar, wormwood, and nitrum, or bran with vinegar, or, again, mustard with vinegar and fig. And after the patient's head is shaved, he again uses the same clysters as before.[9]

4   He gives the patient radishes to chew on and with mustard or
pepper induces the expectoration of phlegm. And he prescribes
suppositories if he cannot loosen the bowels with a clyster. He
has the whole body anointed with vinegar and olive oil and
arouses the patient with sternutatories and aromatic preparations of castor and cow-parsnip dissolved in sharp vinegar. But
if the illness has arisen from an acrid condition of the humors, he

9. Or possibly 'he uses these same substances as clysters.'

iubet ac deinde vinum. post haec acetum cum melle ob virium
tutelam adhibendam probat, tunc iuscellum[42] tenue dat anseris
vel perdicis aut gallinae, et per profectum oryzae sucum vel
ptisanae ex ordeo; tunc panem cum radicibus fluxis ac mollibus
vel cappare, dehinc cum pisciculis.

sic enim quasi acceptis his lethargicos iuvandos existimat,
cum omnimodo tumentia acrioribus virtutibus accensa gra-
55 ventur, hoc est clysteribus supradictis atque potionibus et infusionibus et perunctionibus et odoramentis et fomentis et
apophlegmatismis et vini dationibus intemporalibus et cibis
acrioribus et indigestibilibus et radicibus et cappare et iuscello[43]
innutribili atque corruptibili. in quos errores ceciderit nobilis
videlicet Empiricus claret cum liquidarum materiarum causas
attendit, et neque tempora neque quantitatis modum dare perspexit, sine quibus solas materias nominavit, non adiutoria
constituit.

alia quoque multa varia opinatione composuit, quae non in
principaliter[44] dicenda suscepit, sed expugnando[45] quae ab aliis
posita videbantur adiecit. quae propter fastidium prolixitatis
tacenda melius existimo, quippe cum ex his quae narravimus[46]
praetermissorum conici vanitas[47] possit.

56   X. DE APPREHENSIONE VEL OPPRESSIS, QUOS GRAECI CATALEPTOS APPELLANT

VICINA atque similis est lethargiae passio quam Graeci catalepsin appellant, nos apprehensionem vel oppressionem vocare poterimus, de qua nunc dicemus. nomen igitur ab accidenti sumpsit. sed Hippocrates libro suo Sententiarum et
Diocles libro Prognostico hanc passionem aphoniam appellavit;
Praxagoras secundo libro Peregrinarum passionum catochen[1]
appellavit; item Antigenes Cleophantinus libro quem De fe-

---

[42] viscellum *edd.*: iusculum *Am*

[43] viscello *edd.*

[44] in principaliter *Bendz Eran 43. 39*: imprincipaliter *G*

[45] expugnanda *G*: *corr. Bendz Eran 43. 40*

[46] narrabimus *G*: *corr. R*

[47] varietas *G*: *corr. Am*

[1] catochen *Am*: cathoden *G* (*sic etiam 58, sed cf. 60–61*): ϲωματωden *R* (= c̄at(h)o-den)

has the patient drink fresh water and then wine. After these, he suggests oxymel to maintain the patient's strength. Later on he gives him a thin broth of goose, partridge, or hen and, as the patient improves, a gruel of rice or of peeled and unpeeled barley; and later bread with soft, tender radishes or caper, and then with small fish.

Indeed, he seems to think that the adoption of these measures will help in the treatment of lethargy. But actually the inflamed parts are irritated and in every way burdened by the sharp substances employed, i.e., the above-described clysters, potions, infusions,[10] anointings, aromatic preparations, fomentations, expectorants, the ill-timed prescriptions of wine, the acrid and indigestible foods, the radishes, the caper, and the broth which lacks nutritive value and is prone to spoil. Into what errors the famous Empiric has fallen is clear from the fact that he concerns himself with the properties of the fluid substances he prescribes, but neglects to give the times or the quantities. Yet in the absence of these data what he gives us is merely a list of names of substances, rather than any clearly described remedies.

Heraclides wrote a great deal more on the subject, setting forth a variety of views. This material he did not include in his main discussion, but added in the course of refuting the opinions held by others. But, being averse to prolixity, I think it better to omit this material; for from what I have already said one may gather how useless[11] are the things that I have passed over.

X. ON SEIZURE OR STUPOR (GREEK *CATALĒPSIS*)

AKIN to and like lethargy is the disease which the Greeks call *catalēpsis* ['catalepsy'], a term we may translate *apprehensio* or *oppressio* ['seizure, stupor']. This disease we shall now discuss. It takes its name from a characteristic symptom, but Hippocrates in his book of *Aphorisms*[1] and Diocles in his book *On Prognosis* called it *aphōnia;* Praxagoras, in Book II of his work *On Strange Diseases, catochē;* and Antigenes, the follower of Cleophantus, in his book *On Fevers and Inflammations,* an-

10. Perhaps the reference is merely to *guttatim infundit*, 53.

11. 'Varied,' if G's reading be retained.

1. *Aph.* vi. 51; cf. *Reg. ac.*, Appendix, 4. There is no indication in these passages that the disease was actually called *aphōnia*.

bribus et tumoribus scripsit anaudiam vocavit; Asclepiades
libro quem De periodicis febribus scripsit catalepsin appella-
57 vit, atque plenum corpus scripturae composuit. quo constat
errasse[2] Chrysippum[3] libro quo de ipsa passione scripsit appellans catocham hoc modo: passionem, inquit, quam appellamus catocham.

veteres etiam medici hanc passionem non tacuerunt, sed facile, sicuti etiam nunc plurimi, lethargiam esse senserunt. alii
horum successores, pauci quidem Asclepiadis sectatores, hanc
passionem a lethargo discreverunt et nomine adiecto catalepsim
vocaverunt, equidem nihil ei novitatis ascribentes quod proprium passionis videretur, sed omnia communia quae etiam de
lethargo dixerunt. sed neque alius quisquam hanc passionem
58 cognovit usque ad Methodicorum tempora. nam ex nostris
primus Magnus eius argumenta constituit, atque mox Agathinus, dehinc Archigenes, qui plurimum passionem a ceteris
discernendo separavit. sed neque proprium nomen passioni
omnes unum posuerunt; Praxagoras eam catochen[4] appellavit.[5]
neque si quisquam nomen passionis dedit primus, etiam eius
signa recte agnovisse probatur. neque Asclepiadis sectatores
soli catalepsin vocaverunt, verum etiam et ipse Asclepiades
aliam dixit esse passionem quam lethargiam. sed cum hoc
solum praeciperet, novum non dedit nomen.

59   nunc ne supradicta omnia simplicia atque nuda posuisse videamur, ipsas quoque significationes singulorum prosequemur.
Hippocrates ait repente voce captos, quos aphonos appellavit,
fieri venarum causa cum spiritum sumpserint: multos denique
talia prosequentur, rubor vultus atque oculorum statio sine ulla
palpebratione, manuum neglecta atque distenta abiectio, dentium stridor et membrorum saltus, ac musculorum quibus buccae

---

[2] ⟨non⟩ errasse R

[3] Chrysippum scripsi, coll. 64, 82, Chr. ii. 86: Philippum edd.

[4] catochen Am: cathoden G (cf. 56): cωmatωden Rm

[5] Praxagoras . . . appellavit fort. del.

audia. Asclepiades in his book *On Periodic Fevers* called it *cata-lēpsis* and discussed it very fully. Clearly, then, Chrysippus was in error when, in the book in which he discussed this disease, he referred to it as *catochē* in the following way: 'the disease that we call *catochē*.'[2]

The ancient physicians did not pass over this disease in silence but easily confused it with lethargy, as very many do even now. Some later physicians, a few of them followers of Asclepiades, sought to distinguish this disease from lethargy and, applying a special name to it, called it *catalēpsis*. They did not, however, ascribe to it anything new as belonging specifically to this disease. Instead they ascribed to it all the common characteristics that they had also noted in the case of lethargy. But no one identified this disease as such until the time of the Methodists. For it was Magnus, a member of our sect, who first determined its characteristics, and he was soon followed by Agathinus and then by Archigenes, who completely distinguished the disease from all others. But these men did not give a single, characteristic name to the disease. Praxagoras called it *catochē*.[3] And whoever it was who first gave a separate name to the disease cannot also be said to have correctly recognized its characteristics. The followers of Asclepiades were not the only ones who called the disease catalepsy. And in fact Asclepiades himself declared that it was a different disease from lethargy. But, though he taught this much, he was not the first to give the name to the disease.[4]

Now, rather than content ourselves merely with the bare and simple details given above, we shall also give the description set forth by each of these authors. Hippocrates says[5] that sudden loss of voice (he calls the victims *aphōnoe*) is caused by entrance of pneuma into the veins; and that in many cases the following symptoms occur: face red, eyes staring without any blinking, hands haphazardly stretched out and cast about, gnashing of the teeth, twitching of the limbs, convulsive movement of the

2. Does the mistake of Chrysippus consist in using *we* (= the Greeks), when the disease was not generally known as *catochē?* Such an interpretation is not necessarily invalidated by 74, below, or by ascribing the use of the term to Praxagoras (56, 58). But the explanation is not entirely satisfactory, and the text may be corrupt.

3. The sentence seems out of place.

4. But cf. 56.

5. *Reg. ac.*, Appendix, 4. Note the divergence from the traditional text.

colligantur conductio, quos appellant siagonitas, articulorum
frigus cum spiritus invaserit venas.

60 item Diocles ait defectivas febres tutas atque innoxias esse
frequentius quam sunt continuae, quamquam et in his periclitentur qui in accessionibus apprehensi conticescunt, vel raptu
quodam alterno per membra tentantur cum supra dictis signis,
quod saepe, inquit, est accidens pueris.

item Praxagoras ait esse quasdam febres ex anno duodecimo
usque ad sextumdecimum vel septimumdecimum quae quadam
privata pernicie mortis habeant effectum, atque id in servis
magis quam in liberis evenire, sed excesso dierum numero passiones fiant catochae vehementes, ut etiam voce capiantur aegro-

61 tantes; horum aliquos etiam lethargos fieri. denique, inquit,
de catocha passione quidam liberati, ac deinde sanitatis creduli,
plurimum quicquam sumentes repente in mortem venerunt.
hos denique plurimus modo sequitur somnus atque febrium
instauratio et cetera quae corpus passione habituari[5a] demonstrent.

item Archigenes ait esse difficiles etiam periodicos typos,
horum difficiliores esse tertianos, in quibus cotidianae accessiones fiant sed alterna diei interpositione suae similitudini respondeant, quando in accessione vehemens occurrerit oppressio,

62 et appellavit rhigos. difficilis inquit etiam si cotidianis diebus
[in][6] accessiones sibi similes fiant et in accessione aegrotantes
supra dicta patiantur. dehinc progrediens paululum idem dixit
periodicos typos non esse perniciosos, sicut supra dictum est, sed
horum esse molestos quibus accessionis tempore pressurae vehementes adveniunt, et quodam nubilo corpus demergitur, quod
item rhigos vocavit. sed hoc, inquit, est accidens magis tertianis, aliquando etiam cotidianis, qui similibus respondeant accessionibus.

5a habitari *edd., sed cf. Ac. iii. 87; Chr. i. 79, iv. 109*
6 *om. R*

muscles controlling the jaws (Greek *siagonitae*), and chill in the extremities, since pneuma has entered the veins.

)0   Diocles declares that intermittent fevers are more frequently safe and harmless than are unremitting fevers, but he points out that intermittent fevers are dangerous in those cases where the voice is lost in a sudden seizure and the limbs are shaken back and forth in convulsion, the other symptoms mentioned above also being present. This seizure, he says, often occurs in children.

Praxagoras says that between the ages of twelve and sixteen or seventeen certain fevers occur which involve a characteristic type of breakdown and result in death, and that slaves are more often the victims of this disease than free persons. But, he adds, after a certain number of days[6] the disease may take the form of a powerful seizure (*catochē*), so that the patients are even affected by loss of speech, and some of them also show the symp-

)1   toms of lethargy. And then, he goes on to say, though some may be relieved of the oppressive malady and believe that they are completely well, in most cases, on undergoing any exertion at all, they die suddenly. And the only symptoms in these cases, apart from the general signs that the body is in a state of disease, are an excessive amount of sleep and a renewal of the fever.

Archigenes says that periodic fevers are hard to deal with, particularly tertian fevers (in which feverish attacks occur each day, those of alternate days being similar each to each) when a powerful seizure, which he calls *rhigos*, occurs during an attack.

)2   And he also describes as difficult those cases in which attacks of like intensity come every day and during attacks the patients show the symptoms described above. A little farther on, the same author says that, while periodic forms of fever are not deadly (as he had already pointed out), some of them are difficult to deal with, e.g., those in which there is a profound stupor at the time of an attack, and the body seems plunged in a fog. This, too, Archigenes calls *rhigos*, holding that it is more apt to occur when the corresponding attacks come every other day (tertian fevers), but that it occurs sometimes also when they come every day (quotidian fevers).

6. Or perhaps 'on an odd-numbered day,' *excesso* rendering περισσῷ. Cf. *impari die*, *Ac.* i. 109, where the reference is probably to the third day.

63   item Asclepiades ait cotidianum perseverantem non sine
periculo esse, atque multos ex eo in alium morbum induci, hoc
est ⟨in⟩[7] corporis defluxionem aut hydropem venire et quicquid
potest per corporis debilitatem accedere.[8] apud Romam vero,
inquit, frequentare advertimus has febres cum corporis atque
mentis oppressione in similitudine[9] lethargiae, quae secundo vel
tertio[10] in statu accessionis constitutae statim recalefacto corpore vel cessante vehementia in resumptionem atque resurrectionem mediocrem revocant aegrotantes. at si levi figmento cessaverint, semel apprehenso aegro nullam resurrectionem dabunt,
sed in sudores et respirationem celerem impulsum[11] febricitantem
64 occidunt. item[12] similia de his scribit, et non semel sed frequenter, dicens certa ratione mentis apprehensionem typorum
in accessionibus fieri, atque hoc apud Romam frequentare, dans
etiam causas quibus haec singula fiant.

item Chrysippus particulariter signa passionis percurrit futurae et praesentis vel in peius euntis; discernit etiam ab lethargo, et alia plurima et varia digerit.

quibus ita se habentibus erit indignum tanta dissensione con-
scriptae passionis eorum cuiquam ascribere firmitatem, quippe
cum ceterarum etiam passionum omnibus cognitarum aliqui
plurima accidentia atque signa, aliqui pauca conscripserint,
nec quisquam vera significatione ⟨hanc⟩[13] finierit.

65   haec sunt quae propter eos qui specialiter istam passionem
perniciosam dixerunt ponenda credidimus. quod etiam si la-
teret in partibus, periculum ⟨non perniciem⟩[14] Methodicis affere-
bat, qui generalibus congruas passionibus posuerunt curationes,
etiam quibus particulariter latentia curentur. sciendum igitur
quia haec passio ex iisdem causis antecedentibus fiet quibus

---

[7] *supplevi*

[8] *fort.* accidere

[9] *an* similitudinem, *ut freq.?*

[10] tertio ⟨die⟩ *Wellmann, Celsus 114, n. 3*

[11] impulsum *scripsi*: in pulsum *edd.*

[12] *fort. nomen proprium (an* Themison?) *post* item *excidit*

[13] *suppl.* R: *fort. suppl.* ⟨hanc dif⟩   [14] *supplevi: fort.* ⟨non⟩ *tantum*

3   Asclepiades declares that a persistent quotidian fever is not without danger, and that in many cases the patient lapses from it into another disease, such as bodily dissolution[7] or dropsy or any other disease that may occur with weakness of the body. At Rome, he says, we frequently observe these fevers accompanied by a seizure of the body and mind like that occurring in lethargy; on the second or third day, when the feverish attack is at its highest stage, the body suddenly loses its heat, that is, the violence of the attack abates, and the patient experiences a mild gain of strength and recovery. But if the abatement is merely a false appearance, the fever will again lay hold of the patient and thereafter allow him no relief, bringing him in his feverish state to sweating, rapid respiration, and finally 4 death. Asclepiades makes similar observations about these cases, not merely once but frequently, saying that for a definite reason this type of seizure afflicts the mind during attacks of periodic fevers, and that such cases occur frequently at Rome. He also tries to give a rational explanation of all these phenomena.

   Chrysippus takes up the specific signs of an imminent attack of catalepsy, those of a present attack, and those that indicate the disease is growing worse. He also distinguishes the disease from lethargy, and treats many other varied aspects of the subject.

   In view of this situation and the diversity of written opinion about this disease, it would be wrong to put our reliance on any of these authors. For while they have described, some of them very fully and others briefly, the symptoms and signs of other diseases that are widely known, not one has defined this disease by a true account of its signs.

5   We have considered it necessary to give the above account in view of the opinion of those who have specifically declared catalepsy to be deadly. But even if the disease lay concealed in parts of the body, this would be to the Methodists an indication of danger rather than death. For their treatments are designed to fit general types of disease, including those diseases in which the treatment is directed to what is concealed in some part of the body. And note that catalepsy arises from the same antecedent causes from which other diseases also arise, namely, indigestion,

7. The reference may be to a condition like phthisis. Cf. *Chr.* ii. 196.

aliae quoque passiones efficiuntur, indigestione, vinolentia, carnali cibo, et horum similibus rebus.

⟨Soranus vero⟩[15] cuius haec sunt quae nostra mediocritas latinizanda existimavit se vidisse plurimos memorat ex intemporali cibo vel plurimo puerorum[16] ista oppressos passione. sed non inquit necessarium[17] praecedentium causarum differentiam in curationibus praevidere, siquidem praesentia sint a Methodi-

66 cis intuenda. sic etiam super[18] dicit temporis attendere frequentiam, quod autumno[19] tempore haec passio magis irruat corporibus, atque in puerilibus frequenter aetatibus, item sexus causa mulieribus, et humorosis et vacuis corporibus, et edacibus hominibus, vel post aegritudinem resumptionis tempore inordinate atque impatienter agentibus. praeterea omni febriculae haec passio irruere potest, sive continuis sive dimissionibus intercapedinatis, hemitritaicis etiam febribus vel cotidianis et tertianis et quartanis, quamquam rara atque frequens secundum

67 febrium fiat qualitatem; hinc etiam gravis vel levis pro earum magnitudine fieri intelligatur. frequentius tamen cotidianis accessionibus vel tertianis accessionibus aegrotantes ista passione afficiuntur, et propterea diuturnis accessionibus admoniti tertianis similitudinem servantes[20] ad typum cotidianum. sed omnium earum febrium gravius, quoties cum articulorum frigido torpore fuerit qualitas; levius, quoties tremore aegrotantes afficiuntur. item magis ac magis levius, quoties sine his quae supra diximus solo fervore initium febres accipiunt.

68   sequentur autem eos qui in passionem venire meditantur alia communia cum lethargo, ut segnities et tardus corporis motus, vel nulla querela ex his quae aegrotantes afficiunt, hoc est tacita sui laboris perlatio[21] et veluti somnus ultra modum prolixus vel gravis, item alloquentibus nobis eius tarda responsio. propria autem sunt quae in propriam passionem venturi patiuntur, ut est genarum rubor plurimus sine febrium levigatione, salivarum fluor, pulsus erectio atque plenitudo, ventris retentio aut coacervata atque fluxa effusio.

[15] ⟨Soranus⟩ Rm, coll. 8

[16] puerorum scripsi: persicorum edd.

[17] necessariam G: corr. Rm

[18] insuper Rm: superfluum Hagendahl 257

[19] autumni R (cf. 90)   [20] servant edd.   [21] relatio edd.

excessive drinking of wine, the eating of meat, and similar causes.

Soranus, the author of the very work which I have here humbly sought to translate into Latin, relates that he saw a large number of children stricken by catalepsy as a result of untimely and excessive eating. He holds, however, that for purposes of treatment it is unnecessary to take note of differences in ante-
6 cedent causes. For in the view of the Methodists it is the present condition that must be observed. And, in addition, he bids us note the time when the disease commonly occurs, for it is more apt to attack the body in autumn; and it occurs more often among children. And in females, so far as sex is concerned; and in moist bodies and bodies that have no exercise,[8] and among voracious persons, and those who in the period of recovery after illness live irregularly and do not submit to regimen. Besides, an attack of this disease may supervene on every type of fever, either continuous or intermittent, semitertian, quotidian, tertian, and quartan, though the frequency or infrequency of the
7 disease varies according to the nature of the fever; and the disease is also observed to be severe or mild according to the severity of the fever. Thus patients who are suffering from quotidian or tertian fevers are more frequently attacked by catalepsy, and hence also those who are suffering from the continued tertian fevers which resemble the quotidian type. But in all these fevers the attack is more dangerous when the fever is accompanied by a cold numbness of the extremities, and less severe when there is only trembling. But the attacks are even milder when neither of these symptoms is present, the beginning of the fever being marked merely by the presence of heat.
8   Those who are on the verge of lapsing into catalepsy will show some signs in common with lethargy, e.g., inactivity and sluggish motion of the body, absence of complaint about their pains, that is, endurance of distress in silence, a kind of sleep excessively protracted and heavy, and slow response when we address them. But there are also specific signs that indicate an imminent lapse into catalepsy, e.g., cheeks very red without any mitigation of the fever, saliva flowing copiously, pulse prominent and full, feces retained or else poured out in a fluid mass.

8. Possibly, 'among persons with an excess or a deficiency of bodily fluids.'

eos vero qui sint[22] in passione iam constituti sequitur schema
69 iacendi iugiter supinum, colli distentio, genarum rubor, febris,
vocis amputatio, sensuum torpor atque hebetudo, palpebrarum
distantia, et infixa atque immobilis intentio luminum, tamquam
quicquam intento obtutu cupientium[23] aut boum cervicis repentino motu cadentium. sequitur etiam lacrimatio tamquam
sentientium atque dolentium, saltus latenter commovens musculos qui buccas colligant, quos siagonitas appellant, movens etiam
labia et supercilia et digitos atque manus, singultus creber ac
resonans, pulsus celsior humectus plenus, vehemens retentio
ventris, et neque extenta recolligunt membra neque conducta
distendunt, ventris inflatio, aliquibus tamquam ex vento magis
ac magis circa stomachi sessionem,[24] aliquibus tamquam ex hu-
70 more vel cibo cum sonitu intestinorum, dentium concubitus,
hoc est confixio vehemens, aliquando etiam stridor, et cum statum sumpserit accessio, horum recessus, adeo ut sit quaedam
interiecta distantia, oris hiscens atque dimissa hebetudo, cum[25]
plurimum salivarum fluore per eius obliqua foras decurrit,
nunc attestante sonitu transvoratur; discurrit etiam si quid fuerit liquoris infusum aut invito aegrotante percipitur. item
labia saepissime conducentes contrahentesque et tamquam in
maestitudine constituti suspirant. atque ita si ante oculos
eorum quisquam digitos circummoveat, palpebrant[26] aegrotantes et suo obtutu manuum traiectationem[27] sequuntur.
71 vel si quicquam profecerint, etiam toto obtutu converso attendunt, et inclamati respicientes lacrimantur, nihil dicentes
sed volentium respondere vultum simulantes. odoramentis admotis iucundis delectantur atque iugi adducto spiramento;
odoribus autem tetris delectationem non accommodant, sed adversa voluntate eorum fugiunt putorem. dulcia atque amara
sentiunt si eorum linguae fuerint admota. item perpuncti sentiunt, vel si eorum manum quis extenderit hanc recolligunt, vel
lacessiti horrescunt; et eorum vultus in ruborem florescit, cum

[22] sunt *Rm*

[23] ⟨aspicere⟩ cupientium *R*: *fort.* aspicientium

[24] sensionem *edd.*: *corr. Schmid Mn 136*

[25] qua *Rm*: nunc *A*

[26] *fort.* ⟨non⟩ palpebrant

[27] traiectionem *R*

Those who are already suffering from the disease show the following signs: position in bed constantly supine, neck distended,
69 cheeks red, fever, loss of voice, senses benumbed and blunted,
eyelids unable to close completely, eyes staring steadily and without motion, as if longing for something while gazing intently at
it, or, again, falling with the sudden motion of a bull's neck.[9]
There is also weeping, as if the patients are conscious and grieving, a slight twitching of the muscles that control the jaws
(Greek *siagonitae*), and also of the lips, eyebrows, fingers, and
hands, frequent and noisy hiccoughs, pulse prominent, moist,
and full, persistent failure to evacuate the bowels, failure to
draw back the limbs again after they have been stretched out,
or to stretch them out again after they have been contracted,
and abdominal distention, apparently due in some cases to
wind centering more and more in the lower end of the esophagus,
and in other cases to liquid or food, with rumbling of the intes-
70 tines. There is also a clenching of the teeth, that is, a firm pressing together, and sometimes a gnashing; but during the height
of an attack a parting, so that there is some distance between
them, the mouth gaping open, relaxed and weak. Then most of
the saliva flows out by the sides of the mouth, but some is noisily
swallowed; and whatever liquid is poured in or taken against
the patient's will also runs out. Again, often drawing their lips
together and contracting them, they sigh as if they were sunk in
sadness. And if we move our fingers before their eyes, they
blink[10] and follow the movements of the hand with their gaze.
71 Now if their condition has to some extent improved, they even
turn their eyes [to us] and watch intently. If we call them, they
look at us and weep, and, though they say nothing, they show
by their expression that they would like to answer. When agree-
able-smelling substances are brought near them, they are pleased
and keep drawing their breath in. But when the odors are foul,
the patients show no pleasure but lose their good disposition
and turn away from the stench. They taste sweet and bitter
when these are brought to their tongue. Again, they feel when
they are pricked; and if we stretch out their hands, they draw
them back. When they are shaken, they bristle up; their faces

9. If the text is sound, the reference may be to what takes place at the slaughtering
of animals. In a somewhat different way Aretaeus uses the same comparison (*Sign. ac.*
i. 5).

10. Or, reading ⟨*non*⟩ *palpebrant:* 'do not blink, but follow, etc.'

sudore saepius plurimo atque ferventi, et in dimissione sinceritati propinquantes rursum admonentur.

72   at si ad peiora passio fuerit devoluta, fervor plurimus corporis in superficie, magis sentitur spiratio, oculorum conversio, menti quoque fixa condicio,[28] manuum contractus et musculorum qui buccas colligant tamquam ridentium, sudor igneus, et quibusdam in thorace atque vultu emergentes discolores vel stantes in rotunditate maculae in similitudine[29] scatebrarum corporis quos[30] Graeci ionthos[31] vocant, et e magnitudine repentinus ⟨pulsus⟩[32] casus, gutturis stridor, quem Graeci rhogmon vocant, torpor frigidus et albidus vultus, et in ultimo efflatio[33] atque vitae periculum.

73   alii vero in phreniticam aut lethargicam passionem reciderunt, sicuti et ipsae passiones in semet per temporum motum venire consueverunt. his igitur qui in phreniticam passionem ex ista deveniunt pulsus sensim minuitur atque densatur, et oculorum fixus obtutus mutatur atque mobilis efficitur, leviter etiam tamquam in somno murmurantes non recta secum loquuntur, et incerto motu atque tardo suas transferunt manus vel digitos complicant. qui autem in lethargicam passionem deveniunt inani afficiuntur pulsu atque tardo, et eorum palpebrae concluduntur,[34] et in torpore sensuum vel hebetudine perseverant.

qui autem in declinationem passionis deveniunt plurima vel parva accidente[35] humiditate relevantur, quibusdam accedenti-

74 bus signis. nam plerisque plurimo per intestina exeunte vento vel mucilento humore aut[36] stercore ventris subsedit inflatio. alii vero humore plurimo atque crasso profecta[37] dentium distantia ex ore detracto locuti sunt; et alii sapienter[38] quidem sed concisis sermonibus, alii iugibus.

proprie igitur passionem supra dictam, hoc est catalepticam sive catocham, ut Graeci appellant, designant febres acutae, vocis silentium, sensuum hebetudo, pulsus magnus ac vehemens et plenus et humectus, et oculorum stans atque fixus obtutus.

[28] conductio *A*

[29] similitudinem *R, ut freq. ap. Cael.*   [31] *cf.* iontus *Chr. ii. 89*

[30] quas *Rm*   [32] *supplevi*: ⟨virium⟩ *R*

[33] efflatio *Triller (Kühn 109)*: effatio *G* (= *aphonia?*)

[34] conducuntur *edd., sed cf.* conclusio *75*

[35] *an* accedente?   [37] perfecta *Rm*

[36] aut *Rm*: ut *G: an* et?   [38] sapientes *edd.: corr. Schmid Mn 136*

begin to bloom with ruddiness, and warm, copious sweat appears. And in the remission, just as they become practically free of symptoms, they again experience sensations of the illness.[11]

But if the disease has taken a turn for the worse, there is great heat at the surface of the body, breathing is more audible, the eyes are turned [from their normal position], the chin firmly set, the hands curled up, and the muscles of the jaws contracted so that the patient seems to be laughing; there is fiery hot sweat, and in some cases an emergence of round spots of different colors on the chest and face, like the eruptions on the body which the Greeks call *ionthoe*, a sudden collapse of the pulse from a vigorous state, wheezing in the throat (Greek *rhōgmos*), cold numbness, whiteness of face, and finally the last gasps and imminent death.

But some cases of catalepsy pass into phrenitis or lethargy, in the same way that each of these latter diseases often passes into the other with lapse of time. In the case of those who are passing into phrenitis from catalepsy, the pulse gradually becomes smaller and more rapid; the eyes are no longer fixed in a stare but move about; the patients quietly murmur as if in sleep, and talk irrationally to themselves; with slow and fumbling motion they change the position of their arms or fold their hands. But in the case of those who are passing into lethargy, the pulse becomes empty and slow, the eyelids close, and the senses remain benumbed and blunted.

Again, those who are passing into the declining phase of catalepsy are relieved with either copious or little discharge of fluid. Certain signs are present in these cases. Thus in many instances the abdominal inflation subsides with the passing of a great deal of wind or slimy fluid or excrement through the intestines. In some cases a great deal of thick fluid is removed from the mouth as the position of the jaws becomes normal, and the patients begin to speak. And some speak rationally but in broken sentences, others continuously.

The characteristic signs of the disease in question, that is of *catalēpsis* or *catochē*, as the Greeks call it, are as follows: acute fever, loss of voice, blunting of the senses, a large, strong, full, and moist pulse, and a fixed and steady gaze. It is a swift or

---

11. But presumably the successive exacerbations are weaker.

est autem passio celeris atque acuta etiamsi in chronias venerit
febres. et est magna, atque strictura et raptu corporis, quem
Graeci spasmon vocant, fieri perspicitur, nisi per immodicum
fluxum diaphoreticus tamquam in cardiacis fuerit effectus.

75   huic igitur similis est lethargia, apoplexia, stomachica passio
in febribus vocis ingerens silentium, item animi defectio per
nimiam ieiunitatem, et matricis praefocatio, et lumbricis[39] vocis
depressio, de qua capite de lumbricis scribentes memorabimus.
de aliis vero leviter atque coacte nunc discretionem ponemus.
namque lethargicis maior quidem pulsus sed tardus atque inanis
invenitur, et palpebrarum conclusio; catalepticis autem pulsus
maior sed plenus atque celer et vehemens invenitur, palpebrarum attestante distantia.

item apoplecticis parvus celerrimus durus ac sine febribus
76 pulsus invenitur, siquidem haec repente accidant. item stomachicis qui nimia ieiunitate[40] etiam voce capiuntur pulsus parvus et imbecillis invenitur, cum stomachi solutione vel tumore
manifestius apparente et frigido torpore, qui sequitur post oppressionem factam et non antecedenti febriculae concurrit,[41]
sicut in catalepticis. item stomachici intelliguntur ex eo quod
iam frequenter fuerint admoniti passione, et propterea typorum
tenuerunt tarditatem quibus accessiones longo intervallo respondeant.

item qui ieiunitatis[42] vel abstinentiae defectu, sive ex capitis
causa quam Graeci scotosin vocant, demersi videntur dis-
77 cernuntur[43] hoc modo quod primum oculos habeant distentos,
dentium concadente iunctione, attestante pulsu parvo atque imbecillo, ita ut aliquando interire videatur cum frigido torpore;
sed haec et cito circumscribuntur,[44] et is qui patitur facile re-
surgit. nam si perseveraverint, catalepticam passionem designant.

item non aliter facile resumere perspiciuntur hi qui odore
carbonum vel unguentorum sensuum oppressione vel torpore

[39] ⟨ex⟩ lumbricis *Rm* (*sed cf. Bendz 24*)

[40] nimia ieiunitate *Bendz 90, coll. Ac. ii. 75*: nimietate *G*

[41] febricula cucurrit *G: corr. Rm*

[42] qui ieiunitatis *Hagendahl 258*: a ieiunitate *G*: a ieiunitatis *Schmid 107*

[43] discernuntur ⟨autem⟩ *R*

[44] circumscribuntur *Rm*: circumscribunt *G*

acute disease,[12] even though it may supervene upon a chronic fever. And it is a serious disease and is found to occur in connection with a condition of stricture and bodily seizure (Greek *spasmos*), except in cases where it occurs with colliquative sweating of the kind found in the cardiac disease.

Lethargy, apoplexy, and the disease of the esophagus, when it causes loss of voice[13] and is accompanied by fever, bear a resemblance to catalepsy. So also do fainting occasioned by excessive fasting, hysterical suffocation, and the loss of voice resulting from worms. This last we shall discuss in the chapter on worms.[14] But we shall now briefly and concisely distinguish [from catalepsy] the other diseases mentioned. Thus in lethargy the pulse, while large, is found to be slow and empty, and the eyelids meet. In catalepsy, however, the pulse, while large, is also full, rapid, and strong, and the eyelids do not meet.

Again, in apoplexy the pulse is found to be small, very rapid, hard, and free from any sign of fever; for these attacks take place suddenly. And in those cases of the disease of the esophagus in which the voice is lost because of excessive fasting, there is a small and weak pulse together with a state of looseness in the esophagus or else an obvious inflammation thereof, and a cold numbness which comes after the attack and does not, as in cases of catalepsy, accompany the antecedent fever. Furthermore, sufferers from the disease of the esophagus may be recognized from the fact that they have already had frequent attacks of the disease, and for that reason show the sort of chronic condition found in periodic fevers in which the corresponding attacks come at long intervals.

And those cases in which the patients collapse by reason of hunger or starvation, or because of a disease of the head that the Greeks call *scotōsis* ('dizziness') are distinguished from catalepsy as follows. At the outset the eyes are open wide, the teeth firmly closed, the pulse so small and weak that at times it seems about to vanish, and the body cold and numb. But these symptoms soon pass, and the patients recover easily. If, however, the symptoms persist, it is an indication of catalepsy.

Again, those who suffer impairment or blunting of the senses through smelling coals or ointments are likewise observed to

12. Cf. also *Chr.* ii. 86 ff.
13. Cf. *ibid.* iii. 16.   14. Cf. *ibid.* iv. 106 ff.

afficiuntur. item matricis praefocationem oppressae discernuntur, primo quod ipsa matrix se sustollat, atque supra umbilicum
vel ventrem extans videatur, antecedente querela earum parti-
78 um ante oppressionis tempus. aliquando etiam longis atque
solitis⁴⁵ accessionibus admoneri aegrotantes inveniuntur cum
pulsu parvo celeri imbecillo; his etiam collum latius fiet cum
palpebrarum conclusione atque frigido corporis torpore.⁴⁶

†**ex duplici tertiana confectis in vehementiore accessione
similiter alternis respondente diebus lethargica⁴⁷ fuisse oppressi passione, et veluti complexum⁴⁸ earum fuisse, accessionibus demonstrando lethargicum simul atque catalepticum esse
confirmat aegrotantem, non aliter quam sunt ex typorum complexione in una atque eadem aegritudine reperti.⁴⁹†

haec sunt quae ⟨de⟩⁵⁰ intelligenda passione atque a similibus
discernenda posuimus.

79 ## XI. QUOMODO CURANDI SUNT HAC PAS-
SIONE LABORANTES

Dᴇʜɪɴᴄ ob curationem adhibendam oportet aegrotantem
iacere sicut strictura laborantes saepe docuimus, adhibita
abstinentia pro virium qualitate, atque fomento ex oleo dulci et
calido capiti et medianis partibus, sed praetactis membris quae
frigido mortis torpore afficiuntur, calefactionibus etiam adhibitis
cum obvolutione atque modica strictione ex lanis effecta. item
ori vel faucibus sensim infundendus humor vel mulsum illis
temporibus quibus alias passiones curantes docuimus. clyster
etiam simplex adhibendus si ventris cessaverit officium.

80 in declinatione vero vel dimissione os aegrotantis sensim dis-
tendimus atque hiscere tentabimus. aliis item dimissionibus
cataplasma mediis adhibemus partibus et clunibus ob absti-

---

⁴⁵ solutis G: corr. Rm

⁴⁶ fort. leg. torpore; ⟨ex quibus nihil in catalepticis invenitur, praeterea (transp. ab
80)⟩ duplici tertiana confectis (an confecti?) inveniuntur accessione etc.: torpore. at
duplici tertiana affecti, in vehementiore accessione similiter alternis respondente diebus,
lethargica ⟨simul et hac⟩ oppressi passione, ac veluti harum complexa [fuisse], ⟨quidam
videntur, signorum et⟩ accessionis demonstratione lethargicum simul et catalepticum
aegrotantem esse confirmante, non aliter quam sunt [ex] typorum complexiones in una
atque eadem aegritudine repertae Rm

⁴⁷ lethargicam G: corr. R   ⁴⁹ repente G

⁴⁸ complexu G: corr. A   ⁵⁰ addidi: ⟨in⟩ R

recover easily. And hysterical suffocation may be distinguished from catalepsy chiefly by the drawing up of the womb so that it appears to bulge out above the navel or abdomen, and also by the presence of pain in these parts before the time of the at-
78 tack. And sometimes the patients are found to have been accustomed to attacks over a long period of time. Their pulse is small, rapid, and weak; the neck is distended, eyelids meet, and there is a chill numbness of the body.[15]

† There are also cases where the patient, exhausted by a double tertian fever, is stricken by lethargy in a violent attack with paroxysms taking place correspondingly on alternate days. There is a sort of mixture of two diseases, and from the nature of the attacks it is clear that the patient is suffering simultaneously from lethargy and catalepsy, in much the same way as those who have a combination of periodic fevers in one and the same illness.†[16]

This concludes our account of the method of recognizing catalepsy and of distinguishing it from similar diseases.

79   XI. THE TREATMENT OF CATALEPSY

I N TREATING catalepsy have the patient placed as we have often indicated is necessary for those suffering from a state of stricture.[1] Let the patient fast if his strength permits. Apply a fomentation of warm sweet olive oil to his head and middle parts; but first apply the oil to the limbs, which have a death-like chill and rigidity, and keep warming them, and wrap woolen cloths around them, using moderate pressure. Pour liquids such as diluted honey a little at a time into the patient's mouth or throat at the times indicated in our discussion of the treatment of other diseases. Also administer a simple clyster if the bowels do not perform their function.

80   Now in an abatement or remission of the attack, gradually distend the mouth of the patient and try to open it. And in subsequent remissions apply poultices to the middle parts and the

15. 'None of these symptoms is found in catalepsy' reads a sentence obviously out of place in 80; it either belongs here or is a marginal note to this or some other passage of 75–78.

16. The text and meaning of this whole passage are obscure. In fact, its proper place may be at 73, after *hebetudine perseverant.*

1. I.e., in a moderately light and warm room.

nentiam urinae solvendam; item cervici vel maioribus nervis,
quos tenontas appellant, et musculis qui buccas colligant, quos
siagonitas[1] vocant. iniectione parva olei per clysterem utimur et
cucurbitae appositione, nunc simplici nunc scarificatione adiecta, ob singultum et tumorem ventris atque stomachi. tunc
vaporatione[2] spongiarum atque cerotariis[3] relevatis partibus
mediis caput tondemus, atque apposita cucurbita [ex quibus
nihil in catalepticis invenitur praeterea][4] scarificamus occipitium
et tempora vel cogentibus causis alia quoque capitis loca, si qua
81 potuerint cucurbitae appositionem accipere. tunc fomento utimur olei atque embasin toto adhibemus corpori, acopis etiam
levioribus utentes, quae mitius nervorum faciant laxamentum.
tunc post perunctionem[5] cibum dabimus declinationis tempore
varium atque bibilem, ut ovum sorbile, cerebrum, olus quod non
sit virtutis acrioris, et magis nutribile. dehinc adhibemus lavacrum, sine ullo cibo qui in se habeat vini qualitatem. tunc pro-
ficienti aegroto pomorum quicquam damus, ut ficum recentem
vel pirum ex melle; tunc mulsum vel aquam. atque completo
sanitatis officio et depulsis omnibus quae passionis recursum
fore sollicitant, dabimus vinum tenue leve,[6] sicut Salutaribus
praeceptis docuimus.

82 ## XII. QUOMODO ALIARUM SECTARUM PRINCIPES
ISTAM CURAVERUNT PASSIONEM

MULTI aliarum sectarum principes[1] quos inter etiam Chrysippus scribens de catalepticis in ultima parte libri etiam
catocham nominavit, sed in his qui mediocriter tardasse in
eadem passione inveniuntur acrioribus utitur unctionibus ob
stuporem articulorum vel tremorem, hoc est cyprino admixto
pipere et nitro, et fomento ex aqua salsa concoctis sulfure et
bitumine. dehinc perungit[2] unctione quam appellavit tripticen,[3]
quam conficiendam dixit ex calamo aromatico, schoeno, cachry,
pyrethro, irino, manna, singulorum partibus oleo admixtis atque
contritis.

---

[1] siagontas G: corr. Rm   [2] vaporationes G: corr. R
[3] cerotariis Rm: cerotaria G: cerotario Helmreich 321
[4] seclusi: fort. transp. ad 78   [5] punctionem G: corr. Friedel 28   [6] lene Rm
[1] fort. suppl. ⟨istius passionis curationem tradiderunt⟩ vel sim.
[2] perunget G: corr. R   [3] fort. tripticon (= τρίπτυχον); cf. 83

loins in order to overcome the retention of the urine, also to the neck and the great sinews (Greek *tenontes*), and to the muscles that control the jaws (Greek *siagonitae*). Inject a small amount of olive oil by a clyster, and use cupping, either with or without scarification, to overcome hiccoughs and inflammation of the stomach and esophagus. Then use sponges to apply heat to the middle parts and also apply cerates; and when these parts have been thus relieved, cut the hair from the patient's head. Apply cupping, with scarification, to the occiput, temples, and also, if there is good reason, to any other parts of the head where cup-

81 ping is feasible. Then foment with olive oil, and prescribe a tub bath for the whole body; also use mild restorative ointments to afford gentle relaxation to the nerves and sinews. Then, after an anointing, give the patient soft, varied food in the declining phase of the disease, e.g., a soft egg, brain, and a nutritious vegetable which does not have acrid properties. Then prescribe bathing. Do not at that time give him any food with a winelike character. Later, as he progresses, give him some fruit, such as fresh fig or pear in honey, and then mead or merely water.[2] When the patient's health has been completely restored and all fear of a return of the disease removed, give him a thin mild wine, as we have indicated in our *Precepts on Health.*

82 ## XII. THE TREATMENT OF CATALEPSY ACCORDING TO THE LEADERS OF OTHER SECTS

MANY leaders of other sects have given directions for treating catalepsy. Among them is Chrysippus. In the last part of his book on catalepsy (which he also calls *catochē*) he suggests that in those cases where the patients are found to linger for some time in this disease, sharp ointments be used to overcome the numbness or trembling of the limbs, e.g., henna oil with an admixture of pepper and nitrum. He also uses as a fomentation salt water in which sulphur and bitumen have been boiled. Again he uses an ointment, which he calls *tripticos,*[1] compounded, he says, of sweet flag, rush, cachry, pellitory, iris oil, and frankincense, the several ingredients being mixed in the oil and ground down.

2. Perhaps the meaning is 'a honeyed drink like hydromel.'
1. I.e., 'for massage.'

83   sed haec nos ob acrimoniam reprobamus siquidem sit passio
celeris atque acuta, etiamsi[4] iamdudum tardantibus atque in-
veteratis febribus irruerit: quippe cum chroniae febres ista passione necessario in superpositionem veniant, quam graece[5] epi-
thesin vocant, quae similis fiet[6] necessario acutis passionibus, et
ob hoc mitigationem deposcat. prohibemus etiam supra dictis
rationibus unctionem ex illo liquore articulis adhibendam, vel
ex eo quicquam potandum aut cibo admiscendum; item sternutamenta vel rasuram capitis aut articulorum sinapismum, aut
supponenda podici acria collyria ob provocandum ventrem,
quae appellavit balanos; item diagridium atque castoreum et
omnia gravabilia fomenta, ex quibus tumor magis augetur et
soporifera pressura geminatur.

84   his etiam compeccavit Themison libris quos Periodicos dixit,
adhuc quidem in iuventute constitutus, nec dum[7] Asclepiades in
libris suis eos discreverat. ait enim si iam tardantibus atque in-
sidentibus febribus apprehensiones vel oppressiones advenerint
sensuum, atque in accessione vocis silentium fecerint, ceteris ut
supra diximus similiter adhibitis, ante accessionem tribus vel
quattuor horis servatis, si venter non fluit, diagridii obolum cum
tribus vel quatuor obolis castorei dabimus cum aqua, occipitium
atque tempora capitis inungentes thapsia, quam nos ferulaginem
dicimus, aqua contrita, ut quendam sensum atque levationem
mediocrem per corporis faciat superficiem. cibos etiam inquit
dandos solidiores, nisi praecordia fuerint in tumore constituta;

85 quod si obstiterit, bibiles[8] dabimus cibos. nec dum quidem ait[9]
providens quia etiamsi in aliis partibus tumores fuerint corporis,
sorbiles interea cibi conveniunt, siquidem laxamentum passio
deposcat, quam[10] necessario accendit[11] atque erigit thapsia[12]
manificum[13] tumorem. est etiam castoreum acre inveteratae
qualitatis causa, sicut omnis caro reposita.

prohibemus propterea ob dentium faciendam distantiam im-
mittendos violenter cuneos. etenim ex his commotae partes
atque quassatae asperant tumentia, quam ob rem dentium

[4] etiam si R: etiam sicut G: etiam si cum Rm   [5] an Graeci? v. Ac. i. 4   [6] fort. fiat
[7] necdum ⟨enim⟩ Wellmann, Hermes 57. 397
[8] bibiles Rm, coll. 81: bibulos G   [9] fort. scrib. erat vel fuit
[10] cum Bendz Eran 41. 67 (cum accendat atque erigat): fort. quamquam
[11] accendit Rm: accendet G
[12] thapsia atque erigit A: thapsia ut quae erigat Rm
[13] magnificum edd.; cf. Ac. i. 109

But we reject all these preparations because of their sharpness.
83 For the disease is swift and acute even though it may supervene
upon fevers that linger and persist for a long time. And these
chronic fevers of necessity develop a paroxysm (Greek *epithesis*)
by reason of the presence of disease. This attack is always like
that in acute diseases and for that reason requires soothing
treatment. And for the reasons already given we also disapprove
of anointing the patient's limbs with the liquid described
above, or of having him drink any of it, or of mixing any in
his food. We also disapprove of sternutatories, shaving of the
head, mustard plasters for the limbs, and the insertion of sharp
suppositories (Greek *balanoe*) into the anus for the purpose of
stimulating the bowels. And we reject scammony juice, castor,
and all pungent fomentations, which aggravate the inflammation and add to the drowsiness and stupor.

84   Themison made similar errors in his work *On Periodic Fevers*,
written when he was still a young man, at a time when Asclepiades had not yet distinguished these cases in his own work.
Now Themison says that if, in the course of a chronic and persistent fever, seizure or violent laying hold of the senses occurs,
and the patient loses his voice during the attack, all the previously described remedies should be applied as before; also that
three or four hours before an [expected] attack, if the bowels
are not loose, we should give the patient an obol of scammony
juice and three or four obols of castor in water, and anoint the
occiput and the temples with thapsia (Latin *ferulago*) rubbed
up in water. His purpose is to bring some sensation and a measure of relief to the surface of the body. He also prescribes somewhat solid food, if the precordial region is not inflamed, but if
85 there is that obstacle, then liquid food. In so prescribing, however, he does not realize that so long as there are any inflammations, even in other parts of the body, soft food is proper inasmuch as the disease requires a relaxing treatment. And thapsia
always irritates an inflammation and artificially increases it.
Again, castor because it is stored for a long time has an acrid
quality, like all meat that is kept long.

For a similar reason we reject the violent insertion of wedges
to pry the patient's teeth apart. For these wedges irritate and
injure the parts in question and aggravate the inflammations,
thereby causing the teeth to come together even more violent-

concasus vehementior fiet, cum magis sit utile[14] ac necessarium
in tensione partibus constitutis requiem adhibere, ut declinationis tempore vel potius dimissionibus,[15] laxatis musculis sine
ulla vi digitis immissis dentium facilius distantiam faciamus.

86   nocent etiam suci frigidi, ut hederae fomentatae atque capiti
impositae:[16] etenim tumores constringunt et passionis asperant
motum. et si qua his fuerint genere similia, sicuti in lethargicis
contra sectarum principes scribentes docuimus, prohibemus.
est autem improprium atque loco carens in initiis[17] frigidis uti
fomentis, in declinationibus vero calidis atque ferventibus iuxta
imitationem[18] recentium vulnerum. in his enim priusquam tumor emerserit frigida probantur, sed omnis sensuum pressura
vel apprehensio in ista passione tumoris esse perspicitur, vel hoc
praecedente[19] superfieri.

haec sunt quae de catalepticis sua potentia Soranus ordinavit.

87   XIII. DE PLEURITICA PASSIONE

PLEURITIS a parte corporis quae magis patitur nomen sumpsit:
latus enim ipsa passione vexatur, quod Graeci pleuron[1] vocaverunt. fit autem ex variis antecedentibus causis, ut ceterae
passiones, magis tamen profunda perfrictione aut vinolentia aut
usu venereo, plurimo nimis potu, indigestione continua aut percussu vehementi aut ponderis magna[1a] subvectione, vel cursu
vehementi. sed neque secundum has differentias differens erit
adhibenda curatio. una est enim atque eadem passio ex qualibet veniens causa, quae una atque eadem indigeat curatione.

hanc definiens primo De adiutoriis libro Aristoteles sic tra-
dendam credidit: pleuritis, inquit, est liquidae materiae coactio[2]
88 sive densatio. nec tamen disseruit utrumne totius, quod falsissimum, siquidem phlebotomati aegrotantes liquidum sanguinem

[14] inutile G: corr. R
[15] fort. dimissionis (dem- Rm)
[16] fomentati atque capiti impositi R
[17] in initiis Almeloveen, coll. 150: nimium G: initio Rm
[18] iusta imitatione edd.
[19] praecedentes G: corr. Rm
[1] pleuron G (cf. Sor. Gyn., p. 16. 20): πλεύραν A (cf. Diaet. pass. 22)
[1a] fort. magni   [2] coactio Almeloveen: coctio G

ly. It is more useful, however, and in fact necessary, to give rest
to the parts that are strained and tense, so that in the decline
of the disease, or rather in periods of remission, the muscles may
be relaxed and we may without the use of force insert our fingers
and easily make an opening between the teeth.

86   Liquids with cooling properties, like ivy applied as a fomentation to the head, are also harmful. For they have an astringent
effect on the inflamed parts and arouse the activity of the disease. And in fact, as we showed in refuting the opinions of the
leaders of the various sects on the treatment of lethargy, we
reject all remedies similar in nature to those here discussed.
Furthermore, it is unsuitable and out of place to use cold applications in the beginning, but hot and steaming fomentations in
the decline of the disease, in imitation of the procedure in the
case of fresh wounds. For in the latter case cold applications are
proper before the inflammation develops. But in the case of
catalepsy the benumbing or seizure of the senses is in every
case a manifestation of inflammation or supervenes upon a
preceding inflammation.

This concludes the account that Soranus, with his customary
authority, gives on catalepsy.

87   XIII. PLEURISY

Pleurisy takes its name from the part of the body that is
particularly affected. For the part attacked in this disease is
the side, called *pleuron* by the Greeks. Like all other diseases,
pleurisy arises from various antecedent causes; and more particularly from a heavy cold, intoxication from wine, venery, excessive drinking, continual indigestion, a powerful blow, the
carrying of a heavy weight, or violent running. But the variety
of causes will not occasion a corresponding variety of treatment.
For the disease is one and the same, whatever the cause from
which it proceeds, and it requires one and the same treatment.

Aristotle in Book I of his work *On Remedies* adopted the following definition of pleurisy: 'Pleurisy is the coagulation or
88 thickening of liquid matter.' He does not, however, say whether
all the liquid matter of the body is so affected (a view which
would be false, for patients with pleurisy when subjected to venesection give up fluid blood), or only a small part. But by not

reddant, an vero particulae. sed cum hoc tacuit non promisit.[3]
mitto etiam oculorum suffusionem nihil aliud esse quam liquoris
coeuntis densitatem, nec tamen pleuritim.

item Apollonius qui appellatus est Mys, volumine vicesimo
octavo quod[4] De secta Herophili conscripsit, 'pleuritis,' inquit,
'est communiter passio temporalis atque celeris secundum laterum membranas, quas hypezocotas vocant, atque inter earum
carnem, aliquando etiam in pulmonis partibus, saepissime sine[5]
tumore vel ex solitis[6] causis effecta: proprie autem tumorem[7]
secundum supradictas membranas vel carnem lateribus inter-
iectam, aliquando etiam pulmonis partem.' sed in utraque dif-
89 finitione peccavit. primo enim sunt prolixae atque narrabiles;
secundo plurima alia praetermisit. nam necessario passioni febris inest.[8] correptum autem atque usurpatum dicimus in pulmone passionem posse constitui, sicut ex consequentibus docebimus.

item Asclepiades libro Diffinitionum pleuritim dicit esse humoris fluorem temporis parvi atque celerem interiorum[9] lateris
partium cum febre atque tumore, sed erat melius tumorem dicere atque[10] humoris fluorem: etenim quoties ex complexa passione conficitur, tumorem perspicimus superare.

est igitur secundum Soranum pleuritis dolor vehemens interiorum lateris partium cum febribus acutis et tussicula qua variae qualitatis liquor excluditur. frequentat autem haec passio in
masculis quam in feminis, atque in senibus magis quam iuveni-
90 bus. tussiculosa enim atque frigida senilis est aetas, quo intelligimus profecto hanc passionem pueros difficulter incurrere. frequentat etiam hiberno magis quam autumni tempore quod[11]
hiemi vicinatur; aestate vero difficulter occurrit. est praeterea
passio acuta atque celeris et vehemens, et aliquando sola ex
strictura confecta, aliquando admixta solutione ob plurimum

[3] non promisit] necessarium praetermisit *Rm*

[4] quod *R*: quem *G* (*defendit Bendz 19*)

[5] *an* cum?

[6] solitis *conieci*: solis *G*

[7] tumore *Haller*

[8] inest *conieci*: non est *G*: [non] est *R* (*si recte, legendum videtur* necessaria)

[9] interiorum *A* (*ut infra*): interiorem *G*

[10] quam *Rm*   [11] quod *Rm*: quo *G*

considering this question he failed to make his account definite.[1]
And I need not point out that cataract is precisely liquid matter
that has run together and thickened; yet it is not pleurisy.

Apollonius, surnamed Mys, in Book XXVIII of his work on
the sect of Herophilus,[2] says: 'Pleurisy is generally an acute disease of short duration in the pleural membranes, called *hypezō-
cotes*, and in the fleshy parts connected with these membranes;
it also occurs at times in parts of the lung, is often unaccompanied by inflammation, and arises from the customary causes.[3]
But in the strict sense pleurisy is an inflammation in the aforesaid membranes or the flesh at the sides, and sometimes, too,
in part of the lung.' Apollonius, however, errs in both his defini-
89 tions. For not only are they long and wordy, but they omit many
essentials. For example, fever is always present in the disease.
Moreover, as we shall show below, we consider it hasty and improper to say that the disease may be situated in the lung.

Asclepiades in his book *On Definitions* says that pleurisy is a
flow of liquid matter in the internal lateral portions of the body,
of short duration and acute, with fever and inflammation.
But it would have been better to say that pleurisy is an inflammation rather than a flow of liquid matter.[4] For in the cases of
pleurisy in which there is a combination of these elements we
observe that the inflammation predominates.

Thus, according to Soranus, pleurisy is a severe affection in
the internal lateral parts of the body, with acute fever and a
cough in which fluid of varying character is given up. This disease is more common in men than in women, and in old men than
90 in young men. For old age is cold and subject to cough, and for
that reason it is at once clear that this disease hardly ever attacks children. Again, it is more frequent in the wintertime
than in autumn, which comes just before winter. But in the
summer it hardly ever occurs. Moreover, it is a swift or acute
disease and powerful. Sometimes it involves solely a state of
stricture; but at other times there is present in addition a state
of looseness, as evidenced by the large amount of fluid coughed

1. The text and meaning are uncertain here.

2. Presumably a treatise on medicine according to the principles of this sect.

3. The text here, too, is quite uncertain. Perhaps what is meant is 'visible' inflammation (cf. 97). Or the reference may be to a kind of latent pleurisy free from the usual
symptoms.

4. Or perhaps: 'together with a flow of liquid matter.'

tussiculae liquorem. etenim ventris defluxio non implet in
pleuriticis signorum concursum, sed magnitudinem passionis
docet. quapropter ex his solum dicimus agnoscendam quae supra memoravimus. alia vero concurrunt plurima atque differentia pro passionis magnitudine ac temporum mutatione, quae
quia praetermittenda non sunt prosequamur.

91   XIV. QUAE CONSEQUUNTUR[1] PLEURITICOS

PROSEQUETUR[2] in passione constitutos acuta febricula, dolor
cum tussicula lateris vehemens atque usque ad iugulum et
palam eiusdem partis perveniens, quibusdam etiam brachium
tangens et pectus atque ilium, et est stimulosus ac pulsuosus et
igneus, iugis aut intercapedinatus, servato ordine aut confuso,
et infixus atque perseverans iisdem locis aut mobilis et recurrens
atque mutabilis, cum suspirio et difficili spiratione, quam
Graeci dyspnoean[3] vocant, attestante tussicula aliquibus arida,
frequenter tamen cum liquidis excrementis, et primo spumosis,
dehinc sanguinolentis, ita fellosis, ac inde saniosis. sequitur
etiam aegros supra id latus iacendi facultas, at[4] cum se supra
contrarium latus verterint dolor, ut adduci sentiant suo pondere
pendentia[5] tumentium partium viscera. sequentur etiam vigiliae atque siccitas et asperitas linguae.

92   peiorante passione augentur omnia supra dicta: additur[6]
etiam articulorum frigidus torpor, genarum rubor, oculorum
sanguineus color, ventris fluor spumosus ac felleus, urinae quoque frequens atque paulatim albida egestio, pulsus densior celer
fortis et veluti fluctuans, et suo percussu pressuram significans;
spiratio etiam circumdolens atque frequens et obtusa, vultus et
thoracis roscida humectatio, mentis alienatio, gutturis stridor
vel sonitus interius resonans aut sibilans in ea parte quae patitur; acceptorum etiam per vomitum recursio, et iacendi negata
atque displicens omnis positio, sputa facile siccantia, et magis
salivosis ea quae fuerint contra naturam vel in densitatem coacta. etenim spumosa sanguinis in qualitatem transeunt, san-

---

[1] sequuntur *laterculum capitum apud* G, *fol. 36v*

[2] prosequitur R   [3] δυσπνοιαν G (*sed* dyspnoean *95*, -am *101*)

[4] facultas, at *scripsi, coll. 96*: difficultas, atque *edd.*

[5] pendentia *Bendz Eran 41. 68, coll. Ac. ii. 96 (cf. etiam Chr. iii. 51, v. 95)*: evidentia
G: cadentia *Rm*

[6] addit G: accedit *Rm*

up. Flux of the bowels does not enter into the combination of
signs specifically indicative of pleurisy, but merely indicates
that a particular case of the disease is severe. We hold, therefore, that the disease is to be recognized solely by those signs
which we have mentioned above. But there are many other
diverse accompanying symptoms depending on the severity of
the case and the passage of time. Since these should not be
neglected, let us discuss them at this time.

91   XIV. THE SYMPTOMS OF PLEURISY

THOSE who have pleurisy show the following symptoms:
acute fever, coughing with severe pain in the side, reaching up to the collarbone and the shoulder blade of the side affected, in some cases also touching the arm, chest, and iliac
region. It is a pricking, throbbing, and burning pain, continuous or intermittent, and [in the latter case] appearing at regular or irregular intervals, persistently adhering to the same
places or else moving about, returning, and changing. It is accompanied by sighing, difficulty in breathing (Greek *dyspnoea*),
a cough dry in some cases but frequently with fluid discharges
at first frothy, then bloody, then bilious, and then sanious. Patients are able to lie on the side affected, but when they turn
on the opposite side they experience pain and actually feel the
inflamed organs hanging and being drawn down by their own
weight. There is also sleeplessness, and the tongue is dry and
rough.

92   If the disease grows worse, all the symptoms mentioned become more pronounced. There are, in addition, the following
symptoms: limbs cold and numb, cheeks red, eyes blood red,
frothy and bilious flux from the bowels; also frequent discharge
of urine, a little at a time, of whitish color; pulse thick, rapid,
and strong, but somewhat uneven and indicating the distress
by its beat; rapid and weak breathing accompanied by pain all
around; dewy perspiration on face and chest; mental aberration; a wheezing sound in the throat, or a resonant or hissing
sound within, on the side affected; vomiting of what has been
swallowed; and inability to find a comfortable position in which
to lie. The sputa dry quickly, especially as they become more
unnatural and coagulated. And frothy sputa are followed by

93 guinolenta in livorem, item fellea aeruginosa atque prasina vel
nigra efficiunt⟨ur et⟩[7] saniosa faeculenta vel fumosa et odore
gravia et inaequalia, mutato etiam saepe ordine suae egestionis.
item post felleam vel saniosam qualitatem in sanguineam transeunt vel quamlibet coloris varietatem. tumoris etiam vehementia luctante alia in soliditatem coguntur, alia in nigredinem
veniunt ob fervoris usturam. aliqua ruptis vasculis funduntur,
quae propterea neque saniosa qualitate post sanguinea[8] perseverant, sed spumosa rursum fient,[9] cum singulas per partes tumor quatiens liquida spiritu turbato spumosam sufficit qualitatem. in ultimo autem cogente periculo celerrima fiet spiratio, et
praecordiorum suspensa adductio, pulsus inordinatus aut deficiens aut deserens in his quae in peripneumonicam passionem
aut apostema transire noscuntur.

94   at si ipsa fuerit[10] levigata, singula mitescunt et ventris egestio
coagulatur, aut fellea carebit qualitate, et per tussiculam exclusa saniosa minime in sanguinolenta redeunt.

discernendum etiam quae sint sputa saniosa, et quae sit sanies.
nam saniosa iam mitescentis tumoris atque declinantis solutione
esse probantur; sanies vero ex apostemate, quod etiam vomicam
dicere poterimus, vel certe ex ulcere probatur venire. discernitur autem exercita inventione, hoc est colore et substantia et
odore: frequenter enim tetri odoris est sanies. item saniosa admixtione aquae facile solvuntur, sanies autem difficile.

dolorem vero peiorem alii dexteri lateris probant, ob pulmonis
vicinitatem; alii sinistri, vicinantis cordis causa, forsitan et quia
frequentius sinistra dextris debiliora videntur. item pleuritis

[7] efficiunt *G*: fiunt *Rm*

[8] *fort.* sanguineam

[9] quapropter ea neque saniosa qualitas, post sanguinea perseverat, sed spumosa
rursum fiet *G*: ea neque *om. R*

[10] fuerit *R*: fuerint *G*

1. Or, if *efficiunt* be retained: 'yellowish, rusty, green, or black sputa give way to
sanious, feculent, etc.'

93   bloody, and bloody by leaden-colored. Then the sputa become yellowish, rusty, green, or black, and also sanious, feculent, fumy, of pungent odor, and quite variable,[1] the order in which the different kinds appear often changing. And after being yellowish or sanious, the sputa become blood red or any other color. As the severity of the inflammation continues, the sputa in part coagulate into a firm mass, and in part turn to blackness under the action of the burning heat. Some sputa are given up when blood vessels are ruptured; these sputa do not for that reason remain blood red after changing from sanious,[2] but become frothy again when the inflammation agitates the pneuma and whips up the fluids in the several parts, giving them this frothy quality. And finally, when danger is imminent, the respiration becomes very rapid, the precordial region is drawn up and distended, and the pulse irregular, breaking off or failing in those cases which are obviously passing into pneumonia or empyema.

94   On the other hand, however, if a case of pleurisy improves, the various symptoms are allayed, the discharge from the bowels becomes more solid and loses its bilious character, and the sanious matter brought up in coughing does not give way again to blood-red matter.

And we must distinguish between sanious sputa and sanies itself. For sanious sputa obviously come from an inflammation which is decreasing in intensity and waning through dissolution. But sanies is found to come from an abscess (*apostēma*, which we may translate *vomica*), or at any rate from an ulceration. They may also be distinguished by what is found in practice, that is, on the basis of color, substance, and smell. Thus sanies frequently has a foul odor. Again, sanious sputa are easily dissolved by the addition of water, while sanies can be dissolved in this way only with difficulty.

Some assert that it is worse for the right side to be affected, because of the proximity of the lung; others for the left, because of the proximity of the heart, and perhaps, too, because the parts on the left frequently seem weaker than those on the right. Finally, pleurisy sometimes appears together with a fever,

2. Or, if *sanguineam* be read: 'do not remain sanious after changing from blood red, but become, etc.'

nunc eodem tempore febriculae concurrit, nunc supervenit, nec
antecedit, ⟨nec⟩ cessante[11] febricula perseverat.

95 XV. QUOMODO INTELLIGIMUS PLEURITICAM PAS-
SIONEM IN PERIPNEUMONICAM TRANSEUNTEM
AUT IN VOMICAM VENIENTEM

INTELLIGIMUS eos qui in augmento pleuriticae constituti passionis proni atque faciles in peripneumonicam videntur, cum
ceteris omnibus peiorantibus signis atque in magnitudinem extentis solus dolor minuitur, atque iacendi positio ex parte facilior ac levior supina aegro fuerit visa, aucto genarum rubore,
conductu etiam superciliorum e medio vehementer tamquam in
maestitudine constitutis,[1] articulorum attestante fervore.

eos etiam qui in vomicam transeunt intelligimus ex eo quod
dolor infixus eodem permaneat loco, accedente tussicula arida
atque tremore typico et inordinato, spiratione difficili, quam
graece[2] dyspnoean vocant, cum dolore leviore et pulsu denso.

96   XVI. QUIS LOCUS IN PLEURITICIS PATITUR

QUAESITUM etiam est a veteribus quis in pleuriticis locus patiatur, et quidam pulmonem pati dixerunt, ut Euriphon,
Euenor, Praxagoras, Herophilus, Philotimus. item quidam hypezocota membranam quae latera ex interiore[1] cingit, ut Diocles,
Erasistratus, Asclepiades, et eorum plurimi sectatores.

horum primi aiunt non esse in lateribus tumorem, cum neque
extantia ulla earum partium inspectione sentiatur, neque rubor,
nec motu nec tactu dolor acutus vel fortis, tamquam manifestis
tumoribus. accedit etiam quod facile supra id latus quod patitur iacere possint aegrotantes, supra aliud vero quod passione
liberum videtur si se iactaverint, difficultas spirationis accedat,
siquidem nunc sustentatae pulmonis partes iaceant, nunc vel-

---

[11] nunc antecedit, cessante G, *sed cf. 89, 102 al.*: nunc antecedit, ⟨nec⟩ cessante *Rm*

[1] constitutus G: *corr. R*

[2] Graeci *Haller* (*cf. Ac. i. 4*)   [1] ex interiore] et interiora *edd.*

---

3. Or, retaining the reading of G: 'sometimes precedes a fever and may persist
when the fever has passed.' This does not accord with Soranus' definition and discussion;
but the reference may be to a kind of latent pleurisy. See also 88.

sometimes supervenes upon a fever, but does not precede a fever, and does not persist when the fever has passed.[3]

95 ## XV. HOW TO RECOGNIZE THAT A CASE OF PLEURISY IS PASSING INTO PNEUMONIA OR EMPYEMA

WHEN cases of pleurisy are in their increasing phase, we may recognize those which seem to be on the verge of passing into pneumonia by the fact that all the characteristic signs [of pleurisy] are aggravated and intensified, with the sole exception of the pain. The latter is reduced, and the patient finds lying on his back somewhat easier and less painful. But his cheeks become even redder, his eyebrows are sharply drawn toward each other, as in those who are grieving, and his limbs are hot.

And we may recognize those who are passing into empyema from the following indications: pain becoming fixed in one place and remaining there, dry cough, trembling [due to fever] recurring at regular or irregular intervals, difficulty in breathing (Greek *dyspnoea*), less severe pain, and a rapid pulse.

96 ## XVI. THE PART AFFECTED IN PLEURISY

THE ancients asked what part was affected in pleurisy, and some declared that it was the lung. Among these were Euryphon, Euenor, Praxagoras, Herophilus, and Phylotimus. Again, others declared that it was the pleural membrane, which girds the sides internally. Among these were Diocles, Erasistratus, Asclepiades, and many of their followers.

Those in the former group reason as follows. 'There is no inflammation in the sides, for on inspection none of these parts is found to be swollen, and there is no redness, and no sharp or severe pain from motion or touch; all of which signs are present in obvious cases of inflammation. In addition, patients can lie without difficulty on the side affected, but if they turn upon the side that is free from the disease, they experience difficulty in breathing, for in the former case the [affected] parts of the lung are supported, but in the latter case they feel as if they

97 uti pendere sentiantur. dehinc etiam tussicula signum est ex
accedentibus[2] consequens[3] fibrarum pulmonis esudati corporis
liquoris sive cannae[4] gutturis. singula etiam et tussita[5] de pulmone venire manifestum est, qui neque venis neque arteriis
neque fibris contiguus vel admixtus esse lateri videatur, ut per
ipsum latere[6] accepta excludi posse credamus.

unde igitur dolores? numquidne pulmonis sensibiles partes in
passione constitutae causa sunt? an vero eius tumore latera
vicinantia comprimuntur, et propterea dextrarum fibrarum tumor dextri lateris dolorem facit, sinistrarum sinistri? sed in
peripneumonicis totus tumet pulmo nec ullus tamen sequitur
dolor.

sed huic quidem sententiae contrarii aiunt propterea neque ruborem neque extantiam vel dolorem aegrotantes consequi, siqui-
98 dem in alto tumor esse videatur. quod autem supra patiens latus
quosdam iacere prohibet, alios vero contra mitescendo relevat,
illa causa est quod incumbendo obiectu straminum pressa materia refugiat, atque ex partibus quae patiantur ad sanas partes
rediens dolorem non faciat; at vero partibus non patientibus expressa atque fugata se patientibus impartiens et has distendens
dolorem facit. tussicula vero fiet compatientibus[7] hypezocoti
membranae vicinis atque contiguis partibus, et tussita[8] itidem
sputa per pulmonem feruntur, siquidem in ipsum veniant ex
vicinis accepta per vias mente sensas, quas logotheoretos appellant,[9] sicuti et in vomicis[10] contingit, quamquam frequenter
ad externas partes verticem faciant, vel fracto latere sanguino-

[2] *an scrib.* accidentibus?: antecedentibus *Bendz 92*

[3] consequens ⟨morbum⟩ *R*

[4] cannae *R*: canna *G*

[5] et tussita] extussita *Rm* (*cf. 98*)

[6] latera *G*: *corr. R*

[7] cum patientibus *G*: *corr. R*

[8] et tussita] extussita *Rm*

[9] appellat *G*: *corr. A*

[10] vomicosis *Wellmann, Diocles Frag. 64*

1. The general line of argument is clear enough, but the text of the sentence is very
uncertain. With this section cf. *Anon. Paris.*, p. 93.

97 are hanging down. Again, of the characteristic symptoms of pleurisy the cough is an indication that bodily fluids are being discharged from the lobes of the lung or the windpipe.[1] And the matter coughed up each time clearly comes from the lung; for the lung obviously has no contact or connection with the side, either by its veins, arteries, or lobes, to justify an assumption that the liquid matter could have been obtained from the side and passed off through the lung.'

From where, then, do the pains [in the side] come? Surely the cause is not to be found in the diseased condition of the sensitive parts of the lung. Or does the inflammation of the lung cause the side near [the affected lobe] to be compressed, so that inflammation of the right lobes of the lung causes pain in the right side, inflammation of the left lobes pain in the left side? But in cases of pneumonia it is the whole lung that is inflamed, and yet there is no pain at all.

Now those who are opposed to the view [that in pleurisy the lung is the part affected] reply that neither [visible] redness nor swelling nor [external] pain is present [in pleurisy] for the reason 98 that the inflammation is obviously deep-seated. And the fact that some patients find it impossible to lie on the side affected, while others, on the contrary, rest more easily on that side and are relieved, may be explained as follows.[2] As the patient lies on that side the liquid matter there, because of the counterpressure of the bed, runs off; since it passes from the diseased parts to the healthy parts, it does not produce pain. But when matter is pressed out of the healthy parts and driven off, it runs into the diseased parts, distending them and causing pain. And the cough results because the parts neighboring and contiguous to the pleural membrane are affected along with it; and the sputa are in each case carried through the lung before being coughed up, for they enter the lung from the surrounding parts through pores that can be apprehended only by the intellect (Greek *logotheōrētoe*). This is similar to what happens in cases of empyema (though often the head of the abscess is pointed outward), or in cases of fracture of the side, when bloody sputa are coughed

2. What follows gives a reason why patients feel relieved when lying on the affected side, and pain when lying on the opposite side. This is not what the foregoing sentence promises; and the discrepancy may be evidence of a corruption somewhere in the line of tradition since Soranus' time.

99 lenta excludantur sputa. nam profecto insensibilis omnis est pulmo: debuit igitur nullus fieri dolor. sed si ex oppressione hypezocotis membranae ex pulmone vicino tumente dolor fiet, debuit magis aegrotans tunc dolere quoties iacuerit in latus,[11] siquidem tunc magis incumbens opprimit pulmo. dehinc etiam peripneumonicos dolere oportuit: si enim ex parte tumens pulmo dolorem facit, magis omnis in tumore constitutus facere debuit.[12] patitur itaque hypezocos membrana et propterea dolorem vehementem facit, siquidem sit nervosa atque lateribus

100 infixa. hinc[13] denique quoties tumore densatur, ossibus vicinantibus abstenta ire latius prohibetur, et eorum conversione naturali quatitur motu atque acuti doloris accipit causas. item spiratione[14] thoracis adducti spiritus vicinitate pulsata insustentabiles dolores facit. manifesta namque coniectura est quod ipsa patiatur, siquidem tumoris augmento collectionem in pleuriticis faciat, et expirantibus saepe aegrotis nigra inveniatur. hos denique venenatos quidam vocaverunt.

igitur pleuriticam videntes passionem, non simplicem lateris dolorem, verum etiam febre acuta attestante totum corpus pati videamus,[15] etenim febres totius corporis sunt. plus tamen pati hypezocota membranam recte dicimus, siquidem sint in ipsa dolores constituti.

101 ## XVII. QUAE SUNT SIMILIA PLEURITICAE PASSIONI, ET QUOMODO INTERNOSCUNTUR

SIMILIA pleuriticae passioni dicuntur dolor lateris, collectio in eius medio constituta, item vomica, quam Graeci empyema vocant, suspirium sive spiratio difficilis, quam iidem dyspnoeam vocant, item cum[1] ad nares catarrhus, quem vocant

[11] ⟨patiens⟩ latus *Wellmann, loc. cit.*

[12] debebit *Kalbfleisch ap. Wellmann, loc. cit.*

[13] haec *Rm*

[14] spirationum *G: corr. Rm*

[15] videmus *R*

[1] cum *om. R*

---

3. Unless there has been a confusion between 'side' and 'membrane' (*pleuron* and *pleura* may refer to either), we have here one of the few ancient references to post mortem examination of internal parts. Cf. *Chr.* iii. 111.

9 up. For surely the lung itself is entirely without sensation. And consequently there ought to be no pain there. But if the pain arises from pressure upon the pleural membrane owing to an inflammation in a part of the lung near the membrane, the patient should experience more pain every time he lies upon the [affected] side, for then the lung weighs more heavily upon that side and presses down upon it. And on this assumption patients suffering from pneumonia should also experience pain. For if a lung partially inflamed causes pain, there is all the more reason why a lung completely inflamed should have this effect. Therefore, it is the pleural membrane that is the seat of the disease. And this membrane is the source of severe pain, for it is fibrous
10 and attached to the sides. And so, when it is congested by inflammation, it is checked by the adjacent ribs and kept from spreading out farther. As these ribs rise and fall in their natural motion, the membrane is agitated and acute pain is caused. Furthermore, the motion of the chest in respiration, by reason of the proximity of the air breathed in, causes the pleura to be struck repeatedly, and unbearable pains are the result. The conclusion is therefore obvious that the membrane itself is the seat of the affection. For during the active phase of the inflammation in pleurisy an abscess is produced in this membrane and often, when the patient dies, the membrane is found to be black.[3] In these latter cases some have declared that the patient was poisoned.

But when we see a case of pleurisy, let us view it not as a simple affection of the side but as an affection of the whole body accompanied by acute fever. For fevers involve the whole body. We shall be right, however, if we say that the pleural membrane is more particularly affected, for it is there that the pains are centered.

1   XVII. AILMENTS RESEMBLING PLEURISY: HOW
TO DISTINGUISH THEM FROM PLEURISY

THE following ailments are said to resemble pleurisy: pain in the side, abscess in the middle of the side, internal abscess (Greek *empyēma*), labored or painful breathing (Greek *dyspnoea*), nasal catarrh (Greek *coryza*), and finally asthma. For

coryzan, et anhelatio, siquidem supradictis tussicula atque spiratio difficilis adiuncta esse videatur, et febricula et dolores
accedentes pleuriticam passionem fingant. sed discerni atque
internosci suis proprietatibus possunt.

nam dolor lateris etiam sine febre plerumque est, et longo
tempore perseverat, vel quoties celer est sine varietate sputorum
vel excrementorum esse perspicitur. in pleuriticis vero dolor
acutus cum febribus acutis et sputis supradictis invenitur.
102 item ab empyicis, hoc est vomicosis sive collectione laborantibus, discernitur pleuritis, quod febres noxiae atque acutae et in-
ordinatae in pleuriticis inveniantur. vomicosis vero vel collectione laborantibus, antecedente corporis horrore frigido atque
dolore pungenti, eodem tempore, hoc est quo in vomicam transeunt aegrotantes, sputa sequentur, quae antea nulla fuerant, reiecto prius pure coacervato in latere collectionis causa, laterum
quoque veluti conversionem sentiunt, aliquando etiam sub ipsis
extans vel prominens collectio sentitur. in pleuriticis vero febricula ex initio vehemens atque sputa contra naturam et varia
reperiuntur. item ab spiratione difficili, et ortopnoea, et catarrho quem supra diximus ad nares fieri, et anhelatione, celeritate discernitur et febri atque dolore, siquidem illa tarda sint et
sine febribus, aliquando etiam sine dolore.

103   XVIII. QUOMODO CURANDI SUNT PLEURITICI

IACERE pleuriticos convenit mollibus stramentis, loco lucido
atque calido et mediocriter amplo, schemate quo se melius
ac facilius haberi perviderint, adhibita requie et cibi abstinentia
usque tertium diem,[1] accessionis tempore vigilantia cum articulorum tenaci blandaque defricatione manuum calidarum.
vaporanda etiam quae sunt in dolore constituta calidis pannis,
et cum accessio statum sumpserit lanis limpidis ex oleo dulci
calido expressis contegenda. adhibenda fomentatio lenis capiti
atque inguinibus et sub umbilico locis ex eodem oleo similiter
calido, et magis quando fuerint indulgentia corporis relevati

¹ diem ⟨ab⟩ *A*

---

1. Or perhaps 'a churning sensation,' with reference to the fluids present.

coughing and difficulty in breathing are found in connection with all these ailments, and if fever is present the accompanying pains simulate the disease of pleurisy. But all these ailments can be distinguished from pleurisy and recognized by their special characteristics.

Thus it is common for pain in the side to occur also without fever and to last a long time. And even in the acute cases the sputa and the excrements are not found to pass through changes. But in pleurisy the pain is always acute and accompanied by acute fever and changes in the sputa, as described above. Again, pleurisy may be distinguished from empyema, that is, vomica or abscess, by the distressing, acute, and irregular fevers that are found in pleurisy. But in cases of empyema the body first experiences cold shivers and a piercing pain, and then, as soon as the patient passes into the empyemic condition proper, there are sputa, though there had been none previously, and the pus that had collected in the side to form the abscess is first given up. And these patients have a sort of twisting[1] sensation at the sides, and sometimes also a prominent and conspicuous accumulation may be seen at the sides. But in cases of pleurisy there is a severe fever from the beginning and the sputa are found to be abnormal and of varying color. Again, by its acuteness, fever, and pain, pleurisy is distinguished from dyspnoea, orthopnoea, nasal catarrh, which we mentioned above, and asthma. For these diseases are chronic, without fever, and sometimes even without pain.

XVIII. THE TREATMENT OF PLEURISY

A PATIENT with pleurisy should lie on a soft bed in a well-lighted, warm, and fairly large room. Have him lie in the position in which he finds he is most comfortable. Keep him quiet, give him no food until the third day, and during the attack keep him awake and hold and massage his limbs gently with warm hands. Heat the parts that are in pain by applying warm cloths, and when the attack has already reached its highest stage cover these parts with scoured wool wrung out of warm sweet olive oil. Apply a soothing fomentation to the head, the groin, and the parts below the navel, using the same olive oil similarly heated. More extensive use of this treatment should

aegrotantes. sin minus, addenda[2] etiam cataplasmata ex polline
104 atque lini semine et faenugraeci cum aqua et oleo coctis;[3] tunc
oris collutio[4] et potus[5] aquae calidae moderate quidem ne plurima liquoris humectatio sputorum provocet fluorem. tunc
somno dimittendus aegrotans. at si venter influxerit, poterit
somnus ante dimissionem permittente hoc est declinante accessione accersiri, prohibitis[6] scilicet laxativis cataplasmatibus.

sed si dolor vehemens fuerit, phlebotomiam convenit adhibere: si nullus ventris fuerit fluor, intra tertium diem, sin vero
fuerit adiuncta ventris solutio, in ipsa diatrito erit phlebotomia
adhibenda, ut praediscere possimus utrum sit perseverans atque
superior strictura magis quam solutio. saepe enim concurrens
ventris solutioni sanguinis detractio aegrotanti novissimam in-
105 tulit defectionem. quapropter perspiciendum utrum usque ad
dimissionem accessionis fluor ventris perseveret, vel eius meatio
mordicationem quandam faciat podici vel intestinis. suspecta
etenim habenda est istiusmodi defluxio.

atque ita adhibenda phlebotomia, sed ex alio brachio, quod
fuerit dolenti lateri contrarium, certae rationis causa quam saepe
memoravimus. tunc post mediocrem sanguinis missionem, quae
magis conicienda est ex coniunctione quamquam levissimae solutionis, quiescere permittimus aegrotantem, atque resumptum
laxativa perunctione curari, oris etiam adhibita fomentatione.
digesto scilicet adiutorii turbore, dabimus sorbilem cibum ex
oleo dulci confectum sive melle, ne liquidorum provocentur
sputa importunitate temporis, hoc est initio sive augmento pas-
106 sionis. dabimus etiam pultem calidam atque madidam sine
sale, vel panem ex aqua calida; sed si venter influxerit, pultem

---

[2] *fort.* adhibenda

[3] coctis *R*: cocta *G*

[4] collutio *coni. Bendz 58*: collutione *G*: collutione (utendum) *R*

[5] potu *R* (collutione *retento*)

[6] prohibitis (adhibitis *R*: prohibitus *A*) accersiri *G*

be made in cases where the patient finds relief in this soothing of the body. But if he is not relieved, poultices of flour, flaxseed, and fenugreek seed boiled in water and olive oil should also be 04 applied. Then give the patient a mouth wash and warm water to drink, but in moderate quantity, lest an excessive amount of moisture from the liquid stimulate the flow of sputa. Then let him sleep. And if there is flux of the bowels, it will be proper to induce sleep even before the remission, provided that the attack is declining and so permits of it,[1] but in that event, of course, do not use relaxing poultices.

If there is severe pain, it is well to perform venesection. This should be done before the end of the third day if there has been no flux of the bowels. If, however, the bowels have been loose, we must wait until the end of the three-day period to perform venesection, so that we may be able to tell whether the state of stricture is stronger and more persistent than the state of looseness.[2] For the withdrawal of blood coming at the very time of flux of the bowels has often caused a sudden collapse. 05 We must therefore see whether the flux persists to the time of the remission of the attack, and whether the evacuation causes any griping at the anus or in the intestines. For a discharge of this sort must be watched carefully.

Venesection, then, should be performed, but on the arm opposite the side affected, for the very reason we have often given. And when a moderate amount of blood has been withdrawn, an amount that must largely depend on whether a condition of looseness, however slight, is present, permit the patient to rest, and when he has recovered have him anointed as a relaxing measure, and foment his face. When the disturbance caused by the venesection is over, give the patient soft food prepared in sweet olive oil or honey, to avoid stimulating the expectoration of liquids at an unfavorable time, that is, at the beginning or in 06 the increasing phase of the disease. Also give the patient a well-diluted warm porridge without salt, or bread that has been dipped in water. But if there has been a flux of the bowels, give

1. Sleep is astringent according to the Methodists. Since pleurisy essentially involves *strictura*, sleep is contraindicated during an attack. The rule is relaxed to the extent of permitting sleep during the declining phase of an attack in the event that elements of *solutio* (e.g., flux of the bowels) give the case a complex character (*status mixtus*).

2. Though venesection is to be performed in either case, the amount of blood to be withdrawn will differ, as the sequel indicates.

dabimus crassiorem sed calidam, siquidem tumentes prius partes
incurrat. tunc post cibum somno dimittimus aegrotantes usque
ad solitum accessionis tempus.

quae cum fuerit effecta, erunt adhibenda quae supra memoravimus congrua. adhibendus etiam cucurbitae levissimus raptus, sed cum statum ceperit[7] accessio, adiecta etiam scarificatione. cum ad dimissionem declinando pervenerit, tunc spongiarum vaporatio atque cataplasmata laxativa frequenti mutatione novata. sed si ventris fuerit fluor, erit quidem his utendum ob tumorem, siquidem immutabilis dolor augeat liquidorum
107 defluxionem vigiliarum atque corruptae digestionis causa. iniciendi[8] sunt[9] igitur aegrotantes plantaginis suco [reficiuntur][10]
et aliquando simplici, aliquando admixta acacia, aut ptisanae
suco quo sit praecoctus mali punici cortex, vel myrti aut agrestis celsae coma, quam rubum vocant, aut rosa vel galla et his
similia.

etenim alia quaeque nimium constrictivae virtutis vel multorum admixtione composita immodica[11] densatione maiores membranarum fieri provocant necessario tumores, quos passionis nequitia et tardare faciles et adiutoriis medicinalibus cedere difficiles facit, adiuncta scilicet solutione. quare cum prolixiores
fieri viderimus dimissiones, clystere utemur solutione cessante,
cataplasmatibus autem et cucurbitae[12] scarificatione, cum doloris fuerit dimissio.

108 at si solutus fuerit aut levigatus dolor, ut ordinem accessionum
servans magnitudine tamen minutus esse videatur, urgente etiam solutione, iniectione utemur supradicta, prohibita scilicet
vaporatione, atque cataplasmatibus submotis et scarificatione
supra dicta, apponentes palmulas quas patetos vocant contritas,
atque pannis calidis. potum dabimus calidum quidem sed omnino paucissimum, ut neque liquore plurimo sputorum vel ventris augeatur defluxio et tepore quodam tumentia mitigentur:
omne etenim frigus tussiculam commovet. danda[13] denique
pulticula sed constrictior, vel panis ex aqua calida diligenti infusione atque innovatione calidae elutus et expressus, ut suae
densitatis positu elentescat.

---

[7] caeperit G: coeperit R

[8] iniciendi *Helmreich 322*: initiandi G

[9] *post* sunt *interpunx. edd.: corr. Schmid Mn 138*

[10] *secl. Schmid Mn 139*

[11] in modica G: *corr. Rm*

[12] *fort.* cucurbita ⟨cum⟩

[13] danda *scripsi*: deinde G

him a thicker porridge, which should, however, be warm, since the parts it first passes are inflamed. After giving him this food, permit him to sleep until the expected time for the next attack.

When this attack comes, apply the remedies we mentioned above as being suitable. Also apply cups of very gentle action, but when the attack reaches its highest stage use cupping with scarification. And when the attack declines and there is a remission, apply heat with sponges, and employ soothing poultices, renewing them frequently. Even if there has been a flux of the bowels, these remedies must still be used because of the inflammation, for the constant pain, by causing sleeplessness and spoiled digestion, aggravates the discharge of fluid. In that case give the patient a clyster of plantain juice, either plain or mixed with acacia; or use pearl barley water in which has been boiled pomegranate rind, myrtle leaves, leaves of the wild bramble called *rubus*, rose leaves, oak gall, or the like.

But other remedies having excessively astringent properties or made by mixing many ingredients inevitably aggravate the inflammation of the membranes by their strong astringent action. The stubbornness of the disease makes these inflammations prone to persist and makes it hard for us to get them to yield to curative measures, obviously because a state of looseness is also involved. Therefore, when the remissions are observed to last for a considerable time, if the condition of looseness ceases, use the clyster, but also apply plasters and make use of scarification in connection with cupping during a remission of the pain.

And if the pain has been completely dissipated, or so alleviated that, though it varies with the stage of the attack, it is obviously less intense, but the looseness still persists, use the clyster as described above, but, of course, stop using the hot applications, poultices, and scarification. Instead, chop up juicy dates (Greek *patētoe*) and apply them with warm cloths. Give the patient a warm drink, but only a very little to avoid any increase in the flow of sputa or aggravation of the flux of the bowels through the taking-in of too much fluid. The warmth, however, will serve to soothe the inflamed parts; for everything cold irritates a cough. Then give the patient a rather thick porridge, or bread carefully washed by the repeated pouring-on of warm water, the water being then pressed out, leaving the bread tender and without its former hardness.

109   at si iugi vexatione tussiculae atque conatu frequenti eruptio venulae sanguinem per os emitti coegerit, dabimus plantaginem dimissionis tempore oleris vice mandendam. etenim in accessione omne quod datum fuerit corrumpi atque acescere necesse est, olera praecipue. dabimus etiam decoctorum aquam cydoniorum. at si in ipsa accessione id facere coacti sumus insistente periculo, dabimus poscam; tunc in dimissione cibum, ut liquori soliditas accedat, alicam ex aqua calida in qua fuerint praecoctae palmulae thebaicae vel mala cydonia, ut eorum frigore sanguinis fluor teneatur, fervore vero tussicula leniatur. erit praeterea, si vires aegrotantis permiserint, alternis diebus dandus cibus donec passio declinet. at si imbecillitas coegerit, etiam ante declinationis tempus erit cotidie nutriendus aegrotans.

110   in statu vero mitescentibus atque segnescentibus sputis, et nullis irruentibus novis saniosae etiam qualitatis effectis, sine ventris fluore, convenit post cataplasmata atque vaporationem ante cibum dare bibendum mulsum diebus duobus vel tribus. etenim tussiculam mitigat et spirationem facilem facit, liquidorum tenacitatem laxat et eas partes ex quibus sputa feruntur depurgat. cibum dabimus sorbilem ex melle atque halicam vel siliginis panem et amylum aut ptisanam aut panem ex mulso aut ovum hapalum.

declinante passione, si aliqua fuerit sputorum difficultas ob debilitatem virium vel liquidorum crassitudinem, erit faenugraeci
111 sucus admiscendus melli hoc genere confectus. duobus diebus erit faenugraeci semen infundendum, sed frequenti mutatione aqua innovanda, praefusa scilicet anteriore. tunc donec color virescat aqua coquenda, et eliquata admixto melle aegro supra dicta moderatione bibenda. potest[14] etiam ipsum faenugraeci semen tritum cum melle lambere, vel lini semen assatum melli admixtum, vel vitellum ovi assati nucleis recentibus contritum

14 prodest *Rm*

09   But if the constant agitation and the repeated strain of coughing cause the rupture of a small blood vessel, so that blood has
to be emitted through the mouth, give the patient plantain as
a green to chew on. This should be done at the time of a remission, for during an attack all food necessarily spoils and turns
sour, especially greens. Also give the patient water in which
quinces have been cooked. If, however, you have to stop the
flow of blood in the midst of an attack because of the pressing
danger, give him diluted vinegar; and then, at the time of the
remission, in order that something solid may be added to the
liquid, give him food. This food may consist of spelt groats prepared in hot water in which Theban dates or quinces have previously been cooked, so that the flow of blood may be checked
by the cooling properties of these substances while the cough
may be relieved by the warmth [of the preparation]. And if
the strength of the patient permits, food should be given him on
alternate days until the disease declines. But if his weakness
compels it, he should be fed every day, even before the time of
the decline.

10   And at the highest stage of the disease, if the sputa become
milder and begin to abate, and no new sputa of a sanious nature are produced, and there is no flux of the bowels, it is helpful, after applying poultices and heat but before giving the patient food, to give him mead to drink. This procedure should be
followed for two or three days; for it soothes the cough, eases
respiration, loosens viscous fluids, and cleans out the parts from
which the sputa are carried up. And then give the patient soft
food with honey: spelt groats, bread of fine wheat flour, starch,
pearl barley, or bread soaked in mead may be served, or else a
soft egg.

      In the decline of the disease, if there is any difficulty in bring-
ing up the sputa by reason of the patient's weakness or the
thickness of the fluids, prepare a mixture of fenugreek juice and
11   honey as follows. Soak fenugreek seed in water for two days, the
water being constantly changed, that is, new water added after
the old has been poured off. Then heat the water until it becomes green, strain it, add the honey, and give it to the patient
to drink in moderate amount, as indicated above. The patient
may also take powdered fenugreek seed with honey; or roasted
flaxseed mixed with honey; or the yolk of a baked egg chopped

atque decocto melli admixtum, vel simul omnia admixtis etiam amaris amygdalis.

tunc convenit vario iam cibo aegrotantem reficere pultibus, ovis hapalis, vel cerebro porcino aut haedino aut agnino, coctis cum sale modico, vel pede porcino in ptisana decocto, aut molli 112 gallinaceo pullo vel columbinaceo.[15] tunc post tres vel quatuor dies solutis febribus adhibendum lavacrum, sed a vino temperandum. illis quoque partibus quae dolore tanguntur cerotaria apponenda[16] ex oleo dulci vel cyprino confecta, admixto faenugraeci polline vel meliloto tuso atque creto, admixtis etiam adipibus. utendum quoque medicamine quod diatessaron vocant, cera, resina terebinthina, iri illyrica, pice, aequis ponderibus. dehinc post unum[17] vel duos adhibendum lavacrum, et dandum vinum; apponendum malagma quod diachylon vocant, vel Mnaseu.[18]

haec ratio secundum Soranum curationis. antiquorum vero Erasistratus et Herophilus de pleuriticis nihil dixerunt.

113   XIX. AD HIPPOCRATEM

HIPPOCRATES, volumine quo De ptisana scripsit, ad pleuriticos curandos haec ait. lateris dolor sive ex initio effectus sive supernatus principio vaporis erit curatione tentandus: in qua meliorem probamus ex aqua calida in utriculo[1] vel vesica constitutum hunc ad modum, vel in aeneo vasculo sive testeo, supposito quolibet stramine molli ne quassatio fiat locorum, scilicet qui in dolore sunt. probat etiam spongiam mollem magnam ex ferventi aqua expressam atque involutam, tunc apponendam. circumtectus, inquit, enim atque inclusus vapor plu-

---

[15] columbino *Bendz Eran 43. 45*

[16] ponenda *edd.*

[17] ⟨diem⟩ unum *R: sed cf. Chr. ii. 217*

[18] Mnaseu *scripsi*: diamna *G*: Dia Mannae *R*

[1] utriculo *Rm*: ventriculo *G*

---

3. Or, if *diamannēs* be read, 'the plaster of frankincense.' But this plaster is nowhere else mentioned by Caelius (though it is referred to by Galen), whereas the plaster of Mnaseas is frequently mentioned by Caelius and almost always in conjunction with *diachylon*.

up with fresh pine kernels and mixed with boiled honey; or, indeed, all these together, with the addition of bitter almonds.

Afterward it is well to restore the patient's strength with
varied food, e.g., porridges, soft eggs, brains of pig, kid, or lamb,
cooked with a moderate amount of salt; or pig's trotters cooked
12 in pearl barley water, or tender young chickens or squabs. Then
after three or four days when the fever has completely broken
up, prescribe bathing; but do not allow the patient any wine.
And to those parts which are still affected by pain apply cerates
made with sweet olive oil or henna oil, with the addition of
fenugreek flour or melilot pounded up and sifted, and also of
fat. Use also a preparation of four ingredients (Greek *diates-
sarōn*), containing wax, resin of the terebinth tree, Illyrian iris,
and pitch, in equal weights. Then after one or two days prescribe bathing, give the patient wine, and apply the emollient
plaster of juices or that of Mnaseas.[3]

The above is the system of treatment of pleurisy according
to Soranus. Of the ancients, neither Erasistratus nor Herophilus
had anything to say about the treatment of this disease.

13   XIX. REPLY TO HIPPOCRATES

B[UT] in the book which he wrote *On the Ptisan* Hippocrates
has the following to say on the treatment of pleurisy.[1] 'In
treating pain in the side, whether it is present at the beginning
of an illness or a later development, the application of heat
should first be tried. We believe the best arrangement for heating is as follows: use hot water in a small skin or bladder container, or in a bronze or earthen vessel, and place some soft
padding beneath the vessel to avoid irritating the parts which
are in pain. It is also advisable to apply a large, soft sponge
wrung out of hot water and wrapped round. For heat, if con-

1. *Reg. ac.*, pp. 119. 10—121. 20 Kuehl. (II. 268–78 Littré). There are many divergences, not only in details but in the most important ideas, between the traditional Hippocratic text and Caelius' version. I shall call attention in these notes only to a few of
the divergences. It is impossible to say definitely which are due to pre-Caelian and which
to post-Caelian corruption; and the text Soranus worked with may have differed considerably from that on which Galen wrote his commentary. R emended the text of
Caelius on the basis of the traditional Hippocratic text, but this procedure may be
carried too far.

rimo tempore perseverat. admovendus[2] etiam tamquam odoramentum ori vel naribus aegrotantis ut spiramento adductus[3]
suo ingressu laxamentum partibus administret. utendum inquit etiam ⟨hordeo vel⟩[4] ervo in[5] aceto miti macerato et cale-
114 facto, et celeriter sacello incluso, tunc apposito, sive cantabro
eodem genere fervefacto. vel aridae atque siccae vaporationes
adhibendae, ut sunt ex sale sive milio frixo in sacellis laneis
aptissime appositae. etenim leve[6] atque conducibile est milium:
solvet[7] namque naturali quadam mollitudine illos dolores qui
iugulum in ipsis passionibus pulsant; non aliter etiam illos qui
has partes ⟨non⟩ pulsaverint solvit.

at si dolor vaporationibus minime fuerit mitigatus vel absces-
sus,[8] non oportet plurimo tempore in hac perseverare curatione:
etenim pulmonem vaporatio siccat atque purulentum fieri cogit.
sed si doloris significatio ad iugulum vel ad brachium tetenderit
cum gravedine, ut etiam pectus vel mamillam tangere videatur,
oportet in brachio venam dividi, sed in eo ex[9] quo multa fieri detractio possit, donec plurimum rubrior sanguis excludatur, vel
115 ex rubro ⟨ac⟩[10] limpido lividus. utraque, inquit, enim eveniunt.

sed si sub pectore fuerit dolor et ad iugulum non tetenderit,
emolliendus est venter aut helleboro nigro aut peplio: nigro, admixto dauco vel seseli aut cumino sive aniso, vel aliud quod-
cumque tranquillum admiscendum putat; ⟨peplio vero⟩,[11] id
est portulacae,[12] silphii[13] sucum praestare. quae enim admiscemus sibi similigena haec sunt quae supra diximus. deducit autem melius ventrem helleborum nigrum quam deducit[14] peplion;
peplion[15] autem helleboro nigro ventositatem melius tollit per
podicem provocatam. haec denique utraque dolorem solvunt.
mitigant etiam alia plurima: haec sunt, inquit, deducentia sive
trahentia per effusionem summa quae ipse scivi atque posui;

[2] admovenda G

[3] adductus ⟨vapor⟩ R: adducta G   [6] lene *edd., sed gr.* κοῦφον

[4] *suppl.* R   [7] solvit R, *ut infra*

[5] ervo in *conieci*: bono G: orobo in *Rm*   [8] *fort.* abscissus *vel* abscisus

[9] in eo ex] interiorem *Bendz Eran 41. 69, coll. 122*

[10] ex rubro ⟨ac⟩ R, *coll. gr.* ἀντὶ καθαροῦ τε καὶ ἐρυθροῦ: cum rubro G

[11] *suppl. Rm*

[12] portulacam G   [14] deducit *om.* R

[13] silphii *Rm*: vel peplii G   [15] peplios G

fined and covered on all sides, lasts a very long time. Apply this
heat like an aromatic substance to the patient's face or nose,
so that it may be drawn in by the act of inhaling, and, on entering, bring relief to the parts.[2] Also use barley or vetch soaked in
mild vinegar; boil and quickly place in a small bag, and then
14 apply. Bran similarly heated may also be used. Or apply dry
heat, which may best be done with salt or roasted millet in wool-
en bags. For millet has a gentle and soothing quality, and by
its natural softness dispels those pains that reach the collarbone in this type of disease. And it likewise dispels those pains
that do not reach these parts.[3]

'But if the pain is not relieved or checked by the application
of heat, do not continue this treatment for very long. For heating dries the lung and causes it to become purulent. But if there
are indications of pain extending as far as the collarbone or
arm, together with a feeling of heaviness that seems also to affect the chest or breast, open the vein[4] in that arm from which
a large withdrawal of blood can be made. The withdrawal
should continue until the blood flowing out is very much red-
15 der or turns bluish from clear and red. For either of these cases
may occur.

'If, however, the pain is under the chest, and does not reach
the collarbone, soften the bowels with either black hellebore or
peplium. To the black hellebore should be added Cretan carrot,
seseli, cumin, anise, or any other soothing substance; but to the
peplium, i.e., purslane, it is best to add silphium juice. For the
substances we add, that is, those which we have just mentioned,
are homogeneous. Now black hellebore purges the bowels more
effectively than peplium; but peplium is better than black hellebore for overcoming flatulence, forcing the wind out through
the anus. Both these substances dispel pain. And many other
substances offer relief; but, of the drugs which clean out or
withdraw matter through a flux of the bowels, those which I
have indicated are the best I know of and have applied. Also

2. This sentence is quite at variance with the traditional Hippocratic text.

3. In the traditional Hippocratic text this sentence refers to venesection. In any
case ⟨non⟩ should probably be restored in Caelius because of the Greek ἢν μή (note
the corruption ημι already present in the first hand of Parisinus 2253). This makes sense,
though not Hippocratic sense, of the passage.

4. The Greek specifies the internal vein of the arm (see also 117, 122).

⟨conveniunt⟩[16] quae etiam[17] in sorbilibus dantur deductoria quae non satis sunt insuavia aut amaritudinis causa aut alia qualibet ⟨insuavitate⟩,[18] ut copiae vel coloris.

116   ptisanam igitur quando medicamen biberit statim superbibere nihil minus a congrua est ratione, vel quantum accipere consueverit; dehinc paulatim inter ventris deductionem non erit[19] sorbenda. sed quando humorum declinaverit exitus, tunc modicum sorbeat aegrotans vel quantum consuevit;[20] dehinc detractio[21] perseverare debet donec dolor cesset vel nihil contrarium occurrat. haec mihi, inquit, ratio est et in suci usu[22] ptisanae. etenim dixit melius esse statim sorbendi initium sumere et in omnibus magis ⟨quam⟩ ventris antecedentibus deductionibus. sumendum ergo est[23] initium sorbendi tertia vel quarta vel quinta vel sexta vel septima die, nisi intra id tempus fuerit aegritudo praeiudicata. haec sunt quae in primis partibus libri ordinavit.

117   alias quoque passiones curans in ultima scripturae parte rursum peripneumoniam atque pleuritim curans haec ait. in peripneumonico et pleuritico oportet inspicere utrumne acuta febricula, atque dolores alterius vel utriusque sint lateris, et utrum ascendente spiritu dolor admoneat, et tussicula vel sputa fuerint abundantia, flava, vel livida, ac tenuia, vel spumosa, vel florida, aut alia qualibet qualitate a supra dictis differentia. sic agi oportet ut si dolor pungens penetrans ad iugulum vel cinc-

---

[16] *supplevi, coll. gr.* ἀρήγει

[17] quae etiam] *fort.* etiam quae   [18] *suppl. R, coll. gr.* ἀηδίην

[19] non erit *Bendz Eran 41. 69*: noverit *G*

[20] minus sorbeat aegrotans quam consuevit *R, coll. gr.*

[21] adiectio *R, coll. gr.*

[22] succo usus *G, sed cf. gr.*

[23] sumendo ergo est *G: fort. del.* ergo est *et scrib.* sumere (*interpunctione post* deductionibus *sublata*)

suitable are purgatives in gruels, provided that they are not very unpleasant either because of bitterness or some other disagreeable feature, such as quantity or color.[5]

16 'Now immediately after drinking the purgative, the patient should drink pearl barley gruel, taking not less than a reasonable quantity, or as much as he has usually had. Then while the bowels are being evacuated, the gruel should be gradually[6] omitted. And when the outflow of liquid matter abates, let the patient take a small amount of gruel, i.e., his customary amount,[7] and maintain the reduced amount until the pain abates,[8] provided that nothing untoward occurs. This is also my rule in the use of the strained barley water. For it is better and in general preferable for the patient to begin taking it at once, rather than when evacuations of the bowels have already occurred. Thus he should begin to take it on the third, fourth, fifth, sixth, or seventh day, unless the illness reaches a crisis before that time.'[9] So much for the rules which Hippocrates gives in the earlier part of the book.

17 While discussing the treatment of other diseases in the latter part of the work, Hippocrates again takes up the treatment of pneumonia and pleurisy, and writes as follows:[10] 'In cases of pneumonia and pleurisy examine whether the fever is acute, whether the pains are on one side or on both, whether there is a sensation of pain as the breath is exhaled, whether the patient coughs, whether the sputa are copious, and whether they are reddish-yellow, bluish, or thin, frothy, and bright colored, or have other characteristics. The proper procedure is as follows. If there is a piercing pain penetrating and extending to

5. The text of this whole paragraph is badly corrupted, though the general meaning may be ascertained on the basis of the Hippocratic text.

6. The traditional Greek text has κατὰ λόγον ('the gruel should be omitted, as is reasonable'). Caelius (Soranus?) seems to have read κατ᾽ ὀλίγον. Cf. Schmid, p. 57.

7. This is a misunderstanding of the Hippocratic text, which means 'let the patient take less gruel than his customary amount,' but the Latin almost literally translates the individual words of the Greek, and it seems unwise to emend as R does.

8. The Hippocratic text: 'make gradual additions, provided that the pain has abated.'

9. The Hippocratic text is quite different: 'to begin taking it at once rather than to wait until inanition has occurred and then to begin taking it on the third, etc.' The Hippocratic sense would be approximated by reading ⟨quam⟩ ventris antecedentibus deductionibus sumere initium sorbendi tertia etc. But one can hardly assume that Caelius wrote this.

10. Reg. ac., Appendix, pp. 162. 13—164. 13 Kuehl. (= II. 456–64 Littré).

tum vel brachia tetenderit, venam incidamus in quacumque
parte facilior fuerit visa. detractionis autem modus conveniens
secundum corporis habitudinem atque temporis aetatis vel re-
118 gionis considerationem accipitur. plurimam enim detractionem
ostendit celer atque acutus dolor, quae usque ad animi defectionem erit facienda; tunc clyster adhibendus.

si inferius thorace fuerit dolor et plurimum aegrotanti[24] dis-
tenderit ventrem, ⟨purgatione utendum⟩,[25] sed medio tempore
purgationis, hoc est quo ventris officium ⟨non⟩[26] cessat, nihil
inquit accipiendum; sed post perfectam effusionem mulsum ex
aceto exhiberi iubet, quod oxymeli vocant. item quartanum
typum[27] medicamine curans, tribus aliis[28] diebus adhibendum
clysterem probat, et si passio ⟨non⟩[29] fuerit relevata, tunc inquit
purgatione utendum.

119 praecavendum etiam monet donec dies septem intacti febribus
transigant aegrotantes; tunc, inquit, tuto sucum dabimus tenerum atque parvum. at si facilius agere coeperit sputa, attestante spiratione meliore et sine ullo dolore, atque ut supra
dictum est cessante febricula, paulatim crassiore ac plurimo et
bis in die utendum praecipit suco. sin vero difficile[30] haec fuerint relevata, leni potu atque sorbili utemur cibo, hoc est suco
parvo et semel in die, tempore scilicet quo levius aeger habuerit.
atque id intelligi urinae inquit inspectione. tunc dandum sor-

---

[24] aegrotans G: aegroti R

[25] supplevi: ⟨danda purgatio⟩ R

[26] supplevi: ⟨nondum⟩ R

[27] quartum diem R

[28] fort. ab initio (gr. ἐξ ἀρχῆς)

[29] suppl. R

[30] facile G: ⟨non⟩ facile R

---

11. Cinctum here refers to the diaphragm rather than the waist. The Greek has
μάζον, 'breast.'

the collarbone, chest,[11] and arms, open a vein[12] on whichever
side seems more feasible. The amount of blood withdrawn depends on the condition of the body and considerations of the
18 season, the age of the patient, and the region.[13] For a swift
and acute disease requires the letting of a large quantity of
blood and the procedure should continue even until the patient faints. Then employ a clyster.

'If the pain is below the chest and causes considerable abdominal distention, employ a purgative.[14] But in the midst of
the activity of this purgative, that is, while the evacuation of
the bowels is not completed, the patient should not take anything. After the bowels are completely purged, however, give
the patient a mixture of honey and vinegar (Greek *oxymeli*).
And in the case of a quartan fever, before using the purge, administer a clyster on each of the [first] three days, and if the illness does not abate, then employ the purge.[15]

19 'Avoid [giving food] until seven days have passed and the patient is without fever;[16] it is then safe to give a thin gruel in
small quantity. And if the patient has begun to bring up sputa
more easily, and his respiration is easier and free from pain,
and the fever, as we have said, has passed, have him take gruel
twice each day, gradually increasing the thickness and the quantity. But if these symptoms do not readily yield to treatment,
prescribe very moderate drink, and liquid food, that is, a small
amount of the thin gruel, and only once a day, at a time when
the patient is somewhat better. This time may be determined
by an examination of the urine. And it is not until the urine and

12. The Greek specifies the internal vein of the arm (see also 122).

13. Soranus (or Caelius) probably read χώρην for the traditional χροίην ('color'). Cf.
Schmid, p. 57.

14. This version is based upon a problematical emendation of the text in partial
accord with the traditional Hippocratic text. It is possible, however, that Caelius
actually began the new sentence with *tunc clyster adhibendus si inferius*, etc. In any case
Soranus seems to have punctuated καὶ συντείνῃ λίην τῷ πλευριτικῷ τὴν κοιλίην, ὑπο-
κάθαιρε. . . .

15. τεταρταῖον of the Greek has been misunderstood, and I have translated on this
assumption rather than assume (with R) post-Caelian corruption of the Latin text.
The Greek means: 'Use the purge on the fourth day: [that is to say] employ a clyster
on each of the first three days, and if there is no relief, then use the purge.'

16. The Latin may also be interpreted 'until the patient passes seven days without
fever,' but this is probably not what Caelius (Soranus) had in mind and is certainly not
what the Hippocratic author intended.

bile quidem, nec prius tamen quam urina atque sputa visa fuerint mitiora.[31]

sed si medicatus plurima excluserit, necessario parvum atque
120 tenuem dabimus cibum: non enim potest inanitate[32] somno vel
plena affici digestione, neque passionis atque naturae conflictus
sustinere, quos Graeci crises appellant. sed cum corporis defluxio tenuem fecerit aegrotantem, retentione cessante qua[33]
naturali vigore corporis nutrimenta tardantur, sucorum nihil
valebit retinere. intelligimus autem mitiora sputa quando sunt
⟨puri⟩[34] similia; item urina cum fuerit rubrior ervi[35] ⟨in⟩[36] similitudine.[37] nihil etiam, inquit, prohibet doloribus[38] lateris adhibere tepores atque cerotaria, et unctionem crurum et clunium
pingui atque calido oleo frequentare, praecordia vero semine
lini cataplasmare usque ad papillas.

121 his Soranus respondens ait in calefactionibus acres esse sales
ac necessario tumorem provocare, febrem accendere; poscam
etiam constringere et stricturam passionis augere. item milium frixum graveolens et nidorosum atque capiti grave, maxime
acute febricitantium, esse perspicimus. spongiis etiam erat melius quemquam in dimissione patientes partes vaporare atque
oleo calido perfundere.

est praeterea improprium ac sine ratione tunc uti phlebotomo
quoties ad superiora dolor tetenderit, prohibere autem quoties
ad inferiora descenderit. oportet ergo sub hoc argumento
neque difficultate inferiorum[39] impeditos phlebotomare, neque
etiam podagricos, siquidem inferiora[40] tumere videantur. sed
⟨neque⟩[41] necessario quoties dolor ad superiora tetenderit phlebotomiam adhibendam videmus, siquidem saepe peiorante ven-

---

[31] matura *Rm, coll. gr.* πέπονα, *sed cf.* segniora *124,* mitescentibus atque segnescentibus *110, et* mitiora *infra*

[32] ⟨prae⟩ inanitate *R*

[33] *an* quo?

[34] sunt ⟨puri⟩ *A* (*gr.* τῷ πύῳ): ⟨saniei⟩ sunt *Schmid Mn 139*

[35] ervi *Rm, coll. gr.* ὀρόβων: vini *G*

[36] *suppl. Schmid Mn 140*

[37] *fort.* similitudinem

[38] ⟨et aliis⟩ doloribus *A* (*gr.* τὰ ἄλλα)

[39] inferiorum *scripsi*: tumorum *G*: articulorum *Bendz Eran 41.70*: tumorum ⟨partibus
inferioribus⟩ *R*

[40] interiora *G: corr. Rm*   [41] *suppl. Bendz Eran 41.71*

the sputa are observed to be ripe that the [thicker] gruel should be given.

'But if the patient has had a complete evacuation as a result of the purge, we must give him a small quantity of light food. 20 For because of his inanition he can neither sleep nor perform the function of digestion completely, nor endure the conflicts between nature and the disease (Greek *criseis*). And, since the flux from the body has weakened the patient, and there has been an interruption of his power of retention (a power which enables him to retain nourishment so long as his body has its normal strength), he will not be able to keep back any fluids.[17] Now we can recognize that the sputa are ripe when they are like pus; and urine when it is reddish and resembles vetch.[18] And there is no reason to avoid the use of warm applications and cerates for pains[19] of the sides, and the frequent anointing of legs and loins with grease and warm olive oil, and the application of flaxseed plasters to the precordial region as far as the nipples.'

21   In opposition to these prescriptions, Soranus writes as follows. Salts have a sharp quality when used in applications of heat and always irritate the inflammation and increase the fever. Again, vinegar water has an astringent property and aggravates the state of stricture involved in the disease. Furthermore, roasted millet is strong-smelling, as we know, and its fumes cause heaviness of the head, especially for those who are suffering from acute fever. And it would be better for one to warm the affected parts with sponges and bathe them with warm olive oil at the time of remission.

It is, moreover, inappropriate and unreasonable to make use of venesection whenever the pain spreads upward, but to reject it whenever the pain descends to the lower parts. According to such reasoning, we should have to reject venesection for those who suffer from ailments in the lower parts, even for those who have podagra, for here it is clearly the lower parts that are inflamed. Moreover, even when the pain extends upward, we know that venesection should not always be employed, for when a flux of the bowels becomes worse, this type of treatment must

17. This sentence diverges sharply from the Greek. The meaning of the Greek is: 'but when the unconcocted fluids have been passed off and these obstacles have been removed, there will be no further bar [i.e., to the giving of food].'

18. Or 'wine' (G).

19. The Greek refers to *other* pains in the sides, but it is doubtful whether the omission from the Latin is due to a textual corruption.

122 tris fluore hoc adiutorii genus prohibeatur. neque etiam, ut
ait, oportet interiorem venam dividi, siquidem et exteriori et
media divisa corpora releventur, quippe cum econtrario interiorem prohibeant[42] propter magnitudinem, ne tumor augeatur.
item sanguinis mutatio iners est detractionis moderationi, sicuti
De adiutoriis scribentes demonstrabimus. sese denique idem
Hippocrates impugnat in consequentibus dicens usque ad animi
defectum faciendam detractionem, quod magis vehementer est
nocens, siquidem sit periculosa defectio. et cum[43] sit temporaliter defectionis causa sensu carens aegrotans dolore relevatus,
videbitur cum resumptus fuerit rursum dolere, cum magis atque
magis eiusdem magnitudinis passiones[44] debilia corpora vehementius afficiant.

123   item purgativa medicamina, quae Graeci cathartica[45] vocant,
acrimoniae causa stomachum tumentem atque hypezocota membranam acuunt in tumorem et in periculum;[46] ventris[47] effusionem
provocantia manificam[48] passionis ingerunt vehementiam. nutrire
etiam cibo post medicamen non oportebat. pugnat enim purga-
tioni faciundae illatum cibi nutrimentum, quippe cum medicamine corruptum officii sui careat viribus. mitto etiam quod ex
initio acescere facile ptisanae sucus perspiciatur, confectus
quippe ex ordei suco qui sit digestione difficilis. dehinc aegrotantis corpus non valeat[49] tantum sustinere nutrimentum quantum sanitatis tempore solitum videbatur. item mulsum ex
aceto, quod oxymeli appellavit, sine discretione accipimus. est
etiam immodica usque ad septimum diem cibi abstinentia,
124 quam custodiendam ordinavit, quippe cum nullus vehementiam

[42] *fort.* prohibeat

[43] cum *conieci*: neque G: neque ⟨si⟩ R (⟨non⟩ dolere *infra*)

[44] passionis G: *corr.* R

[45] καθαρκτικὰ G (*sic*)

[46] in periculum] impetuosam *Rm*: in periculosam *A*: *fort. scrib.* in periculo, *interpunctione transposita post* tumorem

[47] *fort.* ⟨et⟩ ventris

[48] magnificam *edd.*; *cf. Ac. i. 109*

[49] valet *R*

20. This was omitted at 114 and 117.

22 be rejected. And it is not necessarily the interior[20] vein, as Hippocrates says, that should be opened. For the body is also relieved when the exterior or the middle vein is opened. And, in
fact, they [Hippocrates and his followers] should advise[21] against
opening the inner vein, because of its size, in order to avoid aggravating the inflammation. Change [in the color] of the blood
as a criterion for limiting the amount of blood withdrawn is
similarly ill-advised, as I shall show in my work *On Remedies*.
And then Hippocrates contradicts himself when he goes on to
say that the withdrawal of blood should continue until the patient faints. This is an extremely harmful procedure, for fainting is dangerous; and though the patient, having lost consciousness by reason of his collapse, is for a time relieved of his pain,
it will be observed that he suffers pain again when he recovers
consciousness. For diseases of the same intensity have an increasingly severe effect on bodies as the latter grow weaker.

23   Furthermore, because of their property of sharpness, purgative drugs (Greek *cathartica*) aggravate the inflammation of the
esophagus and cause inflammation of the pleural membrane
with consequent danger; and by exciting a flux of the bowels
they artificially aggravate the severity of the disease. Moreover, Hippocrates should not have prescribed food after the
purge, for the giving of such nourishment is an obstacle to the
effectiveness of the purge. The food decomposes under the action of the drug and lacks the power to perform its function.
And I need not point out that the pearl barley water turns sour
from the very beginning, for it is prepared from barley, which
is hard to digest. And, again, the patient's body cannot deal
with as much nutriment as seems to have been customary for it
during health. Moreover, the prescription of honey and vinegar
(Greek *oxymeli*) is, as we have it, not specific enough.[22] And
abstinence from food until the seventh day, as he prescribes, is
124 excessive.[23] For no one can endure a severe disease unless he is

21. Or perhaps the meaning is that they *do* (elsewhere) advise against opening the
inner vein, for the reason indicated. But I have not found such a passage; and it is not
certain, in any case, who 'they' are.

22. E.g., as to dosage or proportions of ingredients; but the meaning may be 'indis-
criminate,' i.e., not specifying sufficiently the type of patient to be so treated.

23. Cf. 119. The Hippocratic prescription of food directly after the purge does not
contradict the present passage, for here the prescription referred to is for cases where
there is no complete inanition.

passionis sustinere valeat, nisi nutrimento quamvis parvo to-
leratus; et neque in declinatione passionis aliquid humanius cibo
largiatur,[50] sed in iisdem sorbilibus perseverandum existimat
sucis. at cum fuerint sputa segniora, tunc (existimat) erit
primo aeger nutriendus, quomodo necessario haec declinante
passione occurrunt. intoleratum[51] in ceteris relinquendum temporibus aegrotantem apertissime indicavit,[52] cum semper plurimum utilitatis adiutorium cibi, quam cetera possunt adiutoria,
largiatur.[53]

omne etiam corpus erit unctione coaequandum, et non eius
particula, quippe cum totum cibo nutriatur, ipsa quoque unctio
non exerta anxietatem ingerit aegrotanti[54] atque[55] latentem difficultatem, atque accessione veniente corpus[56] provocat ⟨in⟩[57]
incendium.

125   XX. AD DIOCLEM

DIOCLES etiam similiter phlebotomat aegrotantes, eadem discretione adhibita. purgat etiam catharticis medicamentis,
quapropter eadem dignus accusatione iudicatur. cibum vero
iuvenibus undecima die dandum statuit, sed aestatis tempore
elixum magis et frigidum, hiemis vero assum atque ferventem.
est enim summae imperitiae[1] in ordinandis qualitatibus non
passionum genera sed tempora hiemis vel aestatis attendere,
scilicet ut aestate tumore laborantes frigido cibo nutriti altiora
percutiantur.[2]

126   XXI. AD PRAXAGORAM

PRAXAGORAS signa docens futurae pleuritidis praecavendum
iubet dando bibendum piper cum mulso ex aceto vel abrotanum aut absinthium. phlebotomat etiam non ultra quintum

---

[50] largitur R
[51] occurrunt intolerato. G
[52] an iudicavit?
[53] largiantur G: corr. R
[1] inperitiae Rm: peritiae G (ironice?)
[2] altiora percutiant G: altius percutiantur Rm

[54] aegrotantiae G: corr. R
[55] atque scripsi: qua G: quae Rm
[56] corporis Rm
[57] suppl. Schmid Mn 140

sustained by nourishment, however small. And Hippocrates does not prescribe a more liberal diet even in the declining phase of the disease, thinking that the same liquid foods should be continued. Indeed, it is only when the sputa become milder that Hippocrates thinks the patient should begin to take nourishment, on the ground that sputa are always less frequent during the decline of the disease. But he specifically prescribes that the patient must be left unsustained by nourishment at all other times, though, in fact, food always confers more benefit upon the patient than do all other remedies.

Furthermore, the whole body, and not merely parts of it, should be equally anointed.[24] For it is the whole body that is nourished by food. And unless an anointing is extensive, it causes the patient distress and internal pain and, as an attack comes on, makes the body burn.

25

XX. REPLY TO DIOCLES

DIOCLES also prescribes venesection in certain cases of pleurisy, and adopts the same criterion.[1] And he also purges with cathartics. He is therefore, in our judgment, open to the same criticism. And in the case of young patients he holds that food should first be given on the eleventh day, in summer boiled and cold, in winter roasted and hot.[2] But it betrays a complete lack of understanding to make the seasons of winter and summer rather than the nature of the ailments themselves the basis for prescribing the various qualities.[3] The obvious result of such a procedure is that those suffering from inflammation in summer are more seriously stricken by being fed cold food.

26

XXI. REPLY TO PRAXAGORAS

IN DISCUSSING the signs of a coming attack of pleurisy, Praxagoras says that precautions should be taken by giving the patient a drink of oxymel with pepper, southernwood, or worm-

24. Perhaps: 'should be relieved by the anointing.'

1. Cf. 117–18.

2. Cold and hot probably here refer to the essential quality of the food, i.e., whether cooling or heating in its action, rather than merely to the temperature of the food when served.

3. E.g., hot, cold, etc.

diem, sed eos qui non perfrictionem[1] incurrerint, neque frigido
tempore, et neque senes, neque debiles[2] corpore ante aegritudinem fuisse videantur. omnia inquit corpore curanda, et fame
magis utendum: dandum bibere mulsum ex aceto, aliquando
etiam hyssopo admixto, item sucum ptisanae sorbilem, si celerius
quarta die, si tardius sexta, atque ex illo cotidie; item celerius
senibus atque a[3] sanitate debilibus. dehinc usque ad septimum
diem ventrem emolliendum iubet, et unctionibus utendum pa-
vide[4] persuadet, atque respirationem inquit intuendam utrum
127 sit calida et odoris tetri. quibus autem redundantia est humorum in venis, exceptis senibus et a[5] sanitate debilibus, helleboro nigro purgandos existimat. item deponendos secunda vel
tertia die aegrotantes in aquam calidam iubet, vel utribus eos
calefacere, fovendo crura[6] donec dolor excludatur.

hic vero etiam non futuram pleuritim ex his quae ordinat
efficit. omnia enim constrictiva atque acria esse videntur, ut
mulsum ex aceto et piper et absinthium, quae necessario tumores accendunt, eo maxime tempore quo etiam aqua sumpta
128 in qualitatem devenit fellis ob nimium in alto fervorem. dehinc phlebotomari oportet etiam eos qui ex frigore incurrisse
videntur, et eos qui senilibus annis videntur affecti: non enim
necessario debiles esse probantur. quapropter etiam illos[7] qui
in sanitate corporis debilitate videbantur affecti: exigit enim
magnitudo passionis adiutorium. purgativa vero medicamina,
quae cathartica appellantur, praerumpunt corpus atque solici-
tam eidem passioni solutionem provocant. item fames tantum
noxia quantum refectio commoda. numquam[8] igitur sexta die
cibum iudicamus dandum, longa est enim ieiunitas; et neque

---

[1] per frictionem *A*: *fort.* ⟨ex⟩ perfrictione
[2] ⟨si⟩ debiles *R*: *fort.* ⟨qui⟩ debiles
[3] in *R* (*cf. 128*)
[4] impavide *Schmid Mn 135, fort. recte*
[5] in *R*
[6] latera *Rm*
[7] illos *Rm*: illis *G*   [8] numquam *conieci*: numquid *G*: non *R*

wood. He also prescribes venesection, but not after the fifth day, and only in cases which do not result from cold; not, however, in cold weather, nor for the aged, nor for those who evidently were physically weak before their illness. Everything must be cured by the body, he says, and abstinence from food is particularly advantageous. But the patient should be given oxymel, sometimes with the admixture of hyssop; he should also be given pearl barley gruel. The latter may be first taken as early as the fourth day or as late as the sixth, and every day thereafter. And it should be given sooner to old people and to those who were physically weak even from the time they were healthy. He then prescribes that the bowels be kept soft right up to the seventh day. And he bids us use anointing with great caution, and directs us to watch the patient's breath to see if 27 it becomes warm and foul smelling. With the exception of old people and people who were physically weak even from the time they were healthy, those who have an excess of humors in their veins should, in his opinion, be purged with black hellebore. Moreover, he bids us give the patients a hot-water bath on the second or third day, or warm them with [hot water in] skin containers, while fomenting the legs until the pain is dispelled.

But Praxagoras by these very prescriptions brings about pleurisy, which would not have developed but for them. For all his remedies are seen to be sharp and astringent, e.g., oxymel, pepper, and wormwood. These inevitably aggravate inflammations, and particularly at a time when even the water that is drunk takes on a bilious quality because of the very deep-28 seated heat. Furthermore, venesection should also be prescribed for those who are found to have incurred the illness after a cold and those who are old. For these patients are not necessarily weak. And, in fact, venesection should be prescribed for those, too, who apparently were physically weak even in health. For the severity of the disease demands external help. Furthermore, purgative drugs (Greek *cathartica*) wrench the body asunder and cause a flux which aggravates the disease itself. And starvation is as harmful as a substantial diet. Thus in our judgment one should in no case wait until the sixth day to give food, for this is too long a fast. Nor should one always wait until the fourth day; indeed, food should often be given even on the

semper quarta die, saepe enim etiam tertia die caput[9] implet:
fit autem hoc ex aromatibus. dehinc calidae aquae fomentatio
importuna est et frigescere facit aegrotantes.

129   XXII. AD ASCLEPIADEM

ASCLEPIADES secundo volumine Celerum vel acutarum passionum pleuriticos phlebotomat, praedicens primo ab his,
quibus[1] locis consistunt vel commorantur, utrum regio adiutorium phlebotomiae permittat adhiberi. se enim vidisse testatur
apud Athenas atque urbem Romam phlebotomia vexatos vel
peius acceptos esse pleuriticos; in Pario vero atque Hellesponto
resumptos ac relevatos. prohibet praeterea[2] sitim atque clysterem vel ante cibum bibere. at[3] si, inquit, oportuerit deducendi
ventris causa, adhibendum semel vel secundo clysterem. potum dat magis ac plurimum mulsum, aliquando etiam et rutam
130 et hyssopum cum mulso. nocere inquit radicem herbae quam
Graeci phlomon vocant: quapropter omnino dandam negat,
vel certe semel dandam ubi dolor coegerit. cibum inquit dandum praecauta secunda die, siquidem alternis admoneantur
diebus, et quarta, siquidem gravior sit quinta. tertia,[4] inquit,
die dabimus sucum et, ut saepe sufficiens, semel probavimus
dandum. at si pulsus defecerit,[5] nutriendos etiam post accessionem quintae[6] diei permittimus. declinante passione vinum
damus et varium cibum.

huic Soranus occurrens ait semper phlebotomandos pleuriticos
strictura cogente, et apud Romam denique nos, inquit, utemur
131 phlebotomo, nulla regionum discretione confusi. etenim quaerendum utrum Asclepiades proprietate regionis noceri suspicatur
eos qui fuerint in eadem[7] phlebotomati pleuritici, an vero proprietate passionis. ex quibus si primum putat, hoc est regionum
proprietate, vexari omnes oportuit, non solum pleuriticos, verum

___

[9] caput ⟨autem⟩ R: *fort.* ⟨item⟩ caput

[1] quae G

[2] propterea *edd.*

[3] et *edd.*

[4] sit quinta. tertia] *locus obscurus* (*cf. 132*); *fort.* sit quinta ⟨vel⟩ tertia, *vel sim.*

[5] pulsus defecerit *Schmid Mn 141, coll. Ac. ii. 133*: plus defecerint *edd.*

[6] *fort.* quartae   [7] eadem *A*: eodem G

third day. Praxagoras' treatment also congests the head, the use of aromatic substances bringing about this result. And, finally, the fomentations with hot water are harmful, causing the patients to become chilled.

XXII. REPLY TO ASCLEPIADES

IN BOOK II of his work *On Swift* (i.e., acute) *Diseases* Asclepiades recommends venesection in [certain] cases of pleurisy, but first indicates, on the basis of the place where the patient happens to be living or sojourning, whether the location permits of treatment by venesection. For he asserts that he has seen cases of pleurisy at Athens and Rome in which venesection had a harmful and adverse effect; but that cases in Paros and the region of the Hellespont were relieved and benefited by this treatment. Again, he rejects abstinence from drink, the clyster, and drinking before eating; but if it is necessary in order to clear out the bowels, he prescribes the use of a clyster once or twice. As drink he generally prescribes a large amount of mead, sometimes also rue and hyssop with mead. He considers the root of the mullein (Greek *phlomos*) harmful, and for that reason declares that it should never be prescribed, or at most once, when the pain makes it necessary. We should give the patients food, he says, but avoid doing so on the second day (for the paroxysms come on alternate days), or on the fourth, which is a more trying day than the fifth.[1] But gruel should be given, says Asclepiades, on the third day, and it is generally sufficient to give it just once. But if their pulse grows weak, feed them, he says, even after the attack of the fifth day. And when the disease declines, give them wine and varied food.

In opposition to Asclepiades, Soranus says that venesection should be employed in all cases of pleurisy when the state of stricture requires it. We apply this treatment at Rome, too, he says, and are not troubled by any regional distinctions. And we must ask why it is that Asclepiades believes that in a given region venesection is harmful in cases of pleurisy. Is it because of the nature of the region, or the nature of the disease? If his reason is the former—that is, the nature of the region—then venesection performed in that region should be harmful in *all*

1. The text is uncertain. Cf. also 132.

etiam synanchicos et[8] qui fuerint phlebotomia[9] curati, et epilepticos etiam quos phlebotomandos imperat aptissime. at si
secundum, hoc est proprietate passionis vexari putat, non apud
Romam solum phlebotomatos pleuriticos sed in omni regione
noceri debuit iudicare.[10]

132 clysterem vero recte prohibet propter acrimoniam, sed non
recte semel vel secundo adhiberi permittit. multo enim melius
est omnino innoxium quicquam quam leviter nocens. hinc
etiam phlomi herbae radicem tamquam natura noxiam repro-
bans ⟨non⟩[11] recte semel adhiberi ubi dolor coegerit. dehinc
omni ex parte ratione caret prohibere clysteres tamquam augentes incendia, et rutam vel hyssopum adhiberi, quae sunt vehementius ardentia ob suae qualitatis acrimoniam.

item mala atque caduca intentione confirmat circa[12] quartum
diem cibum dandum generaliter, ac necessario quartum[13] diem
servandum. his enim qui iugibus afficiuntur febribus, quoties
initium ex die sumpserint, quarta die necessario dandus est
133 cibus; non aliter qui maiore hemitritaeo aegrotant et ex nocte
sumpserint initium. ipse quoque Asclepiades in phreniticam[14]
passionem venturos graviter indicat[15] affici quarta die. neque
tuto ante dimissionem declinante accessione dandus, ut existimat, cibus est, atque semel datum sufficere nisi pulsus fuerit
defectio. non enim oportuit virium debilitate captata cibum
dare, cum fuerit nostrae potestatis opportune ante aegrum quam
deficiat reficere. vinum etiam et varium cibum declinante passione dandum recte consulit, sed non suo conveniens iudicio.
etenim phreniticis atque lethargis ante declinationem vinum
dedit.

[8] et *fort. secl.*

[9] phlebotomia *conieci*: phlebotomati *G*: phlebotomando *A*

[10] indicare *edd.*

[11] *suppl. R*

[12] *fort.* citra

[13] quintum *edd.*

[14] *fort.* pleuriticam (*sed cf. Ac. iii. 36*)

[15] *fort.* iudicat

---

2. E.g., the third or the fifth. Or if *citra* be read, 'before the fourth day.' The text is
quite uncertain. Cf. 130.

cases, not merely in cases of pleurisy, but in those of synanche, which are treated by venesection, and in those of epilepsy, too, for which Asclepiades very properly prescribes venesection. But if his reason is the second one—that is, the nature of the disease—he should conclude that harm results from the treatment of pleurisy by venesection not only at Rome but everywhere.

And he is right in rejecting the use of a clyster because of its sharpness, but he is wrong in permitting it to be used once or 32 twice. For a treatment that is completely harmless is much better than one that is even slightly harmful. Similarly, with regard to the root of the plant mullein, he is wrong in prescribing its use even once, when the pain seems to require it, while rejecting it generally as harmful by nature. Again, it is entirely illogical to reject clysters on the ground that they would add to inflammations, and yet to prescribe rue or hyssop, both of which produce more intense burning because of their natural sharpness.

Furthermore, it is an erroneous and futile idea that prompts him to assert that food should, in general, be given around the fourth day[2] but not on the fourth day itself. For the truth is that in all cases of unremitting fever which begin in the daytime, food should be given on the fourth day; and the same 33 holds for cases of major semitertian fevers which begin at night. Again, Asclepiades himself points out that patients on the verge of phrenitis suffer a severe attack on the fourth day.[3] Furthermore, it is not safe, as he proposes, to give food during the decline of an attack, before there is a real remission. Nor is it safe to say that unless the pulse grows weak a single feeding is sufficient. For Asclepiades should not have waited for the actual collapse of the patient's strength before giving him more food, since it was quite feasible to nourish him sufficiently to prevent the collapse. Asclepiades is right in prescribing wine and varied food in the decline of the disease, but in so doing he is inconsistent with his own rules. For in cases of phrenitis and lethargy he prescribes wine before the declining phase.[4]

3. The point of the sentence is doubtful. Perhaps there is a textual confusion of phrenitis and pleurisy. At any rate, if the statement holds for pleurisy, it is probably the feeding on the fifth day (cf. 130) that is being criticized as coming too soon after an attack.

4. Cf. *Ac.* i. 130; ii. 38, 42.

134   ## XXIII. AD THEMISONEM

AT THEMISON alias quidem pleuriticos recte curavit, peccavit
autem quarta die cataplasmando, dehinc cerotarium apponendo, ex[1] aliquo virtutis ferventis ungendo[2] atque ruta: sunt
enim acria. dehinc cerotarii tempus declinante est passione.

135   ## XXIV. AD HERACLIDEM

HERACLIDES TARENTINUS sanguinis extimens[1] abundantiam,
secunda die utitur clystere bis aut tertio, atque post paululum phlebotomat, conturbans corpora requie indigentia. etenim
quaerendum quid magis esse[2] confirmat,[3] utrumne fluorem ventris, aut tumorem et retentionem stercorum. sed si fluor est,
hunc duplicat adhibendo clysteres; at si tumor est, hunc eorum
duplicat acrimonia. credas etiam eandem iniectione suspensam
raptu quodam patientibus advenire partibus et propterea vehementius nocere. hic quoque etiam ⟨nulla⟩[4] phlebotomiae utilitas: vexatae etenim tribus clysteribus vires sanguinis prohibent
136 detractionem. dehinc neque omnes neque secunda necessario
phlebotomandi sunt die, sicut supra docuimus.

cataplasmat etiam aqua solutis pollinibus, quod Graeci omen
lysin appellant, admixto fico vel panace aut chamaepity, quorum
complexio ob qualitatis acrimoniam noxia iudicatur. probat
post usum cataplasmatis malagma quod Apollophanis appellamus, sive polyarchion, item sua inventione conscriptum, quae
omnia sunt acerrima et propterea recusanda. dat praeterea
mulsum praebibendum in quo praecocta vel praeinfusa fuerit
ruta.

[1] et Rm: an ⟨et⟩ ex?

[2] fort. scrib. ungendo, ⟨ut est⟩ * * atque ruta

[1] fort. sanguinis extimans (= existimans) abundantiam vel sanguinis extimans
abundantia ⟨pleuriticos fieri⟩, vel tale quid

[2] fort. esse ⟨timendum⟩   [3] confirmet A   [4] ⟨nulla est⟩ Rm

XXIII. REPLY TO THEMISON

THOUGH Themison's treatment of pleurisy is sound in other respects, he errs in prescribing a poultice on the fourth day followed by a cerate, and in anointing the patient with some substance possessing a burning quality, and rue. For these substances are acrid; moreover, the proper time for a cerate is when the disease is declining.

XXIV. REPLY TO HERACLIDES

SINCE Heraclides of Tarentum considers an excess of blood dangerous,[1] he prescribes the use of a clyster twice or three times on the second day, and venesection a little later. In so doing he agitates the body at a time when it needs rest. And, indeed, we must ask him which condition he considers to be more serious, flux of the bowels or inflammation along with retention of feces. If it is the flux, he adds to it by using clysters; and if it is the inflammation, he aggravates it by the sharp quality of the clysters. One may assume that this very sharpness, deposited in the body by injection, reaches the affected parts with a violent thrust and for that reason does even more severe damage. And under these circumstances the venesection is also without advantage. For the impairment of the bodily strength by three clysters should bar the withdrawal of blood. Furthermore, as we have shown above, not all patients should be treated by venesection, nor should the treatment necessarily take place on the second day.

Heraclides also prescribes a poultice consisting of a solution of flour in water (Greek *ōmēlysis*), to which fig, allheal, or ground pine has been added. Such mixtures are harmful, in our judgment, because of their acrid quality. After the application of the poultice, Heraclides recommends the emollient plaster of Apollophanes, as it is called, or that of Polyarchus, or one of his own invention. But all such preparations are extremely acrid and should therefore be avoided. Besides, Heraclides prescribes that the patient first drink mead containing a decoction or infusion of rue.

1. Or, reading *ex(is)timans:* 'considers an excess of blood [the cause of the disease].'

at si sputa excludi coeperint, dat medicamen bibendum quod
137 conficit ex hyssopo, iride, et melle. si, inquit, non fuerint congrue vel sufficienter exclusa, addendas absinthii drachmas sex.
sed si nausea occurrerit, apium vorare iubet aegrotantes vel
olivam ex aceto mandere. haec quoque sunt acria et stomacho
inhaerentia. ipse denique tentatione expertus ex supra dictis
eversionem fieri stomachi, ordinat ob nauseam retinendam incongrua[5] scilicet quae constringere possint. ait enim[6] si non recesserit sputorum emissio sequenti die iniciendos,[7] ut quae[8] excludenda commoveat iris, eadem clyster per ventrem detrahi
138 provocet: noxia noxiis committens, siquidem etiam per clysterem iniecta ex eadem sint materia ex qua sunt ea quae bibenda
ordinavit. quo fiet ut commovens tumorem magis faciat excludenda quae putat retineri.

dat etiam iuscellum[9] gallinaceum cum mulso ex vino vel suco
ptisanae, quae sunt in corruptione[9a] facilia atque inflantia et ventrem in fluorem moventia. dari praeterea vinum iubet his qui
fuerint viribus debiles nisi caput (inquit) doluerint, non advertens quia temporis opportunitate permittente omnibus convenit
dare, utque[10] econtrario resistente neque imbecillibus. etenim
si, ut existimat, valentes viribus vexat, multo magis imbecillos.
139 neque recte sentit ita dandum nisi caput doluerint: dolor enim
si prohibet capitis, non aliter etiam lateris[11] prohibere[12] perspicitur, prius quam passio declinaverit. importune[13] datum,
namque omnia quae patiuntur exagitat, nec solum caput.

dicit etiam declinante passione gobiones pisces dandos, accedente profectu etiam carnem atque panem, non coniciens quia
omnis acrimonia tussientibus vel spirationis difficultate laborantibus vel spuentibus sanguinem inimica est, etiam declinante

---

[5] incongruam G: corr. R

[6] fort. etiam

[7] inicienda edd.

[8] ut quae Bendz Eran 41. 71: atque G

[9] viscellum edd.

[9a] fort. corruptionem

[10] atque Helmreich 324, sed cf. adn. ad Ac. i. 85

[11] lateribus edd.: an laterum?

[12] prohibete G: corr. R

[13] importunum G: corr. Rm

And if the patient begins to bring up sputa, Heraclides has
7 him drink a drug compounded of hyssop, iris, and honey. But
if the sputa are not eliminated properly or in sufficient quantity,
he prescribes the addition of six drachms of wormwood. And if
nausea occurs, he recommends eating some parsley or an olive
soaked in vinegar. Yet these substances are also sharp and tend
to cling to the esophagus. Furthermore, having found in actual
practice that the substances first prescribed cause gagging, in
order to check the nausea he prescribes measures[2] that by reason
of their astringent effect are obviously unsuitable. Thus he says
that if the coughing-up of sputa is still not completed by the
following day, the patient should be given a clyster, the enema
serving to withdraw through the bowels the same matter that
the iris was to help to discharge upward. But these procedures
8 are harmful and employ harmful substances. For the substances
that Heraclides orders injected as a clyster are the same as those
he orders drunk. The result is that by aggravating the inflammation he adds to the matter which requires elimination and
which he believes is being held back.

He gives the patients chicken broth and either honey-wine or
pearl barley gruel, all of which decompose easily, cause flatulence, and provoke flux of the bowels. Besides, he prescribes
wine for those who are weak, unless, as he says, there is pain in
the head. He is not, however, aware that it is proper to give wine
to all patients when circumstances permit, but that when the
circumstances are unfavorable wine should not be given even
to the weak. For if, as he supposes, it harms the strong, much
9 more does it harm the weak. And he errs in thinking that wine
should be given unless the head is affected. For if pain in the
head is an obstacle, it is equally true that pain in the side should
constitute a bar [to the prescription of wine] before the disease
declines. The fact is that wine wrongly prescribed irritates all
parts that are affected, and not only the head.

Heraclides also says that, when the disease declines, gudgeon
fish should be given the patient and, as convalescence progresses,
also meat and bread. But he is not aware that even in the declining phase of the disease anything sharp is harmful in cases
where the patient coughs, suffers from difficulty in breathing,

2. Or perhaps 'substances,' if the reference is to the preceding rather than to the
following sentence.

passione. simile enim quiddam facit quale contingere videmus
in externis corporis partibus vulneribus constitutis, quae cum
sunt adhuc tenera cicatricis[14] novitate acrioribus exusta facile
resolvuntur.

140

XXV. DE PERIPNEUMONIA

CONSEQUENS atque vicinum est peripneumoniae dicere curationem quae non, ut priores voluerunt, a parte corporis
quae patitur nomen sumpsit, sed ab ea quae plus patitur, siquidem neque sine febribus esse videatur. perficiunt hanc passionem causae quae etiam pleuriticam faciunt, ut venenum
sumptum, vel ex opio atque hyoscyamo confecta tussientibus
medicamina, vel his similibus virtutibus; item catarrhus vel
coryza vel, quod est rarissimum, synanchica praecedens passio.

141 nam frequentius antecedente pleuritica peripneumonia sequitur,
quo fiet ut perniciosior sit antecedente,[1] siquidem vexatis prius
viribus atque adiutoriis ex parte incassum praerogatis in secundam veniant aegri passionem. afficiuntur autem iuvenes magis
atque aetatis mediae; at senes vel pueri atque mulieres difficile.

hanc igitur quidam diffinientes passionem, ut Demetrius
Herophilus[2] libro duodecimo De passionibus, peripneumonia,
inquit, est tumor in toto pulmonis corpore: ex parte enim si
fuerit pleuritis dicitur. addere autem debuit 'cum febribus,'
siquidem sine his peripneumonia esse non possit.

142

XXVI. QUAE EST PERIPNEUMONIAE
INTELLIGENTIA[1]

DIFFINIRE Methodici iuxta Sorani iudicium declinant.
Asclepiadis sectatores aiunt esse peripneumoniam parvi
temporis solutionem cum tumore atque febre. 'solutionem,' inquiunt, ob humorum emissionem; 'parvi temporis' ad discre-

---

[14] cicatrices *edd.*

[1] antecedente *fort. del.*

[2] *cf. Ac. ii. 4*

[1] *initium capitis ad* hanc igitur *(141) statuendum videtur*

or spits blood. For the effect is somewhat the same as we see
happening in the case of wounds on the surface of the body.
So long as these are still tender because of the freshness of the
scar, they are easily opened if attacked by sharp substances.

XXV. PNEUMONIA

40

As is fitting, we shall now discuss pneumonia and its treatment, a subject closely connected with the above. Pneumonia does not derive its name, as previous writers have held,
from the part of the body which is affected, but rather from
the part which is more affected than the others, for this disease
is not observed to exist without fever.[1] The same causes which
give rise to pleurisy give rise to pneumonia, e.g., the taking of
poison, or of cough medicines compounded with poppy juice,
henbane, or drugs having similar properties. Again, catarrh or
coryza[2] and very infrequently synanche may precede pneu-
41 monia. But pneumonia often supervenes upon pleurisy and is
consequently more dangerous than pleurisy, since the patient
passes into pneumonia after his strength has already been impaired and some of the remedies have already been employed
without avail. Young men and those of middle age are more
frequently stricken; old men, children, and women rarely.

Some writers give a definition of this disease. Thus in Book
XII of his treatise *On Diseases* Demetrius the Herophilean declares[3] that pneumonia is an inflammation in the whole structure of the lung, pleurisy being the name given when only a
part is affected. He should have added 'with fever,' for pneumonia cannot occur without fever.

XXVI. DEFINITION OF PNEUMONIA

42

The Methodist physicians, following Soranus' principle,
avoid defining diseases. Asclepiades and his followers say
that pneumonia is a state of flow of short duration, with inflammation and fever. They speak of pneumonia as a state of flow
on the ground that it involves elimination of fluid matter.

1. And therefore, according to the Methodists, the whole body is affected.
2. Nasal catarrh (cf. *Ac.* ii. 101; *Chr.* ii. 94).
3. The text of *G* presents a harsh anacoluthon but is probably not unsound.

tionem phthisicae passionis quae est et ipsa solutionis, vel efflu-
entis humoris per tussiculam exclusio; 'peripneumoniam'[2] inquiunt ad discretionem aliarum passionum parvi, ut supra diximus, temporis solutionem ingerentium, ut oculorum vel aurium;
adiecerunt etiam 'cum tumore atque febre' siquidem solutio,
hoc est eruptio, parvi temporis ad pulmonem fiat peripneumonia
ad eas partes sine febribus.

huic Soranus occurrens diffinitioni ait: 'cum semper strictura
in his obtineatur,[3] non oportuisse passionem rheumatismum vel
solutionem dici cum tumore, sed forte tumorem cum rheumatismo: etenim parva maioribus postponuntur. est igitur secundum nos peripneumonia strictura vehemens atque acuta pulmonis, cum sputis et siti et febricula celeri atque acuta.'

143   XXVII. QUOMODO INTELLIGITUR PERI-
                        PNEUMONIA

INTELLIGITUR ex his quae concurrunt. etenim peripneumonicos sequentur febres acutae, gravedo thoracis, et sensus laborantium quadam difficultate laterum atque medii scapularum;[1]
iacendi etiam facultas supinae positionis atque paulo erectior,
frequens etiam sedendi delectatio, atque supra latus iacendi
difficultas, ita ut praefocabilis esse sentiatur; vultus rubor tamquam florens, oculorum veluti pinguis aspectus, atque etiam
splendor scilicet in partibus albidis quae praeter pupulam videntur, et magis cum alterna conversatione aspiciunt aegro-
144 tantes. sequitur eosdem etiam anhelitus celeritas, tussicula
sanguinolenta atque fellea vel fumosa[2] iactans sputa, et in comparatione pleuriticorum fulviora vel spumosiora, spiratio difficilis, desiderium frigidi atque plurimi aeris haustu[3] rapiendi,
frigidi etiam potus appetitio, os siccum, lingua aspera ac primo
subalbida dehinc rubra, pulsus vehemens et celer, anxietas,
iactatio, vigiliae iuges, ingemens atque turbulentus somnus.

peiorante passione thorax etiam extantior fiet, accedente
spirationis persecutione cum quodam sibilatu vehementi atque
145 aspero; sequitur etiam colli ac vultus inflatio, et oculorum aut

---

[2] peripneumonia *edd.*   [3] obtineat *R, fort. recte*

[1] medio scapularum *Bendz 90, coll. Ac. ii. 149*: medium papularum *edd.*

[2] spumosa *Rm*   [3] haustu *R*: hausti *G*

They say that it is of short duration to distinguish it from phthisis, which also involves a state of flow, phthisis being the emission of fluid matter through coughing. And they call it pneumonia[1] to distinguish it from other diseases that involve a state of flow of short duration, as we have just said, e.g., of the eyes or ears. They add 'with inflammation and fever,' for otherwise a brief state of flow or emission of fluid at the lung would constitute pneumonia there, despite the absence of fever.

In opposition to this definition Soranus says: 'Since a state of stricture always prevails in these cases, the disease should not be defined as a state of flow or looseness accompanied by inflammation, but perhaps rather as an inflammation accompanied by a state of flow. For the unimportant ought to be subordinated to the important. In our view, therefore, pneumonia is a severe and acute state of stricture of the lung, accompanied by sputa, thirst, and a swift and acute fever.'

XXVII. HOW TO RECOGNIZE PNEUMONIA

Pneumonia may be recognized by its symptoms, which are as follows: The patient has acute fever, heaviness of the chest, and the feeling of some pain in the sides and between the shoulder blades. He finds it possible to lie in bed in a supine position, or raised a little, and frequently even likes to sit up; but he finds it hard to lie on his side, for this gives him a choking sensation. The face is flushed bright red, the eyes have a somewhat languid appearance, and there is also a glaze in the whites, which are visible around the pupil, particularly when the eyes shift their glance from side to side. There are, in addition, the following indications: rapid panting, a coughing-up of blood-red, yellow, or fumy sputa, yellower and frothier than those in pleurisy, painful respiration, a longing to draw in an abundance of cold air, a great desire also for cold drink, dry mouth, rough tongue at first whitish, later red, a strong and rapid pulse, uneasiness, tossing, long stretches of sleeplessness, groaning and restlessness in sleep.

As the disease grows worse, the chest becomes more distended, the patient gasping for breath and making a strong and rough hissing sound; neck and face are puffed up, eyes either

1. I.e., from *pneumōn*, 'lung.'

immobilitas aut difficilis motus, visus nubilosus vel nubilus,[4]
mentis alienatio, articulorum frigidus torpor attestante livore,
lingua crassior atque conductione breviata, sudor superiorum
partium, pulsus latens aut formicabilis,[5] quem Graeci myrmecizonta[6] vocant, in ultimo etiam pectoris resonans stridor, quem
rhogmon appellant.

at si salutaribus prosperata signis passio coeperit in melius
vergere, omnium supra dictorum fiet paulatim deductio, ali-
146 quibus etiam semel amputata decisio. quidam denique in
pleuriticam passionem redeuntes relevati vixerunt, accedente
dolore et plurima spirandi difficultate.

etenim praedicta quae peripneumoniam designant vel concurrentia complent sunt haec: febres acutae, spirationis celeritas
ac difficultas, tussicula atque sputorum varia emissio, gravatio
sine ullo dolore, aut cum parvo praefocationis sensu. est autem
passio generaliter acuta atque strictura suffecta, adiuncto levi
humoris fluore, quem rheumatismum vocant. quo fiet ut magis
stricturam vocemus, etiam si dolor non fuerit, quippe cum inesse
gravedinem atque pressuram videamus, et asperitatem et siccitatem et accessionem vel his similia signa.

147   XXVIII. QUIS LOCUS IN PERIPNEU-
                     MONICIS PATITUR

PATI in peripneumonicis Diocles venas pulmonis inquit,
Erasistratus vero arterias, Praxagoras eas inquit partes pulmonis pati quae sunt spinae coniunctae. etenim omnem inquit
pulmonem pati Herophilus; si febrem, inquit, fuerint passi,
pleuriticam facit. Asclepiades vero eas pulmonis partes pati
quae arteriae sunt adhaerentes, quas appellant bronchia. item
Apollonius Herophilus[1] inquit ipsius pulmonis venas atque arterias pati.

Soranus autem, cuius verissimas apprehensiones latino sermone
describere laboramus, totum inquit corpus passione vexari, sed

---

[4] vel nubilus] *om. Bendz 16, ut glossema*

[5] *cf. Ac. ii. 167 (Isid. iv. 6. 4* formidabilis*): formicalis Chr. ii. 198, Diaet. pass. 38,
nisi hos locos emendare malis*

[6] myrmizonta *edd.; cf. etiam Chr. ii. 198; Diaet. pass. 38* myrmitonta, *sed semper*
μυρμηκι- *apud Graecos*

[1] *cf. Ac. ii. 4*

motionless or barely moving, face beclouded or overcast, mind wandering, limbs chilled, numb, and bluish in color, tongue thick and made shorter by contraction, sweating in the upper parts, pulse submerged or antlike (Greek *myrmēcizōn*), and toward the end a wheezing in the chest (Greek *rhōgmos*).

But if the disease is attended by favorable circumstances and begins to change for the better, there is a gradual abatement of all the symptoms described above, and in some cases the symp-
46 toms are banished and disappear all at once. In certain cases pneumonia abates and the patients live, but they lapse back into the disease of pleurisy with pain and considerable difficulty in breathing.

Thus the signs that are indicative of pneumonia and make up the symptoms of the disease are the following, as we have given them: acute fever, rapid and painful respiration, cough, emission of sputa of various colors, a feeling of heaviness with no pain or with a slight choking sensation. The disease is, in general, acute and arises from a state of stricture, though it is accompanied by a mild flow of liquid matter (Greek *rheumatismos*). And we prefer to call it a state of stricture, even if there is no pain, for the reason that we find present in the disease heaviness of the head, languor, roughness, dryness, feverish attacks, and the like.

47   ## XXVIII. THE LOCUS OF THE AFFECTION IN PNEUMONIA

THE affection in pneumonia is situated, according to Diocles, in the veins of the lung, and according to Erasistratus, in its arteries. Praxagoras holds that those parts of the lung are affected which are joined to the spine. But in the opinion of Herophilus it is the whole lung that is affected; Herophilus adds that if the patient suffers fever, the case leads to pleurisy. But, according to Asclepiades, the affection is in those parts of the lung, called the *bronchia*, which connect with the windpipe. And Apollonius the Herophilean declares that the veins and arteries of the lung itself are affected.

But, according to Soranus, whose very accurate judgments we are now striving to set forth in Latin, it is the whole body that is attacked by the disease, the lung, however, with particu-

148 pulmonem vehementius; quod quidem aestimatum et non ad expressam fidem accipiendum iudicavit. est etiam inutile curationi, quippe cum nihil obstet locorum neglecta specialis apprehensio, ubi totum corpus laborare senserimus; et neque mutabilis sit adiutoriorum qualitas pro patientibus locis, sed talis perseveret in genere donec passio ipsa perseverat.

manifestum autem ex supra dictis quomodo possunt similia quaeque peripneumonicae passionis internosci accipimus. pleuritici enim vehementi dolore lateris afficiuntur. dyspnoeici vero, quos anhelosos dicere poterimus sive suspiriosos, sine febribus esse noscuntur, et non solum celeri atque acuta afficiuntur passione sed aliquando etiam tarda atque obtusa (nam Graeci chroniam vocant) et cetera.

149 ## XXIX. QUOMODO CURANDI SUNT PERI-
PNEUMONICI

CONVENIT peripneumonicos iacere in loco medie lucido atque calido et ita haberi vel componi ut reclinato leviter thorace collocentur. ad hoc enim positionis[1] sive schematis genus ipsi quoque aegrotantes releventur.[2] dehinc abstinentia adhibenda usque ad primam diatriton si nulla obstiterit urgentior causa. servandi etiam a somno vigiles accessionis tempore, adhibita articulorum leni atque calida manuum defricatione; calefactionibus etiam lenibus ex pannis utendum. tunc cum statum sumpserit accessio, lanarum appositione thoracem secus atque medio scapularum, sed quae sint ex oleo calido ac dulci expressae.

declinante accessione os colluendum ac deinde potus dandus 150 aqua calida. tunc somnus permittendus, adhibita etiam phlebotomia permittentibus viribus. sed si intra diatriton in passionem venerint aegrotantes, quod quidem est rarissimum, erit tum phlebotomia adhibenda; si autem non, in ipsa diatrito. tunc unctione;[3] dehinc aqua ora fomentamus. et damus sorbilem cibum atque tenuem ex alica. etenim ptisana inflationem facit, item oryza constringit, simila quoque in initiis gravis est.

[1] positionis Rm: passionis G
[2] relevantur Rm
[3] unctione ⟨utendum⟩ R: fort. unctio

1. Possibly the meaning is 'and so on [with the other diseases].'

lar severity. Yet Soranus considers this statement merely an
expression of opinion, not to be taken as matter for absolute
48 trust. Moreover, it does not help so far as the treatment is concerned, the failure to recognize the part specially affected being
no bar to the use of proper measures. For obviously the whole
body is affected; and the character of the remedies does not
vary with the parts affected, but remains of the same type so
long as the nature of the disease is unchanged.

Now, from what has been said, our criteria for distinguishing
diseases similar to pneumonia are evident. Thus in cases of
pleurisy there is a severe pain in the side. And cases of dyspnoea
(a term which we may translate *anhelatio* or *suspirium*) are, as
is known, unaccompanied by fever; the disease, moreover, is
not necessarily swift and acute but, in fact, is sometimes slow
and inactive (Greek *chronia*), and so forth.[1]

49   ## XXIX. THE TREATMENT OF PNEUMONIA

PATIENTS suffering from pneumonia should lie in a place moderately light and warm. Their position should be so arranged
that they lie with their chests sloping a little. For it is in this
type of position or arrangement that the patients themselves
find relief. Give them no food until the end of the first three-day
period, unless there is a pressing reason for doing otherwise;
also keep them from sleeping at the time of an attack by gentle
and warming manual massage of their limbs; and apply heat
gently, using cloths. Then at the time when the attack reaches
its highest stage, apply woolen cloths wrung out of warm sweet
olive oil to the chest and between the shoulder blades.

When the attack declines, wash the patient's face, and then
50 give him warm water to drink. After that let him sleep. Perform
venesection if the patient's strength permits. And if the disease of pneumonia develops before the end of the [first] three-
day period, which, to be sure, is very infrequent, perform venesection at the time it develops; otherwise, at the end of that
period. Then anoint the patient, apply fomentations to his face,
and give him a thin gruel made from spelt groats. For pearl
barley produces flatulence, and rice is binding. Again, simila[1] is

1. A type of wheat flour.

conficiendus itaque erit, ut supra diximus, sorbilis sucus melle
atque anetho et oleo. at si aeger sorbilia quaeque horruerit vel
recusaverit, alicam dabimus ex aqua calida aut ovum sorbile.
tunc usque ad declinationem totius passionis alternis cibabimus
diebus, si vires aegrotantis permiserint.

151   atque ita thoracem cataplasmamus et interscapulam, quod
Graeci metaphrenon appellant, leni scilicet cataplasmate vel
mulso mediocriter decocto aut pane ex aqua calida et[4] polline
atque faenugraeco et aqua mulsa vel fici aridi decoctione. eius
quamquam sit reflata sucositas, tamen manet veluti mellosa
dulcedo. tunc cucurbita eisdem locis cum scarificatione adhibenda sed dimissionis tempore; leves autem, quas cuphas[5] appellamus,[6] etiam in accessione adhibere possumus, et frequentes
atque multis partibus. tunc vaporatio spongiarum et cataplasmatum apta: et si sese ad tempus gravari sentiunt aegrotantes,
eorum appositionem aegre tolerantes, tamen ex his plurimum
152 deinde commodi consequentur. erunt adhibenda angusto licet
tempore detracta, atque rursum apposita, quo etiam tussiculae
mitigetur inquietudo, et ea quae egeruntur facilius lapsa sine ullo
tormento reddantur. erit decoctum mulsum dandum vel faenugraeci decoctio cum melle; facit etiam nucleorum contritio mulso
admixta vel amylum aqua contritum. dabimus etiam eclegmata
sorbilia ex lini semine ac faenugraeci, nucleis et melle decocto et
ovorum vitellis confecta.

cum statum sumpserit passio, gestatione levi utemur; cum
vero declinaverit, vario nutrimus cibo servantes ac praecaventes
multo tempore ex liquamine et oleo cibos, siquidem tussiculam
153 commoveant. tunc lavacrum adhibemus et ultimo vinum damus. pectori autem atque a tergo circulatim cerotaria apponimus ex oleo dulci confecta vel cyprino, admixta iridis radice decocta vel meliloto, et secundum aliquos sampsucho. sed est hoc
acerrimum quamquam sit calidae virtutis. post cerotarium vero
apponimus ⟨malagma⟩[7] quod appellatur diachylon, vel Mna-

---

4 ex G: corr. Bendz Eran 41. 76   6 cf. vocant Ac. i. 79
5 κούφας G   7 addidi

PNEUMONIA   235

too heavy to be given at the beginning of the disease. Prepare
the gruel, then, as we have said, adding honey, dill, and olive
oil. But if the patient dislikes or refuses any kind of gruel, give
him spelt groats soaked in hot water, or a soft egg. Thereafter,
if his strength permits, feed him only on alternate days until
the decline of the disease as a whole.[2]

51   And apply poultices to the chest and also between the shoulder blades (Greek *metaphrenon*). The poultices should, of course,
be mild, consisting of mead moderately boiled down, bread
dipped in hot water, flour, fenugreek, hydromel, or a decoction
of dried fig. Though the moisture of this type of poultice evapo-
rates, there remains something of a honey-like sweetness. Then
apply cupping to the same regions, with scarification, but only
at the time of a remission. At the time of an attack, however,
cups of mild action (*cuphae*) may be applied in large numbers
and to many parts. After this treatment it is well to apply heat
with sponges and poultices. And even if, at the time, the patients feel that their condition is being aggravated and they
can scarcely endure these applications, yet afterward they
52 will gain greatly because of them. Make these applications,
but discontinue them after a short time, and then renew them
later. The purpose of this procedure is to relieve the distress
caused by the cough and to enable the sputa to flow more readily and to be given up without any pain. Also give the patient
boiled mead or a decoction of fenugreek with honey. Ground-up
pine kernels mixed with mead is also beneficial; so is powdered
starch in water. Prescribe also soft electuaries compounded of
flaxseed, fenugreek seed, pine kernels, cooked honey, and the
yolks of eggs.

When the disease reaches its highest stage, prescribe gentle
rocking. And when it declines, nourish the patient with varied
food, carefully avoiding for a long time foods prepared in fish
53 sauce and olive oil, since these aggravate a cough. Then prescribe bathing, and finally give the patient wine. And apply to
the chest and around the back, in a circle, cerates made with
sweet olive oil or henna oil to which a decoction of iris root or
melilot has been added, or, according to others, marjoram.
Marjoram, however, though it has a warming quality, is quite
sharp. After the cerates apply the emollient plaster of juices,

2. As opposed to the declining phase of a single attack.

seu;[8] aliqui etiam adhibuerunt illud quod Nileos[9] appellatur,
item Cephisophontis,[10] quae non sunt ita vehementia et propterea permittenda. horum sane compositiones De medicaminibus scribentes Interrogationum docuimus libris.

ex antiquis autem Erasistratus et Herophilus de ista passione
154 nihil dixerunt. Hippocrates vero libro Regulari, quem diaeteti-
cum vocavit, peripneumonicae inquit remedium aptandum ex
cocco atque galbano atque attico melle, vel abrotano ex aceto
mulso atque pipere admixto et helleboro nigro. summum, inquit, est etiam panacem in mulso ex aceto confecto decoquere
et liquatum dare bibendum. sed haec somnia[10a] Soranus esse
iudicavit et propterea reprobanda, adiciens quod mulsum ex
aceto factum constringat et sit inconveniens tumori.

item Diocles ait peripneumonicos qui annum sextum natu ex-
cesserint post iniectionem suco cibari oportere; sed fortiores
155 atque validos viribus levius, imbecilliores vero plenius. omnes
tamen communiter parum refici iubet qui ultra annum quartum-
decimum fuerint hac passione aegrotantes, adhibens acerrimos
clysteres et propterea noxios. dehinc sine ratione ad dierum
numerum cibum dandum putat. item libro quem De passionibus atque causis et curationibus scripsit phlebotomandos dicit,
et[11] adhibendum tempus tacuit. dehinc ventrem commovendum
existimat, exagitans atque exsucans[12] interiora. addit etiam
unguentum naribus admovendum, vel[13] sucum scammoniae,
quam diagridium appellamus, et helleborum et opium suco
consparsum, obsidens odoramentis perniciosissimis caput.
156 usque ad quintum diem mulsum ex aceto solum dandum praecepit, excitans profecto tumorem constrictivae virtutis causa et
immoderata abstinentia vires absumens. utitur etiam cum his
potionibus vexativis absinthio infuso et thymo, decoctis et eis-

---

[8] Mnasei *edd.*

[9] Nileus *edd.*

[10] Cephisophontis *scripsi* (*cf. Chr. ii. 34, iii. 55: an* Caf- *scrib.?*): Antisophantis *G*:
Apollophanis *Rm*

[10a] *fort.* ⟨acria⟩ omnia   [12] exsiccans *Rm*

[11] sed *Wellmann*   [13] vel *scripsi*: et *G*: *secl. Wellmann*

---

3. *Reg. ac.*, Appendix, p. 164. 21 Kuehl. (= II. 464 Littré). The Hippocratic text
has κόκκαλος, 'pine kernels,' that of Caelius *cocco*. The latter term would normally refer

or else that of Mnaseas. Some apply Nileus' plaster or that of Cephisophon. These are not so strong and are therefore permissible. And I have discussed their composition in the section on drugs in my treatise entitled *Questions and Answers*.

54 Now, of the ancients, neither Erasistratus nor Herophilus has anything to say about pneumonia. But Hippocrates in his book *On Regimen*, which he calls *diaeta*, prescribes the following remedies for pneumonia: pine kernels,[3] galbanum, and Attic honey, or southernwood in oxymel with pepper and black hellebore added. Another excellent preparation, he says, is allheal boiled down in oxymel; this is strained and given to the patient to drink. But Soranus considers this all nonsense and therefore to be rejected. He points out that oxymel has an astringent action and is harmful in a case of inflammation.

Diocles declares that patients with pneumonia who have passed their sixth year should be given a clyster and then nourished with gruel, the stronger and sturdier being given a smaller
55 portion of the food, and the weaker a larger. But for all patients generally, who have this disease and are past the age of fourteen, he prescribes little food. And he prescribes clysters, which are sharp and therefore harmful. Again, he adopts the illogical view that the food should be given according to the number of days. And in his book *On Diseases and Their Causes and Treatment* he writes that venesection should be employed, but does not indicate the time for this treatment. And he prescribes evacuation of the bowels, thereby causing the inner parts to be agitated and drained. He also prescribes the placing of an aromatic ointment at the patient's nose, say, scammony juice (Latin *diagridium*) with hellebore and poppy-juice sprinkled thereon. But in so doing he causes the patient's head to be pervaded with the
56 most harmful aromatics. Until the fifth day the only nourishment he prescribes is oxymel. But, because of its astringent property, oxymel undoubtedly aggravates the inflammation; and the excessive fasting saps the strength. Along with these irritating drinks, Diocles employs decoctions of wormwood and thyme, pouring them into the drink. He also gives these pa-

---

to oak gall or possibly the Cnidian berry; and it is possible that there is a misunderstanding of the Hippocratic text (so Vietmeier, p. 27) or that Soranus had before him a variant reading κόκκος. But I interpret *cocco* in the sense of pine kernels on the analogy of κόκκος, which does occur with that meaning.

dem, dans quoque transvorandum atque sorbendum passum cum aceto et mulso confecto. quae omnia, ut ratio demonstrat, sunt acria et propterea tumori contraria.

item Praxagoras eandem pleuriticorum atque peripneumoni-corum tradidit curationem.

Asclepiades vero secundo libro Celerum vel acutarum pas-sionum phlebotomiam recusavit, siquidem nullo dolore aegro-tantes afficiantur, et propterea si fuerit adhibita ex initio sanguis
157 tenuis atque subtilis exire videatur, sed errans plurimum, ut Soranus ait. neque enim moderatio detractionis sanguinis mu-tatione demonstratur, neque etiam solos dolentes phleboto-mandos accipimus, sicut idem Soranus libris quos De adiutoriis conscripsit edocuit. dehinc ipse Asclepiades ait quosdam peri-pneumonicos dolere; oportuit igitur etiam nunc, sicut in pleuri-ticis, non ex causa reprobare phlebotomiam, sed a commoranti-bus inquirere utrum in omnibus peripneumonicis obesse regiona-liter videatur. prohibet etiam cataplasmata et vaporationes, quorum est utilissimus usus ob relaxandam stricturam. item reprobat clysteres atque omnia medicamina, et quidem recte,
158 sed non suis conveniens placitis: in phreniticis enim clysteres adhibuit. item libris quos De vini datione scripsit, in febrici-tantibus iugibus inquit utendum clysteribus. dat etiam cum aqua mulsa hyssopum vel tragoriganum: et sunt haec acria atque medicosa, quae Graeci pharmacode appellant. mites-cente, inquit, interea passione cataplasmata adhibenda atque cibis asperioribus diebus nutriendos aegrotantes existimat, cum nos oporteat saepe levioribus diebus cibos dare, tunc puriores siquidem dimissiones occurrant.

item Titus huius sectator bis in die adhibendam inquit de-

tients raisin wine mixed with vinegar and honey to drink down. But these are all sharp substances, as reason indicates, and therefore harmful in a case of inflammation.

Praxagoras sets forth the same treatment for pneumonia as for pleurisy.

Asclepiades, however, in Book II of his work *On Swift* (or acute) *Diseases* rejects venesection [in pneumonia] on the grounds that the patients do not suffer any pain, and that if venesection is employed at the outset only thin and watery 57 blood will be seen to flow out. But, according to Soranus, he is completely mistaken, for a change in the blood that flows out[4] is not an indication for limiting the amount withdrawn. And, as Soranus also points out in his work *On Remedies*, we do not agree that venesection should be performed only on those who suffer pain. Furthermore, Asclepiades himself tells us that there is pain in some cases of pneumonia. Therefore, he should not have rejected venesection in pneumonia on general grounds, but should have made inquiries of the inhabitants of the region in question, as he did in the case of pleurisy, to determine whether venesection is harmful for all sufferers from pneumonia in that region.[5] Asclepiades also rejects poultices and applications of heat, though they are very useful for relaxing a state of stricture. Again, he rejects clysters and all [purgative] drugs; and properly so, though not in accordance with his own precepts. 58 For he prescribes clysters in phrenitis; and in his work *On the Prescription of Wine* he says that in cases of fever clysters should be given continually.[6] He also prescribes hyssop or goat's marjoram in hydromel. But these substances are sharp and drastic (Greek *pharmacōdē*). When the disease abates somewhat, he recommends the application of poultices; and he prescribes nourishing the patients with food on the days when the fever is more intense. In our view, however, food should often be given on the days when the fever intermits, for then the remissions are more perfect.

Titus, a follower of Asclepiades, prescribes a massage twice a

4. I.e., a change from thick to thin blood. Hence, if thin blood is the first to issue, it is not an indication against venesection.

5. Cf. 129. Caelius (Soranus) does not approve of Asclepiades' criterion but holds that consistency requires that Asclepiades apply it in pneumonia as well as in pleurisy.

6. I.e., daily.

fricationem, quam quidem veluti quassantem in acutis passionibus reprobamus.

Themison vero alia quaedam de passione recte composuit, sed
peccat iubendo eos secunda vel tertia die gestari, quoniam non-
159 dum sumpserit passio statum. iubet etiam cum scarificatione
adhiberi cucurbitam declinante accessione, cum sit adiutorii
genus districtivum[14] et propterea proprium dimissionis. dat
etiam bibere aquam frigidam vel frigidae vicinam: et non est
consequens sorbilibus cibis atque curationi laxativae potus constrictivus. si, inquit, incensa atque longa fuerit accessio, ut
ardore ac siccitate difficultatem faciat excludendi ea quae tussicula emitti coguntur, dabimus pityidas vel nucleos aut cucumeris semen bibendum cum aqua aut secundum modum collecta, et sunt haec maxime contraria. augmenti etenim atque
accessionis tempore etiam aqua, quae nullius est qualitatis,
160 noxia perspicitur. utitur etiam amygdalis amaris quae ob
amaritudinem tumores vehementius accendunt.

item Heraclides Tarentinus eandem iudicavit curationem adhibendam quae pleuriticis est ordinata. multi Empirici potionibus atque sorbilibus cibis usi sunt; item pityida et ruta et menta
et tragorigano et abrotano et pulegio atque origano,[15] alii haec
singula, alii secum mixta adhibentes. sic denique amylum cum
aqua praecoctum atque melle [mixta][16] admiscuerunt, tunc
amygdala amara, et haec sorbilia movent ramo hyssopi. dant
etiam irin et gentianam decoctam cum pulegio et anagallide
herba et eryngio et marrubio et his similibus: quae omnia ratione
circumscripta reprobanda sunt.

161 ## XXX. DE CARDIACIS

CARDIACAM passionem aiunt quidam duplici significatione
nuncupari, communi et propria. sed communem dicunt
eam quae substantiam in stomacho atque ore ventris habuerit,

---

[14] destrictivum G: corr. Vetter, TLL (cf. Bendz Eran 43. 55)

[15] tragoriganum et abrotanum et pulegium atque origanum G: corr. R   [16] om. R

day. But we reject this on the ground that it would irritate patients in acute diseases.

And Themison, though his discussion of certain other aspects of the disease is correct, errs in prescribing passive exercise on the second or third day. For the disease has not yet reached its
59 highest stage. Again, as the attack begins to decline, he orders the use of cupping with scarification. But this remedy has a dissolving property and is therefore suitable for a period of remission.[7] He also gives the patients cold water to drink, or water that is nearly cold. But an astringent drink does not go well with gruels or with a relaxing treatment. And if, says Themison, the paroxysm is intensely feverish and long continued, so that the heat and dryness make it difficult for the patient to cough up the sputa, give him pine seed or kernels or cucumber seed to drink with water, or a mixture of them in suitable proportions. But these prescriptions are extremely bad. Indeed, in the increasing phase of the disease and at the time of an attack, even the water, which has no [medicinal] property, is obviously
60 harmful. Themison also makes use of bitter almonds; but because of their very bitterness they greatly aggravate the inflammation.

Heraclides of Tarentum prescribes the same treatment [for pneumonia] as he sets forth for pleurisy. And many other Empirics prescribe potions and liquid foods. They use pine seed, rue, mint, goat's marjoram, southernwood, pennyroyal, and marjoram. Some employ these separately, others in mixtures. And, in fact, they add starch, previously boiled with water and honey, and also bitter almonds, and stir these fluid mixtures with a twig of hyssop. They also prescribe iris and gentian boiled down with pennyroyal, pimpernel, eryngo, horehound, and the like. But all these remedies, since they are rejected by reason, should be barred.

61 XXX. THE CARDIAC DISEASE

SOME employ the term 'cardiac disease' in two senses, one general and the other special. They use it in the general sense to refer to that disease which has its essence in the esopha-

7. I.e., the decline of the attack must proceed to completion before cupping is permissible. Cf. 151.

ubi etiam mordicatio sequitur supradictarum partium, ut Hippocrates primo et secundo libro Epidemion commemorat, et
Erasistratus libris quos De ventre scripsit. propriam autem dicunt eam quae cum sudore fuerit atque pulsu imbecillo, de qua
nunc dicere suscepimus.

162   nomen autem haec sumpsit passio, ut quidam volunt, a parte
corporis quae patitur, siquidem putent principaliter cordis esse
aegritudinem. alii vero aliter sentiunt, siquidem vulgus quadam
consuetudine propria atque dominantia magnis[1] nominibus ap-
pellet, ut magnum mare sacrum mare, atque luem deificam vel
epilepticam passionem. est igitur in nobis proprium atque vi-
gens, et dominium vitae continens cor: quapropter tamquam
magna passio ⟨ab ea parte⟩ quae[2] summae potestatis habetur[3]
nomen sumpsit.

163   XXXI. QUID EST CARDIACA PASSIO, VEL QUO-
              MODO EIUS AGNITIO TRADENDA

DEFINITIONES enim Soranus dicere declinavit. cognitio igitur sive intelligentia eius passionis ab Artemidoro Sidensi
Erasistrati sectatore tradita est hoc modo: cardiaca, inquit,
passio est tumor secundum cor. item Asclepiadis sectatores
aiunt tumorem secundum cor corpusculorum coacervatione
sive obtrusione effectum.

Soranus vero, cuius haec sunt, tumoris inquit signum nullum
subesse quod in cardiacis videatur. item cor pati non valde
plurimis probabile videtur. sed ait cardiacam esse passionem[1]

    [1] magis G: corr. Rm
    [2] ⟨ab ea parte⟩ quae ⟨vim⟩ R: quam G
    [3] habet edd.
    [1] esse passionem] passionem esse R

1. I.e., On Abdominal Diseases.

2. Greek cardia is used in two senses, (1) the heart, (2) the upper orifice of the
stomach (English cardia), and it may have been a confusion of these senses that led some

gus and the upper orifice of the stomach and is characterized
by griping pain in these parts; this form of the disease is referred
to by Hippocrates in Books I and II of the *Epidemiae*, and by
Erasistratus in his work *On the Abdomen*.[1] But the term is also
used in a special sense to refer to the disease which is accompanied by sweating and a weak pulse. This is the form we have
now undertaken to discuss.

62   Some believe that this disease takes its name from the part
of the body affected, for they consider it chiefly an affection of
the heart.[2] Others, however, disagree. They say that people are
generally accustomed to give impressive names to objects of
special importance and power, for example, to call the great
sea the 'sacred sea' and to speak of the 'sacred scourge' (i.e.,
epilepsy).[3] Now in our bodies the heart is unique and powerful
and has control of life. Therefore, since this is an important disease, it derives its name [they say] from that part of the body
which is supremely dominant.

63   ## XXXI. WHAT THE CARDIAC DISEASE IS, OR
        HOW THE DISEASE IS TO BE DESCRIBED

SORANUS was reluctant to give definitions.[1] But Artemidorus
of Side, a follower of Erasistratus, gives his notion or con-
cept of the cardiac disease. Artemidorus says that the cardiac
disease is an inflammation in the region of the heart. And the
followers of Asclepiades say that it is an inflammation in the
region of the heart due to a heaping-up or stoppage of the corpuscles.

But Soranus, whose work this is, declares that no sign of an
inflammation can be observed in cases of the cardiac disease;
that, furthermore, there are very few who think it likely that
the heart itself is affected. He does hold, however, that the car-

---

to consider the heart the part affected. Note also the distinction, probably referred to
in 161, between what is generally called 'cardialgia' (heartburn?) and the cardiac disease proper. Cf. also 180 ff. and *Anon. Paris.*, p. 99.

   3. Cf. *Chr.* i. 60.

   1. It may be that *enim* is to be closely connected in thought with the title, i.e.
'What the cardiac disease is, *or rather* how the disease is to be described, *for* Soranus
was reluctant to define diseases.'

solutionem celerem atque acutam qua disici corpora per omnes
164 viarum particulas apprehendit. fit autem magis aestatis tempore, atque in viris potius quam in mulieribus, et calidis atque
iuvenibus corporibus vel habitudine plenis et exercitis. sed
praecedentes causae quibus haec passio sufficitur multae atque
variae sunt, magis autem iugis indigestio vel vinolentia aut post
cibum lavacra aut post cenam vomitus aut maestitudo vel timor,
in quae² consentiens corpus solvitur in sudores. emergit autem
frequentius quinta vel sexta die in febribus continuis, vel
ardentibus atque flammatis.

165   XXXII. QUOMODO INTELLIGIMUS EOS QUI IN
CARDIACAM VENIRE POSSUNT, AUT ETIAM
IN IPSA CONSTITUTOS

INTELLIGIMUS eos qui in cardiacam passionem declives atque
proni videntur et eos qui sunt iam in eadem constituti ex his
signis quae concurrunt. sequitur enim in passionem pronos febris acuta atque celerrima et flammosa, pulsus celer densus
humilis et quasi humectus toto accessionis tempore, aliquando
etiam usque ad dimissionem, ut etiam si fervoris relevatio fuerit
quadam circumscriptione collecta, non tamen simili profectu
pulsus quoque erigi videatur, quippe cum magis sui comparatione demersior esse noscatur. aliquando etiam ut inordinatus
occurrit, sed non ita ut deficiens intelligatur, sed celeritate co-
166 actus implicatis saltibus ordine¹ careat modo.² sequitur etiam
fastidium, sitis immodica, somnus parvus et facilis in suscita-
tione,³ hallucinatio, hebetudo, iactatio; item genuum gelidus
stupor atque cubitorum et tibiarum, crescente accessione vel
usque ad eius finem. haec concurrunt aliquando non praevexa-
tis viribus, sed ratione passionis effecta; aliquando vero prae-
vexatis ob nimiam sanguinis detractionem, vel ventris coacervatam effusionem, vel cuiusque materiae corporis immoderatam
eliquationem, ut peiorantibus febribus dissolutio fiat. addunt

² quibus *Rm*

¹ ordine *Rm*: ordinibus *G*

² ⟨et⟩ modo *Rm*   ³ *fort.* suscitationem

1. Or, with the reading of *Rm*, 'lacks regularity and measure.'

diac disease is a swift and acute state of dissolution, by which term he means that the bodily substance is dissipated through 64 all the minute pores. The disease occurs more often in summertime, in men rather than in women, in warm, young bodies, and in those that are full-figured and athletic. And the antecedent causes which give rise to this disease are many and varied; the usual causes, however, are continual indigestion, excessive drinking of wine, bathing after taking food, vomiting after dinner, and grief or fright in which the body is sympathetically affected and dissolved in sweat. The disease most often appears on the fifth or sixth day in the course of continuous and ardent or burning fevers.

65 XXXII. HOW TO RECOGNIZE THOSE WHO MAY LAPSE INTO THE CARDIAC DISEASE AND THOSE WHO ALREADY HAVE THE DISEASE

WE RECOGNIZE those who seem to be tending toward or lapsing into the cardiac disease and those who already have the disease by the following characteristic signs. Those on the brink of the disease have an acute, swift, and burning fever; their pulse is rapid, thick, submerged, and moist, as it were, during the whole period of the attack and even sometimes up to the remission. Indeed, even if relief from the burning heat is obtained by a checking [of the fever], the pulse does not show a like improvement and become stronger, but is found, by comparison, to be even more submerged. Sometimes, in fact, an irregular pulse occurs, not to such an extent that it is found to fail, but that because of its rapidity its beats become confused 66 and it merely lacks regularity.[1] Other symptoms are nausea, excessive thirst, little and light sleep, wandering mind, dulness [of the senses], tossing, and a cold numbness of the knees, forearms, and lower legs as the attack increases, or indeed, until its end. These symptoms sometimes occur as effects of the disease before the patient's strength is seriously impaired; but at other times they occur when the strength has been impaired by excessive loss of blood, or copious discharge from the bowels, or widespread liquefying of all types of bodily matter, so that, as the fever becomes worse, there is a state of dissolution. In addi-

vel attendunt quidam etiam aeris aestus, vel utrum temporaliter abundent solutiones, aut aeger sit lactea corporis habitudine, vel communiter si tenerum atque albidum et diffusum ac pingue habuerit corpus, et aquatum colorem, sitne etiam hac passione
167 tentari consuetus. sed haec, ut Soranus ait, sunt incerta et instabilia.

at vero si iam fuerit praesens, sequitur aegros articulorum frigidus torpor, aliquando etiam omnium crurum vel manuum aut totius corporis, pulsus densus celer parvus imbecillis inanis et quasi fluens. increscente passione etiam demersus obscurus tremulus et formicabilis[4] et inordinatus ac deserens, attestante halucinatione, desponsione cum vigiliis iugibus. et quibusdam repentinus atque coacervatus per totum corpus sudor, quibusdam vero primum cervice tenus et vultus,[5] parvus tenuis aquatus, dehinc per totum, ut supra diximus, corpus plurimus; tunc crassus et tractuosus atque viscosus vel male redolens tamquam lotura carnis; respiratio parva atque anhela et insustentabilis.
168 et per profectum rara locutio ac tremula, ora pallida, oculi concavi, thoracis gravedo, debilitatis causa animi defectus imminentibus accessionibus. aliquando etiam translátis lingua humecta, aliquibus vero ob complexionem tumoris parvi in visceribus constituti arida atque sicca, attestante desiderio frigidi potus.

deficiente aegro[6] visus obscuritas, articulorum livor, unguium uncatio, quam gryposin vocant, et plurimis mentis integer sensus, quibusdam vero falsitas intellectus, cordis saltus crebrior, dehinc deficiens, corporis superficies rugosa, et ea quae pereuntibus frequenter occurrunt, ut solutio ventris.
169 perniciosum etiam signum est involuntaria lacrimatio, hoc est sine ulla ratione, vel oculorum ex aliqua parte saniosa atque pu-

---

[4] cf. 145 n.

[5] vultum R: an vultu?

[6] aegro Rm: ergo G

tion, some observe whether the air is warm, whether cases involving a state of looseness are common in that season, whether the patient's body has a milk-white appearance and is generally tender, white, flabby, and heavy, whether his complexion is watery, and whether he is usually attacked by this disease.
67 But, as Soranus says, these are not fixed and definite indications of the disease.

Now if the disease is already present, the patients show the following signs. There is a cold numbness of the extremities, sometimes of both legs and arms or even of the whole body. The pulse is thick, rapid, small, weak, empty, and fluid, as it were. As the disease increases in intensity, the pulse is submerged, indistinct, quivering, antlike, irregular, and failing. There is also wandering of the mind, despondency, and continual sleeplessness. In some cases there is a sudden and copious perspiration over the whole body. But in other cases perspiration first appears at the neck and face, small in amount, thin, and watery; later it appears copiously over the whole body, as in the other cases, being now thick, clammy, sticky, and of bad odor, like water in which meat has been washed. The respiration is small, gasping, and unbearably difficult. As the disease advances, the patient speaks rarely and in a trembling voice.
68 The face is pale, eyes sunken, chest heavy, and because of weakness the patient faints when attacks impend. In some cases the tongue is moist after such fainting;[2] but in other cases, because they involve the presence of a small inflammation[3] in the vital organs, the tongue is parched and dry and there is a desire for cold drink.

As the patient becomes worse, his vision grows dim, his limbs become leaden colored, and there is a curving of his nails (Greek *grypōsis*). In most cases the mind is unimpaired, but in some cases such impairment occurs. The beating of the heart becomes more rapid and then fails; the surface of the body is wrinkled, and there are the other symptoms which frequently occur in the dying, including flux of the bowels.
69 Involuntary weeping, that is, weeping without any reason, is also a deadly sign; so is a partly sanious and purulent appearance

2. Or perhaps 'after the copious sweating.'

3. I.e., involve an element of *strictura* in combination (*complexio*) with the basic *solutio*.

rulenta similitudo, vel ex oculi circulo qui[7] nigro cum[8] colore apparet nata albedo[9] quae in unguis similitudinem, vel nascentis vel
crescentis lunae cornibus respondens, paulatim sumat augmentum: hanc Graeci onycha[10] vocaverunt. item coacervata atque
non masticata cibi transvoratio cum quodam sonitu perniciem
denuntiat, et magis si immutata atque indigesta post sumptionem fuerint immorata plurimo tempore, et tamquam in
utriculo moto ventre sonitum reddant, quem Graeci bombon[11]
170 vocaverunt. est enim signum mortuorum corporum ut tamquam inanimato atque insensibili tegmine cibus depositus videatur. peius etiam omnibus cibi sumptionibus privari fastidio
atque omnino accipienda recusare, vel etiam vinum non appetere, aut post acceptum cibum gravari potius vel febrire, tunc
rursum in solutionem recurrere, ut leviter resumptum celeriter
restringi, vel accepta reicere, et ventrem fluere, aut labiorum
pati tremorem, mordere etiam in accipiendo cibo vel potu cochlearia vel poculorum labra. etenim deficientis spiritus est
signum tamquam lassantis nec valentis oris partes attollere
sed[12] morsibus involuntariis succumbere.

171 est etiam gravius diaphoreticum delirare, siquidem neque
vini datione neque varietate ciborum ad sublevandas vires con-
stantius uti possumus. item gravius est post dationem ac resumptionem rursum in febres recurrere, tunc cum quadam
maestitudine latenter disici per sudorem atque marcere. etenim
solubile ac dimissum sit aegrotantibus corpusculi robur, atque
vultus visus obtusus, lingua aspera et arida, praecordiorum
etiam raptus ad superiora, et post cibum gravatio. sic enim[13]
aegrotantes multis diebus marcore quodam demersi moriuntur:
172 neque enim parvo atque simplici cibo sufficienter refici possunt,
neque multo ac solido valentius tolerata occurrere digestione.
in quibusdam etiam sine sudore vires solvuntur, et naturalis
vigor disiectione occulta, quam Graeci adelon diaphoresin[14]
vocant, extinguitur, cum omnis corporis habitudo laxior atque
dimissa et friabilis fuerit facta.

[7] quae *edd.*

[8] cum *om. R*

[9] albedo *scripsi* (*an* albido?): albida *G*: albida ⟨macula⟩ *R*

[10] ὄνυχα *G*

[11] βόμβον *G*

[12] *fort. del.* sed

[13] etiam *R*

[14] ἄδηλον διαφόρησιν *G*

of the eyes, and the formation on the black-colored circle of the eye of a white area which, like a nail or the horns of a new or crescent moon, gradually grows larger. The Greeks call this white area *onyx*.[4] Again, the noisy swallowing of food in unchewed masses is a deadly sign. This is especially the case if the food remains unaltered and undigested for a long time after being swallowed and, whenever the belly is shaken, makes a rumbling sound (Greek *bombos*) as if it were in a leather bottle. For it is a mark of a dead body that the food seems to rest in an insensible and lifeless container. It is, again, a bad sign if the patient is prevented by loss of appetite from taking any food and has to refuse it entirely, or has no desire for wine, or, after taking food, is distressed or feverish, and lapses back again into a state of dissolution; so that after gaining a little strength he soon loses it, or vomits what he has eaten, or suffers a flux of the bowels, or a quivering of the lips; and, again, if he bites the spoon or the rim of the cup in taking food or drink. For it is a sign of a failing and exhausted pneuma if the patient is unable to lift the parts of his mouth and gives way to involuntary biting.

It is also a grave sign if a patient with the cardiac disease loses his reason. For in that case we may no longer keep giving him wine or varied food to build up his strength. It is also dangerous if the patient relapses into fever after he has taken food and begun to convalesce. The same is true if he remains in a state of sadness and his body undergoes a gradual dissolution through sweating, with consequent weakening. For the strength of his poor body is broken and destroyed, his countenance has a feeble appearance, the tongue is rough and dry, the precordia drawn upward, and there is a feeling of heaviness after taking food. And thus the patient, after remaining sunk in a state of exhaustion for many days, dies. For it is impossible to restore his strength sufficiently with simple foods in small amount, nor can he deal adequately with a large quantity of solid food, since his digestion is impaired. Now in some cases the dissolution of the patient's strength takes place without sweating, and his natural vitality is destroyed by an invisible dissolution (Greek *adēlos diaphorēsis*). In this process the whole body passes into a state of atony, dissolution, and decay.

4. I.e., 'nail.'

at si in salutaria signa venire coeperint aegrotantes, pulsus re-
surgit, corporis frigus frangitur, et difficultas respirationis minuitur, accedente animi quadam securitate et post sumptionem
cibi virium profectu, somnus quoque altior tamquam post laborem dormientium.

173   XXXIII. UTRUMNE FEBRICITENT CARDIACI

QUAERITUR etiam utrum cardiaci febricitent, et plurimi quidem ante Asclepiadem febricitare cardiacos negaverunt;
alii vero contraria dixerunt, ut Apollophanes Erasistrati sectator. item Asclepiades plurimos inquit non febricitare: libris
enim quos ad Erasistratum fecit et appellavit Contradictorios,
dico, inquit, cardiacos non febricitare. sed secundo libro Oxeon
non inquit febricitare frequenter cardiacos. item Themison
et Thessalus [Demetrius Aponieus][1] quosdam febricitare aiunt,
quosdam negaverunt. Demetrius vero Apameus[2] incipiente,
inquit, passione atque crescente omnes febricitare; post vero
cum vehementescere coeperit passio, febris[3] recedere fertur.
174   igitur qui nullum aiunt febricitare cardiacum dicunt quod febricitantibus plurimus necessario fervor adsit, et gravedo cum
difficili motu corporis, et ariditas, vel tamquam vulnerationis
singularum viarum sensus, et rubor atque extentio praecordiorum. nihil inquiunt horum in cardiacis incurrere, quapropter
neque febricitare probamus. dehinc secundum Asclepiadem
febricula est fervor plurimus in omnibus sive plurimis corporis
partibus, cum mutatione[4] pulsus in vehementem ob obtrusionem
facta; at in cardiacis neque maior est pulsus sed magis humilis,
neque vehemens sed magis imbecillus, neque fervor plurimus
sed magis in aliis parvus corporis partibus, in mediis omnino
175   levissimus. utendum igitur clysteribus in his qui sine febribus
fuerint iubet constantissime. quidam vero conclusioni viarum

[1] *seclusi*

[2] Aponieus *edd.: corr. Almeloveen 711; cf. Chr. ii. 64, v. 89, Sor. Gyn., p. 94.22, 106.10*

[3] febris, passio *edd.*

[4] cum mutatione *scripsi*: commutatióve *G*: commutatione *A*: immutatione *Wellmann*, *Celsus 113, n. 6*

But if, on the contrary, the patient begins to show signs of recovery, the pulse becomes stronger, the bodily chill is dissipated, the pain felt in breathing diminishes, the mind recovers its composure, and there is an improvement in strength after the taking of food. Also the patient sleeps more soundly, like one who has finished a fatiguing task.

73

XXXIII. IS FEVER PRESENT IN THE CARDIAC DISEASE?

THE question is asked whether patients with the cardiac disease have fever. Many before Asclepiades answered in the negative; but others, among them Apollophanes, the follower of Erasistratus, held the opposite view. And Asclepiades himself asserts that in most cases patients do not have fever. In the treatise he wrote in opposition to Erasistratus, a treatise which he called *Refutations*, he does, to be sure, declare that patients with the cardiac disease do not have fever. But in Book II of his work *On Acute Diseases* he says that *frequently* they do not have fever.[1] Again, Themison and Thessalus hold that in some cases there is fever, and in others not. But Demetrius of Apamea says that at the beginning of the disease and in its increasing phase all patients have fever; but that afterward, when the disease begins to grow violent, the fever wanes.

74 Now those who hold the view that no patient with the cardiac disease has fever say that in cases of fever there is, of necessity, a great deal of heat, a feeling of heaviness, discomfort in moving the body, dryness, a painful sensation in every passage, and redness and distention of the precordia. They say that none of these signs occurs in cases of cardiac disease, and they hold, therefore, that there is no fever in this disease. Furthermore, according to Asclepiades, fever is an excessive heat in all or many parts of the body, with a change to a stronger pulse because of the obstruction. Yet in the cardiac disease the pulse is neither larger nor stronger, but more submerged and weaker; nor is there very much heat, but a little in other parts of the body,

75 and least of all in the middle regions. And for that reason Asclepiades prescribes the regular use of clysters in these cases,

1. But cf. 176. The bracketing of *non* or the reading of *noson* for *non* are possibilities if the present passage is considered incompatible with 176.

causam febrium ascribentes, aiunt disiectionem sive diaphoresin diraratis partibus fieri totius corporis, viis[5] vero febrem densatis, quarum ex affricatione quadam nasci ac proficisci fervorem.

Apollophanes omnes inquit cardiacos febricitare secundum Erasistratum, siquidem cardiaca passio ex cordis tumore fieri videatur; febricula quoque magni tumoris fit ex causa. item aliqui novelli scriptores aiunt signum esse periculosae passionis non[6] sine febribus aegrotare, atque malignas passiones acce-dentibus fieri febribus, tunc diaphoresin venire, vel cessantibus sudoribus perseverare febrium reliquias.

176   sed haec utraque Soranus excludit, nam primo dicto respon-dens ait aliud esse signum, aliud accidens. nam signum neque recedit, et semper significato coniunctum est; accidens autem, quod Graeci symptoma vocant, nunc advenit, nunc recedit. ex quibus esse intelligimus singula quae febricitantium accidentia dixerunt, ut corporis difficilem motum, gravedinem, tensionem praecordiorum. etenim aliqui febricitantes nulla ex ipsis pa-tiuntur, si febricula secundum solutionem fuerit facta; sed fervor mordicans atque febrem designans tamquam ex alto quibusdam cardiacis inest.

Asclepiades ait secundo libro Acutarum vel celerum pas-sionum non semper sed frequenter ex[7] febricula fieri hanc pas-
177 sionem. at si omnes[8] cardiacos sine febribus esse voluerit, siquidem non adsint secundum ipsum febrium signa, respondere poterimus eum peccare non videndo vera febrium signa. nam

[5] viis *Schmid 82, n. 17*: in his G
[6] non *posuit R post* aiunt *praecedens*
[7] cum *Rm*: *an* sine?
[8] omnes *om.* R

---

2. And therefore in the cardiac disease fever would not be present.

3. I.e., of the corpuscles.

considering them free from fever. And some who ascribe the cause of fevers to the blocking of the pores say that, when all the parts of the body are dilated, dissolution or diaphoresis takes place;[2] but when the pores are clogged, fever occurs, the heat originating in the rubbing of matter[3] in these pores.

But Apollophanes holds that, according to Erasistratus, fever is present in all cases of the cardiac disease, since this disease apparently arises from an inflammation of the heart; and fever, too, results from any extensive inflammation. Again, some recent writers say that the presence of fever is an indication that the disease is dangerous; that stubborn cases of disease are always accompanied by fever; and that in these cases diaphoresis takes place, but, even when the sweating is over, remnants of the fever still persist.

6   But Soranus rejects both these views. In refuting the first view he says that a true sign [*signum*] and a concomitant symptom [*accidens*] are two different things. A sign never disappears but is always found in connection with the thing signified;[4] on the other hand, a concomitant symptom (Greek *symptōma*) now comes and now disappears. And the particular attributes of feverish persons that have been mentioned are, as we know, instances of just such concomitants, e.g., discomfort in moving the body, a feeling of heaviness, and precordial distention. In fact, some persons with fever do not show any of these symptoms if their fever results from a state of looseness; though in certain cases of the cardiac disease there is present a burning heat indicative of fever, apparently arising from deep within.

In Book II of his treatise *On Acute* (i.e., swift) *Diseases* Asclepiades says that frequently, though not always, this dis-
7 ease arises from fever.[5] But if he concludes that all cases of this disease are unaccompanied by fever merely because what he believes to be the signs of fever are not present, we may answer that he makes the mistake of not observing the true indications of fever. For at the beginning of an attack [of the cardiac

4. I.e., so long as a certain state exists, its true 'signs' are present. On the other hand, a particular 'symptom' may appear after, or disappear before, that which it symptomatizes.

5. The apparent discrepancy between 173 and the present passage may be avoided by a distinction between 'arises from fever' and 'is accompanied by fever.' Cf. 178.

manifeste atque prompte in initiis accessionis articuli frigidi reperiuntur, et pulsus humilis et imbecillus. quod secundo poterit obici, quo putant densitatem viarum esse febrium causam.[9]

item aliqui aiunt complexa aegritudine aegrotare cardiacos qui cum febribus fuerint, atque ita cum aliae fuerint viae laxatae, aliae densatae, raritate diaphoresis fiat, densitate vel adfricatione febricula. nos vero Sorani sequentes iudicium et solutione absoluta fieri febres accipimus, hoc est raritate viarum, ut et ipsis est consequens, sicut libris De febribus docuit.

178   item Erasistrati sectatoribus respondebimus falsum esse omnes febres ex tumore fieri, siquidem quaedam fiant solutione. at si hoc parum etiam probaverint, cardiacam tamen nullo ex tumore fieri non negabunt. nam cum sint aegrotantes integro iudicio mentis et nullo sensu doloris vel ceteris stricturae signis afficiantur, cordis inesse tumorem erit falsissimum atque omnes cardiacos febricitare.

sed neque periculosas passiones signo febrium designari recte dixerunt. est enim cholerica gravis atque periculosa passio, quae numquam cum febribus fiet. antecedere autem febres cardiacam passionem verum est, sed aliquando sudoribus solvi, sicut etiam tumor solvitur in humorem purulentum conversus 179 collectione suffecta. falsum etiam esse perspicimus cessantibus sudoribus manere febriculae reliquias: plerique enim sine febribus reperiuntur.

dicimus igitur, sicut omnes nostri Methodici, quosdam sine febribus [quosdam cum febribus][10] esse cardiacos, ut eos qui sanguinis emissione solvuntur; quosdam vero febricitare. nam-

[9] causa G: *corr. Rm*
[10] *om. R*

---

6. I.e., the failure to distinguish the true 'sign' from the incidental symptom. The reference is to the view of the Asclepiadeans, *quidam vero*, etc. (175).

disease] the limbs are obviously and unmistakably found to be cold, and the pulse submerged and weak. The same objection[6] may be made to the secondary argument that the cause of fevers is the blocking of the pores.

Some hold that persons with cardiac disease who have fever are really suffering from a complex type of illness; that, while some pores are dilated, others are obstructed; and diaphoresis results from the condition of dilation, while fever results from the condition of obstruction and the consequent friction. But we adopt Soranus' views and hold that fevers may also arise in connection with a simple state of looseness, that is, with a dilation of the pores, and that this condition is characteristic of the cases under discussion.[7] This is the view of Soranus in his work *On Fevers*.

78   Moreover, our answer to Erasistratus and his followers[8] is that it is wrong to say that all fevers arise from an inflammation, for they do arise in some cases from a state of looseness. And even if Erasistratus and his followers do not accept this statement, yet they will have to admit that the cardiac disease does not arise from an inflammation. For, since patients with this disease remain of sound mind and do not feel pain or show any of the other signs of a state of stricture, it is quite wrong to say that an inflammation of the heart is present, and that all the patients have fever.

Again, those who say that fever is a necessary indication of a dangerous disease are mistaken. For cholera is a serious and dangerous disease, but is never accompanied by fever. Now it is true that fever precedes the cardiac disease, but this fever is sometimes dispelled by sweating, just as an inflammation is dispelled when, with the formation of an abscess, it turns into 79 purulent liquid matter. It is also obviously erroneous to say that the remains of the fever persist when the sweating ceases. For many cases are found to be without fever.

We therefore hold, as do all our fellow-physicians of the Methodist Sect, that some patients with cardiac disease have no fever, for instance, those in whom the state of looseness is manifested by loss of blood. Other patients, however, do have fever; for if

7. I.e., cases of the cardiac disease accompanied by fever.

8. Cf. 175.

que inanibus et celatis locis vel supra quae iacuerint antea apposita manu, tarda perseveratione occurrat[11] plurimus et
mordicans ascendens fervor ex alto, febrium referens signum,
attestante anhelatione ferventi, cum delectatione frigidi potus.
quibusdam etiam lingua sicca atque aspera invenitur.

180   XXXIV. QUIS IN CARDIACIS LOCUS PRINCI-
                    PALITER PATITUR

PRAEPATI in cardiacis Erasistratus et Asclepiades cor dixerunt,
  alii membranam quae cor circumtegit, alii diaphragma, hoc
est membranam quae a visceribus discernit intestina, alii stomachum, alii pulmonem, atque iecur. sed hi qui cor pati dixerunt aiunt primo ipsius se nominis testimonio iuvari, siquidem
ideo cardiaca dicatur passio, quod ex cordis veniat causa; nam
cardian Graeci cor vocaverunt: secundo quod eidem cordi in
ipsa passione constitutis saltus inesse videatur atque in sinistra
parte secundum papillam thoracis gravedo: tertio ipsius passionis
magnitudo, quae fieri non posset nisi aliqua corporis parte principali atque propria patiente; est autem cor praestans atque salutaris corporis particula, praeministrans omnibus sanguinem
membris atque spiritum.

181   sed his quidam occurrentes primae propositioni responderunt
quod passio a magnitudine nomen sumpserit: secundae, quomodo similis arteriarum cordis est motus, gravedo[1] etiam quibusdam cardiacis occurrit in toto thorace et non solum in sinistra
parte, quae si fuerit, poterit hypezocote membrana patiente
fuisse suffecta, vel quaquam altera vicinante[2] ⟨parte⟩ corporis,
si locis ascribendae sunt causae. tertio dictae respondentes
aiunt multas fieri periculosas passiones quae non patientis cordis

---

[11] occurrit *Rm*

[1] ⟨quod⟩ gravedo *R*

[2] cuiusquam alterius vicinantis *edd.*

---

1. Caelius (Soranus) usually defines the diaphragm as the membrane between the
abdominal and thoracic cavities (cf., e.g., *Chr.* i. 75, ii. 14). The present definition is
inaccurate unless the stomach be considered as included in the term *intestina*. I have
therefore adopted the loose term 'abdomen' in translating.

one places one's hand in hollow and concealed parts of their bodies, or over the places where these patients have been lying, a considerable amount of burning heat may be felt, slowly and steadily rising from below. This sign, in connection with panting and hot breath and a desire for cold drink, is indicative of fever. In some cases, too, the tongue is found to be dry and rough.

XXXIV. THE PART PRINCIPALLY AFFECTED IN THE CARDIAC DISEASE

80

ERASISTRATUS and Asclepiades hold that the part chiefly affected in the cardiac disease is the heart. Others hold that it is the membrane which covers the heart, others the diaphragm, i.e., the membrane separating the abdomen from the [upper] viscera,[1] others the esophagus, others the lungs, and others the liver. Now those who say it is the heart assert that their position is supported, in the first place, by the evidence of the very name of the disease, for it is called the 'cardiac' disease because its origin is supposed to be in the heart, and the Greek word for heart is *cardia*. Their second argument is that the heart is found to palpitate in cases of this disease, and there is heaviness of the chest on the left side near the nipple. Their third argument is that the disease is very serious, and this could not be the case unless some leading and especially important part of the body were affected. And the heart is a pre-eminently important part of the body and is vital to bodily health, furnishing, as it does, blood and pneuma to all the other parts.

81   In opposition to this view, some have replied to the first argument by saying that the disease takes its name from its importance; and to the second by saying that the motion of the heart is like that of the arteries, and that in some cases of the cardiac disease there is heaviness of the whole chest and not merely of the left side. If that is true, the disease, they say, may arise from an affection of the pleural membrane or of any other neighboring part of the body, if diseases must be assigned to particular parts. They reply to the third argument by saying that there are many serious diseases which do not involve

habeant causas. non enim ubi magna fuerit passio necessario
propriam corporis partem pati accipimus, quippe cum omnes
partes propriae sint corpori.

    alii vero propterea magis falsum dicunt esse cor ista passione
182 vexari, siquidem eorum testimonio qui hoc asseverant sit[3] propria pars atque principalis saluti et propterea mox pati coeperit,
morte praeveniat sensum; vulnerata denique cum fuerit, statim
atque sine ulla mora mors vulneris antecedit effectum. at[4] si
multo parvissime fuerit laesa, nihilo minus mortem necessario
perfecit,[5] et non similiter ceteris partibus aut emoritur aut durescit aut in paralysim solvitur.

    sed his rursum primi respondentes aiunt quod vulneratum cor
celerius interficiat, siquidem multis ante praecisis partibus vulnus possit accipere, et pomposa atque coacervata sanguinis fiat
effusio, nec tamen diaphoresis. quod autem neque emoritur
neque edurescit[6] neque paralysi afficitur argumentum est quidem non omnino cor pati negans, sed leviter pati. si enim ceteris similiter partibus corporis est natura confectum, iisdem
necessario similes sustinet causas.

183   nos vero cum Sorani iudicio totum videmus corpus in solutionem laxari, totum necessario pati accipimus. et neque valde
nobis de praepatienti loco certandum est, ne in occulta quaestione versemur. non enim aut significatio aut curatio secundum
haec differenter accipitur, cum oporteat omnibus corporis partibus adiutoria prolatari.

    aliqui denique alios ex corde, alios ex membrana quae cor
circumtegit, aiunt diaphoresi vexari: et propterea eos qui ex

---

[3] sit *Schmid Mn 143*: si *edd.*

[4] ac *Rm*

[5] perficit *R*

[6] durescit *Bendz Eran 41. 72*

---

    2. Cf. 162. The ambiguity in *propriae* here—'special or peculiar' and 'pre-eminent'—
is the crux of the sophism.

an affection of the heart. For where there is a serious disease we must not necessarily assume (they say) that the principal part of the body is affected. The fact is that all parts have a special importance for the body.[2]

Now others adduce the following additional reason to refute the argument that the heart is the part affected in this disease.
2 They say that even on the testimony of those who put forth this argument the heart is the pre-eminent part of the body and essential to life, and that therefore, as soon as it began to be affected, death would forestall any sensation. For when this part is wounded, death follows immediately and without any delay, before the effect of the injury can be felt. Even if the injury is very slight, it still inevitably causes death; the heart does not, like the other parts, either die off [by itself], or become hard, or paralyzed.

But the first group [who assert that the heart is affected in the cardiac disease] declare, by way of rejoinder, that death follows quickly when the heart is wounded because the heart can receive a wound only when many parts in front of it are previously damaged, with the result that there is a rich, gushing flow of blood, and yet no colliquative sweating (*diaphoresis*).[3] And, they add, the fact that the heart does not die off, or grow hard, or become paralyzed is proof not that the heart is entirely unaffected but that it is only slightly affected. For if the heart is naturally constituted in the same way as the other parts of the body, it is necessarily subject to affections similar to those of the other parts.

3 From our viewpoint, however, since we follow Soranus in holding that the whole body is relaxed in a state of looseness, we have to assume that the whole body is affected in this disease. And to avoid becoming involved in the investigation of matters beyond our knowledge, we certainly should refrain from arguing about the part chiefly affected. For this question does not affect our understanding of either the indication or the treatment of the disease, since our remedies must be directed to the body in all its parts.

Now others hold that the colliquative sweating which characterizes this disease in some cases has its cause in the heart, in

3. So that the case is not the same as that of the cardiac disease.

membrana cordis solvuntur adiuncto dolore laborare, qui punctionibus crebris aegrum afficiat, eos vero qui ex corde, gravedinem solam sustinere. sed his quoque respondemus quomodo signa sibi quae fingunt vera existimant esse, cum[7] oporteat, sicuti
supra diximus, patientibus quibusque vicinis atque contiguis[8]
cordi aliquando stimulantem dolorem, aliquando gravedinem
consequi.

184 XXXV. QUOMODO DISCERNIMUS CARDIACOS AB
HIS QUI IN[1] STOMACHO PATIENTE
SUDAVERINT

QUONIAM plerisque stomachicis adest in accessione sudor
atque articulorum frigus cum parvo pulsu et animi defectu et pallore, quae omnia sunt communia cum cardiacis,
horum quoque discretionem faciendam existimo. Asclepiades
igitur haec discernens ait cardiacos atque eos qui stomachi su-
pinitate decoquuntur ita internosci, quod in cardiacis omnis
pulsus sit parvissimus atque imbecillus, cordis vero saltus maior
et vehemens, cum gravedine thoracis atque spiratione praefocabili; in his vero qui stomacho patiente deficiunt atque coacervant ceteris arteriis pulsus cordis[2] imbecillus invenitur, exceptis
ceteris accidentibus, quae symptomata Graeci vocaverunt.

nos vero magnitudinem pulsus in corde fieri cardiacis non in-
185 venimus, quippe cum cor ipsum pati sit existimabile potius quam
verum. gravantur quidem thorace atque praefocabili spiramento
respirant quidam stomacho patiente cum defectione virium
fuerunt depurgati; atque rursum cardiaci quidam nulla spira-
menti praefocatione iactantur. dicendum itaque stomacho
nunc tumente, nunc deficiente in tumore, fervorem atque dolo-

---

[7] existimant esse cum *Friedel 31*: existimantes secum *G*

[8] continguis *G: corr. R*

[1] in *om. R (ex* istomaco *ortum?): cf. 184 fin. et* ex stomaci passione *Diaet. pass. 41,
Aurel., p. 496*

[2] *fort.* atque coacervant, ⟨ut in⟩ ceteris arteriis, ⟨sic⟩ pulsus cordis *etc., vel sim.*

---

1. The text is uncertain. The suggestion in *Thes. Ling. Lat.*, 'coacervant (*sc.*
stercora),' can hardly be right.

others in the membrane surrounding the heart; and that in the former case the patients merely experience the feeling of heaviness, while in the latter case the patients also suffer from a pain which keeps pricking them. But again our answer to those who assert this is that they believe that the signs they invent are true. Yet, since every part near the heart and touching it is affected, sometimes a pricking pain and sometimes a feeling of heaviness must occur, as we have indicated above.

4 XXXV. HOW TO DISTINGUISH BETWEEN THE CARDIAC DISEASE AND DISEASE OF THE ESOPHAGUS ACCOMPANIED BY PROFUSE SWEATING

SINCE in many cases of the disease of the esophagus we find sweating, coldness of the limbs, a small pulse, fainting, and pallor, conditions which all occur in the cardiac disease too, I think a distinction should be made between the two diseases. Asclepiades, seeking to make this distinction, says that persons who have the cardiac disease and those who waste away through atony of the esophagus may be distinguished as follows. In cases of the cardiac disease the pulse is always very small and weak, while the heart beat is large and strong, and there is heaviness of the chest and a choking sensation in breathing; but where fainting and collapse are due to an affection of the esophagus, the heart beat, compared to that of the other arteries, is found to be weak,[1] not to mention other differences in the concomitant conditions (Greek *symptōmata*).

But we have never found that a strong heart beat occurs in 5 cases of the cardiac disease. And, in fact, it is only a supposition rather than a demonstrable certainty that the heart itself is affected. Indeed, some patients with disease of the esophagus suffer heaviness in the chest and a choking sensation in breathing when overcome by a collapse of strength. On the other hand, some of those who have the cardiac disease are not troubled by any choking sensation in breathing. And so we should say that, when the esophagus is either in a state of inflammation[2] or in a state of atony combined with inflammation,[3] heat and pain are

2. *Strictura (status strictus).*

3. *Complexio (status mixtus).*

rem fieri sub his partibus pectoris quae costis teguntur, vel ex adverso inter palas, aliquando etiam post cibum pressuram. at vero si defectione fuerit stomachus affectus, fluor sequitur salivarum et humecta callositas et nausea vel vomitus liquidorum atque cibi, frigus etiam articulorum.

186   initio enim nunc fervore nunc frigore afficiuntur; in cardiacis vero neque dolor, neque post cibum gravedo, neque vomitus esse perspicitur, et torpor frigidus idem atque aequalis perseverat. dehinc sudor aliquando cardiacis crassus excluditur et male redolens ut saniem vel cruorem simulet; his vero qui stomacho patiuntur tenuis omnino atque aquatus sudor invenitur. item animi defectio stomacho[3] incipiente magis accessione fiet, cardiacis vero recedente. at si vero utraeque passiones eodem concurrerint tempore, obscuratur discretionis fides sed nihil curatio impeditur, siquidem iisdem adiutoriis curentur.

item in cholericis et tetanicis vel tumentibus aut matrice[4] praefocatis plurimus sequitur sudor, adiuncto frigido torpore, qui ita discernitur cum singularum passionum fuerit consideratio perspecta. in alia enim vomitum, in alia colla inclinari, in alia matricem tumere, in alia tumorem vehementem esse necesse est.

187   at si nihil ex antecedentibus causis quae passionem facere valent fuerit repertum, si tamen praesens atque provocata corporis solutio quae cardiacam designet, certo inesse passionem dicimus, nec satis necessarium unde illa solutio venerit invenire. non enim curatio pro differentia antecedentium causarum mutanda accipitur.

vocatur autem secundum aliquos quaedam passio etiam cardimona, quam Graeci cardiogmon vocaverunt, quam necessario sequitur dolor oris ventris, quem plurimi idiotae cordis dolorem vocaverunt.

[3] *fort.* stomachico *vel* stomachicis: ⟨ex⟩ stomacho *A*

[4] aut matrice] matrice, aut *R*

---

4. *Solutio* (*status laxus*).

5. *Cordis dolor* = Greek *cardialgia*. Cf. our term 'heartburn.' Caelius (Soranus) either disregards or implicitly criticizes the use of *cardia* to signify 'the esophageal orifice of the stomach' as well as 'the heart.' Cf. 161.

caused in those parts of the chest which are covered by the ribs, or in the back, between the shoulder blades; sometimes, too, there is a feeling of drowsiness after eating. But if the affection of the esophagus involves [only] a state of atony,[4] there occurs a flow of saliva, moisture and numbness, nausea or the vomiting of liquids and food, and coldness of the extremities.

6 That is to say, at the beginning [of the disease of the esophagus] the patients sometimes suffer from heat, and sometimes from cold. But in cases of the cardiac disease neither pain, nor a feeling of heaviness after eating, nor vomiting is observed to occur; but a constant state of cold numbness continues without change. And in the cardiac disease the sweat given off is sometimes thick and foul-smelling, so that it resembles sanies or corrupted blood; but in disease of the esophagus the sweat is found to be quite thin and watery. Again, the fainting that is due to an affection of the esophagus takes place at the beginning of an attack, while that due to the cardiac disease takes place as the attack is declining. Now if both diseases occur at the same time, it is more difficult to make a reliable distinction between them, but that is no obstacle to the treatment, for both diseases are treated by the same procedures.

Copious sweating accompanied by cold numbness also occurs in cases of cholera, tetanus, inflammation of the womb, and hysterical suffocation. But a distinction may be made on the basis of a consideration of these several diseases. For, in the first, vomiting always occurs; in the second, the neck is bent; in the third, the womb is inflamed; and in the last, there is a severe inflammation.

7 Now, even if we should be unable to find any of the antecedent causes which may produce the cardiac disease, yet if the kind of collapse which is indicative of this disease has been brought about and is present, we may with certainty declare that the disease is present. And it really is not necessary to discover the cause of the collapse. For we do not vary our treatments according to differences in the antecedent causes.

There is also a disease called by some *cardimona* (Greek *cardiōgmos*). In this disease there is always pain at the mouth of the stomach, a condition which many laymen call pain of the heart.[5]

generaliter autem cardiaca passio est solutionis, atque una acutarum et vehementium passionum. sed aliquando huic miscentur quaedam stricturae accidentia, ut tensio vel tumor partium mediarum, quae non speciali concursu ac significatione sint cardiacis ascribenda.

188 XXXVI. QUOMODO DISCERNIMUS CARDIACOS AB HIS QUI PROSPERO SUDORE LIBERANTUR, QUEM GRAECI CRITICUM VOCANT

QUOMODO etiam prosperi sudores, quos Graeci criticos vocant, habent quiddam circa visum similitudinis cum cardiacis ob ipsam redundantiam, quippe in solutionem vehementium vel continuarum febrium salutari motu venientes, utile duximus eorum ponere discretionem. multi etenim imperiti medici prosperos atque mediocres sudores constringentes morbosa aegrotantibus reddiderunt[1] corpora, diaphoreticos adiuvantes causa mortis extiterunt. quare eorum differentiam necessario ducimus ordinandam, quae varia ratione colligitur. nam primo ex praeteritis, dehinc ex genere passionum et magnitudine et temporibus et sudoris ipsius ordine et quantitate et qualitate significatio firmatur.

189   ex praeteritis, inquam, cum consideramus utrum signa futuri sudoris diaphoretici an salutaris praecesserint. ex genere passionum, cum qualitatem attendimus passionis. si enim solutio inest, sudor etiam inutilis ac diaphoreticus esse monstratur; sin vero strictura inest, attendenda magnitudo. parva enim passio diaphoresim pati non potest; si autem magna fuerit, attenden-

---

[1] morbos aegrotantibus reddiderunt *Friedel 21* (*deleto* corpora), *coll. Diaet. pass., p. 214. 3* (passiones aegrotantibus reddiderunt), *et Aurel., p. 494*

---

1. Throughout this chapter cf. *Diaet. pass.* 40, Aurel. 3.

In its essential nature the cardiac disease involves a state of looseness and is one of the acute and severe diseases; but sometimes there are also present certain symptoms involving a condition of stricture, e.g., tension or inflammation of the middle parts. These symptoms, however, are not to be considered as specifically connected with, and indicative of, the cardiac disease.

8 XXXVI. HOW TO DISTINGUISH THE CARDIAC DISEASE FROM ILLNESSES IN WHICH SWEATING IS INDICATIVE OF A SUCCESSFUL CRISIS (THE GREEKS CALL SUCH SWEATING *CRITICOS*)[1]

ALSO bearing some outward resemblance to the cardiac disease are those illnesses in which a successful crisis is marked by sweating called *criticos* by the Greeks. For here, too, there is copious sweating, but it is a beneficial symptom and makes for the dissolution of severe and persistent fever. We therefore consider it important to distinguish between the two sets of cases. For in cases of beneficial and moderate sweating many inexperienced doctors, by using astringent measures, cause the patient to lapse back into disease; while in the colliquative sweats [of the cardiac disease], by helping along the flow, they bring about the patient's death. It is therefore necessary, in our judgment, to set forth the difference between the two kinds of cases, a difference which may be inferred from various considerations. For the diagnosis is in each case confirmed, first by the prior circumstances, and then by the nature, gravity, and time of the disease, and by the regularity, quantity, and quality of the sweating itself.

39   We rely on the prior circumstances when we consider whether the antecedent signs were indicative of the coming of an unwholesome or a beneficial sweat. We rely on the nature of the illnesses when we note the character of the disease in question, for the presence of a state of looseness is an indication that the sweating is harmful and unwholesome. But if a state of stricture is present, the extent of this state must then be noted. For a minor illness cannot give rise to unwholesome diaphoresis; but if the illness is a severe one, we must consider the factor of

dum tempus. in statu enim totius passionis atque temporalis
accessionis vel limpida dimissione criticus magis sudor ostendi-
tur; in initio autem vel augmento perniciosus.

ex ordine, inquam, sudoris ipsius: aequalis enim bonus, inaequalis malus sudor iudicatur. ex quantitate signum accipimus moderationem considerantes: modicus enim sudor bonus,
immodicus malus accipitur. sed[2] denique sudantes excessa
190 moderatione diaphoresin incurrerunt.[3]   ex qualitate autem
significationem accipimus cum tactus iudicium adhibemus.
salutaris enim sudor calidus tenuis et non male redolens probatur; perniciosus autem sudor frigidus et sucidus et male redolens
atque loturae[4] carnis similis invenitur.

dehinc ex praesentibus atque concurrentibus signis confirman-
da significatio. nam diaphoreticis magis parvus atque creber
et imbecillis et inanis pulsus invenitur, thorax etiam gravatus,
cum respiratione frequenti, et iactatione, ac desponsione animi,
vocis etiam tenuitate, attestante pallore. recte autem sudantibus pulsus erectior, respiratio facilior ac levior efficitur, et in
somnum[5] prona delectatio,[6] et omnium adversorum minutio
cum animi atque corporis relevatione.

191   XXXVII. QUOMODO CURANDI SUNT CARDIACI

DEHINC cardiacorum ordinamus curationem: deridendi etenim
sunt qui hoc passionis genus incurabile iudicantes reliquerunt. multos enim omnes medici[1] iuxta sententiam Sorani
liberari videmus. livore namque commoti argumentatione
turpi aiunt quidam eos liberari non qui sint, sed videantur esse
cardiaci.

quapropter Sorani nos iudicium servantes iacere facimus
locis refrigerantibus atque umbrosis et obscuris, ut sunt plerumque hypogea vel speluncosa atque ad aquiloniam partem con-
clusa, vel certe solis tactu difficilia. semper enim atque magis

    [2] sed del. Friedel 21, coll. Diaet. pass., p. 215. 11, Aurel., p. 495

    [3] fort. incurrunt; cf. Diaet. pass., p. 215. 12, Aurel., p. 495

    [4] loturae A, coll. 167 (cf. etiam Diaet. pass., p. 215. 15, Aurel., p. 495): putridae G,
    fort. retin.

    [5] somnum Rm (cf. Diaet. pass., p. 215. 21): somno G

    [6] sic etiam Aurelius: deiectio Diaet. pass., p. 215. 22

    [1] methodici Bendz Eran 41. 72

time. For sweating which occurs at the highest stage of the whole disease as well as of a particular attack, or during a period of pure remission, is more likely to be indicative of a successful crisis, while sweating which occurs at the beginning of an illness or in its increasing phase is more likely to be unfavorable.

We rely also on the regularity of the sweating, for an even flow is considered favorable, an uneven flow unfavorable. We also obtain a clue from the quantity of sweat, with reference to moderation. For sweating in moderation is good, in excess bad. And, in fact, excessive sweating indicates a lapse into unfavor-

90 able diaphoresis. The quality of the perspiration also aids our diagnosis. In determining this quality we rely on the sense of touch. For sweat that is warm, thin, and not ill-smelling may be considered beneficial; but that sweat is unfavorable which is found to be cold, thick, foul-smelling, and like water in which meat has been washed.

In addition, the diagnosis should be corroborated by the group of symptoms found present in the disease. Thus in the colliquative sweats of the cardiac disease the pulse is found to to be small, rapid, weak, and empty, the chest heavy, and breathing rapid; the patients are restless, despondent, thin-voiced, and pale. But in cases of beneficial sweating[2] the pulse becomes stronger and respiration easier and gentler; the patients tend to fall asleep, all their unfavorable symptoms abate, and they are relieved both in mind and in body.

91   XXXVII. TREATMENT OF THE
                         CARDIAC DISEASE

W E NOW set forth the treatment of the cardiac disease. For we have only scorn for those who consider this type of disease incurable and leave the patient untreated. As Soranus points out, we physicians have all seen many cases of cures. Yet some writers, prompted by ill-will, declare, in an unfair type of argument, that those who became well only seemed to have the cardiac disease, but did not actually have it.

But we follow Soranus' judgment, and we have the patient lie in a cool, shady, and dark place, such as a cellar or a cave facing north or, in any case, hardly touched by the sun. For at

2. I.e., indicative of a successful crisis.

in ista passione solem praecavendum accipimus, et propterea
vehementiae eius ingressum, si qua ex parte venerit, prohibemus.
192 convenit etiam neque maiora loca esse, solubilis[2] enim plurimus
aer esse perspicitur. sed neque satis brevia: sunt enim prae-
focabilia et quae facile fervorem ex ingressu hominum conci-
piant, quos naturalis spiratio aerem accipere atque reddere anhelitus raptu necessario cogit.

denique si non fuerit naturaliter frigidus locus, hunc[3] affecta-
bimus specularia detrahentes, nisi sol obstiterit aut aeris inaequalitas. adiungitur frigori inducto purgatior aer ingrediens
locum, qui sua novitate ac miti accessu reficiat aegrotantem.
flabellis etiam latenter aerem frigerandum dicimus, aqua frigida
aspergentes solum. et ea quae influxione[4] sui, quam Graeci
aporrhoeam vocant, spirationem facilem aegrotantibus facere
193 valent circum proici iubemus, quae tamen sine ullo percussu
atque odore gravi valeant aerem facere constrictivum, ut vitis
folia aut myrti aut quercus et pini atque lentisci et mali punici
vel rosae atque his similium. sic enim corporis fluor aeris occur-
rentis afflatu densatus prohibetur.[5] decocto denique supra dictarum materiarum liquore, frigido tamen, terram perfundimus.

cooperimenta praeterea atque stramenta tenera et tritiora
probamus, etenim nova vaporatione sui corpora resolvunt. generaliter autem ipsa lecti concubatio neque dura, siquidem vigilias faciat, neque satis mollis, ut est floccorum vel levium plu-
194 marum, erit procuranda. etenim recessu facili corpori cedens
utrimque[6] orarum circumlevigat tegmina, quae amplexu quodam corpus cingendo vaporatione[7] sui resolvant. denique etiam
cum fuerit mollior, erit[8] coarctanda straminum velamento ne
facili, ut supra diximus, recessu concava faciat[9] stramina. lecti
etiam latitudo atque spatium tantum probatur quantum sufficiat aegro alterna conversatione alterius loci frigus accipere, ac
desertum vapore carere, quo mutua vice semper veluti nova
repetendo frigida inveniat, ut sine ulla lectorum mutatione in
195 eodem lecto mutatio fieri videatur. in altera enim parte aegro
constituto, alteram sternere poterimus, quippe cum saepe

[2] solubilibus G: corr. Rm   [3] hoc R

[4] effluxione Rm

[5] sic enim . . . prohibetur fort. transp. post perfundimus infra

[6] utrique G: corr. Rm   [8] fuerint molliores, erunt G: corr. R

[7] vaporationes G: corr. R   [9] fiat [sc. concubatio] Rm (omisso stramina)

all times, and particularly in this disease, we are taught to guard against the sun; therefore, from whatever direction it comes, we keep its strong rays from entering the place where the 92 patient lies. And this place should not be too large, for a large amount of air obviously has a dilating property. At the same time the place should not be too small, since it then quickly becomes hot and suffocating as people enter and breathe the air in and out under the compulsion of a natural respiratory process.

But if the place is not naturally cold, make it so by removing the windowpanes, unless the presence of sun rays or unsuitable weather prevents this. The effect of cold is enhanced as clean air enters the place, and with its freshness and mildness revives the patient. Also cool the air by fanning it quietly, after sprinkling cold water on the floor. And place about the room sub93 stances which by their emanation (Greek *aporrhoea*) can make it easier for the patient to breathe, and can render the air astringent without injuring the patient by any pungent odor. Such substances are the foliage of vine, myrtle, oak, pine, mastic, pomegranate, rose, and the like. The effect is to check the outpouring of matter from the patient's body by the astringent property of the air that blows upon him. And the procedure is to boil down any of these substances and pour the liquid, when it is cold, over the floor.

Again, we recommend thin and well-worn covers and bedclothes. For new ones relax the body by their greater warmth. And, in general, see that the bed is not too hard, for that will keep the patient awake, nor too soft, as a bed of wool or light 94 feathers would be. For the body would easily sink into it causing the bedclothes on both sides to be raised; these covers enveloping and encircling the body would by their warmth further relax it. And even if the bed is soft, draw a cover tightly over it to keep it from sinking in easily in the middle and becoming concave, as described above. The bed should be wide and spacious enough for the patient to change from one side of it to the other, experiencing the coolness of the fresh side while the other side is relieved of the heat of his body. By changing sides in this way the patient always has a cool, fresh place to lie in, and there is no necessity of having a second bed, the change being effected 95 in the same bed. Thus, while the patient is lying on one side of the bed, we can arrange the bedding on the other side. For

translati aegrotantes ex lecto ad lectum senserint defectionem,
atque parvo motu asperata passionis fuerit magnitudo.

tunc amplexu atque ligatione paulo[10] tenaci utemur articulorum, iubentes eos quiescere non solum corporis officio, sed, si
fieri poterit, etiam cura animorum, lecto mutato ad grabata aegros transferendo.   augetur enim solutio meatu[10a] quolibet; multum denique sanguinem[11] fluentibus prodesse immobilitas valuit.

196   in statu autem accessionis fovendum dicimus caput oleo frigido atque hispano recenti adhibito, etiam aequali motu aeris ac-
commodato.   densantur enim corpora aeris motu percussa,
atque plurimus sudor non solum cedentis aeris verum etiam ir-
ruentis tamquam repercussu[12] abstinetur.   utendum etiam spongiis teneris ex aqua frigida expressis, quibus ora atque colla
aegrotantes circumtegentibus[13] virium resumptionem faciamus,
temporum intervallis innovantes.   tunc totum etiam pectus
atque oris partes[14] eodem modo praecuramus[15] frigida[16] infundentes spongias, admiscentes etiam aceti quiddam ac iugiter
mutantes, ne perseveratione tactus ex vapore tepescant, et
amisso frigore non valeant facere densitatem.

197   aliquando etiam linteola tenuia tingentes similiter aut suco
plantaginis aut polygonii aut portulacae aut herbae pulicariae
vel semper viventis aut myrti aut rubi comae aut rosarum, vel
mali punici decoctionibus[17] aut hypocistidis herbae aut acaciae
resolutae ex posca aut oleo hispano vel lentiscino, pectori atque
ori ventris apponimus.   at si sudorum perseveraverit fluor,
probandam etiam asperginem quae suo frigore ac propria virtute vel obstrusione constringat iudicamus, cuius ⟨generis⟩[18]
frigerantia atque obtrudentia tactu et densantia sunt haec: terra
samia et cimolia, frigerantia vero rosa arida, contusa atque
creta, in isto[19] etiam alumen scissum, plumbum exustum atque
lotum, gypsum, atque mala punica, oenanthe, acantha aegyptia,
quam nos latine spinam aegyptiam dicere poterimus.

---

[10] paulum *Rm*   [10a] *fort.* motu

[11] sanguine *edd., sed cf. Chr. ii. 128 ff.*

[12] repercussus *G: corr. R*

[13] *fort.* aegrotantium circumtegentibus: aegrotantis circumtegentes *Rm*

[14] oris partes] *an* os ventris, *ut 197?*

[15] praecuramus *scripsi (cf. 207)*: percurramus *G*: percuramus *R*

[16] frigidae *G: corr. Helmreich 327, coll. Ac. ii. 200, iii. 59*

[17] *fort.* decocto *vel* decocti   [18] *suppl. A*   [19] in isto *scripsi*: in ista *G*: *om. R*

when a patient has to be carried repeatedly from one bed to another he becomes exhausted and his illness is aggravated even from this little movement.

Now bandage and bind the patient's limbs, though not very tightly, and have him cease not only from bodily activity but, if possible, also from mental concern. And if the bedding is to be changed, transfer the patient on a portable couch.[1] For the state of looseness is aggravated by any motion at all. Furthermore, immobility can greatly benefit those who suffer hemorrhage.

)6   At the highest stage of the attack apply cold olive oil and fresh Spanish oil to the head. Also keep the air moving evenly, for a body regularly fanned by air currents is condensed, and excessive sweating is checked as the currents of both the receding and the advancing air repeatedly strike the body. Also use light sponges wrung out of cold water, having them applied round the mouth and neck of the patient in order to restore his strength. Keep renewing these sponges at intervals. Then treat the chest and the facial parts in the same way, dipping the sponges in cold water to which some vinegar has been added. Keep renewing these sponges to prevent their becoming warmed by the heat of the body through prolonged contact, for if they lose their chill they lose their astringent property.

)7   Sometimes we apply small, thin, linen cloths to the chest and the parts over the mouth of the stomach, moistening the cloths as before, or using the juice of plantain, knotgrass, purslane, psyllium, houseleek, myrtle, bramble foliage, rose, or decoctions of pomegranate, hypocist, or acacia dissolved in diluted vinegar, Spanish oil, or mastic oil. But if the copious sweating persists, we also recommend a dusting powder which will constrict the flow by its cooling action and its characteristic repressive property. Examples of cooling substances of this type, which upon contact have a styptic and condensing quality, are Samian and Cimolian earth; dried rose petals powdered and sifted are also cooling; and in this category are fissile alum, lead roasted and washed, gypsum, pomegranate, oenanthe, and Egyptian acantha, which in Latin we may call *spina Aegyptia* ['Egyptian thorn'].

1. I.e., to the other side. The patient is not to roll over but to be carried on a sort of stretcher. Possibly, however, the meaning is that the patient is no longer to use the large bed (where he can roll from side to side) and is to lie on a small cot.

198   haec singula commixta atque corpori aspersa per linteolum
rarum sudantibus locis vel omnibus locis prodesse probantur.
oportet autem haec singula diligenter conteri atque ad summam
tenuitatem deduci, ut patentibus irruentia viis[20] ingressu quodam vehementem faciant constrictionem, et nulla corpus asperitate afficiant qua possit aeger aliter inquietari. hinc namque
commotus Thessalus, unus e principibus nostris, eorum usum
iudicavit cohibendum. etenim recte quoque valentibus, inquit,
parva cuiusquam asperitas contagio vigilias facere solet; stramentis irruens terga iacentium vel alias corporis partes lacessendo inquietat.

199   est autem possibile ex supra dictis et oleo hispano aut alio
similis virtutis unctionem facere constrictivam, non irrationa-
biliter. namque plurimi medici ad retinendos sudores mannam
thuris ovi alboribus conterentes, ita ut crassitudinem mellis
similarent, tota corpora perunxerunt. retenta etenim, ut ita
dixerim, his virtutibus corporis superficie, necessario solutio
constringetur. probamus etiam cataplasmata eiusdem virtutis,
sed alia simplicia, alia ex simplicibus composita vel variata. pro
magnitudine etenim passionis extendi atque minui virtutes me-
200 dicaminum debent, ex quibus sunt haec: palmulae nucales,
quas cariotas appellant, tritae cum oleo hispano aut myrteo aut
lentiscino aut melino aut roseo asperso admotoque;[21] vel polenta
praeterea et palmulae saepe vino infusae aut aceto aut posca
vehementius profuerunt. utemur etiam praeinfusis thebaicis
palmulis et malis cydoniis elixis singularibus, vel admixto amylo
diligenter contrito atque creto (cogente passione etiam galla tusa
atque creta admiscenda erit, vel acacia vel alumen et hypocistidis sucus aut rhus syriacus); cataplasmatibus aliis[22] simillimae
virtutis, ut palmulis et malis contritis singularibus vel cum al-

[20] patientibus irruentia in iis *G*: corr. *Bendz Eran 41. 73*
[21] aspersae admotaeque *Rm*
[22] cataplasmatibus. ⟨utendum et⟩ aliis *R*

8   If we take these several substances, mix them, and dust the body with them, using a thin linen cloth, we shall find that the sweating parts and, in fact, all the parts[2] are benefited. But the individual ingredients must be carefully ground down and reduced to the utmost fineness so that they may make their way into the open pores and produce a strong astringent action by their entrance, and at the same time not injure the body by any roughness, which if present would greatly upset the patient. It was, in fact, because of fear of such a result that Thessalus, one of the leaders of our sect, advised against the use of these substances. For, he says, even in the case of the healthy, a small degree of roughness in any of the ingredients generally causes sleeplessness through contact with the body; for the material gets into the bedclothes, irritating the back or other parts of the body and preventing sleep.

9   It is also possible, and not improper, to make an astringent ointment by mixing the aforementioned substances with Spanish oil or some other oil of like nature. And, in fact, many physicians, in order to check sweating, use as an ointment for the whole body frankincense granules beaten up with the whites of eggs to obtain a thickness like that of honey. For if the surface of the body is stopped up, so to speak, by substances of this type, the outpouring will necessarily be checked. We also recommend plasters having the same properties, some consisting of a single simple substance, others of various simples compounded or mixed. And the strength of the drugs should be increased or decreased in proportion to the severity of the

0 disease. Nutlike dates, called *caryōtae*, pounded up with the addition or admixture of Spanish, myrtle, mastic, quince, or rose oil, may be used for this purpose. And, in addition, pearl barley with dates, dipped in wine, vinegar, or vinegar water, often proves very beneficial. Use also Theban dates previously dipped in these liquids or else boiled quinces, alone or with the addition of starch, thoroughly pounded up and sifted. If the disease requires it, add as an ingredient of these plasters oak gall similarly powdered and sifted, acacia, alum, hypocist juice, or Syrian sumach. Other plasters of similar properties may also be used for this purpose, e.g., dates and apples, chopped up

2. Or, construing these words with *aspersa:* 'dust the powder over the sweating parts and, in fact, over all the parts.'

tero ex his, vel vitis foliis atque amylo[23] et rubi,[24] quam Graeci
201 baton appellant, virgultis contusis et contritis, myrto etiam et
polygonio et semper viva herba, quam aizon vocant, et plantagine et rosa et uva lupina et portulaca et intybo, cum polenta
vel palmulis et pane.

horum singula apponenda sunt pectori aegrotantis et praecordiis ac frequentissime mutanda, quo frigida perseverent atque
extenta medeantur. possunt etiam rhus syriaci sextarii[25] quatuor infusi die atque nocte in aquae sextariis viginti decoqui,
donec quarta liquoris remaneat, atque ita colandus ac rursum
coquendus horis[26] duabus donec coagulata omnia fiant inducti-
biliaque, digitis[27] convoluta nullam corpori infectionem dimit-
202 tant, ut unam vel eandem qualitatem sufficiant. similiter enim
imposita constringunt fluida atque laxata corpora, et stomachi
vigorem repraesentant.

at si tumor aliquis in praecordiis fuerit, non sine praecautione
erit cataplasmatibus localibus utendum supra dictis; denique
erit panis admiscendus, quo nimietas constrictivae virtutis tem-
peretur. at si plurimus fuerit tumor, adhibendum simplicis pol-
linis cataplasma sive panis infusi, quod Graeci omen lysin vocant, iisdem scilicet locis sed neque calidum, ne corpus provocet
in sudorem.

nos denique iuxta Sorani iudicium praecordiis imponere hoc
203 cataplasmatis genus solemus: palmulas quas Graeci patetos vocant conterentes cum melle leviter praecocto, asperso lini semine
atque contrito ita ut qualitatem faciat inductibilem et, ut saepe
diximus, quae attrectata manibus nihil de se inquinamenti
dimittat (Graeci denique amolynton vocaverunt). tunc linteolo
illitum apponimus medicamen. utimur etiam pane cum palmulis, atque secundum pectus vel thoracem prioribus et a tergo
partibus aliqua ex supra dictis apponimus.

204 potum dabimus frigidum parvum atque paulatim, ne liquoris
multitudine corpus irrigatum laxetur, sed magis tactu frigidae
qualitatis densetur. tempus autem cibandi, si adiuncta febri-

---

[23] amylum *G: corr. R*

[24] rubus *G: corr. Rm, nisi scrib.* rubo

[25] sextariis *G: corr. R*

[26] horis *Rm*: unciis *G*

[27] ⟨et⟩ digitis *R*

separately or together, vine foliage, starch, and cuttings of
ɔɪ bramble (Greek *batos*), bruised and pounded down. Myrtle,
knotgrass, houseleek (Greek *aeizōon*), plantain, rose, strychnos,
purslane, or endive, in combination with pearl barley, dates, or
bread, may also be used.

Apply any one of these preparations to the patient's chest
and precordia, renewing it often so that the cooling properties
and the efficacy of the remedy may be prolonged. You may
also cook four sextarii of Syrian sumach for a night and a day[3]
in twenty sextarii of water until a fourth part of the liquid is
left; then strain this and cook it again for two hours until it
all coagulates and can be smeared, and, when rubbed with the
fingers, leaves no sediment on the flesh, that is, has an even,
ɔ2 homogeneous quality. The application of this substance, as of
the others, has an astringent effect on loose and dilated bodies
and restores strength to the esophagus.

But if there is an inflammation in the precordial region, the
local applications of plasters should not be made without caution. And in that case add bread to the aforesaid preparations
to moderate the excessively astringent properties. But if the
inflammation is extensive, use an application consisting simply
of moistened flour or bread (Greek *ōmēlysis*). This should be
applied to the above-mentioned parts, but it must not be hot
or it will cause the body to sweat.

In accordance with Soranus' precepts we generally employ a
ɔ3 plaster prepared as follows. Take dates of the kind the Greeks
call *patētoe;* chop them up in honey moderately cooked in advance, add flaxseed, and pound up the mixture until it can be
smeared and, as we have often said, leaves no sediment when
handled (Greek *amolyntos*).[4] Then apply the drug, smearing it
on with a small linen cloth. Or use a preparation of bread and
dates; and to the parts in front, i.e., the region of the chest or
thorax, and to the back we apply any of the previously mentioned preparations.

ɔ4   Give the patient cold drink in small quantity and a little at
a time, so that the body may be condensed by contact with the
cooling property of the drink, rather than be moistened with too
much fluid and consequently dilated. And if a case of the cardiac

3. Or perhaps 'without interruption.'
4. I.e., 'leaving no stain.'

cula diaphoresi fuerit, erit ex fervore corporis accipiendum, sicut
primo libro De febribus scribentes docuimus. at si sine febribus
fuerit passio, ex pulsu signum accipere poterimus cum leviter
erectum senserimus atque alia concurrentia fuerint levigata.
etenim numquam aegros nutrire potest accessionis tempore
quicquam datum, quippe cum magis opprimat atque anxium
faciat aegrotantem.

205   quapropter affectandum artis industria aliis ex rebus vires
usque ad dimissionis tempus servare, et ita cibo nutrire. utimur
namque odoramentis: haec enim sensim quodam nutrimento
reficiunt ac resumunt latentem adiectionem corporis facientia,
et cum quadam constrictione ac densitate. denique neque
simpliciter aut indiscrete omnibus debemus bene olentibus uti
odoramentis aut omnibus acrioribus. alia etenim percutiunt,
alia diaphoresim provocant in fluorem. sit igitur polenta infusa
atque panis assus aceto infusus, vel mala cydonia aut myrta et
206   his similia. haec enim defectu extinctam corporis fortitudinem
retinent, sicut ratio probat atque Democriti dilatae mortis exemplum fama vulgatum. utendum etiam mulso bene decocto, ne
ventrem fluidum faciat. oportet namque tribus sextariis etiam
tres uncias mellis admiscere, et ad tertiam decoquere partem,
et exinde singulos dare cyathos bibendos. sic enim corporis
servabimus vires usque ad cibi tempus. aliquando etiam pira
concoquenda duracina quae crustumina vocant, vel cydonia
mala. cum nondum audemus quicquam de vino dando tentare,
207   his utemur quae leniora procul dubio probantur. erit enim
suave atque stomachum reficiens et constringens supra dictum
mulsum.

tunc cum cibandi tempus venerit—quod plurima cum cautione
erit apprehendendum, siquidem plerisque ex initio accessionis
febrium sudores concurrant, plerisque etiam in statu aut de-

5. The mere heat and odor of warm bread kept him alive for three days. See Diog.
Laert. ix. 43; cf. Asclep. ap. *Anon. Lond.*, col. 37. 34. According to another version it
was the odor of honey (cf. Ath. *Epit.*, p. 46E).

6. The proportion of honey to water is thus approximately 1:12 before boiling,
and 1:4 after boiling.

disease is accompanied by fever, the time of giving food will depend on the heat of the body, as I indicated in Book I of my work *On Fevers*. But if the disease is without fever, our indication will come from the patient's pulse, when we find that its strength is somewhat restored and the other symptoms of disease have also been relieved. For food given at the time of an attack can never nourish the patient, since it is an additional burden to him and causes distress.

05 We must therefore apply our skill to find other means of preserving the patient's strength until the time of remission, and only thereafter nourish him with food. Thus we make use of aromatic substances, for they gradually refresh and restore the body with a kind of nourishment, imperceptibly adding strength while producing an astringent and condensing effect. We must not, however, make use of all pleasant-smelling or all pungent substances without exception and indiscriminately. For some are irritant, and others provoke a flow of colliquative sweat. Use may be made, however, of pearl barley and toasted bread

06 steeped in vinegar, or of quinces or myrtle and the like. For these substances preserve the bodily strength when it is all but snuffed out by the collapse. This is proved by reason as well as by the well-known story of the delayed death of Democritus.[5] Also use diluted honey well boiled down to prevent flux of the bowels. Add three ounces of honey to three sextarii [of water], and boil down to one-third of the original.[6] Give it to the patient to drink in doses of one cyathus. For in this way the bodily strength will be preserved until the time for giving food. And in some cases cook the hard[7] pears called Crustumerian,[8] or else quinces, and until such time as you care to risk giving any wine, use these instead; they will doubtless be

207 found to be milder than wine. And the diluted honey mentioned above will also prove pleasant and will have a tonic and strengthening effect on the esophagus.

Then when the time for giving food comes—a time which must be determined with the greatest caution, for in many cases the sweating takes place from the beginning of the feverish attack, but in many other cases at its height or in its de-

7. Perhaps 'sourish.' See *R.E.*, *s.v.* 'duracinus.'

8. From the town of Crustumeria near Rome.

clinatione—cum itaque inhumectum atque siccum fuerit corpus, erit praecurandum unctione olei frigidi, lentiscini, aut his-
pani. ora etiam fovenda aqua frigida ex spongia, singulis partibus attrectatis;[29] tunc collutione oris aqua frigida dentium limus
detergendus. dandus cibus simplex, sed aliquantulum coagula-
tus ac frigidus, ne statim sudorem corpori moveat adiectus.
208 sit autem eius materia panis ex aqua frigida diligenter elutus ut
sui careat difficultate, itemque oryza et alica ex aqua frigida, vel
suavitatis causa quiddam decocti mellis admixtum, pultes etiam
non oleatae, ova hapala. at si vires minime fuerint reparatae,
febribus declinantibus ut totius passionis minui magnitudinem
demonstrent, varius est dandus cibus: ut cum praedictis demus
aliquid pomorum, ut pira duracina et cetera quae stringere
209 valent et vini similitudinem servant. sed haec nunc cocta, nunc
sincera dare debemus, mala etiam cydonia atque ea quae orbiculata vocant, et mespila, et paleales uvas vel pensiles quae iamdudum fuerint siccatae, et damascena.

carnis etiam quiddam sed neque indigestibilis neque difficilis
neque pinguis neque bromosae, sed eius quae sit et digestione
facilis et corporis densabilis ac nutribilis et sufficiens levamento
fortitudinis extinctae, ut sunt pulli columbarum, vel gallinae
pastae, assae, perdices, attagenes, quorum omnium pectora
magis offerenda et horum interius,[30] cocta ac tenuiter accurata
ex oleo et aqua et anetho et sale. facile enim corrumpunt[31]
curiosae atque gravabiles[32] conditurae. item si friabilis fuerit
caro assata, tamquam cornea efficitur: quapropter si quisquam
delectatione affectus accurari voluerit, erit primo coquenda,
tunc assanda. dandi etiam porcini pedes, ora, auriculae, et
summitates articulorum; dandum etiam cerebrum et vulva; dehinc haedina caro, vel mollium caprearum vel silvestrium capra-
rum aut aprorum clunes, quas Graeci psoeas[33] vocant.

[29] singulis partibus attrectatione G: ⟨cum⟩ singularum partium attrectatione R

[30] interiora Rm

[31] fort. corrumpuntur

[32] gravabiles R: gravabilis G   [33] ψόιας G

cline—when, therefore, the body has become dry and is without moisture,[9] begin by anointing it with cold mastic oil or Spanish oil; and apply cold water to the face with a sponge, rubbing the various parts; then wash the mouth with cold water and remove the film from the teeth. And give the patient simple food but somewhat solid and cold, to prevent a sudden outbreak of 208 sweating as soon as the body receives it. The food may be bread carefully washed in cold water so as to remove difficulty [of digestion], or rice or spelt groats soaked in cold water. To these some cooked honey may be added as sweetening. Also porridges prepared without olive oil may be used, as well as soft eggs. But if the patient's strength has not been in any measure restored, give him varied food when it is obvious, from the decline of the fever, that the severity of the whole disease is diminishing. Thus, in addition to the foods already mentioned, some fruit may be given, such as hard[10] pears and other fruits that have an astringent property and winelike nature. And these 209 should be given sometimes cooked and sometimes raw; also give the patient quinces, so-called 'round apples,' medlars, grapes preserved in chaff or by hanging and long since dried, and damsons.

Some meat may also be given. It must not, however, be indigestible or hard to digest, or fat, or ill-smelling, but must be easy to digest, binding, nourishing, and capable of restoring the patient's lost strength, e.g., squabs or well-fed hens, roasted, or partridges and francolins. It is best to give the patient the breast, especially the inner part thereof, cooked and simply prepared with olive oil, water, dill, and salt. For elaborate and heavy seasoning may easily cause [the food] to spoil.[11] Again, if friable flesh is roasted, it becomes horny. Therefore, if one is fond of this food and wants it properly prepared, it will have to be boiled first and then roasted. Pig's trotters, snout, ears, knuckles, brain, and womb may also be given, and, in addition, kid's flesh, and the loins (Greek *psoae*) of young roes, wild goats, or boars.

9. I.e., not only has the sweating ceased, but the whole attack seems past. The connection of ideas is somewhat obscure. Previous editors have taken the clause *tunc cum cibandi . . . declinatione* with the preceding; but it seems preferable to take it with what follows, despite the mild anacoluthon.

10. Cf. 206.

11. I.e., in the body, through failure to be properly digested.

210   item ex mari mullos, squillas, bancos, acus, labraces; at si
fastidiosi fuerint aegrotantes, damus spondylos, et conchylia,
buccina, peloridas; si haec omnia fastidio erunt, dabimus ostrea
211 et echinos. item olerum intuba, plantaginem, asparagos. si
neque ita vires surrexerint, tamquam in continuationem humaniorem indulgentiam pro dedignatione passionis accipientes, ad vini dationem descendimus, quod ita summum
generaliter probamus ut album atque non confusum et medii
temporis eligamus: qualia saepe ita vina probantur quae surrentina dicuntur vel falerna et trifolina[34] vel albana, quae in Italia
nata probantur, item graeca, chia et lesbia. at si febres tenuerint corpus, leviora atque tenuiora offerenda erunt vina, ut
sunt in Italia sabina et tiburtina et gentiliter surrentina appel-
212 lata, vel in Asia tripolitica.[35] at si febres nihil obstiterint, erit
melius surrentinum vel trifolinum atque albanum. si vehementer corpus in solutionem disici viderimus et[36] frigido torpore vexari sine ulla febricula, dabimus nutribiliora ac firmiora vina, ut
setinum et falernum. sunt enim haec efficacia et quae facilius
omnia quae de vino speramus accelerent, sufficientia fortificare
et totam relevare habitudinem corporis, omni etiam parti atque
particulae sese insertare, et per omnes tenues vias celeri motu[37]
percurrere, alia quoque nutrimenta secum trahere, et inducta
corporibus insinuare.

sed haec cum primum dantur, medio cibo sunt offerenda cum
213 alica vel quolibet simili suco, aquata etiam atque parva moderatione temperanda,[38] vel certe cum pane dissoluto atque infuso
danda; dehinc paulo plus, ac mediocriter mixta cum aqua frigida
ac recenti, vel nivium liquore.

coniciendum etiam ut mediocriter cibum demus, sed per intervalla frequentius, praesentientes iam fuisse digesta praedata.
quapropter melius erit paulatim atque frequenter offerre, quam
semel aegrum nutriendo gravare. multi etenim largioribus cibis

[34] tripolina G: corr. R
[35] tripolitica Am: trifolina G
[36] ex G: ⟨et⟩ ex R
[37] motu Am: potu G
[38] temperata A

---

12. These are various kinds of mussel.

10   And, as seafood, red mullet, squill, bancus, garfish, and bass may be given. But if the patients have no desire for these, give them spondylus, conchylium, bucinum, and peloris.[12] And if all these are likewise distasteful, give them oysters and sea urchins. And, of vegetables, endive, plantain, and asparagus may be

11 given. If even then the patient's strength does not revive, we must conclude that the use of a liberal diet without interruption is tantamount to disregarding the disease, and we therefore have recourse to wine. In general, our highest preference is for a clear white wine, somewhat sharp and of moderate age. Of this kind the so-called Surrentine, Falernian, Trifoline, and Alban wines, which come from Italy, are often very good; so also the Greek wines from Chios and Lesbos. And if the body is feverish, milder and thinner wines should be given, e.g., in Italy, the Sabine, Tiburtine, and Surrentine wines, as they are commonly

12 called, and in Asia the wine of Tripolis.[13] But if there is no fever, Surrentine, Trifoline, or Alban wine will be better. And if you see the patient's body being dissolved in an acute state of looseness, and suffering from cold numbness without any fever, give him stronger and more nutritious wines, like Setian and Falernian. For these wines are powerful and will speedily bring about all that we expect of wine. They are able to revive and strengthen the bodily condition as a whole, to find their way into every part, large and small, to course with rapid motion through every narrow pore, to bring with them other nourishment, too, and to spread this nourishment through the body.

But when these wines are first given, they should be given at the time of eating, together with a gruel of spelt groats or some

13 similar gruel. And they should be mixed with water and thus somewhat moderated in strength; or bread may be soaked and softened in the wine. And later a little more wine should be given, moderately mixed with cold fresh water or melted snow.

And it is reasonable to give food in small amounts but at frequent intervals, being sure that the small amount previously given has already been digested. That is, it will be better to give the patient food in small amounts at frequent intervals than to burden him by feeding him just once. For many patients, if

13. If *tripolitica* is a sound reading, the reference is to Phoenician Tripolis. But the text is uncertain, and the two groups of wines, for cases with and without fever, respectively, are not mutually exclusive, as we should expect them to be.

oppressi refracti sunt potius quam resumpti. nam sicut parva
scintilla plurima coacervatione lignorum opprimitur, vel lucernae flamma marcescens[39] olei multa infusione frustratur, parva
autem adiectione atque sumptione recrescit et rursum ardescit:
214 non aliter corporis virtus insumpta ex[40] immodicis nutrimentis
oppressa mortis dabit effectum.

signa autem detrahendi vini haec sunt: primo torpor atque
stupor corporis infractus, pulsus erectior, sudoris quoque fluor
primo non frigidus, dehinc abstinetur,[41] somnus insequens, et ad
omnia quaeque facilis aegrotantis arrisio. tunc denique oportet
non dense atque semel vinum detrahere, sed paulatim subdu-
cere, et magis si febres nullae fuerint repertae. at si post sudoris
abstinentiam febrium fuerint accessiones subsecutae, et aegrotantes sufficienter resumptos senserimus, omnino vinum extemplo detrahimus.

sin vero adhuc imbecillos viribus viderimus, dabimus vinum
215 moderatione cautissima. at si forte cibum reiectaverint, debilitate stomachi concurrente, constrictivis medicaminibus utemur,
non solum anterioribus partibus sed etiam posterioribus pectoris
apponentes, addita articulorum ligatione, et appositione cucurbitae multa flamma subiecta, quae infigenda erit ori ventris
atque interdum a tergo, nunc ante cibum, nunc post cibum, qui
quidem frequenter ac paene continue erit offerendus. at si in
toto non tenuerint cum vino accipientes, tunc ex aceto dabimus
quicquam. si neque ita, rursum ex aqua tentabimus dare.
plerique enim ex vino atque aceto sumentes cum accepta non
tenuissent, aqua coniuncta magis cibos tenuerunt. in his vero
qui fastidio vexantur, erit tentandum ciborum varietate pug-
nare: solent enim veluti tentandi pulmenti causa ex multis parva
sumendo unam facere cibi sumptionem.

216   affectanda etiam odoramenti resumptio erit, vel nutribilium
cataplasmatum atque inductionum appositio. at si omnis spes
fuerit absumpta, erit per clysterem cibus iniciendus, sed neque

---

[39] flammam accersens G: corr. A

[40] ex om. R: fort. scrib. et   [41] abstentus Rm

weighed down by excessive food, are weakened rather than strengthened. And just as a small glimmer of fire is snuffed out when a great quantity of wood is heaped upon it, or the fading flame of a lamp dies out if a large amount of oil is poured in, but becomes larger and burns again with the addition and absorp-

4 tion of only a small amount, so the exhausted bodily powers, overwhelmed by excessive nourishment, suffer death.

Now the indications for taking wine away from the patient are as follows. To begin with, the numbness and languor of the body abate, and the pulse becomes more prominent; also the flow of sweat first loses its coldness and then ceases; the patient is able to sleep, and has a ready, approving smile for everything. In such cases, then, the wine should be withdrawn, not suddenly and all at once, but gradually, particularly if there is no fever. But if feverish attacks ensue after the sweating has ceased, and it is obvious that the patient's strength has been adequately restored, take the wine away all at once.

But if the patient is found to be still weak, continue to give

5 wine, but limit the amount most carefully. And if he happens to vomit his food and there is an attendant weakness of the esophagus, use astringent remedies, applying them not only to the chest but also to the part of the back opposite the chest. In addition, bind the patient's limbs and apply a cup, with much flame, over the part where the upper orifice of the stomach is located, and occasionally to the back. This should be done sometimes before giving food and sometimes after; and food should be brought to the patient frequently and, in fact, almost continually. But if the patient does not at all retain his food when he takes it with wine, then give him something soaked in vinegar. And if that does not help either, try again with food soaked in water. For many who have taken food with wine and vinegar, and have been unable to retain it, succeed in retaining what they take with water. And where patients suffer from loss of appetite, try to overcome this by serving various kinds of food. For usually they take a little bit from each of many varieties, by way of sampling the food, and thus have a complete feeding.

6 Try also to use aromatic substances as restoratives and also to apply nourishing plasters and liniments. But if all other hope is gone, food will have to be injected by a clyster. This food

ptisanae aut cuiusquam labilis qualitatis quod facile lubrica
faciat intestina. est enim hoc perniciosissimum in cardiacis,
quippe fastidio attestante, ventris fluorem commovere. quapropter erunt haec ex lenticula adhibenda, et primo parvissima,
tunc vino cum aqua panis attritus et expressus. sic enim corpori
fiet additio, atque vires resurgunt, et stomachus iamdudum supinus fortificatur, altiora constringentur.[42]

217   at si omnes partes fuerint solutione laxatae, similiter haec
omnibus sunt adhibenda, in illis etiam quae occulta diaphoresi
contabescunt. differentia etenim accidentium mutata videtur, genus autem passionis idem manet. dehinc si profectus
quisquam fuerit supra dictorum adiutoriorum, erit implenda
resumptio usque ad perfectionem desideratam, sed tunc a lavacro temperandum aut multo tardius adhibendum. at si febres
perseveraverint, ut in marcorem venire aegritudo meditetur,
quem Graeci marasmon vocant, ad eius curationem descende-
mus, sicuti libris De febribus scribentes docuimus.[43]

    haec est secundum Soranum cardiacorum methodica curatio.

218 XXXVIII. QUOMODO ALIARUM SECTARUM PRIN-
CIPES CARDIACOS CURAVERINT

ANTIQUORUM plurimi cardiacorum curationem tacuerunt, aliqui vero memoraverunt, ut Serapionis atque Heraclidis sectatores et quidam Herophili,[1] item Asclepiades et Themison,
parvissime quidem, at iisdem deceptionibus implicati. phlebotomant enim et clysteres adhibent acerrimos, et ob calefaciendum articulorum frigus pannos applicant calidos et lanas oleo
infusas ac sulfure fumigatas. terunt etiam oleo veteri ac
sicyonio cum pipere sulfur et cachry et ammoniaci guttam et
laserpicium cum bulbis. cataplasmant praeterea ex lasere et
bulbis, sympasmatibus utentes, quae nos aspergines dixerimus,[2]
219 item ex[3] calce cum pipere; cibis acribus utentes atque edacibus,

[42] constringuntur *Rm*
[43] docebimus *G: corr. Friedel 49, coll. 204*
[1] *cf. adn. ad Ac. ii. 4*
[2] ex faecibus *add. Wellmann, Celsus 85, n. 2, coll. Ac. ii. 223*
[3] ex *Wellmann, loc. cit.*: et *G*

should not, however, be pearl barley or anything else of a smooth character, which would easily render the intestines slippery. For in these cases of the cardiac disease, since there is no desire for food, it is most dangerous to stimulate a flux of the bowels. Therefore, the food injected should consist of lentil, at first in very small quantity. Later bread pounded up in wine and water and pressed out should be injected. For thus nourishment will be brought to the patient's body, his strength will revive, the esophagus after a long period of atony will be invigorated, and the inner organs will be given tone.

7   And if all the parts of the body are relaxed in a state of looseness, our remedies must likewise be directed to all these parts, including those which are being consumed by hidden diaphoresis. For the various symptoms may appear changed, but the nature of the disease remains the same. And if any success attends the application of the aforesaid remedies, let the repairing of the body continue until it is as complete as required. But in such a case bathing should not be prescribed, or at least not until much later. On the other hand, if the fever persists so that the disease threatens to pass into a wasting decay (Greek *marasmos*), we shall have to proceed with the treatment of this condition, as I have set forth in my work *On Fevers*.

This concludes Soranus' account of the treatment of the cardiac disease according to the Methodists.

8 XXXVIII. TREATMENT OF THE CARDIAC DISEASE
        ACCORDING TO LEADERS OF OTHER SECTS

THOUGH most of the ancients say nothing about the treatment of the cardiac disease, some do mention it, among them the followers of Serapion and Heraclides, certain followers of Herophilus, as well as Asclepiades and Themison themselves. While they say very little, they are all involved in the same snares. For they employ venesection and harsh clysters, and to warm the patient's cold limbs apply warm cloths and wool steeped in olive oil and fumigated with sulphur. They also rub up pepper, sulphur, cachry, gum ammoniac, silphium, and bulbs in old Sicyonian olive oil. In addition, they apply plasters prepared with silphium and bulbs, and employ dusting powders
9 (Greek *sympasmata*, which we may translate *aspergines*), also

alio,[4] salsamento, et lasere. et per totum diem atque noctem
vino usque ad ebrietatem replerunt. alii vero in aquam frigidam
aegros deposuerunt. Eudemus Themisonis sectator ait per clysterem aquam frigidam iniciendam.

sed haec omnia gravia atque execrabilia et aegrotantibus perniciosa esse perspicimus. etenim phlebotomiam nihil iugulatione differre ratio testatur, quippe cum haec faciat quae ipsa
nititur passio, mentem disicere, et corpus in mortem per sudores
solvere, ac ad sua primordia revocare defluxionem, atque casum
virium augere.

220   quibus denique commoti eorum successores aiunt esse eos
phlebotomandos qui proni ac declives in cardiacam sint passionem, non advertentes quia ipsa quoque in passionem prona
declivitas nulla re alia corpus affici quam solutione testatur.
clysteres etiam adhibentes corpora resolvunt et ob acrimoniam
aperiunt, quos utiles probaverunt.[5] sed aiunt coacervatam
atque celerem per superficiem corporis insumptionem retineri
cum ad ventrem vel intestina fuerint[6] conversa fluentia. hoc
quidem si more mechanico ac simili miraculo se facere posse
promittunt, ut aperientes ventris interiora superficiem corporis
221 claudant, erit credibile quod promittunt. sin vero, ut in omnibus videmus, superficie[7] fluentia augeri potius quam minui interiorum fluxu debilitate crescente cognoscunt, contrarius procul dubio clysteris usus accipitur, atque fluentium relaxator.

dehinc consequens non est, immo etiam incongruum iudican-
dum, articulos igneis medicaminibus confricare, ut ex alto ad
semet materiam ducant. inicere quoque intestinis acriora, ut

---

[4] a(l)lio *scripsi, coll. 224*: alii *G*

[5] quos utiles probaverunt *transp. R post* adhibentes

[6] fuerit *A* (*ed. 1722*), *sed cf. Ac. ii. 221, Chr. ii. 150, v. 88, Cael. Aur. Gyn. ii. 48, Diaet. pass. 89, Helmreich 329*

[7] superficiem *G: corr. R*

---

1. Or perhaps 'diversion' (cf. 228, *revocare materiam ad id quod patitur*). It is just possible that the reference is to the dissolution of the body into its constituent elements. But for ἀρχαί = 'vital organs,' cf. Galen I. 318 K.

quicklime and pepper. They use acrid and pungent foods, such as garlic, pickled fare, and silphium; and they fill the patient with wine all day and night even to the point of drunkenness. Some plunge the patient into cold water. And Eudemus, a follower of Themison, declares that cold water should be injected by a clyster.

But it is obvious to us that all these remedies cause the patient distress and danger and are to be condemned. For, as reason attests, venesection is no different from murder, since it accomplishes what the disease itself aims at, the disruption of the mind, the fatal dissolution of the body in sweat, the extension[1] of the flux to the vital organs of the body, and the acceleration of the patient's collapse.

Influenced by these leaders, their successors hold that venesection should be employed where the patient is on the verge of passing into the cardiac disease. But they do not see that the very condition of being on the verge of this disease indicates that it is precisely from a state of looseness that the body is suffering. And the clysters which they employ in the belief that they are helpful merely hasten the dissolution of the body, bringing about openings[2] by their sharp properties. But these writers assert that the swift and precipitate dissolution of the body through its surface is checked when the flow is directed, instead, to the stomach and intestines. Now if they were to say that they could by a mechanical method or some other such marvelous device succeed in closing the surface of the body while opening the interior of the bowels, we might believe what they say. But, in fact, as we observe in all cases and as they well know, the flow from the surface is increased rather than decreased by an intestinal flux as the patient becomes progressively weaker. We therefore consider the use of the clyster harmful beyond any doubt, as promoting the flow of matter.[3]

Now surely it is not only out of place but should, in fact, be considered harmful to rub the limbs with drugs of fiery quality in order to draw matter from the interior of the body to the surface. But it is evidently the same type of error to inject sharp

2. *Aperiunt* seems to be used in the sense of Celsus v. 4 (= στομοῦν).

3. I.e., not only through the intestines but from the surface of the body.

illuc concurrens ex articulis materia atque ex omni corporis superficie attrahatur rursum ad altiora corporis conducta, similis
erroris esse probatur. est igitur melius propria viarum ac naturae[8]
spiramenta servare, et non infracta corporis fortitudine acutiori
222 atque celeri solutioni corpus aptare. ferventia vero et ignea et
urentia ad visa mentis simplicia, quae appellant phantasiam,
sunt frigori atque torpori congrua, ad virtutem tamen incongrua.
est enim solutioni accidens atque comes corporis frigidus torpor,
qui ferventibus rebus aucta passione necessario duplicetur:
serviunt enim dominantibus appendentia. dehinc acria, siquidem non sint mitigativa, celeritatem passionum acutiorem faciunt adiuvando.

prohibemus iniectionem aquae frigidae, siquidem celerrime
calefacta interiorum fervore adiuvet solutionem, faciat etiam
delectatione quadam ventris officium provocari. non aliter et
in aquam frigidam deponendos prohibemus aegrotos: non enim
manet lenis atque mitis constrictio. item ex sinapi cataplasma
223 prohibemus, siquidem sit recorporativae virtutis, quam Graeci
metasyncrisin[9] vocant, cum passio atque eius celeritas mitem
demonstret atque exigat curationem. praeterea sinapismi acrimonia hortationem fieri sudorum nemo est qui nesciat. sicut
enim semper lacrimam commovet oculorum acrioris humectatio
collirii, non aliter supradicta contingunt.[10] item bulborum puta-
mina molliunt, non constringunt. illa vero quae eorum corpulenta videntur recorporativae virtutis esse noscuntur. reprobamus etiam aspergines ex calce atque faecibus et pipere.
224 haec enim singula corpus incendunt et in ignis vicem suburunt
et superficiem corporis vulnerant, quo fiet ut saepe transitum
faciant in gravissimos tumores. non sunt haec denique ex genere
mitium adiutoriorum. est etiam iners allium dare atque laser
et salsamenta vel communiter acriores cibos. sunt enim digestione in ventre difficiles, atque inspiratione corporum tardi,[11] et
inflant.

[8] naturae *R*: natura *G* (*fort. retin., omisso* ac): *an* naturalia?

[9] μετασύγκρισιν *G*

[10] constringunt *Bendz Eran 41. 73*

[11] in spiratione corporum tardi *edd.*: *fort.* inspirationem corporum tardant

drugs into the bowels, so that matter may flow there from the limbs and be withdrawn from the entire surface of the body to the inner organs. It is consequently better to keep the pores open to a normal and proper degree than to prepare the patient's body for a sudden and swift flux by destroying his strength. 2 And hot, fiery, and burning medicines seem, on first glance (Greek *phantasia*), to be proper remedies for chill and numbness. But in their actual effect they are harmful. For cold numbness of the body is a symptom and concomitant of a state of looseness and necessarily becomes worse when the disease is aggravated by the application of hot remedies. That is, concomitant conditions follow the course of the dominant condition. And sharp drugs, since they are not soothing, help to render the disease swifter and more acute.

We also condemn the use of a clyster of cold water, for it is swiftly warmed by the heat within the body and adds to the state of looseness, stimulating the movement of the bowels by provoking the desire. So, too, we refuse to prescribe the placing of patients in cold water, for the mild and gentle astringent effect does not persist. We likewise bar the use of a mustard plaster; for it promotes a change in bodily condition (Greek *metasyncrisis*),[4] whereas the cardiac disease, because of its acuteness, clearly requires a mild treatment. Furthermore, everyone knows that sweating is stimulated by the sharpness of the mustard plaster. For this sweating is caused in much the same way as the moisture of a sharp eye-salve causes tearing of the eyes. And again the peelings of bulbs have an emollient, not an astringent, effect. And the fleshy parts obviously have a metasyncritic effect. We also reject powders made with quicklime, 4 dregs,[5] and pepper. For each of these ingredients inflames the body and scorches it like fire, injuring its surface. Hence these remedies often cause the development of severe inflammations. Moreover, they do not belong to the class of mild remedies. And it is unsound to give the patient garlic, silphium, salted fare, or sharp foods in general. For they are hard to digest in the stomach, are sluggish in passing through the body [after digestion],[6] and cause flatulence.

4. See p. xx. The mustard plaster is suitable during remission in chronic diseases.
5. Presumably of wine.
6. Or perhaps with altered reading: 'interfere with the body's breathing.'

haec nunc communiter[12] omnibus respondenda. etenim Tarentinus Heraclides phlebotomat atque clysterizat et calidis et
laxativis utitur cataplasmatibus. nunc quomodo Asclepiadem
adhuc quidam recte locutum accipiant, et ea quae posuit prin-
cipalia retractemus.

225
XXXIX. UTRUM RECTE ASCLEPIADES
CARDIACOS CURAVERIT

Hic quoque secundo libro Celerum vel acutarum passionum
providens ne qua sit in corpore cruditas, clysteres adhibet
operantissimos ob transversionem faciendam. primo nescius
quae sit operans in cardiacis causa, et tamquam Herophili[1] sectator indigestionem atque corruptionem intuendam existimans.
secundo ignarus quia post antecedentem diem esse in corporibus
indigestio potest: at vero cardiacorum passio frequenter quinta
vel sexta die emergere perspicitur. tertio est gravis atque noxia
clysteris iniectio non solum solutione laborantibus[2] celeri, sed
226 etiam in[3] strictura affectis, siquidem commoveat atque turborem
corporis efficiat, quando fuerit operosior ac frequens, ut Asclepiades iubet; in diaphoreticis vero interfectivus[4] esse probatur.
ipse denique Asclepiades de peripneumonicis scribens confitetur
noxios esse clysteres, dicens: 'clysterum genus non in peripneumonicis solum noxium, sed in omnibus etiam sine febre passionibus insidiosum atque vexabile corporum eorum usum iudicamus.'[5] item specialiter indicans iniectionum vexatione eas corporum solutiones augeri atque iactationes et sitim vehementem,
siquidem sint, inquit, virium captrices. item clysterum vexa-
227 tionem etiam in pleuriticis demonstravit, similiter et in phreniticis tamquam interfectricem metuit ventris turbatam solutionem: quorum debuit memor neque in cardiacis clysteres adhibere. alios enim plurima stercorum gravatione oppressos et
propterea sudantes salutare est relevare clystere ad ventris[6]

[12] communiter R: comiter G

[1] Herophilus G: corr. Rm

[2] loborantibus G: corr. R (cf. 234)

[3] in om. R, fort. recte (ex istrictura ortum?)

[4] interfectivus Bendz Eran 41. 74: interfici livor G: interficiens Haller

[5] iudicans R   [6] ventris Schmid 93, n. 34: mentis G

Such, then, is the general reply we must make to all those writers. In fact, Heraclides of Tarentum employs not only venesection but clysters and warm, relaxing poultices as well. And now, since some still hold that Asclepiades' discussion of the subject is sound, let us review the chief points that he sets forth.

25   XXXIX. IS ASCLEPIADES' METHOD OF TREAT-
ING THE CARDIAC DISEASE SOUND?

Asclepiades, too (in Book II of his treatise *On Swift* [i.e., acute] *Diseases*), seeking to rid the body of any undigested matter, prescribes powerful clysters to accomplish the removal. But, in the first place, he does not know what the efficient cause in the cardiac disease is, and, like a follower of Herophilus, thinks he must look to the indigestion and spoiling of food. And, secondly, he is unaware that indigestion can be present in the body the day after [food is taken], while the cardiac disease frequently does not appear until the fifth or the sixth day thereafter. Thirdly, the injection of a clyster is distressing and harmful not only to those suffering from an acute state of looseness but also to those suffering 26 from a state of stricture. For when the clyster is a strong one and frequently administered, in accordance with Asclepiades' instructions, it has an irritating effect and arouses considerable bodily disturbance. But in cases of the cardiac disease the clyster is deadly. And, in fact, Asclepiades himself in writing about pneumonia admits that clysters are harmful. He declares that treatment by clysters is not only harmful in pneumonia but is dangerous, too, in all diseases without fever, and holds that their use distresses the body. He also points out in particular that a bodily state of looseness, restless tossing about, and violent thirst are aggravated because of the agitation produced by the clysters. For these conditions, he says, rob the patient of his strength. He likewise calls attention to the harmful effect 27 of clysters in cases of pleurisy. Similarly, he considers a violent flux of the bowels deadly in cases of phrenitis. But he should have been mindful of all this and should not have prescribed clysters in cases of the cardiac disease. Now in other cases, where the patient is burdened by the weight of fecal matter, and sweats for that reason, it is proper to relieve him with a

alienitatem detrahendam, sed hoc simplici atque miti usu clysteris: quos ita affectos non dicimus esse cardiacos.

item post iniectionem adhibet cataplasma sinistrae mamillae constrictivae virtutis; sed corpus ob excludendum frigidum torporem calefaciendum probat unctionibus olei veteris ac defricandum manibus calidis et pannis circumtegenda loca. ex quibus calefactiones atque unctiones superioribus dictis exclu-

228 dendas asseruimus. constrictiva vero cataplasmata non solum sinistrae mamillae erunt apponenda, sed omni pectori atque praecordiis. erat autem Asclepiadi consonans approbanti tumorem in corde constitutum similiter laxativa cataplasmata eidem adhibere. dehinc est incongruum atque non consequens affectare per clysterem e corde aliquid trahere et constrictivis cataplasmatibus e superficie corporis materiam ad id quod patitur revocare, ut stricturam, quam esse in tumore cordis adverterat, duplicare videatur.

iubet etiam dari vinum noctibus, diurnis, atque iugiter, sed id vinum cui salem miscuerimus, et appellavit tethalassomenon. cito enim, inquit, currit ac labitur et ad omnia corporis membra

229 perveniet.[7] cibum dat betam cum lenticula, et appellavit seutlophacen, vel lenticulam cum ptisana aut oryza aut alica, vel aliqua ex maritimis. et quid ultra inquit? ea nos dare convenit quae aegri fuerint voluntati gratissima. probat autem vinum dandum post cibum, siquidem solum facile penetret ac pertranseat corpora, non aliter quam si sine ulla faece per liquatoria fundatur, quorum cavernae nullis obstantibus facile accipiunt atque reddunt accepta. at si post cibum, inquit, datum fuerit, manebit non aliter quam si cum faece, ut supra dictum est, in liquatoria fundantur. iubet etiam meracum mixtum[8] dari.

230 hac enim ratione, inquit, exustae viae tamquam ex igni conductae sudorem retinendo constringunt.

[7] pervenit R

[8] ⟨non⟩ mixtum R, sed cf., e.g., Chr. ii. 109, et meracum temperamento 231, infra

1. Not in so many words. But note that there is no essential contradiction here with 199 or 207, for the anointing in 199 is not of the same kind as Asclepiades prescribes, and that in 207 does not apply.

2. Cf. Ac. i. 145.

clyster and withdraw the foreign matter from the bowels; and for this purpose simple and mild clysters should be used. But we cannot say that such cases are cases of the cardiac disease.

Now after the use of a clyster Asclepiades prescribes the application of a plaster of astringent properties to the left breast; yet he recommends warming the body with anointings of old olive oil, rubbing it with warm hands, and covering the parts with cloths, in order to dispel the chill and numbness. But of these treatments, we have already declared[1] that the use of heat and anointing is to be rejected. And as for astringent plasters, they should be applied not only to the left breast but to the whole chest and the precordial region. Furthermore, since Asclepiades believes that in the cardiac disease there is an inflammation in the heart, it would have been logical for him to apply *dilating* poultices to this part. But it is inconsistent and illogical for him to try to withdraw matter from the heart by a clyster, and at the same time by the use of astringent plasters to send matter from the surface of the body back to the part affected. The result is that he aggravates the state of stricture, which he had held was centered in an inflammation of the heart.

Asclepiades also prescribes the giving of wine continually night and day, but it is the wine to which brine is added (called by him *tethalassōmenos*); for he says that this wine flows swiftly and smoothly and reaches all the parts of the body. As food he prescribes beets and lentils (called by him *seutlophacē*), or lentils with pearl barley, rice, or spelt groats, or else some seafood. And he goes on to say that we should give the patient foods that are most pleasing to him. He also recommends the giving of wine after food. For he holds that if wine is taken alone, it quickly penetrates and makes its way through the body like wine poured into filters when there is no sediment. For in that case the wine readily flows into the holes of these filters, since there are no obstructions, and just as readily flows out of them. But, says Asclepiades, if the wine is given *after* food, it will linger, as when we pour wine which has a sediment into such filters. And he prescribes that a very strong mixture of wine be given. For he holds that in this way the pores are burnt up and contracted as if by fire,[2] and consequently check and constrict the flow of perspiration.

est nunc iners et inertiae plenum tota die atque nocte vinum dare et cibo nutrire. plurima enim adiectione nutrimenti vires opprimi necesse est. item ptisana ventrem commovet in fluorem lapsum suae faciens qualitatis; contraria denique lenticulae qualitati probatur. vinum quoque incongruum atque intemporale et immodicum probatur. incongruum, siquidem sit salsum, quod appellavit tethalassomenon, et propterea ventrem solvat et ex omni corporis parte vires deponat, sit praeterea inflabile atque virium vexabile, non solum aegrotantibus, sed

231 etiam sanis hominibus. forsitan hoc et fervens dederit: tacuit enim frigidum dandum, culpans denique libris quos De lue conscripsit Cleophanti sectatores vinum frigidum dantes.

immodicum diximus, siquidem plurimum det atque extentum, et meracum temperamento quaerit,[9] cum etiam sani quanto plus biberimus, tanto plurimum sudoris effundimus. intemporaliter autem, siquidem ante declinationem dandum iusserit. est praeterea ridiculum quod post cibum dandum vinum propterea dicat, ne citius curans corpora pertranseat, probans econtrario salsum dandum quo citius corpora penetret ac suos effectus exhibeat. hic est ille Asclepiades frigidans atque calefaciens, exantlans atque replens, et contrariis semper utens rebus in his passionibus.

232 ## XL. UTRUM RECTE THEMISON CARDIACOS CURAVERIT

THEMISON vero quaedam recte dixisse perspicitur ob cardiacorum curationem, quaedam prave. vino namque cum amylo trito cum bulbis et ammoniaci gutta cum vino et ovi albore et pipere trito cum sinapi corpora defricanda existimat. dat etiam cibo alleum cum pipere. dehinc in scaphulam deponi iubet aegrotantes quae sit aqua plena calida. item post cibum

[9] *fort. scrib.* quaerat

Now it betrays an utter lack of understanding to give the patient wine and nourish him with food all day and night. For the patient's strength must inevitably be overwhelmed by the excessive intake of nourishment. Again, pearl barley imparts to the stomach and bowels its own quality so that they lapse into a flux; and this quality is contrary to that of the lentils. The wine, too, is obviously unsuitable, ill-timed, and excessive in amount. It is unsuitable because it is mixed with brine (Greek *tethalassōmenos*), and therefore loosens the stomach and robs every part of the body of strength. Furthermore, it causes flatulence and saps the strength not only of the sick but of the healthy. Asclepiades may also have prescribed that the wine be heated. For he does not say that it should be given cold. And, in fact, in his treatise *On Pestilential Fever* he criticizes Cleophantus and his followers for prescribing cold wine.

Again, we consider Asclepiades' prescription of wine excessive, for he gives the patient large quantities over a considerable period; and he requires that a strong mixture of wine be used. Yet even in health the more we drink, the more sweat we pour forth. And his prescription is also ill-timed, for he directs that the wine be given before the decline of the disease. Besides, it is ridiculous for him to say that the wine should be given after a meal to keep it from flowing too quickly through the body, and at the same time to say that it should be given salted in order to flow through the body and produce its effects more quickly. But that is the way of the great Asclepiades, who at one time applies both cold and heat, both drains the body and replenishes it, and always uses conflicting treatments in these diseases.

XL. IS THEMISON'S TREATMENT OF THE CARDIAC DISEASE SOUND?

Some statements of Themison on the treatment of the cardiac disease are obviously correct, while others are wrong. He asserts that the body should be rubbed. For this rubbing he prescribes wine and starch pounded up with bulbs, or gum ammoniac and wine, the white of an egg, and pepper ground up with mustard. As food he prescribes garlic with pepper. And he has the patient placed in a bathtub full of hot water. After feed-

adhibet gestationem, siquidem sint, inquit, imbecilla ac debilia
nimium corporis officia, et indigeant hoc adiutorio, quo partim[1]
etiam caro commoveatur sua[2] promota[3] substantia, hoc est
spiritu atque[4] nutrimento, ex quibus concreta perspicitur.

233 quae omnia facere valet gestatio, omni corpori suffundens materiam. mox denique, inquit, allevatos atque magnitudinem
accipientes pulsus invenimus.

sed haec Asclepiadis nugis[5] sunt adiungenda. demonstravimus enim ferventium medicaminum fricamenta esse necessario
noxia, et sinapi. tentat etiam inflabiles cibos, et quamquam
haec sint omnibus celeribus atque acutis passionibus inimica,
multo tamen vehementius cardiacis. gestatio vero et incongrua
et intemporalis esse probatur. incongrua, inquam, siquidem sit

234 laxativa: omnis etenim motus viarum efficit raritatem. intemporalis autem, siquidem post cibum fieri iubeatur. etenim si
sanos post cibum vexat motio, non permittens naturae quadam
requie ac tacito motu ad suos effectus accepta perducere, quid
sperare de aegris ac solutione laborantibus[6] poterimus? pulsus
vero post gestationem erigitur cardiacorum, non ob resumptionem virium, sed ob turbationem corporis motu conceptam. ex
qua magis adiuvari passionem dissolutione corporis iudicamus.

hic ratio celerum cum febricula passionum curationis terminatur. nunc transeundum ad eos qui[7] sine febribus esse noscuntur.

---

[1] parti G: corr. R

[2] sua Rm: sed G

[3] praemota Almeloveen

[4] atque R: hoc est G

[5] nugis R: nullis G

[6] loborantibus G: corr. R (cf. 225)

[7] fort. eas quae (cf. Ac. iii. 1)

ing the patient he employs passive exercise because, he says, the bodily functions are weak and disabled and need this remedy. For one of its effects is to stimulate the bodily substance by aiding the movement of the stuff, i.e., the pneuma and the

33 nutriment, of which it is evidently constituted; and passive exercise can accomplish all this by facilitating the supply of matter to the whole body. And soon [after this motion] the pulse, he says, is found to be more prominent and increasingly large.

But all this is of a piece with the nonsense of Asclepiades. For we have shown that rubbing the body with drugs whose nature is fiery is always harmful, and this is true of mustard too. Themison also makes use of foods that cause flatus. Now these are harmful in all other swift or acute diseases, but even more so in cases of the cardiac disease. Moreover, his prescription of passive exercise is clearly unsuitable and ill-timed. It is unsuitable because it has a dilating effect; for every kind of motion

34 tends to dilate the pores. And it is ill-timed because it is prescribed after food. For any exercise after a meal distresses even healthy persons by interfering with the quiet and imperceptible motion by which nature enables the food and drink to accomplish their function. And if this is so, what can we expect in the case of the sick and those suffering from a state of looseness? Moreover, the strengthening of the pulse after passive exercise in cases of the cardiac disease is due not to the restoration of bodily strength but to the disturbance of the body resulting from this motion. And we hold that the disease is aggravated more by this disturbance than by the bodily flux.

This concludes our discussion of the treatment of acute diseases accompanied by fever. We must now pass to those which are known to occur without fever.

LIBER TERTIUS

I. DE SYNANCHE

CELERUM cum febricula passionum curationem praescriptis tradidimus libris. nunc autem earum quae sine febribus esse noscuntur ordinabimus, quo cunctarum perfecta distinctio compleatur. initium namque a synanchica passione sumemus quae nomen a suspendii similitudine habet, quod non aliter quam laqueus praefocans interficiat; nam Graeci anchonas suspendia vocaverunt: sive quod spiritum continendo spirationem neget; Graeci enim synechein[1] continere appellant. alii vero etiam cynanchen vel lycanchen hanc passionem vocaverunt, siquidem frequenter haec animalia afficit: nam canes cynes, lupos lycos vocaverunt. quorum quoque similes voces sive ululatus in synanchica passione constituti, cum praefocari coeperint, emittunt.

synanches igitur alia est sine manifesto indicio,[1a] alia cum visibili atque manifesto; et alia intra oris spatium, alia exterius, alia ex utroque, hoc ⟨est⟩[2] exteriore atque interiore, parte dextra vel sinistra aut in utraque. denique quidam specialem discretionem etiam nominibus posuerunt, ut Valens physicus libro tertio Curationum. eam igitur quae sine manifesto tumore est sine nomine reliquerunt. eam vero quae cum manifesto, si in utraque,
aiunt, parte interiorum fuerit, cynanchen vocandam, siquidem faciat difficultatem spirationis atque oculorum prominentiam et linguam procidentem, tamquam canibus avidis saepe contingit cum ea quae minime transvorare possunt, admonente natura, aviditate impavida minas contemnentes invadunt: quae saepe faucibus inhaerentia atque ancipiti retentione tardata, neque percipere neque reddere valuerunt. eam vero quae in altera fuerit parte paracynanchen vocaverunt. item in exterioribus at-

[1] συνέχειν G

[1a] ⟨tumoris⟩ indicio *Schmid 50*

[2] *add. Rm*

---

1. I.e., of swelling and inflammation.

BOOK III

I. SYNANCHE

IN THE preceding books we set forth the treatment of acute
diseases accompanied by fever. We shall now lay down rules
for those known to occur without fever, thereby completing
our account of the different kinds of acute diseases. And we shall
begin with the disease of synanche, which gets its name from its
similarity to hanging, for when it is fatal its effect is like that of
choking by a hangman's noose, the Greek word for 'hanging' being *anchonē*. Or synanche may get its name from the fact that it
cuts off respiration by constraining the breath, the Greek word
'to constrain' being *synechein*. But others have called this disease
'cynanche' or 'lycanche,' since it frequently attacks dogs and
2 wolves, the Greek word for 'dogs' being *cynes* and for 'wolves' *ly-
coe;* moreover, when humans who have the disease begin to
choke, they emit sounds or howls like those made by these
animals.

Now one form of synanche occurs without visible sign,[1] another gives a clear and visible indication; again, one form occurs
inside the cavity of the mouth [and throat], another outside it,
and still another both inside and outside; and [the affection]
may be found on the right side, on the left, or on both. Some
writers, e.g., Valens the Naturalist in Book III of his work *On
Treatments*, use specific terms to distinguish these types of the
disease. They leave without special designation that type
which occurs without any visible inflammation. But that which
occurs with a visible inflammation of the inner parts on both
3 sides they call 'cynanche.' Their reason is that this type causes
difficult breathing, bulging eyes, and hanging tongue; and something of the same sort often occurs in the cases of voracious dogs,
when, goaded on by their nature, they disregard our threats and,
with fearless greed, seize far more than they can swallow. The
prey often sticks in their throat and is checked by a wavering re-
tentive action, so that they can neither swallow it nor give it up.
Again, when [this form of] the disease occurs on one side only,
these writers call it 'paracynanche.' And when the inflammation

que utraque parte tumore constituto hyanchen appellaverunt,
siquidem suum colla his saepissime inflationibus afficiantur, quos
graece[3] hyas appellant.   at si interius atque exterius et in utraque parte fuerit tumor, tunc proprio nomine synanchen memorant nuncupandam; at si in altera fuerit parte, parasynanchen.

4 nihil autem refert speciales differentias proprietate nominum separare.

antecedentes causae quibus haec sufficitur passio aliquae sunt
occultae, aliquae manifestae atque ceteris quoque communes
passionibus, maxime tamen conabiles atque laboriosi vomitus,
plus etiam si post cibum iam corruptum, item vinolentia vel ni-
vis[4] potatio, aut exclamatio vehemens atque eodem modo perseverans, quam Graeci monotonon vocant, item catarrhus, et
acriores cibi praeter consuetudinem accepti, item ferventia atque
ignita medicamina pota, vel purgatio per helleborum provocata,
quibusdam etiam feminis menstrualis retentio purgationis. afficiuntur autem hac passione magis viri quam mulieres, quorum
plus aetatis mediae et iuvenes quam pueri atque senes.

5 hanc diffiniens Asclepiades passionem secundo libro explana-
torio Aphorismorum Hippocratis synanche, inquit, est humoris
fluor sive humectatio faucium vel summitatis ipsarum, saepissime ex capite accidens. sed hoc peccanter diffiniunt.[5] omnis
enim humoris fluor, quem rheumatismum vocant, multi liquoris
est lapsus sive egestio. in synanchicis vero tumor videtur, et
non, ut supra diximus, humoris plurimi egestiones, nisi hoc aliquando ex pressura venerit.

nos vero iuxta Sorani sententiam synanchen dicimus difficultatem transvorandi atque praefocationem acutam, ob vehementiam tumoris faucium sive in locis quibus nutrimenta transvoravi-

6 mus.[6] adiecta est autem transvorandi difficultati praefocatio celerrima sive acuta ad discretionem tumoris tonsillarum sive
uvae. ubi enim synanche fuerit, etiam tumor necessario locorum supradictorum consequetur. sed non ilico ubi tumor fuerit
eorundem, etiam synanche nuncupatur, siquidem qui mediocri
difficultate fuerint transvorandi impediti nondum synanchici

---

[3] an Graeci? v. Ac. i. 4

[4] fort. vini vel nimis

[5] fort. diffinivit

[6] transvoramus R

occurs in the outer parts and on both sides they call the disease 'hyanche.' For the necks of swine (Greek *hyes*) are often affected by swellings of this type. But if the inflammation is in both the inner and the outer parts and on both sides, they assert that the disease is then properly called 'synanche.' And if this form occurs

4 on one side only, they call it 'parasynanche.' But there is no advantage in distinguishing the various forms of the disease by special names.[2]

Of the antecedent causes by which this disease is produced, some are hidden, while others are obvious and are common to other diseases too. These latter causes include, in particular, difficult and labored vomiting, especially if the food has already decomposed, excessive drinking of wine, swallowing of snow, violent screaming that persists on the same note (Greek *monotonos*), catarrh, the eating of acrid foods contrary to one's custom, the drinking of burning and fiery drugs, a purge produced by hellebore, and, in the case of some women, the retention of the menstrual flow. Men are more often attacked by this disease than women, and young and middle-aged men more often than boys and old men.

5   Defining this disease in Book II of his commentary on Hippocrates' *Aphorisms*, Asclepiades says that synanche is a moistening of, or a flow of moisture to, the throat, especially to its highest part, this flow most often coming down from the head. But this definition is wrong. For every flow of moisture (Greek *rheumatismos*) is a running or discharge of a considerable amount of liquid matter. In synanche, however, there is an inflammation but no such discharge of a large quantity of fluid, unless this is occasionally brought about by the patient's distress.

We, however, following Soranus' view, apply the term 'synanche' to difficulty in swallowing and acute choking occasioned by a severe inflammation of the throat, or of those parts which are

6 used in swallowing food and drink. In addition to 'difficulty in swallowing' we include 'swift or acute choking' to distinguish this disease from inflammation of the tonsils or of the uvula. For, while it is true that in synanche there is always an inflammation of the tonsils and uvula, it is not true that whenever there is an inflammation of these parts we have a case of synanche. That is, those who experience merely a mild difficulty in swallowing can-

2. Cf. Galen VIII. 248 K. For a different nomenclature see *Paul. Aeg.* iii. 27.

videntur. haec enim in magno tumore passio intelligitur habere
substantiam. item ad discretionem praefocationis illatae per
laqueum: est enim ipsa quoque acutissima atque celerrima praefocatio, sed non ex tumore descendens.

7   II. QUAE CONSEQUANTUR SYNANCHICOS

SEQUITUR autem eos qui iam passione tentantur querela sine
ulla ratione, atque difficilis motus colli et gutturis, item sali-
vatio plurima praeter tumorem, et subdolens faucium sensus
cum asperitate sensibili, item difficultas transvorandi liquoris soliti salivarum in ore[1] collecti, tunc spirationis velut impedimentum tamquam obstantis crassioris humoris.

surgente vero ac crescente passione, si cum[2] manifesto tumore
fuerit, rubens factus[3] videbitur tumor faucium atque uvae et supra linguam partium et summitatis gutturis, cum difficultate
transvorationis omnium acceptorum, praefocatio etiam pro tumoris modo, spirationis difficultas, et nausearum provocatio.
dehinc sicca tensio, si quis os aegrotantis aperuerit et digito linguam oppresserit, invenitur.

8   crescente vehementius passione, omnium tumor efficitur, colli
atque vultus, et humoris crassioris ac salivarum fluor, oculi prominentes sanguinolenti, et venarum extentio.[4] at si peius[5] in-
creverit, linguae ultra dentes ad exteriora prolapsio, ariditas sive
siccitas faucium, articulorum gelidus torpor, pulsus celer densus,
iacendi difficultas, et magis in supino schemate vel in latere, frequens etiam sedendi cupiditas, item locutio non articulata, sed
confusa atque cum dolore. at si in exitium passio coeperit ferri,
livor vultus, vocis amputatio, gutturis atque pectoris stridor, et
recursio sive recursus[6] poti liquoris, pulsus defectio, quam Graeci
asphygmian[7] vocant, et quibusdam caninus vocis sonitus, qui-
9 busdam oris spumatio. tunc etiam necessario mortis effectus.
at si sine manifesto tumore fuerit passio, sequitur collorum te-

---

[1] in ore *Schmid Mn 145*: more *edd.*

[2] si cum *Bendz Eran 41. 74*: sic ut *edd.*

[3] fuerit, rubens factus *Bendz Eran 41. 74*: fuerit facta, rubens *Schmid Mn 146*: fuerit
rubens facta *G*

[4] *fort.* extantia

[5] ⟨in⟩ peius *E. Wölfflin, Ueber die Latinität des Afrikaners Cassius Felix 419, coll.
Ac. ii. 64, 72; iii. 114*

[6] sive recursus *om. Bendz 16 ut glossema*   [7] ἀσφυγμίαν *G*

not as yet be said to be suffering from synanche. For we take it
that the essence of synanche is its severe inflammation. And this
also serves to distinguish synanche from choking accomplished
by a noose. For while this form of choking is also very swift and
acute, it does not originate in an inflammation.

II. THE SYMPTOMS OF SYNANCHE

7

THOSE who are beginning to suffer from this disease show the
following symptoms. They complain without any apparent
reason and find it painful to move their neck and throat; there is
copious saliva but no inflammation, a slightly painful sensation
in the throat, together with a feeling of roughness, difficulty in
swallowing the regular flow of saliva that collects in the mouth,
and, in addition, a kind of difficulty in breathing, as if a thick
fluid impeded.

And as the disease emerges and gains strength, in cases with
visible inflammation the redness of this inflammation can now be
seen in the fauces, the uvula, the parts above the tongue, and the
upper parts of the throat. And there is difficulty in swallowing
any food or drink. There is, in addition, a choking sensation, increasing as the inflammation increases, difficulty in breathing,
and nausea. And if one opens the patient's mouth and depresses
his tongue with a finger, the parts will be found to be dry and
tense.

8   As the disease becomes even more severe, all the parts become
inflamed, including the neck and face; there is a flow of thick
fluid and saliva; the eyes bulge and are bloodshot; and the blood
vessels are distended. And if the disease grows still worse, the
tongue hangs out of the mouth, the throat is parched and dry,
limbs cold and numb, and pulse rapid and thick. The patient
finds it hard to lie, especially on his back or side, and frequently,
too, he wants to sit up; his speech is indistinct, confused, and accompanied by pain. And if the disease begins to move toward a
fatal conclusion, the face turns blue, the voice is lost, there is a
wheezing sound in the throat and the chest, any liquid taken in
is returned, there is failure of the pulse (Greek *asphygmia*), in
some cases the patient makes a sound like that of a dog, and in
9 some cases there is foaming at the mouth. Death then inevitably
follows.

But if the disease is without any visible inflammation, there

nuitas cum extentione atque subrectione inflexibili, item vultus,[8]
oculorum cavitas, frontis extentio, color plumbeus, spirationis
difficultas plurima, nullo, ut supra diximus, manifesto tumore
sive inflatione aliqua apparente, neque ⟨in internis, neque⟩[9] in
externis partibus, hebetudo plurima atque imbecillitas aegrotantis, et celerrimus vel acutus cum praefocatione mortis effectus.

at si circum colla se ignis sacer[10] infuderit sive in pectore apparuerit et fuerit perseverans, frequentissime bonum portendit,
siquidem ascensus tumoris ex alto ad superficiem venire videatur. at si sine ulla ratione adiutorii cuiusquam medicinalis bene-
10 ficii repente non apparet, salutem negabit. descensus enim a superficie corporis ad altiora monstratur. at si forte non secundo
irruens vel ex alto acceptus ad superficiem fuerit ignis sacer,[11] sed
antecedens passionem aut eidem concurrens, omnia mala significat.

humor autem plurimus sive salivarum fluor in crassitudinem
coactus, si in statu apparuerit, mala ostendit; post statum vero
passionis salutaria pollicetur. alias enim plurimam praefocationem significat, alias corporis laxamentum. in quibusdam
etiam tantum tumor increscit, ut stricturam faciat in faucibus
atque gutture et mento. est autem passio stricturae, acuta atque celeris et vehemens, et saepissime continua, aliquando intercapedinata.

11   III. QUOMODO CURANDI SUNT SYNANCHICI

Oportet in passione constitutos iacere loco lucido atque mo-
deratae amplitudinis, nullo etiam odore corrupto, calido.
est huiusmodi laxativus aer, et qui primus tumentibus partibus
misceatur. iacendi schema esse supinum convenit, paulo levatius capite collocato, firma atque immobili positione, vel qua se
magis relevari aegrotantes dixerint. omnis enim motus dolidus
est tumore oppressis. lanis etiam mundis ac mollibus et non in-
fectis dulci atque calido oleo infusis colla protegenda[1] cum tho-
12 race, adhibita articulorum blanda fricatione. transmittitur
enim naturalis vaporis laxamentum etiam ad illas partes quae

---

[8] vultus ⟨et⟩ R
[9] suppl. R
[10] acer G: corr. R
[11] acer G: corr. R
[1] fort. praetegenda

are the following symptoms: neck attenuated, stretched, and inflexibly erect; face and eyes hollow; forehead drawn; complexion leaden; much difficulty in breathing; absence of any obvious inflammation or visible swelling, either in the internal or in the external parts, as has been indicated; extreme blunting of the senses; weakness; and swift death with choking.

But if erysipelas spreads about the patient's neck or appears on his chest and persists, it is often a good sign, for the inflammation is then apparently arising from the depths of the body to the surface. If, on the other hand, the erysipelas suddenly vanishes without the application of any medicinal remedy, it is a deadly
10 sign; for it means that the inflammation is descending from the surface of the body to its depths. And if it happens that the erysipelas is not a subsequent development, i.e., does not represent the bringing of the inflammation from the depths to the surface, but either precedes synanche or emerges together with it, this is in all respects an unfavorable sign.

Again, if considerable liquid matter or a flow of thickly condensed saliva appears at the highest stage of the disease, it is a bad sign; but if it appears after that stage, it presages recovery. For in the former case it indicates extreme suffocation, in the latter a loosening of the body. In some cases of synanche the inflammation becomes so intense that it produces constriction in the fauces, throat, and chin. And the disease itself involves a state of stricture and is acute, swift, severe, and usually continuous, though sometimes intermittent.

11   III. THE TREATMENT OF SYNANCHE

ONE suffering from synanche should lie in a well-lighted room of moderate size, free from any odor, and warm. The air in such a room has a dilating effect and should from the first be in contact with the inflamed parts. The patient should lie on his back with head raised a little, or should assume the position in which he says he feels most comfortable, and should maintain this position without moving; for every motion is painful to one who is suffering from inflammation. Cover the patient's neck and chest with cloths of clean, soft, undyed wool steeped in warm
12 sweet olive oil. Also rub the limbs gently; for the relaxing effect of natural warmth is also transmitted to the parts affected by

patiuntur. adhibenda quoque requies et abstinentia usque ad
primam diatriton, cum gargarismate laxativo cuius species sive
materias paulo post subiciemus. adhibenda etiam fomentatio
olei dulcis calidi, et apponendae exterioribus partibus vesicae
oleo dulci calido semiplenae.

adhibenda etiam phlebotomia, si vehementer passio coegerit,
intra diatriton: etenim indiget repentina sanguinis detractione
ob celerrimum laxamentum. si autem minus necessitas impulerit, in ipsa diatrito, vel durantibus viribus etiam post ipsam
phlebotomia poterit adhiberi, si tunc necessitas emerserit fa-
13 ciendi. cuius facti rationem De specialibus adiutoriis scribentes
docebimus. igitur intra diatriton phlebotomato erit post detractionem sanguinis caput fovendum atque collum oleo calido,
et ex eodem auribus quiddam immittendum, tunc gargarizandum. potum dabimus aquam calidam vel mulsum, et non coacervatim sed paulatim, ne transvoratione gravi ac percussu tumentia indignentur. at si in ipsa diatrito flebotomiam adhibuerimus, oportet post detractionem factam circumungere corpus aegrotantis oleo dulci atque calido, et faciem aqua calida
mediocriter fovere; tunc sorbilem cibum dare, sed omnino te-
14 nuem vel fluidum, vel panem ex mulso tinctum. at si transvoratio fuerit difficilis, qua obsistente non percipiant aegrotantes
accepta, erit sufficiens viribus fulciendis mulsum guttatim faucibus infusum. perseverandum etiam usque ad declinationem passionis in alterna dierum cibi refectione.

convenit praeterea post phlebotomiam sequentibus diebus cataplasmatibus uti quae circum colla erunt extrinsecus apponenda,
miti tamen simplicitate confecta, ut est panis calidus ex aqua et
oleo, vel mulso diligenter emollitus, vel pollines tritici aut hordei
aut seminis lini aut faenugraeci, singula haec sive commixta ex
calida et oleo et melle, vel aqua in qua fuerit ⟨decocta⟩² hibisci
radix aut contrita et admixta.

15 mutanda praeterea frequentius erunt haec cataplasmata, ne

---

² add. R

the disease. Have the patient rest and take no food to the end of the first three-day period. And prescribe a soothing gargle the nature and composition of which we shall set forth a little later.[1] Also foment the external parts with warm sweet olive oil, and apply bladders half-filled with this oil to the same parts.

If the disease clearly requires it, venesection should be performed before the end of the [first] three-day period. For the speedy withdrawal of blood is required to afford a swift relaxing [of the stricture]. But if the urgency is not so great, venesection may be performed at the end of that three-day period or, if the patient's strength holds out, even after that, whenever the ne-
3 cessity for it appears. We shall give the reason for this procedure in our work *On Special Remedies*. If a patient has been subjected to venesection before the end of the first three-day period and the blood has been withdrawn, foment his head and neck with warm olive oil and pour some of this oil into his ears. Then let him gargle. Give him warm water or mead to drink, not in large amounts but a little at a time, to keep the inflamed parts from being irritated by the painful effect of swallowing. But if venesection has been performed at the end of this three-day period, anoint the patient's body all round with warm sweet olive oil after the blood is withdrawn, and foment his face moderately with warm water. Then give him gruel-like food, making it quite
4 thin and fluid, e.g., bread soaked in mead. But if swallowing is too painful, and the patient is therefore unable to get down the food he takes into his mouth, it will be sufficient for the purpose of sustaining strength to pour some mead into his throat drop by drop. Continue feeding him on alternate days until the declining phase of the disease.

In addition, on the days following venesection it is well to apply poultices externally, placing them around the neck. They should be made of simple and mild substances, e.g., hot bread soaked in water and olive oil or thoroughly softened in mead, or flour made from wheat, barley, flaxseed, or fenugreek seed. These substances may be used separately or mixed together in warm water, olive oil, and honey, or in water in which marsh mallow root has been boiled down or to which the powdered root has been added.
5 Now these poultices will have to be renewed frequently to pre-

1. 16.

perseveratione sui corrupta corporis exhalatione in acorem veniant. erunt etiam calefacienda quo tardius maneant evaporata,
positis extrinsecus saccellis ex cantabro aqua cocto confectis,
vel vesicis calida et oleo semiplenis. convenit etiam spongiarum vaporatio expressarum ex aqua calida, aut admixto oleo,
vel decoctione mitium materiarum laxativae virtutis. apponendae quoque spongiae collo atque gutturi et his partibus quae
haustum negant, vel ori et naribus. iubendus aeger aperto ore
ad semet vaporem rapere, descendentes[3] enim ad altiora haustu
raptae vaporationes tumorem relaxant.

16   sunt etiam gargarismata congrua cataplasmatibus, ut oleum
dulce est atque calidum, vel calida et oleum, tunc mulsum aquatum et decoctum, et lac singulare sive cum melle aut aqua admixtum, ut omnia detergantur quae forte lactis tactu fuerant
derelicta, ne remanentia fervore locorum in acorem veniant.
item utendum decoctione cantabri atque glycyrizae vel lini seminis ac faenugraeci, sed nusquam ad crassitudinem suco decocto, ne[4] ob viscosam tenacitatem humorum fluori connexa
difficultatem faciat[5] spirationis; tunc etiam decoctione hibisci
vel malvae agrestis aut myxarum syrarum aut musci herbae
atque palmularum pinguium vel fici suculenti, item suco halicae
aut ptisanae.

17   at si passio coeperit declinare, convenit etiam cybiraticum[6] et
creticum passum. ea vero quae sunt leviter stringentia, quae appellant stymmata, nunc incongrua iudicamus. his enim utemur
quoties initia fuerint passionis, levibus adhuc querelis affecto
aegrotante aut dolore levi in faucibus vel uva. tunc enim etiam
Thessalus adhibendam poscam iudicavit, siquidem pronos atque
in passionem synanchicam declives, necdum tamen patientes vo-
caverit. utendum denique non solum posca sed etiam decoctione leviter constringentium materiarum, ut rosarum, palmularum thebaicarum, lenticulae, myrti, lentisci [mastichis],[7] quae
singula erunt in mulso decoquenda vel quolibet ex supradictis

---

[3] escendentes *Almeloveen, coll.* surgens, *20*

[4] suco decocto, ne *scripsi*: succi decoctione G

[5] faciat R: faciant G

[6] cybiraticum *conieci* (*cf. Paul. Aeg. iii. 31. 4, 39. 2; vii. 15. 1*): cybariticum G:
Sybariticum *Rm: an* scybeliticum? *cf. Chr. ii. 103*

[7] *seclusi*

vent them from being spoiled by the emanations from the body
and turning sour, as happens if they are kept too long. And in
order that they may give off warmth over a longer period of
time, they will have to be heated by placing next to them bags
containing bran that has been boiled in water, or bladders half-
full of hot water and olive oil. It is also well to apply heat with
sponges wrung out of hot water to which may be added olive
oil or a decoction of mild substances with relaxing properties.
Apply the sponges to the neck and throat and to the passages
that are congested, the mouth and nostrils. And have the patient
inhale the steam with open mouth, for the warm vapors thus
drawn in pass to the deeper parts of the body and relax the congestion.

6   In conjunction with poultices, gargles, too, are suitable, e.g.,
warm sweet olive oil, or warm water and olive oil, or honey diluted with water and boiled. Milk may also be used, either plain
or mixed with honey or water to wash away all the particles
which may otherwise be deposited by the milk as it comes in contact [with the inflamed parts]; for if such particles remain there,
they may turn sour because of the heat of these parts. Again, a
decoction of bran and licorice, flaxseed, or fenugreek seed may
be used as a gargle. But the preparation must never be boiled
down to the point where it becomes thick, for in that case, because of stickiness, it would impede the flow of liquid matter and
cause difficulty in breathing. A decoction of marsh mallow, wild
mallow, sebesten plums from Syria, moss, thick dates, or juicy
figs may also be used; and so may spelt or pearl barley water.

7   Now if the disease begins to subside, raisin wine of Cibyra or
Crete is helpful.[2] But substances with mildly astringent properties (Greek *stymmata*) we consider unsuitable at this stage. They
may be used, however, at the beginning of the disease, when the
patient is as yet only slightly affected or has only little pain in
the fauces or uvula. Thessalus, too, holds that diluted vinegar
should be used at that time, since he considers the patients to be
on the verge of the disease of synanche rather than actually suffering from it. And so [in the initial stage] make use not only of
diluted vinegar but of decoctions of mildly astringent substances, such as roses, Theban dates, lentils, myrtle, and mastic.
Boil down any of these substances in mead or in one of the liq-

2. As a gargle?

suco, quoties viderimus constrictivam virtutem admixtione laxa-
18 tivi liquoris esse frangendam. facit etiam oryzae sucus, atque
diacodion medicamen mulso resolutum ac saepe substantia servata faucibus illitum, non aliter etiam quod diamoron appellatur
et dioporon et diamyrrhinon, sive andronios[8] et Polyidi[9] sphra-
gis, et anthera cum melle, et omne medicamen quod confectum
sit ex malo cotoneo[10] aut punico vel rosae floribus vel mali punici
cortice sive galla vel omphacio aut lycio et his similibus.

sed in augmento passione constituta illis utemur quae supra
iamdudum memoravimus. humorem praeterea ex fervore nu-
tritum si glutinosum viderimus factum, tamquam in oculis su-
pernatantem, spongia calida detergimus; sin vero in alto fuerit
constitutus, dipyreno immisso[11] praetecto eius capite lana molli
19 ac limpida. etenim si remanserit praefocationem magis accele-
rat. at si nimium altiora tenuerit ut videri non possit, erit te-
nuandus dando mulsum, sed praecoctum. est enim efficacioris
virtutis quam si non fuerit coctum. quidam etiam ptisanam
dederunt parvo sale admixto. sed sunt fugienda quae usque ad
sensum veniunt mordicationis, siquidem tumoribus provocatis
fluor quoque humorum crassescat.

at si venter officium non agnoverit, etiam clystere utemur,
inicientes aquam calidam cum oleo, nunc solam, nunc admixto
20 melle. etenim surgens ex isto liquore vaporatio collaxat[12] tumentia, et egestus venter facilia facit spiramenta non solum synanchicis, sed etiam sanis hominibus. manens enim alienitas
gravat, atque oppressione quadam acerrimas facit corporis exhalationes, quibus tumentia provocentur, caput impleatur. sed
post clysteris usum erunt etiam cucurbitae cum scarificatione
apponendae dimissionis tempore; at si continuatio fuerit, initio
lucis, quo tempore etiam ceteris districtivis adiutoriis uti conducit. apponendae aliae igitur collo tenus vel gutturi, quae loca
anthereona Graeci vocaverunt, item cervici sive nervis maiori-
21 bus, quos tenontas appellant, item singulas[13] ex utraque parte
sub aurium lacunis, quibus in locis etiam faucium positio esse
perspicitur.

[8] Andronis *R*

[9] Polyidae *G: an scrib.* Polyidu?

[10] *i.e.,* cydonio

[11] dypyrena immissa *G: corr. A (cf. Sor. Gyn., p. 148. 20):* dipyrene immisso *Rm*

[12] colla laxat *Rm*   [13] singulae *Rm, fort. recte*

uids mentioned above, whenever it is clear that the astringent property of the substance must be weakened by the addition of an emollient fluid. Rice water is also useful, as is the poppy-head drug dissolved in mead; and when this drug is spread undissolved over the throat it is also often beneficial. The same is true of the so-called mulberry, fruit, and myrtle drugs, Andron's compound, that of Polyidus, anthera with honey, and all drugs prepared from quince, pomegranate, roses, pomegranate rind, oak galls, omphacium, lycium, and the like.

But when the disease is in its increasing phase, use those remedies which we mentioned above. Furthermore, if you see that the liquid matter [in the mouth and throat] is condensed by the heat and becomes sticky like the liquid on the surface of the eyeball, wipe it away with a warm sponge; and if it collects deep [in the throat], insert a probe for this purpose, covering its head with soft, clean wool. For if the fluid remains there, it hastens suffocation. And if it gets so far down that it cannot be seen, thin it by giving the patient mead. But first have the preparation boiled, for it is then more effective than if not boiled. Some also prescribe pearl barley water to which a little salt has been added. But those substances which actually produce a biting sensation should be avoided, for they irritate the inflammation and cause a thickening of the fluids.

And if the bowels do not function, use a clyster, injecting warm water and olive oil, sometimes with and sometimes without the addition of honey. For the vapor arising from this liquid relaxes the inflamed parts; and the emptying of the bowels renders the air passages freer not only in persons with synanche but in healthy persons as well. For if this waste matter remains, it causes distress and a feeling of heaviness and gives rise to acrid vapors within the body, which irritate the inflamed parts and congest the head. Now after the clyster employ cupping with scarification at the time of a remission; but if the disease continues without remission, apply the cups early in the morning, a time when it is also well to employ the other dilating remedies. Now some cups should be applied along the [front part of the] neck and throat (Greek *anthereōn*); cups should also be applied to the [back of the] neck and to its large sinews (Greek *tenontes*). Apply a cup also on each side under the opening of the ear, where the jaw is hinged.

at si passio perseverarit et aeger ad perferendam curationem
fuerit mollis, ut ferri cuspide metu se contingi prohibeat, sanguisugas, quas Graeci bdellas[14] appellant, apponemus iisdem locis quae supra memoravimus. tunc post earum casum, si minime factam sanguinis detractionem viderimus, cucurbitas apponemus, ut praefecta sanguisugarum vulneratione raptu cucurbitae detractio compleatur. et olei fomento utemur, atque
cataplasmatibus consequentibus et vaporationibus, dehinc epithematibus oleo calido infusis. tunc superpositis spongiis ex
22 eadem materia expressis vaporamus. etenim saccellorum siccam
vaporationem tamquam densabilem reprobamus. at si maior
fuerit tumor, ipsam quoque linguam scarificamus atque fauces
et palatum tenui ac longiore phlebotomo: etenim locali sanguinis
detractione tumentia relaxantur. tunc post scarificationem mi-
tibus gargarismatibus utemur.

si declinare passio coeperit, etiam subunctionibus faucium vel
interiorum utemur, ut melle decocto, vel medicamine confecto
decoctione agrestis malvae et faenugraeci seminis et lini, cum
amylo et melle et oleo vel uvae passae medio, proiecto ac secreto
semine, contritis[15] cum pane vel decoctione lini seminis vel melle
et passo cretico, quibus incocta sit radix agrestis malvae vel
23 alicae atque lini seminis pollines. at si passio perseveraverit,
secundo vel tertio scarificationem adhibemus, non solum gutturi
vel tonsillarum vicinitati, quam Graeci anthereona[16] vocant, et
nervis maioribus cervicis[17] quos tenontas appellant, sed etiam
occipitio et palis et interscapulae,[18] quod Graeci metaphrenon
vocant, et pectori. etenim quamquam vehementer loca transvorationis patiantur, ceterae quoque partes corporis necessario
consentiunt. multi denique non advertentes rationem revin-
cendae passionis, sola aversione materiae pugnantes, atque in
24 liquidis causas[19] ponentes, principaliter aiunt inguinibus cucurbitas infigendas, tunc praecordiis, tunc supra mammas cum
scarificatione, dehinc gutturi atque collo eiusque partibus.

at si declinatio fuerit confirmata, dabimus cibo pultem atque
ova sorbilia vel porcinum cerebrum, longe servantes omne quod
fuerit acre sive immodice apertibile[20] vel inurens vel vinosum vel
asperum aut aridum vel quod valeat transvorationis loca la-

---

[14] βδέλλας G

[15] contrito Rm

[16] antheona G: corr. Rm

[17] cervices G: corr. R

[18] inter scapulas vel interscapulo Almeloveen

[19] causas Schmid Mn 146: causis G: causam Rm

[20] apertibile vel apperibile Rm, coll. 34: appetibile G

But if the disease continues, and the patient is so afraid to undergo this treatment that he will not permit himself to be
touched with the iron point, apply leeches (Greek *bdellae*) to the
very parts just mentioned. Then after the leeches have fallen off,
if the amount of blood withdrawn appears to have been insufficient, apply cups where the leeches have made their wounds, so
that the withdrawal may be completed by the action of these
cups. Foment the parts with olive oil and use suitable poultices,
hot applications, and epithems containing warm olive oil. Then
heat the parts by placing over them sponges wrung out of this
2 oil; but we disapprove of the use of dry heat from bags, since
such heat has a condensing effect. But if the inflammation is extensive, also scarify the tongue, fauces, and palate with a long,
thin lancet. For the inflamed parts are relieved by the local withdrawal of blood. After the scarification employ soothing gargles.

And if the disease begins to decline, paint the throat, and in
particular the deeper parts, using boiled honey, or a preparation
made by boiling down marsh mallow, fenugreek seed, and flaxseed, with starch, honey, and olive oil, or the pulp of raisins (the
seed being separated out and cast away) ground up with bread,
or a decoction of flaxseed, or honey, and Cretan raisin wine in
which marsh mallow root or spelt and flaxseed flour have been
3 boiled down. But if the disease still persists, perform scarification a second and even a third time, and not merely at the throat
and the region of the tonsils, a region which the Greeks call
anthereōn, and at the large sinews of the neck (Greek *tenontes*),
but also at the occiput, the shoulder blades, the space between
the shoulder blades (Greek *metaphrenon*), and the chest. For,
though the parts used in swallowing are most severely affected,
the other parts of the body are also of necessity affected. In fact,
many writers who do not understand the principles of overcoming this disease and conduct the fight merely by withdrawing
4 matter, ascribing diseases to the humors, declare that cups
should be applied in the first instance to the groin, then to the
precordia, then over the breasts, with scarification, and finally
to the throat, the neck, and its parts.

But if the decline of the disease is corroborated, feed the patient porridge, soft eggs, or hog's brain; but carefully avoid all
food that is sharp, excessively aperient, burning, winelike, rough,
dry, or such as could injure the parts used in swallowing. For the

cessere. facile etenim passio ex occasione parva recurrit. apponenda etiam cerotaria ex oleo dulci aut cyprino vel glaucino[21] aut irino confecta vel malabathrino, cum radice hibisci. tunc lavacro utendum ac deinde vino.

25   IV. QUOMODO SYNANCHICOS ALIARUM
             SECTARUM PRINCIPES CURAVERUNT

ANTIQUORUM Hippocrates libro quem Ad sententias cnidias conscripsit ex utroque inquit brachio synanchicos phlebotomari. sed hoc erit evitandum, siquidem coacervata sanguinis effusio animi faciat defectionem, et propterea prohibeat tantum detrahi quantum sufficiat ad relaxandam stricturam. dividit etiam venas sub lingua constitutas quod est non solum inutile verum etiam noxium, siquidem incongrua sit ex locis patientibus sanguinis per venas detractio. plurima etenim in exitum provocata materies confluens, necessario completis locis abstenta, modum superat detractionis, ut gravatae partes potius ad-
26 ventu quam relevatae recessu materiae videantur. dehinc sublevandarum venarum causa erit laqueus circumdandus, et tunc maxime quando sine ullo manifesto tumore synanchica fuerit passio; laqueus autem quod praefocationem augeat nulli dubium est. quin etiam sanguinis fluorem ex supra dictis venis difficile posse abstineri perspicitur. neque enim aliqua constrictiva adhibere sine ullo periculo poterimus, neque divisa colligare erit cuiquam possibile. est etiam naturale tumentia loca post divisuram in fluorem sanguinis facile devenire.
27   utitur quoque gargarismatibus calidis atque vaporationibus, quorum materiam non enarravit. dehinc caput corradi et iugiter vaporari iubet spongiis, tunc contegi cerotario atque lana. potum dat aquam calidam et mulsum. passione declinante suco cibandos dicit, cuius speciem non enarravit, nescius etiam quod

---

[21] gleucino *Rm*

3. The reference may possibly be to the flower *glaucium* rather than to *glaucium* (or *gleucium*), 'must.'

1. *Reg. ac.*, Appendix, 9 (I. 151. 2 Kuehl. = II. 412 Littré).

2. I.e., though the amount initially withdrawn is large, the operation will have to be terminated before the total amount withdrawn is sufficient.

disease may easily recur if given the least opportunity. Also apply cerates made of sweet olive oil, or oil made with must,[3] or oil of henna, iris, or malabathrum, together with marsh mallow root. After that prescribe bathing and then wine.

IV. HOW LEADERS OF OTHER SECTS TREAT SYNANCHE

25

To BEGIN with the ancients, Hippocrates in his book *Against the Cnidian Maxims*[1] declares that venesection should be performed on both arms in cases of synanche. But we must reject this procedure, for the sudden flow of blood in such profusion causes fainting and makes it impossible to continue the withdrawal sufficiently to relieve the state of stricture.[2] He also opens the veins under the tongue. This procedure, however, is not only useless but harmful, since the withdrawal of blood from the veins of parts directly affected is a mistake. For when a large quantity of matter flows together under the impulse to escape, it is inevitably checked by the congestion of the parts in question, so that more blood is present than can be withdrawn, and the parts as a result are found to be weighed down by the arrival of this mat-

26 ter, rather than relieved by its withdrawal. Again, in order to raise these veins, a knot will have to be tied round them,[3] particularly in cases where the disease of synanche occurs without visible inflammation. But there can be no doubt that this knot will aggravate the choking sensation. Furthermore, it is obvious that the flow of blood from these veins can be checked only with difficulty. For it will not be possible without danger to apply any astringent substances, nor will anyone be able to bind up the opened veins. Indeed, it is natural for inflamed parts after the opening of their veins to produce a ready flow of blood.

27 Hippocrates also employs warm gargles and hot applications, the composition of which he does not indicate. He then has the patient's head shaved, warmed repeatedly with sponges, then covered with a cerate, and wrapped with wool. He prescribes warm water and also mead to drink. When the disease declines, Hippocrates says that the patient should be fed with a gruel, but he does not specify its nature. And he is unaware that in most

3. Possibly around the tongue (?).

in plerisque declinatio post quinque dies vel sex adveniat, et sit
immodica usque ad eius initium cibi abstinentia. vaporare vero
oportet, sed non caput magis quam colla atque gutturis exordium, quod Graeci anthereona vocant: tunc post vaporationem
fovere atque cerotarium declinante passione apponere. item neque potum quantum dandum vel quomodo vel quando manifestavit.

28   praeterea secundo libro De morbis clysterizandos inquit atque
purgativis medicaminibus relevandos, quae Graeci cathartica
vocant, quorum ex acrimonia magis tumentia provocantur.
phlebotomari quoque ex locis sub mamilla constitutis noxium
atque putidum iudicamus. noxium, siquidem plurima oporteat
corpora dividi, cum neque facile sub visum venae devenire possunt;[1] putidum, siquidem sine ulla difficultate ex brachio potuerit sanguinis approbari detractio. dehinc iugis atque coacervata materiarum detractio, clysterum et purgativorum medica-
29 minum et phlebotomiae, vexabilis esse perspicitur. item si plurima, inquit, praefocatio occurrerit, clysteris auliscum, quem nos
tibiam dicere poterimus, faucibus inquit immittendum, incendens hyssopum, sulphur, bitumen, quorum rapere odorem praecipit aegrotantem per eandem fistulam. quorum sine dubio
promptus est error. nititur enim immittere fistulam faucibus,
quae neque aerem tenuissimum percipere possunt vi passionis
oppressae; dehinc austero fumo aegros implendos existimat, quo
saepe etiam sani praefocatione afficiuntur. ultimo etiam ex
duobus brachiis atque venis sub lingua constitutis sanguinem
detrahendum probat, quod supra damnantes frustravimus, non
enim sine multa corporis vexatione fiet.

30   Diocles vero, libro quo De passionibus et causis et curationibus scripsit, sanguinosos inquit homines ex utroque brachio
phlebotomandos, eos autem qui minus sanguinis habuerint solum scarificandos. tum felle taurino cum herba pediculari,
quam staphida agrian vocant, et nitro et cocco cnidio iugiter

[1] possint R

4. The traditional Hippocratic text does include the neck. The criticism of Caelius
(Soranus) seems to be directed (1) to the absence of two distinct processes corresponding
to *vaporatio* and *fovere* and (2) to the timing of the cerate.

5. *De morbis* iii. 10 (= VII. 130 Littré). The numbering of this as Book II (see also
85 and 153, below) is found as early as Erotian.

cases the decline comes only after five or six days, and that it is
too much for the patient to fast until the beginning of the decline. And applications of heat are necessary, to be sure, but not
any more so for the head than for the neck and the upper part of
the throat (Greek *anthereōn*).[4] Again, the parts should be fomented after the application of heat; and a cerate should be applied only in the declining phase of the disease. Furthermore,
Hippocrates does not make clear how much is to be given the patients to drink, nor how or when it is to be given.

28   Again, in Book II[5] of his work *On Diseases* he prescribes clysters and purgative drugs (Greek *cathartica*) for the relief of these
patients. But the inflamed parts are only aggravated by the
sharpness of these remedies. And we consider it harmful and unnatural to perform venesection in the region under the breast [as
Hippocrates prescribes]. The procedure is harmful, for it requires
the cutting of much tissue, since the veins there do not readily
come into view. And it is unnatural, for the withdrawal of blood
can be made from the arm without any difficulty. Furthermore,
the continual withdrawal of matter in large quantity through
clysters, purgative drugs, and venesection obviously distresses
29 the patient. And, if there is considerable choking, Hippocrates
has a small clyster pipe (Greek *auliscos*, which we may render
tibia) inserted in the throat; then, burning some hyssop, sulphur,
and bitumen, he instructs the patient to draw in the vapor from
these substances through the pipe. But in this he unquestionably
makes a palpable error. For he seeks to introduce the pipe into
the throat, though the throat is so overcome by the force of the
disease that it cannot admit even the thinnest air. Again, he
thinks the patients should be filled with pungent fumes when,
indeed, even healthy persons are suffocated by them. Finally, he
prescribes that blood be withdrawn from both arms and from
the veins under the tongue. We have already condemned and
refuted this procedure, for it cannot be carried out without considerable harm to the body.

30   Diocles in his book *On Diseases and Their Causes and Treatment* asserts that in the case of full-blooded persons venesection
should be performed on both arms; but in the case of those who
have little blood only scarification should be performed. And
then he prescribes repeated anointing with ox bile and stavesacre
(Greek *staphis agria*), nitrum, and Cnidian berry. He also pre-

inquit ungendos, utens etiam gargarismatibus iisdem. dat quoque sub lingua piper continendum, vaporans spongiis collum et cerotariis contegens, praecipiens aegrum tenuandum ultra quam fas est.

31 neque nunc solos phlebotomandos sanguinosos probamus, sed omnes passione affectos permittentibus viribus; neque ex utroque brachio, ut supra docuimus. neque acerrimis utendum unguentis et gargarismatibus, sicut neque in tumoribus oculorum similibus inunctionibus. etenim staphisagria etiam sanos plerumque synanchicos fecit, cum repente inflationem faucium fieri cogit. dehinc omnino neque tenuari² deducendo corpus sive eius habitudinem convenit medicinae, sed relaxare tumentia rebus congruis ac remissivis.

32 item Praxagoras quarto libro Curationum synanchicos clysterizat et sudoribus provocatis deducit, aliquando etiam phlebotomat, dans quoque medicamen vomificum, quod emeticon appellant. tunc uvam praecidit vel aliquando dividit et pice lenta vulnera curat. sed horum iudicium ex aliis accipiendum probamus. nam vomitus ingens distentione et praefocatione saepe peremit. dehinc tumens uva laxatione indiget, non amputatione, sicut neque aliae quoque corporis partes, quae necessario erunt mitigabiliter relaxandae.

33 Erasistratus secundo libro Anatomicorum de singulis passionibus scripto, in quibusdam inquit synanchicis vaporatione utendum spongiarum atque cataplasmatibus, et ex vino medicamen transvorandum, quod catapotium appellavit, ex castoreo confectum. sed omnia peccanter: etenim vinum constringit, castoreum vero acerrimae esse virtutis nemo negat, quae indubitanter sunt tumori contraria.

Herophilus de synanchicis nihil dixit.

34 Asclepiades vero secundo libro Celerum vel acutarum passionum inquit: synanchicis convenit sanguinis detractio atque ventris depurgatio et cataplasmata et oris collutiones et garga-

---

² *fort.* tenuare

scribes the use of these same preparations as gargles. And he gives the patient pepper to hold under the tongue, applies heat to the neck with sponges, covers it with cerates, and attenuates the patient's body beyond what is proper.

31   But we hold that venesection should be performed not only on full-blooded persons but on all who suffer from this disease, their strength permitting. And, as we have said above, we are opposed to the use of both arms for this purpose. Nor do we approve of the use of sharp ointments and gargles, any more than we should approve of such ointments in cases of inflammation of the eye. Indeed, stavesacre often brings about the disease of synanche in healthy persons by causing a sudden swelling of the throat. And, finally, it is entirely out of keeping with the medical art to weaken the body and its general condition by the excessive withdrawal of matter; it is necessary rather to relieve the inflamed parts with suitable and relaxing remedies.

32   Praxagoras in Book IV of his work *On Treatments* prescribes clysters in cases of synanche; he withdraws matter by inducing sweats, in some cases also employs venesection, and prescribes a vomitive drug (Greek *emeticon*). He then cuts off the end of the uvula or in some cases merely makes an incision, treating the wounds with viscous pitch. But we prefer to follow the judgment of others on these matters. For the tension of violent vomiting often causes the patient to choke to death. Again, an inflamed uvula requires a soothing treatment, not amputation; in this it is no different from other parts of the body, which in such circumstances must always be relaxed by gentle treatment.

33   In Book II of his *Anatomica* Erasistratus deals with various diseases, and in certain cases of synanche recommends applying heat with sponges, and also the use of poultices. And he has the patient swallow down a pill (Greek *catapotion*) with wine, the pill to be prepared from castor. But all this is unwise. For wine is astringent, and no one can deny that castor has a very acrid quality. And such substances are obviously unsuitable in cases of inflammation.

Herophilus has nothing to say about the treatment of synanche.

34   In Book II of his *Swift* (i.e., acute) *Diseases* Asclepiades says that in cases of synanche the following are proper: blood-letting, purging of the bowels, poultices, mouth washes, gargles, and

rismata et superunctiones tenuabiles atque apertibiles,[3] ut sunt
ex hyssopo, origano, et thymo, meliloto, absinthio, fici coctione,
nitro, staphide agria, centaurea, elaterio, felle taurino, cedria,
adiciens etiam cucurbitae usum cum scarificatione, negans quidem quicquam posse sanguinis elicere, sive, inquit, quod cum
febribus sit passio, sive quod maior causa sit tumentium partium, quae contrario raptu superet cucurbitae fervorem, ut[4] non
possit efficere detractionem.

35   tum phlebotomiam probat ex fronte faciendam vel angulis
oculorum vel venis quae sub lingua sunt vel e brachio. at si
maior, inquit, passio fuerit, dividendae sunt fauces, hoc est ton-
sillae et partes supra uvam constitutae. etenim summa est in
his aequalis sive par incisura, quam appellavit homotomiam. dehinc a veteribus probatam approbat arteriae divisuram ob respirationem faciendam, quam laryngotomiam vocant, varie[5] ac
multipliciter peccans.

    omne etenim quod acre fuerit atque tenuans incendet[6] tu-
36 morem;[7] ipse denique in phreniticam[8] venturos passionem multa
inquit affici materie, ad haec eiusdem acrimonia. est etiam
noxia ex[9] patientibus locis phlebotomia, sicut supra docuimus.
item clysteribus utendum ob avertendam materiam vel avo-
candam a locis patientibus inconsequenter iubet. est enim contrarium detractioni per venas ex patientibus locis faciendae,
quam ipse probavit. item inordinaliter scarificandum primo,
dehinc phlebotomandum iudicavit. etenim locales detractiones
insidente atque infirmata[10] et stante[11] passione adhibendas pro-
37 bamus. est etiam inexerciti medici ob febrium causam suspicari
materiam raptu cucurbitae non elici. in usu enim videmus sine
ullo impedimento in febricitantibus effectum cucurbitae prove-

---

[3] aperibiles *Rm*: cf. 24

[4] ut *Rm*: et *G*

[5] varię *G*: corr. *R*

[6] incendit *R*

[7] humorem *edd.*: corr. Bendz *Eran 41. 67*

[8] *an* synanchicam? sed cf. *Ac. ii. 133*

[9] ex *Schmid Mn 147, Bendz 93*: et *edd.*

[10] confirmata *Am*

[11] ⟨non⟩ stante *Rm*

ointments with attenuating and anastomotic properties, such as those made with hyssop, marjoram, thyme, melilot, wormwood, a decoction of fig, nitrum, stavesacre, centaury, elaterium, ox bile, and cedar oil. He also recommends the use of cupping with scarification, but he says that he has not been able to draw any blood by this means, either because the disease is accompanied by fever or because a more powerful factor within the inflamed parts overcomes the effect of the hot cup with a contrary action, so that the cup cannot effect a withdrawal of blood.

35   Asclepiades then prescribes that venesection be performed at the forehead, the corners of the eyes, the veins under the tongue, or the arm. But if the disease is more serious, he says that incisions should be made in the throat, that is, in the tonsils and the parts above the uvula; and he considers it very helpful to have the incisions there equal and symmetrical, for which he employs the term *homotomia*.[6] Again, he follows older writers in recommending an incision of the windpipe (Greek *laryngotomia*) for the purpose of making breathing possible.

But in these prescriptions he commits many diverse errors. For everything that is acrid and attenuating aggravates the in-
36 flammation. And, in fact, Asclepiades himself says that those who are on the verge of phrenitis suffer from a congestion of matter and, in addition, from the acrid property of this matter. Again, venesection at the affected parts is harmful, as we have shown above. And Asclepiades is inconsistent in prescribing clysters to divert or remove matter from the affected parts; for this is the reverse of making a withdrawal through the veins of the affected parts, a procedure of which he also approves. Again, in prescribing scarification first and venesection afterward, he arranges his treatments poorly. For we hold that the local withdrawal of matter should take place when the disease is firmly established and at its highest stage.[7] Moreover, it is indicative
37 of Asclepiades' lack of experience as a physician that he supposes that fever may prevent matter from being drawn from the body by the suction of a cupping instrument. For in actual practice we observe that the cup works successfully and without any obsta-

6. I.e., the same kind of incision is to be made on each side. Or possibly incisions are to be made at the same time in various parts.

7. The meaning seems to be that scarification should be performed after the increasing phase of the disease is complete (22, above), which would be after venesection. But the text and details of interpretation are not certain.

nire, atque eductam detrahi materiam: adducitur namque caro
et spiritus et sanguis. dehinc neque crescente accessione cucurbitas infigimus tempore quo ad altiora materia conducitur.

est praeterea tumentium partium molestissima atque periculosa divisura: vehementes namque sanguinis effusiones efficit, et

38 quae prohiberi minime possint. si enim easdem constringere
voluerimus, celerrima praefocatio consequetur; at si abstinere
neglexerimus, celerior mortis effectus sanguinis effusione perspicitur. vel si forte sanguinis fluorem effugerit quis, cancrum atque gangraenam non effugiet ob augmenta tumoris. nos[12] enim
naturali habitu constituta cum dividuntur[13] quamquam constrictive tractata saepissime tumescere videntes,[14] in tumore
constituta cum divisa[15] fuerint, at[16] si constringendi caruerint facultate, vehementius in tumorem venire desperare[17] poterimus.
nam omnino in tanto tumore in quo digitorum immissio improba
esse perspicitur, atque cataplasmatum et anagargarismatum
usus aeger atque difficilis aegrotanti videtur, quomodo non altiorum divisura inimica saluti probatur?

39   est etiam fabulosa arteriae ob respirationem divisura, quam
laryngotomiam vocant, et quae a nullo sit antiquorum tradita,
sed caduca atque temeraria Asclepiadis inventione affirmata.
cui ne nunc occurrentes latius respondere videamur aut tantum
scelus angusta oratione damnemus, libris quos De adiutoriis sumus scripturi respondebimus. Themison vero sine febribus passiones recte curare Asclepiadem probans huic accusationi subi-
cietur.

40   Serapion primo libro Curationum clysteribus synanchicos eva-
cuat, atque phlebotomia et cataplasmatibus et unguentis acrioribus utitur, et provocativis et apertivis, quae anastomotica[18] appellant. praecavet autem in omni abstinentia cibum vel potum
dare. sed est etiam hic facile accusabilis. etenim acria atque
tenuantia excitare tumorem nemo dubitat; phlebotomia vero
adiecta clysteribus vexabilis esse perspicitur. dehinc dicens ma-

---

[12] nos *Rm*: non *G*

[13] cum dividuntur *Rm*: condividuntur *G*

[14] *fort.* videmus

[15] divisa *R*: divisura *G*   [16] *fort.* ac   [17] sperare *R*

[18] anastomatica *G*: *corr. Rm, litteris graecis; cf. Chr. ii. 123, iii. 13*

7a. The term here refers to intractable ulcerations.

cle in cases of fever, drawing matter up from the body and removing it. Indeed, flesh, pneuma, and blood are drawn up. And we do not apply the cups when an attack is increasing, for at that time the matter is carried down to deeper parts.

Moreover, incisions into the inflamed parts are most painful and dangerous, since they produce strong outpourings of blood
38 which can scarcely be stopped. For if we try to check these effusions, choking quickly ensues; and if we fail to stop the flow, it is obvious that death will soon result from the loss of blood. Or if a patient happens to avoid a serious hemorrhage, he will still incur cancer[7a] and gangrene because of the spread of the inflammation. For, when incisions are made in tissues that are in normal condition, we often find that these tissues become inflamed, even though treatment is given to stop the flow; but, when tissues that are already inflamed are cut into and treatment cannot be given to stop the flow, we may expect the inflammation to become even worse. Indeed, in cases of inflammation [of the throat] so severe that the insertion of the fingers is bad and the use of plasters and gargles is found to be hardly endurable by the patient, how can an incision into the deeper parts fail to endanger his life?

9 And the incision of the windpipe (Greek *laryngotomia*) for the purpose of aiding respiration is fantastic. It is not described by any of the ancients but seems to be a futile and irresponsible idea set forth by Asclepiades. But, rather than attack him now, we shall answer him fully in a work *On Remedies* which we are planning to write. Thus we shall avoid an overlong refutation in the present work; and at the same time it will be unnecessary for us to content ourselves with merely a brief condemnation of so grievous a crime. And our refutation will also be directed against Themison, since he approves of Asclepiades' treatment of diseases unaccompanied by fever.

0 Serapion in Book I of his *Treatments* prescribes purging with clysters in cases of synanche; he also prescribes venesection and the use of plasters and ointments which are sharp, stimulating, and dilating (Greek *anastomōtica*). And he refrains from giving any food or drink, enforcing complete abstinence. But he, too, can easily be refuted. For there is no doubt that sharp, attenuating substances irritate an inflammation, and the combination of venesection with clysters is clearly harmful. Again, in listing the

teriarum nomina, ea ex quibus adiutoria conficiuntur scribere
neglexit, cum nullo alio quolibet adiutorio minus utilis cibatio
atque potus probentur, arte adhibita atque formata.

41   Heraclides Tarentinus tertio libro Curationum de internis scribens, eos, inquit, qui sanguinis multitudine vexantur clystere
praepurgatos phlebotomamus, nunc ex brachio, nunc ex venis
quae sub lingua sunt, vaporationibus spongiarum admotis collo
atque gutturi ex aqua calida in qua fuerit praecocta ruta vel pulegium. tunc cataplasma apponendum[19] probat quod omen lysin appellamus, ex mulso confectum, cui erit admiscenda chamaepitys vel iris illyrica aut ficus. nocte vero inquit cerotarium
apponendum ex irino oleo atque resina iusta parte in compara-

42 tionem ponderis cerae. in his vero quibus locorum[20] crassitudinem suspicatur ungendas inquit fauces melle atque omphacio;
et anagargarismate utitur mulso in quo praecoquit ficum vel
origanum et admiscet piper. dat etiam elaterium in pondere
†denariorum septem,† multis vero obolum dimidium cum melle
et aqua aut mulso. dehinc medicamen quod appellavit emeticon, vomificae[21] virtutis, et conficitur hoc modo: origani atque[22]
heracleotici panacis manipulum accipiens demerge, inquit, in
vasculum rubri aeris, tum rhus quod appellamus rubrum heminas quatuor atque cepulas germanas viginti, quibus circumtolle-

43 mus exteriorem corticem, et has quassantes immittimus.[23] tunc
infundimus vinum chium vel rhodium aut cnidium quatuor heminas,[24] et sub sole ante ortum Caniculae viginti diebus atque
post ortum viginti diebus ponemus. tunc cum fuerit liquor in-
sumptus, infundemus alias quatuor heminas atque alio[25] sub sole
linquimus. tunc iisdem diebus mittimus medicamentum in pi-
lam et conterentes formamus trochiscos, quorum maiores erunt
drachmarum singularum et dimidiae, alii vero drachmarum singularum, item alii dimidiarum drachmarum. singulos dabimus
virium comparationi congruos, cum mulso vel pro eclectario[26]

44 cum melle. etenim vomitum humoris viscosi efficit et ventrem
deducit. aliqui, inquit, etiam elaterium[27] admiscent et tapsiae

[19] apponendo G: corr. Rm
[20] succorum Rm: fort. liquorum vel humorum
[21] (idest) vomificae Deichgräber
[22] sive Wellmann (cf. Deichgräber ad loc.)   [24] heminis edd.: corr. Schmid RPh 134
[23] immittemus. tunc infundemus Rm   [25] alio Rm: alia G: ita R
[26] electuario Rm: an scrib. electario, ut saepe ap. Cael.?
[27] elaterium Almeloveen, coll. 42, 44: melanteriam edd.

names of drugs, he neglects to indicate the composition of his remedies. And, in fact, food and drink, if skilfully prepared and administered, are no less valuable than any other remedy.

Heraclides of Tarentum in Book III of his work *On the Treatment of Internal Diseases* declares that patients suffering from excess of blood should first be purged with a clyster and then subjected to venesection, sometimes at the arm and sometimes at the veins under the tongue. And the neck and throat should be warmed with sponges dipped in hot water in which rue or pennyroyal has been boiled. Heraclides then prescribes the application of the poultice called *ōmēlysis*, prepared with mead to which is added ground pine, Illyrian iris, or fig. And he further prescribes the application at night of a cerate made with iris oil and resin in proper proportion to the weight of the wax. But in those cases in which he suspects a thickening of the parts affected, he recommends anointing the throat with honey and omphacium, and he uses as a gargle mead in which fig or marjoram has been cooked, with an admixture of pepper. He also prescribes . . .[8] elaterium, and in many cases half an obol, to be taken with honey and water or mead. He also prescribes a vomitive drug (Greek *emeticon*). It is prepared, he says, as follows: 'Take a handful of marjoram and Heraclean allheal and place it in a small vessel of red copper; add four heminae of the so-called red sumach; add twenty German onions after removing their outer skin and squeezing them open. Then pour into the vessel four heminae of Chian, Rhodian, or Cnidian wine, and place the vessel in the sun some time within the twenty days preceding and the twenty days following the rising of the Dog Star.[9] And when the liquid has evaporated, pour in four more heminae and again leave the vessel in the sun. Then within that same period of time place the preparation in a mortar, grind it finely, and make it up in the form of troches, the largest weighing one and one-half drachms, others one drachm, and still others half a drachm. Give the patient one pill, the size depending on his strength; let him swallow it with mead or take it as an electuary with honey. The drug will cause the patient to vomit the sticky, fluid matter and also bring about evacuation of the bowels.

8. The weight of 7 drachms indicated in the text is far too much, but it is doubtful that the change to one-seventh suggested by Amman is correct.

9. Cf. Galen VI. 538 K.

sucum obolos tres. at si difficilis fuerit vomitus, penna oleo veteri intincta atque faucibus immissa provocandum probat. utitur etiam aliquando medicamine ex omphacii suco et elaterio
confecto atque diagridio cum nigro helleboro et sale, si fuerint in
vomitum difficiles aegrotantes, vel elaterio cum aceto et ruta, et
rursum elaterio cum sinapi et salibus.

eos, inquit, qui perfrictione synanchici fuerint effecti phlebotomari prohibemus atque clysteribus depurgari; ceteris vero omnibus ex qualibet causa synanchicis effectis erunt haec adhi-
45 benda. fulciendos etiam omnes iudicat vel nutriendos sola aqua
vel mulso; cetera quaeque[28] ciborum prohibet. sed hoc omne experimentum sive tentatio promptissime ex occultis suscipionibus
videtur esse provisa. etenim Empiricus solam servationem intuens, quam teresin vocant, sanguinosos nunc phlebotomandos
existimat, non advertens quia omnes synanchicos ob stricturae
vehementiam oportet phlebotomari, permittentibus viribus.
denique ridendum est etiam quod eos qui ex perfrictione synanchici fuerint effecti phlebotomandos negat, non advertens praesentia, et inquirens factorum causas.

46   noxia etiam sunt cataplasmata quae adhibenda probat atque
vaporationis genus acrimoniae causa earum specierum quas admiscendas iubet, siquidem sunt incendiosae.[29] item vomifica,
quae emetica appellat, etiam non tumentia in tumorem faciunt
devenire. etenim ferulago, quam thapsiam appellant, sufficiens
est etiam putredinem[30] partium quas attigerit facere atque inflare naturali habitu constitutas; non aliter etiam illa quae conficiuntur ex cepe et omphacii suco et rhu rubro vel horum similibus; item oleum vetus acre est. illa vero, quae cathartica appellat, per clysterem adhibenda, quae nos purgativa vocamus,
turborem magnum faciunt atque stomachum vexant et cetera
quaeque nervorum. est praeterea iners tempus dandi cibi non
definire.

47   nostrae etiam sectae quidam adhuc veterum errore detenti in-
suetas graves materias adhibendas probaverunt, nunc urinam
sive fimum humanum cum melle et myrrha[31] atque ruta, nunc

[28] quoque G: corr. Helmreich 330, coll. 46

[29] incendiosae Rm: incendiosa G

[30] uredinem Rm

[31] myrtha G: corr. Rm

Some also add elaterium and three obols of the juice of thapsia.'
Now if vomiting still proves difficult, he recommends stimulating it by introducing into the throat a feather dipped in old olive
oil. And sometimes in cases where it is difficult to induce vomiting he employs a drug made of omphacium, elaterium, scammony juice, black hellebore, and salt; or elaterium, vinegar, and
rue; or elaterium, mustard, and salt.

'We reject venesection and purging with clysters,' says he, 'in
those cases of synanche resulting from a cold; but we prescribe
these remedies in all other cases of synanche from whatever
5 cause.' And he believes that the patients should all be supported
or nourished merely with water or mead; he withholds all other
food. But this whole procedure is purely empirical and a matter
of trial and is clearly seen to be based on speculative guesswork.
Indeed, the Empiricist, having regard merely to observation
(Greek *tērēsis*), thinks that in this disease venesection should be
performed only on the full-blooded.[10] He does not understand
that, because of the severe state of stricture, this treatment
should be used in every case of synanche where the patient's
strength permits. Again, it is ridiculous for him to reject venesection in cases of synanche resulting from a cold, for, instead of
taking account of what is actually present, he concerns himself
with the causes of things.
6   The poultices and the applications of heat that he prescribes
are also harmful because of the sharpness of the substances he
uses as ingredients; for they have a burning quality. And the
vomitives (Greek *emetica*) produce inflammation in parts not
previously inflamed. In fact, ferulago (Greek *thapsia*) is able to
cause rotting of [inflamed] parts with which it comes in contact
and swelling of normal parts. The same is also true of drugs
made with onion, omphacium, red sumach, and the like. Old
olive oil is also sharp. And the purgatives (Greek *cathartica*, Latin *purgativa*), which he orders administered by clyster, produce a
profound disturbance, causing distress even in the esophagus
and in all the bodily sinews. Furthermore, it is inept of him not
to indicate when food is to be given.
7   And even some members of our own sect, still hampered by
the errors of earlier physicians, recommend the use of strange
and harmful substances, e.g., urine or human feces with honey,

10. Cf. 30.

centauream et absinthium et abrotanum et thymum et aristolo-
chiam et tymbram, quam nos satureiam dixerimus, et sinapi,
nunc pythagoricum atque zopyrium[32] trochiscum nomine inven-
toris appellatum, nunc Polyidi[33] sphragida quam adpellant, atque constrictiva tum unctiones et cerotaria ex unguentis sam-
psuchi atque roris marini. quorum singula tumoris sunt provoca-
tiva ob fervoris nimietatem atque desiccandi virtutem et recorporandi, cum sit celeritas passionis ⟨mitigativis⟩[34] ac simplicibus
curanda virtutibus.

48   V. DE APOPLEXIA

APOPLEXIA dicta est quod tamquam ex letali percussu repentinum faciat casum. est autem oppressio saepe[1] sine febribus, repentina, et quae sensibus[2] privet corpora, et semper celerrima et numquam tarda esse probatur. sed eius antecedentes
causae communes cum ceteris esse accipiuntur, magis tamen
iugis adustio et perfrictio vehemens et indigestio frequens lavacris exercita,[3] usus etiam veneris et magis in senibus, item vulneratio membranae, in pueris vero etiam vehemens saltus membranae cerebri.

49   quibusdam igitur ante casum nullum praevidetur signum, quibusdam vero praecedunt quaedam significantia passionem, ut
gravedo vel dolor capitis aut vertigo aut aurium tinnitus et in
solitos usus difficilis motus, vultus maestitudo, saltus membrorum, et magis prae ceteris partibus labrorum, tremula locutio et
veluti minus expressa, aut interruptio proferendi sermonis sine
ulla ratione, vel oblivio mox dictorum, vultus etiam plenitudo,
egestionum difficultas. sed haec communiter antecedunt vel
praeeunt etiam his qui in epilepsiam vel furorem venturi videntur.

irruente passione vocis amputatio sequitur et mentis oppressio
ex repentino casu, immobilitas perfecta totius corporis atque
50 conductio vultus, quibusdam etiam suspensio palpebrarum at-

---

[32] zopyrium *conieci*: isyperium *edd.*: *an* isopyrium?

[33] Polyidę G; *cf. 18*

[34] *suppl. Schmid Mn 147 (qui etiam* ⟨consuetis⟩ *proponit)*

[1] *fort.* semper

[2] sensibus *Rm, coll. 53*: sine febribus *G*

[3] excita *Rm* (*cf. Chr. ii. 32*): *an* excitata?

myrrh, and rue; or centaury, wormwood, southernwood, thyme, birthwort, thymbra (Latin *satureia*, 'savory'), and mustard; or the troche of Pythagoras and that of Zopyrus,[11] called by the name of its discoverer, or the so-called 'seal of Polyidus.' They also employ various astringent substances, including ointments and cerates made with oils of marjoram and rosemary. These substances all aggravate inflammation by reason of their excessive heat and their desiccant and metasyncritic properties, whereas the disease is an acute one and should be treated with soothing and simple drugs.

V. APOPLEXY

48

A POPLEXY derives its name from the fact that it involves a sudden collapse, as if from a deadly blow.[1] It is a sudden seizure, in general without fever, and it deprives the body of all sensation; it is always acute and never chronic. Its antecedent causes, which are the same as those found in other diseases, include, in particular, prolonged exposure to heat; a violent cold; recurring indigestion aggravated by bathing; venery, especially in the case of old men; an injury to the membrane of the brain; and, in the case of children, any violent shaking of the membrane.

49 In some cases there is no visible indication before the coming of the attack, but in others there are certain signs that point to this disease, e.g., a feeling of heaviness or pain in the head, dizziness, ringing in the ears, difficulty in making accustomed motions, sadness of facial expression, quivering of the parts, and of the lips more than of the other parts; trembling voice, words indistinctly pronounced, a breaking-off without any reason in the midst of speaking, or forgetfulness of what has just been said; face full; evacuations painful. But the same antecedent signs appear also in cases where the patient is found to be on the verge of epilepsy or mania.

Now when the attack of apoplexy comes, there are these signs: loss of voice, coma following the sudden stroke, complete bodily 50 immobility, facial spasm, in some cases failure of the eyelids to

11. The text is doubtful. *Isyperium* (G) may possibly conceal some other proper name or the name of an ingredient, such as *isopyron* (fumitory) or *hypericon* (St. John's wort).

1. Greek *plēssō*, 'strike.'

que oris hiscens distantia, pulsus densus et quadam persecutione
fugatus, articulorum gelidus torpor, parva respiratio, color
plumbeus, atque involuntaria lacrimatio.

peiorante passione atque in exitium aegrotantis crescente,
vultus adductio ita ut longior nota videatur imago, praecordiorum prominentia atque totius corporis frigidus torpor, pectoris
stridor, et superiorum partium sudores frigidi, immobilis etiam
et super suspensa palpebrarum ac superciliorum positio.

at si passio fuerit levigata et in salutaria devenerit signa, corporis fugabitur torpor atque frigus redeunte fervore, partes
etiam quaedam saltu errantes movebuntur in his qui omni motu[4]
51 caruerant, et distillatus humor faucibus transvoratur, quamquam difficile, nec tamen prisca intercessione impeditur. punc-
tus etiam vel inclamatus aegrotans palpebram movet atque labia conducit significans sese audire vocantem posse. et universali dicto, quod Graeci catholicon vocant, quidam prima die
moriuntur, quidam duobus vel tribus diebus supervivunt, alii
vero salvantur, quorum alii statim sese resumunt, alii paralysi
partis vel partium corporis vexantur. item quidam parva conversione mentis afficiuntur, ut aut alienentur aut tristes et som-
niosi videantur, ut[5] si eos quisquam e somno excitaverit aliquid
alienum loquantur.

52 est autem passio stricturae, atque celeris et acuta et vehemens,
et in senibus abundans, et hiemis tempore et autumni fine. vocatur etiam a quibusdam paraplexia. vehementius autem in ista
passione patitur caput, sicuti coniciendum ex his quae antecedunt atque corporis oppressione. et sunt difficiles curationes
fortium hominum: debiles etenim[6] oppressionibus magis su-
perantur atque ferre maiora adiutoria minime possunt. hinc
etiam specialiter difficilius ⟨feminas a⟩[7] viris curari perspicimus,
atque senes et pueros a perfectis aetatibus, et tabidos magis
quam qui habitudine vigent, item eos qui praetacti fuerint aegritudine magis quam qui nulla fuerint morbi contagione sauciati.

---

[4] omni motu *Hagendahl 259*: omnino *edd.*

[5] *fort.* et *vel* aut

[6] *fort.* autem

[7] ⟨feminas⟩ *R* (*post* etiam)

close, and gaping of the mouth. The pulse is rapid, as if fleeing from pursuit, limbs cold and numb, respiration small, and complexion leaden. And there is involuntary weeping.

If the disease becomes worse and tends toward a fatal conclusion, the patient's face is so drawn that it appears quite different from normal; there is also precordial distention, cold numbness of the whole body, wheezing in the chest, and cold sweat in the upper parts; the eyelids and brows are raised and immobile.

If, on the other hand, the disease becomes less severe and a recovery is indicated, the cold numbness of the body gives way as warmth returns; and in the case of patients who had lost all power of movement, certain parts can now be moved with erratic jerks. Liquid introduced into the throat drop by drop can be swallowed, with difficulty, to be sure, but not with such obstacles as before. The patient, when pricked or called, moves his eyelids and brings his lips together, indicating that he hears the person calling him. As a general proposition (Greek *catholicon*), some die on the first day, others survive two or three days; but the rest are saved. Of the latter some experience immediate and complete recovery, while others continue to be affected by paralysis of one or more parts of the body.[2] Again, some experience a small mental disturbance. That is, they either suffer some impairment of their reason, or they seem depressed and sleepy, and, when aroused from sleep, they speak irrationally.

2   Apoplexy is a disease involving a state of stricture; it is swift, acute, and violent, common in old men, and most frequent during winter and the end of autumn. It is called by some *paraplexia*. And in this disease the head is the part most severely affected, as may be gathered from the antecedent symptoms and the seizure of the whole body.[3] The treatment of the disease is difficult even in the case of strong persons. And the weak generally succumb to these strokes, being unable to endure the major remedies. Hence, in particular, the treatment of women is more difficult than that of men; and that of old men and boys more difficult than that of men in the prime of life. Again, those who are ill-nourished are harder to cure than those who are in vigorous condition; and those who have previously been attacked by disease are harder to cure than those who have not

2. On the distinction between apoplexy and paralysis see 55, below.
3. Seizure of the whole body indicates that the brain is affected.

53 adiuvat etiam difficultatem hiems, non solum quod corpora denset, verum etiam quod quibusdam adiutoriis oppugnet, ut gestationibus liberis ac nudis.

similis autem ac vicina est apoplexiae lethargia, epilepsia, matricis praefocatio secundum aliquos, et paralysis, et gravatio, quam Graeci caron appellant, et dissolutio. discernitur ergo a lethargo, siquidem omnis lethargus in febrem atque cum febre fiat, rarum habeat pulsum, et neque semper sensibus privet, apoplexia vero et sine febribus fiat, et parvum atque densum faciat pulsum, et repentinum tamquam ex letali percussu faciat casum; item quod ex membranae vulneratione apoplexia fiat, lethargia vero numquam.

54   discernitur etiam ab epilepsia, siquidem epileptici quidem totius corporis conductione agitentur et spumas agant, apoplecti vero numquam; item post accessionem epileptici integro habitu consurgant frequentius, apoplecti vero paralysin partium sustineant; item apoplexia acuta atque celeris semper accipiatur, epilepsia vero etiam tarda saepissime invenitur.[8]

item matricis[9] praefocatione discernitur, siquidem ⟨non⟩[10] praecedat capitis querela matricis praefocationem, item in accessione conducta atque sese sustollens matrix inveniatur, in apo-

55 plecticis vero hoc numquam contingat. dehinc cessante accessione apoplectae feminae nesciunt[11] gesta, illae vero quae matrice fuerint praefocatae resipiant atque narrent quemadmodum fuerint oppressae. item matricis praefocatio tarda esse perspicitur, hoc est chronia, apoplexia vero numquam.

discernitur etiam paralysi[12] apoplexia, quamquam idem multis videatur veteribus, ut Hippocrati et Diocli et Praxagorae et Apollonio[13] Citiensi[14] et Demetrio et si qui praeterea. inquiunt enim apoplectos toto corpore vitiatos paralysi, paraplectos[15] vero

---

[8] fort. inveniatur
[9] ⟨a⟩ matricis R   [11] fort. nesciant
[10] add. R   [12] ⟨a⟩ paralysi R
[13] Apollonio conieci, coll. Chr. i. 140, iii. 56: Asclepiadi edd.
[14] Titiensi edd.: corr. Wellmann
[15] paraplectos R: parapoplectos G: paralyticos Bendz Eran 41. 75

53 been weakened by any disease.[4] Moreover, winter adds to the difficulty of treatment, not only because it condenses our bodies but because it puts obstacles in the way of certain remedies, such as free and unencumbered passive exercise.

Lethargy, epilepsy, hysterical suffocation (according to some), paralysis, torpor (Greek *caros*), and prostration are conditions that are similar to and resemble apoplexy. But apoplexy may be distinguished from lethargy, since every case of lethargy supervenes upon fever and is accompanied by fever and a slow pulse. Moreover, lethargy does not in all cases deprive the patient of his senses. Apoplexy, on the other hand, occurs without fever, produces a small, rapid pulse, and involves a sudden fall, as if from a deadly blow. Again, apoplexy may result from an injury to the membrane [of the brain], but this is never the case with lethargy.

54 Apoplexy may also be distinguished from epilepsy, for epileptics are shaken by convulsions of the whole body and foam at the mouth, whereas this is never true of apoplectics. Furthermore, epileptics usually can stand up after an attack without having suffered any impairment in their general condition, whereas apoplectics suffer a paralysis of parts of the body. Again, apoplexy is always considered an acute and swift disease, while epilepsy is generally found to be chronic as well.

And apoplexy may also be distinguished from hysterical suffocation,[5] for pain in the head does not precede hysterical suffocation. Moreover, in an attack of the latter disease the uterus is found to be retracted and raised, whereas this never takes place 55 in apoplexy. And women who have suffered an attack of apoplexy do not, when the attack is over, know what has taken place; but those who have suffered an attack of hysterical suffocation recover their senses and can describe the attack. Moreover, hysterical suffocation seems to be a slow or chronic disease, while this is never the case with apoplexy.

Apoplexy may also be distinguished from paralysis, though they are considered identical by many earlier physicians, among them Hippocrates, Diocles, Praxagoras, Apollonius of Citium, Demetrius, and others. These physicians define apoplexy as paralysis of the whole body, and use the term 'paraplexy' for

4. Perhaps the reference is specifically to apoplexy, i.e., to previous strokes.
5. Cf. Soranus *Gyn.*, p. 109.

56 particulis. Themison vero capitis vel in capite paralysin cum
mentis impedimento proprie apoplexiam vocat, in aliis vero partibus corporis sine impedimento mentis hanc ipsam paralysin.
sed non oportet certare de his ex quibus curationis ratio non su-
metur. solum tamen commemorandum est quod apoplexia celeris atque acuta natura intelligatur, paralysis vero propria quae
dicitur tarda semper intelligatur.

item gravatio et dissolutio inter resumptionem veniunt et
numquam praecordia suspendunt et neque difficultatem resur-
gendi ut alii[16] faciunt.

57 curationem vero principaliter apoplexiae nullus nobilium pris-
corum tradidit, siquidem paralysi generaliter hanc ascriben-
dam.[17] solus Hippocrates ait apoplexiam vehementem solvere
impossibile, imbecillem vero non facile. item aliarum sectarum
successores aceto atque oleo caput fovent, ceteras autem partes
corporis vino et oleo lanis contegentes rudibus atque intrectatis.
secundo studiose caput fovent admiscentes hederam vel ser-
pyllum aut peucedanum, quorum fugienda est acrimonia atque
constrictiones.

adhibenda est igitur passioni congrua curatio. nam locandi
58 sunt aegrotantes loco lucido mediocriter atque calido. utendum
etiam articulorum blandi tactus continentia, atque limpidae
lanae tectione mediis partibus, capiti[18] et collo. adhibenda
etiam olei fomenta dulcis atque calidi, et expressa ex aqua calida
spongia vultus circumtegendus. potus dandus aqua calida, vel
mulsum distillandum sensim faucibus.

adhibenda etiam phlebotomia, non necessario expectata diatrito, dimissionis tamen tempore vel circa primae lucis exortum
cum ex aliqua parte corporis frigidus torpor visus fuerit egelari.
etenim qui prius quam haec provisa sunt in materiae detractionem festinantes[19] latenter accessionis tempore decepti phlebotomiam adhibent, vel certe iam expirantes aegrotos phleboto-

---

[16] ut apoplexia *Rm*: *fort.* et alia

[17] ⟨putent⟩ adscribendam *A*: adscribunt *Rm*

[18] capitis *G*: *fort.* ⟨et⟩ capiti

[19] festinare *G*: festinavere *R*: *an* festinarunt?

---

6. *Aph.* ii. 42.

6 paralysis of parts only. But Themison gives the name 'apoplexy' specifically to that paralysis of the head or in the head which is accompanied by mental impairment. And he uses the term 'paralysis' for paralysis in other parts of the body without any mental impairment. But we need not argue about these matters, which do not affect the system of treatment. One point, however, should be noted, viz., that apoplexy is by nature a swift and acute disease, while paralysis, in the proper sense of the term, is always found to be chronic.

Finally, torpor and prostration occur during convalescence from a disease; they do not cause precordial distention and generally do not prevent the patient from getting up again, as do other diseases.

7 None of the famous physicians of the past described a treatment specifically intended for apoplexy, since as a rule they included this disease under paralysis. But Hippocrates does say that it is impossible to cure a severe case of apoplexy, and not easy to cure a mild case.[6] And subsequently physicians of other sects fomented the head [in cases of apoplexy] with vinegar and olive oil, and the other parts of the body with wine and olive oil, covering the parts with rough, uncarded wool. They then thoroughly fomented the head a second time, adding ivy, thyme, or sulphurwort [to the liquid]. But these substances are both acrid and astringent and are to be avoided.

Employ, rather, the following treatment suitable to the disease. Place the patient in a moderately light and warm room. 8 Keep holding his limbs with gentle touch, and apply a covering of scoured wool to the middle parts and to the head and neck. Also use fomentations of warm sweet olive oil, and cover the face with a sponge wrung out of hot water. Give the patient warm water or mead to drink, letting it drip into the throat little by little.

Without necessarily waiting for the end of the three-day period, perform venesection at the time when the attack abates, or about dawn of the first day [after the attack], when the cold numbness of the body has in some measure been overcome. But no good can be done by those who hasten to withdraw matter before these indications and perform venesection too soon, because the time element of the attack escapes them. Again, venesection is unavailing if performed when the patient is clearly on

59 mando nihil prodesse potuerunt, siquidem neque materiae fieri
potuerit exitus cum corpus desertum exitum sanguinis negat,
quamquam divisa venula videatur.

adhibenda etiam abstinentia usque ad primam diatriton, tum
unctio calida atque spongiarum calida expressarum vaporatio et
sorbilis cibus, vel panis aqua calida infusus vel mulso. at si ventris officium [non][20] cessaverit, clyster simplex adhibendus cum
cucurbitae appositione cum scarificatione, tempore quo saepissime docuimus, occipitio atque omni spinae. spongiarum vaporatione utendum et cataplasmatibus laxativis. tum radendum
caput totum et multis partibus eius cucurbitae similiter apponendae. et usque ad declinationem passionis alternis diebus cibus dandus, vel si viribus fuerint aegrotantes fatigati, erunt cotidie nutriendi.

60   at si passio declinaverit, cerotaria apponenda et in oleum vel
in calidam et oleum deponendum atque fovendum corpus. tunc
varius cibus dandus adiectis oleribus, tunc piscibus et volantum
carnibus. dehinc etiam lavacrum adhibendum, atque pomorum
quicquam dandum, dehinc vinum. servandus etenim magis est
supra dictorum counatus atque coacervatus usus ob passionis
difficultatem.

at si quisquam ex apoplexia liberatus aliquas corporis partes
paralysi vitiaverit, harum curationem ex libris quos De tardis
passionibus scribentes docebimus sumendam iubemus. eos vero
qui membranae vulneratione in hanc passionem cadunt ita
curandos monemus ut inferius demonstrabimus.

61 VI. DE CONDUCTIONE, QUAM GRAECI SPASMON
VOCANT, ET DISTENTIONE, QUAM TETANON
APPELLANT, ET EARUM SPECIEBUS

CONSEQUENS est de conductione atque distentione et earum
speciebus dicere. utraque igitur passio ab accedente[1] no-

---

[20] *secl. Schmid Mn 148*

[1] *fort. scrib.* accidenti (-te R); *cf. Chr. iii. 90, 96*

---

7. I.e., during a remission.

8. *Chr.* ii. 17 ff.

9 the point of death; for then no matter can issue forth, since the body, bereft of its strength, cannot give egress to the blood, despite the fact that the vein is opened.

Do not give food until the end of the first three-day period; at that time apply a warm ointment, warm the body with sponges wrung out of hot water, and give the patient gruel-like food, such as bread soaked in hot water or mead. And if the bowels do not function, employ a simple clyster and apply cups, with scarification, to the back of the head and the whole spine. This should be done at the time we have often indicated.[7] Use sponges to apply heat, employ relaxing poultices, shave the patient's entire head, and apply cups symmetrically at many of its parts. Feed the patient on alternate days until the decline of the disease, but if his strength is exhausted give him nourishment every day.

50 Now if the disease declines, apply cerates and immerse and foment the body in olive oil or in warm water and olive oil. Then give the patient varied food, adding vegetables, then fish, and the flesh of birds. Thereafter bathing may be prescribed. Some fruit may also be given, and finally wine. But we must not prescribe all these foods and treatments at one and the same time because of the difficult character of the disease.

And if a patient is cured of apoplexy but remains paralyzed in certain parts of his body, treat these parts in accordance with what we shall set forth in our work *On Chronic Diseases*.[8] And treat those cases of apoplexy which result from an injury to the membrane [of the brain] in the manner to be indicated below.[9]

61 ## VI. SPASM (GREEK *SPASMOS*) AND TETANUS (GREEK *TETANOS*) AND THEIR VARIOUS FORMS[1]

IT IS appropriate now to discuss spasm and tetanus and the forms in which they appear. Each of these conditions derives

9. This discussion is not found; the chapter may be incomplete.

1. Though the matter is somewhat confused by such phrases as *utraque passio* (61), it seems that Soranus considered *spasmos* (*conductio*) and *tetanos* (*distentio*) as forms of one basic disease. The difference in outward appearance—contraction in the one case and extension in the other—gave rise to the different terms (but cf. 69). I have used 'spasm' and 'tetanus' in translating, employing the English form of the original Greek terms. But here, as always, these terms are not to be considered in the light of their modern connotations. 'Convulsion' might also have been employed as a translation of *spasmos* (*conductio*).

men sumpsit, conductio a conducendo atque contrahendo, extentio ab extentione patientium partium. sed eius species sunt
emprosthotonia et opisthotonia, quas nos pronum raptum atque
supinum appellare poterimus, alterum ab eo[2] quod in anteriora
conductionem facit, alterum quod ad posteriora.

62   sed antecedentes causae supra dictarum passionum sunt hae:
percussus maiorum nervorum, quos tenontas appellant, vel supra ipsos iacendi iugis positio duris incumbens suppositis, vel
grave quicquam cervicibus impositum, vel meracum potum, aut
profunda perfrictio, aut ut saepe contingit vulneratio nervorum
vel musculorum, atque vinum iisdem vulneribus manentibus potum vel frigidum. et magis eo tempore quo sordibus carentia
purgari vulnera videntur vel in cicatricem venientia saepissime
raptus occurrit; aliquando etiam celerius, hoc est adhuc vulneribus in tumore constitutis.

63   est autem iuxta diffinitionis formam conductio, quam spasmon
Graeci appellant, involuntaria tensio atque conductio partium
cum vehementia[3] et acuto dolore ob stricturae nimietatem. distentionem autem, quam tetanon vocant, Asclepiadis sectatores
dicunt extentionem corporum, ut alii vero[3a] partium: nescii quomodo etiam voluntate tendimus quasdam partes, et in his qui
satyriasi vexantur vel podagra extensio est genitalium partium
vel pedum, nec tamen distentio quam Graeci tetanon vocant.
alii aiunt distentionem esse tensionem musculorum secundum
colla atque buccarum,[4] quos siagonitas vocant, cum tensione ac
64 dolore effecta. alii nostrae sectae scriptores pro tensione conclusionem vocaverunt, sub alio nomine id ipsum significantes. hanc
enim causam passionis esse voluerunt.

sed his omnibus communiter respondendum est quomodo
causa a passione plurimum differt. dicendum est igitur non

[2] ab eo *Barth 1742*: habeo *G*

[3] *fort.* vehementi

[3a] ut alii vero] aut aliquarum *Haller*   [4] buccas *Rm*

its name from a symptom, spasm (*conductio*) from the contraction (*conducendo*) and drawing-together of the parts affected, tetanus (*extentio*) from the stretching of the parts.[2] Tetanus also appears in two special forms, emprosthotonia and opisthotonia, which we may translate *pronus raptus* (procurvation) and *supinus raptus* (recurvation), respectively, for the former draws the patient forward and the latter backward.

2   The antecedent causes of spasm and tetanus are as follows: a blow upon the large sinews (Greek *tenontes*), pressure resulting from lying upon them for a long time in the same position with something hard underneath, the placing of a heavy load upon the neck and shoulders, the drinking of strong wine, a heavy cold, or, as often happens, injury to the sinews or muscles, and the drinking of wine, particularly cold wine,[3] before these wounds are completely healed. And the seizure is more likely to occur at the time when wounds appear to be clean and free from foreign matter, or about to form a scar. But sometimes the attack comes sooner, that is, when the wounds are still in a state of inflammation.

3   To put it in the form of a definition, spasm (Greek *spasmos*) is the involuntary tension and contraction of the parts, with severe and acute pain, by reason of a pronounced state of stricture. On the other hand, tetanus (Greek *tetanos*) is defined by Asclepiades and his followers as a stretching of the body, and by others as a stretching of its parts. But they are unaware that we also stretch certain parts voluntarily. Furthermore, in cases of satyriasis and podagra there is tension of the genitals and of the feet, respectively, but this is not the stretching which the Greeks call *tetanos*. Others define tetanus as a stretching, accompanied by painful rigidity, of the muscles of the neck and those of the jaws
4   (Greek *siagonitae*). Some writers of our own sect speak of 'blocking'[4] instead of 'stretching,' using another name to indicate the same thing, since they hold that this blocking is the cause of the disease.

But our general answer to all such attempts is that the cause of a disease is very different from the disease itself, and it is our

2. In particular, of the neck.

3. Possibly 'or anything cold.'

4. Or 'locking'; cf. our term 'lockjaw.'

quae causa sit distentionis, sed quae sit distentio. etenim causa
siquidem sit occulta discrepat, atque pro captu mentis signorum[5]
varia esse invenitur. ea vero quae concurrunt passioni, hoc est[6]
conductioni, prompta atque manifesta et omnibus intelligibilia
65 esse probantur. et est tentandum, ubi res patiuntur, ⟨ut⟩ ex[7] his
quae non discrepant disciplinam tradamus.

secundum nos igitur distentio est[8] sive extentio, quam ut supra diximus tetanon Graeci vocaverunt, involuntaria[9] tensio,
recto atque inflexibili porrecta cremento collorum ob vehementem stricturam sive tumorem; raptus vero posterganeus, quem
opisthotonon Graeci vocant, est involuntaria retractio[10] ob nimiam stricturam sive tumorem; pronus item raptus, quem
Graeci emprosthotonon vocaverunt, inclinatio colli in anteriores
partes involuntaria ob vehementem tumorem sive stricturam.
66 sed involuntaria haec dicta sunt ad discretionem eorum qui voluntate sua colla hoc schemate componunt; ob tumorem autem
sive stricturam ad discretionem ⟨eorum⟩[11] qui ligationibus tor-
mentuosis[12] organi eas partes positas habent.

tentantibus igitur in has passiones devenire haec obveniunt:
difficilis cervicis motus, iugis oscitatio et magis loqui[13] volentibus, sequitur etiam non sine dolore iacendi positio, atque nervorum maiorum, quos tenontas appellant, levis tentio et durities, punctio interpellans ex spina usque ad occipitium, atque
67 bibendi difficilis transvoratio, contemptibilis tamen, temporum
dolor et magis eo tempore crescens quo hiscere atque os aperire
voluerint patientes, auditus gravis, linguae impedimentum et
imprompta locutio, salivarum fluor continuus, surarum atque
vestigiorum dolidus sensus, et sine ratione veluti ridens vultus
cum quadam mobilitate suarum partium.

ascendente passione atque erumpente, distentio dura et durities partium fiet cum dolore vehementi colli atque musculorum
qui buccas colligant, rubor vultus et colligatio supradictorum

---

[5] ⟨ac⟩ signis *Rm*

[6] haec esse *G: corr. A*

[7] amandum, ut vires patiuntur, ex *G: corr. Schmid Mn 148, coll. Chr. iv. 130*

[8] est *transp. R post* involuntaria *infra*

[9] involuntaria ⟨colli⟩ *R*   [11] *add. R*

[10] retractio *A*: refractio *G*   [12] tormentuosi *R*

[13] loqui *Triller Clinotechnia 54, coll. Gariop. v. 2 (cf. Aurel., p. 721. 16; Schmid 66):*
locis *G*

task to say not what the cause of tetanus is but what tetanus itself is. For the cause, being beyond positive knowledge, is the
subject of disagreement; and, in fact, various causes are assigned
in accordance with various interpretations of the outward signs.
But the actual indications of the disease, that is, of the spasm,
65 are manifest, obvious, and perceptible to all. And we must strive,
if possible, to base our teaching upon facts about which there is
no disagreement.

We must therefore define the stiffening or stretching, which,
as we said above, the Greeks call *tetanos*, as an involuntary
straining of the neck and its rigid prolongation straight upward,
because of a pronounced state of stricture or inflammation.
Again, tetanic recurvation (Greek *opisthotonos*) is an involuntary bending back, also due to a pronounced state of stricture or
inflammation; and tetanic procurvation (Greek *emprosthotonos*)
is an involuntary bending forward of the neck, likewise due to
66 severe inflammation or stricture. We specify that these conditions are involuntary, to distinguish them from cases where the
neck is voluntarily held in such a position; and we specify that
these conditions are due to inflammation or a state of stricture,
to distinguish them from cases where the body is shackled to an
instrument of torture and twisted into such a position.

Persons who are about to lapse into these diseases show the
following signs: difficulty in moving the neck; frequent gaping,
especially when they wish to speak; some pain in lying; slight
tension and stiffness of the large sinews (Greek *tenontes*); an intermittent pricking sensation from the spine to the back of the
head; some difficulty in swallowing liquid, but not very pro-
67 nounced; pain in the temples, increasing particularly when the
patient has a desire to open his mouth in yawning; hearing impaired; tongue impeded; speech not fluent; continuous flow of
saliva; painful sensation in the calves and soles; a sort of expression of laughter without any reason, the parts of the face retaining their mobility.[5]

As the disease emerges and breaks forth, the parts become
very tense and stiff. There is severe pain in the neck and the
muscles that control the jaws; also flushing of the face, contraction of the aforesaid muscles, a firm clenching or fixed setting-to-

5. Possibly the reference is to a twitching of the parts of the face.

musculorum, dentium quoque concubitus, hoc est incumbens
68 confixio, sudor plurimus, articulorum frigidus torpor, pulsus
obscurus, extensio colli, spiratio difficilis, contractio crurum atque manuum et infusi et destillati liquoris in os recursio per
nares fiet, quibusdam etiam mentis alienatio cum celerrima spiratione sequetur, gutturis et pectoris stridor.

sed tetanicis recto ductu distenta magis videntur colla atque
ita ut inflexibilia fiant. opisthotonicis vero contractus ad poste-
riores partes fiet cum nimia tensione atque dolore dorsi et clunium; his etiam crura conducuntur et neque manus distenduntur. digitos conductos atque implicitos habent, ut Hippocrates
ait, et maiorem digitum, hoc est pollicem, cum ceteris tenent,
69 ut frequentius contingit. se quoque continere non possunt, sed
quadam mobilitate resiliunt cum dolor irruerit. hi sunt peiores
tetanicis, et omnes ab alteris, quoties non sine vulnere sed in
vulneribus propriorum ac salutarium locorum his fuerint affecti
passionibus. emprosthotonicis autem colla conducuntur in anteriorem partem atque mentum pectori configitur; tenduntur
ilia et praecordia cum frequenti delectatione urinae egerendae et
difficili flexu digitorum.

liberari vero ex his omnibus difficile est aegrotantes si in vulneribus spasmus emerserit, vel si spinae fuerit innata durities.
70 at si sine vulneribus[14] spasmus irruerit, facilius liberantur. febrem vero secundum Hippocratem in spasmum venientem salutarem accipimus, spasmum autem in febrem perniciosum, quamquam ⟨alii⟩[15] eius excludant sententiam dicentes quia secundum
ipsum febres corpora gravant, multo magis geminant incommodum cum vehementibus doloribus. laxat enim, inquiunt, tumorem naturalis ac mediocris fervor; febrium vero acer et contra naturam immodicus vexat. quapropter ex minutione eorum
quae passionis sunt spem futurae sanitatis melius accipimus.

[14] vulneribus *Schmid Mn 148, coll. Aurel., p. 722. 24*: febribus *edd.*

[15] *supplevi*

gether of the teeth, copious sweat, cold numbness of the limbs,
58 pulse indistinct, neck stretched, respiration painful, and cramp
in legs and hands. Liquid introduced into the mouth by dripping
flows back by way of the nostrils. In some cases there occur mental disturbance, very rapid respiration, and wheezing in the
throat and chest.

In cases of ['upright'] tetanus the neck is usually found to be
stretched directly upward and in such a way as to be quite rigid.
But in cases of opisthotonos the stretching is backward, with
great pain and tension in the back and loins. The legs are drawn
up and the hands, too, are unextended. The patients hold their
hands clenched with fingers folded in, as Hippocrates says. It
frequently happens that they hold the large finger, that is, the
69 thumb, with the other fingers. They cannot remain in a normal
position but quickly snap back when the attack seizes them.
These cases are more deadly than those of ['upright'] tetanus.
And all cases in which the patient incurs this disease in any form
while suffering from a wound in an important and vital part are
graver than otherwise. And in cases of emprosthotonos the neck
is drawn forward and the chin is firmly fixed upon the chest, the
flanks and precordia are tense, there is frequent desire to discharge urine, and the fingers can be bent only with difficulty.

Patients hardly ever recover from any of these forms of disease, if the spasm supervenes upon a wound or if the stiffness
70 originates in the spine. But if the spasm occurs apart from any
wound, recovery is easier. Now Hippocrates, as we know, holds
that fever supervening upon spasm is a favorable sign, while
spasm supervening upon fever is a deadly sign.[6] Others, however,
reject this view, holding that, according to Hippocrates himself,
fever burdens the body, greatly aggravates the illness, and en-
tails considerable distress. For, they say, natural warmth in
moderation relaxes congestion, but the heat of fever, being
sharp, unnatural, and excessive, aggravates inflammation. We
shall therefore do better to rest our hopes for the patient's future
recovery on the abatement of the conditions connected with the
disease.[7]

6. Cf. *Aph.* ii. 26.

7. I.e., rather than on the coming of fever.

71   VII. QUOMODO DISCERNIMUS RAPTUM, QUEM
GRAECI SPASMON VOCANT, A TREMORE
ATQUE SALTU

Discernens raptum a tremore atque saltu Demetrius Herophili sector in corporibus inquit raptu vexatis motum
fieri per extentionem atque conductionem, in iis vero qui tremore afficiuntur agitatione crebra, item in his qui saltu afficiuntur levabilem et possibilem[1] motum fieri indicavit,[2] et magis in
partibus sensibilibus ac nervis qui voluntario motu subiecti
72 sunt. spasmum vero etiam in colligationibus membrorum fieri
sensit, et non solum in quibusdam sensibilibus partibus, verum
etiam in his quae sensu carent. atque ita inquit gaudio quaedam
membra saltum sustinere, quaedam vero numquam; item senectute tremorem fieri non raptum asseruit. addendum tamen quomodo sine ulla distentione saltus movetur atque tremor efficitur;
cum tensione autem vehementi raptus membrorum fiet.

item secundum Asclepiadem extensio atque conductio par-
73 tium tarda et perseverans esse perspicitur, spasmus vero bre-
vissimi temporis et celerrimi tremor. sed saltum ab his discernentes quidam Asclepiadis sectatores aiunt non extensione vel
conductione fieri, sed levatione[3] ac depositione. quod quidam
non consenserunt. etenim ex tanta levatione[3] inquiunt atque
depositione ⟨quam⟩[4] sustinent, aeque[5] levata ut[6] deposita, extentionem atque incurvationem vel flexum ⟨fieri⟩[7] probant. hos
denique motus manuum, quos ita fieri perspicimus, medium
aiunt esse saltum raptus atque tremoris magnitudine ac[8] distantia temporis; iugem extentionem atque conductionem in tre-
74 more fieri magis quam in saltu, raram vero in raptu; item par-

---

[1] cf. impossibili Chr. ii. 87: pulsabilem Rm: passibilem Haller: an ponibilem vel
deponibilem vel (de)positivum (cf. 73)?

[2] an iudicavit?

[3] lavatione G: corr. R

[4] add. R

[5] aeque Rm: atque G: eaque Almeloveen

[6] ac Rm: aut Almeloveen

[7] add. R

[8] ac A (cf. 74 fin.): hac G

I

VII. HOW TO DISTINGUISH SPASM (GREEK SPASMOS) FROM TREMOR AND SALTUS[1]

IN DISTINGUISHING spasm[2] from tremor and saltus, Demetrius the Herophilean declares that in bodies attacked by spasm the motion takes place by way of extension and contraction, while in those attacked by tremor the motion takes place by repeated shaking. Again, in cases of saltus Demetrius points out that the motion is one of rising and falling and takes place especially in sensitive parts and in sinews that are moved voluntarily.

72 He is aware that spasm, on the other hand, takes place also in ligaments of various parts of the body, and not merely in sensitive parts, but also in those lacking sensation. Certain parts, he says, experience saltus with a feeling of pleasure; but other parts never experience saltus at all. And he declares that it is tremor, not spasm, that is caused by old age. It should be added, however, that saltus and tremor take place without any tension, whereas parts affected by spasm undergo a severe tension.

According to Asclepiades, [alternate] extension and contrac-
73 tion of parts is a chronic and persistent condition; but spasm is a tremor of very short and swift duration. Now some followers of Asclepiades distinguish saltus from these other cases, and declare that it involves not extension and contraction but raising and lowering. Other followers of Asclepiades do not agree. They assert that, as a result of so much raising and lowering to which the parts are subjected in equal degree,[3] a tension and a bending or flexion also take place. Thus, they say, the cases in which we observe the hands rise and fall in this way are cases of saltus midway between spasm and tremor with respect both to the extent of the motion and to the frequency of alternation. They hold that extension and contraction alternate more frequently
74 in tremor than in saltus and quite infrequently in spasm; also

1. The terminology in this chapter is as follows:

Greek	Latin	English
spasmos	raptus (but generally conductio in chap. 6)	spasm (or convulsion)
tromos	tremor	tremor
palmos	saltus	saltus

2. Or 'convulsion' (see 61 n.). Observe that here raptus (spasmos) is used both for what appears outwardly as a contraction and for what appears outwardly as an extension. This is somewhat at variance with the usage in the preceding chapter.

3. Or possibly 'in rapid succession.' The text of the whole sentence is uncertain.

vam extentionem ac conductionem in tremore, maiorem vero in
saltu, item ingentem in raptu. dehinc nomen quoque dicunt
communius esse atque late diffusum saltum; solemus etiam[9]
cordis saltum vocare et arteriarum motum. Hippocrates denique inquit frontis venas saltum sustinere, et neque tremor in
his partibus fiet, est enim passio nervorum. sed his respondendum est oportere etiam venas atque arterias et raptu vexari
atque tremore affici, quantum in ipsis est, siquidem etiam motus
earundem partium alios atque alios fieri magnitudine atque
temporis distantia differentes[10] videamus.

VIII. DE CURATIONE

75

Aegrotantes iacere oportet loco sufficientis magnitudinis,
lucido mediocriter atque calido, nullo etiam odore infecto,
mollibus atque calidis stramentis. prima enim celeritatis morborum mitigatio est straminum mollities. dehinc sine cibo facimus[1] aegrotos usque ad primam diatriton, si vires permiserint,
summo cum silentio iacentes. tum lanis mollibus ac mundis
oleo dulci et calido infusis colla circumtegemus et buccarum
musculos, quos siagonitas vocant, et maiores nervos cervicis
(tenontas appellant), tum clunes atque omne quod doluerit. sed
ob permanentem fervorem erunt extrinsecus apponendi saccelli
vel cuiusquam materiae vaporationes aut vesicae oleo calido
repletae aut panni calidi aut, ut supradictum est, saccelli lini
semine torrido pleni vel cantabro fervente aqua et oleo decocto.
articulos quoque manibus tenentes calefacimus, et sudorem ob
pressuram ac turborem venientem pannis calidis excipimus.
frigescit enim permanens et consensu partium [in] passionem
geminat.[2]

76

9 *fort.* enim

10 differenter G: *corr. Rm*

1 facimus ⟨durare⟩ R: *fort.* linquimus

2 consensum partium in passionem germinat G: *corr. R*

---

4. Greek *palmos*.

5. Soranus does not explicitly state what his own views are on the distinction in the
terms *spasmos*, *tromos*, and *palmos*. It is even doubtful whether the sentence beginning

that the *amount* of extension and contraction is small in cases of tremor, greater in cases of saltus, and very great in cases of spasm. And they point out that the term 'saltus' is quite general and has a wide usage, being customarily applied also to the throbbing of the heart and the pulsation of the arteries. Again, Hippocrates declares that the blood vessels of the forehead are subject to saltus[4] [i.e., pulsation] and that no tremor takes place in these parts, tremor being an affection of the sinews. Our answer to these views, however, is that veins and arteries may also be subjected to attacks of spasm and tremor, so far as their nature permits. For it is obvious that, even in the case of the same parts, motions take place from time to time that differ in intensity and in their frequency of alternation.[5]

5   VIII. THE TREATMENT [OF SPASM AND TETANUS][1]

HAVE the patient lie in a room that is sufficiently large, moderately light and warm, and free from odors. See that the bed is soft and warm, for the first step in relieving the acuteness of these diseases is to provide the patient with a soft bed. Have the patient fast until the end of the first three-day period, if his strength permits, and have him lie perfectly quiet. Using soft, clean wool dipped in warm sweet olive oil, cover the patient's neck, the muscles of the jaw (Greek *siagonitae*), the large sinews of the neck (Greek *tenontes*), the loins, and, in fact, every painful
6 part. In order to maintain the heat, place small bags outside [the covered parts] and use any suitable substance to give off heat, or apply bladders filled with hot olive oil, or warm cloths. The small bags just mentioned may, for this purpose, be filled with hot flaxseed or bran that has been cooked in hot water and olive oil. Also warm the extremities by holding them with the hands, and use warm cloths to soak up the sweat which results from the patient's seizure and his agitation. For if this sweat is not removed, it grows cold and, through a sympathetic affection of the parts, aggravates the disease.

---

addendum tamen (72) sets forth his view or that of Demetrius. Perhaps the chapter as we have it is incomplete.

1. Though the treatment here described is ostensibly for spasm or convulsion generally, the emphasis is on tetanus in its various forms.

at si vehementes fuerint dolores, erit adhibenda phlebotomia
dimissionis tempore atque ante tertium diem, si passio coegerit;
si minus, in ipsa diatrito aut post ipsam viribus permittentibus.
77 tunc ⟨os⟩³ colluere aqua calida permittimus et potum accipere.
in ipsa vero diatrito oleo dulci atque calido et mulso corpus
omne perungemus, ora etiam aqua calida foventes. tunc cibo
nutrimus sorbili atque tenui ex alica vel amylo aut pane ex mulso vel pane insucato ex eodem mulso. oportet enim etiam cibum
ebibi potius quam masticari ob dentium conclusionem, quam
leviter digitis aperire tentabimus prohibentes ligneos, ut plerique
adhibent, cuneos. etenim quassationem partium atque indigna-
78 tionem faciunt toto tempore cibi sumendi permanentes. tum
ceteris diebus ea quae fovimus cataplasmatibus curamus, dehinc
etiam spinam totam lini semine cum polline et faenugraeci semine, singularibus vel commixtis, ex aqua mulsa cataplasmamus, superponentes extrinsecus quicquam de supra memoratis
calefactionibus, quo possint cataplasmata multo tempore calida
permanere. item per clysterem oleum calidum inicimus vel calidam et oleum aut aquam in qua fuerit decoctum semen faenugraeci vel radix agrestis malvae. simul etenim et stercora detrahimus prementia⁴ et tumentes partes fovendo relaxamus.
79 utimur praeterea cucurbitis, et magis cum passio sumpserit
statum, sed in accessione levibus, in dimissione vero etiam scarificatione adiecta. erunt autem infigendae occipitio et collo, sed
aliquando ante impositas cucurbitas expressas spongias ex aqua
calida et oleo aut decoctione faenugraeci aut lini seminis aut
hibisci apponemus. apta etenim vehementer ex his vaporatio
lentescentis liquoris nervis⁵ laxandis accipitur, et quae musculos
buccarum, quos siagonitas vocant, sit sufficiens relaxare. tunc
80 post vaporationem cataplasmatibus utendum. aliqui denique
non sine ratione commoti etiam teneris et exercitis pellibus agnorum vel haedorum oleo calido tinctis atque madefactis loca
patientia vaporaverunt.

³ *supplevi*

⁴ praeminentia G: *corr. Rm*

⁵ lentescenti liquori ⟨ac⟩ nervis R

---

2. Here the term 'light' (*levibus* = κουφαῖς) seems to be equivalent to 'without
scarification.'

Now if the pains are severe, perform venesection at the time of a remission; this should be done before the third day if the case is urgent, otherwise at the end of the three-day period or even thereafter, the patient's strength permitting. The patient may then wash his mouth with warm water, and he may take some to drink. At the end of the three-day period anoint the whole body with warm sweet olive oil and diluted honey, and foment the face with warm water. Then give the patient a thin gruel made from spelt groats, starch, or bread with mead, the bread being thoroughly steeped in the mead. For the food should be capable of being sipped up rather than chewed, because the teeth are shut tightly. Try, however, to open the teeth gently with the fingers, but do not use wooden wedges, as many writers advise, for if they remain inserted for the whole period of feeding they cause concussion and injury. On succeeding days apply poultices to the parts previously fomented, and then also to the whole spine. As poultices, use flaxseed with flour or fenugreek seed, either separately or mixed together, in hydromel. To keep the poultices hot a long time, place over them any of the aforementioned preparations for giving off heat. Also inject a clyster of warm olive oil, or warm water and olive oil, or water in which fenugreek seed or marsh mallow root has been cooked. For in this way the pressing fecal matter is removed, and at the same time the inflamed parts are relaxed by the fomentation.

Employ cupping too, and particularly when the disease has reached its highest stage. During an attack use only mild[2] cupping, but during a remission scarify the flesh in connection with the cupping. Attach the cups to the back of the head and to the neck; but, before putting the cups in place, it is sometimes well to apply sponges wrung out of hot water and olive oil, or a decoction of fenugreek seed, flaxseed, or marsh mallow. For the heat of the viscous fluid obtained from these substances is very suitable for relaxing the sinews;[3] it also serves to relieve the tension of the muscles of the jaws (*siagonitae*). Then after the application of heat employ poultices. Some physicians on reasonable grounds also warm the affected parts with thin, well-worked lamb skins or kid skins immersed and soaked in warm olive oil.

3. Or, with the reading of *R:* 'the heat from these substances is very suitable for the removal of viscous liquid matter and for relaxing the sinews.'

damus etiam oleum calidum ore continendum et quamquam
omni tempore conveniat, magis tamen cum cataplasmata apponimus hoc probamus faciendum, quo ex interioribus quoque
buccarum colligatio laxatur, cibum dantes alternis diebus donec
passio declinet, si vires aegrotantis permiserint. in iisdem perseverabimus, solam aquam calidam vel mulsum calidum dimissionis tempore offerentes.

81   tunc cum ex parte passionem mitigatam senserimus, embasim
olei vel aquae et olei adhibemus, cuius rationem atque ordinem
libris Specialium adiutoriorum docebimus. dehinc cotidianis diebus humaniore cibo nutrimus, praecaventes etiam nunc dura
quaeque ac difficilis transvorationis dare mandenda, sed magis
pultes offerentes vel olera vel cerebra vel pisces teneros et omne
quod facile accipi ac digeri potest, ne ob vehementem masticatio-
nem naturales colligationes buccarum, quas Graeci chalinos vo-
82 cant, moveantur. erunt praeterea loca ipsa quae patiuntur cerotario curanda ex oleo dulci vel cyprino confecto, item diachylon
medicamento, et quod appellant Mnaseu.[6] tunc etiam acopis
utemur quae fiunt ex amylo atque adipe et ex infusionibus ac decoctionibus faenugraeci et lini seminis et his similibus. tunc lavacrum adhibemus, praecaventes aquam frigidam. dehinc dabimus etiam vinum, ut saepe docuimus, qualitate atque natura et
quantitate congruum.

83   veterum medicorum Erasistratus tetanicam passionem non
memoravit. Herophilus vero nihil plus inquit nisi quod vehemens opisthotonia rectiora faciat ea quae nodorum spinae evul-
sione arcuata videntur, et quod febricula irruens passionem solvat. item Serapion primo libro Curationum sic inquit curandos
tetanicos quemadmodum phreniticos, quapropter sumendae
sunt contra ipsum responsiones quas de phreniticis dicentes docuimus. item ex his curationem huiusmodi passionis tradiderunt.[7]

---

[6] Mnasei *G*

[7] *fort.* item ⟨alii⟩ ex his c. h. p. tradiderunt *vel* etenim ex his c. h. p. tradidit

---

4. That Soranus wrote διὰ μυελοῦ ('of marrow'), which was, in the course of tradition, corrupted to δι' ἀμύλου ('of starch'), is shown by a comparison with Aurelius 20
(see also *Chr.* ii. 26). On the basis of this and other evidence Schmid concluded (p. 56)
that the part of Aurelius dealing with acute diseases is not an abridgment of Caelius

And give the patient some warm olive oil to keep in his mouth. Though this is always proper, it is particularly recommended when the poultices are applied, so that the corners of the mouth may be soothed from within too. Give the patient food on alternate days, if his strength permits, until the disease is in its declining phase. Continue the same foods as described above, and give him only warm water or warm mead at times of remission.

Then when the disease is found to have abated in part, give the patient a bath in olive oil or in water and olive oil. We shall give an account of the bath and its preparation and use in our treatise *On Special Remedies*. Later the patient may be fed every day and with a more liberal diet; but anything tough or hard to swallow should still be avoided. He should rather be given porridges, vegetables, brains, or tender fish, or, in fact, anything that can be taken in and digested easily. The purpose is to avoid intense chewing, which would require excessive motion of the corners of the mouth (Greek *chalinoe*). In addition, a cerate made with sweet olive oil or henna oil may be applied to the parts affected; also the plaster of juices and the so-called plaster of Mnaseas. And then restorative ointments made of starch,[4] fat, infusions and decoctions of fenugreek seed and flaxseed, or substances like these may be used. Then prescribe bathing but avoid the use of cold water. Finally, give the patient wine of suitable nature and quality and in the proper amount, as we have often indicated.

Among the ancient physicians, Erasistratus fails to mention the disease of tetanus. And Herophilus says merely that a severe attack of opisthotonos tends to straighten out the [normal] curvature in the line of spinal vertebrae; and that an attack of fever breaks up the disease. Serapion in Book I of his work *On Treatments* declares that tetanus is to be treated in the same manner as phrenitis. Therefore, the same objections that we raised against his views in our discussion of phrenitis may now be raised again. [Others] of this sect[5] have also set forth a treatment for this type of disease.

Aurelianus, as had been held by Daremberg, but goes back to Methodist sources independently of Caelius.

5. I.e., Empirics. But the text is uncertain, and, in fact, there is no specific reference to Serapion in the section on phrenitis. Perhaps: 'for his treatment of tetanus is taken from his treatment of phrenitis.'

Hippocrates libro quem Ad sententias cnidias scripsit cerotario inquit ungendos opisthotonicos et aqua calida eorum crura
84 fovenda. iacere iubet in lineis stramentis utens ad ventrem movendum collyriis, quae appellavit balanos, et potionibus ex radice bryoniae et dauco atque vino confectis. offert praeterea farinam coctam tepentem in partem cibi, ut saepissime facit, permittens etiam vinum superbibendum quando voluerint aegrotantes. tetanicos vero phlebotomat, non advertens adhibendam
vere phlebotomiam, sed non solam. non enim dignum atque
sufficiens tantae passionis unum adiutorium esse probatur. item
collyria sive balani et potiones supra memoratae et vinum intemporaliter datum patientibus contrarium atque saluti noxium
85 monstratur. talia[8] enim tempore importuno[9] nervis officiunt.

item secundo libro quem De morbis[10] scripsit ait esse aliquando conducibile[11] tetanico sine vulnere effecto atque primaevo
corpore et habitudine vigenti aestatis tempore plurimae frigidae
ablutionem,[12] siquidem fervorem reclamet ac revocet. dat etiam
nigrum helleborum cum pipere, et lacte asinino carne concocto
potat atque sternutamentum commovet. mirandum igitur
quod in his qui tali passione afficiuntur frigida utendum existimat Hippocrates, qui iamdudum ait frigida quaeque esse ini-
86 mica ossibus, nervis, dentibus, et cerebro. sternutamenta etiam
commovere tumores nulli dubium est. item asininum lac nulla
ratione laxare tumentia probatur; dehinc stomachum evertet
siquidem sit tetri odoris et saporis. item helleborum nigrum nervos obsidet atque purgando vel deducendo corpus exagitat.

[8] alia G: corr. Rm

[9] importuna G: corr. Rm

[10] moribus G: corr. R

[11] fort. conducibilem

[12] ablutione G: corr. R

---

6. *Regimen in Acute Disease* (Appendix), I. 166. 6 Kuehl. (= II. 470 Littré).

7. The reference in the Hippocratic text is not to opisthotonos but to a form of
tetanus of the loins, perhaps a kind of emprosthotonos (σφοδρῶς ἔμπροσθεν ἀντισπῶνται).
Perhaps Soranus (Caelius) is thinking of *De morbis* iii. 12–13 (VII. 132–34 Littré),
where tetanus and opisthotonos are successively discussed.

8. Can this be a misinterpretation of πλεῖστον?

9. 'Tetanus of the loins' in the Hippocratic text.

Hippocrates in his book *Against the Cnidian Maxims*[6] declares that in cases of opisthotonos[7] a wax salve should be applied and the patient's legs fomented with warm water. He has the patient lie on linen sheets, and for the purpose of moving the bowels employs suppositories (Greek *balanoe*) and potions prepared with bryony root, Cretan carrot, and wine. He also gives the patient warm cooked meal by way of food, as he often does,[8] and then allows him to drink wine whenever he wishes. He prescribes venesection in cases of tetanus[9] but does not observe that, while venesection should, to be sure, be employed, it should not be employed alone. For a single remedy is obviously unsuitable and inadequate for so serious a disease. Moreover, the suppositories (*balanoe*), the above-mentioned potions, and wine prescribed at the wrong time are clearly unsuitable and impede the patient's recovery. For such remedies given at the wrong time are harmful to the sinews.

Hippocrates also says in Book II of his work *On Diseases*[10] that in a case of tetanus that occurs without a wound, in a young and vigorous person, and in summer time, washing the body with a large amount of cold water is sometimes helpful. For this treatment, he says, brings about a restoration and recovery of heat. He also prescribes black hellebore with pepper, and ass's milk[11] cooked with meat, and he provokes sneezing. Now it is amazing that Hippocrates prescribes the use of cold water in cases of such a disease when he has always held that anything cold is harmful to the bones, sinews, teeth, and brain.[12] And there is no doubt that sneezing aggravates inflammation. Moreover, it is clear that ass's milk does not in any way relax congested parts; in fact, it causes gagging because of its foul odor and taste. Again, black hellebore attacks the sinews and has an agitating effect as it purges and withdraws matter from the body.

10. Unless our text is badly corrupted, Soranus seems to have confused his sources here. The words 'esse aliquid . . . revocet' refer directly to *Aphorisms* v. 21 (IV. 538 Littré) = *De usu liquidorum* 6 (VI. 134 Littré), rather than to *De morbis* iii. 13 (VII. 134 Littré), where only the cold douche is referred to. In fact, it would be tempting to read (*h*)*umoribus* instead of *morbis*—the first edition has *moribus*—were it not that the next sentence 'dat etiam . . . commovet' has nothing to do with the *De usu liquidorum* but in most respects agrees with *De morbis* iii. 12 (VII. 132 Littré).

11. There is no reference to ass's milk in the traditional Greek text.

12. *Aph.* v. 18: 'cold is harmful to bones, teeth, sinews, brain, and spinal marrow; but heat is beneficial.'

Diocles libro quo Passiones atque causas atque curationes scripsit, tetanicis inquit adhibenda mictoria medicamina, quae appellavit diuretica, tum ventrem deducendum atque vacuandum.
dat etiam bibendum passum aquatum pueris vel his qui ex vulnere in passionem ceciderunt. prohibet etiam cibum dari et
87 iubet ea quae passione tenduntur vaporari et emolliri. item tertio libro De curationibus similiter clystere utitur et vinum dulce
dat bibendum, adhibens vaporationes nunc siccas nunc humectas, et ungit cerotario atque lanis patientia contegit loca.

sed ex his primo mictoria vesicam moventia omnes provocant
nervos qui tunc summo atque attento sensu habituantur.[13] dehinc clysteres acerrimi adurendo tumores asperiores efficiunt,
quos adhibendos existimant. est etiam vinum repugnans priusquam passio declinaverit, et[14] quamquam omne, magis tamen
dulce, quod opportune[15] datum inflat. denique etiam sanos et
88 indigestos atque inutiles et implicitos facit. est etiam profecto
peccantius prohibito cibo vinum dare. item vaporationes hu-
midae siccis atque aridis repugnant, et usus cerotariorum soli
passionis declinationi conveniens invenitur.

Praxagoras tertio libro Curationum vaporationibus utitur et
clystere et vomitu. quanta autem vexatio sit vomitus arbitror
superfluum dicere. est enim etiam impossibilis usus eius in his
qui neque ad transvorandum potum os aperire possunt.

Heraclides Tarentinus secundo libro Interiorum passionum
tetanicos et opisthotonicos clystere curat et praepotat iure gallinaceo et lasere, cum primo sint haec ventris inflabilia, item la-
seris virtus acerrima, clysterum vero incendiosa.

89 dehinc Asclepiades secundo libro Celerum vel acutarum passionum incipiente, inquit, dolore tetanicos aqua calida fomentamus, nocte atque die scilicet, ut praeter incongruae qualitatis

---

[13] habitantur G: corr. TLL VI. 2481. 80: agitantur *Almeloveen*
[14] *fort. del.*
[15] ⟨et⟩ opportune *Barth 1743: fort.* inopportune

---

13. Or perhaps merely 'night and day.' Cf. 92.

Diocles in his book *On Diseases and Their Causes and Treatment* says that drugs which promote urination (Greek *diurētica*) should be given in cases of tetanus. He then prescribes the purging and evacuation of the bowels. He gives raisin wine mixed with water where the disease occurs in children or as the result of a wound. He withholds food and prescribes heating and emollient remedies for those parts that are made tense by the disease. 87 Again, in Book III of his work *On Treatments* he similarly prescribes clysters, gives sweet wine to drink, employs heat both dry and moist, and smears the affected parts with a cerate and covers them with woolen cloths.

But, in the first place, the diuretics, in affecting the bladder, excite all the fibers that are then most sensitive and strained. Furthermore, the clysters that he thinks should be applied are very sharp and by their burning action increase the intensity of the inflammations. Again, wine is harmful before the disease declines. And though all wine, even when given at the proper time, causes congestion, this is particularly true of sweet wine; in fact, it spoils the digestion even of healthy persons and makes 88 them sluggish and confused. And surely it is worse to give the patient this wine than to give him the food that Diocles withholds. Moreover, the applications of moist heat go counter to those of dry; and the use of cerates is found to be suitable only in the declining phase of the disease.

Praxagoras in Book III of his work *On Treatments* recommends applications of heat, clysters, and emetics. But I think it is unnecessary to point out how much irritation is caused by vomiting. For, as a matter of fact, the use of emetics is impossible in these cases, since the patients are not even able to open their mouths to swallow the potion.

Heraclides of Tarentum in Book II of his work *On Internal Diseases* recommends treating cases of tetanus and opisthotonos with a clyster, and has the patients drink chicken broth and silphium juice. But these substances cause abdominal flatulence; in addition, the silphium has very acrid properties and the clyster burns.

89 Asclepiades in Book II of his *Swift* (i.e. acute) *Diseases* says that, when the pain commences in cases of tetanus, fomentations with hot water should be employed—indeed, for a whole night and a day.[13] But, quite apart from the effect of the impact of a

percussum etiam temporis peccato atque immodicae quantitatis
dolentia provocentur, cum sit tunc mitigationis atque blandi-
menti opportunitas.

interea, inquit, saccellis ex milio confectis vel cachry vel salibus, quae quidem sine dubio ob acrimoniam acutis passionibus
sunt contraria, tamquam acre collyrium his qui acutis doloribus
oculorum afficiuntur. hic praeterea etiam inquit aridas vaporationes operantius mederi quam cataplasmata medentur,[16] non
advertens quia tunc nervi ob colligationem tumoris indigent
90 laxamento atque indulgentia, ex siccis autem vaporationibus, ut
etiam ipse confitetur, siccantur et tenuantur et arescunt corpora. convenit etiam, inquit, cataplasma simplex, quod omen
lysin appellant, pueris atque mulieribus, et viris quorum corpora
fuerint dimissa atque molliora vel tenera, cum potuerit id omnibus conveniens dicere. quid enim tam vanum atque, ut ita
dixerim, ridiculum quam ob usum cataplasmatum naturam vel
aetates ac vitae consuetudinem praeservare? dehinc possunt
pueriles aetates vel muliebria corpora non libere educata neque
molliora inveniri, quo fiet ut communiter in omnibus utilissimum
91 cataplasmatis adiutorium prohiberi videatur[17] ob istius errorem
qui non manifestis intentionibus res advertendo falsis curationibus implicatur. adhibet etiam clysteres acerrimos atque vehementius operantes, salutarem putans ex his febrem generari, quo
raptus sive adductio materiae e partibus patientibus ad intestina
fiat. quae igitur maior accusatio esse potest acerrimi clysteris
quam quod febrem facere promittatur? quid enim utile ex eo
sperare possumus ex quo id perficitur quod etiam sine tetanica
passione grave corporibus existimatur?

probat etiam vehementes fervores similis acrimoniae, iubens
saccello sale pleno aqua calida tincto partes quae patiuntur va-
92 porari, tunc duobus cauteribus alternis sales incendi, ut ex ipsis
invadens quaedam spiratio penetret altiora. sed horum acrimoniam iam pridem reprobavimus. idem[18] ignem plurimum accendens et superponens aegrotantem omnes spondylos spinae oleo

---

[16] medentur *om. R*

[17] *hic interpung. edd.*

[18] *fort.* item

harmful substance, the ill-timing of the remedy and its excessive
use aggravate the painful parts, for at that time a soothing and
gentle treatment is required.

Again, he prescribes the application of bags of millet, cachry,
or salt.[14] But, because of their sharpness, these substances are
doubtless as harmful in acute diseases as sharp eye salves are in
cases of acute eye affections. Asclepiades goes on to say that dry
applications of heat are a more effective remedy than poultices.
But he does not understand that in these cases the sinews require relaxation and tender treatment because of the strain im-
90 posed by the inflammation. And, as Asclepiades himself admits, bodies become dry and attenuated from applications of dry
heat. Asclepiades does, to be sure, recommend the simple poultice called *ōmēlysis* for children and women, and for men whose
bodies are flabby, soft, or tender. But he could have said that
this poultice is suitable in all cases. For what is so futile and, if I
may say so, ridiculous as to base the use of poultices upon an observation of the patient's nature, age, or mode of life? Besides,
there are children and women whose bodies are not abundantly
nourished and soft. Thus the universally beneficial remedy of a
91 poultice will apparently have to be barred because of Asclepiades' error, viz., his failure to perceive the obvious effects of
things and his consequent involvement in mistaken treatments.
Asclepiades also prescribes the use of sharp clysters that have a
powerful effect; he believes that these clysters will produce a
beneficial fever which will cause matter to be carried off or withdrawn from the affected parts to the intestines. But what more
serious objection can be raised against a sharp clyster than that
its use is expected to result in a fever? For what useful result can
we expect from a treatment which produces a condition that is
considered harmful to bodies even without tetanus?

Asclepiades also recommends the application of strong heat,
though this, too, has sharpness. He has the affected parts heated
by a bag that has been filled with salt and dipped in hot water.
92 Then, using two iron cauteries alternately, he continues to heat
the salt so that a hot emanation from it may enter the body and
penetrate to its depths. But we have already rejected this sort of
sharp remedy. Asclepiades also kindles a large fire and, placing
the patient close to it, rubs all his spinal vertebrae with oil and

14. I.e., for dry heat.

per diem atque noctem iugiter fricat. at est vehementer culpa-
bile: omnis etenim impressio et tumentia et dolorem geminat.
item iugiter diem atque noctem id facere iubet. usu etiam sanos
potest quadam vexatione in consensum mittere, quippe cum
saepe in uno latere iacentes atque eodem tardantes schemate
93 vexemur. item plurimus ⟨ignis⟩¹⁹ densat; denique etiam in ferventibus lavacris corporis superficies ⟨densari⟩²⁰ perspicitur. et
quid ultra dicam, cum sit recorporativae²¹ virtutis paroptesis,
tetanos autem mitigatione indigeat ob celeritatem sui.

item ait cucurbitam utilem magis quam phlebotomiam huic
probari passioni nisi, inquit, febres prohibuerint materiae detractionem vel in venis plurima fuerit plenitudo. tunc enim erit
phlebotomia adhibenda in ipsa vehementiae summitate. difficile enim inquit detractionem fieri corpusculorum posse tempore
94 dimissionis. sed dicimus contra neque raptum cucurbitae posse
febribus cohiberi, sicut in ipso saepe opere probavimus. neque
melior phlebotomia vel praelatior usus cucurbitae esse potest.
etenim in augmento phlebotomia locum habet, quo tempore cucurbitam adhibere non licet; neque cucurbitae tempore phlebotomiam, quo noxia probatur. tempus etiam phlebotomiae illud
est quod etiam aliorum amputantium adiutoriorum, ut est dimissionis in totius augmento passionis. in accessione enim simpliciter mitigantibus utemur adiutoriis. Asclepiades autem ob
extinctam falsis intentionibus causam neque aptum scire potuit
phlebotomiae tempus.

95   declinante igitur passione aegrotantes nutrit, atque sucis et
sorbilibus cibis. sera igitur si ⟨declinatio⟩²² fuerit, quam expec-
tandam ob nutriendum putat, aut ut saepe contigit post decem
dies effecta, immodica atque interfectrix [ex]²³ tanta abstinentia
iudicatur. dehinc quae aegro adhibenda sint docere neglexit,
utrumne piscium an volantium vel quadrupedum, sed omne genus corruptibile atque inflabile. hic vero linquens vere resump-

¹⁹ *addidi:* ⟨frictionis usus⟩ *R*

²⁰ *addidi, nisi fort. scribas* densari *pro denique supra*

²¹ recorporativae *coni. Schmid Mn 150:* evaporativae *edd.*

²² *add. R*

²³ *om. R*

---

15. Or perhaps merely 'day and night.' So, too, below in this paragraph. Cf. 89.

16. Cf. *Ac.* i. 105.

continues this for a day and a night.[15] But this treatment is strongly to be condemned. For all such pressure irritates the inflamed parts and increases the patient's distress. And he prescribes that the treatment be given continually for a day and a night, though, in fact, he could produce a similar pain in healthy persons by such irritation. For often we feel pain when we merely lie on the same side and in the same position for a long time.

93 Moreover, the use of considerable fire has a condensing effect; and, in fact, even hot baths cause the surface of the body to be condensed. But why need I say more, when it is clear that baking the body has a metasyncritic effect, while tetanus requires soothing treatment because of its acuteness.

Asclepiades also holds that cupping is more suitable in this disease than venesection, unless fever bars the withdrawal of matter [by cupping] or there is a plethora of matter in the veins. And in these latter cases, he says, venesection will have to be employed at the height of the attack, for he considers the withdrawal of the corpuscles[16] hardly possible at the time of remission.

94 But our answer is, first, that the suction of the cups, as we have often indicated in this very work, cannot be checked by fever; and, secondly, that cupping is neither better than venesection nor preferable to it. The fact is that during the increasing phase of a disease venesection is proper but cupping may not be used; on the other hand, venesection may not be used at the time suitable for cupping, for then venesection is harmful. And the proper time for venesection is that which is also proper for other remedies involving a radical removal, namely, a period of remission during the increase of the disease as a whole; for in the period of attack we use remedies that are exclusively soothing. But Asclepiades, because his system was vitiated by mistaken notions, could not know what time was proper for venesection.

95 Again, he gives the patients nourishment during the declining phase of the disease and employs liquids and gruel-like food. But if the decline, which he thinks he must await before giving nourishment, comes late or, in fact, as is often the case, comes after as much as ten days, such a protracted period of starvation is clearly excessive and nothing short of murder. Moreover, he fails to indicate what foods, whether fish, birds, or quadrupeds, are to be given to the patient, but prescribes the entire class of foods that decompose and produce gas. Indeed, he neglects really

tiva[24] adiutoria quae magis fuerant demonstranda, aliena ordinavit. haec sunt quae Asclepiadi respondenda probamus.

96   communiter autem repudianda[25] est omnis alia quaeque[26]
fuerit acrior materia. etenim quidam, sicut Clodius Asclepiadis
sectator memoravit, laser, quem Graeci opon cyrenaicon vocant,
cera involutum bibendum tradiderunt. dant etiam castoreum
praebibendum, et ferulagine cum euphorbio colla perungunt
atque spinam. item plerique superficiem vulnerant ignis ustura,
et ex sinapi atque fico adhibent cataplasma. alii frigida fovent
cum nimiam viderint tensionem, et post perfusionem frigidae
fricant calidis rebus. alii utuntur etiam baccis[27] et thymo et origano et nepeta et hysopo et herba salvia et butyro et cedria et
herba pulicaria et semperviva. ausi etiam quidam iuscellum[28]
ranarum dare.

97   quae omnia prompta atque manifesta peccata probantur.
alia enim ob acrimoniam tumorem provocant, ut euphorbium et
ferulago et laser et sinapi vel his similia; alia constringendo perfectam stricturam contendunt, ut herba pulicaris,[29] quam psyllion[30] vocant, et semperviva, quam aizoon vocant, et aqua frigida. iuscellum[31] autem ranarum experimentum esse dicitur et
est odiosum, in semet nihil habens commodi quod ratio probet.

98   IX. DE HYDROPHOBIA

DEINDE hydrophobia quae nomen sumpsit ab accidenti. est
enim vehemens timor[1] aquae: nam Graeci timorem phobon
vocant, aquam hydor appellant. quidam[2] denique detracta
litera delta adicientes gamma hygrophobiam vocaverunt, quod
omnem liquorem metuat. sed consuetudo magis primum obti-
nuit nomen, siquidem plus aquam timeant aegrotantes vel quod
inter ceteros liquores plurimum praestet. alii quoque phobo-
dipson appellant quod cum timore sitiat. item Polybus pheugy-
dron, siquidem aquam fugiat; nos denique aquifugam dicere poterimus. item Andreas [qui][3] cynolysson vocavit, veluti ex rabie
canina morbum conceptum.

[24] resumptoria *edd.*   [25] repudianda *R*: respondenda *G*: *fort.* reprobanda
[26] quaecumque *Rm*   [27] ⟨lauri⟩ baccis *R*   [28] viscellum *edd.*
[29] pulicaria *Ac. ii. 197, iii. 96, sed* pulicaris *Sor. Lat., p. 69. 21 (Rose)*
[30] silphion *G: corr. R*   [1] tumor *G: corr. R*
[31] viscellum *edd.*   [2] quidam *Schmid Mn 150, Bendz 91*: qui *G*
[3] *om. R: errorem a scriptura* quinolysson *ortum docet Schmid Mn 151*

restorative remedies, which should preferably have been employed, and prescribes, instead, remedies that are unsuitable. So much for our refutation of Asclepiades.

96 And, in general, we must reject the use of any acrid substance whatever. Thus some physicians, according to Clodius the follower of Asclepiades, prescribe the drinking of silphium juice (Greek *opos Cyrenaicos*, 'Cyrenaic juice') mixed with wax. And they prescribe that castor be drunk; also they anoint the neck and spine with thapsia mixed with spurge. Many of them injure the surface of the body with scorching fire, and apply poultices of mustard and fig. Others bathe the patient with cold water, though they see that the condition is one of extreme tension, and after the cold bath they massage him with substances that produce heat. Still others use berries, thyme, marjoram, catnip, hyssop, sage, butter, Syrian cedar oil, fleawort, and houseleek. And some indeed have gone so far as to employ a frog soup.

97 But it is clearly and obviously a mistake to use any of these substances. For some, such as spurge, thapsia, silphium, mustard, and the like, irritate an inflammation by their acrid properties; others, such as fleawort (Greek *psyllion*), houseleek (Greek *aeizōon*), and cold water, by their astringent action make the state of stricture complete. And the frog soup may be called an experiment. It is offensive and brings no advantage which reason can attest.

98 ## IX. HYDROPHOBIA

WE MUST next consider hydrophobia, which takes its name from its characteristic symptom, a violent fear of water; for the Greek word for 'fear' is *phobos*, and for 'water' *hydōr*. Some then substituted the letter gamma for delta and called the disease *hygrophobia* because the fear extends to every liquid.[1] But custom generally preserved the former name because patients fear water more, or perhaps because water is pre-eminent among all the liquids. Some also call the patient *phobodipsos* because he shows both thirst and fear. Polybus calls him *pheugydros*, since he flees from water; and we may translate this term by the Latin *aquifuga*. Andreas calls the disease *cynolyssos* on the ground that it is incurred from a mad dog.

1. Greek *hygros*, 'fluid.'

99　　antecedens[4] autem causa[5] passionis est canis rabidi morsus,
vel, ut[6] quidam memorant, ceterorum quoque animalium quae
sint simili rabie obnoxia, ut luporum, ursorum, leopardorum,
equorum et asinorum, ⟨vel⟩[7] hominum hydrophobarum.[8] quidam denique in hydrophobicam passionem devenerunt solius
aspirationis odore ex rabido cane abducto,[9] cum deflectione[10]
quadam naturalis spiratio vexata venenosum aerem adducit et
vitalibus[11] inserit partibus. item alii rabidi animalis unguibus
laesi in rabiem devenerunt. memoratur denique sic mulierem
in hydrophobicam passionem venisse cui facies fuerit leviter a
100　parvulo catulo lacessita. item quidam a gallo gallinaceo pugnante leviter laesus in rabiem venisse dicitur. sartrix etiam
quaedam cum chlamidem scissam rabidis morsibus sarciendam
sumeret, atque orae[12] stamina componeret lingua et artuum
iuncturas lamberet assuendo,[13] quo transitum acus faceret faci-
liorem, tertia die in rabiem venisse memoratur. est praeterea
possibile sine manifesta causa hanc passionem corporibus in-
nasci, cum talis fuerit strictio sponte generata qualis veneno.[14]
interea post morsum quidam celerius in passionem veniunt, quidam tardius, ideo etiam post annum aut eo amplius afficiuntur,[15]
sed magis plures post quadraginta dies.

101　　　　## X. QUAE EST DIFFINITIO SIVE AGNITIO
HYDROPHOBIAE

EST agnitio hydrophobiae appetentia vehemens atque timor
potus sine ulla ratione ob quandam in corpore passionem.
adiectum est autem 'sine ulla ratione' atque 'ob quandam in
corpore passionem' quod alii timeant potum, ut veneni admixti
suspicione, vel arte providentes quia si intemporaliter sumpserint periclitabuntur. neque ilico hi ratione timentes hydrophobi esse vel dici possunt.

---

[4] antecedens *Schmid Mn 152, Bendz 91*: accendens *edd.*

[5] causā *G: corr. R*　　　　　[6] velut *G: divisim Schmid Mn 152*

[7] *post* asinorum *interpung. edd.: corr. Schmid Mn 152* ⟨vel⟩ *addito*

[8] hydrophoborum *Rm, et sic saepius (99–137), sed cf.* ὑδροφόβας, *nec non* aerophobas,
pantophobas *(108)*

[9] adducto *A*　　　　　[10] defluxione *Triller ap. Kühn 180, coll. Ac. i. 121, fort. recte*

[11] vitalibus *Triller ap Kühn 180, coll. Chr. v. 180*: talibus *G*: principalibus *Rm: fort.*
altioribus *vel* altis

[12] ore *R*　　　　　[13] assugendo *Barth 1743*

[14] qualis e veneno *Rm (sim. A)*: qualia venena *G*

[15] afficiantur *G: corr. R, sed pro* ideo *fort. scrib.* adeo ⟨ut⟩ *vel sim.*

9   The antecedent cause of the disease is the bite of a mad dog
or, as some say, of other animals that are subject to similar madness, such as the wolf, bear, leopard, horse, and ass, or the bite of
a human being who has hydrophobia. But some cases of hydrophobia arise merely from the wafting of an odor from a mad dog,
when normal breathing is vitiated by a chance emanation;[2] poisonous air is then breathed in and distributed to the vital parts.
In some cases the patient is affected by rabies as a result of being
injured by the claws of a rabid animal. And it is related that a
woman became ill of hydrophobia when her face was slightly
0 scratched by a small puppy. Again, a case of rabies is said to
have been caused by a slight scratch of a poultry-cock as it was
struggling.[3] And once when a seamstress was preparing to patch
a cloak rent by the bites of a rabid animal, she adjusted the
threads along the end, using her tongue, and then as she sewed
she licked the edges that were being joined, in order to make the
passage of the needle easier. It is reported that two days later
she was stricken by rabies. Moreover, it is possible for this disease to originate in the body without any visible cause, when a
state of stricture, such as that which comes from poison, is produced spontaneously. Now some incur the disease quickly after
the bite. Others do so more slowly and are affected only after a
year or even longer. But in most cases the disease comes after
forty days.

X. DEFINITION OF HYDROPHOBIA OR MEANS
OF RECOGNIZING THE DISEASE

THE characteristic mark of hydrophobia is a powerful craving
for drink and an irrational fear of it, occasioned by a disease
in the body. The words 'irrational' and 'occasioned by a disease
in the body' are added, for sometimes people are afraid of a drink
because they suspect that poison has been added. Or they may
be purposely exercising caution, knowing that if they drink at
the wrong time their health will be endangered. But these are
rational fears, and people who have them cannot be said to be
suffering from hydrophobia.

2. Possibly: 'by a chance deflection [of the odor].'

3. Or, perhaps, 'of a fighting cock.'

102　XI. QUAE SEQUUNTUR EOS QUI IN HYDRO-
PHOBICAM PASSIONEM PRONI AC
DECLIVES ESSE VIDENTUR

SEQUITUR eos qui in istam passionem proni ac declives esse
noscuntur, cum iam praetangi coeperint, anxietas quaedam
sine ulla ratione, atque iracundia et corporis difficultas in solitos[1]
motus, somnus etiam suspensus atque turbatus, vel vigilia, et
simul cibi corruptio, stomachi gravedo, crurum atque brachiorum
extensio, oscitatio iugis, et impigens[2] lavandi[3] voluntas, insueta
etiam querela aeris tamquam austrini, quamvis serena fuerit
quies, item difficilis toleratio atque taedium et recusatio im-
brium, parva bibendi voluntas contra consuetudinem.

103　obtinente passione, appetentia bibendi atque timor, et primum ad ipsius aquae visum, secundo etiam si eius audierint
sonitum vel nomen, dehinc timor fomentationis olei, pulsus
densus parvus inordinatus, quibusdam febricula, saltus stomachi, torpor atque stupor articulorum, subreptio atque extentio
praecordiorum ad superiores partes, et officii ventris abstentio,
urinae reddendae paulatim frequentatio, tremor atque conductio nervorum, vox obtusa et velut latrabilis, et corporis spirae[4]
similis sive canina involutio, spiratio difficilis, iactatio corporis
omnis ad ingressum hominum, tamquam secum aquam afferen-
tium, rubor vultus atque oculorum, et corporis tenuitas, attestante pallore cum sudore partium superiorum, veretri frequens
tensio cum seminis involuntario iactu, lingua prominens.

104　in ultimo etiam singultus et vomitus fellis, ac frequentius nigri, quibusdam etiam timor[5] manus oculis tenus admotae vel
circumtractae. quidam se agnoscere fatentur[6] esse naturalem
vel consuetum aquae liquorem cum sibi monstratur, sed commoveri cum viderint, ut se ipse quoque Soranus vidisse testatur in
hac passione constitutum sese hortatum liquorem ut sumeret,
nec tamen potuisse. aiunt et militem quendam, ut Artorius

---

[1] in solitos *Bendz Eran 43. 40*: insolitus *G*

[2] pigens *Bendz Eran 43. 45* (*retento* levandi)

[3] lavandi *Rm*: levandi *G*

[4] spui *G*: *corr. A*

[5] tremor *Rm*

[6] fateantur *G*: *corr. R*

XI. THE SYMPTOMS OF THOSE WHO ARE
ON THE VERGE OF HYDROPHOBIA

THOSE who are on the verge of hydrophobia show the following symptoms when the attack is just beginning: anxiety
without reason, irascibility, difficulty in performing ordinary
movements, light and troubled sleep or wakefulness, decomposition of the food that has been eaten, sensation of heaviness in the
esophagus and of strain in the legs and arms, continual yawning, and a growing disinclination to bathe.[1] Moreover, the patient frets about the weather, though normally it does not bother
him, and complains that the damp south wind is blowing, however bright and calm the day may be. He can scarcely endure
rain, which disgusts and nauseates him. And, contrary to his
usual custom, he has little desire to drink.

As the disease takes hold, the patient has a desire for water
and also a fear of it, at first when he actually sees the water, but
later when he hears its sound or the mere mention of its name.
He also fears fomentation with olive oil. The pulse is rapid,
small, and irregular; in some cases there occur fever, palpitation
of the gullet, numbness and loss of sensation in the limbs, precordial elevation and tension, failure of the bowels to function,
frequent passing of small amounts of urine, tremor and spasm
of the sinews, voice thick and like a bark, body gathered up
like a coil or a [sleeping] dog, breathing painful, shaking of the
whole body at anyone's entrance for fear that he is bringing water with him, face and eyes red, body drawn, pallor, sweating in
the upper parts, frequent tentigo with involuntary ejaculation
of semen, tongue hanging out.

Finally, there are hiccoughs and vomiting of bile, generally
black bile. In some cases the patient shows fear when a hand is
moved up to his eyes or passed round them. Some patients say
they recognize that it is common ordinary water when it is
shown them, but that on seeing it they become agitated. And
Soranus asserts that he actually saw a person who was suffering
from this disease exhort himself to take the water, but that the
person was unable to do so. There is also the case, which
Artorius relates, of the soldier who had hydrophobia. He was

1. This interpretation is doubtful. 'A growing disinclination to get up' or 'an unremitting desire to vomit' are other possibilities, depending on the reading adopted.
But see Theo. Prisc., p. 123. 10 (Rose).

memorat, in passione constitutum sibi indignatum quod in bello
nulla timuerit vice, sed nunc aquam cum vidisset, quae esse
105 consuetudini iocunda solet,[7] metu inenarrabili terreretur. item
Eudemus Themisonis sectator memorat fuisse hydrophobum
medicum, qui cum praenosceret periculum suppliciter ingredientes exoraret, et cum lacrimarum fluore guttis destillantibus
tangeretur, exiliens vestem consciderit. dehinc Soranus memorat se infantem hydrophobum vidisse ubera matris expaves-
centem. item ait quendam Atheniensem sibi retulisse quod viderit hydrophobum ex domo fugatum ad locum venisse ubi inclusus corpore implicato vitam finiverit; sed in ipso loco fuisse
canem iacentem quem rabie accensus repente accurrens mo-
morderit.

communiter autem est passio stricturae atque vehemens et
acuta vel celeris. etenim ob nimium tumorem et humoris defec-
106 tum aegrotantes celeriter interficiuntur. nec Demetrio danda
fides est dicenti quod etiam tarda haec passio possit esse, hoc est
diuturna, quam Graeci chroniam vocant, siquidem dicat in ista
passione levi timore[8] affectos biennium transegisse. neque Asclepiadis sectatores intelligibile quiddam asserunt qui propterea
passionem tardam putant, quia post plurimum tempus morsus
inflicti morte afficiuntur, cum non oporteat illud tempus aegrotanti imputari quo nondum rabie vexatur: quippe cum passio
necdum corpus afficiat, et cum emicuerit non habeat superpositiones seu dilationes, quod[9] specialiter tardis accidit[10] passionibus, et ob hoc celerrime aegrotantes interficiat, non solum ut
acuta sed etiam ut continua passio.

107 ## XII. QUAE SUNT SIMILIA HYDROPHOBIAE ET QUOMODO INTERNOSCUNTUR

SIMILES sunt hydrophobicae passioni phrenitis, mania, quam
nos furorem sive insaniam dixerimus. sed hae discernuntur,
siquidem plus in ipsis caput patiatur, in phreniticis vero etiam
febres sequantur; item in hydrophobicis[1] plus stomachus et sine

[7] solebat Rm
[8] timore Rm: tumore G
[9] ut in his qui Rm: sicut qui A
[10] afficiuntur edd.
[1] ⟨vero⟩ add. R (omisso item)

angry with himself because he, who had never feared the vicissitudes of war, was now affected with indescribable fear whenever he saw water, normally so pleasant and useful to him. Eudemus, a follower of Themison, tells of a doctor who had hydrophobia. When he realized the gravity of the case, on his knees he implored visitors.[2] But when the tears trickled down and touched him, he leaped up and tore his clothes to pieces. Again, Soranus tells us that he saw a baby who had hydrophobia shrink in terror from its mother's breast. He also relates the following case told him by an Athenian. The Athenian had seen a victim of hydrophobia, driven from home, come to a certain place where he later died in seclusion, his body contorted. Once when a dog was lying in that place the patient, in an attack of rabies, suddenly ran up and bit it.

In general, hydrophobia is a disease which involves a state of stricture; it is severe and acute, i.e., swift; for, because of the severe inflammation and lack of moisture, the patients die quickly. And we must not believe Demetrius when he says that the disease may also be slow, that is, of long duration (Greek *chronia*); and when he says, by way of proof, that patients have had this disease for two years with only a mild fear [of water]. Nor does it make sense to say, as do the followers of Asclepiades, that the disease may be considered chronic because the patients die a considerable time after the bite is inflicted. For the period of time before the patient is attacked by rabies should not be included in the reckoning, because the disease has not as yet affected the body. Furthermore, when it does emerge, it does not exhibit exacerbations and remissions, as is specifically the case with chronic diseases. And that is why the victims of hydrophobia die quickly, for it is not only an acute disease but one that is unremitting.

XII. DISEASES RESEMBLING HYDROPHOBIA AND THE METHOD OF DISTINGUISHING THEM

MANIA (Latin *furor* or *insania*) and phrenitis resemble hydrophobia, but may be distinguished from it as follows. In phrenitis and mania the head is the part principally affected; and in phrenitis there is also fever. In hydrophobia, however, the

2. To help him? According to *Rm:* 'to keep at a distance.'

febribus esse perspiciatur, et acuta sit atque celeris passio, mania vero etiam tarda frequentius inveniatur. Eudemus Themisonis sectator inquit melancholiam esse hydrophobicam pas-
108 sionem, sed ab hac quoque discernitur, siquidem tarda sit melancholia, acuta vel celeris hydrophobia. alii quoque aerophobas[2]
aiunt esse similes supra dictis sed internosci, siquidem aeris sit
timor qui generaliter phreniticis ascribitur. etenim phrenitici
quidam aerem lucidum extimescunt, quidam obscurum. item
Andreae sectatores memorant esse pantophobas,[3] quos nos om-
nipavos dicere poterimus, siquidem omnia timere dicantur, si
vere tamen haec esse poterit passio. discernitur autem quod
non solius potus sed omnium rerum timorem faciat.

109 ## XIII. UTRUMNE ANIMAE AN CORPORIS
PASSIO SIT HYDROPHOBIA

QUAESITUM etiam utrum animae an corporis passio sit hydrophobia. etenim quidam[1] esse aiunt animi passionem,
siquidem appetere vel desiderare sit animae speciale non corporis. denique purpuram cupientes vel statuam vel militiam
aut regnum aut pecuniam neque venis neque nervis aegrotare
dicuntur vel arteriis, sed animae affici passione. quo fiet ut
etiam hydrophobia animae sit passio, est enim appetentia potus,
quippe cum timor[2] et maestitudo et iracundia passiones sint
animae. timent igitur aquam hydrophobae,[3] quo necessario
110 animo aegrotare noscuntur. nam omnis phantasia cuius diver-
sitates Latini visa vocaverunt, ut Tullius, sive illa naturalia sive
contra naturam fuerint, animi non corporis esse noscuntur. hydrophobae[3] igitur phantasia iactantur, scilicet ea quae contra
naturam esse videatur, quo assumitur eos animi affici passione.
sed his qui haec asserunt consentiendum non est. etenim
appetere vel delectari potu, sicut etiam mandere, ex corporis
quadam nascitur passione. timor enim[4] per consensum animae

[2] aerophobos *A*   [2] *fort. scrib.* ⟨appetentia et⟩ timor
[3] pantaphobos *Rm*   [3] hydrophobi *Rm*
[1] quidem *G: corr. A*   [4] etiam *Rm*

---

1. Not in all cases. Cf. 103.
1. Cf. *Acad post.* i. 11. 40; *Acad. prior.* ii. 6. 18.

esophagus is the part principally affected, and the disease is observed to occur without fever.[1] Moreover, hydrophobia is swift
and acute, whereas mania is generally found to be chronic as
well. Eudemus, a follower of Themison, declares that melancholy is the same as hydrophobia. But it, too, may be distinguished. For melancholy is a chronic disease, while hydrophobia
is swift or acute. And some say that aerophobia is also similar to
hydrophobia, but that it may be distinguished, for aerophobia
is the fear of air which generally accompanies phrenitis, some
patients dreading the bright light of day, others darkness. Andreas and his followers say that there are pantophobes, whom we
should in Latin call *omnipavi* ['all-fearing'], since they are said to
fear everything, if, indeed, such a disease can actually exist. But
in any case it is to be distinguished from hydrophobia, for it involves a fear not merely of drink but of all things.

XIII. IS HYDROPHOBIA A DISEASE OF THE SOUL OR OF THE BODY?

THERE is also the question whether hydrophobia is a disease
of the soul or of the body, for some say that it is a disease of
the soul, on the ground that desire or longing is a function peculiar to the soul rather than the body. Their argument is as follows. Those who are greedy for the purple or for statues, military
glory, royal power, or wealth are said to be affected not by a disease of the veins, sinews, or arteries but by a disease of the soul.
And so, they say, hydrophobia, too, being the desire for drink, is
a disease of the soul. Again, since fear, sadness, and anger are
affections of the soul and those who have hydrophobia fear water, it must consequently be admitted that theirs is an affection
of the soul. Again, all mental images, the various forms of which
the Latin writers, for example, Cicero,[1] call *visa* ['visions'],
clearly belong to the soul and not to the body, whether they are
normal or abnormal. And persons who have hydrophobia are
tormented by an imagination (*phantasia*) which is evidently
abnormal. Hence the conclusion that they are the victims of a
disease of the soul.

But we cannot agree with those who adduce this argument.
For a longing for drink or delight in drinking, as in eating, arises
from an affection of the body. And we observe that fear, too,

111 corpori[5] compatientis nasci perspicitur. quo fiet ut corporalem
esse passionem hydrophobicam manifeste perluceat. etenim
antecedens morsus ex quo causa descendit utique corporis fuit
et non animae. antecedentia autem atque consequentia, ut est
singultus et difficilis corporis motus et gravedo et his similia corporis esse noscuntur. nam animae passiones, ut philosophi volunt, nostri sunt iudicii; hydrophobica autem passio ex corporis
necessitate descendit. quo fiet ut sit corporis passio, sed etiam
animae occupet qualitatem, tamquam in furiosis vel melancholicis.

112 XIV. QUIS LOCUS IN HYDROPHOBICIS PATITUR

VICINA etiam quaestio est supra dictae quisnam in hydrophobicis locus corporis patiatur. equidem Democritus, cum
de emprosthotonicis diceret, nervos inquit, coniciens hoc ex corporis conductione atque veretri[1] tentigine. item Asclepiadis
sectatores alii membranam aiunt cerebri, siquidem secundum
Asclepiadem omnis passio quae mentem turbaverit in ipsa con-
sistat, ut phrenitis, lethargia, epilepsia. quo assumitur ut etiam
hydrophobica passio eidem membranulae ascribatur, quae animum conturbat.

alii aiunt diaphragma pati siquidem in ipso sit dolor consti-
113 titus. Artemidorus Erasistrati sector et Artorius Asclepiadis
sector de hydrophobia scribentes atque plurimi nostrae sectae
scriptores aiunt stomachum pati, siquidem singultus sequatur
et vomitus fellis et appetentia insatiabilis bibendi, quorum singula stomachi passionis esse noscuntur; consentire tamen etiam
membranas cerebri. sed nonnulli Asclepiadis sectatores stomachum atque ventrem pati dixerunt: etenim bibendi appetentiam
non solum stomachi parvissimis viis sed etiam ventris fieri probant, vomitum quoque utriusque partis effici passione. item
Gaius Herophili sector libro quo De timore aquae scripsit, ait
114 cerebrum et eius membranam pati: etenim voluntario motu ser-

[5] corporis G: corr. R
[1] veteri G: corr. Rm

1. That the reference in *veretri tentigo* here and in 103 is probably made with the
male sex alone in mind is indicated by 115, below. Normally the phrase is applicable to
both sexes.

arises from a sympathetic accord between body and soul. Hence it is abundantly clear that hydrophobia is a disease of the body. And, indeed, the antecedent bite from which the disease is derived assuredly has for its object the body and not the soul. Moreover, the symptoms preceding and attending the disease, such as hiccoughs, distress in moving the body, a sensation of heaviness, and the like, are clearly bodily symptoms. For affections of the soul, in the meaning of the philosophers, are affections of our judgment. But the disease of hydrophobia derives from a bodily force and is therefore a bodily disease, though it also attacks the psychic nature, as do mania and melancholy.

XIV. THE PART OF THE BODY AFFECTED IN HYDROPHOBIA

CONNECTED with the previous question is the question of the part of the body affected in hydrophobia. In the course of a discussion about emprosthotonos, Democritus says that it is the fibers and sinews that are affected [in hydrophobia], basing his conclusion on the bodily spasms and tentigo.[1] Some followers of Asclepiades say that it is the membrane of the brain; for, according to Asclepiades, every disease that disorders the mind is centered in this membrane, e.g., phrenitis, lethargy, and epilepsy. Hence it is assumed that the disease of hydrophobia, because it causes mental confusion, is to be attributed to the same membrane.

Others say that the diaphragm is affected, since pain is present there. Artemidorus, a follower of Erasistratus, and Artorius, a follower of Asclepiades, and many physicians of our own sect in writing about hydrophobia say that the esophagus is the part affected, for there are hiccoughs, vomiting of bile, and an insatiable desire to drink, each of which is a clear sign of disease of the esophagus; but these writers say that the membranes of the brain are also affected. Still other followers of Asclepiades declare that both the esophagus and the stomach are affected; for they hold that the desire for drink is produced in the minute pores not only of the esophagus but also of the stomach and that vomiting, too, takes place from both these parts. Gaius the Herophilean in his book *On Hydrophobia* says that the brain and its membrane are the parts affected. For it is there that the

vientes nervi atque stomachum colligantes initium vel originem inde sumpsisse noscuntur.

Magnus vero Ephesius secundo libro Epistolarum ait sigillatim esse dicendum omnia quae difficultate motus in hac passione afficiuntur pati, hoc est cor, stomachum, diaphragma, caput, ilia. non enim pulsum malignum fieri posse suspicatur nisi praepatiente ea parte corporis unde initium sumit, quae necessario sine ulla fuerit vexabili passione. pulsus mutari in peius numquam potest neque difficultas spirationis fieri, si diaphragma atque pulmo naturali positione maneant ac nullo modo tentata:

115 neque tentigo frequens atque ultra naturam, nisi virilia sive radius virilis fuerit in tumore constitutus; neque visa mentem fallentia, quae Graeci phantasmata vocaverunt, nisi capite patienti fieri possunt, siquidem in ipsa vel in ipso sensus omnes sint constituti, vel quod sensuales viae ex ipso ad cor referantur.

quorum nihil est ad medicum necessario pertinens. sufficit enim agnovisse caput pati tempore quo mens fuerit alienata, quippe cum etiam ex antecedentibus signis pati noscatur. prae-

116 cedit enim quibusdam dolor capitis atque aurium tinnitus, visus quoque falsitas provolantium veluti animalium minutorum tamquam culicum, quapropter palpebratione frequentant, nec non etiam vultus fervor cum rubore per ora insinuans, attestante lacrimarum fluore cum angulis oculorum sanguinolentis, extantibus venis ex utraque parte temporum, apparet.

sed horum singuli ratione commoti vera quidem sed deficiente haec posuerunt. praepatitur enim ea pars quae morsu fuerit vexata, unde initium denique passionem sumere nemo negat. patitur enim totum corpus, quod probamus ex his quae singuli dixerunt. cum enim alii alias asserunt pati partes, omnes pati confitentur. fit autem probabilius ex his quae manifeste hydro-

117 phobicos sequuntur, saltus membrorum, raptus sive contractio nervorum, sitis, timor, tentigo, abstinentia vel retentio egerendorum.

---

2. I.e., collectively. But if this interpretation is correct, the author's argument is incredibly bad.

nerves used for voluntary motion and those that connect with the esophagus are known to have their ultimate beginning or origin.

Magnus of Ephesus in Book II of his *Letters* says that the several parts in which this disease causes difficulty of motion may be said to be individually affected, viz., heart, gullet, diaphragm, head, and groin. For he supposes that the pulse cannot become abnormal unless that part of the body whence the pulse originates has been previously affected, though, of course, this part [the heart] cannot be seriously affected. And the pulse, he holds, can never change for the worse, nor can there be difficulty of respiration unless the diaphragm and the lungs move
5 from their normal position and are in some way attacked; nor can there be frequent and unnatural tentigo unless the male organ, or penis, is inflamed. Nor, finally, can the mind be the victim of illusions (Greek *phantasmata*) unless the head is affected; for all sensation is centered in the mind or the head, the channels which carry sensation passing from there to the heart.

But none of this necessarily concerns the physician; it is sufficient for him to understand that when there is mental derangement the head is affected. That the head is affected can be understood also from the antecedent signs. For in some cases pain
6 in the head and ringing in the ears precede this disease. The patient also imagines that he sees small animals like gnats flying before his eyes, and for that reason frequently blinks his eyes. His face becomes hot and a redness spreads over it; tears flow, the corners of the eyes are bloodshot, and the veins of both temples stand out.

Now various writers have set forth the above conclusions, but, while their reasoning is sound, it does not go far enough. The fact is that the part affected in advance of the disease is the part which the animal has bitten. No one will deny that it is from here that the disease originates. And the whole body is affected [during the disease], as is clear by putting together what these various writers have said. For when some declare that certain parts are affected, and others others, they admit[2] that all the
7 parts are affected. And this is corroborated by the symptoms which are clearly observable in those who have hydrophobia, viz., quivering or palpitation in various parts, spasm or convulsion, thirst, fear, tentigo, and failure to evacuate matter.

plus tamen stomachum pati atque ventrem recte dicimus. in
ipsis enim plurima sunt accidentia signa et manifestiora, ut singultus, saltus, retentio, conductio vel contractio, sitis intolera-
bilis. sed nihil horum ad curam necessario refertur: ubi enim
passionem invenerimus eidem parti iuxta magnitudinis comparationem adiutoria adhibemus.

118   ## XV. UTRUM NOVA PASSIO SIT HYDROPHOBIA

QUIDAM logicorum quaesiverunt pro[1] loco utrum nova passio
sit hydrophobia, ut si novam invenirent, novam etiam
causam atque curationem inquirerent. quod a nobis quidem
alienum est. fieri enim potest ut particulares vel speciales passiones novae fieri possint, generales autem vel principales, quarum dominio ceterae quaeque subiciuntur fieri numquam possint. hae denique consuetis atque congruis curationibus similiter curantur. sed ut plenius omnia perspiciantur, singulorum
placita sive visa vel existimationes ordinamus.

etenim quidam aiunt novam esse hydrophobicam passionem,
quidam negaverunt, et alii omnino, ut Artemidorus Sidensis, alii
119 specialiter, ut Caridemus sectator Erasistrati. item [non][2] novam esse passionem plurimi dixerunt sed ob astructionem pro-
bandae novae passionis aiunt neminem veterum hanc memorasse
passionem, sed soli, inquiunt, novelli inventores eandem adver-
terunt. certe si fuit[3] apud veteres, nec tamen memorata cognoscitur. secundo confundit atque turbat haec passio non
solum inertes sed etiam artifices, quo probatur ob tantam osten-
tationem magnitudinis nova inveniri. dehinc aliarum passionum causae apprehensibiles sunt, scilicet activae atque operantes, quas synecticas vocant; istius autem passionis incomprehensibilis est, quod est signum probabile novae passionis. additur etiam quod sit incurabilis.

120   sed his contraria sentientes falsum esse inquiunt quod hanc
passionem nullus veterum memoraverit. etenim Democritus

[1] primo *Haller*

[2] non *om. R, quod si retineas scribendum videtur* sed ⟨alii⟩ ob astructionem *etc.*

[3] fuit *conieci*: sunt *G*

---

1. The Dogmatists.

But we shall be right in holding that the esophagus, stomach, and bowels are more affected than the rest of the body. For here occur most of the more obvious symptoms, e.g., hiccoughs, palpitation, retention [of waste matter], spasm or convulsion, and unendurable thirst. But none of these symptoms necessarily controls the treatment. For wherever we find the disease we apply remedies to that part, taking into account the severity of the attack.

8

XV. IS HYDROPHOBIA A NEW DISEASE?

SOME physicians of the Rational School[1] have raised the question, as a topic for discussion, whether hydrophobia is a new disease; for if they found it to be new, they would also seek a new cause and treatment. But such an inquiry seems strange to us. For, while it may be that certain particular or special diseases are new, the general and leading types of disease to which all the special diseases are subordinate can never be new. And we treat diseases of the same general type in similar fashion by the application of customary and suitable remedies. But, in order that the whole matter may be more fully examined, we shall set forth the opinions or views or judgments of the several writers.

Some say that hydrophobia is a new disease, others say it is not. Of the latter group, some, among them Artemidorus of Side, deny generally that any disease is new, while others, among them Caridemus, an Erasistratean, deny specifically that hydrophobia is new. In fact, most writers hold that the disease is new; but, by way of proof that it is new, they declare that none of the ancient writers mentions hydrophobia and that only recent writers have noticed it. And even if it did exist among the ancients, still, as they point out, it was never referred to. Furthermore [they say] this disease perplexes and troubles not merely the unskilful but even the most able physicians; and, in view of this clear indication of its importance, there is reason to hold that it is a new disease. Again, the causes of other diseases, that is, the active and efficient causes (Greek *synecticae*), are understandable; but the causes of this disease are beyond our grasp, an indication tending to show that the disease is a new one. They point out, in addition, that the disease cannot be successfully treated.

But those who hold the opposite view reject as false the statement that none of the ancients mentions this disease. Their

qui Hippocrati convixit non solum hanc memoravit esse[4] passionem sed etiam eius causam tradidit, cum de opisthotonicis
scriberet. ipse quoque Hippocrates, etsi non principaliter de
ipsa passione tractans, sensu tamen dictorum hanc memorasse
monstratur, in Praedictivo libro dicens phreniticos parvibibulos,
sono quolibet pulsatos, tremore affici. alienatione autem mentis hydrophobas[5] vexari videmus, quapropter hos Hippocrates
phreniticos dixit parvibibulos, quos brachypotas vocant, hoc est
121   quod modicum biberent ob timorem liquoris. item Polybus
hanc passionem memoravit dicens aquifugas cito interire, quos
pheugydros appellavit. Homerus quoque hanc agnovisse passionem probatur. conicit enim per figuram cum de Tantalo
dicit; item ubi inducit Teucrum occisis octo Hectorem non potuisse percutere, atque ita locutum ut diceret se hunc interficere
non posse rabidum canem. cum igitur memoravit Homerus ex
quo fieri hydrophobae[6] possunt, erit consequens ut et quod fieri
possint scierit. item comicus Menander inducens senem iras-
centem istius passionis imaginem vinolentis adscripsit, dicens
non posse bibere eos qui vinum usque ad vexationem potant.
122   ratio quoque hoc ostendere videtur. etenim superioribus temporibus aut erant canes aut non erant. sed non fuisse nemo quis
dicere audeat: passionis etenim causam prompte Homerus memoravit. si igitur fuerunt, etiam rabie affecti sunt. quo fiet ut
cum fuisse causa ex qua hydrophobae[7] fierent atque homines qui
fierent vel pati potuissent demonstretur, erit rationabile ut apud
antiquos haec passio fuisse credatur. expavescere autem sive
confundi, ut aiunt, non solum inertes sed etiam artifices hac passione non necessario signum est eandem incurabilem pronun-
tiandi. etenim plurimae aliae passiones non aliter videntium[8]
mentem confundunt, ut satyriasis, apoplexia.

[4] esse *om.* R

[5] hydrophobos R (*cf. 99*)

[6] hydrophobi *A*

[7] hydrophobi R

[8] medentium *Schmid Mn 154*

---

2. *Prorrhetic* i. 16; cf. *Coan Prenotions* 95 (V. 514, 602 Littré).

3. *Odyssey* xi. 582.

4. *Iliad* viii. 296.

proof is as follows. Democritus, who lived at the same time as Hippocrates, not only states that there is such a disease but also gives its cause in the course of his discussion of opisthotonos. And Hippocrates himself, though he does not deal formally with hydrophobia, certainly alludes to it, as is clear from the sense of his remarks. For in his book entitled *Prorrhetic*[2] he says that phrenitics drink little, are agitated by every sound, and are affected by tremor. Now we know that persons with hydrophobia also suffer mental aberration. Hence Hippocrates must be referring to these cases of hydrophobia when he speaks of phrenitics as *brachypotae* (which we may in Latin render *parvibibuli*, i.e., 'drinking little,' on account of a fear of liquids). Polybus, too, alludes to hydrophobia when he says that those who flee from water (Greek *pheugydroe*) die quickly. And it is clear that Homer himself recognized this disease, for he alludes to it figuratively when he speaks of Tantalus.[3] This is also the case when he brings forward Teucer, who, after killing eight men, could not strike Hector and has him say that he cannot kill this mad dog.[4] Since Homer mentions that from which hydrophobia may come, it follows that he knows that such a disease is possible. Again, the comic poet Menander introduces an angry old man[5] and draws a picture of this disease, ascribing it to excessive drinking of wine and indicating that those who drink until they become ill are no longer able to drink.

2   Reason seems also to indicate this [i.e., that the disease is not new]. For in former times there either were or were not dogs. But surely no one would venture to say that there were not. Indeed, Homer clearly refers to the cause of the disease. If, then, there were dogs, there were also dogs that were affected by rabies. And, since it is clear that the cause of hydrophobia existed, as well as people who had hydrophobia or might have had it, it is reasonable to believe that this disease was present among the ancients. Again, from the argument that physicians, skilled as well as unskilled, are frightened or perplexed by the disease, it does not necessarily follow that the disease must be considered incurable.[6] For many other diseases similarly perplex the minds of observers, e.g., satyriasis and apoplexy.

5. The play in question has not been identified.

6. 'And even if incurable, a disease is not necessarily new.' Some such idea is to be supplied here (cf. 123). The alternative is to read *novam* for *incurabilem*.

123   item causa praecedens eius passionis incomprehensibilis, ut
putant, non est, quam plurimi medicorum atque philosophorum
tradiderunt. at si esset incomprehensibilis, quod ex ea sequetur
manifestum esse[9] apprehensibile nulli negant. vel si esset in-
comprehensibile id quod sequitur, hoc est passio, non tamen incurabile; at si incurabile, non necessario novum, ut neque carci-
noma. sed aiunt principaliter ex his quae sequuntur vel designant hydrophobicam passionem nihil esse eiusdem proprium,
ut singultus, qui quamquam eos sequatur, sit tamen communis
eorum qui hydrophobae[10] non sunt. sitis etiam sequitur atque
124 vomitus fellis, sed febricitantibus haec saepe contingunt. item
turbatio mentis atque timor, sed etiam phreniticos saepe comi-
tantur. si igitur nihil proprium sequitur hydrophobas,[11] sed sunt
omnia communia aliis passionibus, non poterit nova passio nuncupari.

nos quoque his consentimus. videtur etenim haec passio
etiam frequentare quibusdam temporibus vel locis, ut apud Cariam atque Cretam. haec enim insula aliorum venenosorum animalium difficilis atque paene libera sola canum rabie vexatur
frequentissime. poetarum quoque testimonium longe vetustissi-
mum atque non rectis necessario verbis destinatum accipiendum
ducimus.

125   item Hippocrates magis phreniticos memoravit non hydrophobas[12] parvibibulos. nam inquit eos, quod in quibusdam
phreniticis frequentare videmus, aut fastidio possessos non solum ad cibum verum etiam ad potum, vel certe traductos visis,
quae Graeci phantasiam appellant, ut, ait Eudemus, accipiendum non existiment potum, vel suspicione delirationis affecti
admixta putent venena liquori. tremunt quoque nonnumquam
debilitate nervorum et ad omnem sonitum commoventur, scilicet
alienationis proprietate et non necessario hydrophobicae passionis. quapropter aliis utendum est rationibus ad demonstrandum non[13] esse novam hydrophobicam passionem.

23   Moreover, the antecedent cause of this disease is not, as they think, incomprehensible. Indeed, many physicians and philosophers have set forth this cause. But, even if it were incomprehensible, no one will deny that its obvious result may be readily grasped. And even if this result, that is, the disease itself, were incomprehensible, still it would not necessarily be incurable. And, if incurable, it would not necessarily be a new disease—witness the case of cancer. But the principal argument advanced [against the proposition that hydrophobia is a new disease] is that none of the signs which mark or designate this disease is exclusively characteristic of it. Thus hiccoughs are a sign of hydrophobia, but are also found in those who do not have the disease; thirst and the vomiting of bile are also signs of hydrophobia, but

24   often occur in cases of fever. Similarly, mental confusion and fear [are characteristic of hydrophobia], but often occur in phrenitis, too. If, then, there is no sign exclusively characteristic of hydrophobia, but all the signs occur also in other diseases, hydrophobia cannot be called a new disease.

We, too, agree with this conclusion. Furthermore, this disease seems to occur frequently at certain times and places, e.g., in Caria and Crete. In fact, the island of Crete, which is almost entirely free of other poisonous animals, is frequently scourged by mad dogs. And we hold that the testimony of the poets must be accepted, for it is by far the most ancient evidence that we have, even though not necessarily couched in direct language.

25   But when Hippocrates speaks of those who drink little, he is referring to phrenitis, not hydrophobia. For he says that they may have a distaste for both food and drink, a condition which we frequently observe in phrenitis; or, indeed, as Eudemus says, they are so deluded by their imagination (Greek *phantasia*) that they believe they should not drink anything; or in their madness they may suspect that poison has been mixed with the drink. And their trembling is sometimes due to weakness of the sinews; and their agitation at every sound is undoubtedly an indication of mental aberration and not necessarily of hydrophobia. We must therefore have recourse to the other arguments to prove that hydrophobia is not a new disease.[7]

7. That is, while approving the conclusion that hydrophobia is not a new disease, Soranus seems to be objecting to one of the arguments commonly adduced.

126   XVI. QUOMODO CURANDI SUNT HYDROPHOBAE[1]

C URANDOS hydrophobas[2] convenit iacere loco mediocriter calido atque lucido, adhibita articulorum defricatione, servatos
etiam insomnes usque ad laxamentum temporale, his quoque
partibus quae rapiuntur vel conductione vexantur calidis atque
mundis lanis aut[3] pannis praetectis. adhibendae etiam molles
vaporationes in statu accessionis dulci atque calido oleo clam
lanis tinctis, vel foris a cubiculo infusis, tum immissis, ne visu
liquoris aegrotantes in commemorationem timoris reducantur.
127   at si aliqua fuerit indulgentia passionis (quae erit apprehen-
denda, si etiam febres fuerint, ex minutione fervoris; si etiam
non fuerint, minutione timoris) erunt phlebotomandi ex brachio
quo vena facilior occurrerit. ita in fluenti sanguine avertenda[4]
sunt aegrotantium ora, atque manu excipiendus est fluor, ne sonitu perculsi commoveantur. in diatrito vero erunt primo perungendi, sed pannis oleo tinctis, eorum enim tractu latenter
corpora perungentur; extergendi quoque. at alia foventur[5] aliis
calidis atque mundis[6] consequenter pannis vel linteolis.

tunc post perunctionem cibus dandus tenuis et sorbilis, quo
128 latenter cum cibo etiam potus inducatur, et panis aqua infusus
vel alica ex aqua: facile enim accipiunt. sed oportet magis tempora dandi servare cibum et potum. quod fiet hoc genere, ut ex
obliquo fabulantes de consueta vita loquamur[7] lavacra memo-
rando atque bibendi copiam. tunc si aegri his dictis placidi permanserint, fidenter offerimus potum dimissionis tempore in-
vento. at si commoti vel irati fuerint audito lavacro vel potu,
erit differenda oblatio. dandus interea potus in fictili vasculo
subtili caverna perforato tamquam sunt papillae uberum; et
dandus aegrotantibus praefecto obstaculo oculorum vel tempo-

[1] hydrophobi *A*

[2] hydrophobos *A*

[3] ut *G: corr. Rm*

[4] advertenda *G: corr. Rm*

[5] *fort.* foveantur *vel* fovenda

[6] immundis *edd.*

[7] loquantur *edd.*

---

1. ἔριον κάθαρον (Soranus) may refer, in particular, to scoured wool.

2. Presumably as it strikes the basin or the ground.

XVI. THE TREATMENT OF HYDROPHOBIA

26 IN TREATING a case of hydrophobia have the patient lie in a moderately warm and light room. Massage his limbs and keep him from sleep until there is some temporary relief. Cover with warm, clean[1] wool or cloths those parts that are affected by spasm. And at the highest stage of the attack apply gentle heat, using wool dipped in warm sweet olive oil without the patient's seeing it; the wool may be soaked in this oil outside the sick room and then brought in. These precautions are taken to prevent the patient from lapsing back into a state of fear through sight of the liquid.

27 Now if there is some abatement in the disease (which may be observed from a lessening of the fever in cases where fever is present, and in other cases from a relaxation of the state of fear), perform venesection on the arm in which the vein is easier to reach. While the blood is flowing, turn the patient's face away and intercept the flow with the hand to prevent the patient from becoming agitated and disturbed by the sound of the blood.[2] At the end of the three-day period anoint the patient for the first time, but employ cloths dipped in olive oil, for by their use the body can be anointed [with a liquid] without the patient's seeing it; also dry the patient's body. And foment the various parts, using suitable pieces of warm, clean cloth or linen.[3]

After the anointing give the patient thin, gruel-like food, so that he may have drink with his food without being aware of it. 28 He may have bread or spelt groats that have previously been soaked in water, for the patient readily takes these. Now the proper time for giving food and drink must be carefully watched. This time is determined in the following manner. In talking to the patient, lead up indirectly to matters of daily life and mention bathing and drinking. Then if he remains calm during this discussion, you may confidently offer him drink, having discovered a period of remission. But if, on hearing about bathing or drinking, he becomes excited or angry, postpone giving him drink. And when giving drink use a small [inclosed] earthen vessel perforated with a thin opening like the nipple of a breast. Cover the patient's eyes or the windows of the room while the

3. The text and meaning are doubtful. *Immundis*, if retained, may refer to unscoured wool; *alia* may possibly refer to *diatrito* ('the next three-day period').

129 raliter clausis fenestris. est enim omnifariam mitigatione passionis[8] providendum, ut nulla occasio detur excitandi furoris.
oportet denique etiam ministros aptissimos esse, et primo ut sint
taciti neque fabulas inicientes, sed eius respondentes dictis et
ita[9] respondentes ut cedentes[10] ac sine ulla constantia eum con-
sentiendo coerceant, atque eius visa quae mentis falsitate efficiuntur eidem sensim displicere atque incredibilia faciant.

dehinc convenit laxativis cataplasmatibus thoracem curare et
a tergo inter utrasque palas, quod Graeci metaphrenum vocant.
130 cum autem statum sumpserit passio, etiam cucurbita apponenda
iisdem locis cum scarificatione. tum spongiarum vaporatione
utendum, quae quidem latenter erunt ex oleo atque calida exprimendae et apponendae obvolutae pannis vel linteolis, ne humoris sensus aut sonitus exagitent aegrotantem. tunc etiam caput detondendum et iisdem adiutoriis concurandum; gestatio
adhibenda in lectulo suspenso sive portatoria sella.

at si passio perseveraverit, iisdem perseverabimus adiutoriis.
illud etiam erit affectandum, ut si omnino potum recusaverint,
qualibet tamen parte quiddam liquoris assumant, et nulla in-
131 dignatione aegrotantes afficiantur visu perterriti. quod ita facere poterimus si calidam atque oleum ex clystere per podicem
iniciamus, et[11] hoc si fieri potuerit diurnis diebus, parvum quidem, tunc enim potuerit contineri. nam si fuerit plurimus humor, sua redundantia ac pondere provocat excludi. erit enim
eius continentia utilis ad minuendam sitim. nam neque solum
dysentericis iniectum medicamen superiora invadens saepe stomachum atque caput vexare accipimus, siquidem eo necessario
perveniat, sed etiam calidam[12] et oleum pervenire posse concipi-
mus, quo partibus iisdem irrigationis praebeat laxamentum.
post iniectionem denique manibus admotis impressione moderata ex inferioribus ad superiora ducentes liquorem ascendere
provocamus.

[8] passioni *A*
[9] ipsa *G: corr. A*
[10] cedentes *Rm*: cedenter *G, sed cf.* differenter (*G*) *74*
[11] ut *G: corr. R*
[12] calida *G: corr. R.*

drink is being taken. For every means must be employed to relieve the disease, so that there is no occasion for the patient's
anger to be aroused. And his servants must be carefully chosen.
They must, to begin with, be quiet and not given to storytelling.
They should reply to what the patient says, but in such a way
as to be acquiescent and not insistent, and yet, while agreeing
with him, to maintain control over him. And the servants should
gradually get him to disbelieve and reject the illusions which his
troubled mind produces.

Then [after giving drink] apply soothing poultices to the chest
and in the back between the shoulder blades (Greek *metaphrenon*). And when the disease reaches its highest stage, apply
cupping with scarification at these same places. Then apply heat
with sponges. These sponges should be squeezed out of olive oil
and hot water away from the patient's sight, and applied in a
wrapping of cloths or linen,[4] so that neither the sight, touch,
nor sound of the liquid may cause him agitation. Then clip the
hair from his head and treat this part with the same remedies.
Also prescribe passive exercise, employing a hammock or a sedan
chair.

Now if the disease persists, continue the same treatments. And
if the patient refuses drink altogether, an effort must be made,
nevertheless, to have him receive some quantity of liquid without being terrified by the sight of it and provoked to anger. This
can be done by injecting warm water and olive oil through the
anus as a clyster, repeating this daily, if possible. Only a small
quantity should be injected, for in that case it will be possible to
retain the liquid. On the other hand, a large quantity of liquid,
because of its tendency to flow back and its weight, is more apt
to be driven out. The retention of the fluid will also help to lessen
thirst. For in cases of dysentery, as we know, a drug injected in
this way moves upward and, of necessity, reaches the esophagus
and the head,[5] often causing pain in these parts. Now in the present instance we hold that the warm water and olive oil can reach
these same parts and, by moistening them, bring relief. After
making the injection, apply moderate pressure with the hands,
drawing them from the lower to the upper parts; and in this way
get the fluid to rise.

4. Perhaps 'in a wrapping of wool or linen cloths.'

5. Soranus is thinking primarily of the vapors from the injected substances.

132 declinante passione erunt aegrotantes resumendi, sed multo tempore a lavacro abstinendi atque vino, ne in periculum redeant. at si ex ista passione, ut saepe contingit, satyriasis fuerit effecta, erunt adhibenda ea quae paulo post dixerimus.

antiquorum autem medicorum nullius istius passionis tradidit curationem. aiunt denique Themisonem quamquam volentem non potuisse, siquidem ex rabido cane quondam [fuerat][13] vulneratus, etsi eius curationem assumeret mente, quippe scripturus, continuo admonitus in eandem laberetur. Democritus vero iubet origani decoctionem dari atque ipsum poculum quod 133 bibunt in sphaerae rotunditatem formari. est autem hoc genus decoctionis acerrimum atque stomachum vexans et incendens. in quo etiam idem sibi repugnare perspicitur: ait enim hydrophobiam esse incendium nervorum.

item quidam medici, ut Artorius memorat, alios in vasculum plenum frigida miserunt, alios in puteum posuerunt saccis immissos vel inclusos, ut necessitate bibere cogerentur, alii[14] in aquam calidam, nescii quod passionis curatio illa sit non ut bibant aegrotantes, sed ut bibere velint. quod fiet cum passio fuerit adiutoriis destructa. multi denique etiam bibentes raptu affecti sunt graviore. quapropter etiam toto corpore infundendos, ut putant, et in aquam frigidam magis vexabile comproba-134 mus: omne etenim frigus extendit tumentia. nam propterea, ut Artorius dixit, raptu interficiuntur.

item Aristoxenus ad corruptionem atque abundantiam liquoris intentus, praedandum dicit potum atque clysteribus utendum communiter omnibus depurgativae vel temperativae virtutis, sed haec tumorem passionis incendendo[15] geminant comitantia. item Tullius Bassus etiam sternutamentis utitur et clysteribus, cum generaliter haec passio mitigatione indigeat ob acutissimam celeritatem, et non, ut hic putat, corporativis[16]

[13] seclusi, sed fort. scribere malis ⟨cum⟩ fuerat vel sim.

[14] alios Rm

[15] intendendo edd.: corr. Bendz Eran 41. 67

[16] recorporativis Rm, sed cf. Chr. i. 183, iii. 54

6. 175 ff.

7. Cf. two other versions in Philumenus De venenatis animalibus, chap. 1: (1) Themison incurred the disease from a bite and was cured; (2) Themison incurred the disease from a friend who had it, and, though the illness was stubborn, it was finally cured.

2   When the disease declines, restore the patient's strength; but do not permit bathing or wine until a long time has passed, in order to avoid a dangerous relapse. If, as is often the case, the disease produces a condition of satyriasis, apply the treatment which we shall presently set forth.[6]

None of the physicians of old has described a treatment for hydrophobia. It is said that Themison wished to do so but was unable. The story[7] is that he was once bitten by a mad dog and, though he undertook a treatment, having worked it out in his mind, and was about to put it in writing, he suddenly had a recurrence of the pains and lapsed back into the disease. Democritus prescribes a decoction of marjoram and requires that the vessel from which the patient drinks be rounded in the form of a sphere. But this type of decoction is very sharp and burns and irritates the esophagus. In prescribing it, Democritus clearly goes counter to his own teaching, for he says that hydrophobia is a kindling of the sinews.

According to Artorius, some physicians place their patients in vessels filled with cold water[8] or shut them up in sacks and place the sacks in wells, so that they are simply forced to drink; others immerse their patients in hot water. But these physicians are unaware that the cure of this disease consists not in getting the patient to drink but in getting him to drink voluntarily; and this will be accomplished only when the disease is overcome by the remedies applied. Indeed, in many cases [of forced drinking] the patient even as he drinks suffers a worse convulsion. So, too, we consider the treatment by complete immersion of the body, and in cold water, particularly harmful, for the reason that anything cold aggravates inflammation; and that is why this treatment, as Artorius tells us, brings on a fatal seizure.

Aristoxenus, concerned as he is about decomposition and humoral excess, prescribes for all patients generally potions and clysters of purgative action, and such as will temper [the humors].[9] But these measures excite the inflammation in this disease and aggravate the symptoms. Tullius Bassus employs sternutatories and clysters, although this disease, because of its extreme acuteness, generally requires soothing treatment. The

8. Cf. Celsus v. 27. 2.

9. ἐπικεραστικός. Cf. 136; *Chr.* iv. 11.

adiutoriis sit asperanda,[17] quae Graeci metasyncritica vocant.
item Niger eius amicus etiam album helleborum dedit. Eudemus autem phlebotomans helleborum dat secunda vel tertia die,
135 atque cucurbitas affigit usque ad partium pustulationem. item
Agathinus libro De helleboro conscripto iubet etiam dari helleborum in initio passionis. alii podicem cataplasmandum iubent
helleboro, alii collyria ex ipso facientes, quae appellaverunt balanos, podici supponunt.

sed erunt communiter omnes culpandi, cum sit passio acuta
atque celeris et vehemens ac saepissime continua, quippe cum
numquam puram atque sinceram habeat dimissionem. et est
helleborum recorporativae virtutis ac propterea tardis passionibus conveniens, quas Graeci chronias appellant, et in earum
principaliter lenimento, atque regulis ciborum aegrotante prae-
parato, quod Graeci diaetam vocant, quod utique non sine tempore prolixo fieri potest. sine his igitur nihil veneno differet
136 helleborum datum. est etiam grave usque ad pustulationem
corporis cucurbitas apponere, et simile quiddam tumentes oculos
ligneo baculo inungere. item quidam castoreo potandos iubent
hydrophobas,[18] alii rosaceo oleo, alii diagridio aut elaterio aut
lacte vel pinguibus incongrue iusculis, et agitantes atque gra-
vantes aegros, et non eo tempore quo permitti potuit usus supra
dictorum praecautionis causa ⟨ac⟩[19] effugiendae passionis. nunc
etsi iam[20] praesens indigeat congrua curatione, clystere[21] depur-
gant vel temperant vim veneni, quae semper post effectam passionem contemnenda est, urgentiore cogente coenoteta.

item nihil aliud quam potum dare quoquo modo nituntur,
nunc gelu vel nivem offerentes aegrotis, nunc viridem ficum vel
137 pirum aut cucumerem et his similia. alii calami perforati initium ori aegrotantis immittunt, dehinc ex alia parte per aliam
cavernam aquam infundunt. alii poculo lineo[22] panno superim-
posito[23] vel beluae pelle[24] potandum putant, scilicet supersti-

[17] aspergenda G: exasperanda Rm
[18] hydrophobos A
[19] add. R
[20] etsi iam scripsi: etiam G: etiam si R
[21] cautere Schmid 101
[22] ligneo Rm
[23] subter imposito G: corr. Reinesius 511
[24] felle Reinesius 511

disease should not, as he recommends, be aggravated by alterative remedies (Greek *metasyncritica*). Niger, the friend of Bassus,
prescribes white hellebore. And Eudemus uses venesection and
prescribes hellebore on the second or third day; he also applies
35 cups, keeping them on until the parts in question blister. In his
book *On Hellebore* Agathinus prescribes this drug at the beginning of the disease. Others recommend the application of a hellebore plaster to the anus. And still others make suppositories
(Greek *balanoe*) out of hellebore and insert them in the anus.

But those who suggest these methods are one and all to be
censured, for the disease is acute, swift, violent, and practically
always continuous. In fact, it never exhibits a complete and perfect remission. But hellebore has a metasyncritic property and is
therefore suitable for chronic diseases (Greek *chroniae*). It
should be used chiefly in the interval of remission in such diseases, and only when the patient has been prepared for it by a
regulation of his food (Greek *diaeta*). For this procedure a considerable period of time is required. But the giving of hellebore
36 in any other circumstances is the same as giving poison. It is also
harmful to keep cups applied until the body blisters; indeed, it is
something like rubbing inflamed eyes with a wooden stick. Some
physicians mistakenly prescribe the drinking of castor in cases of
hydrophobia, others prescribe rose oil, and still others scammony
juice, elaterium, milk, or thick broths. In so doing they excite
and burden the patient, and not at a time when the use of these
substances might be permissible as a preventive measure and a
means of escaping the disease. It is now, when the disease is actually present and requires suitable treatment, that these physicians purge with a clyster or seek to overcome the effect of the
poison. But this effect should always be disregarded after the
disease is actually present, since a more urgent pathological condition now requires attention.

And some physicians are concerned only about giving the patient drink. They use every means, sometimes giving them ice or
snow, sometimes a green fig, a pear, a cucumber, or the like.
37 Some place one end of a hollow reed in the patient's mouth and
then pour water into the reed through the hole at the other end.
Others think the patient should drink from a cup covered with a
linen[10] cloth or the skin of a hyena; [in the latter case] they are ob-

10. Or reading *ligneo* (*Rm*), 'from a wooden cup covered with a cloth.'

tione traducti quod naturalis autoritas beluarum quae canibus est contraria timorem aegrotantium solvat. sed haec quae vulgus per experimenta probata putat longe aliena ab arte monstrantur. alia quoque quae facienda ordinaverunt ratione reicienda sunt, ut ea quae sunt vinosa ante declinationem offerenda. item frigida sunt ob tumorem incongrua. constringunt enim atque extendunt stricturae difficultatem, ex qua sine dubio hydrophobica passio confecta probatur.

138   ## XVII. DE ACUTO TORMENTO, QUOD GRAECI ILEON APPELLANT

TORMENTUM dictum est quod existiment aegrotantes convolvi atque torqueri suorum intestinorum verticula, vel quod spiritus ob abstinentiam clausus sese involvens vinctiones atque tormenta efficiat, vel quod vehementia dolorum supra eas partes quae patiuntur aegrotantes arcuati convolutique plicentur. Salimachus autem ait quosdam Pythagoricos apud Siciliam medicantes graeco nomine phragmon vocare, siquidem obtrusis na-
139 turalibus ventris officiis fieri videatur. item hanc passionem tertio libro Acutarum vel celerum passionum Asclepiades diffinivit hoc modo: tormentum est contortio extenta atque longi temporis intestinorum. sed hoc improprie dixit quod sit etiam longi temporis tormentum. est enim acuta atque celeris passio. denique hoc intestinorum dicimus tormentum esse contortionem extentam atque perniciosam.

sunt enim eius antecedentes causae communes quae etiam alias facere valent passiones, sed magis perfrictio, indigestio, atque cibi gravabiles et inflabiles vel novi, aut venenum potum aut cibo datum, aut fungi comesti.
140 sequitur autem in passione constitutos ventris vehemens inflatio et intestinorum, et dolor nimius iliorum aut ossium quae a pube usque ad ilia perveniunt, quae Graeci ephebia appellaverunt, totius quoque ventris atque superpositae cutis inflatio

---

1. *Tormentum* from *torqueo*; εἰλεός or ἰλεός from εἴλω. *Torqueo* and εἴλω mean 'twist,' and so 'squeeze' or 'block.'

viously led astray by a superstition that the natural power of hyenas, opposed as it is to dogs, will dispel the patient's fear. But these notions, which are popularly thought to have been proved sound in actual practice, are obviously quite out of keeping with the medical art. Reason also dictates the rejection of other prescriptions of these physicians, for instance, the giving of wine-like substances before the decline of the disease. And cold remedies are also unsuitable because of the inflammation, for cold has an astringent effect and aggravates the distress occasioned by the state of stricture, the state which is certainly involved in hydrophobia.

138   XVII. ACUTE INTESTINAL OBSTRUCTION
(GREEK *ILEOS*)

INTESTINAL obstruction (*tormentum*, 'ileus') gets its name either because the patient has a feeling that the folds of his intestines are tied up and twisted;[1] or because the pneuma is blocked and shut off, the resulting involution of the flow producing cramps and twisting pains; or else because the violent pains over the parts affected cause the patient to be bent over, twisted, and doubled up. Salimachus says that some Pythagorean physicians in Sicily give the disease the Greek name *phragmos* ['fence, obstruction'] because it clearly involves a blocking of the normal

139 functioning of the intestines. And Asclepiades in Book III of his *Acute* (i.e., swift) *Diseases* defines this disease as follows: 'Ileus is a severe and prolonged twisting of the intestines.' He errs, however, in saying that ileus is a prolonged disease, for actually it is acute and swift. We therefore define this disease of ileus as a severe and dangerous twisting of the intestines.

Its antecedent causes are the same as those which may produce other diseases too. The chief antecedent causes are a severe cold, indigestion, foods that produce a feeling of heaviness or cause gas or are strange, the drinking of poison or the taking of poison in combination with food, or the eating of [poisonous] mushrooms.

40   The signs of this disease are as follows: extreme flatulence of the stomach and intestines, severe pain in the flanks and in those bones (called *ephēbia* by the Greeks) which connect the pubes with the ilia, a puffing-up of the whole abdomen, the skin cover-

⟨et⟩[1] membranae maioris quam peritonaeum vocant, scilicet quae omnia interius tegit atque continet viscera, consensus etiam vesicae et officii ventris perfecta abstinentia, stomachi

141 eversio per nauseam, salivarum fluor, sitis vehemens, spiratio hirta atque anhelatio, articulorum frigidus torpor, pulsus densus, singultus, exitus per podicem venti nihil relevans.[2] ac si quicquam per clysterem fuerit iniectum, aut non admittitur ob nimietatem stricturae, aut admissum retinetur exitu negato, aut si fuerit redditum erit connexum pinguibus ac vesiculosis.[2a] mulieribus etiam matricis adductio ad superiora fiet, vomitus quoque humorum pinguium qui in ventriculo et ipsius orificio adhaerescebant contumaciter.

his vero qui perniciosius atque specialius iactantur etiam ster-
142 corum vomitus fiet, tunc quoque pulsus concidit, nigrescit corpus cum nimia linguae asperitate, aliquando etiam, ut Heraclides Tarentinus memorat quarto libro De internis passionibus, intestinorum verticula distentis cutibus apparent cum peritonaeo disiecto sola fuerit superposita cutis. alii vero memorant ventum per podicem redditum sine odore tetro perniciosum fore, ac si fuerit odoris tetri salutem promittere. in illis enim ob nimiam stricturam tamquam liquatus spiritus purior excluditur; in his autem ob quandam laxamenti facultatem infectus exhalationibus stercorum excludetur.

143 torminosam[3] igitur ab ista passione quam specialiter tormentum diximus magnitudine differre monstramus. hi enim levi dolore afficiuntur et ob hoc ventriculosi sive torminosi vocantur. item discernuntur dolore ventris. ventriculatio enim superius magis ventre est atque sub praecordiis, et saepe sine intestinorum tormento. discernitur etiam a coli vexatione. est enim principaliter coli vexatio unius intestini passio, atque tarda,
144 quam Graeci chroniam vocant, et diutissime perseverans; tormentum autem solius acutae passionis est omnium intestinorum vexatio.

item alii hanc passionem chordapson vocaverunt quod non aliter quam chordae intestina tendantur: nam veteres Graeci intestina chordas vocaverunt. sed hoc quoque nomen alii com-

---

[1] *add. R*
[2] relevans *scripsi, coll. Ac. iii. 194, Diaet. pass. 44*: relevantis *edd.*
[2a] viscosis *Haller*
[3] torminosa *edd.*: *fort.* tormina

ing it, and the large membrane (Greek *peritonaeos*) which incloses and holds together all the [lower] viscera, sympathetic pain in the bladder, complete stoppage of the functioning of the
141 bowels, gagging and nausea, copious flow of saliva, inordinate thirst, rough breathing and panting, cold numbness of the limbs, rapid pulse, and hiccoughs. The passing of wind through the anus brings no relief, and if an injection is made by clyster, it is either blocked by the strong stricture or, if let in, is retained and cannot be discharged or, if discharged, is mixed with fatty and frothy matter. In the case of women the womb is drawn upward. And the thick fluids which clung stubbornly to the stomach and its [upper] orifice are vomited.

And when the condition of the patient becomes particularly
142 dangerous, he even vomits excrement. In such cases the pulse also collapses, the body grows dark, the tongue is very rough, and sometimes, according to Heraclides of Tarentum in Book IV of his *Internal Diseases*, sections of the intestines may be seen swelling out the skin, when the peritoneum is ruptured and only the skin covers the intestines. Some say that the discharge of wind through the anus without a foul odor is a deadly sign; but that if the odor is foul it is a favorable sign. For in the former case, they say, the gas that is driven out is in a sense filtered and purified because of the strong state of stricture; while in the latter case the gas is tainted by the emanations from excrement because of a certain element of looseness.

143 Now cases of abdominal cramps differ in severity from the disease we specifically call 'ileus' (*tormentum*). For in the former the patients are subjected to comparatively mild pain; they are said to suffer from the coeliac disease or abdominal cramps. And the abdominal pain in the coeliac disease may be distinguished [from that in ileus]. For in the coeliac disease the pain is present particularly in the upper abdominal and precordial regions, and often there are no intestinal cramps. Again, ileus is distinguished from the disease of the colon, for the latter is essentially a disease of a single portion of the intestines and is a chronic disease
144 (Greek *chronia*) and may last a very long time. Ileus, however, is always an acute disease and involves all the intestines.

But some give the name *chordapsos* to this disease because the intestines are stretched like strings (*chordae*). And, in fact, the ancient Greeks called the intestines *chordae*, and some writers,

mune vocabulum tormento posuerunt, ut Hippocrates, Praxagoras, Euriphon Gnidius. alii differre dixerunt, ut Diocles libro
⟨quo⟩[4] De passionibus atque causis et curationibus scripsit. etenim tormentum non sine ructationibus dixit,[5] atque permisso[6]
per podicem vento sine stercorum egestione, ventrem quoque
non necessario durum fieri, et clysteris iniectionem accipere,

145 doloris etiam initium superioribus magis accedere; ⟨in chordap-
so⟩[7] autem[8] reicere aegrotantes, si mediocris fuerit passio, humorem, si vehemens, stercora; et neque iniectionem clysteris
admittere, ventrem quoque durum atque extentum iugiter in
orbem tumoris sublevatum, inferiores[9] autem intestinorum partes doloribus affici, stomachum quoque immobilem ac fixum vel
inflexum permanere.

146   sed de his huic dissentire necessarium non est. oportet enim
intentionem adhibere atque intelligere quod sit passio stricturae,
atque acuta vel celeris et vehemens. quapropter habendi sunt
aegrotantes loco mediocriter calido atque lucido, adhibita requie
cum silentio et abstinentia cibi usque ad primam diatriton, prohibito quoque somno donec accessio declinet. incipiente autem
eadem, articulorum adhibenda est blanda ex manibus calefactio,
et partes quae doluerint contegendae mundis et mollibus lanis.

147 apponenda etiam mediocris vaporatio, qua mitigari dolor possit,
ut sunt panni calidi atque linteola, vel vesica calida[10] et[11] oleo
semiplena, vel saccelli ex cantabro calido completi, vel polline
vel lini semine ex aqua mulsa.

cum autem statum sumpserit accessio, iubemus eos, si pati
potuerint, iugiter foveri oleo dulci atque calido, scilicet usu dextero, quo praerepto nuper infuso mox novum superfundatur
oleum. at si dolor coegerit, phlebotomandi erunt scilicet ex bra-

148 chio dimissionis tempore. et si ante diatriton id factum fuerit,
foventes primo os, deinde colluere permittimus ex aqua calida,
dabimus potum parvum ob mitigandum. si enim plurimum
sumpserint, gravatis tumentibus provocabitur passionis asperitas, sicut fiet cum grave quisquam cataplasma apponendum putaverit ex plurima atque corporosa inductura. at si in ipsa dia-

[4] addidi

[5] ⟨fieri⟩ dixit R

[6] emisso R

[7] add. R

[8] autem scripsi: item G

[9] interiores G: corr. Rm

[10] calido Schmid Mn 147 (retento ex)

[11] et Bendz Eran 41. 76: ex edd.

e.g., Hippocrates, Praxagoras, and Euryphon of Cnidos, use 'chordapsos' as a term equivalent to 'ileus.' But others say the two terms differ in meaning. Thus Diocles in his book *On Diseases and Their Causes and Treatment* says that ileus is always accompanied by belching and the passing of wind but no fecal matter through the anus; that the abdomen does not necessarily become hard; that the bowels admit the injection of a clyster; and that the beginning of the pain is generally in the higher parts. But in *chordapsos*, he says, there is vomiting of fluid matter in mild cases and of excrement in serious cases; the bowel does not admit the injection of a clyster; the abdomen is of unrelieved tenseness and hardness and is swollen in a circular area of inflammation; there is pain in the lower parts of the intestines, and the esophagus, too, remains stiff, tense, and inflexible.

146   Now we need not express any disagreement with Diocles on these matters. For the important thing is to have in mind the nature of the disease and to understand that it is a disease involving a state of stricture and is acute (i.e., swift) and violent. Keep the patient, therefore, in a room that is moderately warm and light; have him remain perfectly still and quiet; do not give him any food until the end of the first three-day period; and do not permit him to sleep until the attack declines. But at the beginning of the attack warm the patient's limbs gently, using your hands for this purpose, and cover the painful parts with 147 soft, clean wool. And apply mild heat to relieve the pain, using warm cloths and linens, or a bladder half-full of hot water and olive oil, or bags filled with hot bran, flour, or flaxseed dipped in hydromel.

When the attack reaches its highest stage, have the patient continuously fomented, if he can stand it, with warm sweet olive oil, skilfully arranging the treatment so that, as soon as the previous supply of oil is used up, a new supply is ready to be poured on. And if the pain requires it, perform venesection at the arm 148 during a period of remission. If venesection is performed before the end of the three-day period, first foment the patient's face [after the venesection], then allow him to rinse his mouth with warm water, and give him a little to drink in order to soothe him. For if he drinks a great deal, the inflamed parts are further burdened and the disease increases in severity, just as happens if someone prescribes a heavy poultice requiring the application of

trito fuerit adhibita phlebotomia, parum differentes ob resumptionem unctione corpus curamus, et sorbile damus quiddam
149 tenue, atque panem ex aqua calida, non quidem plurimum. ea
enim quae ob appositionem cataplasmatis exterius admoti asperantur, haec magis plurimum distenduntur cibis uberioribus
gravata. alternis denique diebus cibum dabimus donec passio
declinet. dehinc cataplasmata adhibemus ex pollinibus et lini
atque faenugraeci seminibus ex mulso confecta vel calida et oleo,
illud curantes ut calida perseverent plurimo tempore et neque
valida atque robusta inductione gravabilia fiant pondere: faciunt enim aegrotis dolores augeri.

tunc etiam cucurbitas apponimus, sed eas quae sint osculo la-
150 tiores[12] atque labiis flexis, lenius enim atque blando tractu arri-
piunt membra; tunc etiam scarificatione utemur. vel in cucurbitarum vicem, ne earum pondere grave quicquam aegrotantes
sentiant, vitrea apponimus vascula vel testea, quae Graeci amphoras[13] vocaverunt. tunc spongiis vaporamus expressis ex calida et oleo vel decoctione faenugraeci aut lini seminis aut agrestis
malvae, et rursum cataplasmamus. inicimus etiam per clysterem oleum calidum vel calidam et oleum ⟨vel⟩[14] ex supra dictis
151 decoctionibus quicquam. est etiam consuetum nobis aquam
oleo dulci aequali modo commixtam cum hibisco coquere donec
aqua insumatur, tunc oleum remanens concepta lenitate[15] atque
pinguedine ex radice supra dicta inicere per clysterem. nam si
solum oleum fuerit cum radice hibisci non admixta aqua decoctum, necessario nidorosum fiet. adhibemus etiam encathismata ex calida et oleo[16] vel quarumcumque laxativarum materiarum decoctione.

cum autem declinare passio coeperit, etiam embasim adhibemus ex oleo, vel calida et oleo, aut decoctione laxativarum ma-
152 teriarum, non sine cautione. declinanda est enim perfrictio,
quapropter erit facienda in calido loco vel balnei fornice, quem
appellant architholum[17] sive cameram.[18] at si sensus aliquis
permanens erit duritiae, cataplasmabimus ex ordei farina et
adipe porcino recente et pice liquida. tunc cerotaria apponemus
et malagmatum leniora, ordinantes etiam lavacrum et varium
cibum et vinum ultimo, praecaventes multo tempore frigida

---

[12] latiore R   [13] ambicas *Reinesius 668; cf. Chr. iii. 23, iv. 94*
[14] *addidi:* ⟨et⟩ R   [15] *fort.* lēvitate   [16] oleum G: *corr.* R
[17] architholum *Haller:* achicholum G: aliqui tholum *Rm: an* Graeci tholum?
[18] *fort. scrib.* camaram

a large, ponderous mass. But if the venesection is performed at the conclusion of the three-day period, after a brief delay to permit the patient to recover, anoint his body, and give him a thin gruel and some bread dipped in warm water. But do not give a large amount, for the parts which are irritated by the external application of a poultice are even more severely strained when they are burdened by excessive food. Give food, then, on alternate days until the disease declines; and apply poultices made with flour, flaxseed, and fenugreek seed moistened in mead or in hot water and olive oil. See that the poultices remain warm a long time and that the matter applied is not so stout and bulky that the poultice becomes burdensome by reason of its weight. For such poultices increase the distress of patients.

Also apply cups, using those with broad mouths and curved lips. For their action is milder and they draw up the parts [to which they are applied] with a gentle pull. Also employ scarification. But to keep the patient from feeling burdened by the weight of [metal] cups, you may apply in their stead the small glass or earthen vessels that the Greeks call *amphorae.* Then warm the parts with sponges wrung out of hot water and olive oil, or a decoction of fenugreek seed, flaxseed, or marsh mallow. After this treatment use poultices again. And inject a clyster of warm olive oil, or warm water and olive oil, or any of the decoctions just mentioned. It is also our custom to boil marsh mallow root in water mixed with sweet olive oil in equal parts; when the water is all boiled off, the remaining oil, which has obtained a mildness and thickness from the marsh mallow root, is then injected as a clyster. But if only the oil is boiled with the root and water is not added, the oil necessarily becomes too pungent. Prescribe also sitz baths of hot water and olive oil or a decoction of any of the relaxing substances.

And when the disease begins to decline, prescribe a bath in olive oil, or hot water and oil, or a decoction of relaxing substances. But be very careful, for the patient must not take cold. The bath should therefore be taken in a warm room, such as the vaulted room (Greek *architholos* or *camara*) of a public bath. But if any feeling of hardness persists, apply poultices of barley meal, fresh hog fat, and liquid pitch. Then employ cerates and mild emollient plasters. And prescribe bathing, varied food, and finally wine. But for a long period avoid giving the patient any-

quaeque atque indigestionem et inflabiles vel acres et minus
digestibiles cibos.

153   veterum autem medicorum [ut][19] Hippocrates secundo libro
De morbis communiter inquit frigeranda superiora, particulariter autem adhibenda vomifica medicamina, et phlebotomia ex
brachio et capite. tunc ⟨in⟩[20] sacculum[21] aqua calida plenum deponendos[22] iubet aegrotantes, facere etiam collyrium decem digitorum, quem appellavit balanum, atque hunc summo tactu
felle taurino ungendum; tunc si nihil perfecerit,[23] clysterem ad-
154 hibendum. vel si hoc quoque minus valuerit, et[24] folliculo artis
aerariae immittendum inquit ventum per podicem, quo distantia ventris atque intestinorum replicatis folliculis[25] fiat. tunc
statim adhibendum clysterem probat, detracto supradicto folliculo, et podicem cum spongia obstruendum, atque in aquam
calidam aegrotantem deponendum. utendum inquit primo tempore passionis melle decocto atque vino. secundo libro Epidemion multum vini meraci atque frigidi dari iubet, donec somnus
vel dolor fiat crurum.

    suspicione causarum sollicitatus: existimat enim vel constituit
155 fieri passionem incendio superiorum et frigore inferiorum. contrarias igitur virtute materias adhibendas iudicavit, non intuens
passionem ex tumore fuisse confectam. denique principio vomitus, quem adhibendum probat, asperat eius celeritatem, siquidem disiciendo[25a] corpora commoveat. phlebotomare autem
convenit non post vomitum, sed laxamenti causa, non ut Hippocrates affectandum putat, ob frigidandum corpus. dehinc ex
brachio, non ex capite neque simul ex multis partibus phlebotomare: etenim repentina sanguinis effusio defectum faciens non
sinit congruam fieri detractionem, vel quantum magnitudini
passionis est conveniens.

156   collyrium autem felle taurino perunctum omnifariam nocens
accipimus. etenim ob acrimoniam fellis atque mordicationem
tumentia provocat in fervorem, et ob longitudinem digitorum
decem immissum premit eas partes quae neque tenuem liquorem

[19] *om. R*
[20] *add. A*
[21] vasculum *A: cf. 133*
[22] deponendo *G:* deponere *A*
[23] profecerit *Rm*
[24] et *om. R: fort.* ex
[25] *an* resimplicatis verticulis?
[25a] *fort.* dissecando

2. *De morbis* iii. 14 (= VII. 134 Littré). Cf. 28 and 85, above.
3. *Epid.* ii, 6, 26 (V. 136 Littré).

thing cold; and take care not to cause indigestion by giving him foods that produce gas or are acrid and hard to digest.

3   Among the ancient physicians, Hippocrates in Book II of his work *On Diseases*[2] prescribes a general cooling treatment for the upper parts, and, in particular, prescribes emetics and also venesection at the arm and head. He then has the patient placed in a tub filled with hot water. He also prescribes a suppository (Greek *balanos*) ten digits long, its tip smeared with a coating of ox bile. Now if these measures bring no improvement, he orders a

4 clyster. And if this, too, is of no avail, he prescribes the injection of air through the anus by means of a metal-worker's bellows, the purpose being to dilate the stomach and intestine by opening and closing the bellows. He then removes the bellows and has a clyster immediately injected. The anus is then stopped up with a sponge and the patient placed in a hot water bath. Hippocrates also prescribes the use of cooked honey and wine in the early stages of the disease. And in Book II of the *Epidemiae*[3] he says that a large quantity of cold undiluted wine should be given the patient until sleep comes or there is pain in the legs.

    In these prescriptions he is influenced by what he suspects to be the causes of the disease, for it is his opinion or conviction that the disease is caused by burning heat in the upper parts and

5 cold in the lower. He therefore recommends the employment of remedies of opposite qualities and is not aware that the disease involves a state of inflammation. And so, to begin with, the emetics he prescribes add to the acuteness of the disease, for vomiting tears the body asunder and agitates it. And venesection is a suitable remedy, but not after vomiting. It should be performed in order to relax the patient and not, as Hippocrates believes, for the purpose of cooling the body. Venesection, moreover, should be performed on the arm and not on the head or on many parts at the same time. For [in this last case] the sudden [initial] outpouring of blood causes a collapse and thereafter prevents a suitable withdrawal from taking place, that is to say, an amount of blood corresponding to the seriousness of the disease.

6.   And we consider the use of a suppository smeared with ox bile quite harmful. For the acrid properties of the bile and its griping effect produce violent heat in the inflamed parts. And the insertion of a suppository ten digits long causes pressure on parts which cannot receive or hold even a thin fluid without a feeling

sine gravatione accipere vel ferre valent. nam ex[26] aerario folliculo quid dicere oportet, si ubi inflationis metus est immittendum extrinsecus existimat ventum, atque (quod est maximi pec-
157 cati) frigidum, his partibus quae etiam naturali tactu praegra-
vantur, non aliter quam si quemquam in tetanica passione constitutum, cum sit potestatis laxativis curare virtutibus, eundem
organis distendere contendamus.

advertendum igitur quoniam magis roborat vexationem vel
duplicat corporis inflationem adiciens graviora, quo etiam per
clysterem liquoribus magis praegravet corpus, et tumentia importune vento vexata etiam liquoris percussu intemporali fe-
riantur. item spongia apponenda, quam probat, extenta magis
premit. utitur autem vino, malis quidem sed suis similibus
158 consiliis. neque enim temporaliter declinationem passionis ob-
servavit; praeterea usu immodico, siquidem plurimum dari iubeat et intemperatum,[27] quod saepe in sanitate constitutos alienari
mente[28] perficit; tunc etiam incongrue, siquidem frigidum,[29] omne etenim frigidum tumentia auget. repugnanti iudicio vinum
dare perspicitur, effectum somno atque dolori crurum ascribens.
somnus etenim levigata atque soluta passione efficitur, dolore
autem peiorante et asperato tollitur, quod ita manifestum est ut
demonstratione non indigeat.

159 Diocles autem libro quo De passionibus atque causis et curationibus scribit, phlebotomat in passione constitutos atque cataplasmatibus curat ex polline, quod Graeci omen lysin vocant, et
adipe et vino et faece. tunc praepotat atque clysterizat ex
abrotani semine cum mulsa[30] ex aceto, et aristolochia et cumino
et nitro et feniculi radice decocta ex vino, admixta aqua marina
vel passo vel acriore vino, sive lacte cum decoctione lini seminis
et mellis, vel similibus.

quarto autem libro De curationibus iuvenes, inquit, atque ha-
160 bitudine robustos, et magis quibus dolor ad latera fertur, phlebotomandos probo ex manu dextera interiorem venam,[31] et sub-
mittendos in aquam calidam, fotis ventri inicere admixto sale

[26] de A
[27] intemperato edd.
[28] mentem G: corr. Rm (cf. Ac. i. 6)
[29] frigido edd.
[30] mulso A, fort. recte
[31] manus dexterae interiore vena Rm: fort. manu dextera interiore vena (an ⟨vel⟩
suppleto post dextera?)

of distress. And what are we to say about the smith's bellows and
57 the notion of Hippocrates that air, and cold air, too (which is a
serious error), should be injected from outside into parts which
are already burdened by the natural effect [of the disease]? And
this in a disease where we must guard against gas! It is as if in a
case of tetanus we were to try to stretch the patient with instruments, when it was in our power to treat him with relaxing
remedies.

We must, therefore, remark that Hippocrates increases the
patient's distress, that is to say, aggravates the flatulent condition by adding heavy burdens. For in injecting fluids by a clyster
he weighs down the body even more; the inflamed parts that are
already sorely irritated by the injection of air are now also stung
by the untimely impact of the fluid. Likewise, the use of the
sponge, as he prescribes, adds to the pressure on the distended
parts. And his use of wine is unsound, though in accord with his
58 customary practice. For in timing the prescription of wine he
does not wait for the disease to decline. And his use of wine is
excessive, for he prescribes the giving of a large amount; and he
prescribes undiluted wine, which often causes mental disturbance even in healthy persons. And the wine he uses is unsuitable,
for it is cold. In fact, anything cold aggravates inflamed parts.
And Hippocrates evidently prescribes wine with conflicting purpose when he indicates both sleep and pain in the legs as expected effects, for sleep comes when a disease is alleviated and
overcome, while sleep is banished when a disease is aggravated
and the pains increased. And this is so obvious that it requires
no proof.

159   Diocles in his work *On Diseases and Their Causes and Treatment* recommends venesection for those who have this disease,
and treats them with poultices of flour (Greek *ōmēlysis*), fat,
wine, and the lees of wine. Then he uses, both as potion and as
clyster, southernwood seed with oxymel, or birthwort, cumin,
nitrum, and a decoction of fennel root in wine with an admixture
of sea water, or raisin wine, or a sharp wine, or milk with a decoction of flaxseed and honey, or the like.

In Book IV of his work *On Treatments* he prescribes the letting
of blood from the interior vein of the right hand in cases of young
160 persons in sturdy health, and particularly in cases where the
pain moves to the sides. He then has these patients placed in hot

clysterem, et rursum in aquam calidam deponere et fovere.
praepotandos autem iubet etiam medicamentis, hoc est panacis
dimidia drachma in mulso ex aceto tepido resoluta, et myrrhae
obolos duos cum peristereonis herbae foliis in vino albo, vel cumino aethiopico. adiuvat etiam plurimos plumbi catapotium
transvoratum, impellit enim pondere et excludit obtrudentia.
diurnis, inquit, praeterea diebus sitientibus potandum vinum
dulce vel aquam temperatam[32] aut marinam cum vino albo, aut
161 centauream herbam aut nitrum vel eius spumam, ut ea quae potuerit solvat. danda etiam sorbilia, vel cantabri lotura cum
melle vel bromi sucus vel ptisanae aut cum farina olera cocta,
alia ex adipe, alia ex halica atque sale. sorbendum etiam et
iuscellum scari piscis et carabi et buccinarum et cancrorum.
tunc resumptio, inquit, adhibenda, cuius quidem materies per-
currerit quas superfluum est recensere. etenim ex supra dictis
varia atque iners commixtio materiarum demonstratur.

non enim solos oportet iuvenes phlebotomari, sed etiam alios
in aliis aetatibus constitutos; neque semper e dextera manu vel
162 interiore vena, sed etiam ex sinistra atque exteriore facta. detractio enim[33] tumentia relaxat; usus autem ⟨clysterum⟩[34] acrimoniae causa erigit in fervorem tumentia. est praeterea vexabilis praebibendi medicaminis potio. etenim sunt acria atque
mordentia, et quae non sint mitigativa celeritatis neque tumoris relaxantia. plumbum vero transvoratum premit quidem
atque impellit pondere, sed tactu necessario frigidat atque intestina densitate coacta vexatione distendit. iuscella autem in
corruptione[35] facilia et inflantia esse noscuntur; item ptisanae[36]
eadem perficere. vinum quoque in augmento inimicum.

163 Praxagoras tertio libro Curationum clysterem iubet adhiberi,
dans medicamina purgativae virtutis, atque per vomitum cor-

---

[32] *fort.* aqua temperatum

[33] *post* exteriore *interpung.* R: facta enim detractio Rm: *fort.* facienda detractio.
⟨quae⟩ enim

[34] autem ⟨clysterum⟩ Rm: atque G   [35] *fort.* corruptionem

[36] *fort.* ptisana *Bendz 53:* ptisanae ⟨succus⟩ R (⟨succum⟩ A)

---

4. Or, reading *aqua temperatum*, 'sweet wine diluted with water.'

water, and after the fomentations he prescribes the injection into the bowels of a clyster containing an admixture of salt. After this he orders the patients again to be placed in hot water and fomented. And he prescribes that they be given drugs to drink, such as half a drachm of allheal dissolved in lukewarm oxymel, or two obols of myrrh with leaves of holy vervain in white wine, or Ethiopian cumin. Many are aided, he says, by swallowing a lead pill, for by its weight it dislodges and drives out the obstructing matter. Moreover, if the patient desires it, says Diocles, he should daily drink sweet wine,[4] or a mixture of [fresh] water or sea water with white wine, or centaury, nitrum, or aphronitrum,[5] in order to dissolve as much of the obstructing matter as possible. He also prescribes soft food, e.g., bran water with honey, a gruel of oats or pearl barley, vegetables cooked with flour, some with fat, others with spelt groats and salt, or a broth made from parrot wrasse, crayfish, bucina, or crab. He says that the patient should thereafter be given a diet to build up his strength, and he gives a list of substances. But it is unnecessary to repeat these now, for it is clear from what has already been said that Diocles prescribes a motley and inept mingling of substances.

Moreover, venesection should be performed not merely on young persons but on those of other ages as well; and not in every case on the right hand or the interior vein, but sometimes on the left hand and the exterior vein. Now this withdrawal [of blood] relaxes the inflamed parts, but the use of sharp clysters irritates these parts so that they burn. Moreover, the drinking of the drugs is harmful, for the substances are acrid and griping; they do not relieve the acute condition or relax the inflammation. And the taking of lead, to be sure, presses and drives along [the obstructing matter] by its weight, but necessarily produces a cold effect by its touch. Its astringent action condenses the intestines, causing irritation and increased tension. And it is well known that broths are prone to decompose and cause gas. This is also true of the pearl barley gruel. Wine, too, is harmful in the increasing phase of the disease.

In Book III of his work *On Treatments* Praxagoras prescribes a clyster, purgative drugs, and emetics to dry out the body. He

5. Aphronitrum seems to be either a pure or a slightly caustic variety of nitrum (native sodium carbonate), according to K. C. Bailey, *The Chemical Chapters of Pliny the Elder* (nn. to *HN* xxxi. 106, 112).

pora dissecari.[37] contendit etiam potandum mulsum ex aceto
cum pipere atque nitro et recenti lacte[38] cum mulso et aqua.
dat etiam radices circa vesperam comedendas, praedato aut
super dato oleo. utitur praeterea ad podicem collyrio, et inicit
atque praepotat absinthio aegrotantes cum aceto, et vino sin-
cero cum oleo irino. sed vomitu utitur donec stercora faciat
evomi; aliquos etiam post vomitum phlebotomat et vento per
podicem replet, ut Hippocrates.

164   item libris De causis atque passionibus et curationibus vinum
dulce dari iubet et rursum Hippocratis ordinem sequitur, con-
gerens omnia peccata, et nihil aliud quam facere diruptionem
intestinorum affectans, per acrimoniam medicamentorum tentat[39] et inflabilium potionum et iniectione virtute similium:
quae infesta tensione ac tumore intestinorum aut retenta ruptionem[40] perficiunt[41] vel putredinem, aut acervatim exclusa[42]
alio genere interfectionem faciunt.[43]   item omne stercus per
vomitum emissum tumoris intestinorum est argumentum. non

165 enim sine tumore nimio hoc perfici potest. ex[44] intestinis ex-
pressum per ventrem transiens stomacho incidens stercus per
⟨eam⟩[45] partem excutitur, quo probatur manificam[46] mortem
Praxagoras magis quam curationem voluisse scribere.

quibusdam etiam manibus premens intestina magna quassatione vexavit quibus intestinum, quod Graeci typhlon enteron[47]
appellant, in folliculum fuerit lapsum, plurimis stercoribus confertum.[48]   item confectis quibusdam supradictis adiutoriis dividendum probat pubetenus, dividendum etiam intestinum rectum atque detracto stercore consuendum dicit, in protervam
veniens chirurgiam. oportebat enim si ad hoc accedendum necessitas imperabat enterocelicorum approbare curationem.

[37] desiccare *edd.*: *cf. adn. ad Chr. iii. 153*

[38] *fort.* recens lac

[39] ⟨id⟩ tentat *R*

[40] ruptione *G: corr. Rm*

[41] perficiant *A* (faciant *infra retento*)

[42] excluso *G: corr. Rm*

[43] faciant *edd.*

[44] ⟨nam⟩ ex *R*

[45] *add. R*

[46] manificam *Kühn 66* (*fort. scrib.* manu factam): magnificam *edd.*

[47] τύφλον ἔντερον *G*   [48] confertum *R*: confectum *G*

recommends the drinking of oxymel with pepper and nitrum, and fresh milk with honey and water. He gives the patient radishes to eat in the evening, preceding or following this prescription with olive oil. In addition, he employs an anal suppository, and he uses, both as clyster and as potion, wormwood with vinegar and pure wine with iris oil. He employs emetics until he causes the vomiting of excrement. And in some cases he performs venesection after the vomiting and, following Hippocrates,[6] injects air through the anus.

In his work *On Diseases and Their Causes and Treatment* Praxagoras prescribes sweet wine and again follows the system of Hippocrates, heaping up error upon error. He seeks to do no less than to tear the intestines to pieces and tries to accomplish this with his acrid drugs, potions that produce gas, and clysters of like nature. These remedies bring about a dangerous distention and inflammation of the intestines and are either retained, causing the intestines to burst or rot, or are driven out in a mass, producing death in another form. Furthermore, whenever excrement is vomited, there is proof of a state of inflammation in the intestines, since vomiting of this sort cannot take place without considerable inflammation. The excrement is driven out from the intestines, passes through the stomach, and, reaching the esophagus, is expelled through that part. From this it would seem that Praxagoras wanted to describe a hand-inflicted murder rather than a cure.

And sometimes he presses the intestines with his hands and causes great distress in those cases where the part of the intestine which the Greeks call *typhlos enteros* ['cecum'] has slipped into the scrotum, filled with excrement. And in some cases, after the procedures already described have been carried out, Praxagoras recommends making an incision in the pubic region, then cutting open the rectum, removing the excrement, and sewing up [the rectum and the abdomen].[7] But in this prescription Praxagoras resorts to wanton surgery. Indeed, if necessity compelled such measures, he should have prescribed the treatment used in intestinal hernia.[8]

6. *De morbis* iii. 14 (= VII. 136 Littré).

7. See K. Sudhoff, 'Zur operativen Ileusbehandlung des Praxagoras,' *Quellen u. Stud. z. Gesch. d. Naturwiss. u. d. Medizin*, III (1933), 359–62.

8. Perhaps the meaning is: 'he should also have adopted the remedy [i.e., surgery] in cases of intestinal hernia.'

166 temere Erasistratus secundo libro De ventre scribens culpans
copiam atque acrimoniam clysterum ab antiquis ordinatam, ipse
quoque utitur clystere ex nitro atque sale. iniciendum etiam
probat acre collyrium, et similibus utitur cataplasmatibus, hoc
est ome lysi cum myrto,[50] vino, fico, et chamelaea. et abstinet
a cibo usque ad passionis declinationem; tunc dat mulsum te-
pidum, dehinc sorbilem ptisanae sucum. sed hic aliorum accusationi iungendus est. etenim culpans tamquam nocivam acrimoniam iniectionum, non custodit earum vexationem; quin
etiam ex cataplasmatibus constringens atque densans tumentia
167 gravius aegrotantes affecit. est etiam quibusdam usque ad passionis declinationem abstinentia vexabilis; hic autem iam declinante passione mulsum dandum probat, quod ante declinationem fuerat ordinandum.

Herophilus de his nihil locutus est.

Asclepiades tertio libro Celerum vel acutarum passionum aliqua gratissime, aliqua valenter ordinavit, in quibus est etiam
inhibitio vaporationum ex aqua calida, tamquam facile frige-
rantium.[51] sed fricandas inquit partes quae patiuntur oleo plurimo tempore atque operose quantum loca ipsa pati potuerint.
fugienda[52] inquit etiam declinationis tempore lavacra, non con-
168 iciens quoniam usum vaporationum, non genus damnavit. potest enim quisque etiam in alia vaporationum specie perfrigescere nisi dextro usu fuerint adhibitae. defricatio autem adiutorium est chronicae[53] passionis, non acutae vel celeris, sed magis
si, ut iubet, operantius fuerit adhibita atque multo tempore. si
igitur vera intentione loquamur, neque sibi haec quae ordinavit
conveniunt. ait enim debere fricationem adhiberi multo tempore vel quantum ipsae partes patiuntur, cum neque tumentia
ex initio fricationem fieri admittant, quippe cum neque cataplasmata gravia valeant sustinere. lavacra in declinatione adiu-
169 vant passionis solutionem. utitur etiam embasi ex oleo adhibita, et tempus non finit adiutoriis.

[50] *fort.* myrteo

[51] frigentium *edd.*

[52] fuganda *G: corr. R*

[53] *fort. scrib.* chroniae (*Schmid 8*)

9. I.e., *On Abdominal Diseases*, as we learn from Galen (XI. 192. 8 Kühn).

In Book II of his work *On the Abdomen*[9] Erasistratus criticizes the large number of sharp clysters prescribed by the ancient doctors. But he himself thoughtlessly makes use of a clyster of nitrum and salt. And he recommends the insertion of a sharp suppository, and also employs sharp plasters, that is to say, *ōmēlysis* with myrtle, wine, fig, and chamelaea. He keeps the patient from food until the declining phase of the disease; at that time he prescribes warm mead and then a thin pearl barley gruel. But we must include Erasistratus with the others in our criticism; for, though he objects to the injection of sharp substances as harmful, he does not himself avoid their harsh effects. Indeed, his plasters have an astringent and condensing effect upon the inflamed parts and aggravate the condition of the patient. Furthermore, in some cases it is harmful for the patient to abstain from food until the declining phase of the disease. But Erasistratus waits until the disease is already declining to prescribe even mead, which should be given before the decline.

Herophilus has nothing to say about this disease.

Asclepiades in Book III of his *Swift* (i.e., acute) *Diseases* proposes some very mild and some strong measures. And he rejects the use of hot water as a means of applying heat, on the ground that the patients may easily become chilled, but he holds that the affected parts should be massaged with olive oil for as long a time and as energetically as they can endure it. He declares that bathing should be avoided even during the decline of the disease, unaware that what he is objecting to is the method of applying heat, not the principle. For one may also catch cold in any of the other types of heating treatment if the procedure is not carried out skilfully. And massage is a suitable remedy for a chronic disease; it is not suitable for a swift or acute disease, particularly if, as Asclepiades prescribes, it is to be carried out vigorously and for a long period. Indeed, to speak truly, his prescriptions are not even self-consistent. For he says that massage is to be continued for a long period or as long as the parts themselves permit, but the fact is that parts which are inflamed do not from the very beginning permit of massage. Indeed, they cannot even endure heavy plasters. Again, baths help to overcome the disease in its declining phase. But, though Asclepiades does employ a bath of olive oil, he does not fix time-limits for his measures.

Serapion vero tertio libro Curationum alia similia Erasistrato ordinavit, denique eius accusationi iungendus est. utitur etiam catapotio ex plumbi ramento et cocco cnidio et sale et elaterio et resina et castoreo et diagridio, quorum singula acerrimae esse virtutis probantur atque percutientia, et neque celeritati passionum neque tumori congrua.

Heraclides autem Tarentinus libro quarto Internarum curationum existimabiles constituens suspiciones, aliter inquit curandos tumore affectos, aliter eos qui crassioribus intestinis la-
170 borant et stercoribus opprimuntur. utitur autem per diem et per[54] noctem cerotariis ex cera et resina et irino oleo vel cyprino oleo aut anethino.[55] miscet etiam omae lysi panacem tritum et chamaepityn cum absinthio et cyprino oleo. scribit praeterea potiones quibus inquit praepotandos aegrotantes, ex aniso, castoreo, nitro, hyssopo, calamo,[57] mulso ex aceto. clysterem etiam adhibet admixto absinthio vel centaureo aut cucumeris agrestis radice. dat etiam mulsum ex aceto et purgativum po-
171 tandum medicamen ex diagridio. alia quoque virtutum milia conscribit purgativorum medicaminum, quae praebenda iubet non aliter quam cetera[58] acriora medicamina. et nullam curam adhibet mitigationis laxativae respiciens qua possit tumor mitigari.

sed ⟨Soranus⟩[59] ait communiter omnibus aliarum sectarum principibus quomodo intestina tumore densata atque contenta plurima materia et acerrima et vulnerabili, ut illi probant, onerata interfectionem faciunt aegrotantis; denique si forte quisquam iliacam evaserit passionem, necessario ex supradictis dysentericus fiet.

172 item Thessalus primo libro De regulis, quas Graeci diaetas, alia quidem ut Methodicus scripsit, alia culpabiliter, adiciens quod potum ⟨parvum⟩[60] dare debeamus, siquidem ad loca pa-

54 per *om*. R

55 anethonio G: *corr*. R

57 calaminthe R

58 caeteri G: *corr*. R

59 *addidi*

60 *supplevi*: ⟨exiguum⟩ R

10. Or perhaps 'for a day and a night.'

11. Perhaps 'sweet flag.'

Since Serapion in Book III of his work *On Treatments* sets forth various prescriptions similar to those of Erasistratus, he must be included in our criticism of Erasistratus. He also employs a pill made of bits of lead, Cnidian berry, salt, elaterium, resin, castor, and scammony juice. But each of these substances has acrid and penetrating properties and is unsuitable in cases of acute disease and inflammation.

In Book IV of his work *On the Treatment of Internal Diseases* Heraclides of Tarentum makes some plausible conjectures; he declares that those who are suffering from inflammation must be treated differently from those who are suffering an affection of the large intestines and are burdened with excrement. And day and night[10] he employs cerates of wax, resin, and oil of iris, henna, or dill. He also mixes powdered allheal and ground pine with *ōmēlysis*, adding wormwood and henna oil. In addition, he describes the potions which he orders the patients to take. They are made of anise, castor, nitrum, hyssop, reed,[11] and oxymel. And he employs a clyster to which he adds wormwood, centaury, or root of wild cucumber. He also gives the patient oxymel to drink, and a purgative drug made with scammony juice. Heraclides describes countless other purgative drugs which he recommends along with his other sharp drugs; but with regard to the problem of relieving the inflammation he offers no treatment with the required relaxing and soothing effect.

But Soranus asserts,[12] by way of general criticism of all the leaders of the other sects, that when the intestines are congested and strained by inflammation it is fatal to burden them with the sharp and injurious matter which these leaders prescribe. Furthermore, if a patient happens to escape alive from the disease of ileus, he will inevitably fall victim to dysentery as a result of these very remedies.

Thessalus in Book I of his treatise *On Regimen* (Greek *diaeta*) writes in part as a Methodist, but for the rest his work is open to criticism. Thus he holds that only a small amount of drink should be given the patient,[13] on the ground that it passes down

---

12. It is just possible that the traditional text, which makes this paragraph a quotation not from Soranus but from Heraclides, is to be retained. And even if ⟨Soranus⟩ be supplied, the paragraph may belong at the end of 174.

13. The prescription is the same as that of the later Methodists; it is Thessalus' reasoning that Soranus criticizes.

tientia descendat. quod contra sectae disciplinam videtur sen-
sisse, et contra seipsum inconsequenter fuisse commotus, siquidem pro patientibus locis nolit[61] esse mutabilem curationem. secundo libro quem Comparationem appellavit contradicens Era-
173 sistrato haec ait apertissime discordantia sermonibus: 'non enim
pro differentia partium mutatur liquidorum quantitas, sed ob
stricturam vel solutionem.' inconsequenter igitur idem in iliacis
patientis loci causa potus quantitatem minuendam existimat.
erat enim prompte dicendum atque demonstrandum quomodo
consideratione acutae atque celeris passionis minuenda fuit potus quantitas.

item quidam nostri scriptores, Themisonis sectatores, cuminum oleo decoxerunt ob adhibendum fotum, aut tritum lanis
asperserunt. item alii oleo rutam decoquentes iniciunt per clys-
174 terem, et iubent vaporari ex cineribus. mixtos etenim oleo vel
quodam laxativo liquori ex decoctione congruarum materiarum
praefecto in vasculo ex[62] duobus digitis alto atque ambitu simili
loci patientis mittendos, suppositis carbonibus non flammosis
donec liquor insumatur; tunc circumtento[63] linteolis vasculo
atque parum refricto, convertendos in linteola ac refundendos
cineres; tunc colligato vasculo fundo tenus et constricto linteo
fortiori patientia vaporare loca. equidem vere obtunditur admixtione olei et aquae cumini vel cinerum asperitas, sed est melius ex initio usque ad finem recta intentione congrua passionibus adhibere.

175   XVIII. DE SATYRIASI

SATYRIASIS est vehemens veneris appetentia cum tensione ob
aegram corporis passionem. vocatur autem, ut quidam vo-

[61] velit *Rm*

[62] ex *om. R*   [63] *fort.* circumtecto

---

14. Cf. Galen X. 7 Kühn. But the identification of *Comparatio* with the *Syncritica*
is not certain.

15. I.e., the statement in *Regimen* i. Yet *haec* may possibly refer to *pro patientibus
locis . . . curationem*, in which case the words *non enim . . . solutionem* are to be ascribed
to Soranus and not to Thessalus.

16. Cf. 148.

17. The point is that it is better to use substances that are precisely appropriate
than to take substances which are too strong and weaken them before using.

to the affected parts. But Thessalus seems to have arrived at this view in opposition to the principles of the Methodist Sect. Indeed, he contradicts his own opinions. For, in his opinion, therapy should not vary according to the parts affected; and, in fact, in refuting Erasistratus in Book II of his work entitled *Syncritica*[14] he says: 'The amount of fluid to be taken should not depend upon the parts affected but upon the state of stricture or looseness.' But this is clearly inconsistent with his other statement.[15] Thessalus errs, therefore, in saying that, because of the part affected, the quantity of drink must be diminished in cases of ileus. What he should have clearly asserted and shown is that the quantity of drink is to be diminished in view of the swift and acute nature of the disease.[16]

Certain writers of our sect, followers of Themison, employ a decoction of cumin in olive oil for fomentations, or spread the cumin on in powdered form with woolen cloths. Others inject a decoction of rue in olive oil as a clyster, and prescribe the application of warmth by means of wood ashes, as follows: The ashes are mixed with olive oil or some other relaxing fluid previously prepared by boiling down suitable substances. This mixture is then placed in a vessel two digits deep and as long and broad as the part affected. [Hot but] not flaming charcoals are placed under the vessel until the liquid is entirely consumed. The vessel is then tied round in linen cloths, and when it has cooled a little it is turned over so that the ashes pour onto the cloths. The vessel is now tied around the bottom and made fast with a strong linen cloth and is thus used to apply warmth to the affected parts. Now, to be sure, the acrid property of the cumin and of the ashes is weakened by the addition of olive oil and water. But it is better to use remedies which in their essential action are suitable to a disease,[17] and to use these remedies from the beginning to the end of the disease.

XVIII. SATYRIASIS[1]

SATYRIASIS is a state of strong sexual desire with tentigo due to a bodily disease.[2] It derives its name, metaphorically ac-

1. Cf. the section on priapism, *Chr.* v. 89 f., and Soranus *Gyn.*, p. 109. 1 ff.

2. For the addition of this last phrase cf. *Ac.* iii. 101.

lunt, translative a similitudine satyrorum quos, ut vulgus lo-
quitur sive fabula fingit, vinolentos atque in usum veneris pronos daemones accipimus; item ut alii dicunt, ab herbae virtute
quam satyrion vocant, hanc enim accipientes in venerem provocantur cum tentigine genitalium partium.

sed antecedentes istius passionis causae sunt epota medicamina ob usum venereum excitandum, quae satyrica vel entatica
176 vocant, quae sunt acria atque incentiva et nervis improba; item
immodicus[1] atque intemporalis usus in venerem.[2] est autem
communis passio viris atque feminis, quae solet accidere aetatibus mediis atque iuventuti. hortatur etenim in usum venereum
provocans aetatis vigor.

sequitur autem aegrotantes vehemens genitalium tentigo cum
dolore atque incendio, cum quodam pruritu immodico in veneream libidinem cogente, mentis alienatio, pulsus densitas, anhelatio crebra atque celerrima,[3] desponsio, vigiliae, hallucinatio,
sitis, cibi fastidium, et difficilis urinae egestio, ita ut plerumque
177 stercorum abstentio fiat, quibusdam etiam febres. omnibus tamen in ultimo conductio nervorum fiet, quam Graeci spasmon
vocaverunt, et involuntarius seminis iactus.

initio autem se leviter putant relevatos ex usu venereo atque
seminis iactu, sed paulo post vehementer extenduntur. nocentur enim atque vexantur hoc usu, quamquam parvi temporis
relevationem falsam sentire videantur, non aliter quam si sca-
biosi pruritu affecti vel lippientes manuum contactum affectare
frequentent, quod Graeci chirapsian vocaverunt. declinante
passione omnia supradicta minuentur, quae Graeci symptomata
vocaverunt, nos accidentia passionis.

178 haec omnia etiam mulieribus passione affectis, sed plus in ipsis
praevalet prurigo ob naturam. indecenter enim ipsa in loca manus mittunt prurientibus verendis, atque omnes ingredientes ap-
petunt et suae libidini servire supplices cogunt.

[1] immodici G: corr. R

[2] usus veneris R: an usus venereus?

[3] celerrima Almeloveen: creberrima G

---

3. Cf. Chr. i. 121.

cording to some, from a comparison with satyrs. The common tradition and myth, as we have it, describes these satyrs as demons drunk with wine and ready for venery. But, according to others, the name 'satyriasis' is derived from the plant called *satyrion* by the Greeks. For the power of this plant is such that those who taste of it are aroused to lust and experience tension in the genital parts.

The antecedent cause of the disease is the drinking of drugs for the purpose of arousing sexual desire (Greek *satyrica* or 76 *entatica*). These drugs are sharp and stimulating and harmful to the nerves and sinews. Excessive and untimely venery is also a cause of this disease. Satyriasis is an affliction of both men and women and generally occurs in middle age and youth; for it is during these vigorous years that the sexual impulse is most readily excited.

The symptoms of the disease are as follows: severe tension of the genital organs, with pain and a burning sensation, and an unrelieved itching that goads the patient on to sexual lust; mental aberration, rapid pulse, thick and rapid panting, despondency, sleeplessness, wandering of the mind, thirst, aversion to food, great difficulty in urinating, so that retention of the feces 77 generally results; in some cases there is fever. But at the end there is always convulsion (Greek *spasmos*) and an involuntary ejaculation of semen.

At the beginning of the disease the patient feels somewhat relieved by coitus and the ejaculation of semen, but a short time later the severe tension returns. In fact, the patient is greatly harmed by coitus, though he seems to experience a feeling of relief for a short time. But this relief is no more real than that experienced by sufferers from itch or from inflammation of the eyes when they repeatedly resort to rubbing the sore parts with their hands (Greek *cheirapsia*).[3] In the declining phase there is a moderation of all the above-mentioned manifestations of the disease (Greek *symptōmata*, Latin *accidentia*).

78   All these symptoms occur also in women who are affected by the disease, but the itching is stronger in their case because of their nature. This itching of the genitalia makes them put their hands to these parts in shameless fashion; they accost all who come to see them, and on their knees beg these visitors to relieve their lust.

differt autem a satyriasi gonorrhoea, quam nos seminis lapsum
vocamus, siquidem sine tensione veretri sit[4] seminis involuntaria
atque iugis elapsio; dehinc quod satyriasis tarda non sit, quam
Graeci chroniam vocant, ac simile quiddam[5] passioni quae a
179 Graecis sit appellata priapismos. eius memor est in libro Signorum Demetrius Apameus[6] dicens quod hoc in quodam viderit
sene atque in seipsum manu operante, nec quicquam tamen potuisse peragere; tensionem autem fuisse veretri nimiam cum parvo dolore ut cornu[7] putaretur, et ita perseverasse multis mensibus, nullo[8] quoque adiutorio medicinali cessisse, sed tarde[9] atque
longo tempore requievisse. quo fit ut sit priapismus discernen-
dus a satyriasi, siquidem illa celer sit et non tardet in corpore,
fiat[10] sane contractu[11] nervorum et stimuloso desiderio in veneream voluptatem.

180   est autem passio stricturae et celeris atque vehemens. patitur
enim tota nervositas, quod est coniciendum ex mentis alienatione et contractu membrorum. sed plus atque praestantius pati seminales vias accipimus, quas Graeci spermaticos poros appellant; pati etiam eas partes gravius quarum congressione usus
venereus celebratur.

curantes igitur iacere facimus aegrotantes loco calido, atque
vigilanter silere iubemus, lanis limpidis eorum clunes atque pubetenus, quod Graeci etron[12] appellant, cum inguinibus et ipso
veretro contegentes, prohibentes etiam hominum ingressum, et
181 magis iuvenum feminarum atque puerorum. pulchritudo enim
ingredientium admonitione quadam provocat aegrotantes,
quippe cum etiam sani saepe talibus visis[13] statim in veneream
veniant voluptatem,[14] provocati partium effecta tentigine. initio itaque accessionum convenit nos eorum articulos manibus
apprehensos continere et ipsorum manus a locis patientibus ar-
cere. cum[15] statum sumpserit accessio, et[16] ex dulci atque calido
oleo lanas expressas vel decoctione faenugraeci aut lini seminis
vel hibisci apponere.

---

[4] fit edd.   [5] quiddam ⟨habeat⟩ R
[6] Apameus scripsi, coll. Chr. v. 89, Sor. Gyn., p. 91. 21: Attaleus edd. (cf. Chr. ii. 64)
[7] an cornum (cf. Chr. v. 89)?   [9] tardo edd.: corr. Bendz 19, coll. Chr. v. 89
[8] nulli R, sed cf. Chr. v. 89   [10] fort. scrib. fiet (cf. Chr. v. 89)
[11] contactu G: corr. R: fort. scrib. ⟨cum⟩ contractu (Chr. v. 90)
[12] ἦτρον G
[13] visis Rm: usi G   [15] fort. ⟨et⟩ cum
[14] cupiditatem Rm, coll. 182   [16] et om. R, fort. recte

Gonorrhea (Latin *seminis lapsus,* 'discharge of semen') may be distinguished from satyriasis, for gonorrhea is a continual and involuntary escape of semen without any tension of the sexual organs. Furthermore, satyriasis is not a chronic disease (Greek *chronia*). Again, satyriasis is somewhat like the disease called

79 *priapismos* ['priapism'] by the Greeks. In his book *On the Signs of Diseases* Demetrius of Apamea mentions priapism.[4] He says that he saw an old man who suffered from the disease and who sought, without any success, to obtain relief by masturbating. There was, he says, a powerful erection but with such little sensation that the organ might have been made of horn; and this condition remained unchanged for many months and did not yield to any medical remedy, but after a long period of time was finally relieved. Hence we may distinguish priapism from satyriasis, for satyriasis is acute and does not linger for a long period in the body; it is accompanied by tension of the nerves and sinews and by a goading desire for sexual gratification.

Satyriasis is a disease involving a state of stricture and is acute

80 and severe. For the whole system of nerves and sinews is affected, as we may gather from the mental disturbance and the tension[5] of the parts. But clearly it is the seminal passages (Greek *poroe spermaticoe*) that are most particularly affected. Also strongly affected are the parts which are employed in the performance of the sexual act.

In treating satyriasis have the patient lie in a warm room and rest in silence without sleeping. Cover the loins, the pubic region (Greek *ētron*), the groins, and the genital organs themselves with cloths of scoured wool. Do not admit visitors and particularly

81 young women and boys. For the attractiveness of such visitors would again kindle the feeling of desire in the patient. Indeed, even healthy persons, seeing them,[6] would in many cases seek sexual gratification, stimulated by the tension produced in the parts. And so, at the beginning of an attack, take hold of the patient's limbs with your hands and hold them fast. See that his hands are kept away from the parts affected. When the attack reaches its highest stage, apply woolen cloths wrung out of warm sweet olive oil or a decoction of fenugreek, flaxseed, or marsh mallow.

4. Cf. *Chr.* v. 89.   5. Or perhaps 'spasm.'

6. If *usi* (G) be retained, the meaning might be 'in such circumstances.'

in dimissione vero ob vehementiam etiam phlebotomiam adhibere, cogentibus rebus intra diatriton, permittentibus autem
182 in ipsa diatrito. intelligimus sane dimissionem, si etiam febres
affuerint, ex earum indulgentia. necesse est enim quando passio
asperatur, tunc etiam febres extendi, et cum rursum fuerit re-
missa, febres quoque levigari. at si febres non fuerint, ex ceteris
accidentibus, quae Graeci symptomata vocant, cum ea indulgen-
tiora viderimus, ut ruborem, fervorem, pruritum vel in usum venereum cupiditatem aut genitalium tentiginem vel his similia.
post phlebotomiam corpus perungemus atque ora lavantes cibum damus, halicam ex melle vel panem lotum ex aqua et ova
sorbilia.

183 aliis autem diebus eas partes quas lana texeramus cataplasmate curamus ex faenugraeci atque lini seminibus aut pollinibus
aqua resolutis, quod Graeci omen lysin vocant, aut aqua et
melle. tunc etiam cucurbitas apponemus sed in accessionis statu
leves, in dimissione autem cum scarificatione, clunibus atque pube tenus praerasis[17] capillis. apponimus etiam sanguisugas; et
spongiarum vaporatione utimur, praecoctis in aqua quibusdam
laxativis, adhibentes etiam clysterem ex oleo calido aut calida
184 et[18] oleo, tunc rursum cataplasmantes ante cibum. praeterea
etiam encathismatibus utimur, nunc ex oleo confectis vel calida
et oleo, nunc ex decoctionibus mitiganter[19] laxativis. in mulieribus autem etiam pessulum oleo calido infundentes sensim consexualibus[20] manibus in muliebre veretrum mitti iubemus, externas vero partes per latitudinem lanis contegemus vel cataplasmamus et utrique fibrae cucurbitas infigemus.

declinante passione gestationem adhibemus et in oleum vel
185 calidam aegros infundemus, scilicet embasim facientes. tunc
etiam lavacrum adhibemus atque melioribus sucis et variis cibis
nutrimus, fugientes acriora pulmenta[21] atque vinum multo tempore. cerotaria etiam patientibus partibus apponimus, mulieribus vero liquidiora facientes acrium vice utimur, adhibentes
etiam aeque[22] ex adipibus atque medulla et meliloto vel his simi-

[17] perrasis G, sed cf. Ac. i. 79, Chr. v. 74

[18] ex G: corr. Rm (cf. 147, 151, 184)

[19] mitigantur G: corr. Schmid Mn 154

[20] consexualibus conieci: cum sexualibus edd.

[21] pulmētū G   [22] aeque R: aquae G

During a remission perform venesection because of the severity of the disease. If circumstances require it, perform venesection before the end of the [first] three-day period; but if there is
82 no urgency, do so at the end of this period. And in cases in which there is fever, we may recognize a remission by a diminution of the fever. For when the disease is aggravated, the fever is necessarily increased; and, again, when there is a remission the fever also is alleviated. But in cases where there is no fever, we may conclude that there is a remission when we observe an abatement in the other concomitants of the disease (Greek *symptō-mata*), e.g., redness, heat, itching or desire for venery, tension of the genitalia, and the like. After performing venesection, anoint the patient's body, wash his face, and give him such food as spelt groats and honey, bread dipped in water, and soft eggs.

83 On succeeding days apply poultices to the parts that had previously been covered with wool; make the poultices of fenugreek seed and flaxseed, or flour soaked in water (Greek *ōmēlysis*), or honey and water. Then use cupping, mild[7] cupping during the highest stage of the attack and cupping with scarification during the remission. The cups should be applied to the loins and the pubes, the pubic hair being shaved. Also apply leeches. And apply heat with sponges, using relaxing substances previously boiled in water. Inject a clyster of warm olive oil or water and
84 olive oil; and then apply poultices again before giving food. In addition, prescribe sitz baths, now using olive oil or warm water and olive oil, and now various soothing and relaxing decoctions. And in the case of women patients have a woman attendant gently insert into the vagina a plug steeped in warm olive oil. Lay woolen cloths across the external parts [of the genitalia], or apply poultices and attach cups on both sides.

In the declining phase of the disease prescribe passive exercise; then have the patient placed in a tub of olive oil or warm
85 water. Thereafter, prescribe [regular] bathing. And nourish the patient with the more digestible foods, prescribing a varied diet. Avoid acrid foods and wine for a long time. Again, apply cerates to the affected parts, making these cerates fairly liquid and avoiding all sharpness in the case of women patients. And similarly employ pessaries consisting of fat, marrow, melilot, or

7. The term here seems equivalent to 'without scarification.' But this is not always the case. Cf. *Chr.* v. 74.

libus pessaria, de quibus latius in libris quos[23] De mulieribus[24]
scripturi docebimus.

aliorum autem medicorum excepto Themisone nullus hanc
passionem conscribit, cum non solum raro verum etiam coacer-
186 vatim saepissime invasisse videatur. memorat denique Themison apud Cretam multos satyriasi interfectos, quod quidem
quantum creditur factum est ignorantia ciborum, quod frequenter ac plurimam manderent satyrion herbam. ait praeterea
apud Mediolanum iuvenem atque alias decentem nuptam cui-
dam nobili se vidisse satyriasi interfectam.

ponit etiam eius passionis curationem secundo libro Epistolarum ad Asilium scribens, imperans phlebotomiam atque fo-
mentationes et cataplasmata frigidae virtutis adhibenda quibus
possit extingui veneris appetentia, dans etiam potum frigidum.
187 quae omnia sunt inconsequentia atque incongrua, siquidem pug-
nent phlebotomiae laxamento ex quo indulgentia corporis fiet.
et ex[25] cataplasmatibus et fomentis et[26] frigido potu constrictio
atque condensatio ut supra diximus contraria, quippe cum appetentia ac delectatio concubitus accidens sit verendorum partibus[27] ob tumorem, sicut etiam mentis alienatio membranis cerebri tumentibus. quo fiet ut ex frigidis atque constrictivis rebus
augeatur etiam vel geminetur veneris cupiditas.

188   XIX. DE CHOLERICIS

CHOLERICAM passionem aiunt aliqui nominatam a fluore fellis
per os atque ventrem effecto, veluti fellifluam passionem:
nam cholen fel appellant, rhoeam fluorem. alii a multitudine
⟨humorum⟩[1] fluentium qui sint similes felli. non enim inquiunt
esse fella, sed esse liquida in eundem colorem transeuntia. sed
hoc differt nihil, non est enim necessarium de etymologia certare
passionis.

Asclepiades libro De finibus hanc diffinitionem passionis dedit:
cholera, inquit, est humoris fluor, celer ac parvi temporis, ven-

[23] sumus *add. R (add. Ilberg [Sor. Gyn., p. 109] post* scripturi)

[24] muliebribus *Ilberg (loc. cit.)*

[25] ex *conieci:* est *edd.*

[26] ex *G: corr. Rm*

[27] *fort.* verendarum partium *vel* verendis partibus

[1] *add. R*

substances like these. We shall describe these pessaries at greater length in our forthcoming treatise *On Diseases of Women*.[8]

Of other physicians, none but Themison has written about satyriasis, though it is not only not a rare disease but is fre-
6 quently observed to attack large numbers. Thus Themison tells us that many have died of satyriasis in Crete. And this is believed to have been due to ignorance about food, for in many cases people ate copiously of the plant satyrion. He also tells of seeing a young woman in Milan who died of satyriasis. She had previously been quite modest and was married to a person of high station.

In Book II of his *Letters* Themison, writing to Asilius, sets forth a treatment for this disease. He employs venesection. And he prescribes embrocations and plasters of chilling properties so that the desire for venery may be quenched; he also prescribes
7 cold drinks. But these prescriptions are all illogical and unsuitable. For they are inconsistent with the relaxing effect of venesection by which the body is relieved. Furthermore, the astringent and condensing action of the plasters, embrocations, and cold drink is harmful, as we have already indicated. Indeed, just as loss of reason may be due to inflammation of the membranes of the brain, so the prurient desire for coitus in cases of satyriasis is due to inflammation in the genital organs. Sexual desire is therefore increased and aggravated by the application of cooling and astringent substances.

8 ## XIX. CHOLERA

The disease of cholera, according to some, derives its name from the flow of bile that takes place from mouth and bowels, cholera being, so to speak, 'the fellifluous disease.' For the Greek word for 'bile' is *cholē* and for 'a flow' *rhoea*. But others derive the term 'cholera' from the large number of fluid discharges similar to bile. The discharges, they say, are not actually bile, but merely fluids that assume the color of bile. But the difference involved is of no importance, and there is no need to dispute about the etymology of the name of the disease.

In his book entitled *Definitions* Asclepiades gives the following definition of the disease. Cholera, he says, is a discharge of fluid

8. The section referred to is lost. See Soranus *Gyn.*, p. 109.

tris atque intestinorum ex concursu sive obtrusione corpusculorum, atque ut saepe contigit ex indigestione initium sumens.
189 hanc quoque diffinitionem quidam disserentes aiunt humoris
fluorem dictum, siquidem haec sit[2] generaliter cholera; parvi
etiam temporis adiectum ad discretionem coeliacorum, siquidem
etiam ipsis fluor est humoris, sed longo frequentius tempore;
concursu autem corpusculorum, siquidem etiam navigantium
quidam humoris fluxu afficiantur, nec tamen ex corpusculorum
concursu; adiectum etiam frequenter ex indigestione hoc fieri,
siquidem ex aliis quoque causis fiat cholerica passio.

item aliqui nostrorum tradiderunt eandem diffinitionem, solum concursum corpusculorum detrahentes atque viarum rari-
190 tatem adicientes. nos autem superfluum fuisse causas passionis
dicere iudicamus, cum sit necessarium id quod ex causis conficitur edocere. multo autem ac[3] magis superfluum dicimus etiam
causas antecedentes diffinitionibus adiungi, quippe cum nec sola
cholerica passio ex indigestione fiat, neque sola indigestio hanc
faciat passionem, sed etiam aliae[4] speciales atque contrariae[5]
virtutis, quarum nihil ex ista diffinitione monstratur. dehinc
quod[6] rheumatismus sive humoris fluor non solum ventris atque
intestinorum sit, sed etiam stomachi.

191 quapropter, ut Soranus ait, cholerica passio est solutio stomachi ac ventris et intestinorum cum celerrimo periculo. sed antecedentes causas eius passionis dicimus vinolentiam, vel malum
medicamen potum, aut aquarum calidarum potationem, vel
iactationem maritimam primae navigationis quae commoveat
insuetos. sed vehementius hoc facere dicimus ubi continuamus
indigestionem ob plurimam sumptionem cibi, aut insueti aut curiose conditi. quorum sane intellectus aptus rationi est ob causarum scientiam, inutilis vero ac ⟨non⟩[7] necessarius curationi vel
naturae.

[2] sit *A*: sint *G*

[3] ac *om. Bendz (cf. Hagendahl 258)*

[4] aliae ⟨causae⟩ *R*: alias *G*

[5] contraria *G: corr. R*

[6] quod *om. R (et mox* est *pro* sit)*

[7] ac ⟨non⟩ *Bendz 88*: ac *G*: nec *A*

from the stomach and intestines, acute, of short duration, resulting from a crowding or blocking of the corpuscles, and frequently
89 commencing with indigestion. Some writers offer the following
explanation of this definition: (1) cholera is defined as a discharge of fluid, since that is the general character of the disease;
(2) the words 'of short duration' are included to distinguish
cholera from the coeliac disease, in which there is also a discharge
of fluid, but generally over a long period of time; (3) the words
'resulting from a crowding of the corpuscles' are included to distinguish this disease from seasickness, in which there is a discharge of fluid but not resulting from a crowding of the corpuscles; (4) the statement that cholera arises from indigestion is
qualified by the word 'frequently' because this disease may also
arise from other causes.

Some writers of our Sect give the same definition with a single
change; they substitute 'dilation of the pores' for 'crowding of
90 the corpuscles.' But we consider a discussion of the causes of the
disease unnecessary, since it is rather the results of these causes
that must be set forth. And we consider even less essential the
inclusion of antecedent causes in our definitions, for cholera is
not the only disease that arises from indigestion, and indigestion
is not the only condition that produces this disease. Indeed,
there may be other particular causes, and quite contrary,[1] but
none of these causes is referred to in the definition of Asclepiades.
There is the further fact that the discharge of fluid (*rheumatismos*) takes place not only from the stomach and intestines but
from the esophagus as well.

91   And so, to quote Soranus, the disease of cholera is a state of
looseness in the esophagus, stomach, and intestines, involving
acute danger. We hold that the following may be antecedent
causes of the disease: excessive drinking of wine, the taking of a
harmful drug, the drinking of waters of hot springs, and the un-
settlement caused by the tossing of the sea when one unaccustomed to sailing makes a first voyage. But a more violent attack
of the disease results from prolonged indigestion due to overeat-
ing or the eating of strange or highly seasoned food. To be sure,
an understanding of these circumstances is a proper basis for a
reasoned account of the causes of the disease, but is neither useful nor necessary for treating it or for describing its nature.

1. Presumably to indigestion. But the meaning may be 'of diverse kinds.'

huic passioni similis ac vicina est diarrhoea atque stomachi
192 resolutio. sed diarrhoeam Asclepiadis sectatores discernunt. in
cholericis aiunt ventris et stomachi rheumatismum, hoc est humoris fluorem, in diarrhoea vero ultimarum partium profluvium.
nos vero dicimus in stomachi solutione solum vomitum frequentare, et neque simul ventris fluorem; qui si fuerit rursum vomitu
non attestante, solius ventris significat solutionem et appellabi-
tur diarrhoea. in cholerica passione ⟨utrumque⟩[8] concurrit, hoc
est vomitus atque ventris fluor, cum aliis quibusdam accidentibus signis quae post memorabimus.

item indigestionem aiunt[9] genere differre. sed Asclepiadis sectatores magnitudine inquiunt, siquidem parvus ex indigestione
corpusculorum concursus sive obtrusio, maior autem in chole-
193 ricis; tempore inquiunt, siquidem praecedat indigestio choleram.[10] sed horum prompta atque facilis est discretio. etenim
indigestio conficitur ex corruptione ciborum, etiam si quis neque
vomat neque humoris fluorem sustineat, quem Graeci rheumatismum appellant, per ventrem effectum. cholera autem ex vomitu
atque ventris fluore turbatio,[11] etiam si cibus non fuerit corruptus,
et ex aliis antecedentibus causis [fuerit][12] veniens intelligi potest.

194 ## XX. QUAE SEQUUNTUR EOS QUI CHOLERICA PASSIONE AFFICIUNTUR

PRAECEDIT frequenter cholericos stomachi gravedo atque tensio, anxietas, iactatio, vigiliae, tormentum intestinorum cum
sonitu quem Graeci borborismon[1] vocant, ventris dolor atque per
podicem venti[2] fluor nihil relevans, ructationes fumosae, nausea,
salivarum fluor, gravedo thoracis cum membrorum defectu.

surgente passione iugis vomitus, et primo corrupti cibi, sicut
frequenter occurrit, et humoris atque fellis flavidi, dehinc vitellis
ovorum similis, tunc prasii atque aeruginosi, ultimo etiam nigri;

[8] *add.* R

[9] *fort.* ⟨alii⟩ aiunt

[10] cholerica G: *corr.* R, *sed fort. scrib.* cholericam

[11] turbatio ⟨est⟩ R

[12] *seclusi*

[1] *fort. scrib.* borborigmon (*vel* -yg-); *cf. Chr. iii. 18, Sor. Gyn., p. 114. 12*

[2] ventris Rm (*sed cf. Ac. iii. 141*)

Resembling this disease and akin to it are diarrhoea and a
state of flow in the esophagus. Now the followers of Asclepiades
distinguish cholera from diarrhoea. In cholera, they say, there is
a discharge of fluid (*rheumatismos*) both from the esophagus and
from the bowels, but in diarrhoea the flow is only from the lowest parts. And we add that in cases of a state of flow in the esophagus there is only repeated vomiting, and no accompanying flow
from the bowels; and if, on the other hand, there is a flow from
the bowels with no vomiting, it is an indication of looseness in
the bowels only and will be called diarrhoea. But in the disease
of cholera both discharges occur together, vomiting and flux of
the bowels, along with certain other symptoms which we shall
mention below.

Again, indigestion is sometimes held to differ in essence from
cholera. But the followers of Asclepiades say that the difference
is only one of degree, on the ground that in indigestion the
crowding or blocking of the corpuscles is on a small scale, whereas in cholera it is on a large scale. And they say that cholera and
indigestion differ also in time, for indigestion precedes cholera.
But the true distinction between these diseases is easy and obvious. For indigestion arises from a decomposition of the food [that
has been eaten, and may take place] even if there is no vomiting
and no flux (Greek *rheumatismos*) from the bowels. Cholera, on
the other hand, may be defined as a disorder involving vomiting
and flux of the bowels, even if there has been no decomposition
of food, and may arise from other antecendent causes [besides
indigestion].

XX. THE SYMPTOMS OF CHOLERA

THE following symptoms frequently precede cholera: a feeling of heaviness and tension in the esophagus, uneasiness,
tossing, sleeplessness, a twisting pain in the intestines with the
[rumbling] sound which the Greeks call *borborismos*, abdominal
pain, continual passage of wind through the anus without relief,
fumy belching, nausea, salivation, heaviness of the chest, and
weakness of the limbs.

As the disease emerges, there is continual vomiting, first of
decomposed food, as is often the case, and also of yellowish liquid
matter and bile; later the color is like that of egg yolk, then leek-

195 ventris quoque turbatio cum dolore, et egestio vomitorum similis, hoc est spumosa et acerrima, cum frequenti delectatione
vomendi.

crescente passione, aquati atque tenuis liquoris fiet egestio et
aliquando similis loturae carnis; feruntur etiam cum his humoribus plerumque subalbida desputa. sequitur etiam densitas pulsus et articulorum ⟨frigidus torpor⟩[3] atque vultus nigrore fusca-
tus, ardor atque sitis insatiabilis, spiratio celerrima et contractio
vel conductio membrorum, cum nervorum tensione ac surarum
et brachiorum, praecordiorum etiam ad superiora raptus, cum
dolore iliaco simili, aliquando etiam egestio ventris sanguino-
196 lenta, vultus in maciem atque tenuitatem deductus,[4] oculi rubri,
et in ultimo singultus. ita denique acuta atque celerrima passio
esse a veteribus memoratur, ut numquam in secundum veniat
diem.

at si in meliorem partem vergere coeperit, ut levior fiat, articulorum atque corporis frigus infractum[5] mitescit, et pulsus as-
surgens manifestior fiet ex altioribus ad superficiem veniens, parvae etiam atque intervallis longioribus egestiones fient, et paulatim relevatior aeger efficitur.

accessiones autem apprehendimus ex his quae sunt passioni
consequentia. cum enim anxietas atque iactatio, confluentibus
ad stomachum liquidis, et contractio articulorum occurrerit, ac-
197 cessionem praesentem dicimus. at si post vomitum minus sibi
aeger coeperit displicere, stomachi occurrerit relevatio, et miti-
gata ventris mordicatione ventris[6] cuncta minui adversa coeperint, dimissionem pronuntiamus.

generaliter autem passio est vehemens atque acuta vel celeris;
et aliquando solius solutionis, aliquando adiuncta ex aliqua parte
strictura, ut dolores ostendunt stomachi atque ventris et intestinorum, et articulorum contractio. magis autem patitur in ista
passione stomachus et venter et intestina; cetera vero vel omnia
corporis consentiunt.

198 XXI. QUOMODO CURANDI SUNT CHOLERICI

CHOLERICOS oportet primo similiter ut cardiacos locari atque
ut indigestos vel qui cibos excludunt. potum dari decet te-

---

[3] supplevi, coll. Diaet. pass. 42: ⟨frigus⟩ R, coll. 196   [5] infarctum G: corr. R

[4] deducti G: corr. Rm   [6] ventris om. R, fort. recte

5 green and rust, and finally black. The bowels are agitated and painful, and their discharge is frothy and pungent like that which was vomited. There is frequent straining to vomit.

As the disease spreads, a thin watery fluid is discharged,[1] sometimes resembling water in which meat has been washed; and with this fluid whitish sputa are generally carried up. And there are the following symptoms: pulse thick; extremities cold and numb; face darkened; burning heat; unquenchable thirst; very rapid respiration; cramp in the limbs with tenseness of the sinews, especially in the calves and arms; precordial distention; pain like that in ileus; in some cases a bloody discharge from the
6 bowels; face drawn and emaciated; eyes red; and, toward the end, hiccoughs. Ancient physicians say that the disease is so acute and swift that it never lasts a second day.

But if it begins to take a turn for the better and becomes less severe, the chill of the limbs and body is reduced and relieved; the pulse becomes stronger and more prominent, rising from the deeper parts to the surface; the discharges are small and occur at longer intervals; and the patient gradually becomes more comfortable.

We may recognize the attacks by the symptoms of the disease. For when there is a feeling of discomfort, tossing, a flow of liquid matter to the esophagus, and cramp in the limbs, we conclude
7 that an attack is at hand. But if after vomiting the patient begins to feel less uncomfortable, and the distress in the esophagus is relieved, and, with the alleviation of the sharp abdominal pain, all adverse abdominal symptoms begin to abate, we may assert that there is a remission.

In its general character the disease is severe and acute, i.e., swift. Sometimes it involves only a state of looseness, while at other times there is also present, to some degree, a state of stricture, as is indicated by the pains in the esophagus, stomach, and intestines, and the cramp in the limbs. The esophagus, stomach, and intestines are the parts especially affected in this disease; but all the other parts of the body are sympathetically affected.

8 ## XXI. THE TREATMENT OF CHOLERA

To BEGIN with, a patient having cholera should be placed in the same way as patients with the cardiac disease,[1] or indi-

1. The reference is probably to an upward discharge.   1. See *Ac.* ii. 191–92.

pidae, ut quod immutatum corruptione videatur tamquam veneni materia per vomitum depurgetur. at si haec corrupta excludi desierint, erunt aegrotantes servandi in eodem schemate.
provocabiles sunt[1] enim liquidorum[2] fluctionis[3] motus. convenit
etiam articulorum levis atque impressa defricatio cum quadam
perseverabili tenacitate; tunc etiam eorum ligatio, quae[4] cum
199 fuerit[5] densa phthisicum consentire stomachum cogat.[6] sed ne
ex his ligamentis superiora torpescant, erunt saepius commutandae ligationes. tunc stomacho atque ori ventris spongiae
admovendae iugiter ex aqua frigida expressae, dehinc etiam ex
posca, atque iisdem facies detergenda, quo defectione submota
in resumptionem veniant aegrotantes.

utemur etiam odoramentis, sicut in cardiacis ordinavimus,
atque flabris et cataplasmatibus frigidae virtutis secundum thoracem ac ventrem. sed ut non saepius haec mutare cogamur, ne-
200 que contrario permanendo calida efficiantur, spongiis frigida expressis atque superpositis ea frigidamus, ut non solum[7] virtute
constrictiva verum etiam frigido tactu fluorem constringant.

at si dolor vel intestinorum tormenta plurimum coegerint, pro
frigidis spongiis aliqua temperantia admovemus. tunc tec-
tionem[8] mundarum lanarum vel olei dulcis atque calidae infusionibus utemur. similiter etiam propter contractiones articulos
lana circumtegimus et pannis calidis colligamus.

infigimus praeterea cucurbitas leves, quas Graeci cuphas[9] vo-
201 cant, scilicet sine scarificatione. has frequenter detrahemus[10]
atque differentibus locis infigimus, quo latenter ac sensim etiam
strictura quae irruerat resolvatur. at si dolores coegerint, et
plus urgere vomitum viderimus solutione obtinente, ita cucurbi-

---

[1] *fort.* provocabilis est (*cf. Sor. Gyn., p. 119. 19, Cael. Aur. Gyn. ii. 47*)

[2] *fort. secl.* liquidorum

[3] fluctionis *conieci* (*an* -um?): fluctionibus G (*cf. Bendz 23*)

[4] qua G: *corr. Rm*

[5] fuerint G: *corr. Rm*

[6] cogant G: *corr. A*

[7] saepius G (*cf. E. Löfstedt, Uppsala Univ. Års. 1907, p. 50*) *sed nimirum propter* saepius *supra*: tantum *Rm*

[8] tectione R

[9] κούφας G

[10] detrahimus R

gestion, or those who vomit their food. Give him some warm
water to drink so that the decomposed food may be purged as a
poison, by vomiting. And when this decomposed matter ceases
to be vomited, have the patient lie still, without changing position. For fluxes of liquid matter are easily brought about by
shifts in position. A gentle rubbing of the limbs with pressure
and continued holding is also helpful. This should be followed by
bandaging the limbs; and if the binding is tight, it will also have
a sympathetic [astringent] effect on the flux in the esophagus.
199 But, to prevent the upper parts of the body[2] from becoming
numb because of the binding, the bandages should be frequently
changed. And sponges wrung out of cold water, later out of diluted vinegar, should be continually applied to the parts over the
esophagus and the cardiac orifice of the stomach, so that the exhausted patient may be revived and his strength restored.

Also employ aromatic substances, as we prescribed in the cardiac disease, and fans, and apply cooling plasters to the chest and
abdomen. But to avoid having to change these plasters often
200 and, on the other hand, to prevent their becoming warm by
remaining in place too long, cool them by placing over them
sponges wrung out of cold water. Thus the plasters will constrict
the state of flow not only by their astringent properties but by
their cold touch, as well.

If, however, the pain and cramps in the intestines make it
absolutely necessary, apply soothing remedies instead of cold
sponges; then cover the parts with clean wool or bathe them
with sweet olive oil and warm water. In like manner, because of
the cramps in the limbs, cover the latter with wool and wrap
them round with warm cloths.

In addition, apply light (Greek *cuphae*), cups, i.e., cupping
201 without scarification.[3] Remove these cups frequently and apply
them to other places, so that the element of stricture which has
entered may imperceptibly and gradually be overcome. But if
the pains require it and if, because of the prevailing state of
looseness, there is extensive vomiting, apply cups of astringent

2. This would include the head and, with it, the senses. But the interpretation is
doubtful. *Superiora* may possibly mean 'the parts nearer the extremity.' Again, *ex his
ligamentis* is possibly to be construed with *superiora* rather than with *torpescant*.

3. Cf. 183. But the term 'light cups,' as used by Caelius, does not always mean
cupping without scarification; it may merely mean mild cupping in general. Cf. *Chr.*
v. 74.

tas infigemus ut in cardiacis memoravimus, hoc est constrictivas
ori ventris atque subsequentibus partibus, aliquando etiam a
tergo per intervalla dimissionis. damus¹¹ praeterea aquam frigidam sorbendam per intervalla quidem.¹²

202 at si vehementius vires amputati ac solutionem crescere
viderimus, praecuratis aegris, ut in cardiacis docuimus, cibum
damus dimissionis tempore, non expectata prima diatrito, defectionis coacti periculis. dabimus igitur panem ex aqua frigida
diligenter praelotum, halicam vel oryzam ex aqua vel posca, aut
ova hapala aceto prius infusa, et pulticulam sicciorem. at si
accepta reiecerint, paululum requiescentes post intervallum rursum cibo nutrimus. tunc si res coegerint, etiam tertio id facimus, vel quarto. et ob retinendum cibum cucurbitam latioris
osculi unam vel secundam plurima cum flamma infigimus ori
ventris infra costarum finem, eodem tempore quo cibum dabi-
203 mus. tunc post eius sumptionem idem facimus, quo constrictione atque raptu corporis ad inferiora venire et permanere cogantur accepta. oportet praeterea adiutoriorum mediocritatem
intueri, nam plurimo atque iugi cibo¹³ oppressione¹⁴ praefocati
saepe sunt aegrotantes.

at si distantia temporis longiore fuerit vomitus intercapedinatus et ventris effusio iisdem dilationibus dirarata, tunc ut in
declinatione totius passionis ob destructionem dabimus quicquam pomorum, ut pira vel mala cydonia aut sorba aut mali
204 punici grana aut damascena, vel recentium uvarum palealium,
intybi thyrsum, atque volantium pectora sed non pinguium, ut
perdicis vel phassae vel similium, in posca decoctorum vel assorum cum aspergine corticis mali punici in pulverem comminuti,
dehinc e cellario, quam¹⁵ Graeci apotamiam¹⁶ vocant, colymbadas olivas fractas.

¹¹ damus dimissionis G: *transposui*

¹² *fort.* eadem

¹³ plurimi atque iugis cibi *Rm*

¹⁴ *fort.* oppressi

¹⁵ quem G (*retin. Bendz 19*): quod *Rm*

¹⁶ apo tamiu *Rose, Sor., p. 219 (p. 37. 22 Ilb.*)

---

4. Cf. *Ac.* ii. 215.

5. Or 'during these periods [of remission]'; so, of course, if *eadem* be read.

action to the cardiac orifice of the stomach and the parts below,
as we have indicated in connection with the cardiac disease.[4] In
some cases cups may also be applied to the back during periods
of remission. Also give the patient cold water to sip at intervals.[5]

But if it is apparent that his strength is seriously impaired and
the state of looseness is spreading, use the preparatory treatment
described in the chapter on the cardiac disease;[6] then give him
food during a period of remission, without waiting for the end of
the first three-day period. This must be done because of the danger of collapse. The food given may be bread thoroughly washed
and soaked in cold water, spelt groats or rice in water or diluted
vinegar, soft eggs soaked in vinegar, or a somewhat dry porridge. If the patient vomits what he has taken, let him rest a
while and then after an interval feed him again; and, if circumstances require it, repeat this for a third or even a fourth time.
And to help him retain the food, at the time he is being fed affix
one or two broad-mouthed cups to the [region over the] cardiac
orifice of the stomach below where the ribs end.[7] Considerable
flame should be used with these cups. After the food has been
taken, repeat the cupping so that, by reason of its astringent action and its drawing effect, it may cause the food that has been
swallowed to pass to the lower parts of the body and be retained.[8] But moderation is to be maintained in these treatments.
For patients have often choked when continually burdened by
a great deal of food.

But if the vomitings are interrupted by a considerable interval
of time and the discharges from the bowels are similarly spaced,
the following food may be given the patient at this stage (as also
later in the declining phase of the whole disease) to help overcome the disease: some fruit, such as pears, quinces, sorb apples,
pomegranates, and damsons, or some new grapes preserved in
chaff, or a stalk of endive, or the breast of birds that are not fat,
e.g., partridge, ringdove, or the like, cooked in diluted vinegar or
roasted with a sprinkling of powdered pomegranate rind, or,
from the storeroom (Greek *apo tameiu*), crushed olives pickled
in brine.

6. Cf. *Ac.* ii. 207.

7. The phrase probably means 'just below the sternum.'

8. Possibly *corporis* is to be construed with *constrictione atque raptu* as well as with
inferiora.

at si sufficienter aegrotantium surrexerint vires, dabimus
etiam panem ex vino mediocriter austero et aqua frigida temperato. dehinc etiam bibendum dabimus ex ipso mixtum potum, sed eo tempore quo cibum dabimus. multum enim bibere
205 prohibemus, siquidem sitis siccare valeat humecta. at si febres
fuerint consecutae et vires aegrotantis permiserint, abstinentiam cibi adhibemus[17] una die; si autem hoc ferre non potuerint,
dabimus cibum dimissionis tempore. sin vero febres non coegerint et passionem cessasse viderimus, non sine cautione ac diligenti cura resumimus aegrotantem paulatim atque modicis
adiectionibus motus[18] vel ciborum, praecaventes superfluos cibos, ne in commemorationem passio reducatur. resumptis igitur
viribus etiam lavacrum adhibemus. haec est secundum nos cholericorum cura.

206 veterum autem medicorum sententiae variant. Hippocrates
fel cholen[19] appellans cholericam[20] nominavit, atque iliacae passionis esse particulam sive concursum constituit. nunc[21] denique
eius curationem neque memorare dignum est.[22] sed quinto libro
Epidemion cholericorum signa tradens helleboro dicit utendum
cum lenticula, vel singularem sucum lenticulae bibendum; tunc
inquit vomitum provocandum.

quod est non aliter contrarium quam si quis fluore sanguinis
pereuntem vel diaphoresi dissolutum phlebotomare velit, aut[23]
cardiacum sudore defluentem calido lavacro vel sudoriferis va-
207 poribus velit adiuvare, quod id ipsum quod passio nititur adiutorium quoque fieri vehementius cogat. etenim [in] helleboris[24]
vomitus factus etiam his qui nulla solutione afficiuntur chole-

---

[17] abstinentia cibi abstinemus G (*retin. Bendz 64*): *corr. A*

[18] potus *Rm, fort. recte*

[19] cholen *conieci*: quoddam *edd.*

[20] cholericam *Rm*: choleurecam *G*: choleram siccam *Triller Clinotechnia 51, coll. Hipp. Reg. ac. App. 51*

[21] ille *R*

[22] ⟨arbitratus⟩ est *R*

[23] velit aut *Schmid 88*: vel ita ut *G*: vel aut *R*

[24] in helleboris *G*: ex helleboro *Rm*

And if the patient's strength revives sufficiently, give him bread dipped in moderately tart wine which has been diluted with cold water. Then also give him a drink of this diluted wine,[9] but only at the time when food is served; for the patient must not be permitted to drink much, since unsatisfied thirst will help 205 dry up the moist condition. But if a patient has fever, give him no food for a day, provided that his strength permits; if, however, he is too weak, give him food during a remission. And if there is no fever and the disease seems to have abated, restore the patient's strength gradually and with extreme care and caution, moderately increasing his exercise[10] and food, but avoiding excessive food to prevent a recurrence of the disease. And when strength has been restored, prescribe bathing. This concludes the Methodists' account of the treatment of cholera.

206 Now the physicians of old have various opinions about this disease. Hippocrates calls the disease *cholera* from *cholē*, the word for bile;[11] he asserts that the disease forms part of, or appears in conjunction with, ileus. It is therefore unnecessary to describe his treatment at this time. But note that in *Epidemiae*, Book V,[12] after giving the symptoms of cholera, he prescribes the use of hellebore with lentil and the drinking of lentil soup alone. Then, he says, vomiting should be induced.

Such a prescription, however, is no less harmful than if one should seek to use venesection in a case where the patient is dying of hemorrhage or is exhausted by colliquative sweating, or should treat with a hot bath or a sweat-producing vapor bath a case of cardiac disease where the patient is already sweating 207 profusely. For the remedy would aggravate the very condition which the disease itself tends to produce. Indeed, the use of hellebore to induce vomiting is apt to involve the danger of cholera even in cases where there is no previous state of looseness.[13] This

9. *Ex ipso* may mean 'in which the bread had been dipped.'

10. Or reading *potus* (*Rm*), 'drink.' The absence of any previous mention of even passive exercise supports the reading *potus*.

11. Or, with Triller's reading: 'Hippocrates calls the disease "dry cholera" from *cholē*, etc.' The reference in that case is to the type of intestinal obstruction called 'dry cholera' by the author of *Reg. in Acute Diseases*, Appendix, 51 (I. 171 Kuehl. = II. 494 Littré), though 'dry cholera' is not there identified with cholera proper.

12. *Epid.* v. 10 (V. 210 Littré).

13. The text is uncertain. With the reading *fieri* (*G*) the meaning may be: 'Indeed, it is generally dangerous to induce vomiting with hellebore even in cases where there is no state of looseness caused by cholera.'

ricae passionis periculum solet facere,[25] et magis cum non praepa-
ratis corporibus adhibetur. at si quisquam Hippocratem defen-
dens dixerit ab eo non datum, sed memoratum quod quidam
cholericus acceperit vel sibi ipse dederit, frigida utitur defen-
sione. ait enim Hippocrates profuisse datum, quod si displi-
ceret, culpare debuerat.

208   item Diocles libro quo De passionibus atque earum causis et
curationibus scripsit, frigerandos inquit cholericos, et donec depurgentur nihil accipere; tunc cum tempus visum fuerit, dandam
frigidam et in vomitum provocandos; balanos etiam per podicem
indendos. at si hiems fuerit, calida aqua utendum, tunc nigrum
dandum vinum cum polenta, atque post potum somno[26] quies-
cendum. singultui vero absinthium dicit convenire, et ad[27] solutionem bubulum vel caprinum lac dimidiae heminae quantitate
209 cum papaveris albi suci cyatho dimidio et mali punici suco. scribit etiam aliud curationis genus, quo memorat cumino quoque
atque sale et origano et his similibus potis utendum.

culpandus igitur primum est quod calidum potum dari iubeat
cholericis, cum tempus hiemis intuetur et non passionis con-
siderat vires, neque coniciens quod calidum quicquid est laxando
provocet vomitum. addidit etiam nihil dandum donec aegrotantes depurgentur, et non docuit tempus cibi offerendi, neque
demonstravit quia post depurgationem corruptorum dimissionis
tempore erunt aegrotantes nutriendi. denique tempus vini
dandi non memoravit. item absinthium est acerrimae virtutis
et propterea incongrue atque imperite singultientibus ordina-
210 tum: est enim ex tumore stomachi veniens singultus. lac etiam
in eiusmodi passionibus facilius acescit et effusionem ventris provocatam extendit. cuminum quoque et origanum acerrimae virtutis esse nemo est qui nesciat, quo fiet ut aperiantur magis
quam claudantur fluentia, et provocentur mordicationibus quae
forte sunt in tumore constituta.

[25] periculum s. facere (afferre *Rm*: *an* ferre?) *scripsi*: periculum s. fieri *G*: *fort.* periculosus s. fieri

[26] post potum somno *scripsi*: post potum somnum *Friedel 32 (coll. Salut. praec. 57,*
ubi somnum *quidem cod. Aug. CXX, sed* sonno *cod. Lond. praebet*): post positum somnum
G: provocato somno *R*: *fort.* post vomitum somno *vel* postposito somno

[27] ad ⟨stringendam⟩ *Wellmann*: ad ⟨cohibendam⟩ *Rm*

---

14. The text is doubtful.

15. Diocles was seeking to induce vomiting (208); so that if the criticism has any
point it would seem to be in *laxando*.

danger is especially great if the treatment is administered when
the body has not been prepared for it. But if anyone should say
in defense of Hippocrates that he did not prescribe hellebore but
merely reported that a patient with cholera had taken the drug,
that is, had prescribed it to himself, such a defense would be
quite weak. For Hippocrates does say that the taking of hellebore helped the patient; and if he disapproved of the measure,
he should have expressed his disapproval.

In his book *On Diseases and Their Causes and Treatment* Diocles declares that patients with cholera should be made cool and
should take no food until they are completely purged; and that
when the time seems proper they should be given cold water and
induced to vomit. He also prescribes the insertion of anal suppositories. And in winter, he says, hot water is to be used; then
dark wine with pearl barley is to be given the patient, who, after
drinking it, should go to sleep.[14] To overcome hiccoughs, he says,
wormwood is helpful, and to overcome the state of looseness half
a hemina of cow's or goat's milk with half a cyathus of the juice
of white poppy and pomegranate juice. He also describes another kind of treatment in which potions containing cumin, salt,
marjoram, and the like may be used.

Now our first criticism of Diocles is that in winter he prescribes a hot drink for patients with cholera, considering the season of the year rather than the force of the disease and failing to
understand that anything hot induces vomiting by its laxative
action.[15] He asserts that no nourishment should be given the patients until they are purged, but he does not indicate the precise
time when food is to be given and does not point out that the
patients should be given nourishment during a period of remission after the purging of the decomposed matter. And he fails to
mention the time when wine is to be given. Again, wormwood
has a very acrid property and is therefore an unsuitable and inept prescription for patients with hiccoughs; for the hiccoughs
result from the inflamed state of the esophagus. And milk easily
turns sour in diseases of this kind and causes a further outpouring from the bowels. Furthermore, everyone knows that cumin
and marjoram have acrid properties. For this reason their use
will cause those parts that are in a state of flow to be opened
rather than closed, and those parts that happen to be in an inflamed state to be irritated by griping pains.

Praxagoras primo libro De curationibus contra docens[28] iubet
dari plurimum mulsum ex aceto confectum ebibendum, et calido
passo atque absinthio potandos probat. vomentibus vero prius
211 inquit calidum potum dandum. tunc si plurimus, inquit, vomitus fuerit, lavandos aegrotos calida et post lavacrum somno di-
mittendos; at si dormire non potuerint, danda polenta atque bibenda ex mulso vel passo vel frigida. et cum vomitus quieverit,
lenticula nutriendos et vino potandos; at si vomitus perseveraverit, post dationem rursum lavandos atque iisdem utendum.
at si perseveraverint ea quae per ventrem feruntur, manente
etiam vomitu, alia die rursum lavandos atque similia adhibenda.

apparet etiam in hoc morbo erroribus implicari. etenim mulsum ex aceto doloribus est incongruum, ut quod inflet tumentia
ex aceti qualitate; absinthium vero est[29] nocens, ut superius me-
212 moravimus; item calidus potus vomitibus est inconveniens; lavacrum quoque fluenti corpori vehementer inimicum, quod iste
non semel sed saepius adhiberi confirmat; et neque cibo nutriens,
quo facilius vires aegrotantis diversis intereant detrimentis, neque saltem semel sub hac lavacri frequentia dormire permittens,
ut ipse voluit. item mulsum ventrem dissolvit, quippe non decoctum; non aliter etiam dulce vinum. ridiculum quoque est
atque cachinnos commovens pausante vomitu lenticulam dare,
perseverante vero lavacrum adhibere, cum sint haec in utroque
213 contraria. etenim lenticula constringit praesentem fluorem; lavacrum vero corpus coaequat post vomitus cessationem.

item Erasistratus secundo libro Salutarium utitur tepido potu
vomitum provocans vel acrimoniam temperans fellis; contra dolores autem tepidis utitur vaporationibus et cataplasmatibus ex
vino. at si sitis et defectio coegerit, vino potat lesbio cum aqua

[28] *an* dicens?

[29] est *R*: sit *G*

---

16. *Datio* seems to refer to the prescription of hot drink; but it is not clear whether a
second such prescription is now ordered.

17. I.e., at the time when Praxagoras prescribes it.

In Book I of his work *On Treatments* Praxagoras, in disagreement with Diocles, prescribes the drinking of a great deal of
oxymel, and also recommends hot raisin wine and wormwood.
In the case of patients who are still vomiting he first prescribes
1 a hot drink. If there is a great deal of vomiting, he then has the
patients bathed in hot water and after the bath lets them sleep;
but if they cannot sleep he prescribes the drinking of pearl barley with mead, raisin wine, or cold water. When the vomiting
abates, he feeds the patients with lentils and gives them wine to
drink; but if the vomiting persists, after prescribing the drink[16]
he has the patient bathed again, and again employs the same
procedure as described above. And if the discharges from the
bowels continue and the vomiting also persists, he says that another bath should be given the next day and the other prescriptions similarly carried out at that time.

Now Praxagoras seems to be entangled in errors in his discussion of this disease, too. Thus oxymel is not suitable when there
are pains [due to inflammation], for the properties of the vinegar
cause distention of the inflamed parts. Again, wormwood is
2 harmful, as we have indicated above. So is hot drink, where
there is vomiting. And bathing, which Praxagoras says should
be employed not once but frequently, is extremely unsuitable
when the body is in a fluid state. Moreover, his failure to prescribe food makes it more likely that the patient's strength will
collapse because of the various losses which it sustains. And in
prescribing frequent baths Praxagoras does not once give the patient a chance to get the sleep which was the purpose of the
baths. And the mead, since it is uncooked, causes looseness of
the bowels, as does also the sweet wine. Furthermore, it is absurd and laughable to give the patient lentils if the vomiting
abates, and to prescribe a bath if the vomiting persists, for the
3 remedy proposed in each case is unsuitable.[17] The fact is that
lentils have an astringent effect when a flux is actually present,
while a bath restores the composure of the body only after vomiting has ceased.

Erasistratus in Book II of his treatise *On Health* makes use of
warm drink to induce vomiting or to overcome the acrid properties of the bile. Against pains he employs warm applications and
plasters containing wine. But if thirst and exhaustion make it
necessary, he gives the patient Lesbian wine and cold water,

frigida, sed in aquae cyathum vini guttas duas admiscendas
iubens vel tres, ut solum, inquit, odorem vini habere aqua videatur, atque hoc bibendum post singulos imperat vomitus et post
214 singulas ventris effusiones. plus inquit aquae admiscendum si
febres irruerint, et similiter lenticulam dandam et vinum aut
malorum infusionem vel decoctionem aut pomorum aut pirorum.
et etiam lavacrum probat et resumptionem adhibendam.

sed hic[30] quoque excludendus in quibusdam est. etenim contra dolores quomodo calidis sic sine vino cataplasmatibus utendum, siquidem rigore quodam naturali sive mordicatione, quam
Graeci rhigos vocant, vina[31] constringant. est praeterea eorum
datio ante declinationem passionis contraria, et magis cum sine
215 cibo danda ordinantur; et immodice,[32] siquidem post singulos
vomitus id fieri praeceperit, cum propter virium solutionem
oportuerit etiam cibi quiddam offerre, et non solum vinum potandum dare. febribus quoque irruentibus, et quantum credendum est tumore[33] interposito, inconveniens est lenticula et in-
fusiones sive decoctiones constringentium materiarum. harum
enim[34] vomitum cogentium fuerat usus necessarius.

at Herophilus cholericorum curationem secundum se aliis
nullam tradidit.

Asclepiades vero tertio libro Celerum vel acutarum passionum
affectans vomitum ex rapaci haustu transvoratis potionibus,
216 eadem die levat[35] aegrotantes et vino potat cum polenta. et
quid ultra, cum plurima approbet veterum curationum, solum
prohibens ea die levandos[36] nisi vires fuerint reparatae? oportebat etiam vini tempus diffinire, atque post cibum dandum ordinare.

Empiricorum Serapion primo libro Curationum istius passionis medelam tradidit, item Heraclides Tarentinus libro quarto. sed communiter uterque rationali[37] logicorum consentiunt
curationi, adicientes etiam medicamina quae catapotia voca-

---

[30] hinc G: corr. R

[31] vino G: corr. Rm

[32] fort. immodica

[33] tumore conieci: humore edd.

[34] constringentium. materiarum enim aut constringentium materiarum. etenim
Friedel 32

[35] lavat Rm

[36] lavandos Rm   [37] rationalis G: corr. Deichgräber

having only two or three drops of wine mixed with a cyathus of water, merely, as he says, so that the water may have the odor of wine. He has the patient drink this mixture after each vomit-
4 ing and after each outpouring from the bowels. And if fever supervenes, he has more water used in the mixture,[18] and also prescribes lentils and wine, fruit juice, or a decoction of apples or pears. He also prescribes bathing and restorative measures.

But in certain respects the prescriptions of Erasistratus are also to be rejected. Thus, to overcome pains, warm poultices should be used, but without wine, for wines have an astringent action by reason of the chill (Greek *rhigos*) or biting quality which they naturally possess. In addition, it is harmful to give wine before the decline of the disease, and particularly when it
5 is prescribed without any food. Moreover, the prescription is excessive, for Erasistratus prescribes wine after each vomiting when, because of the impairment of the patient's strength, he should prescribe some food and not merely the drinking of wine. Again, when fever supervenes and, as we must conclude, an inflammation has arisen, lentils are harmful, as are also juices or decoctions of astringent substances. For what is then needed are substances to induce vomiting.

Herophilus did not hand down to others his method of treating cholera.

Asclepiades in Book III of his *Swift* (i.e., acute) *Diseases* induces vomiting by having the patients swallow potions in copious draughts; he prescribes vomiting[19] and the drinking of wine
6 with pearl barley on the same day. But we need not go into further details, for Asclepiades follows the old treatments in most respects except that he will not permit the use of emetics[19] on a given day unless the patient's strength has been restored.[20] But he should have indicated the time for giving wine and should have prescribed it after food.

Among the Empirics, Serapion in Book I of his work *On Treatments* describes a treatment for this disease, as does Heraclides of Tarentum in Book IV of his own work. But both of them generally agree with the rational treatment set forth by the Dogmatists, adding, however, pills compounded from many

18. Or perhaps 'he has more wine mixed with the water.'
19. 'Bathing,' if the reading of *Rm* be adopted.
20. Presumably by the wine and pearl barley.

verunt, multis ex speciebus confecta, quae pharmacode dicuntur, necnon potiones etiam ad retinendos exitus fluentium materiarum. ex quibus sunt hyoscyami seminis, quem nos alter-
217 cum dicimus, drachmae duae, anisi drachma una, opii drachma
semis, contrita et superfusa aqua dulci, tunc collecta et in triginta partes divisa. singula faciunt catapotia et dantur in aqua
frigida cyathis duobus. abstinet,[38] inquit, etenim ventrem. his
vero qui fuerint viribus illaesis[39] convenire dicit medicamen ex
myrrha atque papavere et croco confectum, in quantitatem ervi
datum cum vini cyatho.

sed haec vehementius ostendit Heraclides Tarentinus, dans
etiam halicam cum vino ultimae depressionis (hydatode Graeci
218 vocant, nos abusive tortivum[40]) vel cum absinthio et oryza vel
lenticula aut ptisana,[41] cum contrariam virtutem halicae lenticula atque ptisana obtineat. item primo libro Regulari, sive ut
Graeci dicunt diaetetico, nutriens cholericos prima die, ceteris
utens congrue, postera inquit die eos ante vomitum usque ad
tertium diem neque cibo nutriendos, neque os colluere permit-
tendos, si quicquam fuerit suspicione solicitum; post tertium
vero diem continenter atque cum cautione resumptionem faciendam.

sed huic erit respondendum utrum in declinatione passionis
dari dixerit vinum atque varium cibum, an ante ipsam, quod est
219 intemporale atque importunum. sed si in declinatione, cur declinante passione et, quantum creditur, forsitan et exclusa,
usque ad primam diatriton abstinendos existimat aegrotantes?
his enim qui forsitan ob eius defensionem dixerint eum praeca-
vere rursum ne febres irruant, respondemus hoc esse occultum
et non oportere Methodicum esse suspicionibus incertis occupa-

---

[38] abstinent *Rm*

[39] *fort.* illaesi

[40] tortivum *R*: torticum *G*

[41] *fort.* oryzam vel lenticulam aut ptisanam (*omisso* et?)

---

21. In view of the sequel, I refer this and the following sentence to Serapion rather
than to Heraclides.

22. Wellmann (Celsus 93, n. 2) interprets *congrue* as merely 'in harmony with what
was said in the work *On Internal Diseases*.'

23. Or *continenter* may mean 'without interruption.'

drugs (Greek *catapotia pharmacōdē*) and also potions. The purpose of these prescriptions is to check the outflow of liquid matter. One such drug is made with two drachms of henbane seed
7 (Latin *altercum*), one drachm of anise, and half a drachm of
poppy juice. These are rubbed up together and soaked in fresh
water, then gathered in a mass, and divided into thirty parts.
Each of these parts is a pill which is given the patient in two
cyathi of cold water. The pill, according to Serapion,[21] has a
binding effect on the bowels. And he asserts that those patients
whose strength is not impaired are helped by a drug made from
myrrh, poppy, and saffron, a pill the size of a vetch seed being
given in a cyathus of wine.

Heraclides of Tarentum goes even further in setting forth the
treatment. He prescribes spelt groats with wine of the last pressing (Greek *hydatōdē*, 'watery'; Latin, loosely, *tortivum*, 'pressed')
8 or with wormwood, and also rice, lentils, or pearl barley. The
properties of lentils and pearl barley, however, are contrary to
those of spelt. In Book I of his treatise *On Regimen* (Greek
diaeta) Heraclides prescribes nourishment on the first day for
patients with cholera, and, though in other respects his procedure is sound,[22] from the second day, even before there is any
vomiting, until the third day he allows no food, and does not
even permit the patient to wash his mouth if the case is in any
way suspicious. After the third day, however, he prescribes a
moderate[23] and cautious building-up of the patient.

But Heraclides must answer the question[24] whether he prescribes wine and varied food in the declining phase of the disease
or before that stage. In the latter case the prescription is ill-
9 timed and dangerous. But if the prescription is intended for the
declining phase, why does Heraclides hold that no food[25] should
be given the patient until the end of the first three-day period,
when the disease has already been declining and may, so far as
we know, have been completely eliminated? Now some may say
in his defense that he is taking precautions against an attack of
fever. Our answer to this argument—and it is a proper answer—
is that the argument is hypothetical and that no Methodist
ought to be concerned with unverifiable suspicions. But if Hera-

24. Or: 'We must answer Heraclides by asking. . . .'

25. I.e., after what is given on the first day.

tum, et vere.[42] at si ob irruentem febriculam, quae iam praesens
esse videatur, abstinentia putat utendum, erat melius dicere
quia cessante vomitu, emergente febricula abstinentia est adhibenda: quod idem facere vel memorare neglexerit.

220   ## XXII. DE DEFLUXIONE, QUAM GRAECI DIARRHOEAM VOCANT

D EFLUXIO est secundum Asclepiadem rheumatismus sive
fluor parvi temporis ultimarum partium coli atque sessionis sive longanonis ut nos appellamus, quae fit, inquit, ex
conventu sive concursu atque congressu corpusculorum. sed
huic quidam responderunt quod non solum ultimarum partium
coli defluxio esse videatur, sed etiam superiorum. item ex corpusculorum concursu sive conventu, quem enstasin[1] appellavit,
negant fieri posse defluxionem, sed magis abstinentiam vel
221 retentionem. alii rursum defluxionem dicunt fluorem, sive ut
Graeci rheumatismum, parvi temporis intestinorum atque sessionis vel longanonis secundum viarum raritatem. sed superfluum est causas adicere, cum passionem diffinimus, quibus
fuerit confecta defluxio. item alii defluxionem esse dixerunt
ventris turbationem celerem vel acutam quae fit ex corruptione ciborum. sed etiam nunc habet quaedam superflua diffinitio, dehinc etiam sine corruptione ciborum aut simili causa
posse defluxionem fieri praevideamus.

222   sequitur autem defluxione laborantem sine ullo dolore effusio
liquidorum per podicem, hoc est per anum, quae corporis faciat
corruptionem, aliquando etiam perseverando intestinorum vulnerationem ex qua dysenteria saepe sequatur.

utendum denique aegrotante locato[2] silentio atque abstinentia cibi et vini, tunc cataplasmatibus constrictivis secundum
clunes atque ventrem vel pubetenus. alia die si defluxio cessaverit, cibus adhibendus constrictivus, tunc etiam vinum atque
lavacrum adhibendum, et cetera quae resumptionibus convenire videntur.

---

[42] et vere] sed veris *Haller; Wellmann, Hermes 57. 414*

[1] entasim *G: corr. Vietmeier 94*

[2] ⟨commode⟩ locato *R*

clides means that food must be withheld if fever actually supervenes and is already observed to be present, it would have been
better for him to say that, if the vomiting ceases and fever
emerges, no food should be given. But Heraclides makes no such
assertion and does not even refer to such a view.

XXII. FLUX [OF THE BOWELS]
(GREEK *DIARRHOEA*)

20

DIARRHOEA, according to Asclepiades, is an acute[1] discharge
or flow from the lowest parts of the colon, i.e., from the
rectum (Latin *sessio* or *longanon*); the flow, he says, results from
a coming-together, crowding, or massing of the corpuscles. But
some have contradicted him, holding that the flux is not only
from the lowest parts of the colon but also from the upper parts.
They assert, moreover, that, from a massing or crowding-to-
gether (his word is *enstasis*) of the corpuscles, no flux can result
21 but rather a withholding or retention of matter. Others again
define diarrhoea as an acute flow (Greek *rheumatismos*) from the
intestines and rectum due to the dilation of the pores. But in
defining the disease, it is unnecessary to add the causes from
which the flux arises. Still others define diarrhoea as a swift or
acute disturbance of the bowels due to the turning sour of food
that has been eaten. But this definition, too, contains some unnecessary matter, for we observe cases of diarrhoea not due to
decomposition of food or any such cause.
22   In diarrhoea there is a pouring-out of liquid matter through
the fundament or anus without any pain; this causes a wasting
of the body, and sometimes, if the condition persists, an injury
to the intestines, often leading to dysentery.
   When the patient has been placed [in bed], have him remain
quiet and withhold food and wine from him. Apply astringent
plasters to the loins, abdomen, and pubes. The next day if the
flux abates, give him food with binding properties. Then prescribe wine and bathing and the other remedies which are helpful in building up strength.

1. Lit., 'of short duration.'

TREATISE ON CHRONIC DISEASES

CAELII AURELIANI

Methodici Siccensis

TARDARUM PASSIONUM

CAPITA PRIMI LIBRI

CAPITA LIBRI SECUNDI

CAPITA LIBRI TERTII

CAELIUS AURELIANUS
Methodist Physician of Sicca
ON CHRONIC DISEASES

BOOK I

BOOK II

BOOK III

CAPITA LIBRI QUARTI

CAPITA LIBRI QUINTI

BOOK IV

BOOK V

TREATISE ON CHRONIC DISEASES

LIBER PRIMUS
PRAEFATIO

1 PRAESCRIPTIS celerum passionum libris, tardarum placet curationes ordinare, quae solo superpositionis[1] tempore superioribus similes, in lenimento vero varia recorporatione formantur, et peritis medicinae claram aeternamque gloriam quaerunt. celeres enim vel acutae passiones etiam sponte solvuntur, et nunc fortuna nunc natura favente. quo fit ut ignari homines elati saepe medicos fugiant, cum hos proventus incantationibus novis ac ligamentis adscribant aut fortunae, cum quoties repentino nuntio laeti aut territi aegrotantes mutatione qua-
2 dam corporis morbos excludunt, vel ea per intemperantiam gerunt quae ratione occulta sibi profutura nescientes duce desperatione committunt.

in utrumque enim faciles celeres passiones accipimus, pelluntur enim aut fluore sudoris, aut sanguinis per nares, aut ventris. chroniae autem vel tardae passionis morbi,[2] qui iam praeiudicio quodam corpora possederint, solius medici peritiam poscunt cum neque natura neque fortuna solvantur. podagram denique vel phthisin aut elephantiasin vel similes tarditate passiones resolvi nulli sectarum principes meminerunt, sicut saepe febres acutae solvuntur. hinc denique Graeci Asclepium nomen sumpsisse
3 dixerunt, quod dura curando primus superaverit vitia. scribentium igitur medicinam nullus ante Themisonem tardarum passionum curationes principaliter ordinavit. alii vero has omnino tacuerunt tamquam impossibiles iudicantes vel incurabilium passionum; alii aliptarum officio transmittendas crediderunt, alii disperse atque de aliis passionibus scribentes, ut podagra, sanguinis fluore, hydropismo, paralysi, alopecia, vel quartanis typis,

---

[1] suprapositionis *edd.: corr. Bendz 72*

[2] passiones ⟨et⟩ morbi *Rm: fort. seclud.* morbi *et scrib.* passiones quae

---

1. An ancient derivation of the name Asclepius connects it with Greek *ascelēs* ('dried, withered, hard') and *ēpios* ('soft, soothing'): Asclepius soothes that which was dried up or hardened by disease. For a discussion of this and other ancient etymologies of the name see Edelstein, *Asclepius* (Baltimore, 1945), I, 124–28, II, 80–83.

BOOK I
PREFACE

1   HAVING concluded the treatise *On Acute Diseases* I propose now to set forth the treatment of chronic diseases. Chronic diseases resemble acute only during the time of an attack; but during the intervals between attacks they are treated with various metasyncritic measures. Their successful treatment wins outstanding and everlasting glory for skilful physicians. For swift or acute diseases may be cured spontaneously, with the aid sometimes of chance and sometimes of nature. And for this reason ignorant people often proudly avoid physicians and attribute these cures to new incantations or amulets or luck. Sometimes a patient who is suddenly made happy or frightened by an unexpected message will undergo a bodily

2 change that will drive out the disease. Or in ignorance and desperation he will do something rash, which for some unknown reason will help him.

    Now we know that acute diseases terminate swiftly, whether favorably or unfavorably, their departure being accompanied by a flow of perspiration, or a flow of blood from the nose, or a flux of the bowels. Chronic or slow diseases, on the other hand, which are already in possession of the body by a previous crisis, can be helped only by a skilful physician. For neither nature nor luck can effect a cure. Thus not one of the leading physicians of the various sects holds that podagra, phthisis, elephantiasis, or similar diseases are cured by mere lapse of time, as is often the case with acute fevers. And the Greeks say that Asclepius derived his name from the fact that he was the first to excel in the treat-

3 ment of obstinate diseases.[1] Now no medical writer before Themison set forth treatments for chronic diseases in any systematic fashion. Some authors said nothing at all about such treatments, considering them impossible, since the diseases were incurable; others thought that such cases should be turned over to trainers. Still others, like Erasistratus and Asclepiades, scattered their remarks here and there as they discussed various diseases like podagra, hemorrhage, dropsy, paralysis, alopecia,

441

ut Erasistratus et Asclepiades. Themison autem Tardarum passionum tres libros scripsit; item Thessalus secundo libro Regulari earum curationem ordinavit. dehinc Soranus plenissime
cunctarum diligentiam tradidit atque speciale corpus scripturae
formavit, de passione capitis initia sumens, quod nos quoque
faciendum assumimus.

4   I. DE CAPITIS PASSIONE, QUAM GRAECI
              CEPHALAEAN NOMINANT

A PARTE corporis quae patitur passio nomen accepit: nam
cephalen Graeci caput vocaverunt. generatur autem saepius perfrictione aut frigiditate, aut e contrario solis exustione,
aut continuatione vigiliarum. sed vehementius feminas tenet
ob diligentiam capillorum.

sequitur in passione constitutos dolor vehemens capitis totius
aut dimidii, quem consueto nomine hemicraniam vocant, vel
5 certe temporum, quem dolorem crotaphon appellant. occupat
etiam oculorum radices et occipitium atque colla, tendens usque
ad spinae partes, ut cum sedere aegrotantes voluerint vertigine
adficiantur atque oculorum caligine cum nausea et fellis vomitu.
ac si passio vehementescere[1] coeperit, rubri atque prominentes
oculi fiunt, deiectis et conclusis palpebris evitantes lumen, cum
lacrimarum fluore, cibi etiam iugi fastidio, et obtusione visus,
aurium tinnitu et difficili auditu. sequentur etiam vigiliae iuges
aut frequentes, dentium dolor, et accessionis initio sanguinis e
naribus parvissimus guttarum fluor nihil relevans. erit igitur
6 locandus aegrotans, si totum caput doluerit, supinus; si autem ex
parte, ea parte quae patitur. mitigatur enim quodam blandi-
mento straminum pars in dolore constituta. peiorante passione
sequitur vultus depravatio, pulsus obscuritas, et omnes sensus
obtusione afficiuntur.

hac passione alii celeriter atque cum febribus, quem dolorem
proprio nomine sectarum principes capitis vocaverunt; alii tarde
atque sine febribus per intervalla temporum admoniti solo[2] do-

---

[1] vehementer *S: corr. Rm*
[2] ⟨et⟩ solo *R*

and quartan fevers. Themison, however, wrote *On Chronic Diseases* in three books, and Thessalus gave an account of their treatment in Book II of his work *On Regimen*. And then Soranus wrote a full account of the treatment of all these diseases, composing a body of literature on this special branch. He begins with chronic headache, and we, too, have adopted this procedure.

4   I. CHRONIC HEADACHE (GREEK *CEPHALAEA*)

THIS disease derives its name from the part of the body that is affected, the Greek word for head being *cephalē*. The disease often results from severe cold or chill or, on the other hand, from the burning heat of the sun or protracted sleeplessness. It is particularly severe in the case of women because of the necessity of hairdressing.

Those who have the disease suffer a severe pain in the whole head or in half the head, in which case the disease is customarily called *hēmicrania* by the Greeks, or in the temples (Greek *cro-*
5 *taphoe*). The pain attacks the bases of the eyes, the back of the head, and the neck, extending to parts of the spine. Thus, when the patient wants to sit down, he suffers an attack of dizziness, his vision is dimmed, he becomes nauseated, and vomits bile. And if the disease grows severe, the eyes become red and more prominent; the lids are lowered and closed to avoid light; there is a flow of tears, a continual aversion to food, dulling of vision, ringing in the ears, and difficulty in hearing. There is also continued sleeplessness or frequent periods thereof, pain in the teeth, and at the beginning of an attack a flow of a very few drops of blood from the nose without any relief. The patient must in this case be placed on his back if the whole head is in
6 pain; but if only part of the head is affected, he must lie on the side affected. For the part of the head that is in pain is relieved by the softness of the bedclothes. As the disease grows worse, there is a distortion of the patient's features, the pulse is indistinct, and all the senses are dulled.

In some cases headache is acute and is accompanied by fever; in these cases the leading physicians of the sects give it the special name *cephalalgia*. In other cases the disease is chronic and unaccompanied by fever; the patient experiences pain only at

lore capitis oppressi, quam passionem veteres cephalaean vocaverunt.

pati autem aliqui membranam cerebri dixerunt, alii eam
quae testam circumtegit, alii omnem cutem capitis, alii tempo-
7 rum atque buccarum musculos, quos siagonas appellant. nos
vero aliquando istorum aliqua, secundum quod se sensus doloris
extendit, aliquando omnia **[3] secundum quod augmenta[4] vel accessiones passionum[5] ordinate se ingerunt; similiter etiam sicut
dimissiones atque delinimenta convariant, et nunc longiora et
pura, nunc angusta et sordida[6] accidentium malorum reliquias
in accessionem reliquerint; item secundum superpositionis tempore accessiones;[7] item secundum quod nunc diurnas nunc inter-
capedinatas interpositis diebus uno vel duobus, sicut quos typi-
cos aut periodicos appellamus aut hemitritaicos, pro responsione
8 temporum habuerint variantes. igitur de dolore capitis in acutis
febribus accidenti prius de febribus[8] memoravimus; de illo vero
qui sine febribus atque tardus et suae passionis est, nunc dicemus.

cum itaque adhuc parvus fuerit sensus, oportet aegrotantem
iacere loco mediocriter frigido atque obscuro, paulo levatius capite collocato, adhibito silentio atque corporis et animi requie
cum abstinentia cibi usque ad primam diatritum. adhibenda
etiam articulorum levis fricatio cum capitis fomento ex oleo frigido atque viridi, vel suco quolibet admixto qui sine repercussu
valeat astringere, ut polygoni, arnoglossae herbarum, aut intybi
9 aut portulacae aut rubi, quem Graeci batum appellant, aut anulorum vitis, quos helicas vocant, vel uvae lupinae aut anagallidis
vel sideritis herbae aut murtae. hinc etiam cataplasmata adhibenda ex horum singulis, aut admixta pulenta, vel compositum
ex multis eius virtutis medicamen fronti apponendum, ut est
diaiteon.[9]

si vero vehementior fuerit dolor, erit locandus aegrotans loco
amplo atque calido mediocriter et neque plurimum lucido, ne
nimius splendor officiat. apponendae etiam lanae lenes ac

---

3 *lacunam statui*

4 augmenta *conieci*: fomenta *edd.*

5 *an* passionis?

6 longioras (-es *Rm*) et puras, nunc angustas et sordidas *S*: *correxi, coll.* 73

7 superpositionem tempore accessionis *edd.*

8 ⟨libro⟩ de febribus *R*: *fort.* de febribus ⟨scribentes⟩

9 diatheon *S*: *correxi*

intervals and only in the head. This form of the disease the ancients call *cephalaea*.

Some hold that the membrane of the brain is affected, others the membrane surrounding the skull, others the entire skin of the head, and still others the muscles of the temples and jaws 7 (Greek *siagones*). But our view is that in some cases some of these parts are affected, depending on the extent of the sensation of pain, while in other cases all these parts are affected. [. . . Cases also differ] in the degree of regularity with which the exacerbations or attacks appear. Similarly, the remissions or intervals vary, sometimes being protracted and free from symptoms of disease, and at other times short and marked by such symptoms, the latter remaining for the next attack. The cases also vary in respect to the severity of the attacks when they come and, again, in the fact that sometimes the attacks are unremitting and sometimes interrupted by intervals of one or two days, like the recurring fevers we call 'regular' or 'periodic,' or 'semitertian,' 8 varying as they do according to the time interval. Now in our work *On Fevers*[1] we have already discussed that form of headache which takes place as a concomitant of acute fevers. We shall now consider that form which is chronic, occurs without fever, and is an independent disease in itself.

While the pain is still small, have the patient lie in a room that is moderately cool and dark, with his head a little elevated. Keep him perfectly still and have him rested in body and mind. Give him no food until the end of the first three-day period. Rub his limbs gently; apply cold green olive oil to the head, even adding a juice which would have an astringent action without causing congestion, e.g., knotgrass, plantain, endive, purslane, 9 bramble (Greek *batos*), vine tendrils (Greek *helices*), strychnos, pimpernel, vervain, or myrtle. Then apply plasters consisting of any of the above-mentioned substances with the addition, if desired, of pearl barley; or apply to the forehead a preparation such as the willow plaster, compounded from many substances having this astringent property.

But if the pain grows more severe, place the patient in a moderately spacious and warm room. See that it is not very bright, to avoid the harmful effect of too much glare. And, using clean

1. The treatise of Caelius (Soranus) *On Fevers* is lost, but certain early medieval texts contain material from a similar source. Thus the so-called 'epitome' of Aurelius contains a chapter (6, p. 690 Daremberg) on headaches that occur in fevers.

tenues et limpidae iisdem partibus, cum iugi fomento ex oleo
10 dulci atque calido. ac si coegerit dolor, ptygmata erunt vicissim
lanae aeque mollia apponenda, ex oleo calido expressa, temporibus sub buccarum[10] musculis immota; tunc etiam vesicae semiplenae ex oleo calido, vel saccelli ex pollinibus calidis confecti.
manu etiam calida atque digitis molli tactu loca dolentia con-
tingenda cum omni silentio ac requie aegrotantis. si autem dolor ad dentes tetenderit, mulsum calidum vel oleum damus quod
in ore sine ullo motu contineat, nisi quis hoc horrescens in nauseam fuerit provocatus.

11   at si vehementius dolor convaluerit et maiora exegerit adiutoria,[11] permittentibus viribus in ipsa diatrito vel ante ipsam
sanguis erit detrahendus phlebotomia scilicet. sed totum caput
dolentibus, ex eo brachio quod facilius fuerit detractio facienda;
ac si altera pars capitis doluerit, ex eius contraria detractionem
faciemus, quo longius adiutorii commotio a parte patienti remota videatur. tunc os colluere permittimus et aquae calidae
potum damus. in ipsa vero diatrito[12] unctionem adhibemus ex
oleo dulci atque calido. tunc faciemus foveri faciem ex aqua
12 scilicet calida. dehinc potum atque cibum damus, ut est panis
aquae calidae elutione purgatus, quo difficultate deposita politus
fiat; vel certe alica similiter fiat,[13] aut cum mulsa mediocriter
cocta, aut ex pane[14] pulticula confecta, quam torineton Graeci
vocant, cum parvissimo anetho, aqua, sale et melle; item ova
sorbilia. quae quidem cibatio erit alternis diebus adhibenda donec dolores declinent.

       at si passio duraverit, erit tondendus aeger usque ad cutem.
hinc etiam patientes partes levantur cum ex alto reflatio quaedam viarum nuditate permittitur, et localibus interea adiutoriis
13 praeparantur. tunc novacula radendum caput; atque cataplasmatibus et levi cucurbita in accessione, cum[15] scarificatione autem in[16] dimissione, relevandum, ex illis scilicet partibus quae
plus patiuntur vel fortiore dolore vexantur. atque ita sanguisugae apponendae, quas hirudines appellamus, et magis si locorum
inaequalitas cucurbitae non fuerit capax, quo inhaerere minime

---

[10] *fort.* temporum vel buccarum (*cf. 36*)

[11] adiutoria *Hagendahl 260*: diu etiam *S*: remedia etiam *Rm*

[12] diatriton *S*: *corr. R*

[13] alica s. fiat *Rm*: aliqua s. fiant *S*   [15] cum *Rm* (*cf. Ac. ii. 151*): sine *S*

[14] panis *S*: *corr. Rm* (*cf. 88 adn.*)   [16] in *Rm*: et *S*

woolen cloths that are soft and thin, foment the same parts con-
10 tinually with warm sweet olive oil. Now if the pain compels, use
soft folded pads of wool wrung out of warm olive oil. Apply these
by turns to the temples near the muscles of the jaws, holding
them there firmly. Also apply vessels half-filled with warm olive
oil and small bags filled with hot flour. And hold the painful
parts with the gentle touch of a warm hand and fingers, keeping
the patient perfectly still and at rest. But if the pain reaches to
the teeth, give the patient warm mead or olive oil to keep in his
mouth without any motion. But do not use this treatment if
the patient is upset and nauseated by it.

11 Now if the pain becomes even worse and requires more powerful remedies, withdraw blood by venesection, if the patient's
strength permits, at the end of the three-day period or even before that time. In cases where the whole head is in pain, withdraw the blood from that arm where it is easier. But if only one
part of the head is in pain, withdraw the blood from the opposite
arm, so that the disturbing effect of the remedy may be far
removed from the part affected. Then permit the patient to wash
his mouth and give him a drink of warm water. At the end of the
three-day period anoint the patient with warm sweet olive oil
12 and have his face fomented with warm water. Then give him
drink and food, e.g., bread cleansed and washed in hot water
and thus made smooth by the removal of all roughness. Or else
have spelt groats similarly prepared or warmed moderately
with hydromel, or serve a bread porridge, called by the Greeks
torynētos ['stirred about'], with the addition of a very little dill,
water, salt, and honey. Soft eggs may also be given. The patient
should be fed in this way on alternate days until the pains
subside.

But if the disease persists, clip the patient's hair down to the
skin. This will bring relief to the parts affected, since the resulting emptiness of the pores makes possible a kind of evaporation
from the deeper parts. At the same time, these parts will be
13 made ready for the application of local remedies. Then shave the
head with a razor; and to the more severely affected and more
painful parts apply plasters and cupping, mild cupping during
the attack, but with scarification during the remission. Also
apply leeches (Latin hirudines), particularly if the unevenness
of the parts and lack of room make it impossible for a cup to

possit. tunc vaporationes spongiarum ex aqua calida expressarum adhibendae, vel calida et[17] oleo, aut decoctione hibisci,
quam altean vocant. ac si venter non fecerit officium plurimis
diebus, tunc calida[18] et oleo rutae admixto melle erit iniciendus
14 aegrotans. sic enim et intestinorum fotus fiet, et stercorum detractione caput relevatur, quorum motu ac expirationis ascensu
amplius gravabatur. quapropter etiam pridem, si officium venter non agnoverat, oportuit adhibere clysterem priusquam cucurbitae usus accesserit. dehinc cataplasmatum genus nunc
laxativum convenit, ut est ex lini et faenigraeci seminibus atque
polline ex aqua et oleo, admixto melle concocto vel ex panico
diligenter emollito.

declinante passione cerotariis atque malagmatis simplicibus
15 utendum, ut est diachylon. tunc cibus varius dandus praedictae
simplicitati vicinus, ut est cerebrum porcinum vel haedinum,
pisces[19] teneri, turdi, columbarum pulli vel domesticarum gallinarum; olera quoque cucurbitae, malvae, betae, nunc ex aqua
cum oleo atque garo curata, nunc concisa atque trita[20] et ⟨non⟩
interius[21] condita. magis enim ex his facilis venter efficitur,
quod saepe etiam sanitatis tempore omnibus profuit quibus
unius diei ventris dilatio caput implevit. ante cibum praeterea
erit adhibenda gestatio, portatoria scilicet sella sine vehementi
16 motu, quo partes vehementer patientes releventur. tunc etiam
deambulatione utendum et post perunctionem capiti adhibendus
fotus, cum totum corpus[22] supradicto motu laxatum spiramentis
facilibus agitatum sit: etenim densa laxantur et retenta tenuantur.

dehinc cum declinatio firmior esse coeperit, lavacrum adhibendum; tunc in alia diatrito quiddam vini aquati offerendum.
ita cum capitis pausaverit dolor, longo tempore horae solitarum
accessionum erunt evitandae atque e memoria eiciendae. qui-
17 busdam[23] etiam temporibus in requie servemus[24] aegrotos. declinandum etiam omne quod potest accessionem in commemorationem reducere, ut est adustio, indigestio, venus, meracus potus, vel plurima masticatio durioris cibi aut curiose conditi,

---

[17] et R: aut S

[18] calidae S: ⟨ex⟩ calida Rm   [19] piscis S: corr. Rm

[20] cf. contusa et creta pluries G (De morb. acut.)

[21] an ⟨non⟩ curiose? (cf. 17, 23, sed etiam 162): curiosius Rm

[22] toto corpore S: corr. Rm   [23] fort. quibus   [24] an servamus?

adhere properly. Then warm the parts with sponges wrung out of hot water or hot water and olive oil, or a decoction of marsh mallow (Greek *althaea*). And if the bowels have failed to function for several days, inject a clyster of warm water and oil of 14 rue, with honey added. In this way the intestines will be fomented and the head relieved by the withdrawal of the feces. For the motion of the feces and their rising exhalations aggravated the congestion in the head. Therefore, if the bowels do not function, a clyster should be administered even before cupping is used; and in this case a relaxing type of poultice is proper, e.g., one of flaxseed, fenugreek seed, flour, water, and olive oil, with cooked honey added, or one which employs panic thoroughly softened.

In the declining phase of the disease use cerates and simple 15 plasters, such as the plaster of juices. And give varied food as simple as that described above, e.g., hog's or kid's brain, tender fish, thrushes, squabs, or young chickens; also such vegetables as gourds, mallows, and beets, prepared either with water, olive oil, and fish sauce or cut up, pounded, and mildly seasoned. These foods make the movement of the bowels easier; and even in health this is helpful in all cases where the head is heavy as the result of even a single day's interruption of the functioning of the bowels. Moreover, before giving the patient food, give him passive exercise in a sedan chair, avoiding violent shaking. The purpose of this passive exercise is to afford relief to the parts 16 that are severely affected. Then prescribe walking, and, after an anointing, apply a fomentation to the head when the whole body is dilated by the exercise and is activated by unimpeded breathing through the pores. For thus the pressure is relaxed and the congestion reduced.

Then, when it becomes certain that the declining phase is progressing, prescribe bathing. At the end of the next three-day period give the patient some wine mixed with water. And for a long time after the pain in the head has ceased, special precautions should be taken during the hours when the attacks usually came, and all memory of these attacks should be erased. At 17 certain times the patient should be kept at rest. Everything should be avoided which might bring on a renewal of the attack, e.g., exposure to heat, indigestion, venery, the drinking of unmixed wine, continued chewing of food that is too hard or too

necnon etiam vapores vehementes atque ignea lavacra, exclamatio vehemens, iracundia, vel venter nimis adstrictus,[25] et magis post cibum, aut[26] spiritus retentio et eius ad ilia descensus.
sic enim oppressio quaedam omne caput extendit.

dein tardante passione et nunc superpositionibus exasperata
nunc lenimentis levigata, oportet in[27] superpositione temporis
animadversionem habere, his denique quae supra scripsimus uti.
18 etenim quae mitigant celeres vel acutas passiones ea tardarum
superpositioni [non][28] conveniunt. in lenimento vero paulo audacius resumendi sunt aegrotantes, et non, ut nuper, timoris
adiuncta cautione tempore quo superpositionis asperitas de-
clinabat.

adhibenda igitur vectatio pro viribus aegrotantis fertorio vel
sella procurata. ac si purius occurrerit lenimentum et neque
aeger fuerit viribus praevexatus, tunc hominum manibus aut
animalium actu vehiculum adhibemus, aequali videlicet motu,
sed praetecto[29] atque aequabili, lucido et mediocriter calido loco.
19 ac si temperata et sine flatu aeris fuerit qualitas, tunc etiam sub
caelo erit adhibenda gestatio. sed necessario longitudo loci curanda, ne frequenti reversione vehiculi circulatus gressus vertiginem ingerat aegrotanti. tunc etiam deambulatio adhibenda,
sed primo tarda, dehinc medio tempore fortior atque paulo
erectior extentis cruribus.

his vero quibus caput fuerit plurimum relevatum etiam lectio
ante deambulationem erit adhibenda, si studiosi fuerint aegrotantes, sed levi exercenda voce; tunc exercitium atque unctio,
quae aequaliter corpus moveant atque curent, ut vestitos facia-
20 mus currere, nudos vero cum defricatione perungi. tunc manus
suo motu exerere[30] vel certe luctationem iugem facere, adhibito

---

[25] nimis adstrictus] ob eas abstractus *Sm* (= *lectio cod. manuscripti?*)
[26] aut *om. R*
[27] in *R*: igitur *S*: *fort.* oportet igitur superpositionis tempore *etc.* (*Schmid RPh 141*)
[28] *om. R* (*cf. 96*)
[29] praetecto *scripsi*: perfecta *S*: pertecto *Rm*
[30] exercere *Rm*

---

2. E.g., in exercise (cf. 92).

3. Or with a slightly different reading: 'exercise caution at the time of the attacks.'

highly seasoned; also hot steam vapors and hot baths, loud shouting, anger, excessive constriction of the abdomen, particularly after eating, and a holding-back of breath[2] with its consequent descent to the flanks. For thus a kind of pressure is caused which produces tension throughout the head.

Then when the disease becomes chronic and is alternately activated by attacks and allayed by intervals of remission, watch carefully the time element during attacks,[3] and follow
8 the procedures described above. For the same measures which alleviate swift or acute diseases are suitable during the attacks in chronic diseases. But during the intervals of remission employ measures to restore the patient's strength, and proceed with some boldness. This is in contrast to the timidity and caution required when an attack is merely abating in severity, which was the situation discussed above.

[In these intervals,] then, prescribe passive exercise with due consideration for the patient's strength, employing a litter or sedan chair. And if the interval is free from all symptoms of disease and the patient's strength not seriously impaired, we may use a conveyance drawn with a steady motion by men or animals; the course should be covered over, of equable climatic
9 conditions, light, and moderately warm. But if the weather is temperate and no wind disturbs the atmosphere, the riding may be prescribed in the open air. We must see to it, however, that a long stretch of ground is available; for otherwise the conveyance has to be turned about frequently, and this circular motion may cause the patient to become dizzy. Then have the patient walk, at first slowly, and then more actively, for a moderate interval of time, that is, more briskly[4] and with good-sized steps.

In cases where the pains in the head have been completely relieved, prescribe reading aloud before the walk, if the patient is fond of reading. This reading should be done in a gentle voice. Then prescribe exercise and anointing, which will provide uniform motion and conditioning for the body. Have the patient clothed for his running and stripped for his anointing and mas-
20 sage. Also have him practice thrusting out his arms as he moves, or do some wrestling regularly with the help of a trainer, whose

4. Possibly 'over steeper ground.'

doctore cuius praeceptis pareat, prohibitis[31] sane his rebus quae
implere atque commovere caput valent, ut sunt ea quae cum
obiectione plurima corporis fieri iubentur, necnon etiam circu-
latos[32] ductus atque retrogressus cum saltibus. tunc ora lavanda atque articuli fovendi vel lavacrum per intervalla dierum
adhibendum.

deposita autem corporis turbatione erit aqua praepotandus
aegrotus; tunc cibum sumere suci facilioris, id est mediae ma-
21 teriae, quam mesen hylen vocant Graeci. dandum etiam vinum
tenue parvum, sed eo tempore quo cibamus. adhibenda quoque
animi laxatio, quam diachysin vocant, quae fiet aut ludicris rebus aut ioculari facetia. quae singula artis moderatione adhibita cyclorum ductu augeri atque minui debent, praedato[33] initio cui perfectio consummata respondeat.

est autem resumptivi cycli ordinatio formanda hoc modo.
prima die parvo cibo atque aqua nutritus aegrotans, vel si ferre
valuerit ab omni nutrimento abstentus, alia die levi motu erit
22 exercendus atque oleo perungendus. tunc et cibo nutriendus.
medietatem accipiat panis[34] solitae quantitatis quam facile percipere atque digerere solebat. sed panem dabimus limpidum
fermentatum; pulmentum autem ova vel holerum betas aut cucurbitas vel malvas aut lapathos aut bulbos vel pisces teneros, ut
sunt scari, aselli, iulidae, et aviculas, ut sunt turdi,[34a] ficedulae,
vel cerebrum porcinum aut haedinum: in hac perseverantes qualitate atque quantitate duobus vel tribus diebus, iuxta virium
possibilitatem, quo neque parva dando debilitentur neque adiectionibus perturbati opprimantur.

23   tunc detracti panis[35] partem tertiam adicientes, pulmentum
damus turdorum, ficedularum, aut ex pullis columbarum vel
gallinarum. tunc rursum post tres vel quatuor dies aliam tertiam partem panis adiciemus et agrestia dabimus pulmenta, ut
leporis aut capreae. atque ita aequali numero dierum peracto

[31] prohibitis *Reinesius* (*cf. Chr. i. 41; Anon. Paris., p. 86. 3*): adhibitis *S*

[32] circulati *Rm*

[33] praedatio *S*: corr. *Rm*

[34] medietatem accipiat panis *scripsi* (*cf. 26, Sor. Gyn. iii. 15, Cael. Aur. Gyn. ii. 12*):
id est totam accipiat partem *S*: id est ⟨ut⟩ tertiam ⟨panis⟩ accipiat partem *Rm*

[34a] et aviculas, ut sunt turdi] *habet S post* scari: *transp. Rm*

[35] detractae partis *S*: corr. *Rm* (*cf. 25*)

instructions he should follow. (Of course, avoid measures which congest the head and cause agitation and those exercises requiring considerable shaking of the body for their performance, such as circular movements and backward leaps.) Then have the patient's face washed and his limbs fomented; and prescribe bathing at intervals of some days.

When the bodily agitation abates, give the patient water to drink. He should then take food that is readily digested, i.e., food of the middle class (Greek *mesē hylē*).[5] Also give him a thin wine, but in small quantity and only at the time of feeding. And keep the patient in a cheerful state of mind (Greek *diachysis*), employing games or jesting pleasantry. Now every one of these measures should be used with skilful restraint and either restricted or extended according to the progress of the treatment. The early stages should be so managed as to lead to a perfect ending.

The restorative course of treatment should be regulated in the following way. The first day give the patient only a little food and water or, if he can endure, let him take no nourishment at all. The next day have him exercise with gentle motion and anoint him with olive oil. Then nourish him with food, giving him half the amount of bread[6] he had been accustomed to take and digest without difficulty. Serve pure leavened bread, with such food as eggs or, among the vegetables, beets, gourds, mallows, sorrel, and bulbs, or tender fish, such as parrot wrasse, cod, and rainbow wrasse, or small birds like thrushes and figpeckers, or hog's or kid's brain. Adhere to the same quantity and type of food for two or three days, according to the patient's strength. Avoid weakening him by giving him too little or upsetting and overtaxing him by giving him too much.

Then restore a third of the amount of bread of which the patient had been deprived, and give him, as additional food, thrushes, figpeckers, squabs, or young chickens. And then after three or four more days restore another third part of his bread, and let his other food be game, such as hare or roe. When the same number of days has elapsed, restore the rest of the pa-

5. Cf. *Ac.* i. 93.

6. On the division of bread, cf. throughout Soranus *Gyn.* iii. 15 (paraphrased by Cael. Aur. *Gyn.* ii. 12). The bread is divided into two halves; and one of the halves is further divided into thirds. The undivided half is first given the patient, and then, with each subsequent change of diet, one-third of the remaining half is restored.

ultimam partem panis addemus; pulmentum dabimus porcinum
tenerum ex aqua, vel non curiose conditum ex anetho et sale.

praeterea simili modo erit etiam vini facienda partitio atque
per singulas pulmentorum mutationes adiectio. ac si plus
24 aegrotans bibere quam damus voluerit, aquam sumat. simili
modo etiam gestatio atque exercitium sive motus erit augendus
aut minuendus ad comparationem quantitatis ciborum.

perfecto resumptivo cyclo erit metasyncriticus adhibendus,
primo ex parte, dehinc perfectus. est enim passio facilis in motu, et natura caput iniuriis aptissimum, siquidem non facile
rerum repentinas perferat mutationes. prima igitur die erit cibo
abstinendus aegrotans. tunc alia die parva adhibita gestatione
atque unctione corporis vel, si passio permiserit, lavacro, rursum
panis dabimus[36] partem solitae quantitatis quam ante initium
25 curae facile accipere atque perferre solebat. pulmentum dabimus salsum, assum vel coctum. dabimus etiam cappares sinapi
madidatas, atque olivas ex viridi novitate messas, quas colim-
badas vocant, praecaventes ea quae facile caput implent atque
gravant, ut est porrum, allium, cepe. potum dabimus vinum.
et si perferre valuerit[37] aeger, in iisdem duobus vel tribus perseverabimus diebus; sin minus, secunda die salsamentis admiscemus cerebrum vel piscem. tunc sequenti die panis detracti partem tertiam addemus; pulmentum damus holus, cerebrum,
26 piscem tenerum, hoc tribus vel quatuor servantes diebus. tunc
rursum aliam tertiam partem panis addentes, transimus ex
mediae qualitatis materia ad volantum qualitatem. atque in
eadem simili dierum numero perseverantes ultimam partem
panis addemus; pulmentum dabimus porcinae carnis. sed si
multas mutationes facere voluerimus, in quatuor partes medietatem panis dividimus, ut singulas singulis mutationum pulmentis adiciamus, hoc est unam mediae qualitatis materiae ap-
plicantes, aliam volantum, aliam agrestium, aliam porcinae
carnis.

sed ne quid odiosum e qualitate[38] multorum dierum fiat
aegrotanti, hoc est pulmentorum similis oblatio, erit in communi

---

[36] dabimus ⟨tertiam⟩ R, sed cf. 26

[37] voluerit edd.: corr. Almeloveen

[38] quantitate edd.

---

7. I.e., the half initially withheld from the patient.

tient's bread, giving him tender pork [cooked] in water or lightly seasoned with dill and salt.

And in the same way divide up his wine, restoring his allotment in conformity with the several changes in the food allowed him. If he wishes to drink more than we allow him, have him 24 take water. Similarly, the patient's passive exercise as well as his movements in active exercise should be increased or diminished in accordance with the amount of food that he eats.

Now when the restorative cycle is completed, the metasyncritic should be put into operation, at first partially and only later with completeness. For the disease may readily recur. Moreover, the head is naturally prone to injury, not being easily able to endure sudden changes in conditions. And so on the first day have the patient take no food. The next day prescribe passive exercise and an anointing of the body or, if the state of the illness permits, a bath. And again give the patient only half the quantity of bread he was customarily able to take and digest 25 without difficulty before the beginning of the treatment. Pickled fare, roasted or cooked, should be given; also capers moistened with mustard; and pickled olives (Greek *colymbades*), gathered unripe and green. But avoid foods which might easily congest the head and cause a feeling of heaviness, e.g., scallions, garlic, and onions. Give the patient wine to drink and keep him on the same restricted diet for two or three days, if he can hold out; otherwise, on the second day add brain or fish to the pickled fare. And on the next day restore a third part of the bread of which the patient had been deprived, giving him soft food, consisting of vegetables, brain, and tender fish. Continue this diet 26 for three or four days. Then restore another third part of the [withheld] bread, changing over from food of the middle class to poultry. Continue this new diet for the same length of time, and then restore the remaining part of the bread, giving the patient pork. If, however, it is desired to have more changes, divide half of the bread[7] into four parts, restoring one part for each change in the basic diet. That is, allot one part of this bread for food of the middle class, one more for poultry, one more for game, and one more for pork.

But, to avoid causing the patient displeasure on the score of the kind of food given him over a period of many days, i.e., the repeated serving of the same type, introduce various particular

27 qualitate specierum diversitas varianda, ut quibus diebus salsum
damus (Graeci drimyphagian appellant) eiusdem speciem varie-
mus, nunc exempli causa dantes piscem, nunc sardam,[39] nunc cor-
dulam. atque ita in usu[39a] mediae materiae, quam mesen hylen
appellant, nunc turdos, nunc ficedulas sive quas miliacas vocant,
nunc columbarum pullos ac gallinarum. hoc denique etiam in
aliis qualitatibus pulmentorum sive materiarum erit servandum,
ut eiusdem virtutis pulmenta specierum mutatione varientur.
erit praeterea pomorum quiddam adiungendum quod inflare non
valeat. sed tempore quo porcina utemur erunt etiam olera offerenda. solum servandum ne modum quantitatis excedamus sive
28 qualitatem rerum datarum; augetur enim oblatio non solum si
plurima fuerint diversarum specierum, sed etiam si plus nutrire
valuerint. in omni igitur mutatione, hoc est transitu ex qualitate ad qualitatem,[40] prima die oportet curandum aquam bibere,[41] adhibita perunctione; in aliis vero diebus etiam vinum
accipere et lavacro corpus recurare, sed non omnibus necessario
diebus, siquidem facile caput iugi lavatione ad passionis vestigia
revocetur. similiter autem oportet etiam motus corporis augeri
atque minui.

tunc isto cyclo perfecto erit alius adhibendus solo ex vomitu,
29 detracta drimyphagia. in quo oportet prima die[42] parvo cibo et
aquae potu aegrotantem reservare;[43] tunc alia die ⟨post⟩ levis
deambulationis[44] motum vomitum exagitari ex radicibus ra-
phani, vel his similibus speciebus si loci aut temporis causa defecerit copia. oportet igitur radicis cortices in frusta minui parvissima ad librae pondus, quod excedere fas non est; tunc infuso
mulso ex[45] aceto confecto simplici vel scillino, hauriendum atque
mandendum[46] dare aegrotanti, sed paulo prius quam cibum libero tempore accipere solet, ut neque supinus adhuc stomachus,
hoc est cibi adpetitu non admonitus, sine ulla commotione revo-

---

[39] scarum *Sm* [39a] usum *S*: *corr. R*

[40] qualitatem *Rm*: quantitatem *S*

[41] aqua vivere *S*: *corr. Rm*

[42] die ⟨in⟩ *R*

[43] servare *R* (*cf. Sor. Gyn., p. 103. 20*)

[44] ⟨post⟩ levis deambulationis *Rm*: levi deambulatione *S*

[45] ex *Schmid RPh 39*: et *S*

[46] mandendum *Friedel 30*: medendo *S* (*retin. Schmid RPh 39*): mandenda *A*

7 foods within the general types. Thus during the days in which the diet consists of salt fare (Greek *drimyphagia*), vary the foods within this category. For example, on one occasion give fish, on another pickled sardines, on still another the fry of tuna fish. Similarly, in administering the diet of the middle class (Greek *mesē hylē*), serve thrushes, figpeckers, the so-called millet-eating birds,[8] squabs, and young chickens, each on a different occasion. And also in the case of the other types of diet or food, the same rule should be adopted, to vary the particular foods within a given qualitative category. In addition, serve some fruit which will not produce gas. And at the time when pork is used, also serve vegetables. Only we must see to it that we do not exceed the quantity permitted or depart from the quality of

8 food prescribed. For the amount of nourishment given is increased not only if there is an increased amount of the several foods but also if the foods given are more nutritious. Now in every change or passage from one type of food to another, the patient should on the first day drink only water and be anointed. On subsequent days he should also take wine and refresh his body by bathing. But he should not be bathed every day, for continual bathing will cause the head to experience symptoms of the disease again. And the bodily motion, too, should be similarly increased and diminished.

Then with the conclusion of that course of treatment, prescribe another, the object of which is only to induce vomiting.

9 In this treatment the acrid diet is not employed. On the first day of the treatment have the patient take only a small amount of food and drink only water. The next day, after he has had a mild stroll by way of exercise, induce vomiting with radishes or with similar roots if radishes are not available because of the season or the place. Chop up the outer parts of the roots into very small pieces up to a total weight of one pound, which should not be exceeded. Then over the pieces pour oxymel prepared either with plain vinegar or vinegar flavored with squills. Let the patient take this preparation and chew it. But he should do so a little before he is normally accustomed to take food, so that, on the one hand, the esophagus, still relaxed and unstimulated by the desire for food, may not vomit back the substances without

8. Varro speaks of the figpecker and of a millet-fed bird, *miliaria* (*Ling. Lat.* v. 76): with the latter some identify the *cenchris* (Aelian *Nat. an.* xiii. 25) and the ortolan.

30 mat, neque rursum appetentia soliti temporis excitus digestioni
incitet accepta. tunc tenuiter masticans[47] iugiter ex illo mulso
ex aceto confecto sorbens transvoret, atque cum omnem modum
sumpserit levi deambulans motu requiescat, donec ructante stomacho e retento spiritu mordicatione quadam sive fervoris sensu
sentiat altiora pulsari, quod quidem interposita hora occurrere
probamus. tunc aquae tepidae sumens cyathos duos, ne plurimo
potu acrimoniam radicis obtundat, immissis digitis vomitum
provocet. atque cum omnia reddiderit accepta aquam superbi-
bat plurimam, ut et stomachum lavet et reliquias fervoris extinguat; atque ita provocato vomitu reiecto potu rursum bibat.

31 hoc cum tertio aut quarto fecerit et potum liquore limpido reddiderit, capiti levis fotus est adhibendus atque ora aqua calida
fovenda. tunc levi deambulatione movendus est ob tranquilli-
tatem capitis faciendam, nisi sit solvendi torporis ex nocumento
vomitus illati causa perungendus, hoc est ex superioribus ad inferiora membratim deductis manibus defricandus. sic enim
capitis densitas quae videbatur illata solvetur, cum inspiratio facilis totum per corpus fuerit effecta. tunc epotis duobus cyathis
aquae calidae lecto recollocandus et ab omni cibo vel potu abstinendus summa cum requie animi atque corporis.

32   dehinc laxata capitis strictura somno[48] dimittendus, quoniam
prius quam densitas ex adiutorii commotione illata soluta est,
⟨qui⟩[49] in somnum facile devenerunt non solum sine[50] causa capitis gravationem servaverunt, sed etiam maiorem fecerunt, cum
nullo spatio interiecto somnum adiutorio iungentes densitatem
corporis iunxerunt.

est igitur, ut dicimus, cibo abstinendus ne sumpta corrumpat
ex corporis remanente torpore post agitationem vomitus atque
fervorem: quippe cum saepe manentibus in stomacho squamulis

47 masticans ⟨et⟩ R

48 somno Rm: solo S

49 add. R

50 sine Rm: suae S: sua Bendz 41

---

9. According to the Methodists, sleep has an astringent and condensing effect.

10. I.e., that produced by the vomitive treatment, and perhaps also that of the disease itself.

any agitation at all and, on the other hand, that it may not be impelled by its appetite at the accustomed hour to subject whatever it takes in to the digestive process. And so have the patient keep supping up the pieces of radish from the oxymel, chewing them thoroughly, and swallowing them. After eating the entire preparation he should take a mild walk. He should then rest until the pent-up gas makes him begin to belch and to suffer internal agitation with a griping and a burning sensation. This generally occurs after an interval of an hour. Let him then take some warm water, but only two cyathi so as not to take the edge off the sharpness of the radishes, and then let him insert his fingers and induce vomiting. When he has given up all that he took in, have him drink a great deal of water to wash the gullet and quench the burning heat that remains. This will provoke further vomiting, and after giving up the water he should drink again. When he has done this three or four times, and vomits only what he has drunk, in its pure state, foment his head and face gently with warm water. Then have him take some light walking exercise to rest his head, unless it is thought better to have him anointed in order to overcome the oppressive feeling produced by the agitation of vomiting; in the latter case he should be rubbed with the hands, part by part, from the upper to the lower part of his body. For in this way the clogging of the head, which evidently was caused by the vomiting, is overcome, since breathing is rendered easy throughout the whole body. The patient should then drink two cyathi of hot water, go back to bed, refrain from all food and drink, and give complete rest to mind and body.

And only when the congested condition of his head has been relieved should he be permitted to sleep. For the agitating effect of the remedy causes congestion of the head; and those who fall quickly asleep before this congestion can be dissipated not only needlessly retain it but even aggravate the feeling of heaviness.[9] For by following up the [vomitive] treatment immediately by sleep, without any interval, they add a congested bodily condition [to the congestion already present].[10]

Our reason for keeping the patient without food is to avoid the spoiling of food by reason of the sluggishness remaining in the body after the turbulent vomiting and the heat which it produces. For, since bits of the rind or skin of radishes remain in

vel folliculis radicum, requie superaddita atque cibo novo commixto, eius necessario faciant corruptionem, ex qua consequenter
33 caput impletum, etiamsi sua passione praevexatum non fuerit,
necessario constrictum gravescit, cum ex illa putredine corruptionis exhalationes ascensu quodam caput obsidunt. sicut enim
Themison ait, est natura caput carnibus pauperum et nervosum,
et duris cutibus et capillis obtectum et spiramentis difficilibus
natura, tum sensibus quoque universis formatum,[51] insidens
corporibus atque accipiens eorum cunctas exhalationes, cum spiritus naturaliter superna petens ex inferioribus trahit vapores
eos[52] per arteriam atque stomachum, quae sunt corporis veluti
34 maiora fumaria. dehinc alia die lavacro utemur atque pulmento
mediae qualitatis.

tunc post duos vel tres dies ceteras cycli partes adhibemus.
ac si radices loci aut temporis causa defuerint, adfectandus ordine supradicto vomitus ex granis sinapis madidati vel ex liquido
sinapi poto, aut mulso ex aceto et pipere confecto vel cardamomo
aut erucae semine, aut decoctione thymi vel origani aut hyssopi
aut salsamenti[53] cum multis ossibus,[54] cum aceto vel mulso ex
aceto.

tunc profectu cedente atque limpido lenimento perspecto, praesumpto[55] etiam aegrotanti ingravescentem perferre nunc vomi-
35 tum, nunc drimyphagian, audemus integrum atque perfectum
cyclum metasyncriticum adhibere, ut initium a vomitu sumentes
drimyphagian iungamus, ac deinde per ceteras cycli materias decurramus, ordinantes praeterea etiam localia adiutoria, quorum
prima sunt adhibenda leviora et quae longe remotis partibus
admota, transmissa patientibus ingerant curationem; tunc etiam
vehementiora. erit igitur radendum caput, nunc pro capillatura, nunc contra capillaturam, donec cutis rubore adficiatur;
ac deinde in balneo nitri pulvere aspergi et confricari paulo ante-

---

[51] foratum *Rm*

[52] vapores eos *Rm*: corpora ea *S*: *fort.* incorporea

[53] salsamentis *Rm*

[54] cum multis ossibus *conieci*: et multis ossibus *S*: et multis offis *Rm*

[55] resumpto [*sed hoc sensu fort.* praeresumpto *praeferas: cf. 43*] etiam aegrotante et
convalescente ⟨ut⟩ perferre nunc vomitum ⟨possit⟩, nunc drimyphagian *Rm*

---

11. Or, with *Rm*'s reading: 'and the patient's strength is restored, and continues
to grow so that he can endure the vomitive treatment and the acrid diet, in succession.'

the esophagus, if the patient goes to sleep after taking in new food, the latter undergoes decomposition. This decomposition necessarily aggravates the feeling of heaviness and constriction in the head, even if there is no antecedent irritation due to the primary ailment itself. For, from the decay involved in the spoiling of the food, vapors arise and affect the head. As Themison says, the head is naturally lacking in flesh, but has an abundance of fibers and is covered with tough skin and hair and pores that do not naturally permit of easy breathing; it is also the site of all the senses and rests upon the body and receives all the vapors from it. For the pneuma naturally seeks higher levels and carries these vapors from the lower parts through the windpipe and the esophagus, which are, so to speak, the major chimneys of the body. On the following day prescribe bathing and food of the middle class.

After two or three days carry out the other parts of the cycle. And if no radishes are available because of the season or the place, try, in accordance with our instructions given above, to provoke vomiting with one of the following: moistened grains of mustard, a drink of mustard in liquid form, a mixture of oxymel and pepper, cardamum, rocket seed, a decoction of thyme, wild marjoram, hyssop, or salted fish with many bones, in vinegar or oxymel.

Then as the improvement continues and an interval is obtained free from any symptoms of disease, if it is thought that the patient can endure even stronger vomitive treatment and acrid diet, in succession,[11] we may then risk putting into effect the full and complete metasyncritic cycle. That is, begin with the vomitive treatment, follow this with the acrid diet, and then prescribe successively the other diets of the cycle.[12] In addition, prescribe local remedies, employing first the gentle ones and those which, though applied to parts far removed from the affected parts, will be transmitted to the latter and impart treatment thereto. Then employ the stronger remedies. Thus, shave the head, stroking first in the direction of the hair and then in the opposite direction until the skin becomes red. Then at the bath, a little before the patient enters the water, have the head[13]

12. I.e., food of the middle class, fowl, and pork.

13. Perhaps the reference is not merely to the head but to the whole body.

36 quam in solium descendat aegrotans. tunc etiam paroptesis adhibenda erit ex carbonibus aequali vapore medentibus.

alia etiam die cucurbitae infingendae plurima[56] cum flamma, et primo dorso atque cervici vel cervicis[57] nervis, quos tenontas appellant, tunc capiti: quae quidem capiti erunt magno raptu detrahendae. dehinc dropax adhibendus primo cruribus, tunc thoraci et dorso, ex primo cervicis sphondylo usque ad clunes vel earum ultimum sphondylum. plurimi etenim nervi inferiora quaeque communi natura complexi iisdem paria faciunt superiora. tunc primum[58] propungentibus pilis capitis, atque buc-

37 carum vel temporum musculis, quos siagonas appellant, collo vel mento cum subiectis gutturis, quae anthereona[59] vocant, dropacem apponemus. sed ne ceteri corporis partes nudae interea perfrigescant, erunt a duobus ministris mediocriter unctione fricandae, atque ita cum dropacem detraxerimus totum perungi corpus oportebit, ipso quoque capite manu leviter pertractato, et lavacro dabimus aegrotantem.

his itaque adiutoriis relaxatis atque lentescentibus capitis partibus, vocis quoque exercitium adhibemus, quod Graeci anaphonesin vocant, tunc frequentius sinapismum[60] ac deinde ptarmi-

38 cum utile est. plurimum denique prodest post deambulationem sinapi adhibitum in gargarismum madidatum, prius quam lavacro aeger utatur, vel aridum ac masticatum, ac deinde aqua calida sumpta et in ore paulisper retenta, vel piper cum melle. non quidem haec humoris sive phlegmatis detrahendi causa Methodus ordinavit, sed ut etiam oris interiora adiutoriorum agitatione capiti beneficium tradant, quippe cum dolor saepe ipsas quoque partes afficit.[61]

ista igitur regula consequenter[62] etiam [in][63] betae nigrae vel cyclaminis herbae suco in cochlearis quantitate,[64] reclinato capite aegrotantis, pollicis sinistrae manus impressione inflatis na-

39 rium cavernis infuso uti possumus. etenim fit mucilenta humoris excussio qua aegrotans relevetur, non ob detractionem ut

---

[56] plurima *Rm*: plurimae *S*   [57] cervicis *scripsi*: ceteris *edd.*

[58] partium *edd.*: *fort. scrib.* partibus *et transp. post* pilis

[59] anthereona *Rm*: ante rumam *S* (*retin. Bendz 32*)

[60] frequentior sinapismus *R*

[61] afficiat *Rm*   [63] *om. R*

[62] *fort.* istam i. regulam consequentes   [64] *fort.* quantitatem

sprinkled with powdered nitrum and rubbed vigorously. Also employ intense heat, using charcoals, which by reason of their uniform heat have a healing effect.

The next day, using a great deal of flame, apply cups first to the back and the neck and shoulders, especially to the large sinews of the neck (Greek *tenontes*) and then to the head; remove the cups from the head with a strong pull. And apply a pitch plaster first to the legs, and then to the chest and to the back from the first vertebra of the neck to the loins or the last vertebra there. For many nerves and sinews joined to the lower parts connect the latter with the parts above, linking them by reason of their common nature. Then apply a pitch plaster to the [new] hairs of the head when they begin to come through,[14] the muscles of the jaws or temples (Greek *siagones*), and the neck, chin, and parts beneath the throat (*antothereōn*). But meanwhile, to prevent the other parts of the body from becoming chilled, since they are exposed, have two servants rub these parts gently with an ointment, and when the pitch is removed have the whole body anointed. The head, too, should be lightly stroked, and the patient should then be given a bath.

Now when the parts of the head have been soothed and are growing more relaxed by these treatments, have the patient perform vocal exercise (Greek *anaphōnēsis*). Then apply mustard plasters frequently. Sternutatories are also suitable. And it is especially helpful for the patient to use soaked mustard seed as a gargle after he has taken a walk and before he takes a bath; or to chew dry mustard seed and then take warm water, keeping it in the mouth for a short while; or else to take pepper with honey. Methodism prescribes this treatment not for the purpose of withdrawing fluid matter or phlegm, but so that the inner parts of the mouth, stimulated by these remedies, may transmit the beneficial effects to the head; for the pain often affects those parts too.

And in conformity with this principle we may use juice of black beets or of cyclamen, pouring a spoonful of it into the patient's nostrils. Dilate the nostrils for this purpose by pressing with the thumb of the left hand, the patient's head being inclined backward. A violent discharge of mucous fluid takes place, and this relieves the patient not by reason of the with-

14. The text is uncertain.

supra diximus materiae, sed quod[65] adiuncta agitationis utilitas
capiti beneficium tradat. est etiam ex localibus adiutoriis usus
acoporum,[66] ut sunt ea quae conficiuntur ex euphorbio, vel
adarce, opobalsamo, aphronitro, murra, vel aliis similibus virtute rebus. utendum etiam malagmatibus quae valeant ex alto
causas inductione propria detergere, quae Graeci minythica vocaverunt.

meminerimus tamen non prius esse ab adiutorio locali ad aliud
transeundum, prius[67] quam turbatio corporis fuerit delinita, atque patientes partes aliam recte poscere commotionem adiuto-
40 riorum fuerint visae. quapropter si plurimum vexata corpora
viderimus, sufficere intelligimus uno in cyclo unum locale adiutorium; in his vero quae minus vexata noscuntur vel viribus de-
purgata, etiam secundo uti licet. singula igitur adiutoria adhibenda esse meminerimus sequenti die quam mutatio facta fuerit
materiarum, hoc est qualitatis pulmentorum in aliam transitus
qualitatem, ut ex antecedenti abstinentia ductile atque aptum
corpus adiutoriis fiat. specialiter autem erit dropax adhibendus
tempore quo mediae qualitatis utimur materia; paroptesis vero
et sinapismus et ptarmicum, quod sternutamentum dicere poterimus, tempore quo volantum utimur pulmentis. etenim neque adhuc corpus post usum salsamenti debile, neque rursum
plurimum nutribili qualitate videtur esse confertum.

41 cavenda etenim vehementer est capitis commotio, quae saepe
corporis plenitudine fit, quippe cum sanos homines plerumque
vinolentia vel indigestione confusos, capitis motu vexatos in
catarrum atque coryzam venire videamus. solo igitur tempore
quo drimyphagia utemur omne erit locale adiutorium prohibendum, vel si quisquam omni ex parte fuerit viribus plenus,[68] leve
quiddam addiderit: sufficiens quippe cum drimyphagiae vehe-

[65] quo *Schmid RPh 40*

[66] usus acoporum *Triller Clinotechnia 74*: usura corporum *S*

[67] prius *om. R*

[68] *fort.* plenus ⟨et⟩

drawal of matter, as we have said, but because the salutary effect of the agitation produced [in the nose] helps the head.[15] Other local remedies that may be used are restorative ointments made with spurge, adarce, juice of the balsam tree, aphronitrum, myrrh, or other substances of like properties. Employ also emollient plasters, which, when spread on the surface, have the effect of overcoming diseased conditions deep below the surface, substances which the Greeks call *minythica*.

Let us add, however, that one should not pass from one local remedy to another before the bodily agitation caused by the former is relieved and the affected parts seem properly to require another strong treatment. And so, if we find that the body is severely agitated, we may conclude that a single local remedy is sufficient for a single course of treatment. But in those cases where the body is not sufficiently agitated or exhausted, a second local remedy may be used. And we may point out that the local remedies are to be applied in each case on the day following a change of diet, that is, a change from one kind of food to another, the body becoming fit and ready for the remedies as a result of the fast preceding the new diet.[16] In particular, pitch plasters should be applied at the times when food of the middle class is employed; while baking, mustard plasters, and preparations to provoke sneezing (Greek *ptarmica*, which we may translate *sternutamenta*) should be used when a diet of fowl is prescribed. But after the diet of salt fare, the body, though no longer weak, still is evidently not filled with nourishment.[17]

Care should be taken especially to avoid a shock to the head, which often takes place when the body is replete; indeed, we often see healthy persons, particularly those upset by excessive drinking of wine or by indigestion, incur catarrh and coryza when agitated by violent disturbance of the head. And so only when we employ an acrid diet must we avoid the application of any local remedy; or when a patient who is strong in every respect adds even slightly to his bodily substance. For the strength of the acrid diet and its power to restore the substance of deeper

15. Or, with slightly altered reading: 'Our purpose, as we have said [cf. 38], is not to withdraw matter but to have the salutary effect of the agitation produced [in the nose] help the head.'

16. Cf. Soranus *Gyn.*, p. 103. 19.

17. And so local remedies should not be prescribed at that time. This is made explicit below.

42 mentia atque recorporatio altiorum eo tempore totum paene ha-
    bitum mutare videatur, et sit timoris ita corpus adiutoriis exer-
    cere ut eodem tempore superficies cum altioribus agitetur. uten-
    dum etiam fomentis sive vehementioribus illisionibus aquarum,
    quas Graeci cataclysmos appellant, et primo calidarum, deinde
    frigidarum. ordinandae etiam mutationes earum ad usus na-
    turalium aquarum, scilicet earum quae non odore percutiant.
    natationes vero sub divo fieri reprobamus. ceteris enim corporis
    partibus aqua complexis, solum supernatans remanet caput,
    quod necessario perfrigescens inaequalitatem corporis facit.

43   ac si minus cedere passionem viderimus post frequentiam
    eiusdem, iterataque curatione et fortificato corpore aegrotantis
    querimonia permanserit, hellebori usus adhibendus, sed primo ex
    eius insertatione radicibus penetratis vel mulso ex aceto con-
    fecto infusis. dehinc etiam coctis[69] utendum est atque diversis
    ciborum pulmentis, quod quidem latius tertio Responsionum li-
    bro iamdudum docuimus. vehementi enim motu corpus aper-
    tum despuit, ut ita dixerim, passionis carnem, qua depulsa na-
    turalis atque nova succedit. dehinc si etiam his gestis passio
    permanens erit, secundo vel tertio utendum helleboro, sed prae-
    resumptis[70] viribus ex corporis refectione.

44   tunc etiam naturalibus aquis utendum vel siccis vaporationi-
    bus et longa per maria navigatione. etenim fluminales vel por-
    tuosae atque stagni navigationes incongruae iudicantur; humec-
    tantes caput infrigidant exhalatione terrena. maritimae vero
    latenter atque sensim corpus aperiunt et salsae proprietatis
    causa corpus adurunt atque eius habitum quadam mutatione
    reficiunt. affectandus etiam in aeres teneros atque aquilonios
    transitus, vel contrarios his qui passionem asperare valent. ad-
    hibenda praeterea animi laxatio et magis post cibum, omnis enim
    mentis intentio caput implet. haec est secundum Methodicos
    ordinata curatio.

    [69] coquis *edd*.

    [70] praesumptis *S*: *corr. Schmid RPh 43 (cf. Chr. i. 111)*

---

    18. ὕδατα αὐτοφυῆ (Soranus): waters in their native state but also 'having natural
    curative properties' (111). The prescription usually includes both drinking and swim-
    ming.

42   parts seem sufficient at that time to change practically the entire bodily condition. And it is [particularly at such times] dangerous so to tax the body with remedies that the surface and the deeper parts are affected at the same time. Also employ douches or strong streams of water (Greek *cataclysmoe*), using first warm, then cold water. After this treatment a change to baths in natural waters[18] may be prescribed, but the latter should be free from pungent odor. Do not, however, permit swimming in the open air. For, while the other parts of the body are covered with water, the head alone remains above water and necessarily becomes chilled, producing a lack of balance[19] in the body.

43   But if, after repeated attacks and repeated treatments and strengthening of the body, it is found that the disease does not yield but still persists, have the patient take hellebore. A first dose of it should be taken with radishes; the radishes are perforated and, after the hellebore is inserted, are soaked in oxymel. Then prescribe a variety of cooked foods such as we have already described at some length in Book III of our *Answers*. For the body is opened under the violent action [of the hellebore] and sloughs off, so to speak, its diseased flesh; when this occurs, a new and normal flesh takes the place of the old. Now if after these measures the disease still persists, use hellebore a second and even a third time, having repaired the bodily strength before [each new dose].

44   Then make use of natural waters, dry heat, and long sea voyages. Voyages on rivers, bays, and lakes are considered unsuitable, since they cause the head to become moist and cold by reason of the exhalation from the earth; but sea voyages imperceptibly and gradually open the bodily pores, give rise to a burning effect by reason of the saltiness of the sea, and, by working a change, repair the bodily condition. We must try to arrange voyages to places where the climate is mild and the north wind prevails, conditions the opposite of those which can aggravate the disease. In addition, keep the patient's mind relaxed, especially after he takes food. For all straining of the mind congests the head. So much for the treatment as prescribed by the Methodists.

19. Perhaps 'causing malaise' (ἀνωμαλία).

45 plurimi autem diversarum sectarum principes fomenta probaverunt ex oleo rosaceo atque aceto et ruta et herpyllo, peucedano, castoreo, silphio, atque semine herbae quam agnon appellant, samsuco, hederarum coma. ex quibus in accessione caput impletum augmentis asperrimis agitatum atque gravatum
totius passionis duplicat motum.[71] est enim supradictarum materiarum repercussibilis usus et eo adhibitus tempore quo mitigatio convenire perspicitur.

utuntur etiam purgativis medicaminibus, quae catartica vocaverunt, hoc est ventrem deducentibus, ex quibus stomachus
46 inficitur et omnis nervositas vitiatur. item arteriotomiam probant, et usturam ex cauteriis serratis[72] duorum digitorum spatio
super ipsas venulas effectam. tunc longo tempore vulneratione[73]
servata, ferri[74] materiam purulentam[75] ex alto ad superficiem[76]
passionem relevare promittunt. quod nos in accessione noxium
atque exitiale iudicamus ob vehementiam motus; in lenimento
vero inutile atque adiutoriorum medelae contrarium, siquidem
prohibeat eorum beneficia penetrare. non enim fricationes vel
cucurbitae vel dropaces aut sinapismi aut ptarmica aut cataclys-
mi, quos nos aquarum illisiones appellamus, vulneratis locis adhiberi aut perferri aptissime possunt.

47 utuntur etiam frigido lavacro, quod Graeci psychrolusian appellant, quod necessario nervos indurat[77] ac congelare consuevit
obdensatione[78] cutis ac totius corporis. utuntur etiam locali
venarum divisura, ex qua patientes partes implentur. dant
quoque mastichen masticandam, ex quo in passione constituta
densantur constrictivae virtutis causa.[79]

item Themison primo libro Tardarum passionum, quas chronias vocant, phlebotomat atque constrictivis fomentis utitur ad
laxamentum phlebotomiae, frustratus errore sequenti ex fomen-

---

[71] modum *edd.*

[72] serratis *Sm* (*cf. Chr. iii. 57*): ferratis *S*

[73] vulnerationis *S*: *corr. Rm*

[74] ⟨qua⟩ ferri *R*: *sed fort. ponenda virgula post* ferri (= cauterii), *non post* servata

[75] materia purulenta *edd.*

[76] ad superficiem *scripsi*: atque superficie *S*: in superficiem ⟨possit⟩ *Rm*

[77] *fort.* indurare

[78] ob densationem *R*

[79] densatus constrictivae virtutis cassatur *S* (*cum asterisco*)

5 Many leaders of various other sects have recommended fomentations of rose oil, vinegar, rue, thyme, sulphurwort, castor, silphium, the seed of the tree called *agnos*, marjoram, and ivy foliage. But when the head is pervaded by these substances during an attack and shaken and burdened by the impact of their acrid properties, the disease as a whole is aggravated. The use of these substances is to be condemned,[20] especially at a time when soothing treatment is obviously called for.

These physicians also use purgative drugs (Greek *cathartica*), which purge the bowels. But the gullet is contaminated by these drugs, and the whole system of nerves and sinews is injured.

6 They also recommend arteriotomy[21] as well as the application of serrated cauteries over the small vessels themselves at an interval of two digits. Then, keeping the wounds open for a long time, they claim that in this way the purulent matter is brought from the deeper parts to the surface, with consequent relief of the disease. But we hold that during an attack this treatment is harmful and, in fact, deadly because of the violence of the shock; and during the interval of remission the treatment is useless and, moreover, opposed to the healing power of the other remedies, since it prevents their beneficial effects from penetrating. For massages, cupping, pitch plasters, mustard plasters, sternutatories, and douches (*cataclysmoe*, which we translate *aquarum illisiones*) cannot be suitably employed or endured when the parts are injured.

7 These physicians also recommend the cold bath (Greek *psychrolusia*); but this treatment always hardens the sinews and usually thickens them because of its condensing action upon the skin and the whole body. The same physicians also employ local venesection;[22] but this produces a congestion of the affected parts. They also give the patient mastic to chew; but this remedy, too, by reason of its astringent nature, causes congestion of the affected parts.

Themison in Book I of his work *On Slow Diseases* (Greek *chroniae*) prescribes venesection and follows its relaxing effects with astringent embrocations. In this prescription he is mis-

20. Possibly 'causes a rain of sharp blows.'

21. The text of this and the following sentence is doubtful. The operation was performed on the arteries behind the ears or on those at the temples. These same vessels and, in addition, the temporal veins were often cauterized.

22. I.e., venesection at the affected parts.

tis incongruis. item imminente augmento duas praecavens ho-
48 ras, unctiones adhibet acerrimas et durissimam fricationem atque constrictionem articulorum; tunc sinapismum adhibet ultimis membrorum partibus sive summitatibus articulorum ob
avertendam materiam. plurimas etiam fronti sanguisugas ap-
ponit atque humeris et temporibus capitis, quod est contra sectae rigorem. affectandam igitur corporis laxationem, non aversionem materiae eius dicimus: quippe cum non concurrat neque
conveniat quod faciendum putat, ut eodem tempore articulorum
constrictione et sanguisugarum appositione utamur, praeserva-
tis horis duabus antequam passionis implicent augmenta, cum
49 illo tempore sit requies adhibenda; et saepe contingat ut prae-
veniens corpori occupato querela[80] accessionem denuntians ipsum quoque tempus quod elegisse videtur turbare noscatur; sitque nocens appositio sanguisugarum, ex quibus perfrictio[81] atque
commotio vel ex earum morsibus amentia aut si aliquo sanguinem detrahunt gravis aegros vexatio consequitur.

probat etiam apponenda malagmata dolori contraria, quae
anodyna vocantur, vel castoreum aut rutam aut sphondylion
herbam, cum cerotario ex oleo rosaceo atque pice liquida confecto. ex iisdem iugiter iubet odorem capere aegrotantem, omni-
50 fariam caput implens. atque ita si dolores, inquit, mitigati non
fuerint ex calidis rebus, frigidae spongiae apponendae, ad Empiricorum consilia devolutus, qui ex contrariis ad contraria transeundum causis resistentibus probaverunt. utitur etiam scaroticis, hoc est quae cutem exedere[82] vel corrumpere valeant. et
cessante accessione imperat fricationem adhiberi atque fomenta,
quorum item usus non declinantis est accessionis sed in toto re-
cedentis. denique peccatis indulgendum Methodicorum princeps Soranus dignissime iudicavit: adhuc enim, inquit, Themison[83] Asclepiadis erroribus et rudimento temporis Methodici
fallebantur.[84]

[80] querela ⟨et⟩ R
[81] perfrictio Rm: perfricatio S
[82] exedere scripsi: extendere edd.
[83] Themison⟨is et⟩ Wellmann, Hermes 57 (1922) 398
[84] [methodici] fallebatur Deichgräber, RE s.v. 'Themison' 1634

taken, and his error arises from the unsuitable embrocations. And two hours before an attack is expected to begin Themison employs sharp ointments and strenuous rubbing as well as binding of the limbs, then the application of mustard plasters to the ends or extremities of the limbs, to remove matter. And he applies a large number of leeches to the forehead, shoulders, and temples, a practice in opposition to the strict teachings of the Methodist Sect. We hold that the aim should be to relax the body, not to remove matter from the body. And what Themison proposes to do is neither consistent nor useful, for he has us at one and the same time bind the limbs and apply leeches. And he has us do this two hours before an attack of the disease is expected, a time when rest is required. Indeed, it often happens that when a body is beset [by disease][23] the pain which marks the coming of an attack affects the body before [the end of the two hours] and makes that very period, which Themison chose for his treatment, a troubled one. And the use of leeches is therefore harmful, resulting as it does in chill, agitation, possible loss of reason from the bites of the leeches, and severe injury at any point where blood is withdrawn.

Themison also recommends the application of emollient plasters to allay pain (Greek *anōdyna*) and employs castor, rue, cow parsnip, and a cerate made with rose oil and liquid pitch. He prescribes that the patient continually inhale the scent from these substances; but thereby he causes the patient's head to become completely congested. Again, if the pain is not relieved by warm treatments, Themison prescribes the application of cold sponges. In this he has recourse to the principles of the Empirics, who recommend changing from a given treatment to its opposite in stubborn cases. He also uses escharotics, i.e., drugs which have the property of eating into or corroding the skin. And when the attack begins to abate, he prescribes massage and fomentations; but these are correctly used not when the attack begins to decline but when it is completely over. Now Soranus, the leader of the Methodists, has very properly held that we must excuse these errors; for, as he says, Themison was still trammeled by the errors of Asclepiades, and the Methodists were still led astray by the imperfect state of knowledge at the time.

23. Or possibly 'by the aforesaid treatments.'

51 ## II. DE SCOTOMATICIS

SCOTOMATICA passio ab accidenti nomen sumpsit quod repentinas oculis ingerat tenebras. afficit frequenter vacuos homines, hoc est sine aliquo exercitio vitam ducentes, et vinolentos,
vel consuetos ventrem purgare medicaminibus potis et ab eorum
usu repente desistentes, item haemorrhoidis longo tempore affectos et post earum amputationem nulla recorporatione curatos.
vehementescit autem haec passio hieme vel verni temporis initio. praeterea saepe futuram denuntiat epilepsiam: veteres denique parvam epilepsiam vocaverunt.

nam in passione constitutos repentina visus tenebratio atque
nebula cum capitis vertigine consequitur, ut omnia secum mo-
52 veri existiment. item ante oculos quosdam sentiunt marmorum
maculis similes tractus, quos marmarygas Graeci vocaverunt,
cum tamen conversis oculis omni ex parte non deserant visum.
item capitis atque oculorum gravatio et sedere volentibus timor,
siquidem secum omnia putent impelli vel cadere, aurium tinnitus, superiorum corporis sudor, aut repentinus casus cum celerrima surrectione. asperatur praeterea passio si ex alto aspexerint
aegrotantes vel meatum fluminis, aut rotae vertiginem figuli,[1]
item si proni quicquam gesserint, vel maiorem vocem auribus
acceperint.

discernitur ab epilepsia haec passio, siquidem neque sensibus
privat[2] aegrotantes, neque spasmo, id est diverso raptu, adficit.[3]
53 item a capitis passione, quam cephalaean vocant, discernitur
quod dolorem non faciat. separare autem ab ista passione vertiginem sive obscuritatem necessarium non est, siquidem ex his
veluti partibus scotomatica passio confecta esse videatur. est
denique istius passionis affectio saluti innoxia, hoc est sine ullo
periculo, nisi quis mare tenus aut ex alto cadens ratione casus potius quam passionis violentia perire videatur.

[1] figuli *scripsi, coll. 66, Diaet. pass. 5*: sive ignis *edd.*

[2] privet *Helmreich 185*

[3] adficiat *Helmreich 185*

---

1. The precise force of *diverso raptu* is uncertain. The reference may be to different
kinds of convulsion (e.g., tonic and clonic) or to the seizure of various parts of the body

I   II. SCOTOMA

Scotoma takes its name from its characteristic symptom, for it causes sudden darkness [Greek *scotos*] before the eyes. It frequently attacks inactive men, that is to say, men who pass their days without any exercise, those who drink wine to excess, those who customarily purge the bowels by drinking drugs but all at once give up the use of such drugs, and those who have suffered for a long time from hemorrhoids and after their removal have not been accorded any metasyncritic treatment. The disease becomes severe in the winter or in the beginning of spring. In addition, it often presages the coming of epilepsy, and for that reason the ancients call it 'small' epilepsy.

2   Those who have the disease experience a sudden darkening and blotting-out of the vision, with such dizziness that they think everything is moving about them. They see before their eyes sparks (Greek *marmarygae*) like the flashes that come from the spots of shining marble, meeting the eyes from every direction, no matter which way they turn them. Again, in this disease the head and eyes feel weighed down; though the patient wishes to sit down, he fears to move for he thinks everything is giving way or falling about him. There is ringing in the ears, sweating of the upper parts of the body, or a sudden fall followed by swift arising. And the disease is aggravated if the patient watches the flow of a river from a high point or gazes at a rotating potter's wheel or does anything when bending forward or hears a loud noise.

3   Scotoma may be distinguished from epilepsy, since it does not deprive the patient of his senses, nor are there the various bodily convulsions.[1] And scotoma may be distinguished from chronic headache (Greek *cephalaea*), for it does not cause pain. But there is no need to distinguish scotoma from vertigo and the blurring of vision [that accompanies dizziness], for the latter are, as it were, the parts of which scotoma is composed. The disease is not serious, that is, it does not involve danger of death, unless, of course, the patient falls into the sea or from a height. But then the cause of death is the fall rather than the severity of the disease.

---

or to the thrusting of the limbs in various directions (cf. 64). The phrase repeatedly occurs in the section on epilepsy. Cf. also Cass. Fel., p. 168. 18 Rose.

curationem vero eandem adhiberi convenit quae nuper passioni capitis est ordinata, non solum generali sed etiam speciali
ratione.

54   III. DE INCUBONE

Incubonem aliqui ab hominis forma vel similitudine nomen ducere dixerunt, aliqui a phantasia qua patientes afficiuntur,
siquidem veluti ascendere atque insidere suo pectori sentiant
quicquam. Themison vero secundo Epistolarum libro pnigaliona
vocavit, siquidem praefocet aegrotantes. item quidam veteres
ephialten vocaverunt, alii epofelen,[1] quod utilis[2] patientibus per-
hibeatur.

afficit crapula vel indigestione iugi vexatos. accidens igitur
semel, ita ut nullam vigilantibus querelam aut displicentem sanitatem faciat, sed solius somni turbatio noscatur, minime passio
dici potest: sicut neque semel effectus per somnum seminis lap-
55 sus, quem Graeci onirogmon[3] appellant, passio nuncupatur, nisi
iugiter atque cum corporis incommoditate fuerit effectus. est
autem supradicta passio epilepsiae tentatio. nam quod neque
deus, neque semideus, neque Cupido sit, libris Causarum quos
Aetiologumenos Soranus appellavit, plenissime explicavit.

ista igitur passione possessos sequitur corporis tardissimus
motus atque torpor, et magis per somnium gravedo atque pressura et veluti praefocatio, qua sibi quemquam irruisse repente
existiment qui sensibus oppressis corpus exanimet, neque clamare permittat. quo fit ut saepe erumpentes non articulata sed
56 confusa voce exclament. quidam denique ita inanibus adficiuntur visis, ut et se videre credant irruentem sibi et usum turpissi-
mae libidinis persuadentem, cuius si digitos apprehendere nixi
fuerint, fugatum existiment. tunc cum somno surrexerint faciem atque transvorationis[4] partes uvidas et humectas sentiunt,

---

[1] epofelen (ἐπωφέλην) Triller Clinotechnia 81, coll. Hesych. Lex. s.v. ἐπιάλης, Artem.
Onirocr. ii. 37 (p. 139. 18–23 Hercher): epibolen S

[2] hostilis Rm (epibolen retento): ut talis Am

[3] onirogonon S: v. Chr. v. 80–82   [4] transforationis edd.

---

1. Incubus and incubo are both used in Latin. Caelius uses the latter word; the former
is the common one in English.

2. Pnigō, 'choke'.

3. Diaet. pass. 53: 'Graeci efialten quod ascendisse aliquem supra dormientem
fingant' (Rose, p. 231; cf. Esc. 7). The noun ephialtēs is probably derived from a verb
'to attack.' Note also the proper name Ephialtes.

In this disease the same treatment should be applied as that
prescribed above for chronic headache, and this is true not
merely in a general way but in specific details.

54   III. INCUBUS [NIGHTMARE][1]

SOME hold that the word 'incubus' refers to a human form or
likeness, others to the vision by which the patient is affected,
for he seems to see something climbing over him and settling
upon his chest. In Book II of his *Letters* Themison calls the affection *pnigaliōn*, since it chokes the patient.[2] Some of the ancients
call it *ephialtēs*,[3] others *epōfelēs* because it may be useful to the
patient.[4]

The disease affects those who have been weakened by continual intoxication or indigestion. But if there is only a single
occurrence [of such a dream], so that when the person awakes he
feels no pain or discomfort, there having been merely a disturbance of his sleep, we can scarcely call this condition a disease. It
is the same as with a single instance of seminal emission in sleep
55 (Greek *oneirōgmos*).[5] The condition cannot be called a disease
unless it occurs continually and with bodily discomfort. But
nightmare when it is a disease is a forerunner of epilepsy. And
Soranus in his work *On Causes*, which he calls *Aetiologumena*,
has shown abundantly that the incubus is not a god or a demi-
god or Cupid.

Those who suffer from the disease of nightmare show extreme
sluggishness of bodily movement and stiffness. And particularly
during the dream there is a feeling of heaviness and oppression
and a sort of choking. They imagine that someone has suddenly
attacked them and stunned their senses, exhausting them and
preventing outcry. Thus they often jump up and cry out with
56 confused and indistinct sounds. Some are seized with such gro-
tesque visions that they imagine they see the attacker urging
them to satisfy a shameful lust. If they try to take hold of his
fingers, they find that he is gone. Then when they awake from
sleep, the face and the parts used in swallowing feel moist and

4. I.e., may be a good omen. But with the reading of *Rm* the meaning is: '*epibolē*,
because it appears to attack the patient' (Greek *epiballein*, 'to attack').

5. Cf. *Chr.* v. 80–81.

attestante gravedine cervicis cum tussicula levi molli stimulatione commota. plurimum autem possessis accidit pallor et corporis tenuitas, quippe cum somnum timendo non capiant. apparet igitur stricturae passio ex gravedine, tarda autem ex temporis tractu, et non semper sine periculo salutis: cum enim vehementer impresserit praefocatio quosdam interficit. memorat denique Silimachus Hippocratis sector contagione quadam plurimos ex ista passione veluti lue apud urbem Romam confectos.

quapropter curandos oportet iacere loco lucido atque mediocriter calido, adhibita requie animi et corporis, abstinentia usque ad tertium diem, quem Graeci diatriton vocaverunt. tunc colla tegenda atque caput et[5] stomachus[6] lanis limpidis ex oleo calido praetinctis;[7] adhibenda etiam oris collutio ex potu aquae calidae. ac si plurima stomachi vel capitis vel colli fuerit querela, adhibenda phlebotomia, et post detractionem perunctio ex oleo calido. tunc ora fovenda, cibus dandus simplex, suci facilioris, parvus, sorbilis. et si passio perseveraverit, cataplasmata adhibenda, cucurbita quoque, nunc simplex, nunc adiuncta scarificatione, ex utraque parte gutturis, quam Graeci anthereona vocant, nos rumam. tunc vaporatione utendum, et alternis diebus cibus dandus. illa vero adiutoria quae adhibenda diurnis erunt diebus adhibenda, sed longe remotius a nocturno tempore. tunc etiam gestatio atque varius cibus et lavacrum et aquatum vinum. illis vero partibus quas curamus erunt primo cerotaria apponenda, tunc malagmata, ut diachylon aut diamelilotu aut diasamsucu,[8] fricatio etiam capitis, et densi pectinis capillorum decursio. suspiciones etiam sive metus imminentium somniorum avertendi procul, fabularum lenitate robore adiecto. plerique enim sibi fingentes vel formantes futura voluntarios paene causarum motus efficiunt.

ac si passio tardaverit levioribus admonita monitis,[9] convenit etiam radicum vomitus atque drimyphagia, capitis quoque detonsio, acoporum[10] usus acriorum, item dropax. sic enim aut ex supradictis adiutoriis aegritudo solvetur, aut si peioraverit, epilepsia necessario sequetur.

---

5 et *om. R*   6 stomacho *edd.*   7 praecincto *edd.*

8 diamelilotum aut diasamsucum *S*

9 motibus *Rm*

10 acoporum *Triller Clinotechnia 74*: ac corporum *edd.*

humid; there is a feeling of heaviness at the neck, and also a light cough provoked by a mild pricking sensation. Those who have suffered from the affliction for a long time are pale and thin, for because of their fear they do not get sleep. From the feeling of heaviness we gather that the disease involves a state of stricture; from the length of time it lasts we consider it a chronic disease. And this disease is not always without danger to life; 57 for, since it causes severe choking, it is in some cases fatal. In fact, Silimachus, a follower of Hippocrates, tells us that many persons at Rome were carried off by this disease, incurring it through contagion as in plague.

In treating the disease have the patient lie in a moderately light and warm room. His mind and body should be at rest, and he should eat no food until the end of the three-day period (Greek *diatritos*). Cover the neck, head, and region of the chest with scoured wool dipped in warm olive oil. Have the patient wash his mouth with a drink of warm water. If there is considerable pain in the gullet, head, or neck, perform venesection; and after the withdrawal of blood anoint the patient with warm olive 58 oil, and then wash his face. Give him simple food, easy to digest, in small amount, and soft. If the disease persists, apply poultices and then cupping, first dry and then with scarification, under both sides of the throat (Greek *anthereōn*, Latin *ruma*). Then apply warmth. Prescribe food on alternate days; but have the other required remedies administered every day, in no case, however, near night. Afterward prescribe passive exercise, varied food, bathing, and wine mixed with water. To the parts being treated apply first cerates and then emollient plasters, such as the plaster of juices and the plasters made with melilot and marjoram. 59 Massage the head and run a fine comb through the hair. Keep all thought or fear of impending nightmares away from the patient, strengthening his mind with stories that do not excite him. For many patients, by trying to imagine or conceive what is to be, cause their diseases to become active almost at will.

But if the disease becomes chronic and is subject only to mild exacerbations, it will be proper to prescribe radishes as vomitives, an acrid diet, shearing of the head, the use of sharp restorative ointments, and pitch plasters. The disease will either be cured with the help of these remedies, or, if it becomes worse, will inevitably be followed by epilepsy.

60 ## IV. DE EPILEPSIA

E PILEPSIA vocabulum sumpsit quod sensum atque mentem
pariter apprehendat. appellatur etiam puerilis passio, siquidem in ipsis abundet aetatibus; et sacra, sive quod divinitus
putetur immissa, sive quod sacram contaminet animam, sive
quod in capite fiat quod multorum philosophorum iudicio sacrum atque templum est partis animae in corpore natae, sive ob
magnitudinem passionis. maiora enim vulgus sacra vocavit—
sacrum dictum mare, sacra domus, velut[1] tragicus poeta sacram
noctem, hoc est magnam.

61 fit plerumque vel nascitur ex vinolentia aut indigestione aut
contusione vel, ut Asclepiades, percussu atque divisura membranorum[2] quae cerebrum tegunt, aut nimio timore. sed eius
passionis species duae esse probantur: una quae somno similis
altissimo videatur, alia[3] diverso raptu corpus afficiat, quarum
prima gravior iudicatur, siquidem sit similis apoplexiae. quarum
quidem commixtio tertiam facere speciem potest: plerique enim
raptu atque contractu corporis adfecti vel adprehensi secundo
in altissimum soporem devenerunt. sed horum differentia generaliter inutilis curationi invenitur.

62 pronos autem seu declives aut venturos in ipsam passionem
sequuntur communia accidentia etiam ceterarum passionum
quae ex membrana cerebri oriuntur, ut gravedo atque vertigo
capitis et interior sonitus, consensus etiam occipitii, oculorum
intentio, aurium tinnitus, aut difficilis auditus, et cum vertigine
visus obtusio, vel quaedam prae oculis quasi propendentia macularum marmoris similia, quae Graeci amarygmata[4] sive marmarygas vocant, vel araneorum cassibus aut nubibus tenuissimis
63 similia, aut parvulis volantum animalibus ut sunt culices. item
velut scintillarum micas aut circulos igneos circumferri prae oculis sentiunt aegrotantes, linguam quoque inflexibilem, cum saltu
musculorum et dolorem a tergo inter scapulas. sequitur etiam
gutturis durities, atque praecordiorum iugis inflatio, cum osci-

---

[1] velut *fort. divisim scrib. cum Bendz 55*

[2] membranorum *Reinesius 661*: membrorum *S*: membranarum *Rm*

[3] alia ⟨quae⟩ *R*

[4] marmarygmata *Rm*

IV. EPILEPSY

EPILEPSY takes its name from the fact that it is a seizure both of the senses and of the mind.[1] It is also called 'the children's disease,' since it is common in childhood. And it is called 'the sacred disease' either because it is thought to be sent by a divine power or because it defiles the soul, which is sacred, or because it is centered in the head, which, in the judgment of many philosophers, is the sacred abode of that part of the soul which originates in the body, or because of the great power of the disease, for people generally call what is powerful 'sacred.' Thus the sea and a powerful family are called 'sacred'; and the tragic poet speaks of the night as 'sacred,' that is to say, mighty.[2]

61   Epilepsy generally occurs or commences after drunkenness, indigestion, an injury, or, as Asclepiades says, a blow, especially one which penetrates the membranes covering the brain, or else extreme fear. There are two forms of epilepsy. One appears to be like a deep sleep; the other racks the body with various convulsions. The former type is considered more serious, since it is like apoplexy. Now a combination of the two types may produce a third; for in many cases the patient is attacked or seized by bodily spasm or convulsion and then passes into a profound sleep. But, in general, the differentiation of these types is found to have no bearing on the treatment.

62   Those who are on the verge of an attack of epilepsy show symptoms in common with those of other diseases originating in the membrane of the brain, e.g., heaviness of the head and dizziness, head noises, sympathetic pain in the back of the head, eyes staring, ringing in the ears or impairment of hearing, and blurring of vision accompanied by dizziness. Certain objects may appear as if dangling before the eyes, like the sparkling points in marble (Greek *amarygmata* or *marmarygae*) or spiders'

63   webs or thin clouds or small winged animals, such as gnats. And patients see sparks flashing or rings of fire spinning before their eyes. The tongue feels rigid, the muscles quiver, and there is pain in the back between the shoulder blades. There are also the following symptoms: stiffness of the throat, constant pre-

---

1. As well as of the body. Cf. *Diaet. pass.* 55; Isidore *Orig.* iv. 7. 5.

2. Cf. *Ac.* ii. 162. See M. Haupt, *Hermes*, I (1866), 21–26; F. Bücheler, *Kleine Schriften*, II, 189; O. Temkin, *The Falling Sickness* (Baltimore, 1945), p. 6.

tatione, sternutamento, et salivarum fluore, et cibi fastidio, aut
immodico appetitu, vigiliae iuges, aut plurimus et inanis somnus, insomnia turbata, et ciborum difficilis digestio,[5] vel nulla ex[6]
manifesta causa veretri tentigo, et frequens veneris delectatio,
aliquando etiam per somnum seminis lapsus, quem Graeci oni-
64 rogmon[7] vocaverunt, mens suspensa cum anxietate, et nullis ex
maioribus causis facilis iracundia, atque paulo ante gestorum
oblivio, et eorum quae caliginem facere valent facilis sensus.

obtinente passione occupato corpore, sensuum privatio; accessione dominante, sequitur et quibusdam immobilitas perfecta
cum ore demisso attestante pallore, cum aspiratione tarda et pulsu
magno atque alti soporis simili oppressione. alios vero raptos
diversa diductio atque saltus et vultus contortio vel oculorum
sequetur, quae saepe perseverans etiam post accessionem strabos
fingit aegrotantes; atque contrario[8] quibus tarda[9] fuerit correc-
65 tio[10] naturalis visus simulant aequitatem. sequitur etiam gutturis stridor et singultus cum rubore vultus et venarum inflatione, et aliquando pulsus atque spirationis cessatio, tunc per
intervalla resumptio, palpebrarum quoque suspensa positio, et
illisio dentium atque stridor, et linguae prolapsio, quae saepe
quassatione saepe incisura vexatur. sequitur etiam praecordiorum ad superiora raptus, vel stercorum et urinae involuntaria emissio, sudor roscidus rigenti corpore, aliquibus etiam con-
fusae vocis emissio, et ante dimissionem per os atque nares spumarum fluor.

accessione cessante, omnium gestorum ignorantia, atque cor-
66 poris dimissa volutatio cum maestitia vultus aegrotantis. sequitur tunc oscitatio, et distentio corporis veluti voluntaria, et in
solitos usus[11] piger motus, et totius corporis marcor, oculorum
etiam permanens turbatio, atque venarum frontis extantia, aliquibus etiam mentis alienatio, et nulla notorum agnitio.

alio autem tempore plurima ex antecedentibus[12] consequentur
quae supra memoravimus, hoc est tenebratio vel caligo, cum

[5] digestio *conieci* (*cf. Cass. Fel., p. 169. 13*): egestio *edd.*

[6] nulla ex *Bendz 93*: nulla, et *S*: nulla, et ⟨sine⟩ *R*

[7] onirogonon *S*: v. *Chr. v. 80*

[8] *fort.* ⟨e⟩ contrario

[9] parva *Rm*   [10] corruptio *Rm*: correptio *A*

[11] insolitus visus *S*: *corr. Bendz* (*cf. 69; Cael. Aur. Gyn. ii. 108; Hagendahl 260*)

[12] *fort.* accidentibus (*vel* acced-)

cordial distention, yawning, sneezing, flow of saliva, distaste for
food or else an uncontrolled desire for it, continued wakefulness
or else excessive and unprofitable sleep, troubled dreams, difficulty in digesting food, tentigo without any apparent reason,
frequent desire for venery, sometimes an effusion of semen dur-
64 ing sleep (Greek *oneirōgmos*), mind unsettled and troubled, a
tendency to become angry for no good reason,[3] forgetfulness of
what has just recently taken place, and a susceptibility to anything that blurs the vision.

As the disease emerges and takes hold of the body, the patient
is bereft of his senses. As the attack gains full sway, in some
cases the patient remains completely immobile; his face is pale
and lowered, respiration slow, and pulse large; he is overcome as
if by a deep sleep. But in other cases the patient suffers a convulsive seizure; his limbs are flung about and keep shaking. His
face and eyes are distorted, and this condition often persists, so
that even after the attack he continues to squint. On the other
hand, those who have been successfully treated over a period of
65 time retain their natural appearance without distortion. Other
symptoms occurring during the attack are: wheezing in the
throat, hiccoughs, reddening of the face, distention of the blood
vessels, sometimes a breaking-off of the pulse and respiration
followed by resumption after a time, eyelids remaining unclosed,
clenching and gnashing of the teeth, tongue protruding so that
it is often injured as the teeth strike it or even bite into it, elevation of the precordia,[4] involuntary discharge of feces and
urine, dewlike sweat appearing on the rigid body, in some cases
the utterance of confused sounds, and before the attack abates
an effusion of foam through mouth and nose.

When the attack abates, the patient has no recollection of
what has happened; his body ceases to toss, and his face is sad.
66 He yawns and stretches his body as if voluntarily; his expression
is strange. His movements in ordinary activities are sluggish,
his whole body faint; the distortion of his eyes still persists, and
the veins of the forehead remain distended. In some cases there
is mental aberration and a failure to recognize familiar persons.
Thereafter many of the previously mentioned symptoms

3. The phrase 'for no good reason' may possibly belong with what precedes.

4. Cf. ὑποχονδρίων μετεωρισμός (Soranus): praecordiorum suspensa conductione
(*Diaet. pass.* 54).

proni quicquam gesserint aegrotantes, aut navem aut rotam
figuli celeri motu ferri conspexerint, aut aquam fluentem vel
altitudinem aut rupem viderint, aut strepitum vel clamorem
audierint, aut vehementer refrixerint, vel igneis lavacris usi fue-
67 rint, aut odoribus nimium bonis vel malis adfecti, ut storacis in-
censi aut thuris aut bdellii aut gagatis lapidis vel bituminis aut
cervini cornu.

praeterea accessionum motus nunc ordinatos nunc inordinatos
aegrotantes accipiunt, et nunc intervallis longioribus ut mensium duodecim, nunc angustioribus plurimum vel parum, ut
eodem mense vel die frequenter agitentur. noctibus quidem[13]
inquietati [et][14] quidam antecedentibus signis accessionem fore
denuntiant, quidam sine ullo denuntiativo motu, quo fiet ut
magis periclitentur. alii enim praenoscentes futura, motibus solitis admoniti, in domibus se continendo tutantur accessionem
68 praevenientes: quam cum sentiunt propinquare, eligunt locos
quibus tuto ac sine ulla turpitudine iactentur. alii vero istorum
ignari publicis in locis cadendo foedantur, adiunctis etiam externis periculis quae passionis non esse videantur, loci causa prae-
cipites dati, aut in flumina vel mare cadentes, aut in balneis ventris solutione coacti.

signa autem sunt post lenimentum futurae rursus accessionis,
ex quibus affici in passionem venturos memoravimus: somnus
turbatus vel cibi corruptio sine ulla manifesta causa, item veretri sine ratione tentigo et veneris appetentia vel seminis per somnum iactus, quem onirogmon[15] Graeci vocant, iracundia, maesti-
69 tudo, et cetera quae nuper posuimus, item segnities cum pigro
motu in officia solita, et gravatio cum quodam somnifico maerore, vultus decolor atque venarum[16] inflatio, oculorum quoque

13 quidam *Rm*

14 *seclusi*: et quidam *om. R*

15 onirogonon *S*: *v. Chr. v. 80*

16 venarum *Bendz 93, coll. Chr. i. 65*: maior *edd.*

which indicate the onset of the disease, e.g., dizziness and
dimness of vision, may occur when the patient does something
while bending forward, or watches a ship or a swiftly rotating
potter's wheel, gazes at flowing water, looks up[5] a great height
or a cliff, hears a loud noise or shout, suffers a severe chill, takes
67 too hot a bath, or smells strong odors whether pleasant or unpleasant, such as that of burning storax, frankincense, bdellium,
lignite, bitumen, or stag's horn.

Again, some patients suffer attacks regularly, others irregularly; and in some cases the attacks come at long intervals, e.g.,
twelve months, and in other cases at more or less frequent intervals, successive seizures often coming in the same month or
even the same day. Some patients becoming restless at night
can tell in advance, by the appearance of antecedent symptoms,
that there will be an attack. But in other cases there are no such
premonitory symptoms, and the danger is therefore greater. For
those who are forewarned by certain disturbances regularly occurring at such times and who therefore know that an attack is
to come, anticipate it by keeping to their houses and guarding
68 themselves. And when they sense that the attack is at hand,
they choose places where they will be safe when tossing about
and where they will not be subjected to any shame. But the
others who have no such premonitions may fall down and undergo an ugly attack in public places. In addition, there are in
such cases external dangers which have nothing to do with the
disease itself. Because of the nature of the place they may fall
headlong into a river or sea. And they may have to void their
bowels in the public bath.

The signs of the coming of a new attack, after an interval of
remission, are the same as those which we mentioned above[6] as
indicating that a person is about to incur the disease, viz., troubled sleep, indigestion for no apparent cause, tentigo without
any reason, desire for coitus, ejaculation of semen during sleep
(Greek *oneirōgmos*), proneness to anger, sadness, as well as the
69 other indications set forth above. The patient is listless and goes
about his accustomed tasks with sluggish movements; he has a
feeling of heaviness and is sleepy and depressed. His complexion
is unnatural, and his veins distended; his eyes have a sort of

5. Apparently not 'down': cf. 69. But note *ex alto despectio*, 114.
6. See 62–64.

veluti depravatio cum deiecto quodam visu. nam suspicere
difficile est aegrotanti, hoc est aerem supernum attendere: quod
si tentaverint, facile rursum abducti visivas[17] quoque oculorum
partes ad inferiora convertunt. vel si repentino motu caput in
alteram converterint partem, vertiginem sentient cum tremore
atque torpore, cum digitorum contractu vel dolore, aut crurum
70 gravedine et summitatis[18] manuum vel pedum. ex quibus multis vel cunctis interrogatione acceptis passionem dicere poterimus, nisi praesentibus in accessione facilius nobis cognitio fuerit
declarata, vel aetatis aut aliqualibet[19] causa aeger sua narrare
non potuerit accidentia, quae supradicta ratione apprehendere
poterimus et accessionem futuram praenoscere, conicientes etiam temporum responsionem, quamquam summatim accessionum ordo saepe servetur.

communiter autem haec passio frequens est in pueris, et magis
tempore quo dentium nativitates habentur. accidit etiam pri-
71 maevis atque mediis aetatibus, senibus vero difficile, nam vehementius afficit proximos nativitati infantes quam pueros aut ver-
genti aetate atque seniores, siquidem viribus invalidi passionum
impetum tolerare non possint. solet denique haec passio puber-
tatis tempore sive novae purgationis in feminis aut primi partus
quadam naturali novitate facile detergeri corporis mutatione
suffecta. quod si minime venerit plerumque patienti consenes-
cit, nisi aut longo tempore natura pugnante aut medicinae diligentia fuerit superata.

irruit autem omni tempore corporibus, sed magis verno. frequenter[20] simile pati epilepticis et[21] a matrice praefocatae mu-
72 lieres[22] inveniuntur, siquidem non aliter sensibus privantur, sed
discernuntur quod in ultima accessionis parte per os atque nares
spumarum fluore[23] afficiantur. haec est passionis cuncta specialis significatio.

curationis autem adhibendae causa erit necessario adhibendum genus, quod sit passio stricturae atque vehemens et diffi-

---

[17] visivas *conieci*: vicinas *edd*.

[18] summitate *S*: *corr. Rm*

[19] *fort.* alia qualibet, *cf. Bendz Eran 43. 99*

[20] *fort. interpung. post* frequenter

[21] et *fort. om.*

[22] mulieres *Rm*: mulieri *S*   [23] fluore ⟨non⟩ *R*

distortion, his gaze is lowered. In fact, it is difficult for him to raise his eyes, that is, to look upward; and if he tries to do so, he is soon discouraged and lowers the pupils of his eyes again. And if he turns his head suddenly to one side, he experiences a feeling of dizziness; this is accompanied by trembling, numbness, and cramp or pain in the fingers or heaviness in the legs 70 and the extremities of the hands and feet. On finding, through questioning, that many or all of these symptoms are present, we are able to say what the disease is. Of course, if we happen to be present during an attack, the recognition of the disease is surer and easier. And if, because of his age or any other reason, the patient cannot tell us his symptoms, we shall be able to find out about them in the manner described and thus to prognosticate a future attack. The time of previous attacks should be considered, even though there is only a very limited regularity in these attacks.

In general, it may be said that the disease is most common in children, and especially when they are cutting teeth. It also occurs in young people and those of middle age, but rarely in 71 old people. And it is more violent in young babies than in older children and in persons of declining or advanced age, for weak bodies cannot endure violent diseases. Now ordinarily this disease may easily be gotten rid of at the time of puberty, or, in the case of girls, at the beginning of menstruation or at the birth of the first child.[7] For the body at these times naturally undergoes a kind of renovation and change. But if the disease is not then removed, it generally remains with the patient all his life, unless it is overcome by nature, after a long struggle, or by medical treatment.

Epilepsy attacks bodies at all seasons and especially in the spring. Hysterical suffocation in women is often found to resem- 72 ble epilepsy, for in either case the patient is bereft of her senses. But the diseases may be distinguished, for toward the end of an attack of epilepsy there is foaming at the mouth and nostrils. This completes our account of the special signs indicative of epilepsy.

In prescribing a treatment for this disease, we must bear in mind the type of disease it is, namely, one involving a state of stricture, violent, hard to deal with because it keeps returning,

7. Cf. Hipp. *Aph.* ii. 45; v. 7.

culter frequentans, tarda, superpositionibus atque lenimentis
variata, †cuius quidem superpositiones nunc plurimis tempora
temporibus accessionis generalia superpositionis occurrerunt. †[24]
sed quae forte superpositiones plurimis ex accessionibus fuerint
confectae nunc cotidianos, nunc tertianos, nunc hemitritaicos
73 faciunt typos. difficile est enim hanc passionem in continuationem venire, siquidem praeventu mortis interveniente minime
continuatio intelligi possit, et sit impossibile iugibus diebus aut
sensibus privatum aut motu carentem aut diverso raptu affectum in vita manere. item lenimentorum aliqua pura ac limpida, aliqua turbata concurrunt, et aliqua latiora, aliqua angusta, aliqua horum mediocria. patitur enim communiter omnis nervositas, sed principaliter caput, sicut ex antecedentibus
conicere poterimus et ex his quae post accessionem remanere
videntur.

curandum autem oportet primo, cum tenebricositate vel vertigine vexatur, iacere loco lucido atque mediocriter calido, alti-
74 oribus stramentis capite sublevato. et si raptus fuerit consecutus, digitis erunt palpebrae differendae atque iugiter ab omni
motu servandus ob spasmi passionem. iubendum etiam ministris manibus calidis nunc caput atque frontem cum blanda fricatione, nunc collum atque gutturis partem, quam anthereona
vocant, contingere;[25] aliis etiam manuum summitatem atque
pedum tenere iubemus, praeterea frigescentia corporis vaporari,
corrigi etiam ea quae forti[25a] raptu torquentur. ac si minime consenserint, erunt in eodem schemate servanda, ne ulterius tor-
queantur; tunc quodam laxamento captato corrigenda, ne nimio
occurrentia certamine superare cupientes nervorum quassa-
75 tiones faciamus. linguam quoque relocare curabimus aut mentum corrigere vel coaequare, tunc calidis pannis thoracem vaporare atque inter scapulas, quod Graeci metaphrenon vocant.
laxatis enim diaphragmatis partibus, quod nos thoracis atque
ventris discrimen dixerimus, laxato etiam hypodymate, sive

---

[24] *locus corruptus. fortasse erat sententia auctoris* cuius quidem superpositiones ⟨nunc
ex singulis⟩ nunc ⟨ex⟩ plurimis accessionibus occurrunt *vel similis. an* genera alia *pro*
generalia? *latet fortasse adnot. marg.*: tempora et genera superpositionis

[25] *fort.* continere

[25a] *an* forte?

and chronic, i.e., characterized by periods of activity and periods of remission.[8] . . . Where the period of activity consists of a series of attacks, the exacerbations sometimes take the quotidian form, at other times the tertian, and at still other times the semitertian. But it is hardly possible that this disease should assume an unremitting form. It is inconceivable that such a state could persist, since death would supervene. For a patient cannot live deprived of his senses, unable to move, or continuously racked by various convulsions over a period of days. Again, the intervals of remission in epilepsy are in some cases completely free and clear of symptoms of disease, but not in others. And these periods are sometimes long, sometimes short, and sometimes of moderate duration. In this disease there is a general affection of the whole system of nerves and sinews; but the head is particularly affected, as may be gathered from the symptoms preceding the attack as well as those which may be observed after the attack.

When he is first assailed by darkness and dizziness, the patient should lie down in a light and moderately warm room, and the bedclothes should be so arranged that his head is elevated. If the convulsion ensues, hold his eyelids apart with your fingers, and keep him from all motion by reason of the convulsion. Instruct servants to rub first the patient's head and forehead and then his neck and the part of the throat called *anthereōn* by the Greeks. This rubbing should be done with warm hands and a gentle touch. Other servants should be instructed to hold the ends of the patient's hands and feet. And apply heat wherever the body is cold. If a part of the body is contorted by a powerful spasm, put it back in place. But if it resists replacement, keep it in the new position to prevent further twisting; and then, when there is a relaxation, take advantage of it to replace the part. By thus avoiding the use of force to overcome the resistance when it is strong, we shall avoid injury to the sinews. Also see to it that the tongue is replaced and the chin straightened and made even. And using warm cloths apply heat to the chest and the region between the shoulder blades (Greek *metaphrenon*). When there is a relaxation of the diaphragm (which we may in Latin call *discrimen*—that which separates the chest from the

8. The text is corrupt at this point. The idea may have been something like: 'These periods of activity consist sometimes of a single attack and sometimes of many attacks.'

membrana quae latera ex interioribus contegit, sine ullo periculo
poterit collectus spiritus exhalari. apponenda etiam vesica oleo
calido semiplena pubetenus atque vesicae partibus, ut ipsae
quoque mitigatae conquiescant. ac si dentes conciderint, ut
praefocationis excitent metum,²⁶ immissione digitorum ⟨in⟩²⁷
sinistram compaginem, quam Graeci chalinon vocant, hiscentes
76 dimittemus, ne spumarum emissio tardetur. tunc per intervalla
aegrotantem inclamantes excitamus, et eius ora spongia ex aqua
calida expressa detergemus, dehinc caput fovemus iugiter.

cum statum sumpserit accessio, plurimo atque dulci oleo calido et lanis mollioribus infuso omnia contegimus, magis autem
occipitium et maiores nervos quos tenontas appellant, tunc gutturis atque rumae partes, quas anthereona²⁸ appellant, cum temporibus et buccarum musculis, quos siagonas appellant. sudores
etiam si fuerint ingruentes, raptim detergemus, ne corpora perfrigescant. tunc collectum humorem detrahimus appositione
77 digiti, aut lanae aut spongiae melotae²⁹ involutae: perseverans
enim longioris temporis facit accessionem. ac si minime resu-
mentem viderimus, erunt cucurbitae leves apponendae, quas
Graeci sicyas appellant, stomacho atque thoraci et interscapulis
atque praecordiis.

sed si infans aetas fuerit patientis, erunt maiora prohibenda ob
debilitatem virium; sed eum nutrix amictu contegens oleo fovens
conclusu corporis corrigere meditetur. aut si spumarum quicquam comparuerit quod in ore teneatur, mulsum tenue destillet
paulatim et neque iugiter, quo commorationem faciat spirandi.
tunc lac offerat dimissione perfecta, siquidem sit crassius atque
78 maioris nutrimenti. dehinc cum forte potuerit post accessio-
nem³⁰ mammam sumere, erit melle papilla linienda quo facilior
sumptio fiat, atque nervorum laxatio celebretur, corpus quoque
necessario nutriatur, tenuetur³¹ praeterea etiam liquidorum
crassitudo, et venter molliatur,³² conicientes etiam singula
passionis³³ accidentia, quae ita corrigere debemus ut a generali regula nihil dissentire videamur.

tunc etiam curationis diligentiam per nutricem aegrotanti

---

²⁶ meatum S: corr. R

²⁷ supplevi

²⁸ anthereonas S: corr. R

²⁹ an melotidae vel melotidi? (cf. Chr. ii. 74)

³⁰ accessione S: corr. R

³¹ tenuetur Rm: tenuatur S

³² molliatur Rm: mollitur S

³³ passionis Rm: passioni S

abdomen) and of the *hypodyma*, the membrane [pleura] which lines the sides internally, the air collected there can then be exhaled without any danger. Also apply a vessel half-filled with hot oil to the pubes and the region of the bladder, so that these parts, too, may become relaxed and calm. And if the teeth are clenched so that there is danger of choking, insert the fingers in the left corner of the mouth (Greek *chalinos*) and thus pry the teeth apart, to avoid any obstacle to the emission of the foam.
6 Then from time to time arouse the patient by calling to him, wipe his face with a sponge squeezed out of warm water, and foment his head continually.

When the attack attains its highest stage, cover all the parts with soft wool thoroughly soaked in warm sweet olive oil, particularly the occiput, the large sinews called *tenontes*, the parts of the neck and throat, which the Greeks call *anthereōn*, the temples, and the muscles of the jaws, called *siagones*. If sweat appears, wipe it away immediately to prevent the body from becoming chilled. And remove the fluid matter that collects [in the mouth] by using a finger or a probe wrapped round with wool
7 or sponge. For if this matter remains, it adds to the length of the attack. And if the patient does not seem to be recovering from the attack, apply mild cupping (Greek *sicyae*) to the region over the esophagus, to the chest and precordia, and between the shoulder blades.

But in the case of an infant avoid severe measures because of the patient's limited strength. Have a nurse foment the baby with olive oil and wrap it in covers, trying to keep its body straight by thus confining it. If any foam appears in the mouth, the nurse may give the baby some well-diluted honey, but only a few drops at a time and not continuously, since swallowing suspends breathing. And when the attack completely abates, let her give it some milk, since that is thicker and more nutri-
8 tious. After the attack, if the infant is able to take the breast, spread honey over the nipple in order to facilitate this taking, and thus bring about the relaxation of the sinews, provide the body with necessary nourishment, dilute the thickened bodily fluids, and soften the bowels. And we must keep the particular symptoms of the disease in mind and correct them without going counter to the general regimen required by the disease.

Try also to have the baby receive careful treatment through

praestare tentabimus, iubentes et[34] a lavacro abstinendum atque
sine vino atque ⟨carnis⟩ esu[35] perseverare, tunc deambulationibus atque exercitio levi gestari quo humeros magis exerceant, ut
79 est sphaerae ludus vel exultationis cuiuspiam. item iubendum
cibum sumere suci facilioris vel interea mulsum. ac si forte ipsam quoque hac passione vexari viderimus, erit ab officio remo-
venda, non aliter etiam si qualibet passione affecta malo suco
atque corpore habituari videatur: nam hoc Graeci cachexian vocaverunt. erunt igitur his perfectis[36] aliae nutrices exhibendae
ex quarum[37] sano lacte infans nutriatur. quomodo autem sanum lac vel communiter nutrices bonae probentur Muliebribus
libris, quos Graeci Gynecion vocant, docebimus. interea ipse
quoque infans erit a lavacro servandus; tunc post tertium diem
in domo lavandus,[38] et primo oleo calido, tunc oleo et aqua calida
80 fovendus. vitanda praeterea quorum timore infantes afficiuntur, ut saepe fictae formidines.

in aetatibus vero quae ferre maiora adiutoria possint, accessione transacta erit phlebotomia adhibenda. aliqui enim medici
statim phlebotomandos probant, sicut etiam Thessalus se velle
demonstrat. aliqui prima diatrito servandum[39] existimant, quo
speculentur utrum post unam accessionem passio soluta recessisse videatur (sit[40] praeterea non solum inane, verum etiam
noxium phlebotomiam adhibere), quippe cum praedicendum
probent ex accessione secunda utrum passio augeatur et hoc
phlebotomiae exigat adiutorium, et phlebotomatus cibi refec-
81 tione toleretur. alii vero discernenter[41] aiunt hoc adiutorii genus
adhibendum, ut qui forte iam consueti passione afficiuntur, re-
servato[42] ordine lenimentorum, statim accessione facta phlebo-
tomentur; hi autem qui in prima incursione passionem accipiunt,

[34] eam *Rm*

[35] ⟨carnis⟩ esu *R: fort.* ⟨venereo⟩ usu *vel* ⟨carnis⟩ usu (*cf. 126*)

[36] praefectis *R*

[37] quorum *S: corr. A*

[38] locandus *edd.*

[39] primam diatritum servandam *Rm*

[40] *fort.* ⟨ut⟩ sit

[41] discernentes *Rm*

[42] servato *R*

9. Cf. Soranus *Gyn.*, p. 71. 21–27; Cael. Aur. *Gyn.* i. 132.

the wet nurse. Thus have the nurse abstain from bathing, from drinking wine, and from eating meat. Have her take walks and develop the upper arms and shoulders with light exercise in which the body is shaken, such as ball playing and any form of
79 leaping.[9] Instruct her to take food that is easy to digest and from time to time some mead. But if you find that she, too, is a victim of this disease, do not permit her to nurse the baby. And take the same action if she has any disease that seems to affect adversely the fluids or solid matter of her body, bringing about a condition which the Greeks call *cachexia*. If this is the case, another nurse should be substituted, so that the baby may be nourished with wholesome milk. We shall in our work *On Female Disorders* (Greek *Gynaecia*) set forth the method of testing the wholesomeness of milk[10] and, in general, the suitability of nurses.[11] For a time have the baby, too, go without bathing. Then after the third day bathe it in the house, and foment it first with warm olive oil and then with olive oil and warm water.
30 Moreover, avoid everything which might frighten the baby, for example, pretenses of terror.[12]

But in the case of older patients who can endure more drastic remedies, perform venesection after the attack is over. Now some physicians prescribe venesection as soon as the attack terminates. This is the procedure which Thessalus says he favors. Others, however, believe that we should wait until the end of the first three-day period to see whether the disease has been overcome and dissipated after the one attack, for in such a case venesection, they say, would be not only useless but harmful. They advise the physician to determine on the basis of a second attack whether the disease is increasing and requires this treatment of venesection and whether the patient, if treated by vene-
31 section, can have his strength sufficiently restored by food. Still others, however, hold that a distinction should be made in applying a treatment of this type. Thus they say that venesection should be performed immediately upon the conclusion of the attack in cases where the patient is customarily subject to attacks at regularly spaced intervals; but that in cases of a first

10. Soranus *Gyn.* ii. 21–23; Cael. Aur. *Gyn.* i. 130 f.

11. Soranus *Gyn.* ii. 19–20; Cael. Aur. *Gyn.* i. 126–29.

12. The reference, however, may be to horror tales or possibly to toys or other objects which might cause fear.

in tertium diem, sive ut Graeci vocant diatriton, differantur, siquidem sit incerta accessionis recursio.

nos vero, ut Soranus docuit, neque omnes intra diatriton phlebotomamus, et magis eos qui primo incursu passionis afficiuntur.
plurimi enim aegrotantes corrupto cibo admonentur, et est prae-
82 cavendum indigestione sauciatos phlebotomare. neque rursum
omnes in tertium diem probamus reservandos. cogente enim
passione, nullo subiecto indigestionis obstaculo, erit arripienda
phlebotomiae commoditas non solum[43] his qui iam saepe admoniti passione videntur, sed etiam in illis qui primo invasu afficiuntur. cessante etenim accessione inesse passionem conicimus,
siquidem generaliter sit maligna et frequentius tarda quam celer,
nisi adiutoriis medicinalibus destructa a corpore depellatur, aut
ullo naturae aut fortunae beneficio, nisi tardando corpus tenuerit
83 ut solius medicinae diligentiam poscat. iudicare etiam est incertum utrum passio post accessionem primam inesse corpori an
soluta videatur, siquidem ex occulta veniat apprehensione causarum: et oportet Methodicum sine ulla falsitate regulas inten-
dere curationum.

videmus denique phlebotomiam[44] convenire, nam passionales
coenotetes argui videbuntur si utrum passioni conveniat fuerit
dubitatum. sed quia sola temporum quaestio flagitari perspicitur,[45] erit coniciendum ante secundam accessionem[46] adhiberi
posse phlebotomiam, siquidem initium vehementiae atque magnitudinis causa passio transcedat,[47] ut saepe contusio corporis aut fractura vel ignis ustura. stare autem nec declinare
84 poterit passio. horum enim difficilium morborum proprium est
sine ullo districtivo[48] adiutorio non celeriter temporum nequi-
tiam[49] transire, hoc est accessionis augmentum. sed neque propter abstinentiam cibi, quam necesse est post phlebotomiam ad-

43 solum ⟨in⟩ R
44 phlebotomiae S: corr. Rm
45 praespicitur edd.
46 accessionem conieci: passionem edd.
47 transcendat R
48 districtivo coni. Bendz Eran 43. 55, coll. Ac. ii. 159, iii. 20: destructivo S
49 nequitia S: corr. Rm, nisi scribas tempora (vel tempus) nequitiae

attack the treatment should be postponed to the end of the three-day period (Greek *diatritos*), since a recurrence of the disease is uncertain.

But in our sect, in accordance with the teachings of Soranus, we do not in every case perform venesection before the end of the three-day period; particularly we do not in cases of a first attack. In fact, many patients are predisposed to a new attack because of the decomposition of the food they have taken, and 2 in such cases of indigestion venesection must be postponed. But again we do not recommend the postponement of venesection in all cases to the third day. For when the disease requires it and there is no obstacle in the form of indigestion, the opportunity to perform venesection should be grasped at once, not only in the case of those who seem to have had attacks in the past, but also where the patient is suffering his first attack. For even when the first attack abates, we may assume that the disease is still present, since, in general, it is a stubborn disease and more frequently chronic than acute, unless overcome by medical remedies or by the help of nature or good fortune (i.e., without becoming chronic and taking hold of the body, so that only medi-3 cal treatment can be of any avail). We cannot say with certainty whether the disease is still present in the body after the first attack or has been overcome, for such a question involves causal notions beyond the possibility of verification; and a Methodist physician ought to concern himself solely with the proper rules for treatment without entering into any deceptive questions.

Now venesection is obviously a proper remedy. For to doubt this would be to go counter to the theory of the general types [*coenotētes*] of diseases. And so, since it is merely a decision as to timing that is required, our view is that venesection may be performed before the second attack. Our reason is that the disease, because of its violence and power, persists beyond the initial stage, just as is the case with bruises, fractures, and burns. And it is quite possible for the disease to continue at its peak and not 84 decline. Indeed, it is characteristic of these troublesome diseases that, in the absence of a dissolving remedy, they cannot quickly get over the difficult period,[13] namely, the increasing phase of the attack. And the fasting which must follow venesection is no

13. The text and meaning are doubtful: *nequitia* (κακοήθεια) frequently refers to chronic stubbornness or deterioration.

hibere, erit hoc adiutorium declinandum, quando corporis vires
ferre valuerint, hoc est ut et sanguinis detractionem et abstinentiam[50] tolerent. denique etiam aliis passionibus affectos, ut exempli causa synanchicos, sine ulla ratione[51] phlebotomamus.

    quare sicut superius diximus post casum rectos[52] epilepticos
cessante accessione parvo tempore differimus, quo turbore spi-
85 ritus atque liquidarum materiarum deposito tranquillentur. erit
enim speculandum ne qua indigestio sive corruptio cibi subesse
videatur, quod ita intelligere poterimus si nauseantem vel ruc-
tantem fumosas exhalationes aegrum viderimus, attestante mordicatione atque tormentis intestinorumque inflatione. quae si
non fuerint, perfecte digestum iudicabimus, quippe cum forsitan
praeoccupato corpore iamdudum futurae accessionis causa aut
parvum sumpserit cibum aut in totum abstinuerit. sed si, ut
supra dictum est, corruptus extiterit cibus, erit phlebotomia in
tertium diem differenda, fovendum caput cum ceteris partibus,
86 oris[53] adhibita collutione, cum vini abstinentia. tunc erunt
somno dimittendi atque a cibo servandi usque ad primum diem.
sed si quicquam corruptionis ex indigestione superare viderimus,
erit per vomitum depurgandum. ac si nulla fuerit corruptionis
vel indigestionis suspicio, erit statim adhibenda phlebotomia,
moderata detractione, ex brachio scilicet, sed cum praecautione
defectus,[54] quem Graeci lipothymian vocant, siquidem facile
passionis accessionem imitetur. tunc post phlebotomiam erit
adhibendus fotus[55] atque oris collutio cum parvissimo potu, et
somno abstinendus.[56]

87   ac si accessio in secundum diem duraverit, praedicto periculo
eius propinquis vel ministris, atque adiutoriorum ex ratione ve-
nientium exitum incertum, ne nobis quicquam male gestum im-
putetur, si forsitan vi passionis superatus aegrotans vitam finierit, et intemporaliter nos quisquam adiutorium adhibuisse ar-
guat, phlebotomiam adhibemus, tamquam in continuationibus

---

[50] abstinentiae *edd.*

[51] *fort.* cibatione

[52] *an* surrectos?

[53] oris *R*: hiis *S*

[54] ⟨animi⟩ defectus *R*

[55] fotus *Rm*: potus *S*

[56] somno abstinendus] cibo abstinendus *Sm, fort. recte: an* somno dimittendus *vel*
somnus adhibendus?

reason to avoid venesection, provided that the body is strong enough to endure both the withdrawal of blood and the fasting. Thus in other diseases—for instance, synanche—we perform venesection without any question.

And so, as we have said, when the attack is over and the epileptic has arisen from his fall, postpone venesection a short time so that the confused condition of his pneuma and humors may be allayed and he may regain his composure. And examine the patient to see whether there is any indigestion or decomposition of food. This condition can be recognized if the patient is nauseated or belches with fetid exhalations and if there are griping pains, cramps, and flatus in the intestines. In the absence of these indications we may conclude that his food is completely digested. And, in fact, it is possible that if the patient has suffered previous seizures, he has, in anticipation of an attack, either taken little food or abstained completely. But if, as we said, the food has not been properly digested, postpone venesection, as we indicated above, until the third day. Foment the head and the other parts and wash the mouth; but do not give the patient wine. Then permit him to sleep, giving no food until the end of the first day. Now if we observe that any of the decomposed food arising from indigestion is still present, it will have to be cleared away by vomiting. But if there is no trace of such decomposition or indigestion, perform venesection at once upon the arm, withdrawing a moderate amount of blood but guarding against fainting (Greek *leipothymia*), which may easily be mistaken for an attack of the disease. Then after venesection apply fomentations, have the patient wash his mouth, give him very little to drink, and keep him from falling asleep.[14]

Now if the attack lasts to the second day, first inform the patient's relatives or attendants that there is danger and that the result of the remedies to be applied is uncertain, although they are based on reason. The purpose of this announcement is to forestall a charge that the case was mishandled and that a treatment was administered at the wrong time, if it should turn out that the patient is overcome by the violent disease and dies. Having made this clear, perform venesection, choosing, as in the case of unremitting fevers, a time when there is some small

14. Avoidance of sleep is commonly prescribed by the Methodists during attacks in diseases involving *strictura*. But, since sleep is generally permitted after venesection, the reading of *S* is questionable.

parvam indulgentiam pro dimissione accipientes, ut si exempli causa parum requievisse agitatione seposita aegrum viderimus, ut nullo raptu tentetur, vel contrario si forte oppressis sensibus motu caruerit, aliquas partes corporis movere videatur, ut palpebras quae iamdudum mortis[57] similitudine possessae siluerant.

88   dehinc post detractionem sanguinis, procurata facie ex spongia calida, erit mulsum in os aegrotantis distillandum, tunc secunda die dandi mulsi cyathi duo vel tres, tertia vero die ante horam solitam erit perungendus oleo calido atque dulci, toto corpore sub stramentis. tunc detectus aqua calida ora foveat, et post aequatum corpus accipiat sucum parvum suculentum[58] mollem lenem calidum digestibilem, ut est panis vel alica ex aqua confecta aut pulticula ex pane, quam torineton[59] vocant, ex oleo, aqua, sale, vel melle condita, ex prima diatrito usque ad declinationis tempus: quod probare poterimus ex minutione ac-

89 cessionum sive accidentium. alternis diebus cibum sumat, ne passione affecta nervositas etiam illatione cibi gravata digestionis officium sustineat, sed magis laxamentum ex abstinentia consequatur.

tunc si venter non fecerit vel si suum officium non impleverit,[60] ob detractionem gravatum quo corpus relevetur, erit iniciendus calida[61] et oleo per clysterem. tunc praesentato ventris officio, erit tondendus atque novacula omnis capillatura radenda. ita in alia diatrito cucurbita occipitio apponenda collo, vertici, et temporibus capitis, cum scarificatione; et communibus cataplasmatibus utendum quibus omne caput cum nervis maioribus, quos tenontas appellant, contegamus. tunc buccarum muscu-

90 los, quos siagonas appellant, atque omnes inter scapulas partes, cum stomacho usque ad locum quo discernitur venter, quem

[57] mortis *Rm*: motus *S*
[58] suculentum *A* (-cc-): luculentum *S*, *Helmreich 177 (sed cf. Chr. i. 103)*
[59] torsiniton *S*: *cf. Chr. i. 12, Cael. Aur. Gyn. ii. 7 (= Sor. Gyn., p. 100. 30, ubi hanc vocem non invenies)*
[60] vel si suum officium non impleverit *secl. Bendz 42 ut glossema*
[61] calidae *S*: *corr. Rm*

15. Perhaps this phrase is to be construed with *distillandum*.

measure of relief, for we cannot wait for a real remission. If, for example, you note that the patient has stopped shaking and has calmed down somewhat, being no longer convulsed, or, on the other hand, in a case where the senses were attacked and the patient lacked the power of movement, if he now appears to move any parts of his body, for instance, the eyelids, which had previously been immobile as in death, [such circumstances will indicate the proper time for venesection].

Then after the blood has been withdrawn, attend to the patient's face, using a warm sponge,[15] and permit some mead to drip into his mouth. And on the second day give him two or three cyathi of mead. On the third day before the usual hour[16] anoint him with warm sweet olive oil, keeping the whole body under covers. Then uncover him and let him wash his mouth with warm water. After his body has become normal,[17] have him take a little liquid food, wholesome, soft, mild, warm, and digestible, e.g., bread or spelt groats soaked in water or a porridge (called *torynētos*) consisting of bread prepared with olive oil, water, salt, and honey. This food should be used from the end of the first three-day period to the time of the decline of the disease. It will be possible to recognize the decline by an abatement of the attacks or of the symptoms. The patient should take food only on alternate days, so that the nerves and sinews already impaired by the illness will not have to support the task of digestion while burdened by the taking-in of food [every day]. On the other hand, abstinence from food [on alternate days] will afford them a greater measure of relaxation.

Then, if the bowels do not perform or fulfil their function or help relieve the body burdened by the withdrawal of blood, inject a clyster of warm water and olive oil. After the bowels have functioned, cut the patient's hair and use a razor to shave off all of it. And, at the end of the second three-day period, apply cups, with scarification, to the occiput, neck, crown of the head, and temples. Employ the usual poultices to cover the entire head as well as the large sinews (Greek *tenontes*), the muscles of the jaws (Greek *siagones*), the entire region between the shoulder blades, and the region of the esophagus as far down as the membrane

16. I.e., of the expected exacerbation.

17. The precise interpretation of this phrase is doubtful: cf., e.g., *inaequalitatem Chr.* i. 42, and *coaequare, Chr.* i. 75.

diaphragma vocant, ac deinde praecordia atque vesicam simili
curatione laxamus.

singula etenim passione raptus[62] vexata accessionis tempore
accipimus; ac si aliqua in parte corporis querela extiterit cucurbita imponenda. sed neque coacervatim neque uno tempore
omnes erunt partes curandae, sed partiliter atque diverso, ut
nunc stomachus, nunc vesica, nunc inter scapulam[63] relevetur,
quo necessario caput relaxatum adquiescat. tunc spongiae
vaporationibus[64] qui curationis laborem[65] sustinuerunt recura-
91 mus, atque ungentes[66] oleo communi sive, quia iam licitum est,
cyprino vel irino, tunc cerotariis mollibus, ac deinde scarificatis
locis inducta apponimus cerotaria.[67] convenit etiam embasin[68]
adhibere, de qua Adiutoriorum libris docuimus. dabimus cibum
plurimum atque panosum. si aliqua in parte capitis gravedo vel
dolor aut punctio aut torpor occurrerit, erunt sanguisugae circulatim apponendae. quae si sufficientem fecerint detractionem
adiutoriorum modum dabunt; sin minus, his detractis, cucurbitas infigemus, ut per earum vulnera detractio procuretur. tunc
rursum cataplasmatibus utemur atque vaporationibus spongiarum; dehinc cerotario partes contegimus.

92 profectu accedente dabimus olera non acriora. atque ita gestationem adhibemus sellarem: etenim vehiculi motus rotarum
vertiginem caliginemque facit aegrotanti, quae passionis imaginem ferat. tunc deambulatione movendus pro temporis aere[69]
atque loco lucido et longo ductu, ne iugi conversione vertiginem
sentiat. dehinc si ferre valuerit, etiam vocis atque corporis exercitio utemur monentes ut neque spiritum retineat, neque pronus vel circumflexus aut saepe conversus aliquid gerat, sed pingui unctione defricatus stanti exercitio moveatur.

93 tunc cum facilitas corporis fuerit accepta, lavacrum adhibemus caput foventes sine ullo percussu, manibus subterpositis:
implet enim sensum eius demersio. tunc etiam in aqua calida,
quam rigolyton[70] vocant, deponendi sunt aegrotantes, ne per-

---

[62] *fort.* passionis raptu

[63] interscapulum *Helmreich 179, coll. Chr. iii. 10, 29*: interscapulae (releventur) *Rm*

[64] evaporationibus *S: corr. Schmid RPh 45*

[65] ⟨eos⟩ qui curationis laborem *Rm*: qui curationem labori *S*

[66] ungimus *Rm*

[67] *an* cataplasmata, *ut infra?*

[68] envasin *S: corr. Rm*

[69] tempore et aere *Rm*   [70] rhigolyton *Rm*: pygolithon *S: fort.* r(h)igolyticon

(Greek *diaphragma*) by which the abdomen is separated [from the upper organs]. Again apply similar relaxing treatment to the precordia and the region of the bladder.

At the time of an attack note the particular parts affected by the convulsion; and if there is pain in any part of the body, cupping should be employed. Do not, however, apply this treatment to all parts at one and the same time, but treat one part at a time, skipping from one region of the body to another. Thus the esophagus may first be relieved, then the bladder, and then the region between the shoulder blades. In this way the head will necessarily be afforded relaxation and rest. Then, using sponges, apply warmth again, and anoint the patient with ordinary olive oil or, since it is now permissible, henna or iris oil. Then use soft cerates, and later rub them over the scarified parts. Bathing, which we have discussed in the work *On Remedies*, is also suitable. And give the patient a substantial bready diet. If there is heaviness, pain, pricking, or numbness in any part of the head, apply leeches arranged in a circle. If they withdraw enough blood, there will be no further need of such remedies. But, if not, remove the leeches and apply cups, withdrawing blood through the openings made by the leeches. Then once more employ plasters, apply heat with sponges, and cover the parts with cerates.

As the recovery progresses, give the patient vegetables that are not acrid. Also prescribe passive exercise. This is to be taken in a sedan chair, for the motion of a carriage on wheels causes the patient vertigo or dizziness, which brings about a condition resembling the disease itself. Then, with due regard to the season of the year, have the patient take a walk in a light place and over a long stretch, for he will feel dizzy if he has to turn constantly. And if his strength is adequate, prescribe also exercise of the voice and body, warning him not to hold his breath or to lean forward, bend over, or turn about frequently. He should be rubbed down with a thick ointment and should perform the movements of the exercise standing up.

And when his body is observed to move freely again, prescribe bathing. Foment the head, supporting it with the hands; but do not dash the water over it, for if the head is immersed, the senses will be congested. Then place the patient in a hot-water bath, called *rhigolyton*,[18] to prevent his nerves and sinews from being

18. I.e., 'cold-dissolving'; but the text is doubtful.

cussu frigoris nervositas afficiatur. post lavacrum vero parum
differentes quo fervor ex capite relevetur, dabimus aquam prae-
bibendam, tunc cibum varium, simplicem, media qualitate confectum. et post primam vel secundam diatriton dabimus quaedam in cibo quae vinosae sint qualitatis, ut sunt poma, quo cor-
94 pus vinum daturi praetentemus ut tuto dare possimus. atque
ita servandum ne his gestis somnus suspensus vel concisus aut
adiuncta phantasia sequatur, et insomnia faciat turbulenta,
quod ex relatione patientis discere poterimus. item si gravedo vel
torpor in aliqua parte corporis fuerit, ut[71] dolor aut punctio vel
saltus, erit in aqua calida perseverandum atque illa prohibenda
quae vinosae qualitatis danda praecepimus.

   sin vero ex his nulla fuerint prosecuta, dabimus lavacro remoto mediocriter vinum lene parum, ut exempli causa semun-
ciam vel unciam, medio scilicet cibo, aquatissime temperatum.
95 tunc in alia diatrito lavacro vinum iungemus. sed prae ceteris
erit animi laxatio procuranda, quo corpus consentiens nullis obstantibus curis facile sanitatis repetat qualitatem.

   ac si resumptio recurrens nihil virium[72] perficere permiserit,[73]
quo etiam carnatum corpus ostendat, bono attestante colore,
erit consuetudini dimittendus aegrotans. eadem sane curatione
utendum etiam in his qui, cum nondum sunt epileptici, eo tamen
ferri videantur. hoc enim solum servabimus: cum signis ad[74]
passionem minantibus fuerint absoluti, eos consuetudini revocemus.[75] facilius est enim imminentium aversionem quam praesentium depulsionem facere.

96   sin vero passio tardaverit, et propterea plurimis fuerit accessionibus[76] variata, erit partienda curatio secundum superpositionem et lenimentum, ita ut superpositionis tempore iisdem
utamur adiutoriis quibus acutas passiones curari praescripsimus.[77] neque enim phlebotomum reprobamus, permittentibus
viribus, si quidem[78] longo interstitio superpositiones occurrere
videantur. in lenimento vero resumendos dicimus aegrotantes,

[71] aut *Rm*

[72] nihil virium] *fort.* virium nihil

[73] praetermiserit *Bendz 94*

[74] ad *om. R*

[75] *exspectaveris* cum signa passionem minantia fuerint assecuta, eos ab consuetudine
revocemus *vel sim.*

[76] *fort.* accessionibus ⟨ac lenimentis⟩

[77] perscripsimus *S: corr. Almeloveen*   [78] siquidem *S: div. Rm*

affected by the impact of cold. After the bath wait a short while to permit the heat to rise from his head; then give him water to drink. After that give varied but simple food of the middle class. After the first or second three-day period include in the food things of a winelike quality, for example, fruits. In this way test the body in advance of giving wine, to be sure that the latter may safely be given. And watch to be sure that after these measures the patient's sleep is not light or broken off or accompanied by visions and confused dreams. This condition may be determined from the patient's report. Again, if there is heaviness, numbness, pain, pricking, or throbbing in any part of the body, continue the use of the hot-water bath and omit the food of winelike quality previously prescribed.

But if none of these conditions is present, omit the bath and give a somewhat mild wine in small amount, say half an ounce or an ounce; this should be taken along with food and should be mixed with a great deal of water. Then at the end of the next three-day period prescribe both wine and bathing. But, above all else, see to it that the mind is relaxed, for then the body in sympathy with the mind will easily regain its state of health, there being no cares to impede the recovery.

Now if repeated treatment to restore the patient's strength has proved completely successful, so that his body is well covered with flesh and his complexion good, let him return to his normal mode of life. And, of course, deal in the same way with patients who are not yet epileptic but seem to be tending toward the disease. But be careful to permit them their customary activity only when they are completely free from premonitory signs of the disease. For it is easier to ward off a threatening disease than to overcome one that is actually present.

But if the disease becomes chronic and its course is therefore marked by numerous attacks, the treatment will have to be divided into two parts, one for the attack, the other for the interval between attacks. During the attack we employ the same remedies as we have indicated are used in the treatment of acute diseases. Thus we do not reject venesection, if the patient's strength permits and if the attacks are found to occur at considerable intervals. But we hold that in the period of remission the patient's bodily strength should be restored and metasyncritic treatments should be instituted, according to the cyclical

cum[79] recorporativa curatione dirigendos iuxta cyclorum regulam,[80] sicut latius, cum de capitis passione diceremus, scripsimus.

97 quapropter ob resumendum corpus adhibenda gestatio sella vel cathedra, aut deambulatio aut vocis exercitatio. item lectionem,[80a] perunctionem aliptarum praeceptis ordinatam sine ulla capitis inflatione geramus, ne immodico labore affectum corpus vexare potius quam reficere videamur. tunc lavacrum longioribus[81] intervallis adhibendum. varius dandus cibus, panis limpidus atque studiose elaboratus, pulmentum vero ex mediae qualitatis materia, ut ova, pultes, olera quae non sunt acerrimae virtutis, item volantum leviora et piscium teneriora.

dehinc post resumptivum cyclum adhibendi recorporativi, et primo ex parte, tunc perfecti. in quibus esse vomitus ex radicibus debet vel similibus materiarum rebus, ut nuper docuimus; atque ita drimyphagian, exinde contiguas sibi pulmentorum materias ordinamus.

98 item adiutoria localia, ut exempli causa primo capillos decurramus ex pectione, nunc pro capillatura, nunc contra capillaturam, tunc tonsuram adhibentes, dehinc novacula caput radentes, et[82] cucurbitas aliis atque aliis capitis partibus recorporativas imponamus. tunc dropacis[83] raptum adhibemus sed longe primo[84] remotis partibus, tunc vicinis, dehinc patientibus, dantes etiam masticandum sinapi vel piper aut staphisagriam. item sternutamentum ex helleboro vel strutio[85] et pipere et castoreo vel his similibus adhibemus, narium quoque apophlegmatismum

99 adicientes atque fricationem[86] balnearum nitri pulveris et ceteris sympasmatibus[87] quae ruborem facere valeant, ut sunt ex pyretro, staphisagria, adarce, euphorbio, pipere, calcis gleba, et pumice; tunc cataplasma ex sinapi atque malagmata quae detergere et papulis[88] afficere corpus valeant. item acopa acriora, sed quae tetri odoris non sint, toto corpore illinienda, magis tamen capiti atque ori, conclusis palpebris: quae immittenda sunt etiam

---

[79] ⟨et⟩ cum R: *fort.* et

[80] *iusta cyclorum regula* S: *correxi, coll. Chr. ii. 211, iii. 67*

[80a] lectionem ⟨et⟩ R:*fort.* lectio. et

[81] longioribus *Bendz 94*: languorum S

[82] et *om.* R

[83] tropacis S: *corr.* R

[84] longe primo] primo longe R

[85] strut(h)io *Ihm, TLL 2. 980. 40, coll. Cels. v. 22. 8*: astrutio S: *cf. etiam Chr. i. 116, ii. 37*

[86] fricatione S: *corr.* Rm

[87] caeterorum sympasmatum *Rm*

[88] pabulis S: *corr.* Rm

regimen. We have described this procedure at some length in our discussion of chronic headache.[19]

7   Now to restore the bodily strength prescribe passive exercise in a chair, walking, or vocal exercise. Also prescribe reading aloud; and have the patient anointed under the direction of a trainer. But we must avoid congesting the head, lest we seem to be subjecting the body to greater distress and injury instead of restoring its strength. Again, prescribe bathing at long intervals. And give the patient varied nourishment, including pure bread carefully prepared and food of the middle class, such as eggs, porridge, vegetables other than those of acrid properties, light fowl, and tender fish.

Then, after the restorative course of treatment, employ the metasyncritic, first in part, and then in its entirety. In this connection use radishes or similar substances as emetics, in accordance with our previous discussion; then prescribe the acrid diet and follow this with the other types of diet, one after the other in order.

8   Also apply local remedies. For example, begin by combing the hair, running the comb first in the same direction as the hair and then in the opposite direction. Then cut the hair, shave the head with a razor, and apply metasyncritic[20] cupping at various parts of the head in a manner suitable for metasyncrisis. Then employ pitch plasters for their drawing effect, applying them first far from and then near the affected parts and finally to the affected parts themselves. And give the patient mustard, pepper, or stavesacre to chew on. Also employ a sternutatory of hellebore, soapwort, pepper, castor, or the like. Make use of remedies to purge away phlegm through the nostrils. And at

9   the bath have the patient rubbed with powdered nitrum or the other dusting powders which have rubefacient properties, e.g., those made from pellitory, stavesacre, adarce, spurge, pepper, limestone, or pumice stone. Also apply a mustard plaster and emollient plasters which have a detergent effect and can produce eruptions on the body. And apply such restorative ointments as do not have a bad odor, smearing them over the whole body, particularly over the head and face, with the eyelids closed. Also insert these ointments in the openings of the ears.

19. *Chr.* i. 24 ff.   20. Cf. 168.

aurium cavernis. gargarizandum sinapi, adhibenda etiam aquarum illisio, qua patientes partes percussae mutari cogantur, quod
Graeci cataclysmum appellant.

his deinde perfectis cyclis resumpto corpore helleborum adhibemus, sed longe superpositionis servantes occursum.[89] in om-
100 nibus quidem adiutoriis exercitioribus adhibendis, tunc magis in
helleboro, monemus praecavendum. denique si nullam accessionem denuntiaverint signa, his qui ordine servato admonentur,
ante decem vel duodecim dies vel generaliter pro longitudine
lenimenti, porrectius erit adiutoriorum regula dirigenda; in his
vero qui inordinate[90] admonentur, eo tempore adhibenda curatio quo conicere possumus medium praeteritae atque futurae
accessionis. sic igitur hoc genus diligentiae intuendum, ut cum
aeger somnum decusserit, primo requiescat paululum iacens, non
101 solum suspicans indigestionem cibi, verum etiam donec perfectione[91] quadam propria corporis fuerit facta digestio, ne ex vigi-
latione sequenti atque laxamento membrorum et tenuitate vel
purgatione ⟨liquidorum⟩[92] spiritus iamdudum somno turbatus
atque crassus fiat,[93] quo etiam saepe officia impediri noscuntur,
cum nondum totum recurrens occupaverit corpus. unde saepe
factum est ut experrecti[94] his quae ilico intueantur fallantur, nisi
perfricatis oculis intenderint, neque clamare vel currere facile
possint, siquidem vi quadam somni nunc arteria, hoc est gutturis
via, asperetur et raucos faciat, nunc fatigata corpora densitate
nervorum irruente spiritu crassiore[95] afficiat percussioni vel
102 quassationi[96] similes plagas ingerendo. has igitur ob causas
aeger plurimo tempore somno deposito tardare debet, praecavens lucis autoritatem[97] quam mox discusso somno intueri mini-

---

[89] occursum ⟨quod⟩ R

[90] inordinate *Bendz 88*: ordinate S

[91] perfectione *Rm*: persecutione S

[92] *supplevi*: ⟨humorum⟩ R

[93] turbatus crassus fiat *R*: turbati atque crassi fiant *S*: *an latet* crassescat *vel sim.*,
unde orta est loci corruptio?

[94] experrectis S

[95] irruens spiritus crassior *Rm*

[96] percussioni vel quassationi *Rm*: -e vel -e S

[97] austeritatem *Triller Clinotechnia 89*

Have the patient use mustard as a gargle. And prescribe a douche (Greek *cataclysmos*) in which water is thrown against the affected parts to effect a change in their condition.

With the completion of these courses of treatment and the restoration of the bodily strength, prescribe hellebore; but be certain that no attack is approaching. Caution is necessary in applying all drastic remedies, but particularly so in the case of hellebore. Now, while there are no signs of an approaching attack, in cases where the attacks are regularly spaced,[21] the more drastic treatment should be given ten or twelve days before [the next attack is expected], or generally in proportion to the length of the interval between attacks. But in cases where the attacks are irregular, this treatment should be applied at a time guessed to be midway between the previous attack and the one to come. And set up the following procedure in the treatment. When the patient wakes from sleep, let him lie quiet for a while, not merely because of the possibility that his food has not been digested, but to permit of the complete digestion and distribution of the food in accordance with the normal bodily process. The carrying-out of this process will avoid the possibility that, in the ensuing period of wakefulness, with the relaxing of the body and the thinning-out and purging of the body fluids, the pneuma may still be agitated and thick from the preceding sleep. Such a condition is often observed to interfere with certain functions, since the pneuma is not yet able, with its ebb and flow, to penetrate the whole body.[22] And so it often happens that when such persons are roused from sleep they cannot make out the very things they are looking at, but must first rub their eyes. Nor can they readily cry out or run. For the windpipe, the channel of the throat, sometimes becomes rough under the influence of sleep, and hoarseness results; and sometimes the body is overcome as the nerves and sinews become dense, the pneuma now flowing thicker. Sleep produces this effect by a series of thrusts, as if it were beating or shaking the body. And so for these reasons the patient should rest for a considerable time after waking from sleep; and strong light should be avoided to prevent the vision from being assailed suddenly. In fact, just after sleep it is

21. Cf. 67.

22. The text and interpretation throughout this section are uncertain, and the versions here given are quite tentative.

me potest, ne repentino percutiatur visus. item disputationibus vehementibus animum exercere declinet.

tunc resumptus atque relevatus somni plenitudine, sub stramentis leni unctione tangatur semel, vel[98] secundum corporis singulas partes[99] laxamenti mediocris causa, atque frigoris cautione levem et delectabilem gestationem,[100] ut fertoria sella vel cathedra. sed prohibenda erit exclamatio siquidem vehementer

103 moveat partes patientes. tunc deposito turbore motus, unctione olei fricetur; conductis et extentis brachiis flexo atque extento motu relevans singula crura commoveat, quo fortioribus motibus faciat aptiora. fovenda etiam ora aqua calida: nunc enim erit lavacrum prohibendum. atque ita post perunctionem cibum accipiat parvum suculentum et levem, ut ova, pultes, pisces[101] teneri, quaeque ex volantibus parvae aetatis atque formae, ut ficedulae, turdi, declinans omne quod fuerit acrioris virtutis, sive inflare valentis aut carnosae vel gravis. quapropter etiam a vino erit abstinendus, vel per intervalla ab omni cibo servandus. relevatur enim hoc genere corpus ieiunitate reflatum.

104 sin vero aliqua signa accessionis futurae apparuerint, ut somnus turbatus vel cibi corruptio vel iracundia inanis ac sine ratione, item maestitudo vel sternutamentum aut aurium tinnitus vel prae oculis scintillarum fingibilis visus aut inflatio praecordiorum et per somnum seminis involuntarius iactus, quem onirogmon[101a] vocant, et horum similia, non solum ad[102] vitae regulam transeundum est, verum etiam initium ex abstinentia sumendum; tunc levis adhibendus motus atque perunctio et cibus quo corpus salutaribus officiis non deseratur. ut enim iisdem ci-

105 borum regulis perseverare tutum non est, sic e contrario iugis immobilitas atque cibi abstinentia vacuato corpore solitis nutrimentis vires extinguit futuris temporibus necessarias.

quaesitum etiam utrum contradicentibus[103] signis accessionem fore an praesentem sive factam iudicemus. sed tunc erit acces-

---

[98] vel *om. R*   [99] *fort.* tangantur semel vel secundum corporis singulae partes
[100] gestationem ⟨adhibeat⟩ R
[101] pisces *Rm*: piscis *S* (*sine virgula post* pultes)   [101a] onirogonon *S*
[102] ad ⟨hanc⟩ R: *fort.* ad ⟨tenuem⟩ (*cf. 107*) *vel* ad ⟨aliam⟩
[103] ⟨ex⟩ praedicentibus (*alii* praecedentibus) *Rm*

---

23. Possibly 'when his strength has been restored and his condition relieved by copious sleep.'

impossible to look directly at light. Again, the patient should avoid exciting his mind with violent disputes.

Then, when he has recovered from the fulness of sleep,[23] while he is still under the bedclothes, have him mildly anointed just once. The ointment is to be applied to the various parts of the body as a moderate relaxing measure. Also prescribe mild and agreeable passive exercise, having the patient carried in a sedan chair; but be careful to avoid chilling him. Do not permit him to use a loud voice, since the affected parts are thereby violently 03 disturbed. Now when the excitement created by the passive exercise has abated, have the patient anointed with olive oil. Have him flex and extend his arms, and also exercise his legs by raising them, bending and stretching first one and then the other, to prepare them for more vigorous motion. Foment his face with warm water; for at this stage bathing is still not permissible. And after the anointing let him take a little food that is juicy and light, e.g., eggs, porridge, tender fish, and young birds belonging to small species, like the figpecker and the thrush. He should avoid everything that has acrid properties or may cause gas, and everything that is fleshy or heavy. He should therefore avoid wine, too, and from time to time abstain entirely from food. For in this way, by fasting, the body is relieved of flatus.

04 But if any signs of a coming attack appear, such as troubled sleep, indigestion, display of temper without basis or reason, dejection, sneezing, ringing in the ears, the seeing of what appear to be flashes of light before the eyes, precordial distention, involuntary ejaculation of semen in sleep (Greek *oneirōgmos*), and symptoms like these, not only must the patient submit to a regimen, but he should begin by fasting. Then gentle exercise, anointing, and food may be prescribed, so that the body may not be deprived of its normal functions. For, just as it is unsafe 5 to continue with the same diet as before, so, on the other hand, continued immobility and fasting would empty the body of its customary nourishment and rob it of the strength it needs for the future.

The question is raised whether, when the signs are contradictory,[24] we should conclude that an attack is to come or that it

24. Or, reading *praedicentibus*: 'whether from the premonitory signs, etc.'

sio iudicanda, quoties ceciderint in ea aegrotantes: quo discere
poterimus quo tempore diatriti tempus sit numerandum, ut recte
possint curationes suis reddi temporibus. nam denuntiata[104]
signa iam praesentis[105] accessionis esse contenditur.[106] nos vero
praetangi nervositatem atque in accessionem urgeri recte probamus, ut augmenti indicia tamquam praeludere videantur, ut
sunt in hemitritaicis febribus frequenter accessione imminente
corpora praeoccupata, cum noctis anxietate pulsata diei fore
106 asperitatem significant. ita igitur vel simili ratione praemonitus
epilepticus, tamquam si accessione vexaretur, erit usque ad
primam diem abstinendus, et neque similiter agendus ut pridie,
cum fuisset in lenimento purissimo.

quapropter abstentus una die, sequentibus levi motu antecedente unctione atque parvo cibo nutriatur, aquam bibat. tunc
si rectius habuerit ut laudabilior sanitas appareat, augenda oblatio cibi, alternis scilicet diebus, nunc qualitate nunc quantitate.
tunc nisi ex omni parte signa supradicta ⟨cessaverint⟩,[107] erit
rursum abstinendus una die. sin vero fuerint expulsa vel de-
pugnata, non erit ilico reddenda aegrotanti consuetudo, tam-
107 quam nihil sit quod sollicitudini remansisse videatur. neque
rursum inani suspicione, tamquam iam imminentis superpositionis metuentes adventum, in tenui vitae regula retinere debemus patientem. ut enim opportunitas adhibita abstinentiae fu-
turas amputat superpositiones atque earum occasiones detrahit,
sic importune adhibita corpus vexat atque fatigatione affectum
tarde surgere facit in solitas vires. quapropter cum summa cautione et sine ulla nimietate servati, blanda regula resumendi sunt
aegrotantes, quo asperatas accessiones fore ⟨non⟩[108] metuamus.

tutius autem esse probamus, ut supradictum est, longe ante

---

[104] denuntiantia *Rm*: *fort.* denuntiativa *Bendz Eran 43. 55*

[105] praesentia *edd.*

[106] contendit *edd.*

[107] *add. Rm*   [108] *add. R*

---

25. Cf. *Chr.* i. 99.

is already present and existing. Our view is that the attack should be considered as commencing at the time when the patient is seized and falls. From this we may determine the time from which the three-day period is to be reckoned, and we may thus assign each treatment to its proper time. Now it is held that the premonitory signs are part of an already existent attack. We, on the other hand, rightly hold that the system of nerves and sinews is first affected, being subjected to [a strain which culminates with] the attack, so that the premonitory signs are seen to be a sort of prelude to the attack. It is similar to what often happens in cases of semitertian fevers when the body first gives signs of a coming attack; its agitation and restlessness at night indicate that there will be an attack the next day. And so the epileptic who has had the premonitory symptoms described above or similar symptoms should be given no food the entire first day, just as if he were actually suffering an attack; and his general regimen should no longer be the same as it was the day before, when he was enjoying an interval of complete remission.

And so, let the patient fast for one day; and on the following days, after anointing him, have him take mild exercise and a small amount of food; and give him water to drink. If his condition then improves so that he seems to be in a good state of health, increase his nourishment every other day, now enriching the quality of the food, and now increasing its quantity. Then, if the premonitory signs mentioned above do not abate, have the patient fast again one day. But if these signs are banished or overcome, the patient must still not be permitted to return immediately to his customary regimen as if there appeared to be no further cause for concern. On the other hand, do not keep the patient on a restricted regimen without good reason, merely because of suspicion and fear of the imminent approach of an attack. For, while it is true that fasting prescribed at the proper time may avert a coming attack and remove the possibility of its occurrence, yet, when prescribed at the wrong time, fasting injures the body, causes fatigue, and impedes the return to normal strength. And so the patient's strength should be restored by the use of a mild diet and regimen. But extreme caution should be exercised and nothing done to excess, so that we shall not have to fear that we are aggravating the future attack.

And, as we said before,[25] we consider it safer to have recourse

108   futuram accessionem ad hellebori usum accedere, quo accepto si irruerit accessio, erunt omnia mitigativa adhibenda quae accessionem valeant temperare. in strictura enim constitutis altioribus, hoc est stomacho et ventre, mitigativa laxatio[109] adhibita etiam medicamini excludendo praeparat viam et praefocationis amputat metum. sin vero post purgationem nullum periculum subierit praefocationis,[110] causa refectionis adhibenda resumptio est cum his quae valeant accessionem temperare, ut odoramenta sine ullo percussu medentia atque nutribilia, ut est panis calidus, melo, cucumis, et his similia. destillandus etiam helleborismus, sed ex melle decocto.

109   ac si initio vomitus ex accessione emerserit, cucurbita multa cum ⟨flamma⟩[111] supposita ori ventris[112] infigenda, tunc sequenti parti secundum quod medicamen ad inferiora teneatur, donec accessio levigetur temperamentis supradictae rationis, ne concursus passionis et adiutorii praefocet aegrotantem. erit igitur sustollendus aegrotans subiectione manuum ex utraque alarum parte, cum capitis sustentatione, atque leviter inclinandus. tunc si medicamen ad superiora cucurrerit et transvorationis ceperit partes, quo spiramenta obstruere videatur, illisis dentibus

110   atque ore clauso, vel erumpens per naturales vias quae ad fauces de capite feruntur in nares defluxerit, ac rursum decurrens gutturis meatum clauserit, praesens praefocatio metuenda. quapropter immissis digitis ex utraque parte buccarum circa maiores dentes oris facienda distantia. tum imponenda ptygmata multiplicia, quae si forte defuerint, cuneos ex ferulis scissis mittere poterimus, quo[113] hiscentem[114] aegrotantem servemus, atque medicamen ad faucium partes veniens spatio quodam exceptum facilius excludatur. servanda etiam tempora quibus medicamen faucibus occurrit, adiuvantes eius exclusionem in faciem inclinantes aegrotantem, atque eius ora calida spongia detergentes,

111   distillantes etiam in os mulsum. sic enim veluti despumans resumit, aut[115] deponit accessionis pressuram relevatus aegrotans.

---

[109] laxatio *R*: laxatione *S*

[110] *fort. post* causa *transponenda virgula*

[111] *add. Rm*

[112] ventri *S*: *corr. Rm*

[113] quo *R*: quod *S*

[114] hiscentem *Schmid RPh 45*: scientes *S*

[115] resumitur ac *Rm*

---

26. Perhaps 'upper.'

to the use of hellebore long before the future attack is expected.
8 If, however, an attack supervenes upon the taking of hellebore,
employ all the relaxing treatments that can overcome the
paroxysm. For, since internal[26] parts, i.e., the esophagus and
stomach, are suffering from a state of stricture, the application
of a soothing and relaxing remedy prepares the way for the expulsion of the hellebore and removes the danger of suffocation.
And if no danger of suffocation arises after the purge, restorative remedies should be employed for the purpose of building
up the patient's strength, along with the treatments that can
alleviate the attack. Thus employ aromatic substances which,
without being pungent, have a healing and nourishing effect,
e.g., hot bread, melon, cucumber, and the like. And give some
drops of hellebore mixed with cooked honey.
9   If, as he begins to vomit, the epileptic comes out of the attack, apply a cupping instrument over the cardia, using a great
deal of flame. And then apply cups to the lower parts where the
drug passes as it descends. Continue this cupping until the
effects of the attack are relieved by the type of treatment set
forth above, to avoid the possibility that the conflict between
the disease and the remedy will choke the patient. First, then,
lift him by placing your hands under his armpits while supporting his head, and place him so that his body is on a moderate in-
cline. If, even then, the drug moves upward, passing into the
parts where swallowing takes place, obstructing also the passage of air (the teeth being clenched and the mouth closed),
10 bursting into the natural channels which connect the head and
the fauces, flowing into the nose and down again, and blocking
the throat passage, there is immediate danger of choking. In
this case insert the fingers at both jaws where the larger teeth
are, and thus pry open the mouth. Then insert pads of lint folded
over many times. But if these are not available, wedges split
off from a rod may be inserted to keep the patient's mouth open.
And the drug which comes up to the throat and collects there at
any time will thus be easily removed. Watch for the times when
the drug appears in the throat and help to remove it by placing
the patient with his head inclined downward, wiping his mouth
with a warm sponge, and letting diluted honey drip into his
11 mouth. In this way he recovers as the foaming abates, and, obtaining relief, he overcomes the oppressive attack.

ac si non sufficiens hellebori fuerit agitatio, quam Graeci spa-
ragmon vocant, et parvo eventu successerit, perseverante passione erit etiam secundo vel tertio hellebori usus adhibendus, sed
praeresumpto[116] viribus aegro: quippe cum non iisdem uti omnibus necesse sit, et destruendae passionis causa una sola sufficiens
et perseverans exhibitio ⟨non⟩[117] approbetur.

utendum etiam aquis naturalibus, hoc est naturali virtute
medentibus, sed quae nulla odoris vexatione adficiant aegrotan-
112 tem. adhibenda igitur natatio et sole corpus torrendum, quod
Graeci heliosin[118] vocant, sed praetecto capite. utendum etiam
potabilibus medicaminibus, vel electariis ex hyssopo et origano
et thymo confectis. principaliter enim corpus mutant, recorporationem faciendo ob acrimoniam; dehinc etiam corpus sucorum naturalium tenuant qualitate. emolliendus namque venter; et peregrinatio imperanda terrena atque maritima, si ferre
navigationem potuerint patientes. tunc etiam exercitia vehementiora, quae labore corpus afficiant, affectanda quo magis
113 fortitudo quam corporis robur augeatur. est enim semper gravabilis carnatio, et magis si tenuibus fuerit imposita viribus, et
in his passionibus quae in nervis esse noscuntur.

unde neque facile curationis est credendus effectus, quo depul-
sam passionem iudicemus, nisi legitima accessionum tempora
soliti concursus sine ulla inquietudine atque plurima[119] transi-
erint aegrotantes, somnos quoque sine ullo impedimento duxe-
rint, et vigilias placidas ac liquida sanitate moderatas, nulla
etiam difficultate officiorum animae vel corporis impeditas, attestante cibi sufficienti appetitu cum digestione congrua et corporis nutrimento mediocri, vel egestionum naturalium moderato
exitu, bono attestante vel immutato colore.

114   servanda praeterea multo tempore omnis nimietas, ut frigus,
ustio, indigestio, vinolentia, libido, lavatio, et magis ea quae
specialiter passionem in commemorationem ducunt, ut odores
percussibiles, aut splendor nimiae lucis aut resultantium mate-

[116] praesumpto *S*: corr. *Schmid RPh 43 (cf. Chr. i. 43)*
[117] add. *R*
[118] heliasin *S*: corr. *Rm*
[119] pressura *Bendz 95*

But if this [first] treatment with hellebore does not cause a sufficiently violent agitation (Greek *sparagmos*) and is attended with small success, and the disease still persists, it will be necessary to employ hellebore a second or even a third time, building up the patient's strength again before [each new treatment]. For, while the same number of treatments is not required in every case, a single application does not generally suffice to overcome the disease permanently.

Natural waters, i.e., those having a natural curative property, may also be used, provided that they have no strong odor which 12 might affect the patient. Prescribe swimming [in such waters]; also baking in the sun (Greek *hēliōsis*), with head protected. Employ potions or electuaries made with hyssop, marjoram, and thyme, for these herbs primarily transform the body, bringing about metasyncrisis by reason of their acrid nature. They also overcome the condensation of the body by the properties of their natural juices. Keep the patient's bowels soft. And have him take a trip on land or even on sea if sailing is not too much for him. Again, he should try severe forms of exercise which impose considerable strain on the body; such exercise will increase the body's strength without correspondingly increasing its bulk. 13 For excessive corpulence is always harmful, and especially so when the underlying bodily strength is slight, and also in diseases known to center in the nerves and sinews.

We must not conclude too readily that our treatment has been effective and that the disease has been routed. We must first observe that the patient has without any discomfort passed many periods when an attack would usually have appeared; also that he sleeps without any difficulty, and when awake is calm, perfectly rational, and self-controlled; that his mind and body function without any difficulty; that his appetite for food is adequate, digestion good, and bodily nourishment moderate; and that the waste matter passed is moderate in amount and of good and unchanging color.[27]

14 And, even then, all excesses should be avoided for a long time, e.g., intense cold and heat, indigestion, excessive drinking of wine, sexual desire, and bathing. And those things which are especially apt to cause a recurrence of this disease must also be avoided, e.g., pungent odors, extremely bright light or flashes

27. It is possible that the reference is to the patient's complexion.

riarum, item strepitus, clamatio, circulatus cursus, extentio aut
ex alto despectio sive fluminum celerrimus fluor. ut enim ulcerum recentes cicatrices facili occasione solvuntur, non aliter haec
passio vel alia quaeque similis nequitia parvo impulsu repetit
corpus, quippe quod proxime dimisisse videbatur.

115   ac si forte neque ita fuerit aeger ab epilepsia liberatus, nihil
minus[120] adhibendum sed magis perseverandum[121] curatione probamus. dabit enim haec diligentia vel ex parte beneficium, quo
neque frequentius admoneatur aegrotans, neque longioribus accessionibus opprimatur, neque turpiter in foro[122] vel publicis in
locis apprehensus etiam post passionis impetum animi luctatione[123] vexetur. quibus enim prima vel optata non proveniunt,
erunt[124] secunda mitigationis causa capienda. haec est secundum ordinem methodica epilepticorum curatio.

116   aliarum vero sectarum principes varia rerum temperatione
sive experimento curationis adiutoria cumularunt, caput foventes aceto atque oleo rosaceo, puro vel immixto castoreo, in
accessione frigidis utentes, articulos quoque omnes ligatione constringentes, sternutamento commoto ex aceto naribus interius
flato cum sinapi, vel castoreo oleo irino infuso cum chalcantho,
vel sulphure vivo aut strutio[125] incenso, vel his quae ad matricis
praefocationes incendenda posuerunt, item hyssopum, et origanum, et thymum,[126] vel ignis flammam oculis offerentes cum
titillatu quodam et oppressione praecordiorum ad inferiores
partes.

117   iubent praeterea motum corporis adhibere, gestationem vel
deambulationem, aut supra sindonem volutari, sinapisandas
etiam manus aegrotantium atque pedes, et ante accessionem perungi tapsia caput, et spiritum continere. alio vero tempore, hoc
est dimissionis, vini atque carnis imperant abstinentiam, et magis porcinae vel bubulae et caprinae. prohibent praeterea supra
pellem caprinam dormire sive iacere aegrotantem, siquidem passionis faciat motum. adhibent etiam clysterem iugem atque
acerrimae virtutis, et medicamina urinalia,[127] quae diuretica vo-

---

[120] maius *Bendz 87*

[121] perseverandum ⟨in⟩ *R*

[122] foro *Rm*: furore *S*

[123] *fort.* laceratione *Schmid 105*

[124] erit *S*: *corr. Rm*

[125] astrutio *S*: *cf. 98*

[126] hyssopo et origano et thymo *R*

[127] diurinalia *S*: *corr. R*

from reflective substances, loud noise, shouting, movement in a circle, stretching, looking down from a height, and watching swiftly flowing rivers. For, just as the scars of recent wounds readily open if there is an opportunity, so this disease or any other disease equally malignant needs but little impulse to renew its attack on the body which apparently had just shaken it off.

15   And even if it turns out that the patient is not cured of epilepsy by the treatment described, we consider it all the more necessary to continue with it. For this treatment may confer some partial benefit, so that the patient will not suffer frequent attacks or attacks of long duration and will not suffer an unsightly fit outdoors and in public places, with the mental distress that follows such a seizure. Those who do not succeed in obtaining the highest and most desirable benefits from the treatment will at least obtain secondary benefits, because the treatment lessens the intensity of the disease. This concludes the account of the systematic treatment of epilepsy according to the Methodists.

16   The leaders of the other sects in their treatment heap remedy upon remedy, mingling diverse substances and proceeding empirically. They foment the head with vinegar and rose oil, either plain or with an admixture of castor, using cold substances during the attack; again, they bind and constrict all the limbs. They provoke sneezing by blowing into the nostrils fumes of vinegar and mustard, or of a mixture of castor, iris oil, and chalcanthum, or fumes obtained by burning virgin sulphur, soapwort, or any of the substances which these same physicians burn for cases of hysterical suffocation. They also use hyssop, marjoram, and thyme. Or they place a flame close to the patient's eyes, at the same time tickling him and pressing the precordia toward the lower parts.

17   In addition, they prescribe bodily motion in the form of passive exercise, walking, or the rolling of the patient in a sheet. And they have his hands and feet treated with mustard, and his head anointed with thapsia; they order the patient meanwhile to hold his breath. Later—that is, during the remission—they forbid the use of wine and meat, especially pork, beef, and goat's meat. In addition, they forbid the patient to sleep or lie on a goatskin, believing that this would activate the disease. And they continually employ clysters of sharp properties, as well as

cant, atque purgativa per ventrem, quae cathartica vocant, et
horum magis cui nomen est hiera, quae non erunt, inquiunt, ter-

118 tio minus singulis mensibus offerenda; tunc capitis divisuram accuratam,[127a] quam chiasmum,[128] dehinc scarosin vel medicamine
sive ignis ustura,[129] item terebrationem testae, vel arteriotomiam, vel usum venereum, aut e contrario eunuchismum faciendum probantes. dant etiam bibendum lac asininum cum sale,
vel sanguinem[130] testudinis marinae, vel humanum,[131] aut vituli
marini, et non solum sanguinem verum etiam coagula quae lacti
miscentur. item mandendam mustelam, sed longo desiccatam
tempore, et tunc carnem[132] hominum, atque equorum [quo-
rum][133] impetigines quas in cruribus habent, sive asinorum vel

119 mulorum, item testes vel veretrum marini[134] sive fluminalis canis,[135] et porcelliones,[136] hoc est animalia quae humectis et aquo-
sis locis saepe nascuntur, a Graecis appellata onisci, dehinc squa-
mulas ferri cum aqua in qua fuerit candens ferrum praetinctum.
dant etiam cameli cerebrum fumo siccatum atque concisum, sed
infantibus vel pueris odorandum, perfectis autem aetatibus bibendum ad modum cyathi cum mulso ex[137] aceto tribus cyathis;
similiter etiam leporis cor, et cerebrum gaviae. alii vero etiam
ligamenta probaverunt, et magos adhibendos, atque eorum in-
cantationes.

quae quantis sint vexationibus conferta[138] etiam[139] per se pro-

120 batur, sicut latius Adiutoriorum libris docuimus, nunc tamen
paucis memorabimus.[140] constringens igitur fomentum atque
tetri odoris vel[141] aceto et oleo rosaceo et castoreo percutit et
gravat et tumores constringit, et si, ut putant, materiam redarguit, abactam[142] tamen cutibus ad cerebrum et eius membranas
revocat. et[143] sunt haec ceterorum[144] comparatione magis salutaria.

127a *fort.* cruciatam; *sic etiam 127, 143*   128 chiasmum ⟨vocant⟩ R   129 *fort.* igni
(-e) usturam (*cf. Chr. i. 127*)   130 sanguine S: *corr.* R   131 humano S: *corr.* R

132 carnem *Rm, coll. Chr. i. 128*: corda S, *fortasse retinendum, hi enim loci (118 et 128)
aliis quoque rebus inter se discrepant*: ossa *Reinesius 661*

133 quorum *seclusi*, impetigines quas in cruribus *conieci, ne discrepet locus cum 128,
138 (cf. etiam Galen XII. 342, Diosc. Mat. med. ii. 43, Plin. HN xxviii. 226, ubi de
lichene non de corde edendo agitur; nota tamen cor [asinorum] edendum Plin. xxviii. 225*):
quorum crura quasi impetigines *edd.*

134 ⟨vituli⟩ marini *Reinesius 661, coll. Chr. i. 134*

135 canis *Rm, coll. 129*: cancri S: caballi *Reinesius 661* (= hippopotami, *134*)

136 porcellionis S: *corr.* R (*cf. 128*)   137 ex *Rm*: et S   138 confertae S: *corr.* R

139 *fort.* etiam ⟨si⟩   140 memoravimus S: *corr. Rm*   141 ex *Rm*   142 abactum S:
corr. Rm   143 *fort.* at   144 ceterorum *scripsi*: exteriorum *edd.*

drugs [taken by mouth] to promote urination (Greek *diurētica*), others to purge the bowels (Greek *cathartica*), and especially a purge called *hiera*. These drugs, they say, should be adminis-

18 tered no fewer than three times a month. And they also recommend an elaborate[28] [cruciform] incision of the head, which they call *chiasmos*. And they try to produce a scab by employing drugs or burning with fire; and they prescribe trephining the skull, arteriotomy, venery, or, on the contrary, castration. They give the patient ass's milk with salt to drink, or the blood of a sea turtle, or human blood, or that of a seal—and not merely the blood but also the rennet. They have the patient eat weasel flesh that has been dried a long time, human flesh,[29] the calluses

19 which horses, asses, and mules have on their legs,[30] the testes or generative organs of the beaver,[31] wood lice (Greek *oniscoe*—animals often generated in moist and swampy places), and iron filings together with the water in which the glowing hot iron has previously been dipped. They also prescribe camel's brain, cut up and dried in smoke; this is merely to be smelled by infants or children but is to be drunk by adults, a cyathus of it with three cyathi of oxymel. Hare's heart and sea gull's brains are similarly prescribed. And some also rely on amulets and on the magi and their incantations.

The great harm involved in all these prescriptions is clear

20 upon examination. I have shown this at some length in my work *On Remedies* and shall now merely review the matter briefly. To begin with, the astringent and foul-smelling fomentation, with its vinegar, rose oil, and castor, pervades the body, causes a feeling of heaviness, and further constricts the inflamed parts. Even if, as they suppose, such a fomentation disperses the [harmful] matter, still this matter is driven back by the skin [which prevents its egress], and the fomentation tends to draw it to the brain and its membranes. But even such remedies are helpful in comparison with the others.

28. For this use of *accuratam* (= περίεργον?) cf. *Chr.* iv. 11; see also *Chr.* iv. 58. But the text is uncertain.

29. Or 'hearts' if *corda* (*S*) be read; but cf. 128.

30. With the reading of *S*: 'the hearts of horses, asses, and mules having calluses on their legs.' But cf. *Chr.* i. 128, 138.

31. According to the reading of *S*, 'sea and river crabs'; but, while these are frequently prescribed in various forms, they are out of place here. *Fluminalis canis* probably is the beaver; *marinus canis* is doubtful (cf. Servius *Aen.* v. 822: *ceti dicuntur canes marini*, a statement which would include the seal; cf. 134, below), but may merely be a synonym for beaver, based on a confusion. See *Chr.* i. 129 and note.

praeterea est vehementer noxium frigidis[145] caput accessionis
tempore fovere. quae enim dimissione relevata mitescunt,
eadem frigida densatione magis gravantur. item ligationes ner-
121 vos densant, atque corporis oppressio quam fieri iubent. defricatio intemporalis, hoc est accessionis tempore, geminat passiones. accidentia enim si temporaliter quidem videntur lacessitis
sitis sensibus in resumptionem venire, totam tamen passionem[146]
peiorat,[147] non aliter quam si quisquam turbatos oculos manu-
tigio, quod Graeci chirapsiam vocant, temporaliter fricando relevare videatur. item non aliter sternutamenta medicaminibus
commota accessioni non convenire probamus: quippe cum neque
in linimento passionis constitutos hoc adiutorio facile inquietare
liceat, nisi certo regulae ductu praeparatos, quo caput releve-
122 tur gestatione tenui ac deambulatione, siquidem hoc adiutorii
genus initio impleat, caput dehinc medeatur. quid[148] sperandum
in his qui accessione agitati earum partium plenitudine vexantur,
si etiam sternutamento fuerint convitiati, cum magis oporteat
passionis illatam solvere turbationem?

est praeterea acetum molestum naribus insufflare sive solum
sive cum alia qualibet percussibili materia. constringit enim
atque densat tumentia, et turbata perturbat, et ea concurrere
compellit quae accessionis violentia excludi coguntur. item non
aliter inutiles[149] atque satiabiles[150] sunt incensiones sive fumiga-
123 tiones et odoramenta ex pice, bitumine, spondilio, castoreo, galbano, acerrimae atque gravabilis virtutis causa[151] et iniucun-
dioris, adeo ut etiam recte valentium impleant caput, et eorum
qui numquam aut difficile earum partium querelam prodiderint;
nunc tamen his odoramentis acceptis vertigine atque gravedine
urgeantur,[152] et non aliter tumentes oculos fumigatio adficiat

---

[145] frigidat S: corr. Rm

[146] fort. tota tamen passio

[147] peiorant S: corr. R

[148] quid R: quod S

[149] mutiles S: corr. R

[150] vitiabiles Bendz (cf. Hagendahl 261)

[151] causae S: corr. Haller in marg.

[152] urgentur R (et paulo post adficit)

Again, it is particularly harmful to apply cooling substances to the head at the time of an attack. For whatever is relieved and soothed by relaxing remedies is aggravated by the condensing effect of cooling substances. And the binding of the limbs and pressure on the body which they prescribe also have a constrictive effect on the nerves and sinews. Moreover, massage[32] when performed at the wrong time, i.e., at the time of an attack, aggravates diseases. For, even if the symptoms seem to be relieved temporarily by the stimulation of the senses, still the disease as a whole is made worse. It is the same as when one who is troubled by his eyes seems to find temporary relief in manual massage (Greek *cheirapsia*). Again, we do not consider it proper to use drugs to provoke sneezing at the time of an attack. In fact, even in the quiescent interval of the disease, one should not use this remedy, which may so easily upset the patient, unless he has been prepared for it by a definite regimen, including the relief of the head with mild passive exercise and walking. For sternutatories first pervade the head and only thereafter exert a healing effect. What, then, can we expect when a patient, who is experiencing the agitation of an attack and is distressed by clogging of the head, is at the same time subjected to the harsh effects of a sternutatory? And this at a time when it is particularly necessary to overcome the disturbed condition produced by the disease.

Again, it is harmful to blow fumes of vinegar, either alone or with some other pungent substance, into the patient's nostrils. For this has an astringent and condensing effect upon the inflamed parts and further agitates what is already disturbed, forcing a congestion of that which should be eliminated by the force of the attack. Equally unprofitable and tending to congest the head is the use of fumes from incense and scented substances like pitch, bitumen, cow parsnip, castor, and allheal. For they have such acrid, congesting, and unpleasant properties that they may cause clogging of the head in perfectly healthy persons and those who have never, or hardly ever, suffered a disorder in this part. But in the present cases, when the patient inhales these scents, he complains of dizziness and heaviness in the head, the strong fumes causing inflammation of the eyes as well as inflam-

32. Unless the reference is to the first part of 117, above, it may be necessary to assume a lacuna at 116–17: there is no specific reference to massage in the text as we have it.

quam etiam tumentes cerebri membranas. necessario enim cogit
in similem venire passionem.

percutit etiam ignis flamma sive eius affectatus splendor mul-
tus. denique etiam in lenimento epilepticos constitutos lucis
124 importunitas atque eminens percussio in commemorationem facit accessionis venire. noxia etiam praecordiorum pressura,
quam adhibendam probant, iudicatur: mitiganda enim sunt accessione commota, et non violenter atque contrario conatu repri-
menda. gravis etiam sine dubio videtur supra sindonem iussa
volutatio, quippe cum levi conversione corpus affectum non solum lenimenti tempore epilepticos in vertiginem mittat, verum
etiam recte valentes similiter afficere videatur.

articulorum quoque sinapismus accessionis tempore tumorem
geminans etiam passionem necessario peiorem facit. est item
intemporalis[153] ante accessionem perunctio[154] ferulaginis, quam
Graeci tapsian vocant, cum oporteat motam passionem atque in
125 peius coactam mitigare potius quam provocare. et quoties eius
necessarius est usus lenimenti tempore, toties atque melius suae
virtutis impleat beneficium, cum importune adhibitus partes faciat emori (has denique Graeci necroses vocant).

item spiritus retentio, quam faciendam probant accessionis
initio, sensus implet; non, ut quidam volunt, repercusso spiritu
futuram prohibet accessionem. premit etiam[155] potius quam
discutit ea quae iam suo motu densari videntur.

abstinentia vero vini atque carnis, quam iugiter fieri iubent,
vel unius anni spatio, impedit recorporationis faciundae profectum, quem augere necessario mutationum varietas potest. quod
facile ignaris notum fiet ex vitae consuetudine, quae si eadem
126 fuerit procul dubio corpus infirmat: quippe cum iugis potatio
aquae demissum faciat corpus, et neque numero dierum vel
mensium curandi regula sit constituenda, sed passionis tempori-

153 intemperabilis S: corr. Rm
154 punctio S: corr. Rm, coll. 117   155 enim Rm

mation of the membranes of the brain. That is, these fumes always affect the eyes in the same way as they do these membranes.

The use of flame or a very bright light obtained from flame has an agitating effect. In fact, when a case of epilepsy is in its quiescent stage, the untimely use of light with its sharp, penetrating action may cause the recurrence of an attack. And we also consider it harmful to press upon the precordia, as these physicians recommend. For the parts agitated by the attack should be relaxed and not, on the contrary, violently pressed down. And the rolling of the patient on a winding sheet, as prescribed, is undoubtedly dangerous; for, when the body is subjected even to slight turning, dizziness results. And this occurs not only in the case of epileptics in the intervals of remission but likewise in the case of perfectly healthy persons.

Moreover, the application of mustard to the limbs at the time of an attack increases the intensity of the inflammation and always aggravates the disease. And it is out of place to anoint the patient with ferulago (Greek *thapsia*) just before an attack; for at that time, when the disease is stirring and becoming worse, it is necessary to soothe it rather than to provoke it. Of course, whenever the use of this substance is necessary during the intervals of remission, it gives better and fuller proof of its beneficial properties. But when used at the wrong time thapsia causes mortification (Greek *necrōsis*) of the parts.

And the holding-in of the breath, which the physicians recommend at the beginning of the attack, causes a blocking of the senses; such repression of the breath does not, however, prevent the emergence of the attack, as some believe. For the breath presses upon, but does not disperse, that which by its own movements seemed already to be condensing.

These physicians prescribe continued abstinence from wine and meat, even for as long as a year. But this restriction is an obstacle to the metasyncritic process, which is always promoted by a continually varied regimen. This truth will become clear even to the inexperienced from the fact that lack of variety in the normal regimen undoubtedly weakens the body. Furthermore, the continual drinking of water leaves the body flabby. And again, we must not make our system of treatment depend on a number of days or months, but upon periods connected with

bus, quorum mutatione[156] regulae commutantur, ut sub eorum rigore datio[157] aquae vel vini ministretur. hoc etiam de carnis usu erit coniciendum.

caprina vero pellis odoris tetri causa noxia capiti iudicatur, non speciali atque privata ratione. item iugis atque acerrima clysteris iniectio intestina conradit atque nervos vitiat. urinalia quoque medicamina, quae diuretica vocant, vesicae infectione 127 capitis membranas commovent. item purgativa medicamina, quae cathartica vocant, defluxionem corporis facient atque stomachum evertunt. capitis etiam accurata divisura[157a] quam chiasmum vocant, et testae perforatio, et ustura cutis medicamine vel igne suffecta, quam scaroticam vocant, et arteriotomia patientes partes insumit et utilibus renititur rebus, siquidem nulla recorporativa[158] adiutoria iisdem locis adhibere permittat.

at vero concubitus sive venus quam adhibendam probant ab aliquibus parva epilepsia nuncupata est, siquidem similem faciat membrorum motum diverso contractu, anhelatione et sudore 128 attestante et oculorum conversione cum rubore vultus; ac deinde post effectum displicere faciat sibimet corpus, cum pallore et quadam debilitate vel maestitudine; adeo nervos afficere male videatur, ut saepe imminente accessione per somnum iactu seminis aegri praepurgentur, quod Graeci onirogmon[159] vocaverunt. item eunuchismus vires amputat, non epilepsiam solvit.

lac quoque sumptum facile acescit et propterea gravans epilepticos male probatum videtur. non aliter etiam potus sanguis testudinis, sive hominis, atque vituli marini, et sumptio coaguli, quod Graeci pityan vocant, mustelae quoque sive hominum caro siccata, et equorum impetigines, vel veretrum atque testes 129 canis aquarii, vel porcelliones[160] supra memorati, quos oniscos

[156] mutatione *Rm*: mutatae *S*

[157] datio *conieci*: damnum *S*: donum *Rm*

[157a] accuratam divisuram *S*: *corr. A* (*sed cf. 118*)

[158] recorporativa *Bendz 95*: te comparativa *S*

[159] onirogonon *S*: *cf. Chr. v. 80*

[160] porcellionis *S*: *corr. R* (*cf. 119*)

---

33. Cf. 118 and n. 29.

34. *Canis aquarius*, 'water dog,' is probably the beaver. The testes of the beaver, which were erroneously thought to contain the castoreum, are often mentioned in medical prescriptions. Beavers were called *canes Pontici* (Isidore *Etym.* xii. 2. 22, Servius *Georg.* i. 58), and it may have been a confusion of this term which gave rise to the ad-

the disease; changes in these periods require changes in the regimen, and it is these requirements that determine the prescription of water and wine. Our conclusions about the use of meat must be based on similar considerations.

Again, we consider goatskin harmful to the head, not for any reason peculiarly characteristic of goatskin, but merely because of its foul odor. And the continual injection of sharp clysters irritates the intestines and injures the nerves and sinews. Moreover, the drugs that promote urination (Greek *diurētica*) agitate the

27 membranes of the head through their effect on the bladder; and the purgative drugs (Greek *cathartica*) produce a bodily flux and cause gagging. And the elaborate [cruciform] incision of the head which the Greeks call *chiasmos*, the trephining of the skull, the burning of the skin by caustic drugs or fire (Greek *escharōtica* ['scab-forming']), and arteriotomy all weaken the affected parts and interfere with the use of helpful measures; for they prevent the application of appropriate remedies to the parts in question.

And coitus or venery, which these physicians recommend in cases of epilepsy, has itself been called minor epilepsy by some. For it causes a motion of the parts like that in epilepsy; various parts are subjected to spasms, and at the same time there occur panting, sweating, rolling of the eyes, and flushing of the face.

28 And the completion of coitus brings with it a feeling of malaise along with pallor, weakness, or dejection. Moreover, the harmful effect of coitus on the nerves and sinews of an epileptic is seen in the fact that often when an attack is imminent the patient first suffers an ejaculation of semen during sleep (Greek *oneirōgmos*). Again, castration robs the patient of his strength but does not overcome epilepsy.

And, when milk is taken, it easily turns sour and causes the patient distress; it therefore seems ill-advised in cases of epilepsy. The same is true of the drinking of turtle's blood, human blood, and seal's blood, and the taking of rennet (Greek *pitya*). Dried weasel or human flesh,[33] calluses from the legs of horses,

29 the genitalia and testes of the beaver,[34] the above-mentioned

---

jective *marinus* (*Chr.* i. 119): in fact Gloss. 5. 200. 11 has *ponti canes* in what may be a similar confusion. At any rate, the terms *fluminalis* (119) and *aquarius* are appropriate to the beaver. On the other hand, neither crabs (see 119) nor the various types of fish or sea monsters usually included in the term *canes marini* fit the present context as well as does the beaver.

appellant, et aqua de squamulis sive tinctionibus ferri, et cor leporis, et cameli sive gaviae cerebrum male probatur. etenim
neque ex occultis causis, quas Graeci ἀδήλους αἰτίας[161] vocant, rationes ducunt, neque ex aliqua contagione sive tentatione, ut Empirici volunt, approbata in usum venerunt medicinae: quippe cum intelligi vel apprehendi naturali aut fortuita
rerum dominatione minime possit uti his maxime ita insuetis
atque novis et odiosis generibus materiarum, quarum nihil usu
gravius esse videatur ipsius quoque comparatione passionis, sit-
130　que admirandum quod de aere atque vigiliis vel somno et potu
et cibo vel his quae necessario sumuntur nihil experimenti utile
collegerint, de his vero ita execrandis et crudelibus atque inhu-
manis plerumque etiam periculosis curationes ordinare voluerint. non enim sanguinem tauri potum interficere, ut Themis-
toclem, ⟨aut⟩[162] lac coagulatum vel caseum coactum,[163] aut oratorem et magum[164] recte reprobaverunt, si quisquam humanum
sanguinem facere minime crediderit, quo falso memorata a veteribus cetera videantur.

accusatis igitur sive nudatis summatim veterum curationibus,
non est absurdum etiam cum nominibus errores arguere singulorum.

131　　Hippocrates de epilepsia scribens communiter ait: 'quisquis in
humano corpore agnoverit siccandi vel humectandi aut frigi-
dandi vel calefaciendi causas, idem etiam istius passionis[165] poterit videre rationem.'[166] et neque quomodo neque ex quibus neque quando vel quousque haec fieri debeant tradere curavit.[167]

item Diocles, libro quo De passionibus scripsit, in his qui· ex
vinolentia vel carnali cibo istam passionem conceperint, phlebotomiam probat, antecedentes potius quam praesentes intuens
causas; in his vero qui ex corporis habitudine in istam venerint

[161] locus unicus ubi S litteris graecis utitur
[162] add. R
[163] coactum Rm: coctum S
[164] magum conieci, coll. 119: imaginem S
[165] passiones S: corr. Rm
[166] facere curationem Rm (= Hipp. ἰῷτο)
[167] curabit S: corr. Rm

wood lice (Greek *oniscoe*), water containing iron shavings or in which hot iron has been plunged, hare's heart, camel's brain, and sea gull's brain—all these are wrongly prescribed by physicians. In fact, no reason for using such substances can be adduced on the basis of hidden causes (Greek *adēloe aetiae*), nor can their use in medicine be justified, as the Empirics believe, on the basis of trial and experience. For one cannot understand or comprehend the use of substances of this kind, so strange, unusual, and revolting, on the basis of any natural or even fortuitous power which they possess. In fact, it seems impossible to imagine any more harmful substances from the standpoint of this disease. And it is amazing that in their experience these physicians arrived at no useful conclusion about the proper air for the patient,

30 about having him sleep or remain awake, about his food and drink, and the other necessary parts of the regimen, but, on the contrary, preferred to prescribe treatments involving these abominable, cruel, inhuman, and often dangerous substances. Indeed, they did not reject the drinking of ox blood as deadly, as, indeed, it was in the case of Themistocles;[35] nor did they reject, as they should have, the prescription of curdled milk and pressed cheese or the ministrations of rhetor or magus, if, indeed, any of them believed that human blood was without beneficial effect. And it is clear that the other substances mentioned by the ancients were also wrongly prescribed.

Now that we have summarily exposed and rejected the treatments of the ancients, it is not out of place to refute the particular errors of individual physicians, naming them one by one.

31 Writing on epilepsy,[36] Hippocrates makes the following general statement: 'Whoever understands the causes of dryness, moisture, cold, and heat in the human body will also be able to understand the principles of this disease.' But he does not take the trouble to state how, by what means, when, and to what extent this may be done.

Diocles in his work *On Diseases* prescribes venesection in cases of epilepsy resulting from excessive drinking of wine or eating of meat. But in this prescription he is concerned with antecedent, rather than actually existing, causes. And in cases arising from

35. According to the legend, Themistocles died of a draught of ox blood.

36. *Sacred Disease* 21: 'Whoever understands how to cause dryness, moisture, cold, and heat in men by means of regimen can also cure this disease.'

passionem, humoris crassi detractionem probat adhibendam,
132 quem appellavit phlegma. utitur etiam urinalibus medicamentis, quae diuretica vocant, item deambulatione ac gestatione.
quae si etiam vera essent adiutoria, ob parvitatem tamen numeri et magnitudinis suae magnae passioni difficile possent paria
pronuntiari aut eius destructioni sufficere.

item libro Curationum phlebotomans utitur medicamine catapotio quod stomachum evertit, atque post cenam vomitum facit,
exhalationibus implens caput. potat etiam aceto: sternutamentum commovens prius quam in somnum veniant aegro-
133 tantes, profecto intemporaliter commovet sensuales vias. dat
etiam absinthium, centaurion, et lac asininum et equorum impetigines vel mulorum, neque tempus adiciens factis, et odiosis
aegrotantes afficiens rebus.

Praxagoras vero secundo libro Curationum caput imperat
radendum adhibens fricationes, et cataplasma ex aceto sive vino,
redolentibus[168] speciebus etiam sternutamentum commovens, et
ieiunum vomitum per singulos dies, utens etiam poto lacte cum
mulso atque sale, item deambulationibus plurimis atque vehementi motu celebratis, et potionibus urinalibus, et cibis variis, et
agninae carnis sive haedinae atque porcinae et catulorum, dans
acetum bibendum atque vinum, et post vomitum sternutamenta
134 et odoramenta probans, et spiritus retentionem, item usturam
atque incisuram partibus, adhibens etiam ventriflua medicamina. et cum accessionem viderit commoveri, deprimit partes
quae fuerint in querela atque defricat castoreo, et vituli marini
veretro[169] sive virilibus hippopotami, aut testudinis sanguine vel
rhombi marini, omnia confundens.

non enim initio rasio capitis est adhibenda, nec aceto densan-
dum corpus, neque diurno vomitu vexandum, siquidem fortitudinem tollant; neque plurimo sternutamento, implet enim sensus; neque urinalibus medicaminibus, siquidem corpus nimium

---

[168] sive vino, redolentibus *Steckerl* (*priv. comm.*): sine venere, dolentibus *S*: sine bene
redolentibus *Friedel 28*

[169] *fort.* ⟨coagulo, aut⟩ veretro *etc.*, *vel sim.* (*cf. 135*)

a bodily condition he prescribes removal of the thick humor
132 which he calls *phlegma*. He also makes use of drugs to promote
the flow of urine (Greek *diurētica*) and prescribes walking and
passive exercise. Now, even if these were sound remedies, still because of their insufficient number and strength they could hardly
be considered a match for so powerful a disease or adequate to
overcome it.

Again, in his work *On Treatments* Diocles prescribes venesection and also employs a pill which causes gagging; he induces
vomiting after the patient has eaten, causing the head to be congested with vapors; he prescribes the drinking of vinegar and
induces sneezing before the patient goes to sleep. But surely this
133 agitation of the sensory channels is ill-timed. Diocles also prescribes wormwood, centaury, ass's milk, and calluses from the
legs of horses or mules; but, while burdening the patient with
these offensive substances, he fails to indicate the time for their
use.

Praxagoras in Book II of his *Treatments* prescribes shaving of
the head, massage, and a plaster made with vinegar or wine;
he induces sneezing with aromatic substances, and provokes
vomiting on an empty stomach each day. He prescribes the
drinking of milk with diluted honey and salt, a great deal of
walking done with vigorous bodily motion, the drinking of diuretic drugs, and the eating of varied food, including lamb, kid,
and pork, especially the flesh of the young animals. He gives the
patient vinegar and wine to drink and, after inducing vomiting,
prescribes sternutatories and aromatic substances and also the
134 holding-in of the breath. He also makes use of caustic treatments, incisions, and purgatives. When he sees that an attack is
about to begin, he presses down on the parts affected and rubs
them with castor, or the genital organs of a seal[37] or hippopotamus, or the blood of a turtle or turbot.

But his treatment is a perfect jumble. The head should not be
shaved at the beginning of an attack, nor should the body be
subjected to the astringent action of vinegar or the irritation of
daily vomiting; for such treatments rob it of its strength. And
continual sneezing is harmful, for it agitates the senses. Again,
diuretics should be avoided because they relax the body exces-

---

37. As it stands, the text does not quite accord with 135. Castor and seal's rennet
were ingredients in potions given to epileptics according to Pliny *HN* xxxii. 112; see
also Diosc. *Mat. med.* ii. 75. 2.

laxent; neque purgativis, siquidem non aliter vexent; neque ca-
135 tulorum carnibus, propter suae qualitatis horrorem; neque de-
tentione[170] spiritus accessione imminente, tunc enim tempus est
requiescendi; neque compressionibus, asperant enim tumores;
neque curiosis odoramentis siquidem caput impleant; neque incisura, ob inutilem dolorem; neque ustionibus, superpositionis
enim tempore asperant ob tumorem passionem, in lenimento
vero resumendos vexatione doloris fatigant, et usui recorpora-
tivorum adiutoriorum obsistunt; neque coagulo vituli marini vel
veretro aut testibus hippopotami vel testudinis sanguine aut
rhombi marini. haec omnia experta neque ratione neque regula,
sed tentatione probantur.

136   item Asclepiades primo libro Celerum vel acutarum passionum
eos qui corporis raptu afficiuntur solos imperat phlebotomari,
non advertens quia ex eadem adstrictione generales quaeque species epilepsiae formantur, sed accessione gravior altera[171] com-
parabitur, quapropter magis exigit phlebotomiae beneficium.
item phlebotomatos inici iubet clysteri vel collyrio, quod bala-
non appellant, odoribus tetris adhibitis et fumationibus et naribus aceti [insufflati][172] insufflatione atque volutatione in sindone
praestita.[173] prohibet sane carnales cibos et vinum, sed imperat
venerem, quorum accusationem atque improbationem ex ante
scriptis accipere poterimus.

137   at Serapion primo libro Curationum multis ex rebus diligentiam curandi confundit. ungit enim residuum corpus oleo, colla
vero aceto cum oleo rosaceo, constringens ea quae laxatione indigeant. tunc exercitio adhibito dat mulsum bibendum ex aceto
confectum, ac deinde nihil accipere iubet aegrotantes sed quiescere; tunc deambulare circa vesperam ac rursum conquiescere et
deambulationem repetere; tunc lavari et adhibita requie bibere
hyssopi decoctionem cum aceto atque melle[174] in trium hemi-

---

[170] *an* retentione?

[171] altera ⟨quam altera⟩ R

[172] *om.* R

[173] *fort.* praestrata   [174] melle *Am:* mel *S*

sively; and purgatives are harmful because they, too, have an excessively laxative effect. Moreover, because of its toughness, 5 the meat of young animals should not be taken. Nor should the breath be held back when an attack is imminent, for that is the time when rest is required. And it is a mistake to subject the body to pressure, for that aggravates inflammation, or to strong aromatics, for they pervade the head, or to incisions, for they cause pain uselessly. Caustic treatments are also harmful, for during the attack they aggravate the disease, since a state of inflammation is present; and during the interval between attacks they wear out the convalescent by their irritating and painful effects and interfere with metasyncritic measures. Equally harmful is the use of the rennet of a seal, or the genitalia or testes of a hippopotamus, or the blood of a turtle or turbot. All these substances are recommended not on the basis of any rule of reason but as having been tested by experience.

36 Asclepiades in Book I of his work *On Swift* (i.e., acute) *Diseases* prescribes venesection only in cases in which the patient suffers convulsions. He is not aware that all the generic forms of epilepsy involve the same basic state of stricture but that, during an attack, one type is more serious than another and therefore more urgently requires the help of venesection.[38] Again, after venesection he prescribes the injection of a clyster or a suppository (Greek *balanos*); and he makes use of foul odors and fumes, and blows vapors of vinegar into the patient's nostrils. He also has the patient rolled in a sheet. And, on the one hand, he forbids meat and wine, while, on the other, he recommends venery. From what has already been said it will be easy to see the unsoundness and error of such prescriptions.

37 Serapion in Book I of his *Treatments* assembles a treatment consisting of many elements mingled in confusion. Thus, while he anoints the rest of the body with olive oil, he anoints the neck with vinegar and rose oil, using astringents on the very parts that require relaxing. Then he prescribes exercise followed by a drink of oxymel; after this he orders the patient not to take any food or drink but to rest quietly. Then in the evening he prescribes a walk, followed again by rest; then another walk, followed by a bath; then rest again and the drinking of three heminae of a decoction of hyssop with vinegar and honey. Finally,

38. But the remedy should not be confined to this one type, as Asclepiades holds.

narum quantitate;[175] tunc cibum sumere, erroribus mille stoma-
138 chum vexans ut semel cibo reficiat. utitur etiam ante unum vel
duos dies, si ordine certo accessiones occurrerint, nunc sanguinis
detractione, nunc purgativis medicaminibus; sed nunc per superiora, ut[176] albo helleboro, nunc per inferiora, ut[176] scammonia,
vel nigro helleboro, et his similibus, perniciosis turbationibus
corpus adficiens eo tempore quo requies adhibenda est, ne ulla
occasione accepta accessio generetur. ordinat praeterea quae
specialiter passioni congrua medicamina nuncupavit, ex castoreo
et equorum impetiginibus. sunt autem squamulae anteriorum
crurum sub armorum partibus in ipsis animalibus natae: has
Graeci lichenas vocant sive chelidonas, nos vero, ut supra dic-
139 tum est, impetigines vel hirundines. dat etiam cameli cerebrum
atque fella et coagulum vituli marini. item dat medicamen
quod ex crocodili terreni stercore confectum probat, et leporis
corde et lumbis, et testudinis marinae sanguine, vel testibus apri
vel arietis aut galli gallinacei. adhibet etiam odoramenta et
iniectiones clysteris, non minus ab epilepticis in curationibus
cadens.

item Heraclides Tarentinus secundo libro Interiorum curationum eadem medicamina conscripsit.

multi quoque vetustiores istam curationem ordinantes variis
140 erroribus conciderunt, quos memorare superfluum est, quippe
cum eorum vires proditione temporis expirasse videantur, ex
quibus est Menecrates †zeophletensis†,[177] item Tryphon, Philotimus, Chrysippus, Demarchus et aliorum[178] plurimi. quod est
nudum atque probabile ex conscriptione curationum Apollonii
Citiensis secundo libro de epilepticis, item Nicandri tertio libro.

Themison vero libro primo Tardarum passionum, Asclepiadis
erroribus nondum purgatus,[179] ante accessionem phlebotomandos[180] inquit, si ordo fuerit augmentorum praeservatus; sin vero
errans fuerit perspectus, post accessionem imperat phleboto-
141 miam adhibendam. modum autem detrahendi sanguinis eius
approbat mutatione.[181] quae sunt vanissimae intentiones,[182] sic-

[175] quantitatem R   [176] ut R: aut S
[177] *nimirum ex* Ζεὺς ἐπικληθείς *ortum; cf. Anon. Lond. XIX. 18*
[178] aliorum *scripsi*: horum *edd.* (*sc.* sectatores?)
[179] purgatur S: *corr.* R
[180] phlebotomandus S: *corr.* R   [181] mutationem S: *corr.* R
[182] inventiones *edd.*: *corr. Schmid RPh 47, coll. Ac. ii. 48, Chr. ii. 54, al.*

he prescribes food, having plagued the patient's stomach with countless mistaken treatments before refreshing it just once with 38 food. And a day or two before an attack, if the attacks have been coming with definite regularity, he prescribes, first, the withdrawal of blood and then the use of purgatives. He purges both from above with white hellebore and from below with scammony, black hellebore, and the like. But in so doing he subjects the body to grievous disturbances at the very time when the patient should be kept quiet to avoid giving the attack any opportunity to get under way. In addition, he recommends as specifically helpful in this disease drugs prepared from castor and horses' calluses. The latter are scaly growths on the forelegs under the shoulder parts of these animals; they are called *leichēnes* ['lichens'] or *chelidones* ['swallows'] in Greek, and *impetigines* ['scabby eruptions'] or *hirundines* ['swallows'] in Latin. 39 Serapion also gives the patient camel's brain and bile and seal's rennet. And he prescribes a drug compounded from the excrement of a land crocodile, the heart and loins of a hare, and the blood of a sea turtle or the testes of a boar, ram, or cock. He also employs aromatic substances and injects clysters. Like the epileptics themselves, his treatment falls to the ground.

Heraclides of Tarentum in Book II of his work *On the Treatment of Internal Diseases* describes the same drugs as Serapion.

Also many older writers prescribe treatments for epilepsy but fail because of their various errors, which it is unnecessary to 40 rehearse here. For the influence of these physicians has obviously vanished, time having revealed their shortcomings. Among them are Menecrates [called Zeus], Tryphon, Phylotimus, Chrysippus, Demarchus, and many others. Now the situation is clearly revealed in the account of the treatments given by Apollonius of Citium in Book II of his work when he deals with epilepsy, and also by Nicander in Book III.

In Book I of his *Chronic Diseases* Themison, still under the influence of the errors of Asclepiades, holds that, if the previous attacks have occurred at regular intervals, venesection should be performed before the next anticipated attack; but that, if no regularity has been observed, venesection should be performed 41 after the attack. And he determines the amount of blood to be withdrawn by the change [in its color].[39] But all these notions

39. Cf. *Ac.* ii. 114.

532

ut libris Specialium adiutoriorum docuimus. tunc si in brachiis
vel in cruribus, inquit, aliqua querela extiterit, earundem partium venas[183] dividendas; sin minus, interiorem venam distrin-
gendam lino, coniciens melius esse ex partibus non patientibus
sanguinis coacervatam facere detractionem, siquidem patientes
magis graventur ob irruentem materiae lapsum qui detractae
superet modum.

tunc post phlebotomiam deambulatione utitur et defricatione
alienis manibus adhibita, quo corporis motus conquiescat. dat
etiam cibum ex mediae qualitatis materia, et nulla cogente ra-
142 tione rursum sanguinem detrahit. sed si ordinem servaverint
accessiones, intra quinque dies secundo vel tertio detractionem
facit, de aliis quoque multis atque omnibus corporis partibus, et
talis et brachiis, nil metuens defectionem sanguinem detrahit.

in lenimento vero, ut exempli causa xxx dierum, post accessionem helleboro utitur post quatuor vel quinque dies, tunc sequenti iniciet, atque alia die adhibet lavacrum, et tribus vel quatuor diebus ceteris cursibus cyclum complet. ac deinde rursum
adhibet helleborum post accessionem transactam vel certe radices[184] adhibet, phlebotomo[185] dissecans corpus, quod erat melius
ordinare ante usum hellebori, quo leviora maioribus praepone-
rentur, quippe in recorporativis curationibus.

143   adhibet praeterea clysterem qui vires detrahat aegrotantis, et
propterea sequi non debuerit supra dicta. utitur etiam localibus
adiutoriis, et quidem multis pro differentia, et quibusdam fal-
sissimis, ut est sub occipitio accurata divisura, quam chiasmum
vocari diximus, et ferro circumscripta in capite cutis ustura qua
testa squamulis despumatur, item medium testae,[186] quod Graeci
bregma appellant, terebri perforatione, et in accessione constric-

183 *fort.* venas ⟨exteriores⟩
184 radicium *S: corr. Rm*
185 phlebotomū *S: corr. Rm*
186 media testa *Rm: an* medii testae?

are futile, as we have shown in the work *On Special Remedies*. Again, he holds that, if there is any pain in the arms or legs, the vein[40] should be opened in the part in question; otherwise the interior vein should be drawn out with a thread [and opened]. For he believes that it is better to make a copious withdrawal of blood from parts that are not affected, on the ground that the affected parts are more severely burdened by the flow of blood to them, a flow which even exceeds the amount withdrawn.

Then after venesection Themison prescribes a walk and a manual massage by attendants to calm the body after its exertion. He gives the patient food consisting of substances of the middle class and then withdraws blood again, though there is no cogent reason for this procedure. And if the attacks have been coming at regular intervals, he prescribes a second or even a third withdrawal of blood within five days. And he takes the blood from many other parts of the body—in fact, from all the parts, including the ankles and the arms—and is not concerned about the patient's fainting.

Now in a case where the interval between attacks is, let us say, thirty days, Themison gives the patient hellebore four or five days after the attack. Then on the following day he administers a clyster, and the day after that he prescribes a bath. On the next three or four days he completes the cycle by administering the other treatments. Then he prescribes hellebore again, the effects of the attack now having entirely disappeared, or uses radishes; and he agitates the body with venesection. But it would have been better for him to prescribe venesection before hellebore, so that the milder remedy might precede the more severe; for that is the rule in metasyncritic treatments.

In addition, Themison administers a clyster; but this impairs the strength and should therefore not follow the aforementioned treatments. He also employs many local remedies according to the type of case. But some of these remedies are certainly unsound, e.g., the elaborate [cruciform] incision, which we have said is called *chiasmos*, at the back of the head; the burning of the skin of the head in a circle with an iron cautery, the scales thus being removed from the skull; the trephining of the middle of the skull (Greek *bregma*); the binding of the limbs during an

40. Perhaps the text originally contained a contrast between interior and exterior veins.

tione articulorum, et odoribus tetris atque male olentibus ex pice atque ex spondylio, castoreo, galbano, sinapi cum aceto, quae ex ante dictis erunt protinus refellenda.

144 V. DE FURORE SIVE INSANIA, QUAM GRAECI MANIAN VOCANT

Plato in Phaedro duplicem furorem dixit: unum fieri mentis intentione ex corporis causa vel origine, alterum divinum sive immissum, eiusque Apollinem inspiratorem esse, atque nunc vocari divinationem, ab antiquis vero appellatum furorem. magna Graecorum vetustas manian appellabat, quae nunc mantice dicta est. item alium inquit ex Libero fieri patre, alium ex amore, et appellavit eroticon, alium ex Musis, quem appellavit protrepticon,[1] quod ⟨ad⟩[2] carmen instruere videatur. item Stoici duplicem furorem dixerunt, sed alium insipientiae genus, quo omnem imprudentem insanire probant, alium ex aliena-

145 tione mentis et corporis compassione. item Empedoclem sequentes alium dicunt ex animi purgamento fieri, alium alienatione mentis ex corporis causa sive iniquitate.

de quo nunc scripturi sumus, quem Graeci ⟨manian vocant⟩,[3] siquidem magnam faciat anxietatem, quam[4] appellant anian;[5] vel quod animum sive mentem ultra modum laxet, manon enim dimissum sive mollem appellant; vel certe quod polluat aegrotantes, nam pollui Graeci lymenin vocant; vel certe quod deserta[6] sive solitudinem cupientes faciat aegrotos, nam Graeci destitui atque solitudinem petere monusthae dicunt; vel quod perseverantius corpus teneat et difficile pellatur, et ob id Graeci

146 veluti moniam dixerunt; vel certe quod duros atque perferentes faciat aegrotantes, quod[7] Graeci hypomeneticos[8] vocant.

est autem alienatio tardans sine[9] febribus, quo a phreneticis discernitur, siquidem neque celer neque cum febricula esse vi-

---

[1] *fort.* poeticum (-con): *cf. Phaedr. 265B*

[2] *add. R (cf. Phaedr. 245A)*

[3] *suppl. Bendz Eran 46. 338*

[4] quam *om. A*

[5] anian *Bendz Eran 46. 339*: manian *edd.*

[6] desertam *S: corr. R*

[7] *fort.* quos

[8] hypometicos *S: corr. Rm*

[9] sine *R*: in *S*

---

1. *Phaedrus* 265B; cf. also 244-45.

2. Modern authorities connect *mania* with the root *men*, mind.

attack; and the use of the pungent and offensive odors of pitch, cow parsnip, castor, allheal, and mustard and vinegar. On the basis of what has already been said, all these remedies should at once be rejected.

V. MADNESS OR INSANITY (GREEK *MANIA*)

IN THE *Phaedrus*[1] Plato declares that there are two kinds of mania, one involving a mental strain that arises from a bodily cause of origin, the other divine or inspired, with Apollo as the source of the inspiration. This latter kind, he says, is now called 'divination,' but in early times was called 'madness'; that is, the Greeks now call it 'prophetic inspiration' (*mantice*), though in remote antiquity it was called 'mania.' Plato goes on to say that another kind of divine mania is sent by Father Bacchus, that still another, called 'erotic inspiration,' is sent by the god of love, and that a fourth kind comes from the Muses and is called 'protreptic inspiration' because it seems to inspire men to song. The Stoics also say that madness is of two kinds, but they hold that one kind consists in lack of wisdom, so that they consider every imprudent person mad; the other kind, they say, involves a loss of reason and a concomitant bodily affection. The school of Empedocles holds that one form of madness consists in a purification of the soul, and the other in an impairment of the reason resulting from a bodily disease or indisposition.

It is this latter form of madness that we shall now consider. The Greeks call it *mania* because it produces great mental anguish (Greek *ania*); or else because there is excessive relaxing of the soul or mind, the Greek word for 'relaxed' or 'loose' being *manos*; or because the disease defiles the patient, the Greek word 'to defile' being *lymaenein*; or because it makes the patient desirous of being alone and in solitude, the Greek word 'to be bereft' and 'to seek solitude' being *monusthae*; or because the disease holds the body tenaciously and is not easily shaken off, the Greek word for 'persistence' being *monia*; or because it makes the patient hard and enduring (Greek *hypomeneticos*).[2]

Mania is an impairment of reason; it is chronic and without fever and in these respects may be distinguished from phrenitis.[3]

3. Cf. *Ac.* i. 42.

deatur. vel si quisquam furiosus febricitaverit, discernatur[9a] a
phrenetico temporis consideratione. nam praecedit in furiosis
furor sequenti febricula, et non ita parvo pulso afficiuntur: quae
utraque necessario phreneticos sequentur.

generatur autem frequentius in iuvenibus ac mediis aetatibus,
difficile in senibus, atque difficilius in pueris vel mulieribus, et
147 nunc repente invadens, nunc paulatim increscens, et nunc ex
occultis, nunc ex manifestis causis, ut est ustio, perfrictio, indigestio, vinolentia frequens atque immodica, quam Graeci
craepalen vocant, item vigiliae iuges et amor vel iracundia aut
maestitudo vel timor vel superstitio nimia, item concussio sive
percussio, et intentio nimia sensuum et intellectus ob cupiditatem
disciplinarum vel quaestum pecunialem aut gloriam, item pota
medicamina, vel[10] magis ea quae amorem facere videantur, a
Graecis philtropota appellata, item detractio haemorrhoidarum
veterum sive varicum, aut abstinentia in feminis solitae purgationis.

148   sequentur autem eos qui non repente hac passione afficiuntur,
priusquam morbus enitescat, ea quae etiam epilepticos futuros
afficiunt et apoplectos. signa denique ex ante dictis sumenda
memoravimus, sed haec quidam discernunt, ut communibus
propria iungentes. graves etenim, inquiunt, somni magis epilepsiam fore significant, atque e contrario leves atque parvi,
furorem: sic etiam in iracundia constitutos capitis implemento
affici atque aestimare se in furorem devenisse, et rursum silentio
opprimi ex inani timore, item maestitudo, vel animi anxietas,
et iactatio, vel plurima ciborum appetentia, et oculorum frequens palpebratio, cordis saltus, et somni cum timore terribili
149 vel turbato[11] effecti, item ventris extantia, et frequens descensus
venti per podicem, pulsus parvus atque creber et vehemens.
etenim in epilepsiam declives ac pronos maior atque rarus pulsus sequetur et imbecillus. intuendam etiam inquiunt qualitatem

[9a] discernitur R
[10] et R
[11] fort. turbati

For mania is not an acute disease, nor is it observed to occur with fever; or, if fever *is* present in a case of mania,[4] the case may be distinguished from phrenitis by considerations of time, for in mania the madness precedes any supervening fever and the patient does not have a small pulse. In phrenitis, however, the fever always precedes the madness, and the patient has a small pulse.

Mania occurs more frequently in young and middle-aged men, rarely in old men, and most infrequently in children and women. Sometimes it strikes suddenly, at other times it takes hold gradually. Sometimes it arises from hidden causes, at other times from observable causes, such as exposure to intense heat, the taking of severe cold, indigestion, frequent and uncontrolled drunkenness (Greek *craepalē*), continual sleeplessness, excesses of venery, anger, grief, anxiety, or superstitious fear, a shock or blow, intense straining of the senses and the mind in study, business, or other ambitious pursuits, the drinking of drugs, especially those intended to excite love (Greek *philtropota*), the removal of long-standing hemorrhoids or varices, and, finally, the suppression of the menses in women.

Before the disease emerges, those who are not attacked suddenly by it have the same symptoms as persons on the verge of epilepsy or of apoplexy. These signs may be found, then, in what has already been said. But some seek to distinguish the antecedent signs of these diseases by listing specific signs for each of them in addition to the general signs common to all. Thus deep sleep, they say, is indicative of the coming of epilepsy; light and short sleep, on the other hand, of mania. So, too, they take it as an indication that mania is imminent when a person in a state of anger suffers congestion of the head and believes that he has gone mad or, again, when such a person is overcome by speechlessness resulting from groundless fear. Other such signs, in their opinion, are unhappiness, mental anxiety, tossing in sleep, immoderate appetite, frequent blinking of the eyes, palpitation of the heart, sleep marked by great fear and turmoil, abdominal distention, frequent passing of wind through the anus, and a small, rapid, hard pulse. On the other hand, they say that persons on the verge of epilepsy have a large, rare, and soft pulse. Now these same writers tell us to study the nature of these dis-

4. Cf. *ibid.*, 45 ff.

advenientium morborum, saepe enim quadam contagione in-
geruntur. quae universa secundum nos non tutissimam[12] atque
certam faciunt discretionem supradictarum passionum. etenim
futuris epilepticis vel in passionem pronis vigiliae irruunt
et anxietates et cetera. item in adventiciis morbis aliqua ex iis
eveniunt, ⟨non⟩[13] necessario omnia, vel certe aliqua quae non
enumeraverint signa.

150   emergente enim sive prodita passione, alienatio mentis fiet
sine febribus, et quibusdam vehemens, quibusdam levis, et aliis
alia specie atque visu differens, virtute tamen atque genere uno
confecta. nam furor nunc iracundia, nunc hilaritate, nunc maestitudine sive vanitate occupat mentem, nunc timore commi-
nante inanium rerum, sicut quidam memoraverunt, ut nunc spe-
luncas timeant, nunc lacunas, ne in easdem concidant, vel alia
quae terrori esse possunt.

item esse furorem cum quadam vaticinatione veteres posuerunt. Demetrius etiam parvi temporis mentis extensionem
furorem appellat: item turbore[14] repentino expavescentes atque
percussos quosdam ut etiam oblivione praegestorum afficiantur.

151   sic denique Artemidorum grammaticum Apollonius memorat
nitente gressu crocodilum in harena iacentem expavisse, atque
eius motu percussa mente credidisse sibi sinistrum crus atque
manum a serpente comestam, et literarum memoria caruisse
oblivione possessum. item melancholiam inquit speciem furoris
esse nuncupandam; nos vero ipsam quoque discernimus a furore. est autem insania sive furor nunc iugis, nunc temporis interiecti requie levigatus, efficiens ut aegri nunc non meminerint
sui laboris, nunc oblivionem nesciant suam, et nunc omnium
sensuum alienatione vexentur falsitate possessi, nunc[14a] aliarum

---

[12] tutissima *S: corr. A*

[13] *add. R*

[14] turbine *edd.*

[14a] nunc *Am*: nec *S*

---

5. I.e., signs which these writers would consider characteristic of imminent mania.

6. I.e., the signs supposed by these physicians to be characteristic of imminent epilepsy or imminent mania, as the case may be.

7. The point seems to be that the attempt of these physicians to diagnose, say, as
between epilepsy or mania, at the very first appearance of symptoms, not only before

eases as they first come to the body, on the theory that they often attack the body by a kind of external contact. But all these methods fail, in our opinion, to provide an accurate and definite means of distinguishing which of the aforesaid diseases is imminent in a given case. As a matter of fact, before an attack of epilepsy, sleeplessness, anxiety, and other signs[5] do appear. And when the diseases first attack the body, some of the signs, but not necessarily all, appear;[6] or, at any rate, some signs appear which these writers have failed to enumerate.[7]

o   Now when the disease of mania emerges into the open, there is impairment of reason unaccompanied by fever; this impairment of reason in some cases is severe, in others mild; it differs in the various cases in its outward form and appearance, though its nature and character are the same. For, when mania lays hold of the mind, it manifests itself now in anger, now in merriment, now in sadness or futility, and now, as some relate, in an overpowering fear of things which are quite harmless. Thus the patient will be afraid of caves or will be obsessed by the fear of falling into a ditch or will dread other things which may for some reason inspire fear.

The ancients also associated madness with a kind of prophetic power. And Demetrius calls mania a strain imposed on the mind for a brief period, saying that some persons in a sudden moment of confusion are so terror-stricken that they lose their memory

51 of the past. In fact, Apollonius tells us that when the philologist Artemidorus was lying on the sand he was frightened by the ponderous approach of a crocodile; his mind was so affected by the sudden sight of the reptile's motion that he imagined that his left leg and hand had been eaten by the animal, and he lost his memory even of literature. Apollonius says that melancholy should be considered a form of mania, but we distinguish melancholy from mania.[8] And mania or madness is sometimes continuous and at other times relieved by intervals of remission. Thus the patient sometimes does not remember his tasks, sometimes is unaware of his own forgetfulness, sometimes suffers impairment of all the senses, and sometimes is affected by various

---

the diseases are chronic, but even before the first attack is under way, is doomed to failure. For the lists of signs that they have drawn up will at this early stage prove inadequate.

8. See 183.

152 specierum errore fallantur. sic denique furens alius se passerem existimavit, alius gallum gallinaceum, alius fictile,[15] alius laterem, alius deum, alius oratorem, alius tragoedum vel comoedum, alius stipulam ferens mundi se centrum[16] tenere, alius se sustentandum manu poscebat, vagiens ut infans. horum plurimis accessionis tempore oculi sanguinolenti fient atque attenti; accidunt etiam vigiliae iuges, venarum extensio,[16a] genarum rubor, corporis durities, atque aliena fortitudo.

patitur autem omnis nervositas, ut ex his quae sequuntur vel accidunt conicere poterimus, magis tamen caput: etenim antecedentes plurimae querelae eius partis existunt, cum gravedine 153 atque dolore afficiuntur, singulis quoque sensibus patientibus, quos in capite novimus constitutos. est[17] praeterea passio magna atque tardissima, superpositionibus ac lenimentis variata, ex constrictione confecta. etenim his qui Mnaseam sectantes alium[18] putant, adquiescendum non est, suspicantibus eum furorem qui hilaritate affecerit aegrotantes solutionis appellandum. falluntur etenim nominis voce, siquidem Graeci diachisin animi laxationem dixerunt sive diffusionem, cum hoc animi non corporis ostendat qualitatem. nam quod omnis furens strictura afficiatur, manifestum atque probabile est ex oculis sanguino- 154 lentis, qui in alto[19] constitutam stricturam denuntiant; item quod ipsos oculos atque venas in vultu extantiores habeat, totius corporis attestante duritia, cum fortitudine praeter naturam adveniente ob stricturae consensum. denique lenimenti tempore fatigatos se sentiunt aegrotantes. est item coniectura facienda ex his quae mentis alienationem praecedunt, ut capitis gravedo vel dolor spinae vel scapularum[20] et tardus membrorum motus ⟨et⟩[21] ventris inflatio. peccant denique etiam hi qui animae passionem principaliter, dehinc corporis esse concipiunt, cum neque quisquam philosophorum eius tradiderit curationem, et antequam mente falluntur, accidentia substantia corporis habere videatur. haec sunt quae ad apprehendendum vel discernendum morbum Methodus ordinavit.

---

[15] fictile R: fictilem S

[16] centrum Rm: censum S: sceptrum Haller   [17] est Rm: et S

[16a] sed extantia, 66   [18] aliam Rm: aliud Am

[19] in alto Haller: inlato S: in lato A (cf. ὡς ἐν πλάτει Sor. Gyn., p. 16. 8)

[20] spinae vel scapularum habet S post motus: transp. R   [21] add. R

2 other types of aberration. Thus one victim of madness fancied himself a sparrow, another a cock, another an earthen vessel, another a brick, another a god, another an orator, another a tragic actor, another a comic actor, another a stalk of grain and asserted that he occupied the center of the universe, and another cried like a baby and begged to be carried in the arms. In most cases of mania, at the time of an actual attack, the eyes become bloodshot and intent. There is also continual wakefulness, the veins are distended, cheeks flushed, and body hard and abnormally strong.

In this disease the whole system of nerves and sinews is affected, as we may gather from the symptoms. But the head is especially affected; and, in fact, most of the discomfort preceding the attack is in the head, the patient being affected by a feel-
3 ing of pain and heaviness there. Also the senses are individually affected, and these are, as we know, centered in the head. Mania is a major disease; it is chronic and consists of attacks alternating with periods of remission; it involves a state of stricture. And we cannot agree with the followers of Mnaseas, who think otherwise and hold that those cases of madness which manifest themselves in merriment should be thought to involve a state of looseness. The fact is that these physicians are deceived by the word they employ. For the Greek word *diachysis*, in the sense of relaxation or diversion of the mind, denotes a quality of the mind, not of the body. But it is obvious that there is a state of stricture in every case of mania. This is confirmed by the bloodshot condition of the eyes, a condition that indicates an internal state of
4 stricture; also by the bulging of the eyes and the facial veins, the hardness of the body and its unnatural strength, a concomitant of the state of stricture. Thus in the interval of remission the patient feels fatigued. Our conclusion is further confirmed by the symptoms that precede the loss of reason, e.g., a feeling of heaviness in the head, pain in the spine and shoulder blades, sluggishness in the movements of the limbs, and abdominal distention. Thus those who imagine that the disease is chiefly an affection of the soul and only secondarily of the body are mistaken. For no philosopher has ever set forth a successful treatment for this disease; moreover, before the mind is affected, the body itself shows visible symptoms. This concludes the Methodist account of the recognition or diagnosis of the disease.

155   curationem vero similem epilepticis accipimus adhibendam.
etenim principio convenit iacere loco mediocriter lucido atque
calido et nullo turbore pulsato, nulla quoque picturae distinc-
tione neque fenestris humilibus luminato, neque in superioribus
potius quam in solo. plerique enim furore correpti sese praeci-
pites dederunt. est etiam lectus firmissime atque aversus ingressu[22] cubiculi locandus, quo ingredientes minime videant
aegrotantes, ne vultus varietate lacessiti furoris augeant vani-
tatem. stramina praeterea mollia sunt approbanda, cum defricatione ac retentione articulorum, blando scilicet tactu.

156   et si qua pars corporis saltu fuerit agitata, tepidis vaporationibus erit mitiganda, appositis lanis mollibus ac limpidis atque[23] capiti, collo, et thoraci circulatim. fotus quoque adhibendus olei calidi, admixto aliquando mitigativae virtutis causa
faenigraeci liquore ex[24] eius decoctione confecto, sed minime
pingui, vel certe hibisci infusione aut lini seminis: tunc oris collutio atque potus ex aqua calida.

erunt praeterea multorum ingressus prohibendi, et maxime
ignotorum. mandandum quoque ministris ut eorum errores
quodam consensu accipientes corrigant, ne aut omnibus con-
157 sentiendo augeant furorem eorum visa confirmantes, aut rursum
repugnando asperent passionis augmentum, sed inductive nunc
indulgeant consentientes, nunc insinuando[25] corrigant vana, recta demonstrantes. ac si exilire coeperint, ut difficile teneantur,
vel solitudine potius exasperantur,[26] oportebit plurimis uti ministris, et praecipere aegros latenter retineri ad articulorum fricationem, quo minime provocentur.

si etiam visu hominum fuerint commoti, erit adhibenda ligatio
sine ulla quassatione, praetectis articulis ex lana; tunc fasciola
ligatur.[27] ac si quemquam[28] timere vel revereri consueverint,
158 non erit itidem[29] frequenter inducendus:[30] continuatio enim con-

---

[22] ingressum S: corr. Triller Clinotechnia 92

[23] atque om. R

[24] ex Rm: et S

[25] insinuanda S: corr. R

[26] exasperentur R

[27] ligatis Rm

[28] quicquam S: corr. Rm

[29] itidem ⟨ac⟩ R

[30] inducendum S: corr. Rm

5   As for the treatment, we hold that measures should be taken similar to those employed in epilepsy. Thus, to begin with, have the patient lie in a moderately light and warm room. The room should be perfectly quiet, unadorned by paintings, not lighted by low windows, and on the ground floor rather than on the upper stories, for victims of mania have often jumped out of windows. And the bed should be firmly fastened down. It should face away from the entrance to the room so that the patient will not see those who enter. In this way the danger of exciting and aggravating his madness by letting him see many different faces will be avoided. And the bedclothes should be soft.

6   Rub the patient's limbs and hold them gently. If any part of the body is shaken by a throbbing movement, relieve it with warmth, applying soft scoured wool to the head, too, the neck, and circularly to the chest. Also employ a fomentation of warm olive oil, sometimes adding, for its soothing properties, fenugreek water (obtained from a decoction of fenugreek; but see that it is not thick), or else an infusion of marsh mallow, or flaxseed. Then wash the patient's mouth and have him take a drink of warm water.

Do not permit many people, especially strangers, to enter the room. And instruct the servants to correct the patient's aberrations while giving them a sympathetic hearing. That is, have the servants, on the one hand, avoid the mistake of agreeing with everything the patient says, corroborating all his fantasies, and
7   thus increasing his mania; and, on the other hand, have them avoid the mistake of objecting to everything he says and thus aggravating the severity of the attack. Let them rather at times lead the patient on by yielding to him and agreeing with him, and at other times indirectly correct his illusions by pointing out the truth. And if the patient begins to get out of bed and cannot easily be restrained, or is distressed especially because of loneliness, use a large number of servants and have them covertly restrain him by massaging his limbs; in this way they will avoid upsetting him.

If the patient is excited when he sees people, bind him without doing any injury. First cover his limbs with wool and then fasten with a bandage. Now if there is a person whom the patient has customarily feared or respected, he should not be brought into
8   the sickroom repeatedly. For this frequent repetition gives rise

temptibilitatem parit. vel[31] cum causae coegerint, vel adiutorio adhibendo non succubuerint aegrotantes, tunc erit necessario inducendus,[31a] quo aegri terrore vel reverentia opprimantur. ac si etiam lucem animo contraria commoventem viderimus, erunt eorum oculi adumbrandi, quo ceterum corpus luce tangatur.

adhibenda cibi abstinentia usque ad primam diatriton, ac[32] permittentibus viribus phlebotomia, si passio coegerit, intra diatritum. et si ulla obstiterit causa detractionis congruae fa-

159 ciendae, aliquoties adhibita detractione modus implendus. si horum nihil obstiterit, in ipsa diatrito erit phlebotomia adhibenda.

tunc perunctio, ora fovenda, dandus cibus levis parvus digestibilis, ut panis ex aqua calida, vel alica ex melle leviter decocto confecta, vel sorbile quicquam aut tenerum. exinde usque ad passionis declinationem alternis diebus aeger nutriendus, si vires eius permiserint. proluendus denique etiam clystere simplici si passio poposcerit. tunc etiam praecordia cataplasmatibus relaxanda ob digestionis qualitatem, quo nulla constrictio

160 spiritum abstentum capiti transmittat. attendendae etiam species alienationis cuius accidentia contrariorum coniectura erunt mitiganda, ut eum[33] hilaritate[34] relaxent[35] nuntiantes quicquam quod animum resolvat.

dehinc cum status passionis apparuerit, detonso capite atque raso, cucurbitam infigimus adiuncta scarificatione, et primo ex praecordiis, tunc inter scapulas, quas Graeci metaphrenum vocant (consentiunt enim facilius istis superiora), dehinc etiam occipitio ac vertici et temporibus capitis. ac si vultus vel ora fuerint affecta plurimum, totum corpus erit sanguisugis relevandum, quas hirudines appellamus. tunc cataplasmandum ex

---

[31] sed *Rm*

[31a] inducendum *S: corr. Rm*

[32] ac *fort. transp. post* viribus

[33] *an* cum *vel* aegrum?

[34] *fort.* hilaritatem

[35] *fort.* relaxemus

---

9. Cf. *Ac.* i. 65.

10. Cf. *Ac.* i. 61.

to a lack of regard.[9] But when circumstances require it, as when the patient does not submit to the application of a remedy, this person should then be brought in to overcome the patient's stubbornness, by inspiring fear or respect. And if you observe that the light is upsetting his mind, shade his eyes but let the rest of his body be touched by the light.[10]

Do not give the patient food until the end of the first three-day period; and if his strength permits and the disease requires it, perform venesection before the end of the three-day period. If there is any reason why an adequate withdrawal of blood cannot be made, take the amount required in several operations. But if there is no reason for doing otherwise, perform the venesection at the end of the three-day period.

After venesection anoint the patient, foment his face, and give him a small quantity of light and digestible food, e.g., bread in warm water, spelt groats mixed with honey which has been boiled down moderately, or some other gruel-like or soft food. Thereafter, feed the patient on alternate days, if his strength permits, until the disease declines. And if the case requires it, purge with a simple clyster. Again, relax the precordial region with poultices as an aid to digestion. The purpose is to prevent any state of constriction from causing the pent-up gases to pass to the head. Attention must also be paid to the type of mental aberration involved, for its symptoms will have to be relieved by properly reasoned countermeasures. Thus they [the servants] will soothe a patient with cheerfulness,[11] telling him something to relax his mind.

And when the highest stage of the attack is reached, cut the patient's hair and shave his head; then apply cupping with scarification, beginning with the precordia, and then passing to the region between the shoulder blades (Greek *metaphrenon*). For in these cases the upper parts of the body are apt to be sympathetically affected.[12] Then apply cupping in conjunction with scarification to the occiput, the top of the head, and the temples. And if the face is particularly affected, relax the whole body by using leeches, which we call *hirudines*. Then use poultices of

11. *Hilaritate = dictis hilarioribus* (*Ac.* i. 98). If *cum hilaritatem* be read, the meaning may be 'as when they relieve a patient of hysterical laughter by telling him something to break the tension.'

12. Or 'the upper parts [i.e., the head] and these parts are apt to be sympathetically affected.'

pani ⟨et⟩ [36] ceteris [37] laxativae virtutis; dehinc spongiis vaporandum. et si passio [iisdem] [38] permanserit, secundo vel tertio
161 iisdem perseverabimus adiutoriis. si vigiliae fuerint consecutae, adhibenda gestatio, primo ex lectulo pendenti, tunc etiam fertoria sella. adhibenda etiam aquae distillatio crebra, cuius sonitu saepe aegrotantes inducti somnos capiunt. tunc etiam spongiis calidis oculi vaporandi, atque palpebrarum duritia relaxanda, quo etiam per oculos usque ad cerebri membranas beneficium perveniat curationis.

ac si passio declinaverit, et propterea minime vigilare atque alienari coeperint aegrotantes, dabimus varium cibum ex mediae materiae qualitate. tunc si doloris sensum aegrotantes acceperint, adhibenda embasis ex oleo vel admixto aliquanto [39]
162 liquore quo fuerit hibiscus praecocta. tunc capiti atque scarificatis locis cerotaria apponenda, et ex eis liquefactis [40] corpus omne perungendum miti defricatione. tunc acopis atque malagmatibus utemur, [41] quae nulla nimietate percutiant, motum quoque gestationis adhibentes, et primo gestatoria sella, tunc vehiculo manibus acto. atque toto fortificato corpore erunt in deambulationem cogendi, et vocis exercitium quod cuique convenerit. nam literalis etiam lectio adhibenda est, et quae sit aliqua falsitate culpata, quo interius mentem exerceant aegrotantes. quapropter interrogationibus quoque erunt fatigandi, ut nunc mendacii causa, nunc promendi quod quaerimus exer-
163 ceri videantur. tunc sibi dimittendi, data lectione quae non sit intellectu difficilis, ne plurimo labore vexentur. haec enim si supra vires fuerint, non minus afficiunt quam corporis immodicae gestationes.

item post lectionem aliqua composita [42] vel mimica sunt offerenda, si maestitudine furentes laborent; aut rursum tristitiam vel tragicum timorem habentia, si puerili lusu [43] furentes afficiantur. oportet enim contrarietate quadam alienationis corrigere

---

[36] *add. Rm*

[37] caeteri *S: corr. Rm*

[38] *om. R*

[39] aliquando *Bendz 96*

[40] liquefactis *Rm*: liquefactum *S*

[41] utemur *Bendz 97*: veterum *edd.*

[42] *fort.* comica

[43] luxu *S: corr. Reinesius* (*v. Almeloveen ad loc.*)

bread and other substances with relaxing properties, followed
by an application of heat with sponges. And if the disease persists, keep using the same remedies a second or even a third
ı time. If the patient is wakeful, prescribe passive exercise, first
in a hammock and then in a sedan chair. The rapid dripping of
water may be employed to induce sleep, for under the influence
of its sound patients often fall asleep. And heat should then be
applied to the eyes with warm sponges, and the stiffness of the
lids relaxed; for the beneficial effects of this treatment will pass
through the eyes to the membranes of the brain.

When the disease declines and the patient's wakefulness and
mental aberration are very much reduced, give him varied food
of the middle class. If he then has any feeling of pain, give him a
bath of olive oil, sometimes with the addition of a decoction of
2 marsh mallow. Then apply cerates to the head and the other
scarified parts and, when these cerates melt, anoint the whole
body with them, employing gentle massage. Follow this with
restorative ointments and emollient plasters which do not have
an injurious effect by reason of any strong property. And then
prescribe passive exercise, first in a sedan chair and then in a
cart drawn by hand. When the patient's body has gained
strength, prescribe walking and also vocal exercise, as required
by the case. Thus have the patient read aloud even from texts
that are marred by false statements. In this way he will exercise his mind more thoroughly.[13] And for the same reason he
should also be kept busy answering questions. This will enable
us both to detect malingering[14] and to obtain the information
63 we require. Then let him relax, giving him reading that is easy
to understand; injury due to overexertion will thus be avoided.
For if these mental exercises overtax the patient's strength,
they are no less harmful than passive exercise carried to excess.

And so after the reading let him see a stage performance. A
mime is suitable if the patient's madness has manifested itself
in dejection; on the other hand, a composition depicting sadness
or tragic terror is suitable in cases of madness which involve
playful childishness. For the particular characteristic of a case
of mental disturbance must be corrected by emphasizing the
opposite quality, so that the mental condition, too, may attain

13. The meaning of *interius* is obscure. Cf. 15.
14. This interpretation is conjectural.

qualitatem, quo animi quoque habitus sanitatis mediocritatem agnoscat. tunc proficiente curatione erunt pro possibilitate
164 meditationes adhibendae vel disputationes. sed nunc quoque similiter ordinatae, ut principia levi[44] voce promantur, narratio vero et demonstrationes extenta atque maiore, tunc epilogus dimissa et indulgenti, sicut hi qui de exercenda voce, quam Graeci anaphonesin vocant, tradiderunt. adhibendi denique auditores sunt aegrotanti consueti, qui favore quodam atque laude dicta prosequentes dicentis animum laxent. etenim iucunda exercitamenta corporis adiuvant sanitatem. tunc post meditationem vel disputationem deducendus mox est[45] atque perungendus leviter aegrotans et deambulatione levi movendus.
165   ei autem qui literas nesciat immittendae quaestiones erunt quae sint eius artis propriae, ut rustico rusticationis, gubernatori navigationis. ac si ex omni parte iners fuerit curandus, erunt vulgaria quaedam quaestionibus[46] tradenda, vel calculorum ludus. habet enim quiddam quod animum exerceat, et magis si peritior aegrotanti colludat.

tunc post requiem adhibita deambulatione erunt diligentius perungendi. et primo parva atque simplici defricatione mulcendi, dehinc profectu apparente etiam devexo ductu post humeros atque colla, defricatione potiore et levi deductione, quam
166 Graeci cataspasmon[47] vocant. ultimo fricandum etiam caput. quod ⟨ubi⟩ [48] fuerit relevatum, lavacrum etiam erit adhibendum.

et sicut de epilepticis dictum est, varius dandus cibus, inhibito vino. tunc addendum quicquam pomorum, quo corpus praetentemus. dehinc vinum dandum tenue leve[49] atque parvum, medio cibi tempore; et primo inter quinque dies, tunc inter quatuor, dehinc inter tres atque duos, item alternis diebus, ita

[44] leni *Rm*

[45] deducenda vox est *Sm*

[46] *fort.* ⟨pro⟩ quaestionibus

[47] catapasmon *S: corr. Am, sed fort.* catapsasmon, *ut Rose, ind. Sor., p. 401*

[48] *add. R: aliter* quando *pro* quod

[49] lene *R (cf., e.g., 94)*

---

15. Possibly 'purged' or 'massaged.' According to the reading of *Sm:* 'the patient's voice should be rested.'

the balanced state of health. And as the treatment proceeds, have the patient deliver discourses or speeches, as far as his

4 ability and strength permit. And in this case the speeches should all be arranged in the same way, the introduction to be delivered with a gentle voice, the narrative portions and proof more loudly and intensely, and the conclusion, again, in a subdued and kindly manner. This is in accordance with the precepts of those who have written on vocal exercise (Greek *anaphōnēsis*). An audience should be present, consisting of persons familiar to the patient; by according the speech favorable attention and praise, they will help relax the speaker's mind. And, in fact, any pleasant bodily exercise promotes the general health. Soon after the discourse or speech, the patient should be taken[15] and gently anointed; he should then take a light walk for exercise.

5 Now if he is unacquainted with literature, give him problems appropriate to his particular craft, e.g., agricultural problems if he is a farmer, problems in navigation if he is a pilot. And if he is without any skill whatever, give him questions on commonplace matters, or let him play checkers.[16] Such a game can exercise his mind, particularly if he plays with a more experienced opponent.

When the patient has had his walk and rest, he should be carefully anointed. At first, massage him only slightly and simply. But when his recovery has become more obvious, massage him behind the shoulders and the neck with a downward motion, using a stronger stroke than before; this is the moderate

66 rubdown which the Greeks call *cataspasmos*. In the final stage also massage the head; and when the head is relieved, prescribe bathing.

Serve the patient varied food, as we indicated above in discussing epilepsy. Do not give him wine at first, but add some fruit to his diet to test the body.[17] Afterward give him a small quantity of thin, mild wine at the time of eating. At first, the wine should be given at intervals of five days and, as time goes on, at intervals of four, three, two, and then on alternate days;

16. Or, with slightly altered reading: 'give him certain commonplace activities, such as checker playing.'

17. Cf. 93.

cotidie, interiecta vel variata aquae potatione eodem contrario ductu quo vinum variabamus.

tunc cum nulla coeperit aeger novitate vexari[50] et perferre singula didicerit, erunt addendae aeris mutationes, et si quidem philosophorum disputationes audire voluerint, erunt adhi-167 bendae. etenim timorem vel maestitudinem aut iracundiam suis amputant dictis, ex quibus non parvus profectus corpori commodatur.

ac si passio permanserit et corpus tarditate possederit, super-positionibus ac lenimentis varianda,[51] erunt et[52] superpositiones mitigandae eisdem adiutoriis quae initio furentibus sunt ordinata. in lenimento vero prius adhibendus resumptivus cyclus per variam gestationem, atque vocis exercitium musico monitore compositum, tunc deambulatio atque gestatio et cibus varius et his similia; secundo recorporativus, sicut superius docuimus.

168 utendum etiam localibus adiutoriis, hoc est cucurbitis recorporativis, et rasione capillorum; item sternutamento, et dropace communi atque composito[53] ex nitro, galbano, manna, piretro, euphorbio, et pipere; tunc paroptesi atque cataclysmo et aspergine pulveris nitri.[54] torrendum etiam corpus fervore solis praetecto capite. dehinc sinapismo utendum et exercitio vario ac vehementi. sed haec omnia cum adhibentur, etiam localibus adiutoriis prius erunt praetangendae ac renovandae[55] longe remotae[56] a patientibus partibus; tunc secundae ac vicinae dehinc ipsae. etenim quoties longe remotae[57] praemoventur, transmissa commoditas sine partium curandarum commotione latenter advenit, et nullam facit capitis inflationem.

169 dehinc adhibendus vomitus ex albo helleboro radicibus inserto, et magis si quisquam ex radice pura noluerit digitis vomi-

[50] vexari *Rm*: servari *S*

[51] variata *Rm* (*ut, e.g., 96*)

[52] et *fort. del.*

[53] compositio *Sm*

[54] nitri *R*: nitrei *S*

[55] renovandae ⟨partes⟩ *Rm* (*om.* partibus)

[56] removendae *S*: *corr. Rm*

[57] remotae *A*: remota *S*

finally, it may be given every day. But water should be drunk
in the intervals, the amount decreasing in proportion as the
allotment of wine becomes more liberal.

Then, if the patient shows no new symptoms and has accustomed himself to the various parts of his regimen, change of
climate should be prescribed. And if he is willing to hear discus-
57 sions of philosophers, he should be afforded the opportunity. For
by their words philosophers help to banish fear, sorrow, and
wrath, and in so doing make no small contribution to the health
of the body.

But if the disease persists and becomes chronic, being marked
by attacks alternating with intervals of remission, relieve the
attacks, using the same remedies as those prescribed above for
the initial attack of mania. But in the intervals of remission,
prescribe, first, the restorative series of treatments including
various types of passive exercise, vocal exercise arranged under
the supervision of a musician,[18] walking, passive exercise, varied
food, and the like. Follow this series with the metasyncritic cycle, as we have described it above.

58 Also employ local remedies, including metasyncritic cupping,[19]
shaving of the hair, sternutatories, ordinary pitch plasters, as
well as a plaster compounded of nitrum, allheal, frankincense,
pellitory, spurge, and pepper. In addition, prescribe intense
heat, douches, and dusting with powdered nitrum. Also have the
patient bake his body in the heat of the sun, first covering his
head. And prescribe applications of mustard and varied, intensive exercise. In connection with these prescriptions, first the
parts farthest removed from the affected parts should be treated
by local remedies and restored to health; then the parts next to
these and adjoining them; and, finally, the affected parts themselves. In fact, whenever the remote parts are subjected to a
remedy, the benefits of the treatment are imperceptibly passed
along to the affected parts without disturbing them in any way
and without causing any congestion of the head.

69 Induce vomiting with white hellebore inserted in radishes,[20]
especially if the patient does not wish to provoke vomiting by

18. In particular, a voice trainer, φωνασκός. Cf. Soranus *Gyn. ind. s.v.*

19. In cupping of this kind a great deal of flame is employed, and a strong pull is
required to remove the cups.

20. Cf. *Chr.* ii. 31.

tum provocare: fit enim ut inserto helleboro sponte vomitus
nascatur. tunc etiam ipsum helleborum dabimus, et si oportuerit, non semel sed saepius per intervalla temporum. item
aurium cavernis inicere debemus aquam nitro aspersam, vel
mulsum cum semine urticae, vel sinapi liquido, quo etiam per
sensuales vias ad membranas cerebri recorporativa virtus adveniat, quippe cum etiam aurium tinnitus saepissime aegrotantes afficiat.

dehinc erunt rursum resumendi aliptarum diligentia. utendum quoque naturalibus aquis, ut sunt nitrosae, et magis si
odoris non fuerint tetri, quo membranae capitis quatiantur.
170 utendum etiam peregrinatione terrena atque maritima et animi
avocamentis quibus mentis laxatio fiat.

erit etiam coniciendum ex maestitudine quantum permaneat
passionis, quamquam soluta videatur. non aliter quam si tere-
bratis oculis, quod Graeci paracentesin vocant, ob tardam suffusionem, quamquam sit perfecta curatio, visus impedimenta perseverant, quae quadam consuetudine potius quam passionis
praesentia fieri videbantur. solutam vero vel convictam passionem intelligere poterimus ex his quae de epileptica curatione
memorantes docuimus. haec est secundum Methodum furio-
sorum sive insanorum curatio.

171 aliarum sectarum ⟨et⟩[58] veterum Methodicorum plurimi obscuris in locis habendos inquiunt aegrotantes, neque accidentia
passionis conicientes, siquidem saepe quidam obscuritatem
odisse videantur, neque ipsam passionem, quod sit ex strictura
effecta. etenim densata corpora aeris obscuritas minime reflari permittit; abstentis[59] denique naturalibus officiis, impletum
caput magis gravatur.

adhibendam etiam immodicam abstinentiam, quam Graeci
limanchian[60] vocant, non advertentes quia immoderata cibi
abstinentia vires corporis vexat, et aegrotantem naturali fortitudine desertum adiutoria ferre non patitur. perdit etiam ci-

---

[58] add. R
[59] abstinentis S: corr. R   [60] laemanchiam S: sed v. Vietmeier 27

inserting his fingers after taking plain radishes. For vomiting begins spontaneously if hellebore is placed in the radishes. And then hellebore should be given by itself, not merely once but, if necessary, several times, at suitable intervals. Also inject into the openings of the ears water with a sprinkling of nitrum, or diluted honey to which nettle seed or liquid mustard has been added; by this means a metasyncritic effect may be conveyed to the membranes of the brain through the channels of sensation. For undoubtedly ringing in the ears often affects the patient.

Again, in restoring the patient's health, the services of a trainer should be employed. Use should also be made of natural waters, such as alkaline springs, particularly those free from any pungent odor which might injure the membranes of the 70 brain. A trip abroad by land or sea and various mental diversions are helpful in affording relaxation of the mind.

From the degree of dejection which the patient shows we may infer to what extent the disease persists, even though it may seem to be completely overcome. The case is similar to that found when an operation of piercing (Greek *paracentēsis*) has been performed on an eye for the purpose of removing a chronic cataract and, though the treatment is completed, the defect of vision still persists; the persistence of the defect would seem to be due to a kind of habituation of the patient rather than to the continuing presence of the disease. But we may recognize when the disease of mania is broken and overcome from the same signs which we noted in our discussion of the treatment of epilepsy. So much for the treatment of madness or insanity according to the Methodists.

71 Many physicians of other sects and even the early Methodists declare that patients should be kept in dark rooms; in making this prescription they fail to take account of the symptoms of the disease, for patients often are found to dislike darkness; and they fail to recognize that the disease itself involves a state of stricture. The fact is that darkness prevents a constricted body from breathing freely, and, since the natural functions are thus impeded, the congested condition of the head is aggravated.

These physicians also prescribe a starvation diet (Greek *limanchia*), not realizing that excessive abstention from food impairs the bodily power and, by robbing the patient of his normal strength, prevents him from properly bearing the treatment.

172 bandi tempora, ex quo densata corpora saepe laxantur. non
enim vere admittenda aut credenda sunt ea quae suspicantur,
quibus ipsi insanire potius quam curare videantur. aiunt enim
ferarum similitudinem intuendam, quae deductione cibi posita
ferocitate mansuescunt. non aliter etiam furentes posse iugi
abstinentia mitigari, quippe cum inter sanos homines facile sapere ieiuni videantur, post cibum vero affici hilaritate facilius aut
furore.

iubent praeterea vinculis aegrotantes coerceri sine ulla discretione, cum necessario devinctae partes quatiantur, et facilius
aegros ministrantium manibus quam inertibus vinculis retinere.

173 cupiunt etiam certis medicaminibus somnos altos efficere, papavere foventes, et pressuram potius atque gravationem capitis
non somnum ingerentes. fovent etiam oleo rosaceo aceto admixto; serpillo et castoreo et ceteris simillimae virtutis caput
obsidunt, constringentes ea quae laxatione indigeant.

item alii frigidis usi sunt rebus, passionis causam ex fervore
venire suspicantes, ut Aristoteles et Diocles, nescii quoniam fervor innatus sine dubio tumoris est signum, et non, ut existimant,
passionis est causa. quare peiorare necesse est et maiorem

174 furorem fieri, cum frigida curatione corpora densantur. alii vero
phlebotomiam adhibendam probant ex duobus brachiis usque ad
animae defectionem, ut saepe faciant mori cupientes.[61] etenim
defectio aut[62] virium amputatio sequuntur immodicam sanguinis detractionem, quam non oportebit ex utroque brachio
fieri. dicunt praeterea usum esse clysteris addendum ex acerrimae virtutis liquoribus,[63] iniectione frequenti, ex quibus nihil
utile sed potius dysenteria sequatur, dantes etiam urinalia atque
ventriflua medicamina potanda, quae diuretica vel coeliotica[64]

[61] fort. patientes
[62] fort. ac
[63] fort. liquorum: liquoribus ⟨et⟩ R
[64] fort. coeliolytica Probst, TLL (cf. κοιλιολυσία, Sor. Gyn.; cf. etiam Chr. ii. 50)

Such fasting also involves a loss of [the opportunity afforded at]
2 mealtime; for then constricted bodies are often relaxed. Indeed,
we cannot agree to, or accept, the conjectures of these writers;
for, in making them, they seem to be the madmen themselves
rather than the physicians of madmen. Thus they say that we
must consider as analogous the case of wild beasts, who when
food is denied are supposed to lose their ferocity and grow tame.
In the same way, they say, madmen may be calmed by continual
fasting; for even sane persons seem more readily inclined to be
sensible when they have not eaten for some time, but after
eating have a greater tendency to mirth and folly.

These physicians also prescribe indiscriminately that the patients be kept in bonds. But, in fact, the parts that are bound
must suffer injury; moreover, it is easier to restrain patients by
having servants use their hands than by applying bonds im-
3 properly. And these same physicians try to produce a deep sleep
with certain drugs, fomenting the patient with poppy and causing stupor and drowsiness rather than natural sleep. They also
foment with rose oil mixed with vinegar and assail the patient's
head with thyme, castor, and other substances of similar properties. In so doing, they constrict the very parts which require
relaxing measures.

Some use cooling substances, supposing, with Aristotle and
Diocles, that the disease results from heat. They are unaware,
however, that the internal heat is certainly a sign of inflammation, not, as they think, the cause of the disease. It follows,
therefore, that a case of mania is aggravated and intensified
4 when the body is condensed by cooling remedies. Some recommend bleeding the patient from the veins of both arms until he
faints; in this way they often cause death, and that by their own
deliberate choice.[21] For collapse and loss of strength result from
excessive withdrawal of blood; hence such withdrawal should
not be made from both arms. Again, they prescribe frequent injections of clysters consisting of fluids with very sharp properties. But no good results from this; on the contrary, dysentery
is apt to follow. They also prescribe the drinking of drugs to
promote urination and to purge the bowels, drugs called in
Greek *diurētica* and *coeliōtica*, respectively. And they hold that

21. Or for the last clause possibly substitute: 'a death, in fact, desired by the patient' (so Amman).

Graeci vocaverunt. avertendam etenim e superioribus ad inferiora materiam dicunt, ex quibus corpora tabescunt, nervositas vitiatur.

175   item alii inebriandos aiunt aegrotantes, cum saepe ex vinolentia furor atque insania generetur. alii flagellis aiunt coercendos, ut quasi iudicio[65] mentis pulso resipiant, cum magis tumentia caede lacessendo faciant asperiora, et adveniente lenimento passionis cum sensum recipiunt, plagarum dolore vexentur. vel certe, sicut ratio poscit, vicinis magis ac patientibus locis adiutoria sunt adhibenda; coguntur ergo ut ori vel capiti plagas imponant.

   utuntur etiam decantionibus tibiarum varia modulatione, quarum alteram phrygiam vocant, quae sit iucunda atque ex-
176 citabilis eorum qui ex maestitudine in furore[66] noscuntur; aliam diram vel quae occupata mente pudorem suadeat, iniecto rigore, ut in bello, quam dorion appellant, in his qui risu vel puerilibus cachinnis afficiuntur, cum cantilenae sonus caput impleat, ut etiam recte valentibus apertissime videtur,[66a] vel certe, ut plerique memorant, accendat aliquos in furorem, quo saepe vaticinantes deum accepisse videantur.

   alii vero amorem furentibus aiunt procurandum, quo mentis intentio conversa furoris asperitate purgetur, non intuentes nudissimam veritatem, quod plerisque furoris amor fuerit causa. sic denique alius amore Proserpinae petit[67] inferna, et sibi licitas
177 alienae ac divae coniugis credidit nuptias. alius nymphae ob desiderium Amphitritis sese deditum mari proiecit. ferunt Graecorum commenta loquacia aetheriae prolis[68] feminam humanis exercitatam fatis et saevo poenitudinis dolore commotam sua manu suos extinxisse successus. neque aspernandos ceteros

---

[65] iustitio *Almeloveen*

[66] in furore] furere *Rm*

[66a] videatur *S: corr. R*

[67] petiit *Rm*

[68] et hiereprolis *S: corr. Buecheler Kl. Schriften II. 190*

---

22. I.e., non-Methodist reasoning. Cf. 168.

23. The text and interpretation of this and the next sentence are doubtful; and it is possible that the references were originally to Pluto and Poseidon rather than to case histories of humans who were maddened by their love for goddesses.

matter should be brought downward from the upper parts. But
the use of these measures causes wasting of the body and injury
to the nerves and sinews.

5   Some hold that the patient should be made drunk. But the
fact is that madness and insanity are often the result of drunkenness. Some say he should be flogged, apparently so that he may
regain his sanity by a kind of whipping of his reason. But the
raining of blows upon the inflamed parts will only aggravate
these parts; and, when the attack is over and the patient recovers his senses, he will still be assailed by the pain from these
blows. Indeed, reason[22] would require that such remedies be
applied in particular to the affected parts and those near them;
and so these physicians would have to strike their blows at the
face and head.

    Some recommend that melodies be played on pipes for the
patient, the melodies differing in mode. They say that one mode,
which they call 'Phrygian,' is of pleasant character and serves to
76 arouse those whose insanity is characterized by depression; another mode, called the 'Dorian,' is grave, has a sobering effect
when the mind is impaired, and, as in war, inspires firmness and
strength. The Dorian mode, they say, is for those whose insanity is marked by laughter and childish hilarity. But actually
the sound of music congests the head, as is perfectly clear even
in the case of healthy persons. In fact, it is abundantly attested
that in some cases music arouses men to madness. Thus, as they
chant their prophecies, priests often seem to be possessed by the
god.

    Some physicians hold that love is a proper remedy for in-
sanity, on the ground that it frees the patient's mind from the
agitation caused by madness and thus purifies it. They are not
aware of the obvious truth that in many cases love is the very
cause of madness. Thus one man through love for Proserpina
sought to enter the lower world, thinking he could rightly take
77 to wife a goddess wedded to another.[23] Another threw himself
into the sea because of his longing for the sea nymph Amphi-
trite. In the rich mythology of the Greeks there is a story that a
woman of divine descent, harried by human fates and beset by
the grim pangs of vengeance, killed her offspring with her own
hand.[24] Nor should we disdain the view of those who have actu-

24. Medea, the daughter of Aeëtes. Aeëtes was the son of Helios, the sun-god.

accipiamus, qui ipsum quoque amorem generaliter furorem vocaverunt, ob similitudinem accidentium quibus aegrotantes
afficiuntur. et est impium atque absurdum passioni adiutoriorum [in]⁶⁹ id ipsum probare quod curas. omitto quod sit impossibile amorem furentibus persuadere, siquidem iudicio carentes pulchritudinem probare non possint. nam saepe homines
feras existimant vel ea quae viderint fingendo praesentia putant.
178 dehinc etiamsi amor fuerit acquisitus, quid magis probemus erit
incertum, utrumne prohibendus sit usus venereus an admitten-
dus. sed prohibitus indignari magis cogit aegrotantes cum de-
siderata producuntur; item permissus vexat cum corpore evi-
rato animae quoque substantia turbatur.

   item alii arteriotomian probaverunt, inutili vexatione caput
afficientes.

   his igitur omnibus experimentis inanibus conferta est furio-
sorum curatio. quae ne falsa putentur, erunt denuntiandae per-
sonae atque librorum nomina designanda. Asclepiades autem
secundo libro **⁷⁰ adhibendam praecepit cantilenam; quo etiam
eius discipulus Titus adductus secundo libro De anima memorat
179 flagellandos. sed idem etiam officiis solitis amoveri iubet aegrotantes, et vinculis constringi, et abstinentia ciborum nimia coerceri, et siti affici, tunc vino corrumpi, vel in amorem induci.
cetera primo libro Tardarum passionum supradicta complevit
[item]⁷¹ Themison: phlebotomatos constrictivis⁷² curat fomentis,
qui se sua lege tenere non potuit, adhibens etiam lavacrum atque
vinum plurimum et amorem suadens, adiuncta ciborum copia,
aliis quoque incongruis utens rebus. quae magis Asclepiadi
quam Themisoni sunt adscribenda: nondum enim sese eius li-
beraverat secta ⟨cum⟩⁷³ sic haec ordinasse perspicitur.

---

⁶⁹ *seclusi*   ⁷⁰ *excidisse videtur titulus*

⁷¹ *om. R: post* Themison *interpunx. Kind* (*post* complevit *edd.*), *RE s.v.* 'Soranus'
1127, coll. Chr. Praef. 3

⁷² constrictius *S: corr. Rm*   ⁷³ *add. R*

ally called love a form of insanity because of the similarity of the symptoms which the victims show. And surely it is absurd and wrong to recommend, of all remedies for the disease, the very thing that you are trying to treat; not to mention the fact that it is impossible to get an insane person to fall in love, for, since he is bereft of reason, he cannot properly appreciate beauty. Indeed, those suffering from mania often mistake human beings for wild animals and believe that what they see in their imagination is real. Moreover, even if the patient falls in love, there is considerable doubt as to which course is preferable, to forbid coitus or to permit it. When the patient sees the object of his desire, he will become even madder if venery is forbidden him. On the other hand, if permitted, it will harm him; for it not only deprives the body of strength but also agitates the soul.

Some physicians prescribe the opening of an artery; but this treatment causes injury to the head without any advantage.

And so the treatment of insanity is marked by all these futile and haphazard procedures. Lest this statement be considered erroneous, I shall indicate the physicians in question and name the books in which the treatment is given. Asclepiades in Book II . . . prescribes music; and, under the influence of Asclepiades' account, his pupil Titus, in Book II of his work On the Psyche,[25] holds that flogging should be employed. Titus also prescribes that the patient be taken from his usual pursuits and put in bonds, that he be made to abstain beyond all reason from food and drink, and then enticed by wine and incited to love. The other treatments mentioned[26] are included by Themison in Book I of his work On Chronic Diseases. He uses venesection, then astringent fomentations. He is unable to adhere even to his own principles; he prescribes bathing and a great deal of wine, incites the patient to love, gives him food in abundance, and employs a variety of other harmful procedures. But these procedures should be attributed to Asclepiades rather than to Themison, for clearly when Themison formulated this treatment his sect had not yet freed itself [from the doctrines of Asclepiades].[27]

25. Probably a work on mental diseases.

26. In 171–78.

27. Or perhaps 'he [Themison] had not yet freed himself from the sect [i.e., the doctrines] of Asclepiades.'

180   VI. DE MELANCHOLIA

M ELANCHOLIA dicta quod nigra fella aegrotantibus saepe per
     vomitum veniant: Graeci enim nigrum melan vocaverunt,
fel autem cholen appellant. et non, ut plerique existimant,
quod passionis causa vel generatio nigra sit fella: hoc enim est
aestimantium magis quam videntium veritatem, vel potius falsum, sicut in aliis ostendimus. nam[1] Tullius atram bilem dixit,
veluti altam iracundiam. item Vergilius, Hercule alta iracundia moto, 'hic vero,' inquit, 'Alcidae furiis exarserat atro felle
dolor,' siquidem melancholici semper[2] tristes ac nulla paene hilaritate laxati esse videantur.

181   frequentat autem in masculis magis et mediis aetatibus, difficile vero in feminis vel aliis aetatibus. sed eius antecedentes
causae sunt hae: indigestio, iugis vomitus post cibum, medicamina pota, acres cibi, maestitudo, timor, et cetera quae etiam[3]
valent sufficere.

        sequuntur autem in ipsam pronos vel venturos ea quae etiam
insanos fore denuntiant. eos vero qui iam passione possessi sunt
animi anxietas atque difficultas tenet, attestante maestitudine
cum silentio et odio conviventium. sequitur etiam nunc vi-
vendi nunc moriendi cupido, cum suspicionibus velut insidiarum
182 sibi paratarum; item inanes fletus, atque murmura vacua, et
rursum hilaritas,[4] magis post cibum cum inflatione praecordiorum, et articulorum frigore, et levi sudore, atque stomachi
mordicatione vel oris ventris usque ad interscapulas, quas Graeci
metaphrenum vocaverunt; item capitis gravedo, color viridis
cum nigrore aut sublividus, corporis tenuitas, virium debilitas,
et accepti cibi corruptio cum ructationibus odoris tetri, hoc est
fumosi vel bromosi, vel piscosi; item intestinorum tormenta,
vomitus nunc[5] inanis, nunc fellosus vel ferrugineus aut niger,

---

[1] eam *Rm*

[2] semper ⟨iracundi⟩ *R*   [3] eam *Rm*

[4] *lacunam post* hilaritas *suspicatus est Schmid 84, coll. Escul. 5*

[5] nunc *R*: tunc *S*

VI. MELANCHOLY

MELANCHOLY derives its name from the fact that the patient often vomits black bile, the Greek word for 'black' being *melas* and for 'bile,' *cholē*. The name is not derived, as many believe, from the notion that black bile is the cause or origin of the disease. For such a notion would be put forward only by those who guess at, rather than observe, truth; and it is, in fact, a false notion, as we have shown elsewhere. Thus Cicero speaks of black bile in the sense of profound anger;[1] and when Hercules is stirred to mighty wrath, Virgil says 'and thereupon the wrath of Hercules burned furiously with black bile';[2] for those suffering from melancholy seem always to be downcast and prone to anger and are practically never cheerful and relaxed.

The disease is more frequent among men, especially in middle age; it rarely occurs in women, and is also uncommon in other ages. Its antecedent causes are the following: indigestion, habitual vomiting after eating, the drinking of drugs, acrid food, grief, fear, and other circumstances which are also able to bring about the disease.

The signs of approaching melancholy are the same as those of approaching insanity. The signs of melancholy, when it is actually present, are as follows: mental anguish and distress, dejection, silence, animosity toward members of the household, sometimes a desire to live and at other times a longing for death, suspicion on the part of the patient that a plot is being hatched against him, weeping without reason, meaningless muttering, and, again, occasional joviality; precordial distention, especially after eating, coldness of the limbs, mild sweat, a sharp pain in the esophagus or cardia extending even to the region between the shoulder blades (Greek *metaphrenon*), heaviness of the head, complexion greenish-black or somewhat blue, body attenuated, weakness, indigestion with belching that has a foul, i.e., a fumy, fetid, or fishy odor; intestinal cramps; vomiting, sometimes ineffectual and at other times bringing up yellowish, rusty, or black matter; similar discharges through the anus. In the remis-

1. *Tusc. disp.* iii. 11. Cicero's point is that in the use of the term 'melancholia' there is a connotation that the mind is affected by black bile, not by the emotions of anger, fear, or grief.

2. *Aeneid* viii. 220.

et eiusdem qualitatis per podicem egestio. in lenimento vero eorum mitigatio vel multorum depurgatio.

183   sed hanc passionem furoris speciem alii plurimi atque Themisonis sectatores vocaverunt. differt autem siquidem ⟨in⟩[6] ista principaliter stomachus patiatur, in furiosis vero caput. et est communiter stricturae passio magna, aliquando etiam complexa ob plurimas egestiones. praeterea est ex numero tardarum passionum, quas Graeci chronias appellant.

curatio autem adhibenda est quam furiosis ordinavimus. non enim phlebotomiam probandam[7] attestante dolore, aut hellebori purgationem attestante passione approbamus. sed exterius localia adiutoria atque mitigativa sive[8] corporativa[9] magis ori

184 ventris atque inter scapulas sunt adhibenda. ac si forte aut vomitus immodicus aut egestio ventris coegerit, constrictiva sunt cataplasmata apponenda ventri atque stomacho, ut ex palmulis thebaicis infusis vino vel pusca, admixtis etiam malis punicis vel cydoniis et oenanthe et alumine scisso aut hypocystide vel acacia sive galla et his similibus. dandi etiam cibi constrictivi atque apponendae eius virtutis cucurbitae.

alia vero medicarum sectarum praefectis relinquamus et his qui de furiosis scripserunt. adhibent etiam bibenda medicamina, hoc est aloen et absinthium, iugiter. quae propter vim suam, quam habent plurimam, excludenda probamus, quippe cum sit possibile ex consuetis perficere sanitatem.

[6] *add. R*

[7] probandam *R*: reprobandam *S*: *fort. del.*

[8] *fort.* sed non

[9] *fort.* recorporativa, *sed cf. Ac. iii. 134, Chr. iii. 54*

sion there is an abatement of these symptoms, or at least a clearing-up of most of them.[3]

83   The followers of Themison, as well as many others, consider melancholy a form of the disease of mania. But the two diseases are to be distinguished, for in melancholy the esophagus is chiefly affected, in mania the head. Melancholy is a serious disease, involving essentially a state of stricture; and sometimes a state of looseness is also involved, as the copious evacuations indicate. Moreover, it belongs to the class of slow diseases (Greek *chroniae*).

The same treatment should be administered as we have set forth above for mania. And we do not advise venesection while an attack is in progress, or a purge with hellebore while the disease is active.[4] On the other hand, we do recommend the application of external local remedies, either soothing or metasyncritic,[5] particularly to the region over the cardia and between 84 the shoulder blades. And if excessive vomiting or discharges from the bowels make it necessary, apply astringent plasters to the abdominal and cardiac regions. For these applications, Theban dates soaked in wine or diluted vinegar, with an admixture of pomegranates or quinces, may be employed; also oenanthe, fissile alum, hypocist, acacia, oak gall, and the like. And in these cases give binding foods and apply astringent cupping.

Let us leave other remedies to the leaders of the various medical sects and to those who have written on insanity. They prescribe the continual drinking of drugs, such as aloes and wormwood. But, because of the potency which these drugs possess to a high degree, we hold that they should be rejected, especially since it is possible to effect a cure with the use of customary remedies.

3. *Depurgatio* may here denote that the clearing-up is effected with copious discharges.

4. Or, retaining *reprobandam* (*S*): 'And we do not reject venesection if pain is present, or a purge with hellebore while the disease is present.'

5. The text may be suspected, since soothing and metasyncritic measures are usually opposed to each other in Caelius (e.g., *Ac.* ii. 223; iii. 134).

LIBER SECUNDUS

PRIMO libro Tardarum passionum de capitis diximus curatione, et de scotomaticis, et de incubone, sed et de epilepsia, et de furore sive insania, et de melancholia. nunc ceterarum curationes[1] ordinemus.[2]

I I. DE PARALYSI

IN SENIBUS atque hiemis tempore frequentat haec passio, difficile autem in calidis aetatibus. sed generatur nunc ex occultis, nunc ex manifestis antecedentibus causis, ut quassatione, vulneratione, vel alia qualibet passione, item frigore profundo, vinolentia, indigestione, luxuria, atque libidine frequenti extenta,[1] item medicaminibus potis.

sed est vel fiet paralysis nunc sensus, nunc motus, nunc utriusque. et intelligitur sensus paralysis, quoties fervens atque frigidum non sentiunt aegrotantes, manifesto[2] partium naturalium motu; motus autem, quoties fervens atque frigidum sentiunt,

2 motu partium carentes. utriusque vero paralysin factam accipimus quoties motu atque sensu caruerint. item haec passio nunc partis est, nunc partium, nunc totius corporis, cum apprehensione mentis, quam apoplexiam vocantes, Acutarum passionum libris tradidimus. sed plurimis species duae paralyseos visae sunt, alia conductione effecta, alia extensione.

sequuntur autem pronos et declives in passionem, hoc est qui non repente fuerint percussi, si totum corpus passurum denun-

3 tietur, ea quae epilepsiam vel furorem denuntiant. si vero ex parte, gravedo partis passurae sequetur, ut tardus motus cum stupore et pallore, et torpedo cum sensuum debilitate, quae nunc

---

[1] actiones *S*

[2] *praefatiunculam om. edd. praeter S. cf. Chr. iii. init., Ac. ii. 1, iii. 1, Diaet. pass., p. 206*

[1] *frequenter excitata Rm: an excita?*

[2] *manifeste S: corr. Rm*

BOOK II

I N BOOK I of the work *On Chronic Diseases* we took up the
treatment of chronic headache, dizziness, nightmare, epilepsy, mania or insanity, and melancholy. Let us now take
up the treatment of other diseases.

I. PARALYSIS

P ARALYSIS is most common among old men and occurs most
frequently in winter; it hardly ever occurs in young persons.
It sometimes arises from unobservable antecedent causes, but at
other times from such clearly observable causes as concussion, a
wound, some other disease, extreme cold, excessive drinking of
wine, indigestion, luxurious living, frequent sexual desire, and
the drinking of drugs.

In some cases there is paralysis of the senses, in others of motion, in still others of both. Paralysis of the senses may be recognized when the patient is not sensitive to hot and cold and yet
clearly retains his ability to move the parts normally subject to
motion. Paralysis of motion may be recognized when the patient,
though sensitive to hot and cold, is unable to move parts of his
body. And we may recognize a case of both kinds of paralysis
when the patient is deprived of both sensation and motion.
Again, this disease sometimes affects one part of the body, at
other times more than one part, and at still other times it affects
the whole body and is accompanied by the seizure of the mind,
called 'apoplexy,' which we have described in the work *On Acute
Diseases*. And many hold that there are two kinds of paralysis,
one brought about by contraction, the other by extension.

Those who are on the verge of paralysis of the whole body—
we do not refer to cases where the seizure comes all of a sudden—
show the same symptoms as those who are on the verge of epilepsy or mania. The approach of a partial paralysis, however, is
indicated by a feeling of heaviness in the part in question, a slow-
ing of its motion, dulness, pallor, stiffness, and some loss of sen-

perseverantia, nunc sine ratione recedentia intelliguntur ac rursum recurrentia.

dehinc effecta passione torpor atque stupor gelidus partium fiet plurimus et[3] parvus, et nunc voluntario motu cessante, nunc ex parte manente; et nunc sensu amisso, nunc parvo remanente, nunc etiam dolore attestante; obscurato pulsu et per profectum cessante,[4] pallore et tenuatione partis vitiatae, nutrimento cessante, quod Graeci atrophian vocant; sequente etiam rugatione cum adductione partium vel extensione.

4   aliqui praeterea paralipsin vocaverunt eam quae ex omni parte naturalem motum abstulerit, paralysin eam quae ex plurima parte vitiaverit motum. quibus minime consentire maiorum autoritas iubet: non enim passionum differentiam ostendunt, sed magnitudinem generaliter passionis, ut sunt quaedam partes duobus vel plurimis officiis aptatae, quae nunc omnium, nunc certorum amputatione vexantur. lingua etenim transvorationis officium sustinens, verba distinguere non valebit.

haec sunt communes paralyseos significationes. sed ob singularem[5] partium atque particularum quas supra diximus communiter adprehensionem, specialiter locorum impedimenta tractabimus.

5   supercilium igitur paralysi vitiatum laxius propendebit circa superius palpebrum, vel certe sustollitur, ut etiam ipsum suspendat. item palpebrum superius paralysi vitiatum laxius fiet atque motu caret et oculi pupulam contegit, vel e contrario extentum sustollitur et oculorum pupulam nudat. item inferius[6] palpebrum paralysi vitiatum nunc intrinsecus flectitur, nunc in semet vel exterius refunditur, et motu caret atque oculum non contegit. sequitur etiam involuntarius lacrimarum fluor, quod

---

[3] *fort.* aut *sive* vel

[4] *fort.* attestante (*om. virgula*) *vel seclud.*: cessante ⟨cum⟩ R

[5] singularum *A*

[6] inferius *Rm*: interius *S*

sation; these symptoms are sometimes found to persist and at other times to depart and to recur again apparently without reason.

And then, when paralysis is actually present, there is a cold stiffness and numbness of the parts in greater or lesser degree; the ability to move them voluntarily is in some cases completely lost, while in others it remains present in part; sensation, too, is sometimes completely lost, at other times persists in small measure, and in some cases pain is actually present. The pulse is indistinct and gradually ceases;[1] the affected part becomes pale and thin because of want of nourishment (Greek *atrophia*). And there is a contraction of the affected parts, with consequent wrinkling, or else an extension of the parts.

4   Now some give the name 'paraleipsis' to that condition which involves complete loss of normal motion, and 'paralysis' to that which involves loss of a considerable part of normal motion. But there is nothing in the old writers which lends support to this terminology. And, in fact, the two conditions described do not actually differ in kind but only in degree. That is, if a certain part is capable of two or more functions, in the one case it loses all its functions and in the other only some of them. As an example [of this latter case], the tongue may continue to perform its function in swallowing but may be unable to articulate words distinctly.

So much for the general signs of paralysis. But as an aid toward its special recognition in the various parts of the body, large and small, which are included in our general description, we shall now deal with the disabilities caused by paralysis in specific parts.

5   To begin with, an eyebrow when paralyzed either hangs down loosely over the upper eyelid, or else is so lifted that it also keeps the eyelid raised. Again, when an upper eyelid is paralyzed, it is either relaxed, losing its mobility and covering the pupil of the eye, or, on the contrary, it becomes tense and is raised, completely exposing the pupil. And when a lower eyelid is paralyzed, it is sometimes bent inward, but at other times it is bent outward over itself, losing its mobility and no longer covering the eye. Also an involuntary flow of tears is found in connection with

1. With the bracketing of *cessante* the meaning is: 'The pulse is indistinct; and the affected part gradually becomes pale and thin.' But cf. Esc., p. 34C (ed. 1544).

est utrique palpebrorum vitio commune. et si in risum venerint
6 aegrotantes contortum vel conductum simulant vultum. oculorum vero tunicae sive membrana paralysi vitiata[7] visum im-
pediunt latitudine facta pupularum, quae passio vocatur mydriasis. ac si conductione fuerit paralysis facta, angustior pu-
pula fiet, cessante nutrimento, ⟨et⟩[8] appellatur phthisis.

lingua paralysi vitiata vocem non disserit, sed interius movetur, et nunc nullius significationis vocem reddit, nunc amputatione facta; medio tempore oppressis conatibus conticescit, demonstrata tamen verbi intelligibili prolatione nunc imperfecta,
nunc ex omni parte motu carens. sed discernantur[9] ab ista passione qui forte ex alia vocem amiserint, cum neque colorem vel
7 superficiem lingua mutaverit, neque sensu caruerit neque motu,
neque schema suae mutaverit positionis: quod fieri necesse est
cum fuerit paralysi vitiata.

item odoramenti officium paralysi vitiatum odorum non accipit sensum. sed discernitur ab his qui narium vitio officium
odoris amiserunt, quod appellant ozaenan, quod neque torpor
partium neque pallor neque nutrimenti desertio sequatur, quam
Graeci atrophian vocant.

labium superius paralysi vitiatum invertitur forinsecus, pro-
ditum magis cum risus advenerit aut locutio, conducitur enim
sano cum inferiori. item poto sumpto exterius facit fluere
8 liquorem. hoc quidam caninum raptum esse dixerunt, nescii,
sicut principaliter futuro docebimus lemmate.[10]

item siagon paralysi vitiatus, sic quidem[11] nos musculum qui
buccas colligat dicere poterimus, conducitur aut laxatur. vicinus denique oculus non valebit perfectam facere reclusionem
conducto inferiore palpebro. mentum paralysi vitiatum amisso
motu laxatur aut vehementer sustollitur. fauces paralysi vitiatae transvorationis difficultatem faciunt. gutturis summitas
paralysi vitiata, sive ut ⟨nos⟩ ruma[12] sive ut Graeci bronchos,
moram facit transvorationis et parvam tussiculam,[13] siquidem
non perfectam eo tempore faciat inductionem [ne] super[14] radicem linguae, quam Graeci epiglottida vocant, quo profecto[15] ac-

---

[7] membranae p. vitiatae *Rm*

[8] ⟨et⟩ *supplevi*: ⟨quae passio⟩ *R* (*ut supra*)

[9] discernuntur *Rm*

[10] lemmate *scripsi*: schemate *edd.*

[11] vitiatum siquidem *S*: corr. *Rm*

[12] ⟨nos⟩ ruma *Friedel 31, n. 3*: reuma *S*

[13] mortem facit et (fortem facit aut *Rm*) parvam transvorationis tussiculam *S*: corr.
Bendz 97

[14] ne superet *edd.*

[15] perfecto *edd.*: *fort. del.*

both types of paralysis of the eyelids; and if the patient laughs,
6 his whole face appears to be twisted and contorted. When the
coats or membranes of the eye are paralyzed, the vision is impaired by a dilatation of the pupil, an affection called 'mydriasis.' And if the paralysis is effected by contraction, the pupil becomes narrower with the loss of its nourishment. This disease is
called 'phthisis.'

The tongue when paralyzed cannot articulate words clearly,
but at first moves within the mouth, sometimes uttering sounds
devoid of meaning and at other times unable to make any sound.
After a while, baffled in its attempts, it becomes still. Sometimes,
however, it does succeed in pronouncing a word intelligibly,
albeit imperfectly, but at other times it suffers complete loss of
motion. Paralysis of the tongue may be distinguished from cases
of loss of speech resulting from some other disease. For in these
latter cases the tongue does not change color or the condition of
7 its surface, or lose sensation or mobility, or change position; but
these things always happen when the tongue is paralyzed.

When the organ of smell is paralyzed, it no longer can detect
odors. But this paralysis is to be distinguished from cases of loss
of the power of smell resulting from the disease of the nostrils,
called 'ozaena.' For in the latter there is neither stiffness of the
parts, nor pallor, nor loss of nourishment (Greek *atrophia*).

The upper lip when paralyzed is turned outward and pro-
trudes most when the patient laughs or talks; for it is then contracted together with the sound lower lip. And it causes what
8 the patient drinks to flow out. Some have identified this condition with cynic spasm, but they are in error, as we shall show in
a section specially devoted to this disease.[2]

When the *siagon* (for so we may indicate the muscle which
controls the jaws) is paralyzed, it is either contracted or relaxed. Thus the eye near by will be unable to close completely
because of the pull upon the lower lid. Again, a paralyzed chin
loses its mobility and is either relaxed or sharply lifted. Paralysis of the fauces causes difficulty in swallowing. Paralysis of the
upper part of the windpipe (Latin *ruma*, Greek *bronchos*) makes
swallowing difficult and causes a slight cough. For then there is
not a perfect fit between that part [i.e., the larynx] and the
[organ at the] base of the tongue (Greek *epiglōttis*) at the time

2. *Chr.* ii. 63.

cepta transvorantur.[16] videbitur denique eius extantia plurimum relaxata.

item stomachum paralysi vitiatum difficultas transvorandi
sequetur, vel omnino impossibilitas, unde etiam praesens peri-
9 culum. videbuntur etiam difficilia transvorantibus accepta, veluti acriora aut immaturo tempore comesta. item sequitur
praefocationis sensus cum frigore in quacumque eius parte fuerit
paralysis; illic namque etiam transvorata sistuntur. sed discernuntur ab his qui faucium[17] paralysin ex difficultate transvorandi patiuntur, siquidem etiam decolorationes nutrimento cessante ac frigus, etiam immobilitas faucium necessario concurrat.
item his qui ex stomachi tumore supradictis querelis [si] fuerint
10 adfecti,[18] discernuntur quod etiam dolore atque fervore partium
vexantur.

sic[19] coenum vel eius summitas paralysi vitiatum, quod nos
commune dicere poterimus, quod arteriae atque stomacho inter-
positum videatur, locorum gravedinem faciet, atque sumpti cibi
vel potus[20] in praecordiis permanebunt, cum torpore sensuum ac
tumore manuum, aliquando et crurum, attestante singultu et
inani timore.[21] aliqui etiam revomunt accepta nulla corruptione mutata.

pyloro[22] paralysi vitiato cibus nulla digestione mutatur, sed
tamquam per infundibulum ad inferiora descendit, et circum
11 ventrem laxior locus efficitur inferius inflatiorque; quae per ventrem egeruntur aspera atque plurima erunt et neque fluida.

nestide paralysi vitiato[23] et typhlo entero,[24] quod nos caecum
intestinum dicere poterimus, erunt ea quae per ventrem excluduntur plurima et minus fluida. videntur enim nesteuin cum
naturam servaverint vel nullo fuerint[25] morbo tentata, tunc
plurimum excrementorum acceptorum[26] facere.

[16] convivantur *edd.*

[17] faucium *scripsi*: facilem *S*

[18] qui ex stomachi tumore supra dictis querelis fuerint adfecti *coni. Schmid RPh 152*:
qui ex stomacho sunt humores supradictis querelis si fuerint adfecti *S*

[19] si *edd.*

[20] sumpto cibo vel potu *S*: *corr. Rm*

[21] tumore *Rm*

[22] perulo *S*: *corr. Rm*

[23] vitiata *Rm*

[24] typhlotero *S*: *corr. Rm (sed cf. Chr. iv. 86)*

[25] fuerit *S*: *corr. A*   [26] *fort.* ⟨ex⟩ acceptis *(cf. Am)*

when food is swallowed. And its projection[3] will be found to be quite relaxed.

When the esophagus is paralyzed, the patient finds swallowing difficult or completely impossible. In this case there is immediate danger. When the patient does swallow, he finds it hard to manage his food, as if it is acrid or has been eaten prematurely. And there is a sensation of choking and cold in that part of the esophagus which is paralyzed; for it is there that the swallowed food is impeded in its course. But these cases are to be distinguished from cases of paralysis of the fauces, which involve difficulty in swallowing. For in these latter cases changes of color resulting from want of nourishment always occur, as well as coldness and immobility of the fauces. Again, in inflammation of the esophagus the patient shows some of the same symptoms as in paralysis of the esophagus. But cases of inflammation may be distinguished because the patient feels pain and heat in the parts in question.

Paralysis of the *coenon* (Latin *commune*) or its apex, situated between the windpipe and the esophagus, causes a feeling of heaviness in these parts. Food or drink when swallowed remains on the chest; the senses are numbed, the arms and sometimes the legs are swollen; there are hiccoughs and an irrational sense of fear. In some cases the patient vomits back unaltered what he has swallowed.

If the pylorus is paralyzed, the food undergoes no digestive change[4] but passes downward as if through a funnel. The region just below the stomach becomes more relaxed and dilated; and the evacuations through the bowels are rough, copious, and not fluid.

If the jejunum [*nēstis*] and the 'blind intestine,' which we may in Latin call *caecum*, are paralyzed, the evacuations through the bowels are copious and not very fluid. For, though these parts seem to be empty [*nēsteuein*] when they are normal and unaffected by any disease, yet when paralyzed they seem to convert that which is passed through them into copious excrement.[5]

3. Perhaps the projection of the larynx, the Adam's apple, is meant. But the interpretation of this and the preceding sentences is doubtful in view of the uncertainty of the text.

4. I.e., in the stomach.

5. The text and meaning are doubtful.

colo paralysi vitiato, inordinato motu atque involuntario ster-
corea[27] descendunt sine ulla humectatione, et cum foetore maxi-
mo eorum fiet egestio, sine ullo dolore.

longanone cum sphinctere atque podice paralysi vitiato, erit
involuntaria egestio stercorum nisi ex aliqua hoc fuerit circumin-
12 cisione confectum. aliquando etiam praecedit, vel certe egestionem stercorum non[28] sine tumore vel aliqua simili causa fieri
permittit.

vesica paralysi vitiata involuntarius urinae exitus fiet sine ullo
dolore, neque incisura neque circumincisione antecedente; aliquando etiam per intervalla prohibitus vel paulatim retardatus
aut omnino negatus. et saepe etiam pubetenus extantia partium fiet extenta vesica. sed ⟨si⟩[29] ex tumore vel sanguinis gelati corpusculis, quae Graeci trombos appellant, aut lapide vel
vulnere difficultas fuerit mictus, aut in toto negatio, discernitur
quod sine dolore atque partium livore atque sanguinis mictu apposita manu oppresso[30] pectine urina in paralysi excludatur.
13 praeterea etiam peritoneo paralysi vitiato, ut Erasistratus ait,
urina abstinetur et neque excluditur nisi adhibito catheteri.
non enim vesicae ambitus naturali consuetudine peritoneo im-
buente[31] opprimitur, neque concluditur ad exprimendum liquorem.

radius[32] virilis paralysi vitiatus multo maior aut minor efficitur, et nulla tentigine provocatur. seminales viae, quas Graeci
spermaticos poros vocant, paralysi vitiatae, si laxatione fuerit
paralysis effecta, sine ulla tentigine involuntarius fiet seminis
lapsus, et vocatur haec passio gonorrhoea, quam nos seminis lap-
14 sum dicimus. ac si conclusione[33] fuerit paralysis effecta, iugis
tentigo aegrotantis sequetur, sine ullo dolore atque seminis lapsu, et vocatur haec passio priapismus.

crus paralysi vitiatum aut conductione[34] brevius fiet aut extentione longius, ut plerique putent articulorum delocationem

---

[27] stercora *R*   [30] oppressa *S*

[28] non *om. R*   [31] incumbente *Rm, fort. recte*

[29] *add. Rm*   [32] radix *edd.: corr. Reinesius 662 (cf. Ac. iii. 15)*

[33] conductione *Rm, coll. Chr. ii. 2. sed cf. Ac. iii. 64, Chr. ii. 44, 53, 56, 63, iii. 105.*
nota conluctione *(S) infra, et adn. marg. ad 25*

[34] conluctione *S: corr. Rm*

---

6. The reference may be to suppressed bowel function after an anal operation.
Perhaps the next sentence means: 'Sometimes such an operation precedes [the paralysis]
and does not permit, etc.'

When the colon is paralyzed, the fecal matter descends through it and is evacuated with irregular and involuntary motion. The feces are devoid of moisture but possess a strong and offensive odor; they are passed without any pain.

If the rectum, sphincter, and anus are paralyzed, the evacuation of the feces will be involuntary unless the condition is due 12 to some excision.[6] And sometimes the paralysis prevents evacuation, or at any rate does not permit it to take place without inflammation or some other such condition.

If the bladder is paralyzed, urine is discharged involuntarily and without any pain, in the absence of a previous operation of incision or excision. Sometimes, however, the discharge of urine is impeded at intervals, being retarded somewhat or entirely suppressed; and often the resulting distention of the bladder causes a distention of the hypogastric region. But these cases may be distinguished from cases in which the discharge of urine is partially or completely suppressed by reason of an inflammation, bits of clotted blood (Greek *thromboe*), a stone, or a wound. For in paralysis the urine may be expelled merely by applying manual pressure to the pubes, and the discharge then takes place without pain, without the parts turning blue, and 13 without the passage of blood. And when the peritoneum is paralyzed, the urine is suppressed, as Erasistratus tells us, and the use of a catheter is necessary for its removal. For then the curved surface of the bladder is no longer confined, as it is normally, by pressure from the peritoneum and does not contract to expel its fluid.

The penis, when paralyzed, becomes much larger or smaller than normal but cannot be erected. If the seminal ducts (Greek *poroe spermaticoe*) are paralyzed and the paralysis involves a relaxing, there is an involuntary discharge of semen without any erection. The Greeks call this disease *gonorrhoea;* we call it *semi-* 14 *nis lapsus* ['flow of semen']. But if the paralysis of these ducts takes the form of tension, the patient will experience prolonged erection without any pain or seminal discharge. This condition is called 'priapism.'

If a leg is paralyzed, it becomes either shorter by contraction or longer by extension, so that this condition is often mistaken for a dislocation at the joints. But the cases may be dis-

hic factam. sed discernitur hoc, siquidem concavitas atque distantia[35] loco motos aut eiectos articulos sequatur.

est autem ratione credibile ceterorum quoque interiorum singula paralysi vitiari, ut pulmonem, cor, vel discrimen thoracis
atque ventris, quod Graeci diaphragma vocant, aut hypozygon[36]
vel splenem aut iecur: praeveniri adprehensionem morte[37] patientis. quae saepe latent facta, cum non propria possint appre-
15 hensione signari. Herophilus denique repentinam mortem nulla
ex manifesta causa venientem fieri inquit paralysi cordis. item
Erasistratus memorat paralyseos genus, et paradoxon appellavit, quo ambulantes repente sistuntur ut ambulare non possint,
tunc rursum ambulare sinuntur.

est autem passio generaliter gravis atque difficilis, sed gravior
curatione fiet quoties toto sensu caruerint partes atque motu,
et in corporibus iamdudum debilibus vel senibus aut ex alio morbo praevitiatis, ut epilepsia, febre; item si plurimas tenuerit corporis partes vel vitae[38] necessarias.

16 de nominibus autem specialiter elogiatis paralyticae passionis,
ut mydriasi, phthisi, priapismo, gonorrhoea, et his similibus,
singula praescribemus:[39] de ceteris nunc dicemus. hanc ergo passionem multi sectae nostrae principes stricturam dixerunt ob
duritiam vitiatarum partium atque siccitatem et gravedinem et
torporem. Mnaseas vero conductione factam paralipsin vocat,
fierique etiam aliquando extentione, aliquando solutione. nos
vero iuxta Sorani sententiam illam vocamus solutionem cum
17 plurimae egestiones corporis fuerint visae. etenim manuum vel
pedum et horum similium extentione facta, nulla egestione attestante, et in ligni similitudinem duratis partibus, stricturae
dicimus esse passionem, quippe cum frigescere[40] vel quadam rugatione crispari corpora commune contrariis passionibus esse
videatur. est tamen passio generaliter tarda, et accessionibus
atque dimissionibus variata, et superpositionibus ac lenimentis.

35 distanti a *S*: corr. *A*
36 *fort.* hypezocota
37 adprehensione mortem *S*: corr. *Schmid RPh 49*
38 vitiatae *S*: corr. *Rm*
39 *fort.* praescripsimus   40 *fort.* rigescere *vel* rugescere

7. Or, if *praescripsimus* be read: 'We have already spoken of the various terms used
to describe specific kinds of paralysis, e.g., mydriasis, etc.'

tinguished; for, when the leg is dislocated or slips out of joint, a hollow part or gap is left.

It is reasonable to suppose that each of the other internal organs may also be paralyzed, e.g., the lung, the heart, the membrane separating the thorax from the abdomen (Greek *diaphragma*), the pleura, the spleen, and the liver. But the death of the patient prevents us from recognizing the paralysis. And these conditions often escape notice because there are no spe-
15 cific indications by which we may recognize them. Thus Herophilus tells us that, when death comes suddenly without any apparent cause, it is the result of paralysis of the heart. Erasistratus terms *paradoxos* ['strange, paradoxical'] a type of paralysis in which a person walking along must suddenly stop and cannot go on, but after a while can walk again.

By its nature, paralysis is a serious disease and hard to cure; but it is even more difficult to treat if the paralyzed parts are completely devoid of sensation and mobility, if the patient is old, or has been weak for some time, or has previously suffered an attack of some other disease, such as epilepsy or fever, and if the paralysis affects many parts of the body or parts essential to life.

16 We shall deal later with each of the specially denominated forms of paralysis, e.g., mydriasis, phthisis, priapism, gonorrhea, and the like.[7] We shall now consider other aspects of the disease. Thus many leading physicians of our own sect say that paralysis is a state of stricture because the affected parts are stiff, dry, heavy, and numb. Mnaseas, however, calls paralysis produced by contraction 'paraleipsis' and holds that paralysis sometimes involves a tightening and at other times a loosening. But we, following the views of Soranus, consider paralysis a state of looseness whenever copious discharges from the body are
17 visible. If, however, the paralysis causes such parts as the hands or feet to be stretched out and to become as stiff and hard as wood and there is no accompanying discharge of fluid, we then consider the disease to be one of stricture. For the fact that [paralyzed] bodies become cold or else wrinkled and curled indicates that paralysis belongs to contrary types of disease.[8] But, in general, it is a chronic disease marked by attacks, remissions, active phases, and periods of quiescence. Having given an ac-

8. I.e., manifests itself sometimes in *strictura* and at other times in *solutio*.

cuius praedata atque demonstrata significatione necessario curationem ordinamus.

mox igitur effecta paralysi, lucido loco atque mediocriter calido locandi sunt aegrotantes, et usque ad tertiam diem permittentibus viribus abstinendi. tunc nisi vino fuerint pleni vel cibo,
18 mox phlebotomandi: si copia fuerit, ex brachio; sin minus, ex
qualibet patienti parte contraria, quo laquei constrictione et
phlebotomi divisura in passione constitutae[41] non afficiantur. si
autem pleni fuerint cibo, alia die erunt phlebotomandi. sed
partes paralysi vitiatae fricatione atque calefactionibus recu-
randae, et lana limpida ex oleo dulci atque calido expressa[42] et[43]
circumtegendae et fomento relaxandae. tunc oris collutio permittenda, atque potu aquae calidae erunt providendi. praeterea
accessionum ac dimissionum diligentius tempora observanda,
quae adprehenduntur ex aegrotantium pallore, nunc aucto nunc
19 minuto; vel sensu earundem partium qui[43a] plus aut minus inesse
videatur; item ex motu vel immobilitate, aut gravedine et levi-
tate, aut frigore et fervore.

tunc diatriti tempore adhibenda perunctio ex oleo calido; ora
quoque fovenda ex aqua mediocriter calida; et dandus cibus parvus sorbilis, ut alica lota ex aqua calida infusa aut ova. ac si
transvorationis ⟨vel⟩[44] faucium partes paralysi fuerint vitiatae,
erunt cucurbitae obliquis partibus gutturis atque cervicis apponendae. tunc cibus offerendus, etenim extentae transvorationis officio facile servire coguntur. exinde donec passio declinet alternis diebus dabimus cibum. sequenti denique die post
diatritum, abstento aegro cataplasmatibus utemur ex polline lini
20 seminis et faenigraeci. tunc alia die nisi passio creverit patientibus locis cucurbitas infigentes scarificabimus. ac si plurimae
fuerint partes passione vitiatae, cogentibus magis atque urgen-
tibus ordine praeponimus curationem, vel his locis quae facile
poterunt aegrotos in periculum devocare, aut ex quibus ceteris

---

[41] constituti S: corr. Rm

[42] lanae limpidae ex oleo dulci atque calido expressae S: corr. Rm

[43] et om. R

[43a] quibus S: corr. R

[44] ⟨vel⟩ addidi: ⟨et⟩ R: fort. fauces ⟨vel⟩ transvorationis partes (cf. 21)

count of the disease and set forth its signs, we must now describe its treatment.

As soon, then, as paralysis has developed, place the patient in a light and moderately warm room, and, if his strength permits, allow him no food until the end of the third day. Then, unless he has considerable wine or food in him, perform vene-
18 section without further delay; if possible, withdraw the blood at the arm, otherwise at some other point on the side opposite the paralyzed part, to prevent the latter from being injured by the tying of the knot and the incision made by the lancet. But if the patient is still replete with food, postpone venesection until the next day. In any case, however, massage the paralyzed parts and apply warmth, cover them completely with scoured wool wrung out of warm sweet olive oil, and relax them with fomentations. Then allow the patient to wash his mouth and to drink some warm water. In addition, watch carefully for the times of attack and of remission. These may be recognized from the patient's pallor, which increases in the one phase and decreases in the other; and from the degree of sensation in these parts,
19 which is also smaller and larger in the successive phases; and from the mobility or immobility, heaviness or lightness, and coldness or warmth of the parts.

At the end of the three-day period anoint the patient with warm olive oil; also apply fomentations of moderately hot water to the face. And give him a small amount of gruel-like food, such as spelt groats soaked in warm water, and eggs. If the fauces or the other parts used in swallowing are paralyzed, apply cupping instruments to the sides of the throat and the neck; and then give the patient his food. For when these parts are stretched out, they can easily be made to aid the process of swallowing. Thereafter, until the disease declines, feed the patient on alternate days. Now on the day after the end of the three-day period,[9] having withheld food from the patient, employ poultices of flour
20 made from flaxseed and fenugreek seed. Then on the following day, if the disease has not grown more severe, apply cupping instruments to the affected parts and scarify these parts. And if many parts are paralyzed, apply this treatment first to those parts where it is most needed and urgent, that is, to those places where paralysis can endanger the patient's life, or to those from

9. Presumably the first such period, but the reference may be to successive periods.

partibus facile possit curationis beneficium dari. sic denique
stomacho laxato plurima certe conlaxantur, utpote[45] e contrario
oppressis principalibus partibus ceterae necessario comprimuntur.

tunc ceteris trinis diebus, quas diatriton Graeci vocaverunt,
21 alias quoque partes cucurbita relevamus. si siagon vel mentum
paralysi fuerit vitiatum, erunt cucurbitae temporibus infigendae
atque musculis buccarum vel sub aurium lamnis. ac si fauces
fuerint vitiatae vel transvorationis partes, praedictis utemur
adiutoriis. item manibus paralysi vitiatis erunt humeris vel
eorum summitatibus atque palis et brachiorum musculis aut cubitorum nodis haec adhibenda. item cruribus paralysi vitiatis
vertebris atque genibus cucurbitae infigendae.

quarum quae partes non accipiunt usum, ut supercilia, labia,
22 digiti, sanguisugis erunt relevandae. item si nimiae tenuitatis
causa aut usus difficultate neque sanguisugarum morsum tolerare potuerint, ut in palpebris vel lingua, praefecta vaporatione scarificamus et generaliter cataplasmatibus utimur. tunc
si exegerit passio, secundo scarificamus et spongiarum vaporatione utemur ex aqua et oleo solo expressis[46] vel ex oleo et[47] decoctione lini seminis atque faenigraeci vel hibisci aut malvae
communis vel agrestis. his vero qui secundum linguam vel
transvorationis partes paralysi fuerint vitiati, tempore cataplasmatum atque vaporationum iubemus in os dari oleum calidum vel aquam calidam et oleum continendum, aut mulsum.
simul enim atque eodem tempore ex utraque parte vaporata ve-
23 hementius relaxantur. si venter fuerit retentus, clystere utemur
prius quam partes cucurbita relevamus, et[48] primo ex aqua mulsa; tunc si oportuerit, etiam diurnis diebus ex oleo calido iniectiones adhibemus.

si intestina vel eorum vicinitas paralysi fuerint vitiata, ac si
etiam urina fuerit retenta, adhibitis ceteris adiutoriis atque perfectis, encathismata sunt adhibenda. tunc catheterismus faciendus quo urina detrahatur, ac post detractionem oleum calidum iniciendum atque[49] adnexo folliculo catheteri[50] ex ea parte
quae cystophilos a Graecis est appellata, vel otico clystere, quem

---

[45] fort. utque Bendz 48   [47] et R: aut S   [49] atque om. R

[46] fort. expressarum   [48] et R: ut S   [50] catathere S: corr. Rm

which the benefits of the treatment can readily spread to other
parts. Thus, for example, the relaxing of the esophagus is clearly
accompanied by the relaxing of many other parts, too; just as,
in a contrary situation, when vital parts are paralyzed, other
parts are necessarily affected along with them.

Thereafter at the end of subsequent three-day periods (Greek
21 *diatritoe*), employ cupping to relieve the other parts, too. In
paralysis of the jaw or chin apply cupping to the temples, the
muscles of the jaws, or under the flaps of the ears. In paralysis of
the fauces or of the other parts used in swallowing, employ the
remedies just described. In paralysis of the hands these remedies
should also be applied to the upper arms, shoulders, and shoulder
blades, and to the muscles of the upper arms or to the elbow
joints. And in paralysis of the legs apply the cupping instruments to the hip joints and the knees.

Those parts to which cupping instruments cannot be applied,
e.g., eyebrows, lips, and fingers, should be relieved by the use of
22 leeches. But if, by reason of tenderness or difficulty of application, certain parts, such as eyelids or tongue, cannot be subjected to the bite of leeches, apply heat to these parts, scarify
them, and employ poultices generally. Then if the disease requires it, make use of scarification for a second time, and apply
heat with sponges wrung out merely of water and olive oil, or of
olive oil and a decoction of flaxseed and fenugreek seed, or marsh
mallow, i.e., the common or wild mallow. In cases of paralysis of
the tongue or parts used in swallowing, at the time when the
poultices and warm applications are being employed, have the
patient take into his mouth and hold there warm olive oil, or
warm water and olive oil, or mead. For parts that are warmed at
one and the same time from both inside and outside can be more
23 effectively relaxed. If the bowels do not function, inject a clyster
before using cupping instruments for the relief of the parts in
question. The clyster should in the first instance consist of hydromel; afterward clysters of warm olive oil may be injected,
even daily if necessary.

If the intestines or parts near by are paralyzed and if urination
is also suppressed, prescribe sitz baths after completing the application of the other remedies. Then insert a catheter to withdraw the urine. After this withdrawal, attach a small bulb to
that end of the catheter which the Greeks call *cystophilos*, and

nos auricularem dicere poterimus, tenui ex aulisco[51] formatum,
24 quo possit cavernam invadere directum cathetere. tunc cucurbitas praedictis adhibemus locis, atque vaporationibus et cataplasmatibus eas partes cum podice et veretris[52] vicinis relevamus.

si stomachus fuerit paralysi vitiatus, omnia sorbilia dabimus
quo facilius transvorentur. ac si ea quae sumuntur aliqua ex
parte substiterint impedito meatu, aegrotantium manus in
aquam calidam mittemus, vel parva vascula aqua calida plena
tenenda offeremus. tunc stomacho levem cucurbitam infigemus
sub ea parte quae premi vel impediri videtur; atque ita sensim
vel paulatim eam detrahimus, quo stomachi partes deferendo
25 accipere vel transire faciamus illata, vel vacuum officium in memoriam reducamus.

ac si vomitus irruerit paralysi facta, nihil dentibus interpo-
namus; si vero conductio,[53] immittimus ceram vel tabellam tiliarem[54] aut feruleam, et ductu contrario fasciolae corrigere tentabimus depravata, declinante passione. etenim ante id tempus
difficiles in consensu partes esse perspiciuntur, et propterea quassatio potius quam effectus sequitur.

utemur praeterea eodem tempore etiam cerotariis qualibet
⟨parte⟩[55] paralysi vitiata, et primo simplicibus, ut ex cera et oleo
pingui vel sabino[56] et squinanto, admixta hibisci decoctione vel
faenigraeci semine contuso atque trito,[56a] tunc ex oleo veteri et
26 resina terebinthina. adhibemus etiam embasin ex oleo calido,
tunc calida et oleo,[57] cibum dantes diurnis diebus ex oleribus non
acrioribus atque piscibus petrensibus et volantum parvioribus.
utemur etiam acopis, ut est diasamsucu[58] et diamelilotu,[59] vel
omnibus quae ex adipibus conficiuntur et medullis, et irino oleo
vel malabatrino et cyprino[60] et his similibus, et malagmatibus
talibus, ex quibus est diachylon atque Mnaseu[61] et diamelilotu[62]
et melinum[63] simplex.

[51] ex aulisco *Reinesius 663 (cf. Ac. iii. 29)*: exabilisco *S*   [52] veretro *Rm*   [53] conclusio
Sm (cf. 14)   [54] tiliarem *conieci, coll. Chr. ii. 42, v. 20*: alearem *edd.*   [55] add. *Rm*
[56] sabina *S: corr. Rm*   [56a] *fort.* creto   [57] calida et oleo *Rm*: calidam et oleum *S*
[58] diasamsucū *S*   [59] diamelilotū *S*   [60] cyprino *Schmid 56*: quirino *S*
[61] mnaseum *S*   [62] diamelilotū *S*   [63] meline *S: corr. A*

inject warm olive oil; we may use for this purpose an ear syringe (Greek *ōticos*, which we may translate *auricularis* in Latin), consisting of a thin pipette which will enter the opening, guided by
24 the catheter. Then apply cupping instruments to the parts in question and also ease these parts as well as the anus and the near-by genitals with applications of heat and poultices.

In cases of paralysis of the esophagus give only gruel-like foods, to facilitate swallowing. But if any of this food becomes stuck and its movement is blocked, place the patient's hands in hot water or give him small vessels filled with hot water to hold. Then apply a cupping instrument of gentle action over the esophagus just below the place where the pressure or stoppage seems to be; and slowly and gradually lower the position of the cup so that the parts of the esophagus may again receive and pass on the food that is swallowed and that the food may thus
25 proceed through these parts. That is, the purpose is to restore the functioning of the esophagus, which had been interrupted.

If vomiting occurs in a case of paralysis, nothing need be placed between the teeth; but if there is convulsion, place some wax or a thin tablet of linden wood between the teeth, or use fennel for this purpose. And try to remedy the displaced parts by counterpressure with a small bandage. But do not use this latter procedure until the disease declines; for before that time parts sympathetically affected are found to be hard to deal with, and for that reason they are more apt to be injured than successfully treated.

And when the disease declines, cerates may also be applied in paralysis of any part. The cerates should in the first instance be simple, such as those made of wax and a thick oil, such as Sabine oil, and flowers of rush, with the addition of a decoction of marsh mallow or fenugreek seed pounded and rubbed down; afterward the cerate may be made with old olive oil and resin of the tere-
26 binth tree. Also prescribe a bath of warm olive oil, then of warm water and olive oil. And give the patient food each day, choosing vegetables which are not acrid, rockfish, and the smaller birds. Also employ restorative ointments, e.g., that made with marjoram, that made with melilot, all those made with fat, marrow, and oil of iris, malabathrum, henna, or the like, as well as similar emollient plasters, e.g., the plaster of juices, Mnaseas' plaster, the melilot plaster, and the simple quince plaster.

tunc gestatione corpus movebimus pro virium modo, fertoria
sella sive cathedra longiore, tunc vehiculo manibus acto, dehinc
27 animalibus. sic enim consensu persuasae altiores in corpore materiae ad exteriora concurrunt, cum in embasi ex oleo fuerint
constitutae, motus beneficio praelaxato aegrotante. dehinc
lavacrum adhibemus atque vinum parvum. et consequenter
singula quae passione fuerint vitiata suo officio exercemus, ex-
plorantes etiam vel intuentes si quid aliud in corpore passionis
occurrerit, ex quo paralysis videtur effecta, ut hoc quoque de-
struamus, non hoc[64] quidem quod antecedens causa esse videatur, sed quo etiam eam ipsam passionem necessario intelligamus.

quapropter si vulneratio ei fuerit congrua, gerere debemus sicut in chirurgumenis vel[65] Responsionum libris demonstravimus:
28 reminiscentes si quidem ex vulneribus facta paralysis sive[66] divisura partium necdum[67] proprio nomine vocabulum teneat, sed
appellari claudicationes[68] vel tardationes possunt[69] sive alienationes. sin vero cicatrix fuerit clausa, hanc mollire tentabimus.
item si spinae contortio vel conversio ex causa[70] effecta, hanc
corrigemus. item si febricula aut nimia capitis passio, quam
cephalaean vocant, aut epilepsia,[71] ex iisdem eas quoque destrue-
mus. item si eversio vel inclinatio fuerit matricis, eidem consequenter ordinata adhibemus, sicut Muliebrium passionum libris
docuimus. sin vero articuli fuerit eiectio, quamquam longi tem-
29 poris, eum relocamus.[72] item si quis humoris fluor per quodlibet
officium naturale ultra modum fuerit dimissus, cataplasmata
constrictiva probamus, ut ex palmulis thebaicis, malis cydoniis,[73]
acacia, hypocistide, alumine, et his similibus, apponentes etiam
emplastrorum ea quae constrictivae virtutis a Graecis enaema
appellata,[74] vel si qua valent concludere atque siccare fluentia,
ut sunt vulnerum medicamina quae appellantur melana.

[64] hoc *scripsi*: hac *S*: ⟨ob⟩ hoc *Rm*

[65] vel *fort. secl.*

[66] sive *scripsi*: sit *S*: sit ⟨ac⟩ *R*: sit ⟨an⟩ *A*: sit ⟨sive⟩ *Friedel 38, n. 2*

[67] ⟨quod⟩ necdum *R*

[68] claudicatio vel tardatio p. s. alienatio *R*

[69] possit *Rm*: possint *Friedel 38*

[70] ⟨aliqua⟩ causa *R*

[71] epilepsian *S*: *corr. R*

[72] relocamus *Rm*: recolamus *S*

[73] citoniis *S*   [74] appellata ⟨sunt⟩ *R*

Passive exercise may then be prescribed in keeping with the patient's strength. For this purpose a sedan chair or long litter, later a cart drawn by hand, and, finally, one drawn by animals 7 may be used. For the patient is relaxed by such movements, and when he is given a bath in olive oil, matter deep within the body, sympathetically affected by the motion, comes to the surface. Later prescribe [regular] bathing and a small amount of wine; and exercise each paralyzed part in conformity with its function. At the same time seek to determine whether there is in the body any other abnormal condition from which the paralysis seems to have arisen, so that this condition may also be overcome—not because it seems to have been an antecedent cause but because it is itself an abnormal condition which must be recognized as such.

Thus if a wound was present in conjunction with the paralysis, proceed as we have indicated in the surgical section of 8 our treatise entitled *Answers*. That is, recall whether the paralysis supervened upon a wound, e.g., an actual cutting of parts, even though the wound is no longer present in the strict sense, but is now called limping, sluggishness, or loss of reason.[10] And if a scar has already closed, try to soften it. If the spine is, for any reason, twisted or dislocated, straighten it. If there is fever or chronic headache (Greek *cephalaea*) or epilepsy, try at the same time to overcome these conditions, too. If there is a bending or flexion of the uterus, employ the measures appropriate for this condition, as we have set them forth in the treatise *On Diseases of Women*.[11] If a joint has been dislocated, even if a long time 9 ago, reset it. If there is an abnormally large discharge of fluid in any of the natural functions, apply astringent plasters, such as those made with Theban dates, quinces, acacia, hypocist, alum, and the like; also those astringent plasters which the Greeks call *enaema* ['blood-stanching']; or those which can halt a flow and cause it to dry up, e.g., the drugs, called *melana* ['black remedies'],[12] which are used on wounds.

10. The text is very uncertain, and the interpretation here given is entirely conjectural.

11. Cf. Soranus *Gyn.*, p. 127. 18; Cael. Aur. *Gyn.* ii. 61–63; *eversio* = ἀναστροφή, *inclinatio* = παρέγκλισις.

12. Cf. also Soranus *Gyn.*, p. 121. 1, where a 'black remedy' made of papyrus is used for uterine hemorrhage. There are numerous references to black remedies in other authors; the name may be due to the frequent use of pitch or bitumen as an ingredient.

nunc simpliciter[75] aegros resumemus. ac si passio permanserit, cyclico[76] ductu resumptionis regula dirigemus per variam
gestationem, deambulationem, vocis exercitium, lectionem,
30 unctionem, lavacra. tunc post haec omnia partium adhibemus
fricationem, dantes varium cibum atque vinum, iuxta praescrip-
tam disciplinam omnia augentes atque minuentes. et nunc
usque ad piscium qualitatem ordinamus cyclum, nunc usque ad
volantum, tunc etiam agrestium, ultimo porcinae carnis, sicut
superius de capitis curatione scribentes docuimus.

dehinc adhibemus etiam metasyncriticos cyclos, et primo
partiles,[77] tunc perfectos, nisi ex initio vires aegrotantis eos perferre non valuerint. denique nunc drimyphagia utemur, antecedente cibi parvitate, nunc vomitum provocamus drimyphagian linquentes, et ceteras quoque cycli regulas complemus, et
31 nunc vomitui[78] adiungentes drimyphagian. ipsum quoque vomitum primo ieiunum probamus, tunc[79] ex radicibus vel his similibus qualitate materiis. atque ita post frequentem radicum
vomitum helleboro utemur, primo radicibus inserto vel aceto infuso, quo detracto radices immissae concisae ipso cum liquore
sorbeantur.

utemur etiam localibus adiutoriis in his partibus quae sunt
paralysi vitiatae, ut dropace primo ⟨communi⟩,[80] tunc composito, quem Graeci pharmacoden vocaverunt; psilotro quoque, et
cucurbitis recorporativis multa cum flamma admotis atque violenter remotis, aut circumtractis nunc ex superioribus ad in-
32 feriora. etenim spiritus iamdudum motu vacuatus ex alto ad-
ducetur et quadam provocatione excitus vel accurrens sua cubilia cognoscit singularum viarum meatus[81] invadens, passionis
deturbato languore. hoc igitur facere tentabimus ex multis cu-

---

[75] simpliciter *conieci*: similiter *S*: similiter ⟨ut in epilepsia⟩ *R*
[76] cyclico *Rm*: cyclo *S*
[77] partiliter *vel* ⟨ex⟩ parte *Rm, coll. Chr. i. 90, 97*
[78] vomitui *Rm*: vomitus *S*   [79] tum *R*: nunc *S*
[80] ⟨communi⟩ *Rm, coll. Chr. i. 168*: ⟨simplici⟩ *R (cf. Orib. lat. Syn. iii. 166)*
[81] meatus *scripsi*: motus *edd.*

At this stage prescribe a simple restorative treatment; but if the disease persists, guide the patient through the standard cycle of restorative treatments, viz., various kinds of passive exercise, walking, vocal exercise, reading aloud, anointing, and bathing. After all these treatments prescribe vigorous massage of the parts. Give the patient varied food and wine. Increase or diminish the amount of everything in accordance with the standard teaching [of our sect], prescribing the cycle now only as far as the diet of fish, now up to that of fowl, now up to that of field animals, and now to the last stage, the diet of pork, as we explained above in the chapter on the treatment of chronic headache.[13]

After this prescribe the metasyncritic treatments, first in part, and then in their entirety, unless from the outset the patient's strength proves insufficient to endure them. Thus after a period when almost no food is given, put the patient first on an acrid diet; then give up the acrid diet and provoke vomiting. After this carry out the other treatments of the metasyncritic cycle, finally joining the vomitive treatment with the acrid diet. As for vomiting, it should first be provoked on an empty stomach, and later with radishes or other substances of like properties; and then, after frequent use of radishes for this purpose, employ hellebore. First insert the hellebore into radishes and pour vinegar over them; then, after removing the hellebore, chop up the soaked radishes and have the patient sup them up along with the liquid.

Also apply local remedies to those parts which are paralyzed, e.g., first an ordinary pitch plaster and then one that is composed of several ingredients (Greek *pharmacōdē*, 'drug-containing'). And apply depilatories; also employ metasyncritic cupping, i.e., use a great deal of flame in applying the cups and either remove them violently or draw them about the body, in these cases from the higher to the lower parts.[14] For the pneuma, which had previously lost its power of motion, is thus stirred from the depths of the body and is stimulated and aroused; it throws off the sluggishness caused by the disease, begins to recognize its proper channels, and flows toward them, entering the several passages. Try to aid this process by applying a number of cups along the

13. *Chr.* i. 20–23.
14. Possibly 'now in a circle, and now from the higher to the lower parts.'

curbitis per spinam, recto scilicet ordine post invicem adfigentes;
atque sufficiens tempus adductioni largientes, primo primarum
faciemus detractionem, tunc sequentium, quo sibi adductum
spiritum tradant[82] atque in solitos[83] provocent motus. atque
verso ordine inferiores primo affigentes easdem detrahemus
primo.

33 post cucurbitationem atque dropacis usum pulvere nitri partes
aspergi facimus et fricari, vel sinapi vel ex utroque, tunc etiam
his pulveribus quae sunt ex calce viva, fecla, pumice, pipere,
pyretro, et his similibus virtute rebus. ordinamus etiam unctiones, gestationes varias, acopa quae mordicatione quadam
corpus afficiant vel accendant et emolliant, ut sunt ea quae conficiuntur ex oleo sicyonio,[84] syriaco, castoreo, aphronitro, sulphure vivo, agresti cucumere, ammoniaci gutta, squilla, quam
vulgo bulbum pruriosum[85] vocant, urticae semine, pyretro, pipere, helleboro albo, nigella, galbano, iri illyrica, lemnida,
34 adarce,[86] et his similibus. non aliter etiam malagmata sunt adhibenda quae corpus valeant papulare lacessendo, ut sunt ex
flore salis vel ex nitro, et illud quod Nileos appellatur vel diadaphnidon vel Apollophanis[87] et Caphisophontos,[88] quorum
compositiones Responsionum tradidimus libris, pro modo magnitudinis passionum adhibendas atque lenimentorum, alias
augentes, alias indulgentes.

ordinamus etiam sole corpus torrendum vel paroptesin ex
carbonibus, aut parietibus calefactis vel pavimento, item lapidibus ac testis. hoc faciunt[89] etiam ceromata sub sole ignita vel
terga praeuncta simili modo calefacta, quae substrata accipiunt
aegrotantes volutatione quadam convertendos ac defricandos et
35 mutandos.[90] etiam loca quae deseruerint repetenda, ut veniant
ferventiora, quippe cum naturaliter tergora oleo ac sole facile
fervescant.

---

[82] tradant *R*: tradunt *S*: *fort.* trahant
[83] insolitos *edd.*: divisim scripsi (*et rursum fort.* meatus; *cf. Ac. i. 106*)
[84] sicyonico *S*: *corr. R*
[85] bulbum pruriosum *Reinesius 664, coll. Varronis R.R. ii. 7. 8*: vulum pluriosum *S*
[86] lemnida (*fort.* lemnide *vel* lemnia), adarce *scripsi*: lemnida carie *S*: limnaea (= *pa-lustris*) adarce, *Reinesius 665*: *cf. Chr. ii. 108*
[87] apollophanos *S*: *corr. R*
[88] *fort. scrib.* Caphisophontis (*vel* Ceph-)
[89] *post* faciunt *interpung. edd.*: *corr. Schmid RPh 49*
[90] convertendi ac defricandi et mutandi *S*: *corr. R*

spine, that is to say, one below the other in a straight line. Then, after allowing sufficient time for the cups to draw, remove them in order, first the higher and then the lower. The purpose is to attract the pneuma and pass it along, stimulating it to its natural movements. Then reverse the order, affixing and removing the lower cups first.

After the use of cupping and a pitch plaster, have the parts sprinkled and rubbed with powdered nitrum, mustard, or both. Also use dusting powders made of quicklime, the incrustation on wine casks [tartar], pumice, pepper, pellitory, and substances of like properties. And prescribe anointing and various forms of passive exercise; also restorative ointments which have a biting or irritant effect on the body but at the same time are emollient, e.g., those containing Sicyonian oil, Syrian oil, castor, aphronitrum, unburnt sulphur, wild cucumber, gum ammoniac, squill, which is commonly called 'the bulb that causes itching,' nettle seed, pellitory, pepper, white hellebore, black cumin, allheal, Illyrian iris, Lemnian earth,[15] adarce, and the like. In the same way use emollient plasters, which, by irritating the skin, can cause the formation of pustules, e.g., salt of the best quality, nitrum, the so-called 'plaster of Nileus,' that from bayberries, that of Apollophanes, and that of Cephisophon. We have described these preparations in our work entitled *Answers*. Their use depends on the nature and severity of the disease and on the character of the intervals between attacks; use them freely at times and sparingly at other times.

Also prescribe a sun bath or apply intense heat to the patient's body, using a charcoal fire or heated walls, pavements, stones, or bricks. A similar result is obtained with wax ointments[16] when they are heated by the sun, or with hides smeared with oil and similarly heated. The patient lies on a hide of this kind, and twists and turns his body, causing it to be rubbed intensely and to undergo the required change; whenever a portion of the hide is left uncovered, it is smeared again with oil so that it may become hotter, for hides treated with oil and exposed to the sun naturally and quickly become hot.

15. Or perhaps 'ruddle.'

16. Cf. *Chr.* iii. 40; iv. 102. *Ceromata* may here refer to mixtures of wax, oil, and earth or clay, or merely to earth or clay packs. Cf. also Cael. Aurel. *Salut. praec.* 135, p. 199 (Rose), which suggests the possibility that the prescription refers to rolling exercise on heated wrestling floors.

utemur etiam ob similem corporis curationem, quam Graeci
phoenigmon vocant, harena littori vicina quae sit sole ignita, ut
circumtecta gremio foveat aegrotantem; tunc etiam fomentationibus ex aqua salsa vel marina, aut decoctione baccarum
lauri vel omnium quae ita corpus afficiunt. manente passione
etiam cataplasma ex sinapi adhibemus, vel contusam atque
liquatam ferulaginem,[91] quam Graeci tapsian vocant. corpus
ungemus usque ad cutis ruborem atque mediocrem partium in-
36 flationem. etenim vulnerari sive vexari quosdam ex istius herbae usu immoderationis est vitium, tamquam sinapismi usus
immodicus. generaliter autem similiter medentur etiam vaporationes ex saccellis sale torrido repletis, atque in lavacro igneo
usus flabrorum.

ordinamus etiam si quid partialiter[92] loco patienti poterit adhiberi, ut capiti passione vexato rasionem capillorum, nunc pro
capillatura, nunc contra capillaturam. in mulieribus vero quae
id fieri non facile permittunt, denso pectine exerceri capillos
imperamus, supradicta scilicet diversitate et cum vehementi
conatu, atque primo aliorum manu et raro pectine, tunc magis
denso et aegrotantis manu.

37 ac si odorandi officium fuerit paralysi vitiatum, erunt adhibenda acriora odoramenta, ut ex aceto et sale, aut adiuncto origano[93] in aceto extincto, quo ex eo acriorem profectam[94] exhalationem naribus sapiant aegrotantes; nunc etiam sinapi vel castoreo ex aceto soluto per intervalla vel lasare, quod Graeci opon
cyrenaicum vocant. sed haec erunt naribus quoque immittenda,
vel sinapi cum aceto, ⟨et⟩[95] donec provocentur iubemus eos
violenter[96] emungere. probamus denique betae nigrae vel cy-
clamini herbae sucum cochleare plenum naribus infundendum,
utentes ptarmicis vehementioribus, quae nos sternutamenta vocamus, ex pipere, helleboro, castoreo, strutio,[97] et horum simili-
38 bus. post sternutationem vero magis odoramenta utenda probamus. haec enim vehementius odorationis movent officium,
et solas capitis partes in passione constitutas quadam mutatione
reformant.

[91] contusa atque liquata ferulagine R
[92] partiliter Rm, coll. Chr. i. 90
[93] origono S: corr. Rm
[94] profectam Rm: profecto S
[95] addidi
[96] volenter edd.
[97] astrutio S: cf. Chr. i. 98

17. Irritation of the skin to redness; treatment with rubefacients.

In a similar type of treatment, which the Greeks call *phoenigmos*,[17] use may be made of sand near the shore; when the sand, packed round the patient's body, is heated by the sun, it bakes his skin. Also foment the body with salt water, sea water, or decoctions of laurel berries or of any other substance having a similar effect on the body. If the disease persists, apply a mustard plaster; or triturate and dissolve deadly carrot (Greek *thapsia*) and apply it, rubbing the body until the skin becomes red and there is a mild swelling of the parts. For it is a mistake to use either this substance or mustard remedies so immoderately as to cause a wound or excessive irritation. And with regard to general treatments, a like beneficial effect is obtained by applying heat with bags full of hot salt and by the use of fans in connection with hot vapor baths.

In addition, we recommend the use of whatever special treatments are applicable to the particular part affected. For example, when the head is the part affected have the hair shaved with the razor, stroked first in the same direction as the hair lies and then in the opposite direction. But in the case of women, who will not readily permit this to be done, have the hair combed vigorously with a fine comb, and with a change in the direction of stroking, as above. First, however, let an attendant comb out the patient's hair with a coarse comb; and later have the patient comb herself with the finer comb.

If the function of smell is paralyzed, use sharp-smelling substances, such as vinegar and salt, or marjoram soaked in vinegar, so that the patient may sense a strong odor coming to his nostrils. And from time to time use may also be made of mustard or castor dissolved in vinegar, or laser (Greek *opon cyrēnaicon*, 'Cyrenaic juice' or 'silphium juice'). Now such substances, e.g., the solution of mustard in vinegar, should also be placed in the patient's nostrils. He should then blow his nose vigorously until the passages are stimulated. Pouring a spoonful of the juice of black beet or of cyclamen into the patient's nostrils is also helpful. And use may also be made of strong ptarmics (Latin *sternutamenta*), e.g., pepper, hellebore, castor, soapwort, and the like. After the sneezing, however, it is preferable to employ the aromatic substances, for these more strongly stimulate the function of smell and subject to change and alteration only those parts of the head which are affected by the disease.

ac si lingua fuerit paralysi vitiata, vel transvorationis partes, aridum sinapi dabimus masticandum ante lavacrum; tunc aqua calida os colluere praecipimus. aliquando etiam liquefactum ex aceto sorbere aegrotantem imperabimus[98] et gargarizare. hoc quidem etiam de similibus liquoribus faciemus, ut ex fico, hyssopo, draganto, origano,[99] thymo, pipere, pyretro, staphisagria. haec etiam masticanda dabimus, ipsam quoque lin-
39 guam lasare fricantes ex aqua soluto. tunc etiam cornu cucurbitae in modum adhibemus: adducit enim non aliter quam haec spiritum, et in solitas[99a] provocat vias, quae sunt ex antecedentibus medicaminibus praepurgatae.

item stomacho patiente atque ventre, magis frequentabimus drimyphagian, dantes etiam lasar cum aceto, ex quibus panis erit madidandus adiuncto quolibet pulmento.

ac si podex fuerit paralysi vitiatus aut eius vicina, acriora facimus vel mordicantia inici collyria, quae Graeci balanos vocant; vel sinapi plurimum fico admixto atque in collyrium collectum, longitudine aptum partibus, inicimus. et[100] ea quae in aliis ordinavimus fomenta nunc pro encathismatibus adhibemus,
40 vel per clysterem inicimus aliqua ex acrioribus, ut aquam salsam vel marinam, vel garum, quod appellamus liquamen, ex pisce siluro confectum, et si qua fuerint similis virtutis. quorum omnium dexteros usus atque confectionis genus et adhibendi rationem libris[101] Adiutoriorum specialium docuimus.

oportet praeterea singulas partes in passione constitutas suis ac naturalibus motibus admonere, ut supercilium levando ac deponendo, palpebram concludendo ac distinguendo, linguam producendo atque conducendo. haec sunt aegrotantibus imperanda.
41 hortandi etiam locutionem tentare: quod si minime facere potuerint, ex omni parte officio linguae cessante, erunt suadendi ut animo concepta volvant quae proferre non possunt. saepe enim quae loqui volentes mente perceperint, in alto formans spiritus accepto motu rumpit in vocem. vel certe docendi sunt

[98] imperavimus *S*: imperamus *R*

[99] origono *S*: corr. *R*

[99a] in solitas] insolitas *edd.*

[100] et *R*: ut *S*

[101] libro *edd., sed cf. Ac. i. 70, iii. 81; Chr. i. 141: an excidit numerus?*

And if the tongue or the parts used in swallowing are paralyzed, give the patient dry mustard to chew on before a bath.
Then have him wash his mouth with warm water. We sometimes
prescribe that the patient sip up and gargle a solution [of mus-
tard] in vinegar; this may also be done with juices of similar
properties, e.g., fig, hyssop, tragacanth, marjoram, thyme, pepper, pellitory, and stavesacre. We may also give the patient
these substances to chew in solid form, rubbing his tongue with
a solution of silphium juice in water. After these treatments,
apply a horn to the part in question to serve as a cupping instrument. The horn will draw pneuma in the same way as an ordinary cupping instrument and will attract it to its normal channels[17a] after they have first been cleansed by the drugs.

In paralysis of the esophagus and stomach, make frequent use
of the acrid diet. And give the patient silphium juice mixed with
vinegar, having him soak his bread in the mixture and eat it together with any other food.

In paralysis of the anus or adjacent parts, insert sharp, irritating suppositories (Greek *balanoe*). For instance, add fig to a considerable quantity of mustard, bring the mixture to the consistency of a suppository, and insert an amount corresponding
to the length of the parts affected. And use for sitz baths the
same preparations we prescribed as fomentations in other cases
of paralysis. Or inject as a clyster any of the sharper substances,
e.g., brine or sea water, garum (Latin *liquamen*, 'fish-sauce')
made from the sheat fish, and other substances of like properties.
We have explained in our work *On Special Remedies* the proper
use of all these preparations, the method of compounding them,
and the rules for administering them.

In addition, it is necessary to exercise each paralyzed part in
the performance of its natural motion, e.g., in the case of the eyebrow, raising and lowering; in that of the eyelid, opening and
shutting; and in that of the tongue, extending and contracting.
Instruct the patient to practice these movements.

He should also be urged to try to speak. And even if he is
quite unable to do so because of a complete loss of function by
the tongue, persuade him to think out in his mind the things to
which he cannot give utterance. For it often happens that breath
takes form in the deeper parts and, being set in motion, breaks

17a. Or, reading *insolitas:* 'stimulate the pores, which have ceased to function.'
Cf. 32.

unius exprimendae literae curam suscipere, ut intra se exercendo
manifestius probent: et magis ex vocalibus, ne difficultate sonitus multarum literarum vocis organa concludantur potius quam
reserentur. tunc cum implere valuerint, dabimus lexes atque
nomina quae sint ex multis vocalibus conscripta, ut est 'paean'
42 et his similia. sic etiam numeros dabimus et ex his exclamare
provocabimus aegrotantes. ac deinde lectionem offeramus[102]
vel disputationem.

haec adhibenda sunt etiam si buccarum partes circa labiorum
confinia, quem Graeci chalinon vocant, fuerint in passione constitutae. danda[103] etiam mastiche masticanda vel cera indul-
gentior mordenda, tunc ferulae particula vel per profectum tiliae
tabella. plus enim illorum singula quodam cum certamine
partes faciunt exerceri. tunc danda etiam frangenda arida fa-
barum grana vel amygdala molliora ac nuces, avellanae primo,
tunc etiam glandes, paulatim aucto numero quantitatis.

43 ac si digiti fuerint in passione constituti, erunt commovendi
oblatione cerae emollientis et malagmatum suprascriptorum,
quo non solum motu sed etiam tactu medicamina propria virtute medentur.[104] praeterea eodem exercitii tempore, et in illis
quibus totae manus paralysi fuerint vitiatae, vel earum quaelibet partes, alteres erunt offerendi; etenim[105] pondere pro modo
virium aegrotantes quodam labore inertes[106] exercent. sed erunt
praedictis malagmatibus commovendi, ut primo teneant vel
baiulent aegrotantes, tunc demum ex ipsis simili ratione ferendo[107] manus exerceant.

44 at si crura fuerint paralysi vitiata, si fieri potuerit per seipsos,
sin minus, aliorum impulsu, extensione atque conclusione[108] ex-

[102] offeremus R

[103] dandum S: corr. Rm

[104] an medeantur?

[105] etenim coni. Bendz 35: at enim S: eo enim R

[106] inertes conieci: mortes S: motus (cum exercentur) Rm: vel artus vel partes Almeloveen: fort. manus vel partes

[107] ferendo Rm: feriendi S: fort. feriendo

[108] conductione Rm. cf. 14

out into voice with the words which the patient wanted to speak and had been forming in his mind. Or have him practice pronouncing one letter at a time. He should first go over the sound in his mind and then utter it aloud; and it is preferable to practice with vocalic sounds, for otherwise the difficulty of sounding more than one letter at a time will tend to close the vocal organs rather than open them. Then, when he can pronounce these sounds, give him words, including proper names, to pronounce; the words should be composed predominantly of vowel sounds, such as 'paean' and the like. Also give him counting exercises and urge him to call off the numbers loudly. Then let him read aloud or participate in oral discussion.

These measures are also to be taken if the parts of the jaws near the ends of the lips (Greek *chalinoe*) are paralyzed. And in this case give the patient mastic to chew, or soft wax to bite into, and afterward a piece of fennel, and, when he improves, a tablet of linden wood. For all these devices give the affected parts something to struggle against and thus afford them exercise. Afterward have the patient bite open dry beans, soft almonds, and nuts, first avellans and then chestnuts;[18] and gradually increase the number.

In paralysis of the fingers, stimulate them by applying wax, which has a softening effect, or any of the emollient plasters mentioned above. For the drugs have a beneficial effect on the fingers not merely by reason of the movement which their application requires, but also because their specific properties are in contact with the fingers. Moreover, at the same time give the patient weights to use for exercise. These should also be given to persons suffering from paralysis of the whole hand or any parts thereof. For with the weight the patient can exercise these sluggish parts as vigorously as his strength permits. But, before this, the emollients described above should be employed in order to stimulate movement [in the fingers], so that we may first get the patient to grasp or lift the weights, and then similarly to swing[19] them and thus exercise the hands.

If the legs are paralyzed, the patient should exercise them by movements of extension and contraction. If possible he should

18. Perhaps 'walnuts,' or merely 'acorns.'

19. If these weights can be used as dumbbells, *feriendo* (possibly *feriendi*) may be read ('to strike them').

erceant eas partes, non tamen sine suasione quo[109] non solum[110] motibus exerceantur, verum etiam ipsi connitantur.

erunt denique ob varietatem motus artis industria partes commovendae hoc modo. iacente aegroto cruribus imposita fasciola, superpendenti rotulae, quam Graeci trochilion appellant, alter[111] ex finibus fasciolae inserendus;[112] hinc tenendum dare, nunc ministro, nunc aegrotanti demonstrato motu [ac][113] partili qui nunc adducta fasciola sublevet crura, nunc indulta deponat.

45 sed cum non solum levare ac deponere voluerimus, sed etiam extendere aut inflectere partes paralysi vitiatas, duae erunt fasciolae imponendae, altera genibus, altera talis. tunc per supradictam rotulam traiciendae et apprehensis initiis similiter offerendae patientibus vel ministris, ut vicissim ducant: quo, ea quae genu continet adducta, et ea quae talum continet indulgente, hoc motu crura flectantur; rursum talari adducta, et indulta ea quae genu continet, cruris fiat extensio. ac si sedere potuerint aegrotantes,[114] erit fasciolae medietas pedibus submittenda, cuius initia eidem tradita cogatur labore proprio per seipsum adducendo atque indulgendo suis cruribus motum

46 praestare. simili etiam modo manus in passione constitutae moveri posse noscuntur, ut ex altera fasciola iubeamus[115] quam oportet partem[116] articulis digitorum vicinam, quam Graeci carpon vocant, altera cubitum circumdari.

praemotis igitur vel exercitis ut supradictum est, dabimus[117] ut sella tonsoria sedeant aegrotantes, quae sit obliquis anconibus fabricata, quibus incumbentes sese levare nitantur. et nunc fulciti ex utroque alarum latere ministrorum officio deambulationem tentent, vel incumbentes baculo, aut vehiculo manibus acto, quod infantibus saepe motum discentibus fabricatur, sed magnitudine tamen aegrotantibus coaequandum.

47 dehinc cum gestationis augmenta sufficimus, conficienda sunt

[109] quo *Rm*: qua *S*
[110] solum ⟨aliorum⟩ *R*
[111] alterum *S*: *corr. R*
[112] inserendum *S*: *corr. Rm*
[113] *seclusi*
[114] potuerit aegrotans *R*
[115] iubeamus *scripsi*: iubeat *edd.*: *an* iubeatur?
[116] partem *conieci*: arteriam *edd.*
[117] *an* imperabimus?

perform the exercise unaided; otherwise with the help of an attendant. But even in the latter case he should be encouraged not to rely for his exercise merely on the movements [induced by the attendant], but to join in the effort himself.

For the purpose of varying the exercise the following device should be employed for the movement of the affected parts. If the patient must lie on his back, a bandage is placed round the paralyzed leg. The loose end of the bandage is passed over a suspended pulley (Greek *trochilion*) and is given to the patient or an attendant to hold. A demonstration of the twofold motion of the device is given, both patient and attendant being shown how to raise and lower the leg by alternately pulling and relaxing the cord. But, since we desire not merely to raise and lower but also to stretch and bend the paralyzed parts, we must tie two bandages, one around the knee and the other around the ankle. The ends are then passed, as before, over the pulley and given to the patient or an attendant to pull alternately. Thus when the end connected with the knee is pulled and that connected with the ankle remains slack, the resultant motion is a bending of the leg. Again, when the end connected with the ankle is pulled and that connected with the knee remains slack, the resultant motion is a stretching of the leg. And if the patient can sit up, the middle of the bandage may be passed under the sole of his foot and the ends given to him to hold; he is thus required to impart motion to his leg by his own efforts, alternately pulling and slackening the ends of the bandage. And it is clear that the arm when paralyzed can be similarly exercised. For this purpose we have one bandage placed round the wrist (Greek *carpos*) of the arm in question, i.e., the part near the fingers, and the other round the elbow.[20]

When the paralyzed parts have been moved and exercised as indicated, have the patient sit in a barber's chair which has arms at the sides. Let him try to lift himself by supporting himself on these arms. Again, let him try to walk, either propped up under his arms by attendants on either side of him or resting on a staff. He may also lean on a carriage which is easily moved by hand, a device of the kind often built for babies learning to walk; but in this case the carriage must be built up to the patient's height. Then when the amount of walking which the patient does with

20. The text is uncertain.

ligna quae transgredi pedibus nitantur aegrotantes. tunc etiam perfectis in terra lacunis deambulationem imperabimus, ac deinde calceamentis adiuncto plumbo prius parvo, ut exempli causa uncia, tunc plurimo, atque pro augmentorum gradu usque ad libram deducto. tum etiam itineris celeritas erit augenda, habet enim maioris laboris officium.

varianda etiam omnis regula, ut nunc resumptivos cyclos in metasyncriticos deducamus, nunc econtrario versa vice gradum revocemus. praeterea perseverante passione ad hellebori usum probamus accedendum, non solum semel, sed et cogentibus
48 rebus secundo vel tertio; tunc resumendos atque naturalibus aquis dandos et magis calidioribus, ut sunt in Italia patavinae,[118] vesevinae, et senanae, et caeretanae[119] appellatae. etenim albae sive albulae quae sunt appellatae, quod sint frigidae virtutis, solutione laborantibus vel fluore quorumlibet officiorum naturalium a veteribus sunt approbatae. utendum etiam natationibus marinis, vel supradictarum aquarum: et primo partibus passione vitiatis inflatae vesicae sunt adiungendae, quo natandi laborem minuant. item aquarum ruinis partes in passione constitutae sunt subiciendae, quas Graeci cataclysmos appellant. plurimum etenim earum percussiones corporum faciunt muta-
49 tionem. peregrinatio quoque adhibenda terrena atque maritima. necnon castoreum poto damus, si quisquam eius odoris difficultatem perferre valuerit. recorporativam curationem, quam Graeci metasyncriticam vocant, utilem approbamus partibus in passione constitutis. haec est secundum methodon paralyticorum curatio.

veterum autem medicorum Hippocratis atque Herophili sectatores memorant ea quae in passione constitutos sequuntur, curationem vero nullam tradiderunt. item Diocles, libro quo De passionibus atque causis et curationibus scripsit, eandem dixit conducere curationem quae epilepticis est ordinata.
50 dehinc Praxagoras secundo libro Curationum primo vomitum probat, et his praesertim qui caput fuerint paralysi vitiati, nunc ante cibum, nunc post cibum; tunc revocationes atque ventri-

[118] pantherinae *S*: *corr. Rm*
[119] caritanae *S*

the help of supports has been increased sufficiently, arrange wooden hurdles and have him try to step over them. And after that have ditches dug and make the patient walk down into them. Also add leaden weights to his shoes, first only a small amount, say an ounce, then gradually more and more up to a pound. Then have him increase the speed of his walking, for this will require the use of more effort.

The whole course of treatment should also be varied. Thus begin first with the restorative series and pass to the metasyncritic; then, contrariwise, pass from the metasyncritic to the restorative. Again, if the disease persists, prescribe the use of hellebore, not merely once but, if the condition requires it, twice or three 48 times. Then give restorative treatment and have the patient use natural waters, especially the warm springs, such as the springs of Padua, Vesuvius, Sena, and Caere, in Italy. And, in fact, the so-called 'Alban' or 'Albulan' springs, by reason of their cooling properties, are recommended by the ancients for persons suffering from a condition of looseness or excessive flux in any of the natural functions. Also prescribe swimming in the sea or in the springs we have just mentioned; at first, however, an inflated bladder should be attached to the paralyzed parts to reduce the effort required in swimming. Again, have the paralyzed parts played on by a shower of water (Greek *cataclysmos*). The strong impact of the water is very effective in bringing about a change 49 in the condition of the body. The patient should also take a trip abroad on land or sea. And we recommend the drinking of castor by any patient who can stand its harsh odor. And when parts of the body are paralyzed, we hold that the treatment which seeks to alter the bodily condition (Greek *metasyncriticos*) is helpful. This concludes the account of the treatment of paralysis according to the Methodist Sect.

Among the ancient physicians, Hippocrates and Herophilus merely mention the symptoms of the disease, but set forth no treatment. Diocles in his work *On Diseases and Their Causes and Treatment* says that the treatment he prescribes for epilepsy is also suitable for paralysis.

50 In Book II of his work *On Treatments* Praxagoras first recommends vomiting, especially in cases of paralysis of the head, the vomiting to be induced sometimes before eating and sometimes after. He then recommends the withdrawal of matter from the

flua et urinalia medicamina, quae coeliotica[120] atque diuretica
appellavit. adhibet etiam clysterem iugem et acriorem; bibendum etiam cum aceto asininum atque bubulinum lac probat;
tunc cataplasmata et malagmata et sudoris provocationes. et si
quis vomere facile potuerit, parum hellebori pulmentis interiectis diebus admiscet.

neque mox factam paralysin curans, neque recte[121] a vomitu
incipiens, et in his magis qui caput paralysi vitiati videntur,
51 priusquam ex aliis adiutoriis partes fuerint relevatae. dehinc
sensibilis post cibum omnis est vomitus, et multo gravius iugis.
at Praxagoras iubet cotidianis aut alternis diebus adhibitos, suis
dogmatibus sublatis[122] erroribus, quamquam ventriflua atque
diuretica et clysteres iuges approbaverit. non enim quod mutationem corporis haec facere valeant existimavit, sed quod materiarum facere detractionem atque corpus liquidis vacuare.
item aceto poto dato lac repugnat, cuius magis[123] gravis.

dehinc qualibus cataplasmatibus vel malagmatibus sit uten-
52 dum dicere negligit; sed neque tempus adhibendi discrevit. non
enim quando mitigativis utimur cataplasmatibus tunc erit
malagmatibus utendum. at iste pariter utraque composuit.
item sudores laxatis corporibus fiunt, non ipsi laxamentum
faciunt. sed neque quemadmodum sint provocandi docuit aut
memoravit. item album helleborum parvum datum praefocationis ingerit periculum, et multo potius quoties sunt in vomitum difficiles aegrotantes. mitto communiter eum dixisse interpositis diebus offerendum et tempus non memorasse, cum passionem necesse sit superpositionibus ac lenimentis variare.[124]

53   item Erasistratus de paralysi scribens differenter curandos ait
eos qui conclusione[125] sunt paralysi vitiati, ab his qui extensione
videntur affecti. etenim neque cataplasmata neque malagmata
secundis inquit convenire, non advertens quoniam etiam stric-

120 cf. Chr. i. 174

121 recte A: recta S

122 fort. suis dogmatibus sublatus ⟨et⟩ vel suorum dogmatum sublatus

123 cuius ⟨usus⟩ magis Hagendahl 262: fort. cuius usus (om. magis)

124 fort. variari

125 conductione Rm: cf. 14

body, prescribing drugs to purge the bowels and void the bladder, drugs which he calls *coeliōtica* and *diurētica,* respectively. He continually injects sharp clysters; and has the patient drink ass's and cow's milk mixed with vinegar. Then he prescribes poultices and emollient plasters; and he orders that sweating be induced. And if the patient can vomit easily, Praxagoras adds a little hellebore to his food at intervals of several days.

But his treatment is unsuitable for recent cases of paralysis. And he errs in beginning his treatment with vomitives before the affected parts have been relieved by other remedies, especially in cases where the paralysis is in the head. Again, all vomiting induced after eating causes agitation; but the effect is even more violent when the vomitives are administered continually. Now Praxagoras prescribes this treatment once a day or every other day, while he recommends the use of purges, diuretics, and clysters continually. But his teachings are undermined by his errors. For he is unaware that these treatments can produce a change in the bodily condition; in his opinion their purpose is merely to withdraw matter and drain the body of fluids. Again, vinegar as a drink is inconsistent with milk, being much stronger than milk.

Moreover, Praxagoras fails to tell us what poultices or emollient plasters should be used. Nor does he specify the time for applying them. And the fact is that when we employ soothing poultices we should not at the same time use emollient plasters. But Praxagoras puts them both together. As for sweating, this takes place as the result of the relaxing of the body; it does not itself bring about relaxation. And in any case Praxagoras does not explain or even mention how the sweating is to be induced. Furthermore, the giving of even a small quantity of white hellebore involves the danger of choking, a danger which is even greater in cases where vomiting is not easily induced. And we need not point out that Praxagoras merely says in general terms that the hellebore should be given at intervals of some days; he does not specify the time, though obviously the disease itself is marked by attacks and intervals of remission.

In discussing paralysis Erasistratus writes that those cases in which the paralyzed part is contracted must be treated differently from those in which the paralyzed part is observed to be stretched out. Thus he holds that neither poultices nor emollients are suitable for the latter class. But he is unaware that

tura densata quaedam corpora vi maiore non aliter quam chordae tenduntur; laxata denique medicinalium virtute saepe re-
tenduntur.

item initio curationis clysterem probat, phlebotomiae negligens potentiam, quo adiutorio maius nihil maioribus approbatur. tunc inquit effecta febricula detrahendum cibum, et dandum mulsum ex aceto confectum,[126] profecto densata constrin-
54 gens.[127] tunc observatis temporibus accessionum vel dimissionum, dandam ptisanam probat aut olus, quorum alterum inflat, alterum facile corrumpitur. dehinc aromaticas approbat
potiones, et alias mites, alias vehementes. ventrem quoque facilem cupit, ex quo stomachus necessario vitiatur, et neque
quanta neque quando neque quae danda sint memoravit.

prohibet etiam vinum[128] anni spatio, vana intentione tempus
definiens. dat etiam lac cum melle atque sale, quod est contrarium supradicto mulso ex aceto confecto. utitur praeterea
55 vomitu post cibos, quod iam superius fieri damnavimus. vitiat
etiam deambulationibus harenosis in locis, ex sola intentione sui
dogmatis. etiam ventrem facilem cupit, caduca suspicione deceptus.

Asclepiades vero principaliter de paralysi nihil scripsit. sed
Erasistrato respondit eos (inquit) qui non gravi dolore in ista
passione afficiuntur, phlebotomari non oportere, eos vero qui
privati[129] sensibus peiore strictura vexantur abstinendos primo,
tum iniciendos[130] probat. adhibet etiam purgativa medicamina,
quae Graeci catartica vocaverunt, cum sint haec corruptivae virtutis et propterea corpus elimando consumant potius quam re-
56 laxent. sed specialiter a laxatione paralysi vitiatis adurentia

---

[126] confecto S: corr. Rm
[127] constringent S: correxi
[128] vinum scripsi: unius S: ⟨vinum⟩ unius Rm
[129] privatis S: corr. R
[130] initiandos edd.

even bodies which are condensed by a state of stricture may also, through the operation of this powerful force, be stretched out in the manner of strings, but that such bodies when treated by drugs of relaxing properties are often freed from tension.

At the beginning of the treatment Erasistratus recommends a clyster, though he neglects the powerful remedy of venesection. Yet among the ancients no remedy is more highly valued than that of venesection. Moreover, at the appearance of fever, Erasistratus withholds food from the patient and prescribes honey mixed with vinegar. But he thereby further constricts
4 what is already congested. And with due regard to the time of exacerbations and remissions he recommends pearl barley or vegetables; but the former causes flatus, and the latter decompose easily. Again, Erasistratus gives the patient aromatic potions, some mild, others strong. And he requires that the stomach and bowels be kept open (though if this is done the gullet will, of necessity, be adversely affected); but he does not indicate what is to be given for this purpose, or in what amount, or at what time.

And he forbids the use of wine for a year, foolishly attempting to set a precise time limit. He prescribes milk with honey and salt, a preparation which has properties in direct conflict with those of the mixture of honey and vinegar mentioned above. Again, Erasistratus has the patient vomit after eating, a meas-
5 sure which we have already condemned.²² And in having the patient walk in sandy places, he causes him harm, even from the point of view of his own teaching. Finally, in his desire to keep the bowels loose, Erasistratus is misled by a vain suspicion.

Asclepiades does not give a separate account of paralysis. In answer to Erasistratus, however, he declares that [only] when severe pain is not present in this disease should venesection be avoided; but that when the patient is deprived of his senses²³ and is overcome by a severe state of stricture, food should be withheld and then a clyster injected.²⁴ Asclepiades also uses purgative drugs (Greek *cathartica*), though these drugs have a destructive effect and, for that reason, attenuate and consume the
6 body rather than relax it. But he holds that caustic drugs and

22. 51.

23. Or possibly 'of sensation,' i.e., in the paralyzed part.

24. In connection with venesection? Cf. 57.

inquit medicamina convenire, et fomentationem parvam paulo
ferventius temperatam, non advertens quia plurima extenta
conclusis[131] similem exigunt laxationem atque indulgentiam tensionis et non, ut existimat,[132] constrictionem.[133] utraque etenim
haec passioni subiecta sunt: ut etiam stupor corporis vel frigidus
torpor, quem non semper necessario vaporationibus verum
etiam frigore adhibito relevamus, siquidem contrariis inter se
57 passionibus haec subvecta monstrantur. ordinat praeterea idem
in harenae spatio deambulationem, quod appellant scamma, atque transcensum lignorum et inter plurimum tempus bibendum
vinum.

item Themison primo libro Tardarum passionum in quibusdam peccare cognoscitur, nondum rectam methodon respiciens.
etenim phlebotomat ex ea parte quae passione vitiata est si,
inquit, sensu non[134] caruerit, non curans, ut supra demonstravimus, evitanda omnia quae adiutorio quadam necessitate veluti
vexabili videantur esse coniuncta. dehinc lanam sucidam, quam
oesypon appellant, capiti iubet imponi aceto atque oleo rosaceo
58 infusam; nervis autem cervicis atque spinae et cruribus et brachiis vinum atque oleum cum sale imponendum iubet, constringens atque lacessens incongrue ea quae phlebotomiae[135] miti relevatione laxaverat. tunc tertia die cibum probat, atque quarta
die cucurbitam imponi, adiuncta scarificatione, non interrogans
passionis tempus, solum numerum dierum imprudenter atten-
dens. dehinc sequentibus gestationem probat, et neque in eo[136]
definiens tempus, atque audaciter secundae diatriti expecta-
tionem spernens. dat etiam aloen in potu; et ex aqua calida et
59 oleo intestinis dare laxamentum ordinat. praeterea anatresin
testae faciendam, quam nos perforationem vocamus, iamdudum

[131] conductis *Rm*: *cf. 14*

[132] existimant *S*: *corr. R*

[133] conscriptionem *S*: *corr. Schmid RPh 50*

[134] non *fort. del.*   [135] phlebotomia *edd.*   [136] ea *Rm*

rather hot fomentations in small amount are particularly suitable in cases where the paralyzed parts are stretched out. He
does not realize, however, that in most cases paralyzed parts
which are stretched out require the same relaxing and easing of
the tension as those which are contracted; they do not, as he
mistakenly believes, require any astringent treatment. That is,
in paralysis the parts may be either stretched out or contracted.
The case is analogous[25] to that of stupor or cold numbness of the
body, which cannot always be relieved with applications of
warmth but sometimes requires the application of cold; for these
57 symptoms may occur in diseases of diverse kinds. In addition,
Asclepiades prescribes walking in a sand pit (Greek *scamma*),
stepping over logs,[26] and, after a long time, the drinking of wine.

In Book I of his work *On Chronic Diseases* Themison, as we
know, makes certain mistakes, not having as yet envisioned the
true Method. Thus he performs venesection on the paralyzed
part if, as he says, it is not bereft of sensation; but in adopting
this rule he overlooks the necessity, which we pointed out above,
of avoiding anything in connection with the remedy that seems
likely to cause injury. Again he orders placed over the patient's
head unscoured wool (Greek *oesypos*) soaked in vinegar and rose
58 oil; and on the legs and arms and sinews of the neck and spine
he orders applications of wine mixed with olive oil and salt. But
in so doing he makes the mistake of constricting and irritating
the very parts which he had sought to relax with the gentle relief
afforded by venesection. Then, on the third day, Themison
recommends food; and on the fourth day he prescribes cupping
with scarification. He does not examine the time element of the
disease itself, foolishly considering only the number of days.
Then on the ensuing days he prescribes passive exercise. But he
does not place any time limit on the prescription; and he boldly
disdains waiting for the end of the second three-day period. He
gives the patient bitter aloes to drink, and prescribes loosening
59 the bowels with [a clyster of] warm water and olive oil. In addition, he orders trephining of the skull (Greek *anatrēsis*, which we
may translate *perforatio*), a procedure long since refuted in other

25. But not the same. The first case involves different symptoms (extension and
contraction) in the same disease (paralysis); the second case involves the same symptom (torpor) in different diseases. In the first case the same remedy is used for different
symptoms; in the second case different remedies are used for the same symptom.

26. Cf. 47.

quidem et in aliis methodicis explosam. et harenae deambulationem convenire existimat; atque plagis ferulae caedendas partes in passione constitutas, profecto quae salsae aquae mitigatione atque recorporatione videntur esse curandae.

item Lucius[137] primo libro Tardarum passionum cum his omnibus tum medicosis quoque fomentationibus utendum probat. 60 plurimi etiam alii aceto atque oleo roseo foventes, cum herpyllo et ruta et hedera et castoreo, probant praeterea iuges clysteres atque purgativa medicamina, quae cathartica vocaverunt, et magis hieram cuius usum graeco[138] libro Epistolarum ad Praetextatum damnavimus scribentes. sunt enim ea quae stomachum vitiant fugienda, ut sunt corpus insumentia, et quae moderationis nostrae careant potestate.

item Thessalus secundo libro De regulis scribens plurima recte dixisse probatur, quaedam vero proterva festinatione caduca. etenim post phlebotomiam usque ad tertium[139] imperat abstineri, solum potum diurna cum luce offerendum. tunc transacta tertia die atque hora qua sunt aegrotantes paralysi vitiati, ci 61 bum portat. quibus respondere facile quisquam poterit, si quaerat qua intentione Thessalus oriente luce potum iubeat dari. etenim si continuationis causa id fieri responderit, oportebat etiam cibum eodem tempore approbare. sin vero accessionum frequentia id existimat declinandum, vel suspicione futurarum, et propterea post tertium diem cibum transferendum, quo transacta hora passionis illatae tertia die recte aegros nutrire videamur, oportebat etiam potum non communiter et[140] generaliter diurnis diebus vel initio lucis offerre, sed horarum dimissione captata. dehinc non semper ac necessario tertio[141] 62 die cibum oportet dari, sed etiam quarta continuationis quae initium ex die sumpsisse visa, vel ob typum eadem ratione currentem.

---

[137] Lucius *Rm*: Lusius *S*: *fort.* Lysias *Wellmann Hermes 35 (1900) 369; cf. Chr. ii. 111, iv. 78, Sor. Gyn., p. 94. 21*

[138] *an aliqui numerus ordinalis substituendus?*

[139] tertium ⟨diem⟩ *R*   [140] et *A*: sed *S*

[141] *fort.* tertia *secundum usum Caelianum; cf. Schmid Mus. Helvet. 1 (1944) 124*

27. Cf. 48.

Methodist writings. He considers walking in the sand helpful, and also subjects the paralyzed parts to the cutting blows of a whip. But there seems to be no doubt that these parts should be treated rather with the mild and metasyncritic properties of salt water.[27]

Lucius in Book I of his work *On Chronic Diseases* prescribes the use not only of all the remedies mentioned above but also of fomentations containing harmful drugs. And many others use vinegar, rose oil, thyme, rue, ivy, and castor in fomentations. They also prescribe the continual use of clysters and purgative drugs (Greek *cathartica*) and, in particular, a drug called *hiera*. In our book entitled *Letters to Praetextatus*, written in Greek, we condemned the use of this latter drug. For whatever injures the esophagus should be avoided, and so should everything which weakens the body and is beyond our power to control.

Thessalus in Book II of his work *On Regimen* undoubtedly is right on many questions; but in his careless haste he gives certain erroneous directions. Thus after venesection he orders the patient to go without food until the end of the three-day period and has him drink only at dawn each day; then on the third day, after the precise hour has passed at which the patient had become paralyzed, he prescribes food.[28] Now anyone can easily refute this view by asking Thessalus why he prescribes drink at dawn. If his answer is that this is done because the disease is continuous over a long period, he should also approve of food at the same time. But if his answer is that the food should be withheld because of the frequency of attacks or the expectation of attacks to come and that the giving of food is thus postponed to the third day, and past the hour when the disease began, so that the giving of food will properly be in the third day—if this is his answer, his prescription of drink should also be at the precise hour of the remission and not simply once a day, say at dawn, in every case. And again the food need not be given in every case on the third day but may be given on the fourth day, either in an unremitting case which is found to have commenced in the daytime,[29] or in an intermittent case where the periodicity requires it.

28. I.e., after more than two full days have passed, e.g., from noon Monday to past noon Wednesday.

29. Cf. *Ac.* ii. 132.

idem post haec, similiter ut Themison, quarta inquit die cucurbitas infigendas, non interrogans utrum passio sumpserit
statum, quod est maxime servandum. ait praeterea alternis diebus cibandos usque ad certum numerum dierum, quod infinitum
reliquisse perspicitur. audaciter etiam atque invidiose acopa
quaedam vel malagmata probat excludenda, solius moderationis
neglectae[142] arguens vitia. haec sunt quae etiam Thessalo Sorani diligentia videntur esse responsa.

63   II. DE CANINO RAPTU, QUEM GRAECI
              CYNICON SPASMON VOCANT

IN ISTA passione constitutos sequitur conclusio[1] sive contractio,
repentino motu veniens ac recedens sine ulla corporis turbatione, et nunc utriusque labii in ultimo fine sive oris angulo,
quem Graeci chalinon vocant, ut etiam buccas adducat in pos-
teriorem partem crebrissime, tamquam ridentibus; nunc palpebras vel supercilia ac nares, [ut][2] etiam colla atque humeros
rapiat, et ita patientes faciat commoveri, tamquam onus humeris baiulantes transferendi ponderis causa.

64   differt autem a spasmo et paralysi musculorum qui buccas
conligant, siquidem spasmus acuta atque celer passio perspicitur, caninus vero raptus etiam tarda. item paralysis supradictorum musculorum non, ut Demetrius ait Apameus,[3] eo differt
quod non sit in canino raptu partium conversio (hoc enim contra manifestam rationem intelligitur dictum), sed quod ipsa
conversio coacta celeritate prius facta quam fieri sentiatur.

     curationem vero ex ante scriptis accipiendam ducimus et ma-
gis quam de paralysi monuimus oris[4] partibus.[5]

65   III. DE AURICULAE DOLORE ATQUE HUMORIS
          FLUORE PER AUDITORIAS CAVERNAS

SENSUALES aurium viae sive auditoriae cavernae, quos Graeci
acusticos poros appellant, difficillimis saepe doloribus vexantur, ut etiam occipitium teneant et oculos atque buccarum
musculos, et perseveratione quadam tardissima tempora teneant

---

142 neglecta S: corr. Rm
1 conductio Rm. cf. 14
2 seclusi: et scrib. Rm: fort. scrib. etiam et

3 Attaleus edd.: corr. Almeloveen 711
4 ⟨in⟩ oris R
5 fort. partium

Then on the fourth day Thessalus prescribes cupping, as Themison does, without considering whether the disease has reached its highest stage, though this is a matter that should be carefully observed. Again, he says that the patient should be given food on alternate days up to a certain number of days, but he does not seem to have specified what this number is. And he rashly and disdainfully rejects certain restorative ointments and emollient plasters, only proving how wrong it is to forsake moderation. This is our answer to Thessalus based on Soranus' account.

63   II. CYNIC SPASM (GREEK *CYNICOS SPASMOS*)

In cynic spasm a twitch or contraction comes suddenly and passes away without any bodily disturbance. Sometimes the twitch is at an end of the lip or corner of the mouth (Greek *chalinos*) and continually draws the cheek backward, so that the patient seems to be laughing; at other times the eyebrows, eyelids, and nostrils are subjected to the spasm, and even the neck and shoulders, the patient being so affected that he seems to be carrying a weight on his shoulders.

64   Cynic spasm differs from convulsion[1] and from paralysis of the muscles which control the jaws. For convulsion is a swift or acute disease, while cynic spasm is chronic. And paralysis of the muscles referred to may be distinguished from cynic spasm not, as Demetrius of Apamea says, because there is no change of position of the parts in cynic spasm (for such a statement is obviously unreasonable) but because this change takes place so swiftly that it is completed before one can observe the process.

The treatment of cynic spasm may be based on what has already been said, particularly on the treatment we have prescribed for facial paralysis.

65   III. EARACHE AND RUNNING EAR

The sensory channels or cavities of the ear (Greek *acousticoe poroe*) are often assailed by pains so severe that they also affect the occiput, the eyes, the muscles of the jaws, and, with especial persistence over a long period, the temples and the head.

1. I.e., Greek *spasmos*. Cf. *Ac*. iii. 61.

CHRONIC DISEASES II

et caput. aliquando etiam humoris fluor per easdem cavernas fiet,[1] quem Graeci reumatismon vocant; et ita iugis, ut saepe vulneret altiora atque corrumpat et ossa conterebret et propterea copiam fluentis humoris efficiat.

66 oportet igitur accessionis[2] tempore discernere curationem, in lenimento communem magis, hoc est recorporativam, quam Graeci metasyncriticam vocant, adprobare: ut cum dolor fuerit in initio, adhuc novam passionem iudicantes, quicquam destillari faciamus in has cavernas constrictivum medicamen, vel ex lana limpida sumentes auriculae immittamus, ut est amygdalinum vel roseum oleum vel acetum et his similia. utendum etiam requie corporis atque abstinentia et silentio.[3] suo[4] etenim officio[6] accepta voce aures necessario commoventur, et propterea maiores dolores efficiuntur.

67 ac si passio fuerit augmentis asperata, erit immittendum oleum calidum ac dulce, ac mollibus lanis praetegenda exteriora atque vicina. locandi praeterea aegrotantes calido in loco, et si dolor coegerit, phlebotomandi; atque tertia die levi atque sorbili cibo reficiendi; et ob mitigationem doloris exterius admovenda vaporatio tepidi vaporis, vel saccelli ex polline tenero confecti; tunc cataplasmata laxativa. et cum dolor sumpserit statum, erunt admovendae sanguisugae, quas hirudines appellant, circa fines auriculae, hoc est circulatim auditoriam cavernam habentes, cartilagine praetermissa:[7] vel certe eius posteriora cucurbita admota scarificanda, adhibita vaporatione spongiarum calidarum.

68 darum. ipsam quoque cavernam involuta lana per melotida oleo calido tinctam paulatim penetramus, atque illic lana derelicta ferramentum detrahimus.

tunc declinante passione cerotaria apponemus, dantes varium cibum et vinum. ac si humoris fuerit fluor, quem reumatismum vocant, eadem adhibemus quae initio doloris adhibenda probavimus. dehinc eorum augemus potentiam, ut cavernae ipsi faciamus infundi collyrium, quod appellamus diaglauciu[8] ex

---

[1] fiet *scripsi*: fiat *S*: fit *R*

[2] accessionis *Rm*: actionis *S*

[3] *post* suo *interpung. edd.*: *corr.* Bendz 98, Schmid RPh 50

[4] summo *Rm*

[6] orificio *Helmreich BPhW 39 (1919) 1104*

[7] cartilaginem praetermissam *S*: *corr. R*

[8] diaglaucium *S*

And sometimes there is a flow of liquid matter (Greek *rheuma-tismos*) through these passages. This flow may persist so steadily that it often injures or destroys the deeper parts and bores its way through the bones, thus adding to the quantity of fluid matter.[1]

66   Now it is necessary in treating this condition to distinguish between the active period of the disease and the quiet intervals, prescribing in these latter intervals a more general treatment, namely, the recorporative (Greek *metasyncritice*). But if the pain has just begun and the disease is still judged to be recent, put some drops of an astringent drug into the cavities of the ear, or insert in the outer ear some scoured wool soaked in the drug. For this purpose use almond oil, rose oil, vinegar, or the like. Prescribe rest for the body and fasting. There should also be silence; for, whenever the ears hear a voice, they are necessarily disturbed, and as a result the pains are more severe.

67   Now if the condition is aggravated by attacks, introduce warm sweet olive oil into the ear and cover over the outer ear and the adjacent parts with soft wool. Place the patient in a warm room, and, if the pain makes it necessary, perform vene-section. On the third day refresh him with light gruel-like food. To ease the pain apply heat externally, using warm vapors, e.g., from a bag filled with fine flour; then apply relaxing poultices. When the attack reaches its highest stage, attach leeches, called *hirudines*, round the ends of the outer ear, that is, in a circle containing within it the auditory opening but not touching the cartilaginous ear flap itself.[2] Or else apply a cupping instrument, with scarification, to the parts behind the ear, and heat these

68   parts with warm sponges. And take a probe, wrap wool around it, dip it into warm olive oil, and carefully introduce it into the orifice; then, leaving the wool within the canal, remove the instrument.

When the attack declines, apply cerates and give the patient varied food and wine. And if there is a flow of liquid matter (Greek *rheumatismos*), employ the same measures as those rec-ommended for use at the beginning of the earache. Then increase the strength of the treatment by having inserted into the orifice of the ear the so-called 'glaucium preparation' dissolved in wine

1. By dissolving the bones?
2. I.e., passing behind the ear flap. But the text is uncertain.

vino solutum vel aceto; vel illud medicamen quod appellant
Herae;[9] vel mulsum ex vino factum quod sit praecoctum in mali
punici cortice, cum nardo, vel amygdalis amaris, et aceto, croco,
et myrrha, et alumine, vel ex herbarum sucis constrictivae vir-
69 tutis. tum auriculae vicinantia circulatim cataplasmate[10] ex
cydonio malo ac simili medentium virtute contegemus, vel medicamine[11] quod appellatur diaiteon,[12] quod est siccativae virtutis,
vel icesio aut diadictamnu[13] et his similibus. dehinc si passio
coegerit, radendum est caput et constrictivis cataplasmatibus
contegendum. dandi etiam cibi constrictivi.

et lenimenti temporibus sive dolorum tardantium sive humorum fluentium resumptivus adhibendus cyclus, tunc recorporativus. et localiter ipsis cavernis per clysterem oticum[14] inicienda nunc destillatio aquae cineribus liquatae, quam vulgo
70 lixivium vocant, Graeci coniam, nunc sinapi liquido; atque
etiam admixto fico erunt exteriora cataplasmanda donec rubor
maximus fiat, quem Graeci phoenigmon appellant. item utendum[15] immissione medicaminum ex garo confectorum, quod
vulgo liquamen appellant, vel his virtute similium materiarum.
tunc etiam totius capitis curationem ex illisione aquarum super-
cadentium, quam Graeci cataclysmum appellant; quibus etiam
aurium vicina sunt maxime concuranda. dehinc acopis[16] et
dropacis[17] et malagmatibus acrioribus et aquis naturalibus utendum. sic enim intardata corporibus emoveri atque excludi mutatione poterunt curationis.

71   IV. DE DOLORE DENTIUM

FIUNT dolores dentium nunc omnium, nunc aliquorum, nunc
unius, cum sibi vicinantibus gingivis, ut etiam contumescant
ac saepe ora faciant subinflari, vel eorum aliquas partes crescente passione terebrari. nam saepe dentes et gingivae compu-
trescunt, corruptis ossibus quibus natura inserti sunt, recedentibus tumore cogente gingivis.

sed etiam nunc erit curationis diligentia partienda, ut initio

---

[9] Herae *Rm*: heren *edd.*: *fort.* Hera

[10] cataplasmata *S*: *corr. Rm*

[11] medicamen *S*: *corr. Rm*

[12] diaiteo *S*

[13] diadictamno *S*

[14] oticum *Rm*: modicum *S*

[15] utendum *scripsi*: eundem *S*

[16] acopibus *S*: *corr. Rm*

[17] dropacibus *Rm*

or vinegar, or the so-called 'drug of Heras,' or honey mixed with wine after having been cooked in pomegranate rind with spikenard, bitter almonds, vinegar, saffron, myrrh, alum, or the juice
9 of any plant having astringent properties. Then cover the parts near the ear with a circular plaster made of quinces and remedies of similar properties, or with the so-called 'willow plaster,' which has a desiccant quality, the Hicesian plaster, the dittany plaster, or the like. Then, if the disease requires it, shave the head and cover it with astringent plasters. And give the patient binding food.

During the intervals of remission in cases of chronic earache or running ear prescribe the restorative cycle of treatment and then the metasyncritic. As for local remedies, using an ear syringe, inject into the orifice some water strained by percolating
70 through ashes (Latin *lixivium*, Greek *conia*, 'lye'); at other times inject mustard in liquid form. Also add a fig to this mustard and apply as a plaster to the outer parts until these parts become very red, a process which the Greeks call *phoenigmos*. Similarly, an application of drugs prepared with fish sauce (Latin *liquamen*) may be used. Then prescribe the treatment in which the whole head is placed under a shower of water (Greek *cataclysmos*). It is particularly important that these measures benefit the parts near the ears as well as the ears themselves. In addition, prescribe restorative ointments, pitch plasters, sharp emollient plasters, and natural waters. For by the metasyncritic effect of these treatments chronic disorders can be removed and driven from the body.

71   IV. TOOTHACHE

SOME toothaches affect all the teeth, others a number of them, and still others only one tooth. The gums near the aching teeth are also involved and swell up; and often because of the affection the face and mouth are puffed up, and parts thereof may become perforated by abscess as the disease is intensified. For teeth and gums often rot away when the bones in which the teeth are normally inserted suffer decomposition, and the gums recede under the stress of the inflammation.

In this disease, too, the treatment must be divided. Thus one type of treatment should be administered at the beginning of

doloris vel certe si ita passio recurrendo tardaverit, superposi-
72 tionis alia adhibeatur curatio, alia lenimenti. quapropter adhuc
recentibus[1] passionis motibus, vel in asperitate superpositionis
doloris constitutis, convenit abstinentia cibi atque requies corporis, ut initio[2] causae aqua quae virtute constringat collutioni
oris adhibenda sit, ut est a plerisque conscripta decoctio in aqua
et vino herbae sideritis vel acaciae vel leuces, quam etiam populum[3] vocamus,[4] aut mandragorae (sed non sine cautione, ne quid
ex ipso liquore transvorent aegrotantes), item pentaphylli herbae aut papaveris necnon personatiae; aut herba phlomos[5] in
pusca decocta, vel ex cornu cervini drachmis quinque, et aceti
hemina usque ad sui medietatem decocta, vel ficus pingues[6] cum
aceto decoctae, aut alterci radices cum uvae lupinae suco et vino
73 sufficienti simul coctae. erunt praeterea ex his aliqua,[7] parte in
doloribus constituta,[8] apponenda vel lenientia, vel simili virtute
medentium materiarum.

tunc cum dolor vehementescere coeperit, lecto tradendus est
aeger, atque blando tepore calefaciendus ⟨et⟩[9] supino capite col-
locandus, sed paulo prominentius a cetero corpore sublevato.
tunc articuli fricatione calefaciendi atque musculi buccarum
lana oleo calido infusa circumtegendi, appositis saccellis ex pol-
74 linibus calidis confectis. tunc oris collutio ex oleo adhibenda
dulci atque calido vel faenigraeci suco aut alica aut ptisana vel
glycyrrhiza aut lacte cum melle.

et si nimius fuerit dolor, phlebotomia adhibenda. tunc tertia
die quo sanguinis facta detractio est, sorbilibus atque calidis
cibis aegri nutriendi, sed plus perungendi. alia quoque die si
dolor steterit atque duraverit et officium cessaverit ventris, erit
amovendus[10] ex simplici clystere, et loca in dolore constituta
ferro laceranda, appositis cucurbitis secundum buccarum musculos atque gingivarum locos. aliquando etiam ipsae gingivae
scarificandae, vel circumseparandae a dentibus ferramento quod
pericharactera vocant. est etiam mitigativa ex oleo vaporatio
quae fiet: ex ferventi oleo lanam melotidi involutam tingimus,
tunc gingivis altrinsecus imponemus, hoc est interiori atque ex-

---

[1] recedentibus *S: corr. Rm*   [2] initiorum *S: corr. R*

[3] populum *scripsi, coll., e.g., Cels. vi. 9. 2:* polium *edd., quod si retinere velis, lacuna
post* leuces *statuenda videtur*

[4] vocant *edd.*   [6] ficus pingues *conieci:* de pinguis *S*

[5] phlomon *S: corr. A*   [7] *fort. post* his *transponenda virgula* (*S*)

the toothache or, if the disease has recurred and become chronic, at the time of exacerbation; but another type of treatment is required during the intervals between attacks. Thus, when the pains are of recent origin or occur in an exacerbation of a chronic condition, fasting and bodily rest are called for. And at the beginning of the attack prescribe as a mouth wash an astringent liquid of the type described by many authors, e.g., a decoction of ironwort, acacia, white poplar (*leucē*, Latin *populus*), or mandrake, in wine and water. But the patient must be careful not to swallow any of the fluid. A similar decoction of cinquefoil, poppy, or burdock may be used; or a decoction of mullein in sour wine and water, or a mixture of five drachms of stag's horn and a hemina of vinegar boiled down to half, or a decoction of thick figs in vinegar, or of henbane roots and strychnos juice in a sufficient quantity of wine. In addition, while the part is in pain, apply the more soothing of these preparations or employ other drugs of similar properties.

Then, if the pain begins to grow more intense, put the patient to bed and warm him gently. Have him lie face upward with his head raised a little higher than the rest of his body. Then warm his limbs by rubbing. Cover his cheeks with wool soaked in warm olive oil, and next to the wool place bags filled with hot flour. Then let him wash his mouth with warm sweet olive oil; or the juice of fenugreek, spelt groats, pearl barley, or sweetroot; or milk with honey.

If the pain is excessive, perform venesection; and on the third day from the time of venesection nourish the patient with warm gruel-like foods. And continue to anoint him. The next day, if the pain continues undiminished and the bowels do not function, purge with a simple clyster. Lance the affected parts [of the gums?] with an iron instrument; and apply cups to the jaw muscles and the gums. Sometimes it is also necessary to scarify the gums themselves or to detach them from the teeth with an instrument called *pericharactēr*. Hot applications with olive oil also give relief; thus wrap some wool around a probe, dip it in hot olive oil, and apply it to the gums on both sides, i.e., to the inner and outer parts, and to the teeth themselves, as hot as the

---

[8] parti in doloribus constitutae *Rm*

[9] tepore calefaciendus ⟨et⟩ *Rm*: tempore calefacientibus *S*

[10] admovendus *vel* movendus *Rm*

teriori parti, et ipsis quoque dentibus, quantum aeger ferre fer-
75 voris potuerit. sed praetegenda vicina sunt, lana praemissa, ne
facile pustulentur.

alia quoque vaporationum genera quae sunt a veteribus tradita erunt adhibenda, ut thuris granum igne calefactum, tunc
tenui linteolo involutum, dolentibus dentibus apponatur, et ita
mordeat aegrotantes ut ex ipso vapore resumantur. item thuris
triti pulverem singulatim linteolis pluribus illigamus; tunc
eorum singula oleo calido praetincta aegrotantibus offerimus
mordenda, dentibus scilicet in dolore constitutis. aliqui etiam
scillae parvum modum aiunt oleo concoquendum, quod nos dif-
ferendum probamus ac lenitatis tempore adhibendum, siquidem
76 ob acrimoniam scillae recorporativam habeant virtutem. oportet praeterea etiam mentum vaporari exterius, et spongiis expressis ex aliqua coctione laxativae virtutis ad mitigandam materiam vel ex ipsa adhibere fomentum. tunc cerotaria apponenda probamus ex oleo ciprino vel irino; item malagmata sensim calefacientia. tunc lavacro atque vino et cibo vario utendum.

ac si tardi temporis dolor fuerit effectus, ut chronia passio
videatur, et nunc superpositionibus asperata, nunc lenimentis
emollita, oportebit superpositionis tempore[11] iisdem adiutoriis
perseverare; totum[12] vero corpus resumere, sicut frequenter
77 docuimus. praeterea tempore exercitii erit offerenda cera, quam
aegrotantes mordendo dentes exerceant, sicut nuper demonstravimus de paralysi scribentes. ultimo autem tempore gestatio[13]
erit adhibenda,[14] fricatio capitis atque oris, sed ipsius manibus
aegrotantis parvissima, plurima vero ex alienis, sed longitudine
temporis potius quam vehementia, ne caput nimietate moveatur. tunc ne partes refrigescant vel impleantur etiam a plurimis
erit corpus confricandum, ut duobus ministris ab humeris latera, et aliis duobus ab inguinibus crura.[15]

tunc resumptione paulo fortius erunt partes recorporatione
78 curandae, ut post fricationem strigili non obtuso vel asperis[16]

[11] tempore ⟨in⟩ R
[12] *fort.* tunc
[13] gestationis S: *corr.* R
[14] adhibenda ⟨et⟩ R
[15] crura *Rm*: curata *edd.*
[16] asperis *Rm*: aspero S

1. See 42.

75 patient can stand it. But first cover the adjacent parts by putting wool over them to prevent their becoming blistered, as they are prone to.

Other methods of applying heat are given by writers of old and may also be used. Thus take frankincense grains, warm over a fire, then wrap in a thin linen cloth, and place next to the aching teeth. The irritant properties of this hot vapor will have a restorative effect on the patient. Again, small amounts of finely powdered frankincense may be placed in a number of small linen bags; then each of these is dipped into hot olive oil and given to the patient to bite on with the aching teeth. Others again advise boiling a small quantity of squills in olive oil; but we think that this remedy should be postponed and that it should be employed only during the interval of remission, for, by reason of their acrid

76 quality, squills have a metasyncritic effect. In addition, apply warmth externally to the chin and lower jaw, and foment these parts with sponges wrung out of some relaxing decoction or directly with the decoction itself. This procedure will help soften the [congested] matter. Then apply cerates made with henna or iris oil, and emollient plasters having mild heating properties. Thereafter, prescribe bathing, wine, and varied food.

Now if the toothache becomes a long-standing ailment and is seen to be a chronic disease, marked now by exacerbations and now by intervals of remission, it will be necessary at the time of an attack to keep using the same remedies as described above and to give restorative treatment to the whole body, as we have

77 often indicated. And at exercise time give the patient wax to bite on as a means of strengthening the teeth, as we recently pointed out[1] in the chapter on paralysis. Toward the end [of the restorative treatment] prescribe passive exercise and massaging of the head and face. This massaging should be done almost entirely by attendants, and only in small part by the patient himself; and, to avoid agitating the head excessively, the treatment should be protracted in time rather than increased in intensity. Then, to prevent the parts from becoming chilled or congested, have the body massaged by a number of attendants, two, for example, massaging the sides from the shoulders down, and two others the legs from the groins down.

Then subject the parts to a metasyncritic treatment which is

78 somewhat more vigorous than the restorative treatment. Thus

pannis buccarum musculos usque ad ruborem fricari faciamus,
et nunc dropacem illiniri, tunc[17] etiam ipsos dentes atque gingivas vehementius fricari, dantes praeterea iugiter oleum calidum
sorbendum atque continendum et despuendum; item aquam
frigidam.[18] tunc interpositis duobus vel tribus diebus, ex humore in quo fuerit decocta mali punici cortex adhibemus oris
collutionem, vel in quo sit praetincta ignita galla, vel ex aquis
sua virtute medentibus. item dentium confricamentis utendum
quae constringere atque fortificare valeant, sicuti libris Medi-
79 caminum ordinavimus. vomitus vero post cibum factus omnibus est contrarius, et maxime in ista constitutis passione. item
non aliter venus obesse probatur et vinolentia.

multi autem veterum medicorum accessionis tempore ea medicamina adhibenda iusserunt quae anodyna Graeci vocaverunt,
nos indoloria dicere poterimus: quae aiunt nocturno tempore adhibenda, profecto sensum non dolorem auferentia. adhibent
etiam fumigationem dentibus, ut bitumen cum simili pondere
myrrhae vino conspersae, mollibus prunis impositae, tunc iubentes ore aperto aegrotantem fumum accipere, cum fuerit melius
haec propter inflationem capitis prohibere, et offerre mulsum
80 calidum vel quemquam mitigativum liquorem continendum vel,
ut aiunt, carbonibus infundendum, ut exinde exhalatione facta
solacium capiant aegrotantes. item iubent circumdandos atque
involvendos dentes ex opio, galbano, pipere vel lasere et peucedano et herba quam tithymalon vocant. haec quidem etiam
corruptis dentibus adhibenda probaverunt; necnon tenue linteolum apponendum praelinitum oleo cocto vel sale et cedria,
vel ex croco atque pipere longo et rosa recenti et ⟨iride⟩ illyrica,[19]
galbano, cocco cnidio, styrace, nitro cum melle medicamine confecto. quae omnia ob acrimoniam lenimenti tempore locum potuerint invenire, quamquam sit etiam fugienda satietas medica-
81 minum plurima. omitto quod tithymali sucus appositus dentes

---

[17] nunc *Rm*
[18] aquam frigidam *R*: aqua frigida *S* (*nulla interpunctione post* frigida): *cf. Friedel 32*
[19] ⟨iride⟩ illyrica *R*: *an* ⟨iri⟩ illyrica *vel* irillyrica?

after the massage use a sharp scraper or rough cloths to rub the
cheeks to the point of redness. Again, at times have a pitch
plaster applied to these parts, and at other times have the teeth
and gums themselves vigorously rubbed. And repeatedly give
the patient warm olive oil to take into his mouth, hold there,
and spit out; have him do the same with cold water. Then after
an interval of two or three days prescribe as a mouth wash water
in which pomegranate rind has been boiled, or in which burned
oak galls have been soaked, or other waters with curative properties.[2] And use such dentifrices as can stiffen and strengthen
79 the teeth, as we have prescribed in our work *On Drugs*. But to
provoke vomiting after eating is harmful in general, and particularly so in this disease. Venery and the excessive drinking of wine
are also harmful.

Many of the ancient medical writers have the patient, at the
time of an attack, take drugs which the Greeks call *anōdyna* and
which in Latin we may call *indoloria* ['pain-allaying']. They prescribe these drugs at night. Now the fact is that such drugs
remove the sensation of pain, but not the affection itself. These
writers also prescribe fumes for the teeth. For instance, they mix
equal weights of bitumen and myrrh, sprinkle with wine, and
place over gently burning coals; they then have the patient
receive the vapors with open mouth. But it would be better to
avoid these substances because of their tendency to congest the
30 head, and to substitute warm mead or some other soothing fluid.
These may either be taken in the mouth directly and kept there
or, as these writers say, poured over the hot coals, so that the
patient may obtain relief by inhaling the vapor thus created.
And these same writers prescribe that the teeth be covered over
with the juice of poppy, allheal, pepper, laserwort, sulphurwort,
or the plant they call 'tithymallos' [spurge]. They prescribe the
use of these substances even for teeth that are decayed, and suggest applying a small thin piece of linen first dipped in boiled
olive oil, or in a solution of salt and Syrian cedar oil, or in preparations made from saffron, long pepper, fresh rose, Illyrian iris,
allheal, Cnidian berry, storax, or nitrum, and mixed with honey.
Because of their acrid properties, all these preparations would
be more appropriate for the intervals of remission, though even
1 then a great abundance of drugs should be avoided. Moreover,

2. Cf. *Chr.* i. 111. The reference is to the appropriate mineral waters.

infringat: non aliter etiam pericharacteres[20] exhibiti qui dentium
dolores mitigent, locorum mortem faciunt et ipsorum dentium
laxitatem **[21] qui aiunt ungendas gingivas accessionis tempore
amurca, aut[22] simili modo infecta lana ex oleo veteri et myrrha,
cum vino et oleo resoluta atque ⟨in⟩ crassitudinem[23] mellis de-
ducta, cum secundum methodon aliud sit tempus medicaminum
lacessentium.

    item alii praesente dolore in contrariae[23a] partis auricula aiunt
balsami sucum mittendum, cum sucis supradictis simili modo
82 vel oleo,[24] his omnibus resolutis vel oleo decoctis, aut in quo
decocta sint ederae nigrae folia decem et squillae medium in
olivae magnitudine,[24a] spe avocandae materiae depravati, vel
maioris doloris illati causam anteriorem avocantes, obscurantes
avocatis sensibus aegrotantes. item alii eius partis quae dentis
dolorem sustinet nari ederae sucum infundentes cum olei parte
dimidia, ex ferramento quod rinenchyton[25] vocant, adhibentes
etiam sternutamenta et apophlegmatismos et oris[26] medicamina, quae iugiter aiunt apponenda et sint virtutis lacessentis,
quae stomatica vocant, quorum singula tamquam recorporativa, non mitigativa, in lenimento adhibere probamus.

83   item alii statim ad auferendos dentes dolore pulsatos accur-
runt, nescii quoniam detractio amissio partis est, non sanatio.
quapropter sicut alias quoque partes in tumore constitutas non
detractione sed mitigatione curamus, sic etiam dentes concuran-
dos accipimus. etenim si quisquam dentium fuerit exesus, exigit
primo mitigationem, tunc sui detractionem faciendam, quippe
cum non sit a periculo remotum doloris tempore dentes auferre,
et maxime integros, hoc est qui non fuerint exesi vel corrupti aut
mobiles: consensus etenim superiorum partium necessario se-

[20] pericharacteres *Rm*: ferreici aetheres *S*

[21] *lacunam indicavi. fort. suppl.* ⟨item peccant⟩ *vel sim.*

[22] aut *Rm*: cum *S*

[23] ⟨in⟩ crassitudinem *Rm*: crassitudine *S*

[23a] contraria *S*: *corr. Rm*

[24] oleo *Rm*: folio *S*

[24a] magnitudinem *R*

[25] *fort.* r(h)inenchyten   [26] odoris *S*: *corr. Rm*

3. The text of this and the preceding sentence is very uncertain. For one thing, *pericharacteres* is a doubtful restoration, Caelius himself having prescribed the use of the

the application of tithymallos weakens the teeth. And the use of instruments [to cut round the gums] in order to relieve the tooth-ache only causes gangrene of the [surrounding] parts and loosen-ing of the teeth themselves. [They are also in error] who pre-scribe rubbing the gums with the lees of olive oil at the time of an attack.[3] The same is true of those who prescribe an applica-tion with wool dipped in a mixture of old olive oil and a solution of myrrh in wine and olive oil, the solution having been brought to the consistency of honey. For, according to the Methodist Sect, the period of exacerbation is not the proper time for irri-tant drugs.

2   Some hold that, when pain is present, opobalsam should be injected into the ear on the side opposite the pain, along with the other juices mentioned above or olive oil. They dissolve all these juices by boiling them in plain olive oil or in oil in which ten leaves of black ivy and the inner part of a squill the size of an olive have been boiled. Thus in their perverse hope of bringing out the diseased matter, they succeed only in bringing out an even more severe affection and in beclouding the patient by rob-bing him of his senses. And others inject ivy juice with half as much olive oil into the nostril on the same side as the toothache; they use for this purpose an instrument called *rhinenchytēs*. They also prescribe sternutatories and drugs to purge away phlegm. And they prescribe the continual use of drugs for the mouth (Greek *stomatica*) which have irritant properties. Since in each case they are metasyncritic rather than relaxing, we recommend their use only in the interval of remission.

3   Others hasten to pull teeth as soon as they ache intensely. They are not aware that such removal is the loss of a part, not its cure. But just as we treat other inflamed parts not by remov-ing them but by relieving them, we hold that teeth, too, should be treated in the same way. Thus if a tooth is eaten away, the first requirement is the relief of the affection; only thereafter should the tooth be removed. For the pulling of teeth during an attack of pain is fraught with danger, and this is especially true of sound teeth, that is to say, those which are not decayed, in-jured, or loose. In fact, the higher parts,[4] as well as the [jaw]

instrument (74), though perhaps only as an emergency measure. *Altheres* (*S*) cannot easily be identified with *alt(h)eres*, 43.

4. E.g., the head.

84 quetur et musculorum et oculorum. Herophilus denique et Heraclides Tarentinus mori quosdam detractione dentis memoraverunt. nam Erasistratus plumbeum inquit odontagogum, quod nos dentiducum dicere poterimus, apud Delphum in Apollinis templo ostentationis causa propositum, quo demonstratur oportere eos dentes auferri qui sint faciles, vel mobilitate laxati, vel quibus sufficiat plumbei ferramenti conamen ad summum. si[27] autem putant quod omnis dens dolore vexatus et qui nocet[28] sanos est detrahendus, oportet etiam omnes auferri si omnes fuerint dolore possessi. quomodo autem sint auferendi dentes exesi vel moti, nisi servari potuerint, libris Medicinalium responsionum docuimus.

85   ac si aliquando ex humore gingivarum visi fuerint commoveri, oportet constrictivis uti collutionibus, quarum materiam[29] ex parte superius diximus. adhibendum oleum lentiscinum et aquae[30] caelestes et lac asininum (est enim densabile); item decoctio mali punici vel gallae aut acaciae aut rosae aut murtae nigrae aut mali cydonii vel platani baccae. ungendae praeterea gingivae medicamine quod appellamus diamoron,[31] item dioporon,[32] et diaroos, et diomphaciu,[33] et oenanthino.[34] item si quaedam emerserit gingivarum sanguinatio, corallii tusi pulvis cretus atque[35] intus ponendus, et alumen cum melle; item eruca cum aceto apponenda. sed haec sunt primo concoquenda iugi motu versata.

86   ## V. DE APPREHENSIONE SIVE OPPRESSIONE, QUAM GRAECI CATALEPSIN APPELLANT

Hanc passionem veteres tamquam specialem vel propriam tradiderunt, quasi nullo ex genere venientem, ut Chrysippus memorat. sed[1] de ipsa Niceratus conscripsit librum probans scilicet etiam veteribus medicis cognitam, quod nos confirmamus. sed quia nunc tarda nunc celer a Methodicis adprobatur,

[27] si *Schmid RPh 51*: sic S
[28] necet S: *corr. Rm* (*nisi scribas* nec est sanus)
[29] materiae S: *corr. Rm*
[30] aquas S: *corr. Rm*
[31] diamaron S: *corr. Rm*
[32] diaporos S (diaporon S, *Chr. ii. 170*)
[33] diomphacion S: *an* diomphacon?

[34] oenanthio S: oenanthinum *Rm*
[35] atque *om.* R
[1] sed *Rm*: quod S

muscles and the eyes, are of necessity sympathetically affected. Thus Herophilus and Heraclides of Tarentum report cases of death due to the pulling of a tooth. And Erasistratus says that a lead dental forceps (Greek *odontagōgon*, which we may call *denti-ducum* in Latin) is prominently displayed in the temple of Apollo at Delphi for the purpose of showing that those teeth should be pulled which are ready to come out or are loose and shaky, in short, those requiring for extraction no more than the pull of a lead instrument. But if these physicians[5] hold that every aching tooth which harms sound teeth should be pulled, it follows that, whenever there is general pain through all the teeth, all the teeth should be pulled. Now we have pointed out in our medical treatise entitled *Answers*[6] how decayed or loose teeth should be extracted, but only if they cannot be saved.

And if it appears that teeth have become loose because of a discharge from the gums, use astringent mouth washes.[7] We have described, above, the composition of some of these.[8] And one may use mastic oil, rain water, and ass's milk (for this has astringent properties); also a decoction of pomegranate, oak gall, acacia, rose, black myrtle, quince, or the fruit of the plane tree. In addition, anoint the gums with the so-called 'mulberry ointment' or the ointments that employ fruits, sumach, omphacium, or oenanthe. And if there is any bleeding from the gums, insert at these places finely powdered and sifted coral and alum with honey. Also apply rocket with vinegar; but, before doing so, boil them together, stirring constantly.

V. SEIZURE OR DEPRESSION
(GREEK *CATALĒPSIS*)

THE ancients speak of catalepsy as a unique or peculiar disease, that is, one which, as Chrysippus says, does not belong to any general class. And Niceratus in his book on the disease shows that it was known to the ancients, a conclusion with which we agree. Now we have given a full account of catalepsy

5. I.e., those who pull teeth indiscriminately. But the text is uncertain.

6. Probably in the surgical books of this treatise. Cf. *Chr.* ii. 27; iv. 3; v. 63, 66.

7. There may be some dislocation of the text here, for the material of sec. 85 would ordinarily come before the refutation of the practices of other physicians.

8. Cf. 72.

quamquam sit a nobis Celerum passionum libris plenissime tra-
87 dita, etiam nunc erit ordinanda, quippe saepe in tardum veniens
motum, et propterea chronia nuncupanda.

sequitur autem patientes febricula, et vocis amputatio, cum
oculis patentibus[2] atque impalpebratione, difficilior[3] eo tempore
quo statum sumpserit accessio, et omnis immobilitas, cum palpebrarum impossibili[4] atque horrenti positione, quae declinatione facta aliqua ex parte accipiat motum. etenim admota
manu ac digitis circumtractis oculis tenus, palpebrare cognoscitur[5] aegrotans, atque obtutu internota translatione[6] manus in
88 qualibet parte[7] declinata sequetur converso scilicet vultu. dehinc inclamati intendunt, lacrimantes sine ulla responsione. et
si odoramenta iucunda fuerint admota, declinatione quadam
moveri intelliguntur, frequenter adducentes spiritum hauriendae
exhalationis causa. ac[8] si tetra odoramenta fuerint admota, recusare videntur ac fugere. item dulcia atque amara ori admota,
labiis vel linguae illita, sentiunt; non aliter si ulla fuerint punctione pulsati. ex[9] nostro officio tentam manum suo[10] replicant
vel colligunt. item lacessiti collugent, ingemunt, attestante vultus rubore, cum pulsu magno ex vehementibus atque fortioribus
saltibus confecto.

89 in declinatione vero plurimus saepe sudor sequetur ac fervens,
et in dimissione limpidae sinceritati proximi efficiuntur. ac rursum in accessionem si redeunt aegrotantes, peiorante passione
plurimus fervor accedit cutis, et spiratio celerrima, quam Graeci
tachypnoean vocant, oculorum conversio, manuum contractio,
sudoris ignei defluxio, maculis emergentibus in thoracem atque
vultum, et primo rotundis[11] in similitudine[12] ulcerum quae iontus
appellant.

90 item ab apoplecticis haec discernitur passio, quod in ipsis parvus atque creber pulsus inveniatur, et non ut in catalepticis
maior atque percussibilis; et neque iucundum sive tetrum odorem accipiant; neque dulcia et amara consapiant. item ab his
qui ex stomachi passione obmutescunt, siquidem in his rursum
parvus atque imbecillis pulsus inveniatur, attestante singultu

---

[2] patientibus *S*: *corr. R*   [3] *fort.* difficiliore   [4] immobili *Rm, sed cf.* possibilem
Ac. iii. 74   [5] palpebra recognoscitur aegrotantis *S*: *corr. Schmid 88*   [6] transla-
tionem *R*   [7] quamlibet partem *R*   [8] at *R*   [9] et *Rm*   [10] subito *Rm*
[11] rotundus *S*: *corr. Rm*   [12] similitudinem *Rm, ut freq. ap. Cael.*

in the treatise *On Acute Diseases*.[1] But, since this disease is considered by the Methodists to be acute in some cases and chronic in others, we must discuss it here too. For it often occurs in a slow form and for that reason should then be considered chronic.

The signs of catalepsy are as follows: fever, loss of voice, eyes wide open and hardly ever blinking, the condition becoming more serious at the highest stage of the attack. The eyelids are entirely immobile, being stiff and unable to be lowered. In the decline of the attack their mobility is partially recovered. Thus when the hand and fingers are brought up to the eyes and drawn across them, the patient is found to blink; he discerns the hand as it moves, and wherever it is carried he follows it with steady gaze, turning his head in that direction.[2] And when called, the patient turns toward the caller but weeps without making any answer. If pleasant-smelling substances are brought near him, he shows that he is attracted by turning toward them, and frequently draws in his breath to inhale the odor. But if foul odors are brought near him, he shows his displeasure and withdraws. Again, if sweet or bitter substances are brought to his mouth and smeared on his lips or tongue, he shows that he is aware; so, too, he reacts to pricking. If we stretch out his arm, he retracts or draws it back. When irritated, he weeps or whines. His face is flushed, and his pulse is large, consisting of strong, firm beats.

In the decline of the attack there is often profuse and warm sweating; and in the interval of remission the patient is practically free from any symptoms of disease. Then, if there is a new attack, as the disease grows worse, the skin becomes very hot, respiration rapid (Greek *tachypnoea*), eyes distorted, and hands clenched. A burning hot sweat pours forth; and spots appear on the chest and face, round at first like the eruptions which the Greeks call *ionthoe*.

Catalepsy may be distinguished from apoplexy, for in the latter the pulse is found to be small and thick and not, as in catalepsy, large and firm. Again, the patient in apoplexy is insensitive to smells, whether pleasant or offensive, and does not taste sweet or bitter. Catalepsy may also be distinguished from loss of voice occurring in disease of the esophagus, for again in the latter the pulse is small and weak, and there are hiccoughs and

---

1. *Ac.* ii. 56 ff.   2. The text of the whole sentence is uncertain.

cum manifesto tumore in stomacho apparente. haec est discretio similium passionum. sed ei curatio adhibenda est quae epilepticis dicta est.

91 ## VI. DE VOCIS AMPUTATIONE, QUAM GRAECI
PHONES APOCOPEN VOCANT

Vocis amputatio fiet ex clamore nimio, aut frigore, aut ardore
sive ustura, faucibus asperatis, vel etiam tumore nimio. fit
autem obtusio sonitus emissae per spiritum vocis, atque hirta vel
aspirationis tractu gravata locutio.

recenti denique passioni atque eius initio convenit adhibita
requies cum abstinentia cibi, et spongiarum cum[1] aqua frigida
expressarum admotio gutturi[2] per ambitum faucium, quem an-
92 thereona vocant. ac si passio vehementescere coeperit, ut maiora deposcat adiutoria, adhibenda phlebotomia. tunc sorbilibus
cibis nutriendi, adhibitis etiam gargarismis ex oleo dulci atque
calido, sive calida ex oleo, vel aqua mulsa, aut decoctione uvarum, cantabri, ficuum pinguium, palmularum, glycyrrhizae, necnon etiam suco alicae vel ptisanae, ut ex eorum vaporatione sive
exhalatione ascensum spiritus[3] rapiant aegrotantes. tunc etiam
spongiarum adhibenda vaporatio atque usus electariorum ex
melle decocto et nucleis et lini semine et ovorum vitellis et draganto ex mulso et vino[4] praemollito. dehinc sorbili ex amygdalis
93 medicamine utendum; in declinatione vero lavacro atque vario
cibo et vino, deambulatione vel gestatione.

ac si querela tardaverit aegrotantium, erit in lenimento adhibenda drimyphagia, dropacismus, defricatio, tunc etiam vomitus
ex radicibus atque varia gestatio et vocis exercitatio,[5] quod
Graeci anaphonesin vocant, adhibito praeceptore, sicuti iam dudum docuimus, temporum ordine servato. adhibenda etiam et
arteriaca medicamina quae partes in passione constitutas exerceant, a Graecis amyctica appellata, quorum compositionem
libris Medicaminum conscriptam dedimus.

---

[1] *an* ex? *fort. del.*

[2] gutturi *R*: gutturis *S*

[3] accensum spiritum *edd.*: *fort.* ascensu spiritum

[4] [ex] mulso ex vino *Rm*

[5] gestatione et vocis exercitatione *S*: *corr. R*

an obvious inflammation in the esophagus. That is how we distinguish catalepsy from diseases similar to it. As for treatment, however, the same should be administered in catalepsy as has been set forth for epilepsy.

VI. LOSS OF VOICE (GREEK *PHŌNĒS APOCOPĒ*)

Loss of voice is caused by loud shouting or exposure to cold or heat, with irritation of the throat or severe inflammation. The patient can utter only a weak sound as he whispers his words, and the sound laboriously produced by the breath is hoarse and subdued.

If the affection is a new one and just beginning, rest and fasting should be prescribed. Apply sponges wrung out of cold water externally to the throat, passing along the area under the chin (Greek *anthereōn*). And if the disease begins to grow worse and requires major remedies, perform venesection. Then nourish the patient with gruel-like foods; and employ gargles of warm sweet olive oil, warm water and olive oil, hydromel, a decoction of grapes, bran, juicy figs, dates, or sweetroot, or gruels of spelt groats or pearl barley. Thus the patient will catch the vapor arising as a warm exhalation from these substances. Also apply heat with sponges and use electuaries made with boiled honey, pine kernels, flaxseed, egg yolks, and tragacanth previously softened in a mixture of honey and wine. And there is a liquid preparation made with almonds which may also be used. In the declining phase prescribe bathing, varied food, wine, and walking or passive exercise.

If the disease becomes chronic, treat the patient during the interval of remission with acrid diet, pitch plasters, massage, radishes as vomitives, varied passive exercise, and vocal exercise (Greek *anaphōnēsis*) under the guidance of a teacher, as we have indicated above.[1] In all these treatments the proper time sequence must be adhered to. Employ also medicines for the windpipe, preparations which the Greeks call *amyctica* ['irritant'], for the purpose of stimulating the parts affected. We have described the composition of all these medicines in the section *On Drugs*.[2]

1. Vocal exercise is a regular part of the metasyncritic treatment (cf. *Chr.* i. 37, 164).
2. I.e., of the treatise entitled *Responsiones*.

94   VII. DE INFLUXIONE, QUAM GRAECI
CATARRHON VOCANT

FIET influxio nunc ad nares, quae appellatur coryza, nunc ad fauces, quae appellatur branchos, nunc ad thoracem vel pulmonem, quae appellatur ptisis.[1]

sequitur autem eos qui coryza vexantur gravedo, narium et frontis constrictio, fluor humoris[2] tenuissimi primo, tunc crassi atque viridis, sternutatio iugis, cum lacrimatione oculorum acrioris qualitatis vel mordentis, aliquando etiam tussiculae impar atque obtusa apprehensio, item consensus sessionis oculorum, cum capitis atque vultus inflatione.

95   eos autem qui faucium influxione vexantur, sive quod Graeci branchos, quam nos raucitatem vocamus, sequitur pruritus quidam secundum fauces atque titillatus, vox obtusa et gravis et impedita locutio, ut se praefocari sentiant aegrotantes, aliquando etiam tussicula et transvoratio difficilis.

ac si ad pulmones fuerit facta defluxio, thoracis gravedo sequetur et tussicula vehemens, cum sputis spumosis atque crassioribus tum saniosis, attestante difficultate spiritus, quam Graeci dyspnoean vocant, aliquando etiam febricula quae noctis initio sumat exordium, cum vocis obtusione et vomitu cibi.

96   sed haec passio a peripleumonia discernitur, siquidem sit una ex tardis passionibus et neque celeri atque acuta febricula corpus afficiat. item discernitur a rheumatismo thoracis sive influxione, quod ceteris communibus signis sequentibus dolor etiam inesse videatur in ea parte thoracis quae pati perspicitur.

sunt autem antecedentes,[3] ex quibus influxiones supradictae nascuntur, ut saepe probatur, perfrictio[4] profunda vel extensio vomitus.[5]

veterum igitur Methodicorum alii stricturam hanc passionem vocaverunt, velut expressis humoribus atque coactis in alia ve-

---

[1] ptysis S   [2] fluor humoris *Friedel 30, coll. Diaet. pass. 74*: fluorum oris S
[3] ⟨causae⟩ antecedentes R, *sed cf. Sor. Gyn., p. 95. 27, Bendz 52*
[4] perfricatio S: *corr. Rm*   [5] vocis *Am*

VII. FLUX (GREEK *CATARRHUS*)

FLUX [catarrh] occurs in some cases to the nostrils and is called 'coryza'; in other cases to the throat, and is called 'branchos'; and in still other cases to the chest and lungs and is called 'phthisis.'[1]

Those suffering from coryza have a sensation of heaviness [in the head], and of tightness in the nostrils and forehead; the fluid discharge [from the nostrils] is at first thin and then thick and greenish. There is continual sneezing, accompanied by acrid and irritant tearing at the eyes. Sometimes there is a weak cough and an attack of hoarseness. There is a sympathetic pain at the base of the eyes; head and face are puffed up.

Those suffering from catarrh of the throat, an affection which the Greeks call *branchos* and we may in Latin call *raucitas* ['hoarseness'], have an itching or tickling sensation in the throat. The voice is hoarse and low-pitched, and speech is so impeded that the patient feels that he is choking. Sometimes there occur coughing and difficulty in swallowing.

In cases where the flux is to the lungs, there is a feeling of heaviness in the chest. Violent coughing occurs with thick, frothy, and later sanious sputa; difficulty of breathing (Greek *dyspnoea*) is also present. In some cases there is a fever beginning at nightfall and accompanied by hoarseness and by vomiting of food.

Now this form of catarrh may be distinguished from pneumonia, since it is chronic and does not produce a swift and acute fever in the body. And it may also be distinguished from a [non-catarrhal] state of flow in the chest,[2] because in the catarrhal case, apart from the signs common to both diseases, pain is found in the affected part of the chest.

The predisposing causes from which these catarrhal fluxes arise are generally a severe cold and the strain of vomiting.

Of the early Methodist physicians, some hold that this disease involves a state of stricture. Their argument is that the disease

1. What Caelius (Soranus) seems to mean is 'may lead to phthisis.' Cf. *Chr.* ii. 196, Esc. 13 *in.*, and Theod. Prisc., p. 158. 10. The reading *ptysis* (*S*) can hardly be interpreted either as πτύσις, 'spitting,' or *tussis*, 'coughing.'

2. The distinction, which is not very clearly put, seems to be between (1) a catarrhal flux which terminates in the chest (the origin might, according to some ancient theories, be the head) and (2) a flux which *originates* in the chest.

97 nire loca eam fieri asserentes; alii solutionem, ut Thessalus mani-
festat atque eius decessores, ut Themison. Mnaseas vero et
Soranus, cuius etiam nos amamus iudicium, complexam inquiunt
esse passionem, et nunc strictura superante, nunc solutione.
etenim constrictio atque dolor accidentia sunt stricturae, quae
Graeci symptomata vocant; multorum vero liquidorum egestio
solutionis est signum.

quapropter obtinente strictura convenit aegrotos iacere loco
lucido mediocriter atque calido, adhibita abstinentia usque ad
tertium diem, quem Graeci diatriton vocant, cum requie corporis atque animi, appositis lanis limpidis ac mollibus oleo dulci
98 atque calido praetinctis, colla circumdantes et thoracem. tunc
oris collutio adhibenda sive fotus ex aqua calida. in ipsa autem
diatrito perungi⁶ aegrotantes oleo calido atque dulci, fovenda
facies ex aqua calida, cibus dandus sorbilis ex alica vel farre, oleo
et anetho vel parvo sale confecto vel ex melle, aut alicae ex mulso
confectae⁷ sorbilis transvoratio, non sine cautione atque coniectura utriusque passionis, ne alteram faciat superiorem.

ac si passio permanserit, alia die cataplasmata laxativa adhibemus, his scilicet partibus quae fuerint in querela. tunc cucurbitam infigentes scarificamus, ac deinde spongiis vaporantes
99 loca relaxamus aut calidis lanis contegemus narium partes. tunc
gargarismum damus calidum mulsum, aut decoctionem cantabri
et palmularum pinguium et mixarum⁸ et glycyrrhizae, vel eius
sucum resolutum⁹ ex aliquo liquore laxativo. item electarium
dabimus ex lini seminibus et sesami frixi acetabulis singulis, et
ovi elixi vitello, et nucleis numero viginti, et amygdalis amaris
expolitis decem, amyli¹⁰ drachma una, traganti drachma una
passo cretico demollita,¹¹ et mellis decocti¹² sufficienti.¹³ quod
medicamen in avellanae modum sumptum sub lingua teneant
aegrotantes, tunc defluens ac deliquatum¹⁴ sensim atque paula-

⁶ perungendi *Rm*
⁷ alicae ex mulso confectae *Rm*: alica ex mulso confecta *S*
⁸ noxarum *S*: corr. *Rm* (myx-). *cf. Cass. Fel. ind. (Rose)*
⁹ succo resoluto *S*: corr. *Rm*
¹⁰ ampli *S*: corr. *Rm*
¹¹ demollito *S*: emollita *Rm*: *an* demolliti? demollitis?
¹² melle decocto *Rm*
¹³ sufficientis *S*: corr. *R*
¹⁴ desiccatum *S*: eliquatum *Rm*

occurs when fluids are pressed out [of their normal channels] and
97 forced to run to other places. Others hold that it involves a state
of looseness. This is the opinion openly held by Thessalus and,
among his predecessors, Themison. But Mnaseas and Soranus,
with whose judgment we agree, declare that catarrh is a mixed
disease in which sometimes a state of stricture predominates and
sometimes a state of looseness. For the constriction and pain are
concomitants (Greek *symptōmata*) of a state of stricture; while
the copious discharge of fluids is a sign of a state of looseness.

Now when a state of stricture predominates, the patient
should lie in a moderately light and warm room. He should take
no food until the end of the three-day period (Greek *diatritos*)
but should have complete rest of body and mind. Place soft
scoured wool dipped in warm sweet olive oil around his neck and
98 chest. Then have him wash or foment his mouth with warm
water. At the end of the three-day period anoint the patient's
body with warm sweet olive oil, and foment his face with warm
water. Give him gruel-like food consisting of spelt groats or
ground spelt prepared with olive oil, dill, and a little salt, or
with honey; or let him take spelt groats softened in mead. Watch
both elements of the disease carefully and see that the food prescribed does not cause one of these elements to predominate
over the other.

Now if the disease persists, apply relaxing poultices the next
day to the parts affected. Then employ cupping with scarification, and after this treatment soothe the parts by applications
of heat with sponges or by covering the nasal parts with warm
99 wool. Then have the patient gargle with warm mead or a decoction of bran, juicy dates, sebesten plums,[3] and sweetroot, or a
solution of the juice of the latter in some fluid which has relaxing properties. Also give him an electuary made with a quarter
of a hemina of flaxseed, the same amount of roasted sesame seed,
the yolk of a boiled egg, twenty pine kernels, ten blanched bitter almonds, a drachm of starch, and a drachm of tragacanth
softened with Cretan raisin wine and a sufficient amount of
boiled honey. The patient should take this electuary, made to
the size of an avellan nut, and hold it under his tongue; then,
as it melts and runs down, he may swallow it a little at a time.

---

3. Greek *myxa* also signifies *coryza*. Is the use of the fruit in the treatment a survival
of some magical procedure?

100 tim transvorent; vel mel oleo concoctum. multi autem [sub][15] fabam fractam, quod Graeci etnos acton vocant, idque linguae suppositum ac defluens transvoretur,[16] quo asperitas arteriae liniatur; vel ex amilo et ex menta et amygdalis amaris confectum medicamen, quod habeat palmularum dulcium contritarum drachmas octo, et nucleorum drachmas quatuor, et amygdalae purgatae drachmas duas, glycyrrhizae suci obolum unum, hoc est drachmae partem sextam, draganti drachmam unam, collectis omnibus atque infusis ex vino protropo. ac si venter officium
101 non agnoverit, simplici ventris laxativo utendum. et si fuerit caput gravatum, adhibenda detonsio, appositis deinde laxativis medicaminibus. tunc cibus alternis diebus dandus. cum autem passio mitescere coeperit, danda olera, ut malva, lapathum, atriplex, quam Graeci andraphasin[17] vocant, beta cum ptisanae suco vel alica aut mulso, et pisces teneri et volantum teneriora. ipsis etiam locis apponenda cerotaria ex meliloto concocto[18] confecta, vel malagmata simplicia. tunc lavacrum atque vinum adhibendum.

ac si superans fuerit defluxio, quam Graeci reumatismum vocant, simili abstinentia utendum est frequenter, sed frigido atque obscuro mediocriter loco aegrotantes iacere iubemus, et absti-
102 nendos a potu, quo sitiendo siccentur. cuius usus cum fuerit permissus, vel oris collutio frigida ex aqua paulatim atque parva probatur. tunc appositio spongiarum ex aqua frigida expressarum vel pusca iisdem partibus quae fluore vexantur, hoc est thoraci atque gutturis summitati, quam Graeci anthereona vocant, nos rumam, aut lanae limpidae infusae oleo viridi conveniunt. dehinc dabimus ore continendam vel gargarizandam aquam frigidam vel puscam aut sucum herbae caliclaris,[19] quam Graeci helxinen vocant, aut plantaginis, quam iidem arnoglossam[20] vocant, aut uvam lupinam, quam strychnon nominant,
103 aut intybi aut endiviae decoctionem aut buxi aut rosarum, item lenticulae, palmarum thebaicarum, lentisci virgultis, aut rubi, quam baton appellant, singulis vel in unum mixtis pro passionis magnitudine, aliquando etiam diamoron sive diasycaminon, cuius nota compositio atque Medicaminum libris tradita comprobatur, ex aliquo[21] supradictorum liquore soluta.

tunc etiam epithemata constrictiva adhibemus, ut est mel de-

---

[15] sub *seclusi*: *fort.* dant: subiciunt *Rm*   [16] transvorant *R*   [17] andraphaxin *Rm*
[18] cocto *R*   [19] calidaris *S*: calycularis *Rm*   [20] arnoglossum *R*   [21] aliqua *S*: *corr. Rm*

Or employ honey cooked in olive oil. Many use a thick soup of crushed beans (Greek *etnos acton*), which should be placed under the patient's tongue and swallowed as it flows down; in this way the irritation of the trachea will be relieved. There is also a remedy compounded of starch, mint, and bitter almonds, with eight drachms of crushed sweet dates, four drachms of pine kernels, two drachms of blanched almonds, one obol—that is, one-sixth of a drachm—of sweetroot juice, and one drachm of tragacanth, all mixed together and soaked in wine of the first flow. If the bowels do not function, use a simple laxative; again, if there is a feeling of heaviness in the head, cut the patient's hair and apply relaxing drugs. Then give food on alternate days. And when the attack begins to decline, let the patient have vegetables, e.g., mallows, dock, orach (Greek *andraphaxys*), and beets with pearl barley gruel, spelt groats, or mead; also tender fish and tender fowl. Apply cerates made with boiled melilot to the parts affected, or employ, instead, simple emollient plasters. Afterward prescribe bathing and the use of wine.

Now if the state of flux (Greek *rheumatismos*) predominates, fasting should still be frequently prescribed. But have the patient lie in a moderately cool and dark room and do not permit him to drink; for, if he refrains from drink, he will dry out more easily. Or if some liquid is permitted, let him take a little cold water from time to time as a mouth wash. Then apply sponges wrung out of cold water or vinegar water to the parts affected by the flux, that is, to the chest and the upper end of the throat (Greek *anthereōn*, Latin *ruma*); scoured wool dipped in green olive oil[4] is also a suitable application. Then have the patient hold in his mouth and gargle cold water, vinegar water, juice of the pellitory plant (Greek *helxinē*), plantain (Greek *arnoglōsson*), uva lupina (Greek *strychnos*), or a decoction of endive, box, roses, slips of lentil, Theban dates, mastic, or bramble (Greek *batos*). Any of these may be taken alone or they may be mixed together, depending on the severity of the case. In some cases the mulberry drug (*diamoron* or *diasycaminon*), the composition of which is well known and is set forth in the section *On Drugs*, may be taken dissolved in any of the aforementioned liquids.

Then apply locally such astringent preparations as honey

---

4. I.e., oil of unripe olives (= ἔλαιον ὠμοτριβές). The term *omphacium* sometimes denoted a better type of oil of unripe olives (cf. Pliny *HN* xxiii. 79).

coctum cum alumine schisto, aequis ponderibus, vel aceto et
aloe, aut ex palmulis et malis cydoniis et his similibus; item cucurbitam constrictivam et electaria vel catapotia, ut est diacodion simplex, et vinum scilliticum[22] coctum donec mellis habeat
104 crassitudinem, solum vel cum melle, admixto etiam cumino, item
creticum vinum vel passum similiter decoctum aut tyrrhenum
vel protropum et omne quod adiuncta dulcedine constringit, ut
arteriam leniat atque desiccet humorem. item mel admixto modico cumino concoctum, vel persicae lacrima,[23] vel plantaginis
aridae contusae atque cretae pulvere, vel rosarum aridarum et
aluminis, item trocisci medicaminis trigoni appellati.

tunc cibi ordinandi supradictis iamdudum temporibus, sed
constrictivae qualitatis, ut est oryza vel alica ex pusca vel aqua
frigida confecta, aut decoctio palmularum thebaicarum; item
ova hapala vel pultes parvissimo atque viridi oleo confectae,
105 ⟨ex⟩[24] oryza vel milio aut pulento frixo aut alica aut farre, aut
ex amylo vel ex ges astere,[25] et melle decocto admixto quiddam[26]
supradictis, quo coagulentur et virtutem medendi maiorem sumant. item thebanarum palmularum decoctarum admixtione
in pulmentis uti possumus, vel ex aridis palmulis pane confecto
et oleo viridi atque rore syriaco vel aceto et galla. ipsa quoque
pulmenta aut cibos aridos dare debemus; tunc hapala ova vel lac
decocta cum amylo ad modum cotylae[27] vel duarum, quod est
106 pondus unciarum decem vel viginti. dehinc danda olera constringentia, ut intyba, plantago, cauliculi, sed haec omnia cocta
atque aceto condita; tunc pisces durioris corporis atque volantia
non pinguia sed magis torrida, vel ex aceto et aqua cocta. tunc
declinante passione vinum dandum est asperioris naturae. dehinc adhibenda gestatio praetecto ore, quo spiratio nulla tangatur iniuria. dehinc lavacro utendum.

ac si passio tardaverit, superpositionibus ac lenimentis variata, erit in lenimento adhibenda deambulatio et vocis exercitium
mite; tunc levis unctio ac defricatio. et cibi ex media materia

---

[22] squilliticum *Sm*: scivelliticum *S*: Scybeliticum *Rm*: Scybelitem *Reinesius 666*

[23] lachrymo *S*: *corr. Rm*

[24] ⟨ex⟩ *supplevi*: ⟨et⟩ *R*

[25] astere *Rm*: asteros *S* (*cf. 174*)

[26] quidem *Rm*

[27] cotylae ⟨unius⟩ *R*

boiled down with an equal weight of fissile alum, vinegar, aloes, or the juice of dates, quinces, and the like. And employ astringent cupping and electuaries or pills, such as the simple poppyhead preparation, and wine of squills,[5] boiled down until it has the consistency of honey. This latter preparation may be taken alone or with honey to which cumin has been added. Cretan wine or raisin wine similarly boiled down, Tyrrhenian wine, wine of the first flow, or, in fact, every wine which combines sweetness with an astringent effect may be used to relieve the trachea and at the same time dry up the flux. Use may also be made of honey cooked with the addition of a small amount of cumin, peach-tree gum, or powder obtained from plantain by drying, pounding up, and sifting it, or from dried roses or alum, or the so-called 'trigonos troches.'

Food should be prescribed at the times already indicated. But the food should be binding in character, e.g., rice or spelt groats prepared in vinegar water or cold water, a decoction of Theban dates, soft eggs, or porridges of roasted rice, millet, pearl barley, spelt groats, ground spelt, starch, or Samian clay, and only a very little green olive oil. Honey boiled down should be added in some measure to the preparations just mentioned to give them greater consistency and to increase their healing properties. Boiled Theban dates also may be added to these porridges; bread and dried dates, mixed with green olive oil and Syrian sumach, or vinegar and oak gall may also be used. Serve these foods without drink. Also give the patient soft eggs or milk cooked with starch; the amount given may be one or two cotylae, i.e., ten or twenty ounces. Then prescribe vegetables which have a binding effect, e.g., endive, plantain, and cauliflower; but these must all be cooked and seasoned with vinegar. Then have the patient eat the less tender varieties of fish and lean dry fowl cooked in vinegar and water. When the disease declines, give him wine of a sharp variety. And have him take passive exercise, but first cover his face to protect the respiratory passages from injury. Finally prescribe bathing.

Now if the catarrh becomes chronic and is marked by attacks and intervals of remission, have the patient take walking exercise and mild vocal exercise during the intervals. In addition, prescribe gentle anointing and massage. Give him foods of the

5. Or perhaps Scybelitic wine (Rm). The reading is uncertain, but cf. 207.

dandi scilicet pro qualitate passionis, solutione aut strictura ob-
107 tinente: qui erunt quodam profectu augendi aut minuendi per
regulam cycli usque ad volantum atque agrestium et porcinae
carnis percoctam partem tertiam. sicque[27a] panem ante pulmenti
oblationem, si obtinens fuerit fluor, cum aqua dabimus; etiam
uvarum fabrilium vel pensilium siccatarum acinos vel intybi
thyrsum aceto praetinctum, adhibito lavacro longo dierum intervallo, tum drimyphagia. dandum etiam lasar cum aceto atque liquamine, ac deinde locis patientibus adhibendae cucurbitae recorporativae, quas Graeci metasyncriticas vocant, et
maxime anthereoni, hoc est thoraci vel gutturis circulo, quem[28]
108 rumam vocamus. tunc resinae cabialis, hoc est dicaminis illi-
nimentum vel dropacis; dehinc etiam ex pulvere nitreo lacera
fricatio, quam Graeci smixin[29] appellant, vel smegmata, quorum
compositionem Responsionum tradidimus libris, vel[30] lemnida[31]
cum oleo, aut piretro[32] cum pipere. item unctiones ex syriaco et
opobalsamo et laurino atque irino oleo et butyro et pice liquida
apponenda[33] naribus atque narium cavernis. tunc etiam sinapismus, et gargarismata ex sinapi vel aqua marina aut decoctione
thymi, origani, hyssopi, gleconis,[34] quod nos pulegium vocamus,
109 et horum similibus. dehinc mutatio locorum appetenda et magis maritimorum, tum usus aquarum naturalium ex quibus erit
caput fovendum.

decessores vero medici, nondum rigore methodico obtinente,
in quibus est Erasistratus secundo libro Salutarium praecep-
torum, et Asclepiades tertio Celerum passionum, item Themison
Salutari libro atque primo Tardarum passionum, quas chronias
appellant, meracum potum dari iusserunt. ait enim Asclepiades duplicandam vel triplicandam quantitatem vini solitae

[27a] fort. siccum

[28] quam R

[29] mixin S

[30] fort. vel ⟨ex⟩ vel ex tantum

[31] cf. 33: lemnistida (= adarce?) Rm   [33] an apponendae?

[32] fort. piretrum nisi suppleas ex   [34] gleconis Rm: glaucii S

middle class, with due regard to the nature of the disease, that
07 is, to the relative predominance of stricture and looseness. As
the days pass, give a greater or lesser amount of these foods in
accordance with the cyclical regimen, until a third part of the
food consists, in the successive stages, of cooked fowl, field animals, and pork.[6] If the state of looseness predominates, have the
patient take bread and water before serving him the main dish.
Also give him raisins, i.e., smoke-dried grapes or those hung up
to dry, or a stalk of endive dipped in vinegar. After a considerable lapse of time prescribe bathing and then an acrid diet. Give
the patient laserwort with vinegar and fish sauce. And cups of
the kind that will help to change the bodily condition (Greek
metasyncriticae) should then be applied to the affected parts,
and especially to the chest and the curve of the throat (Greek
08 *anthereōn*, Latin *ruma*). Then prescribe a liniment of resin[7] . . .
or a pitch plaster; then, too, a sharp rubdown (Greek *smēxis*)
with pulverized nitrum or detergents, whose composition we
have set forth in the work entitled *Answers*, e.g., Lemnian earth[8]
with olive oil or pellitory with pepper. Also apply unguents
made with such substances as Syrian oil, opobalsam, laurel oil,
iris oil, butter, and liquid pitch to the nose and the nostrils.
Then use mustard plasters; and have the patient gargle with
mustard or sea water or a decoction of thyme, marjoram, hyssop,
or pennyroyal (Greek *glēchōn*, Latin *pulegium*), or with any simi-
09 lar substance. Again, change of climate, especially by a sea trip,
is helpful; and so is the use of spring waters for fomenting the
head.

Physicians who wrote before the strict Methodist system was
established prescribed the drinking of strong wine in these cases.
Among these physicians are Erasistratus in Book II of his *Hygiene*, Asclepiades in Book III of his *Acute Diseases*, and Themison both in his book entitled *Hygiene* and also in Book I of his
Chronic Diseases (Greek *chroniae*, Latin *tardae*, 'slow'). Thus
Asclepiades says that the proportion of wine should be twice or
three times as great as it is in the usual mixture, that is, he has a

6. The passage is not clear. Cf. *Chr.* i. 22–24. Would two-thirds of the food continue
to be of the middle class? See also Soranus *Gyn.* iii. 15.

7. The meaning of *resinae cabialis hoc est dicaminis* is uncertain. It seems to be a
pine resin, perhaps from a diseased tree (*cabialis* = *scabialis?*). See Ihm, *Pelagonius*,
p. 181; Oder, *Mulomedicina Chironis*, Index, *s.v.* 'resina.'

8. The reading is uncertain. Perhaps there is a reference to *adarce*.

temperationis, adeo ut uni cyatho unum admisceri iusserit, quo
110 vini et aquae quantitas coaequetur. sed hoc facit intardante[35]
passione: etenim recentem atque novam curans, libris quos ad
Geminium scripsit Salutarium, vinum prohibendum tradidit.

Erasistratus vero etiam pileum vini calidi infusione inflatum
capiti imponendum iubet, lateribus vero ac praecordiis lanas ap-
ponendas vino atque oleo calido madefactas. quorum primo
nervorum vitiabilis est meraca potio atque capiti faciens inflationem, dehinc etiam abstinentis vino vel solutae consuetudinis
gravabilis. atque noxius est usus pilei vino calido praefusi[36] vel
lanae tinctae lateribus ac praecordiis circumpositae ob dolorum
vehementiam.

111   item Lucius[37] secundo libro Tardarum passionum, cum de his
quae faucibus accidunt disputaret, hoc est de supradictis fluoribus, etiam aridam ficum torridam atque vino infusam ante cibum dari iubet, siquidem rudis atque nova difficillimae sit digestionis. sed hinc ait mixtum calidum sorbendum, hoc est vinum
cum aqua supradicta meracum.[38] idem admixtam sandara-
cham quae sit ex ovi albore conspersa in quantitate[39] oboli unius
igni imponendam iubet, vel radicem herbae tussicularis,[40] quam
bechion[41] appellavit. tunc per infundibulum ore rapere fumum
adducto vento imperat aegrotantes, cum sit capiti vehementer
contraria supradictorum incensa fumatio.

112   generaliter autem atque communi repulsione arguendos Erasistratum et Asclepiadem arbitramur, primo quod non viderint
pro passionis motu[42] in curationibus urgentiora nimis praeponenda. Themisonem vero et Thessalum memorantes constrictivam curationem, libro †haec demetico†[43] atque secundo Regu-

---

[35] intardante *scripsi, coll. Ac. i. 43*: in tardante *edd.*

[36] praeinfusi *Schmid RPh 43*

[37] Lucius *Rm*: Lusius *S. an* Lysias? *cf. Chr. ii. 59*

[38] temperatum *Bendz 99*

[39] quantitatem *R*

[40] tunsicularis *S: corr. Rm*

[41] bechion *Rm*: vehion *S*

[42] *fort.* modo; *cf. Chr. iii. 62*

[43] libro haec * demetico *S*: libro hac de methodo *coniecit Triller* (*Kühn 82*): *fort. leg.*
libro ** hunc De methodo (*numerus ordinalis est supplendus si non sub* haec *latet*). *cf.*
Gal. X. 73

---

9. Or possibly 'takes it well diluted.'   10. Cf. 109.

cyathus of water added to a cyathus of wine so that the quanti-
110 ties of wine and water are equal. But he prescribes drink only
when the disease becomes chronic; in his treatise *On Hygiene*,
dedicated to Geminius, he discusses the treatment when the
disease is new, i.e., of recent origin, and declares that no wine
should be given.

Erasistratus prescribes covering the patient's head with a
close-fitting felt cap into which hot wine has been poured; and
he orders applied to the sides and the precordial region wool
soaked in wine and hot olive oil. But, in the first place, the drinking of strong wine injures the nerves and sinews and causes congestion of the head and is especially harmful for one who customarily abstains from wine or takes it only occasionally.[9] Furthermore, the use of the cap soaked with hot wine and the application of similarly soaked wool to the sides and the precordia
are injurious because of the severe pains which result from these
measures.

111 In Book II of his *Chronic Diseases* Lucius discusses diseases
of the throat and in particular these catarrhal fluxes, and he prescribes that a dry parched fig soaked in wine be given the patient before food, for a fresh unripe fig would be difficult to
digest. He goes on to say that the patient should sip the mixture,
referred to above,[10] of pure wine and water, and that this should
be taken hot. He also adds to this mixture an obol of realgar
sprinkled with the white of egg, or an obol of the juice of colts-
foot root, which he calls *bēchion;* he has the mixture placed over
a fire, and then orders the patient to inhale the fumes through
the mouth, using a funnel and drawing in the vapor. But the
fumes resulting from the burning of these substances are exceedingly injurious to the head.

12 Moreover, we think that these physicians may all be refuted
on general grounds. Thus, in the first place, we charge both
Erasistratus and Asclepiades with having failed to recognize
that more powerful remedies were required to cope with the
power of the disease. Again, Themison and Thessalus mention
[only] an astringent treatment . . . [Thessalus] in Book II of his
Regimen (Greek *diaeta*).[11] We therefore hold that they, too, are

---

11. Perhaps: 'the latter in Book . . . of his work *On Method*, and in Book II of his
Regimen,' etc. But *demetico* may be a corruption of the name Deimas (so *Rm*, comparing
Chr. iv. 4).

lari, quem dieteticum vocant, culpandos arbitramur, quod non
113 viderint aliquando stricturam fieri superiorum. item plurima
sulphurosa admiscenda quod[44] satis sit probaverunt, et lanis
quibus thorax circumdatur aspergenda, ordinantes etiam odoramenta iris illyricae aridae contusae, atque eius oleum, item opo-
balsamum et melanthium linteolo ligatum naribus frequenter
admovendum, et anisum et cuminum et rutam [et antiflorum][45]
vel distillationem amaricini olei et samsucum et styracem vel ex
eo oleum confectum, quod styracinum dicitur, item hedicroum
vel murram cum thure et sulphure et radicibus silphii, quae omnia caput implent et propterea sunt evitanda, magis accessionis
tempore. in lenimento vero ratione recorporativae virtutis atque interiecto tempore per intervalla adhibenda[46] poterunt
iudicari.

114   VIII. DE TUSSICULA

Tussicula nunc arida nunc humecta corporibus irruit, multos ac pingues humores excludens, et quibusdam sola, quibusdam adiuncta respirationis difficultate, quam Graeci dis-
pnoean vocant, item cum sanguinis egestione aut phthisica passione vel horum similibus affectis corporibus. sed de his tussicu-
lis quae aliarum fuerint appendices passionum singulatim scribentes docebimus; de his vero quae suae sunt atque propria
vexatione corpus afficiunt nunc tradimus curationem.
115   quae ita erit adhibenda ut de catarrho scribentes docuimus,
discreta scilicet specie, quo possint electaria atque pota medicamina vel catapotia sive alia quaeque sub regula medicinali recte
mederi corporibus. monendi etiam aegrotantes ne ultra modum
competentem retinendo spiritum asperent[1] potius tussiculam
quam mitigent, quod quidem si fuerint moderati, eius motum facilius amputare quantum [datum][2] datur spiritum continendo.
116   tum apponendum per quod aeger adducto spiritu accipiat vaporem ex mulso vel alica aut suco ptisanae, vel eorum quiddam

---

[44] *an* quot?

[45] *om. R. mendum ortum esse videtur ex glossemate* melanthium = atriflorem

[46] adhibita *edd.*

[1] asperent *scripsi*: alterent *edd.*

[2] *secl. Bendz 99*

open to criticism for failing to observe that in some cases there is
113 a state of stricture in the upper parts. Furthermore, they recommend mixing a sufficiently large quantity of substances containing sulphur and using these to sulphurate the wool which they
wrap round the chest. They also prescribe the use of aromatic
substances, e.g., Illyrian iris dried and pulverized, iris oil, opobalsam, black caraway seed tied in a small linen bag and frequently applied to the nostrils, anise, cumin, rue, sweet marjoram, drops of sweet marjoram oil, storax, storax oil called
styracinum, and *hedychrun* or myrrh with frankincense, sulphur,
and silphium root. But all these substances congest the head and
are therefore particularly to be avoided at the time of an attack.
During the intervals of remission, however, their application
may be prescribed from time to time by reason of their metasyncritic properties.

114   VIII. COUGH

THE body may be attacked by a cough, in some cases dry, in
others wet, i.e., involving the discharge of thick, copious humors. Again, the cough sometimes occurs alone, but at other
times is accompanied by difficulty in breathing (Greek *dyspnoea*), by a discharge of blood, by the disease of phthisis, or by
similar bodily affections. We shall deal with those coughs which
are concomitants to other diseases when we discuss each such
disease separately. We are concerned here with the treatment of
those coughs which occur independently and affect the body
with their own special kind of disease.

115   Now the treatment in these cases will be similar to that which
we have indicated for catarrh, with the same distinction regard-
ing the nature of the illness.[1] Only in this way can electuaries,
potions, pills, and the other remedies be chosen that will properly heal the body according to sound medical principles. And
warn the patient against holding his breath beyond a reasonable
limit, for otherwise he may aggravate the cough rather than relieve it. But by holding his breath in moderation he should
gently reduce the coughing so far as possible.

116   In addition, set up an apparatus through which the patient
can, as he draws his breath, inhale the vapor of mead, spelt gruel,

1. I.e., whether *strictura* or *solutio* predominates.

sorbeat, aut ex aqua calida vaporem accipiat. videnda etiam
uva, ne ob tumorem sui aut indulta laxitate tussiculam provocet.
tum gargarismatibus vel inunctionibus utendum circa thoracem
atque gutturis summitatem, quam Graeci anthereona vocant.
epithemata etiam apponenda, et nunc laxativa, nunc constrictiva, quorum species ex antedictis erunt accipiendae, ne saepius
eadem dicere videamur.

117   IX. DE SANGUINIS FLUORE[1]

SANGUINIS fluor occultis ex locis veniens velut saepe salutaris
est, ita vehemens ingerit periculum, et quibusdam extemplo
ob redundantiam fluoris celerans mortem corpore disiecto, et
quibusdam in postremum effecta phthisica passione vel vulnere
non coeunte, siquidem primo tumeat dehinc excorietur, atque
fluidum ex vapore fiat.

sunt autem quae conventum sive glutinationem vulnerum impediant plurimae vel innumerabiles causae. etenim natura altiora plurimum fervere necesse est, atque fluida qualitate ma-
118 nare[2] et multo vel assiduo motu pulsari. obstat etiam quod occulta atque alta atque celata sint visu et a vicino medicaminum
tactu remota. frustrantur etenim frequenter eorum illatae
qualitates, priusquam locis patientibus advenient,[3] itineris detrimento, cum non statim vel extemplo illibata partibus patientibus admoventur.

sunt autem passionis antecedentes causae, ut saepe approba-
tum est, percussio vel casus, item exclamatio, vel ponderis per-
ferendi conatio, vomitus vehemens, aut venus plurima, et tussi-
119 cula perseverans, item abstinentia haemorrhoidarum veterum
quae fuerint inertia amputatae nec iuxta methodicam rationem
curatae, item catarrhus. sed non erit secundum has differentias
curationis regula commutanda.

nominatur autem sanguinis fluor duplici significatione, pro-

---

[1] sed habet S in tabula capitum (p. 33):
  IX. De sanguinis fluore; quot vel quae sint differentiae fluoris (= 117-25)
  X. Quomodo intelligamus differentias sanguinis fluoris (= 126-27)
  XI. Quomodo intelligamus ex quibus locis sanguis feratur (= 127-36)

[2] manere R

[3] adveniant Rm

or pearl barley gruel. He may also sip up something of these fluids. Let him draw in the vapor of hot water, too. And see to it that coughing is not provoked by an inflammation of the uvula or a state of laxness and atony of that organ. Then prescribe gargling and also anointing of the chest and the upper part of the throat (Greek *anthereōn*). Also make use of applications, relaxing or astringent as the case requires. For the composition of these applications we refer to what has already been said, and thus avoid repetition.

117

IX. HEMORRHAGE

A FLOW of blood from a part within the body is often a good sign, but, again, may involve grave danger.[1] In some cases the danger is immediate, the excessive flow causing swift death through the collapse of the body. In other cases, e.g., where phthisis has occurred or a wound fails to heal, death may come ultimately. For in these cases first the body is inflamed, then the membranes disintegrate, and the pneuma turns to fluid.

There are numerous causes which interfere with the drawing-together and closing of a wound. For one thing, the deeper parts are necessarily quite hot by nature, and must be suffused with fluid, and thus be moved by extensive and constant pulsation. 118 Another obstacle is the fact that these parts are deep, hidden, concealed from view, and too far removed to be directly touched by the remedies that are applied. For the powers of these remedies are frequently dissipated before they reach the affected parts. In other words, since these remedies cannot be applied immediately or directly to these parts, their potency may be lost on the way.

The antecedent causes of hemorrhage are generally held to be a blow, a fall, loud shouting, the strain of carrying a heavy weight, violent vomiting, excessive coitus, a persistent cough, 119 the retention of old hemorrhoids inexpertly operated upon and treated without regard to Methodist principles, and, finally, catarrh. But the principles of treating hemorrhage do not vary with the different causes.

Now the term 'flow of blood'[2] is used in two senses, one proper

1. Perhaps the meaning is: 'but, again, when the flow is strong, it involves danger.'
2. Cf. *Diaet. pass.*, pp. 233 f. (Rose).

pria et abusiva. nam propria est qua ex supernis partibus labens fluor significatur, ut de capite per sensuales vias. abusiva est qua etiam ex inferioribus ascendens fluor significatur, ut ex pul-
120 mone vel stomacho, nausea aut tussicula exclusus. improprium est enim fluorem vocare id quod ascensu quodam non lapsu fertur. sed haec Graeci versa vice posuerunt, derivationem nominis intuentes. hi enim anagogen vocant, quod magis ex inferioribus ad superiora fluorem significat.

differt praeterea fluor sanguinis a sputo, quod neque fluor sanguinis sputus[4] dici potest. parvae[5] enim materiae significationem sputus refert, fluor plurimae. neque sputus sanguinis fluor, supradicta ratione. parvam enim materiam sanguinis ex gingivis aut uva aut faucibus emissam, sputum magis quam fluorem recte nuncupamus.

121   X. QUOT VEL QUAE SINT DIFFERENTIAE
                        FLUORIS SANGUINIS

D IFFERENTIAS etiam fluoris sanguinis veteres quaesierunt, et quidam aiunt unam solam esse vel intelligi, hoc est vulnerationis, ut Themison ⟨secundo⟩[1] libro Tardarum passionum. alii vero eruptiones, ut Hippocrates, Euryphon: sed Hippocrates solarum venarum, Euryphon vero etiam arteriarum. alii duas differentias posuerunt, eruptionis et putredinis, ut Asclepiades; alii tres, eruptionis et putredinis et osculationis, quam Graeci
122 anastomosin vocant, ut Erasistratus; alii quatuor, adicientes expressionis sive sudationis, ut Bacchius adserens ex gingivis sanguinem sine ulla vulneratione, vel in curationibus fracturarum saepe fasciolarum ligamenta maculis sanguinolentis aspersa reperiri. item Demetrius Herophili sector duas inquit esse prin-

    [4] sputum R
    [5] parvam S: corr. Hagendahl 262
    [1] supplevi

    3. I.e., 'a bringing-up.' Cf. also Cass. Fel., p. 86. 2 (Rose).
    4. I.e., that *fluor*, strictly speaking, should proceed downward.
    1. *Anon. Paris.* has the same threefold division (*Rh. Mus.* 1894, p. 552).

and the other improper. It is used properly of a flow which passes downward from higher parts, e.g., from the head through the sensory channels. And it is used improperly of a flow which passes upward from lower parts, e.g., blood forced up from the lungs or esophagus by gagging or coughing; for it is improper to speak of a flow which runs upward and not downward. But in the case of upward flow the Greek usage is different, and is [properly] based on etymology. Thus for this case they use *anagōgē*,[3] a term which generally refers to a passage from a lower to a higher level.

Again, hemorrhage (flow of blood) must be distinguished from the spitting of blood; that is to say, the mere spitting of blood cannot be called a flow. For one thing, spitting connotes a relatively small amount of matter; flow connotes a large amount. Moreover, the spitting of blood can hardly be considered a flow for the reason set forth above.[4] Thus a small amount of blood ejected from the gums, uvula, or throat is properly referred to as sputum rather than as a flow of blood.

X. THE DIFFERENT KINDS OF HEMORRHAGE

THE physicians of old take up the question of the different kinds of hemorrhage. Some, e.g., Themison in Book II of his *Chronic Diseases*, hold that only one kind exists or is known, that due to a wound. Others hold that the blood itself may break the vessel and flow out; this is the view of Hippocrates and Euryphon. But Hippocrates holds that such a flow may take place only from veins, while Euryphon holds that it may take place both from veins and from arteries. Some, among them Asclepiades, assert that there are two kinds of hemorrhage, viz., that in which the blood bursts forth from a vessel, and that due to the vessel's decay. Others, e.g., Erasistratus, hold that there are three kinds, the two just mentioned and, in addition, that in which the blood flows through an opening [made at the end of the vessel], an opening which the Greeks call *anastomōsis*.[1] Still others add to these the diffusion or 'sweating' from the vessels, and thus speak of four kinds. This is the view of Bacchius, who asserts that there may be bleeding from the gums without any wound and points out that in treating fractures we often find the bandages spotted with blood. Demetrius the Herophilean de-

cipales differentias fluoris sanguinis, unam incisurae, aliam sine
ulla incisura; speciales vero plurimas, quas principalibus subi-
ciendas ordinavit. etenim quam memorat incisura[2] fieri in duas
divisit partes, quarum alteram vocavit eruptionis, alteram pu-
123 tredinis. eam vero quae sine ulla divisura est, in quatuor dividit partes, quarum unam raritate[3] fieri dixit, aliam expressione
sive sudatione, tertiam defectione vel debilitate corporum, quam
Graeci atonian vocant, quartam osculatione. vult enim eam
differre a supradicta, id est expressionis, quam secundam[4] nominavit. osculari enim inquit corpora nimia plenitudine, sive virtute medicaminum osculantium, quae Graeci anastomotica[5] vocant, et magis inquit venarum ultimos fines, exprimi etiam sanguinem sive excludi per venarum latera.

124   item alii Asclepiadis sectatores unam esse dicunt differentiam
fluoris sanguinis, hoc est eruptionem, siquidem omnem sanguinis solutionem eruptione fieri Asclepiades memoraverit, ne-
gantes eam osculationis differentiam, siquidem sit impossibile
sanguinem crassum tenera[6] ferri[7] per oscula vel excludi. item
putredinis esse differentiam[8] negant, siquidem ex iisdem non ex
aliis locis acrior humor fieri[9] videatur. alii vero eundem Asclepiadem non naturaliter[10] putredinis differentiam ab Erasistrato
constitutam expugnasse dixerunt. non enim ex aliis locis acriore
125 veniente liquore pulmonem fieri in putredine accepimus, sed
eundem quadam passione in putredinem vel acerrimos transire
liquores.

nos autem iuxta Sorani iudicium hac quaestione nullis commodis curationes adiuvari probamus, sed dicimus tres esse differen-

---

[2] incisurā S: corr. Rm
[3] raritate ⟨viarum⟩ Rm: varietate S. cf. 125
[4] secundam scripsi: tertiam edd.
[5] anastomatica S: corr. A. cf. Ac. iii. 40; Chr. iii. 73
[6] tenuia Rm
[7] ferri Rm: fieri S
[8] differentias edd.
[9] ferri Rm   [10] rationabiliter Sm

clares that there are two principal kinds of hemorrhage, one involving a cutting of the vessel and the other without any such
cutting; he recognizes that, actually, there are many different
kinds, but he holds that they may all be subsumed under one or
the other of the principal kinds. Thus he says that the flow which
involves a cutting includes two kinds, one the result of the blood
bursting through the vessel, the other the result of the vessel's
decomposition. And the flow which does not involve any cutting
he divides into four varieties, one taking place by reason of the
open state of the pores, the second through diffusion or 'sweating' from the vessels, the third by reason of bodily exhaustion
or weakness (Greek *atonia*), the fourth by an opening [at the
end] of the vessel. For he holds that this last differs from the one
he mentions second, diffusion. Thus he says that such openings
take place in bodies either because of a condition of plethora or
because of the use of those drugs, called *anastomōtica* by the
Greeks, which have the property of bringing about such openings. And he declares that it is especially the ends of the veins
that open; the diffusion or squeezing-out of blood, on the other
hand, takes place through the walls of veins.

Others, however, members of Asclepiades' sect, hold that
there is only one kind of hemorrhage, namely, that in which the
blood bursts forth from the vessel; for, according to Asclepiades,[2]
every flow of blood takes place by such a bursting-forth. These
physicians deny the possibility of flow by anastomosis on the
ground that thick blood cannot be carried or forced through
such narrow openings. They also deny that hemorrhage can be
due to the decomposition of a vessel, for putrid fluid always
seems to come from the same places and from no other. Others,
however, hold that Asclepiades here makes an unsound attempt
to refute Erasistratus' theory that one of the kinds of hemorrhage comes about through decomposition. For, they say, we
know that the lung may putrefy without any purulent fluid
issuing from other places; that is, the lung itself may, by reason
of some disease, pass into a state of decomposition and be transformed into purulent fluids.

But in our opinion—and we express Soranus' view—this de-
bate serves no useful purpose so far as the treatment is concerned. We do hold, however, that there are three kinds of hem-

2. But this is not consistent with 121.

tias fluoris sanguinis, hoc est eruptionis, vulnerationis, et putredinis sive lacerationis ex tussicula venientis, sicut operantium
manus iugi fricatione lacessiti vulnerantur. item sudationis[11]
sine vulnere sive ex raritate[12] viarum effectus fluor osculationis
differentiam tenet sive expressionis vel cuiuslibet alterius causae.

126   ## XI. QUOMODO INTELLIGAMUS DIFFERENTIAS[1] FLUORIS SANGUINIS

QUAESITUM etiam quomodo supradictae differentiae intelligantur vel apprehendantur. sed discernuntur hoc modo.
nam eruptionis esse intelligimus fluorem quoties repente aegrotantes atque limpidum sanguinem fluunt, nulla querela vulneris
praecedente. vulnerationis vero differentiam dicimus sive putredinis vel defricationis, cum adiuncto humore purulento sanguis excluditur, et non repente vel coacervatim, praeterea antecedente longi temporis vel multorum dierum tussicula vel ca-
127 tarrho. item sudationis dicimus esse cum nullus fuerit vulneris
sensus, aut acceptorum[2] cibo vel potu acriorum materiarum mordicationis affectio.

qui sunt loci ex quibus sanguis fluit? loci sunt plurimi: summitas faucium, arteria asperior, quae etiam faux nuncupatur,
pulmo, thorax, hoc est membrana quae interius latera cingit, a
Graecis hypozygos[3] appellata, item membrana quae thoracem
a ventre discernit, a Graecis diaphragma appellata, quam nos
discrimen dicere poterimus, item stomachus, venter, et secundum aliquos iecur, ac lien, et vena maior quae spinae coniuncta est.

128   quomodo intelligimus ex quibus locis sanguis feratur? (intelligimus locos ex quibus sanguis[4] fluor vel lapsus fertur, quod erit
aptissimum ob adhibendam curationem iisdem vel eorum vicinis
partibus, et non, ut quidam existimant, commutandae curationis
causa, cum generaliter eadem cunctis adhibenda probamus.[5])

---

[11] sudatione R

[12] varietate S: corr. Rm

[1] differentiam edd., sed differentias S in laterculo capitum (p. 33)

[2] fort. acceptarum

[3] fort. hypezocos

[4] sanguinis Rm   [5] probemus Rm

orrhage, viz., the bursting-forth of blood from a vessel, the flow due to a wound from without, and the flow due to decomposition or to such abrasion as results from cough. Workers whose hands are irritated and injured by constant rubbing present a situation analogous to this last. And a flow which involves a 'sweating' from the vessel in the absence of a wound or a flow brought about by the open state of the pores is to be ascribed either to anastomosis, or to diffusion, or to some other cause.

126 ## XI. HOW TO RECOGNIZE THE DIFFERENT KINDS OF HEMORRHAGE

THE next problem is how to recognize and distinguish the different kinds of hemorrhage. They may be distinguished as follows: A case of hemorrhage involving the [spontaneous] bursting-forth of blood from a vessel may be recognized by the sudden flow of pure blood, in the absence of any indication of a previous wound. A case of hemorrhage due to a wound or decomposition or abrasion may be recognized when a purulent fluid flows out together with the blood; the flow in this case does not take place immediately and all at once. Again, a cough or catarrh of several days' duration or longer precedes in some of 127 these cases. And we may ascribe a flow of blood to diffusion or 'sweating' when no wound has been felt and there has been no griping sensation from taking food or drink of acrid properties.

What are the places from which bleeding occurs? There are many, viz., the upper end of the throat (*fauces*), the trachea, which is also called *faux*, the lung, the chest, the pleural membrane (Greek *hypozygos*), which forms an interior lining of the sides, the membrane (Greek *diaphragma*, which we may call *discrimen* in Latin) separating the chest from the abdomen, the esophagus, the stomach, and, according to some, the liver, the spleen, and the great vein that is connected with the spine.

128 How can we tell from what parts blood is flowing?[1] (The reason for determining the origin of the flow or escape of blood is that such information is important in applying treatment to those parts or the parts adjacent to them and not, as some suppose, for the purpose of varying the treatment. For we hold that the same general treatment must be applied in all cases of

1. Cf. Esc. 16 (Rose, *Anecdota Graeca*, II, 233).

de[6] his igitur qui ex supernis faucium sanguinem fluunt primo
parvus intelligitur ferri, aut si plurimus, non spumosus. praeterea cum quodam excreatu despuitur. ipsae quoque partes
sumpto cibo vel potu aut gargarismate mordicantis materiae
dolore pulsantur, et inspicientibus nobis expressa lingua visu
129 locorum probatur asperitas. plerumque etiam, ut Erasistratus
ait, tubercula, quae Graeci condylomata vocant, visibus[7] occurrunt, quae sint similia haemorrhoidis, ex quibus sanguis fertur.

his vero qui ex arteria sanguinem fluunt parvus atque flavus
sanguis ferri perspicitur, et saepe salivis vel humoribus com-
plexus, in imaginem capilli unius aut multorum. sequitur etiam
pruritus vel mordicatio, et magis circa extantiam gutturis, cum
quodam titillatu et tussicula levi; tum deinde plurimus sanguinis
fluor, vox hirta cum dolore, qui nunc tactu[8] moveatur, nunc tus-
130 sicula vehementi. plurimus tenuis et spumosus et plurimum
fervens sanguis excluditur, attestante thoracis gravedine et aliquando dolore, cum voce hirta et saepe cibo quodam cum in-
fracto sonitu eo tempore quo sanguis excluditur.

his vero qui ex diaphragmate, quod iamdudum discrimen vocavimus, et cetera praedictis[9] sequentur communia, sed dolor
inferius a pectore fiet rotunditate quadam thoracem pungens.

eos autem qui ex hypozygo[10] sanguinem fluunt multa similia
supradictis sequentur, sed dolor secundum latera vel pectus, aliquando etiam inter scapulas fiet. ipse quoque sanguis minus
flavus minus excluditur.

131   item[11] eos qui ex stomacho sanguinem fluunt sine ulla tussicula
vomitus sanguinis sequetur nigri atque gelati, et nunc solius,
nunc cum admixtione cibi, attestante dolore inter utrasque scapulas ad superiora tendente,[12] et magis eo tempore quo quaedam
remordentia transvoraverint aegrotantes. accedit etiam animi
desponsio, cum fastidio cibi et salivarum fluore[13] et corpore frigido et pulsu obscuro vel demerso.

---

[6] de *om. R* (*cf., e.g., 129*)   [10] *fort.* hypezocote

[7] *fort.* visu(i) *vel* videntibus   [11] item *scripsi*: in *edd.*

[8] titillatu *Rm*   [12] superiores tendentem *S: corr. Rm*

[9] praedictos *S: corr. Rm*   [13] fluor *S: corr. Rm*

---

2. The text and interpretation are uncertain.

hemorrhage.) Now when the flow of blood comes from the upper end of the throat, it is found to be small at first, or, if copious, it does not form foam. Besides, this blood is hawked or coughed up; and the parts themselves are affected with pain when food or drink or an irritant gargle is taken. In fact, if we depress the tongue and look into the throat, we can actually see the rough-
29 ness of the parts. In many cases, as Erasistratus says, there appear small protuberances (Greek *condylōmata*) similar to hemorrhoids, and it is from these protuberances that the blood flows.

When the hemorrhage is from the trachea, the flow of blood is [at first] small and yellowish and often mingled with saliva or other fluids, these appearing like one or more streaks of hair. There also occurs itching or irritation, particularly at the bulge of the throat, as well as a tickling sensation and a light cough. Afterward, the flow of blood is copious, the voice is hoarse, and there is a pain, which is aggravated now by contact,[2] and now
30 by violent coughing. A great deal of thin, foaming, and very hot blood is given up, with an attendant feeling of heaviness, and sometimes pain, in the chest; the voice is hoarse, and, at the time when the blood is ejected, food, too, is often vomited with a dull sound.

In cases of hemorrhage from the diaphragm, which we have called *discrimen* above, the indications are in other respects the same as in cases of bleeding from the trachea, but the pain is felt below the chest and strikes the chest sharply from below in a curved path.[3]

When the bleeding is from the pleural membrane, many symptoms similar to these occur, but the pain is felt in the sides or chest and sometimes also between the shoulder blades. And the blood itself is less yellow and the flow not so copious.
31 When the bleeding is from the esophagus, there is no coughing, but there is vomiting of black, clotted blood, sometimes alone and sometimes mixed with food; pain is felt between the shoulder blades and extending upward, the pain occurring especially when the patient has swallowed acrid food. The patient is dejected and loses his appetite for food; there is an excessive flow of saliva, the body is cold, and the pulse hard to detect, that is to say, submerged.

3. Cf. Esc. 16: 'The patients are girt (*cinguntur*) with the pain below the chest' (Rose, *Anecdota Graeca*, II, 234).

his vero qui ex ventre sanguinem fluunt, cum supradictis, quae sunt cunctis communia, sequetur etiam dolor et mordicatio vel tormentum inter praecordia, et aliquando sanguinis particula per officium ventris excludetur.

132   item his qui ex iecore vel splene sanguinem fluunt, vel ex vena magna quae spinae coniuncta est, ut quidam memorant, sensu loca designantur. nam in dextera parte praecordiorum dolor cum colore[14] aurigineo sequetur eos qui ex iecore fluunt. item in [hiis][15] sinistra parte praecordiorum haec accidunt quoties ex liene sanguis ferri perspicitur, vel secundum spinam quoties ex maiore vena ferri dicitur. sed [haec][16] Soranus alta considera- tione ex his locis per ventrem vel per eius officium ferri sangui- nem magis quam per os posse credibilius approbavit.

133   his vero qui ex gingivis vel uva vel faucium lateribus vel ton- sillis sanguinem fluunt supradictorum nulla sequentur, sed lo- corum vulnerationem[17] ore aperto oculorum approbat visus.

item his[18] qui ex capite sanguinem fluunt acceptum primo vel exceptum internis visceribus, atque ita redditum, si in arteriam defluxerit, excludunt deinde cum tussicula vehementi, et tam- quam[19] de pulmone feratur similitudinem dabit. sin vero in sto- machum defluxerit vel ventrem, commota nausea vomitur, et tamquam[19] ex iisdem locis ferri videatur similitudinem dabit.

134 sed discerni hoc facile potest, siquidem aegrotantibus fervor igneus ora pertractans antecedat, et capitis gravedo, vel dolor, et extensio venarum, et magis earum quae tempora vel frontem cingunt. sequitur etiam faucium titillatus et aliquando per narium[20] quaedam sanguinis distillatio, vel per eas cavernas quae ad fauces ex capite descendunt, quod aperto ore atque exerta[21] lingua visu probatur. et vicina loca quoque sanguinolenta ap-

135 parebunt. aliquando etiam remeantis materiae causa laxiora

---

[14] dolor cum colore *Rm*: dolorum dolore *S*

[15] *om. R*

[16] *om. R*

[17] *fort.* locos vulnerationum

[18] ii *R*

[19] et tamquam *scripsi*: etiam quam *S*

[20] nares *Rm*

[21] exerta *Rm*: experta *S*: *an* expressa (*cf. 128*)?

When the bleeding is from the stomach, in addition to the symptoms just mentioned, sharp pain and cramps occur also in the precordial region, and sometimes a bit of blood is passed by way of the bowels.

When bleeding occurs from the liver, spleen, or the great vein, which, as some say, is connected with the spine, the source of the flow is indicated by the pain. Thus pain in the right precordial region together with jaundice is indicative of bleeding from the liver. But the pain is in the left precordial region when the bleeding is from the spleen; and the pain is along the spine when the bleeding is from the great vein. And Soranus with keen insight holds that in cases of bleeding from these parts the blood is more likely to flow through the bowels and be eliminated by action of the bowels than from the mouth.

But in cases of bleeding from the gums, uvula, sides of the throat, or tonsils, none of the symptoms mentioned occurs, and an inspection of the patient's open mouth will determine where the wound is situated.

In cases of bleeding from the head, the blood is first received [as it flows from the head] by internal organs and is only then discharged;[4] now if the flow is into the trachea, the patient coughs the blood up violently, making it appear as if it originally came from the lungs. And if, instead, the blood flows down into the esophagus or stomach, it provokes nausea and is vomited out, thus giving the appearance of having come originally from these parts below. But these cases may easily be distinguished [from true cases of bleeding from the gullet or stomach], for before the patient vomits blood his face is affected by a burning heat, he experiences heaviness or pain in the head, and the veins are distended, particularly those which encircle the temples or forehead. There is also a tickling in the throat, and sometimes a dripping of blood through the nostrils or the channels that lead from the head to the throat. In the latter case we may observe the dripping if the patient opens his mouth and puts out his tongue; also the adjacent parts will be observed to be bloody. And sometimes, because of the flow of blood,[5] the parts used in

4. Perhaps: 'if the blood, having been received [by the head] from internal organs, then flows down into the trachea, etc.'

5. Apparently the flow of blood from the head into the mouth is referred to, though the meaning is not entirely clear. The parts used in swallowing are then cleared by the subsequent hawking and spitting.

transvorationis efficiuntur loca, et aegrotantes excreatu quodam sanguinem respuunt, accipientes ex supernis adducto spiritu, ut saepe muculenta consueverunt dormientes. praeterea in ore collectus excitat sanguis, vel transvoratus, et in stomachum vel in ventrem veniens premit permanens aegrotantes aut reiectus relevat. et hi qui passione afficiuntur, acceptis vel transvoratis remordentibus materiis, nullam interiorum mordicationem sentiunt, quod necessario eos qui ex stomacho fluunt sequitur.

136   ac si in arteriam fluxerit, tussicula rursum excludetur, quo reiecto aegrotantibus tussicula mitigatur, siquidem nulla inesse videatur interioribus remanens causa quae tussire provocet aegrotantes, nisi forte, quod est rarissimum, aliqua corpuscula gelati sanguinis inhaereant interioribus locis. item de pulmone fluens discernitur, quod iam praecedente tussicula in fluorem veniant, inde tussire non desinant.

communiter autem, ceteris inter se paribus signis, ex arteriis veniens sanguis tenerior ac rubri coloris et spumosus esse perspicitur, ex venis vero crassior et atri coloris. haec est locorum singulatim posita significatio.

137 XII. DE EFFECTU SIVE EXITU SUPRADICTARUM
PASSIONUM, QUEM GRAECI APOTE-
LESMA VOCANT

QUAESITUM de eventu sive exitu vel effectu passionum. nam Erasistratus facile curabiles suculentos homines dixit atque fortes et parvicolles, quos microtrachelos appellavit, hoc est qui minimae longitudinis habeant colla; difficile autem curari posse tenues ac debiles et porrecta collorum longitudine formatos. in his enim, inquit, summa cum difficultate sanguis[1] et tussis plurimam per longitudinem tractus, et[2] quod obsident uvida plurimo tempore habitudinem gutturis sive cannae, quam arteriam vocant, et ob hoc graves atque tardas tussiculas faciunt.

[1] sanguinis *Rm*
[2] tractus ⟨est⟩ et *Rm: fort.* tractus est

swallowing are relaxed; the patient proceeds to take in this blood from the higher parts while drawing his breath, as is often done with mucous matter in sleep, and then hawks and spits it up. In fact, the collecting of blood in the mouth provokes the patient [to spit it out], or, if it is swallowed and passes to the esophagus or stomach, it burdens the patient so long as it remains there, and its ejection brings relief. In cases of this kind the taking or swallowing of acrid substances causes no griping pain within, as always happens in cases where the bleeding originates in the esophagus [or stomach].

On the other hand, if the blood [coming from the head] flows down into the windpipe, it is brought up again with a cough. With the ejection of this blood the cough abates, for there no longer remains in the inner organs anything that might further provoke the patient to cough, unless any bits of coagulated blood happen to adhere within. But this occurs very rarely. And a case of actual bleeding from the lung may be distinguished [from that in which blood has merely trickled into the wind-pipe], because in hemorrhage of the lung coughing precedes the flow and does not abate when the flow appears.

In general, other indications being equal,[6] blood coming from an artery is thin, red, and foaming, while that which flows from a vein is thick and dark. This concludes our account of the signs of bleeding in the several parts.

XII. THE OUTCOME OR RESULT (GREEK *APOTELESMA*) OF THE AFORESAID AFFECTIONS

THE question is raised about the outcome, issue, or result of these affections. Erasistratus declares that full-bodied, vigorous persons and those with short necks, whom he calls *microtracheloe*, can be readily cured, but that thin, weak persons and those with long necks can be cured only with difficulty. For he holds that in the latter case the bringing-up of blood over a considerable distance is attended with great pain; and the presence of fluid matter for a long time brings about a clogged condition in the passage or channel which the Greeks call *artēria* [the 'windpipe'] and causes heavy and long-continued coughing.

6. I.e., in the absence of any other clear evidence of the type of vessel involved.

138   item Asclepiades difficile curabiles inquit suculentos atque
carnosos ob vehementiam spirationis, eadem ratione etiam
aetates medias et pueros. celerius etenim inquit spiritum ferri,
et in sputis perficiendis³ offensione carnium retardari.

plurimi deinde etiam affectiones vitae quaesierunt et regiones
et temporum annales partes. item per putredinem factum
fluorem difficile curabilem dicunt ab eo qui eruptione fuerit effectus, siquidem putrefactae partes non coeant.

nos vero iuxta Sorani sententiam fluores sanguinis alios dicimus esse novos corporibus atque recentes, alios tardi temporis
139   atque inveteratos; et alios solos, alios cum tumore, alios etiam
cum febricula et tussicula; et alios iuges, alios dimissionibus in-
tercapedinatos, ordine servato aut inordinatos, et [in] superposi-
tionibus⁴ ac⁵ lenimentis magnis aut parvis, et detracta virium
fortitudine aut⁶ servata. haec⁷ sunt enim urgentiores differentiae secundum quas diligentiam variamus curationis, sive serva-
to⁸ sive incerto motu existente passione.

sed difficile curabiles fluores prae ceteris dicimus tardos magis
⟨a⟩⁹ recentibus ob iugem perseverationem. item cum tumore
140   vel febribus ab his qui soli esse perspiciuntur. etenim supradicti
spem futurae conglutinationis negant, et ob hoc complexionis¹⁰
contraria saepe adiutoria poscunt, quae sint diversis adversa.
item iuges fluores ab his qui dimissionibus mitigantur. etenim
grave atque minime tutum omne quod nulla fuerit mitigatione
variatum. item inordinati ab his qui ordine servato corpus afficiunt. est enim insidiosa curationi temporum inopinata varietas. non aliter etiam superpositione asperati fluores curatione
difficiles ab his qui in lenimento constituti sunt iudicantur, ob

³ perferendis *Rm*

⁴ et insuper positionibus *S*: *corr. R*

⁵ ac *R*: aut *S*

⁶ aut *Rm*: ac *S*

⁷ hae *R*

⁸ servata *S*: certo *Rm*

⁹ *addidi*

¹⁰ complexionis *A*: complexioni *S*

1. The passage is not entirely clear, but it seems to mean that the respiratory channels are filled with sputa and the breath impinges upon the flesh instead of passing
smoothly through these channels.

Asclepiades, on the other hand, considers full-bodied and fleshy persons hard to cure because of their vigorous breathing. Similarly, he declares that persons of middle age and children are hard to cure, for, as he says, their normally rapid respiration is impeded by the formation of sputa, the breath striking against the flesh.[1]

Many have also discussed the effect of the patient's mode of life, the climate, and the season of the year on the chances of curing the disease. Again, it is said that bleeding caused by decomposition of the vessels is difficult to cure in comparison with that in which the blood breaks out of the vessel, for the decayed parts do not come together again.

Now, in conformity with Soranus' views, we hold that some cases of bleeding are of new and recent origin in the body, while others are chronic and of long standing; that some cases occur alone, while others occur with inflammation, and also with fever and with coughing; that in some cases the bleeding is continuous, in others interrupted by remissions; that the attacks and remissions may come at regular or at irregular intervals, and may be long or short, and may or may not involve the impairment of the patient's strength. These are the more important types of case according to which we vary our treatment, whether the disease exhibits a regular or an irregular character.

But we hold that chronic cases of bleeding are more difficult to treat successfully than those of recent origin, because of their continued persistence, and that cases which are complicated by inflammation or fever are harder to cure than those which occur without these complications. In fact, in the chronic and the complicated cases we cannot confidently look forward to a future healing of the wound; and the very fact that a case is complicated means that it generally requires contrary remedies to combat the contrary states of disease. Again, we consider cases of continuous bleeding harder to cure than those which are relieved by remissions; for every condition that is unrelieved by remissions is serious and dangerous. And the cases in which the attacks occur at irregular intervals are more difficult than those in which they take place regularly; for changes occurring at unexpected times endanger the success of the treatment. Moreover, when a case of bleeding is in a period of attack, it is considered harder to treat than when it is in an interval of remis-

praedictam rationem vulnerum. item hi qui plurimum corpus
141 affecerint atque vires aegrotantis insumpserint. dat enim[11]
adiutoriis medicinalibus fortitudo corporis viam. haec denique
etiam in vulneribus nudis, hoc est in exterioribus partibus corporis constitutis fieri cernimus, cum iuvenibus vel, ut specialiter
dixerim, athletis et laborantibus hominibus facilia vulnera fieri
videamus, senibus vero et omnibus imbecillibus difficilia. quapropter etiam vacuis vel inexercitatis corporibus Asclepiadis dicta minime conveniunt.

item ulceratione facti fluores difficiles curatione ab his qui
eruptione fuerint effecti[12] iudicantur, siquidem transcenso atque
praetermisso initio, novitatis fructu caruerint, quo facilis glu-
142 tinatio fieri solet. negat enim tarditas facultatem. item eruptione facti fluores ab his qui sine eruptione fuerint difficiles sunt
curatione. eius enim factae glutinationes alterius passionis initium referunt.[13] item ex partibus multum motis[14] factos fluores
ab his qui parvo motu agitantur difficiles curatione accipimus.
est enim motus cohaerentium partium disiunctio.

item ex occultis partibus venientes ab his qui proprias[15] tenuerint partes. etenim adhibita adiutoria occultis vel celatis
partibus vitiata suae virtutis sinceritate perveniunt, sanis primo
locis excepta ac deinde transmissa; hi vero qui ex primis locis
fluores[16] indomita adiutoriorum virtute curantur.

143 denique a stomacho vel ventre aut faucibus venientes facile
curabiles approbamus. etenim pota medicamina patientibus
primo locis adveniunt, et non nimio aut iugi naturae motu exer-

[11] enim *Rm*: etiam *S*

[12] affecti *S*: *corr. Rm*　　　　　　　[13] *fort.* initio reserantur

[14] multum motis *Rm*: multis modis *S*

[15] primas *Rm, coll.* primis locis *infra*: *an* propiores?

[16] fluores ⟨veniunt⟩ *R*: *fort.* fluores ⟨venerint⟩, *ut infra*

---

2. I.e., that the young and middle-aged are harder to cure.

3. E.g., cases of diffusion or anastomosis.

4. E.g., the wound may reopen. This seems to be the general idea, but the text is not
quite clear.

sion. For during the attack there is the additional difficulty of the wound, as mentioned above. Cases of bleeding which involve a great deal of the body and exhaust the patient's strength are also hard to cure, for a vigorous body offers the best medium for the action of medicinal remedies. This is also true, as we observe, in external wounds, that is, in those inflicted on the outer parts of the body. For such wounds are easy to deal with in the case of young men, and specifically in the case of athletes and those who perform physical labor; but they are hard to cure in cases of old men and all persons who are weak. Indeed, the view held by Asclepiades[2] is unsound even in the case of nonathletic persons who take no exercise.

Further, bleeding from a wound or sore is considered harder to cure than that which comes about merely by the eruption of blood from the vessel. For, with the passing of the initial stage, the sore lacks the advantage of freshness, which ordinarily facilitates healing. And the longer the sore persists, the more difficult is the healing process. Again, cases of bleeding due to a break through the vessel are harder to cure than those in which there is no break;[3] for the healing of the break may itself be the beginning of further trouble.[4] And it is harder to treat bleeding in which the parts move a great deal than that which takes place with little movement; for such movement causes the parts that should cling together to become separated.

Furthermore, bleeding which originates in the parts that are unseen is harder to treat than that which originates in the very part[5] [from which the flow is observed to issue]. For remedies directed to parts that are hidden or concealed arrive there with their efficacy impaired. The reason is that these remedies are, in the first instance, received by healthy parts and thence transmitted to the affected parts. But when the bleeding originates in a part to which the remedy can be directly applied, successful treatment is easier because the efficacy of the remedy is unimpaired.

Thus we hold that bleeding from the fauces, esophagus, or stomach is readily cured. For drugs which are drunk reach the affected parts directly; and these parts are not themselves subject to extensive and constant natural motion. On the other

5. The text is uncertain, but the distinction is obviously between the hidden parts and those at or near the surface.

citatis. hi vero qui ex hypozygo[17] membrana fluores venerint difficiles curatione iudicantur, et magis si ex diaphragmate, quod nos iamdudum discrimen[18] diximus, item ex arteria, hoc est pulmonis calamo.

omnium praeterea[19] difficilis atque gravior curatione ex pulmone fluens accipitur ob iuge spirationis officium. his enim qui omnem fluorem de pulmone venientem incurabilem dicunt assentiendum non est. sed iuxta Sorani sententiam difficilis est eorum curatio iudicanda, quippe cum vulnerationibus thoracis saepe pulmo penetratus non intulerit mortem, ⟨sed sag⟩ittis[20] exclusis vel cadentibus febri adhibita decisio in cicatricem vulnera fecerit convenire, ut omnes approbant chirurgi, memorantes in bello quendam sagittatum penetrato pulmone convaluisse, sanguinem a sagitta vomuisse, nec tamen mortem fuisse consecutam.

haec sunt quae de effectu sive de eventu fluorum credidimus ordinanda. etenim ex capite veniens fluor generaliter est curatione facillimus, siquidem non multos sustineat motus.

145   nunc nobis necessario dicendum remanet [ne] cui coenoteti[21] sanguinis fluor adscribatur. aliqui etiam Thessali sectatores recenti incisurae sive vulneri passionem[22] subici[23] dixerunt: 'non enim oportet locorum differentia coenoteton mutare virtutem. externam igitur corporis eruptionem recentem dicimus incisuram, quo erit consequens ut etiam interiorum eruptio huic coenoteti subiciatur.' sed his respondemus quoniam passio non chirurgia, sed diaetetica[24] traditur curatione. omne etenim adiutorium quod adhiberi videtur supradictis fluoribus est diaeteticae partis, non chirurgiae. quapropter diaetetices[25] scriptores libris regularibus, quos diaeteticos vocant, de haemoptyicis

---

[17] fort. hypezocote

[18] discrimen A: discretorium S

[19] praeterea ⟨maxime⟩ R

[20] ⟨sed sag⟩ittis conieci (fort. scrib. ut ⟨sagitt⟩is): ut hiis S

[21] ne cui coenotetesi S: fort. num cui coenoteti (alicui Rm)

[22] vulneri passionem scripsi: vulneris passione S: vulneris passioni Rm

[23] subigi S: corr. Rm

[24] dieteticarum S: corr. R

[25] dieteticas S: corr. Rm, nisi scrib. di(a)eteticae

hand, bleeding from the pleural membrane is not easily treated; the same is in even greater degree true of bleeding from the diaphragm, which we have called *discrimen*[6] above, and from the trachea, the tube leading to the lung.

But most intractable of all and hardest to cure is a case of bleeding from the lung, because the action of breathing must go on without interruption. We cannot agree, however, with those who say that every case of bleeding from the lung is incurable.

44 Rather do we hold, in accordance with Soranus' view, that the treatment of these cases is difficult. For it often happens in wounds of the chest that, though the lung is pierced, death does not result; but, after the removal or dropping-out of the arrow,[7] the checking of the fever causes the wound to cicatrize. All writers on surgery refer to such cases and tell of a soldier who, though shot by an arrow which penetrated his lung, was subsequently restored to health; though the penetration of the arrow caused him to vomit blood, death did not result.

This concludes our account of the probable outcome or result of various kinds of bleeding. And, in general, cases of bleeding from the head are the easiest to treat, for no extensive movement of the parts is involved.

45 It now remains for us to consider to what *coenotēs* [general type of disease] bleeding is to be referred. Some followers of Thessalus say that [in all cases] the affection is to be considered as a cut or wound of recent origin; for differences in the part affected do not change the general character of the disease. Thus these physicians hold that, since a break through the body at the surface is a fresh [i.e., nonchronic] wound, it follows that a hemorrhage originating beneath the surface also comes under the same category. But our answer to these writers is that in all the accounts of hemorrhage a treatment based on dietetics and not on surgery is set forth. That is, every remedy applied to these cases of bleeding belongs to dietetics[8] and not to surgery. Hence writers of books on regimen (Greek *diaeta*) discuss cases

6. Or possibly *discretorium* (*S*), despite the contradiction with 127, 130, and the fact that Caelius uses *discrimen* some half-dozen times in this sense, while *discretorium* is found nowhere else.

7. The passage is corrupt, and the translation is here based on a conjectural restoration.

8. The term here includes not only diet and regimen but also the use of drugs, i.e., all nonsurgical therapy.

146 scripserunt, quos nos sanguinem spuentes nuncupamus; chirurgi
vero in chirurgumenis hoc memorare non ausi sunt. ipse quoque
Thessalus secundo libro Diaetetico de fluore sanguinis scribens,
nihil in Chirurgumenis memoravit. et improprium,²⁶ quod sola
diaeta curetur, in adiutoriis adhibendis chirurgiae coenoteti
ascribere.²⁷

nos vero iuxta Sorani iudicium, sive in exterioribus sive interioribus corporis eruptionem factam recentem divisuram recte
dici probamus, atque etiam solutionem cognominamus; sed in
exterioribus attentionem recentis vulneris iudicamus. haec
enim nos necessario rapit, siquidem solutioni divisura domine-
tur, et ligamentorum vel fibularum²⁸ coniunctionem ex initio deposcat; atque haec divisurae²⁹ aptissima videantur, quae non in
147 omnibus sunt congrua solutioni.³⁰ etenim sagittarum divisurae
laxativa necessario accipiunt.³¹

interiorum vero eruptionum divisuras urgente³² solutionis coe-
noteta³³ ipsam magis cogimur iudicare, siquidem prior oculis occurrat solutio, ac deinde divisura ratione atque intellectu mentis
apprehendi videatur. secundo quod, cum sint multae differentiae fluoris sanguinis, omnes uni subici solutioni,³⁴ hoc est eruptionis et ulcerationis et sudationis; quare non cogamur hac
causa³⁵ fluoris differentias quaerere, aut aliae³⁶ coenoteti erup-

---

²⁶ impropriam *S*: *corr. Rm*: ⟨est⟩ improprium *Schmid RPh 53*

²⁷ coenoteta scribere *S*: *corr. Schmid 108*

²⁸ ligamentorum vel fibularum (*seu* fibrillarum) *Almeloveen*: figmentorum vel fabularum *S*: filamentorum sive fibrarum *Rm*: fragmentorum *vel* tabularum *Reinesius 666*

²⁹ divisura *S*: *corr. A*

³⁰ solutionibus *Rm*

³¹ laxativae necessario accipiuntur *edd.*

³² divisura surgente *S*: divisura urgente *R*: *fort.* divisura praesente

³³ coenoteta *R*: coenotetam *S*

³⁴ solutioni ⟨videntur⟩ *R*

³⁵ quare non cogimur hac causa *Rm*: quae non cogatur haec causa *S*: *fort.* quae non
cogat haec causa *nisi pleonasmus offendit* (*cf. Mulomed. Chir. ind., p. 311, Oder*)

³⁶ alicae *S*: *corr. R*

---

9. Or perhaps merely: 'We characterize the case as that of a fresh wound.'

of those who spit blood (Greek *haemoptyicoe*, which we may
46 translate in Latin *sanguinem spuentes*); but the surgeons do not
venture to refer to these cases in their works on surgery. And
Thessalus himself, though he writes about hemorrhage in Book
II of his work *On Regimen*, has nothing to say about it in his
Surgery. Indeed it would have been improper for him in discussing treatments to place that which is treated solely by
dietetics in the class of diseases requiring surgery.

Now we hold, in accordance with Soranus' view, that a recent
[i.e., nonchronic] hemorrhage, whether originating in the outer
or the inner parts of the body, is correctly termed a wound
[*divisura*]; at the same time we may also consider it a state of
flow or looseness [*solutio*]. But, when the hemorrhage originates
in the outer parts, the emphasis, in our judgment, should be
upon its characterization as a fresh wound.[9] It is this aspect that
necessarily claims our attention, since the traumatic condition
preponderates over the state of looseness and requires at the
very beginning a joining-together with ligatures or surgical
pins.[10] Such measures seem proper for a wound but would not be
47 suitable in every case involving a state of flow or looseness. In
fact, wounds made with arrows must be given relaxing treatment.[11]

On the other hand, though a wound is also involved in a case
of hemorrhage originating in the inner parts, we are constrained
to consider such a case predominantly as a state of looseness.
For, to begin with, this is the condition that first meets the eye;
only later is the traumatic condition apprehended by the operation of reason and understanding. Secondly, though there are
many different kinds of bleeding, it appears that all these kinds,
i.e., bleeding due to bursting of the vessel from within, or to a
wound from without, or to diffusion, may be subsumed under
the single term 'state of flow or looseness.' And this circumstance
therefore makes it unnecessary for us to consider the different
kinds of bleeding and to ascribe to one general type of disease
the bursting of the vessel from within, and to another general

10. This is conjectural. With the reading of *Rm:* 'fibers or threads.' As for *figmen-*
torum (*S*), such a word derived from *figo* (different from *figmentum < fingo*) and referring
to some means of fastening tissues together—whether clasps, pins, or stitches—seems
not impossible for Caelius, though I know of no sure occurrence of it.

11. I.e., in order that the arrow may be withdrawn. This seems to be the general
meaning, but the text throughout this passage is uncertain.

tionem adscribere, aliae ulcerationem, et non eidem sive[37] ulcere
148 vel ruptione vel emissione emissum fluorem. tertio quod nullo
adiutorio chirurgiae uti cogamur, sed omnibus congruis solutioni, quae[38] saepe consequenter etiam glutinationem partium
perfecerunt. ad summum quidem est recens incisura sive vulnus coenotes,[39] sed ex medicaminum regula, quam Graeci pharmacian appellant, diaeteticae parti ingesta, apte curatur. quibus etiam supradicta passio concuratur, obtinente[40] iudicio solutionis.

haec sunt fluoris sanguinis coenotetes: eas enim quibus[41] cog-
nominari atque conscribi possunt praescripta lectione tradidimus. nunc curationem necessario ordinamus.

149   XIII. DE CURATIONE

O PORTET igitur ex qualibet parte sanguinem fluentes iacere loco
mediocriter frigido atque obscuro, lecto immobili, et schemate declinato, ut paulo promptius caput levatum habere videantur, stramentis non nimie cedentibus neque calidis, et ut
potuerint uno atque eodem schemate perseverantes, hoc est immobiles; praeterea animi intentionibus resolutos, vehementer
enim motibus corporis animorum curae saepius turbationes ad-
diderunt. erunt etiam solo consternenda folia atque rami len-
150 tisci, vitis, mali punici, talliae, murtae, salicis, pini, et horum
similium, ex[1] quibus sine capitis iniuria constrictivus aer adnatus
atque confectus congrue aegrotantibus inspiramentis inseratur.
non enim cibi atque potus ratio ac diligentia curanda est, quae
intervallis distantibus adhibetur, quo constrictionis faciant com-
modum vel fluentia[2] retineant, potius quam aer, qui impausa-
biliore inspiratione[3] adductus omni parti atque particulae cor-

[37] sive *Rm*: sine *S*

[38] quae *Rm*: qua *S*

[39] coenotetes *S*: *corr. R*

[40] obstinente *S*: *corr. Rm*

[41] quibus *scripsi*: qui hiis *S*: quae ⟨in⟩ his *Rm*

[1] ex *scripsi*: et *S*: *om. R*

[2] fluentiam *S*: *corr. R. cf.* fluentia *infra et adn. ad Ac. ii. 220*

[3] in pausabiliorem inspirationem *S*: *corr. Bendz 27*

type the wounding of the vessel from without. There is no reason for not ascribing all bleeding to the same general condition, whether the bleeding is due to wounding from without, bursting 8 of the vessel, or diffusion.[12] The third point is that there is no necessity for using surgical measures; in every case remedies suitable for a state of looseness may be employed, and these often give rise to a complete healing of the parts. And so, while bleeding essentially is of the nature of a wound or incision of recent origin, yet the treatment is accomplished by prescription of drugs (Greek *pharmacia*) and is therefore to be found in the dietetic[13] part of medicine. This treatment, then, is the appropriate one for bleeding, provided that the state of looseness is considered to predominate.

This concludes our discussion of the general characteristics of hemorrhage. That is, we have, in what precedes, set forth the categories of disease by which bleeding may be characterized and described. We must now take up the treatment.

XIII. TREATMENT OF HEMORRHAGE

9

REGARDLESS of the part from which the bleeding originates, the patient should lie in a moderately cool and dark room. The bed should be firmly fixed, the patient's position reclining so that the head is held somewhat higher than the rest of the body, and the bedclothes not very soft or warm. Have the patient remain, as far as possible, in the same position, that is to say, unmoved. And see that he is relieved of all mental strain, for cares of the mind generally cause bodily movement and confusion. Strew the floor of the room with leaves and twigs of mas-
0 tic, grapevine, pomegranate, olive, myrtle, willow, pine, and the like. For an astringent emanation arises from these leaves and twigs and, without any adverse effect on the patient's head, proves beneficial when breathed in. Indeed, even a systematic and careful administering of food and drink at regular intervals in order to promote astringent action and repress the flow is not so essential as an astringent state of the air. For the air is breathed in unceasingly; it enters every part of the body, how-

12. *Emissione* seems to refer to all cases other than those arising from *ulcus* and *ruptio*.

13. I.e., nonsurgical.

poris ingressu suo fluentia faciat cohiberi, miti densitate per-
suasa.

convenit praeterea aegrotantes delatiore lecti sessione decli-
nari, ut omnifariam immobiles curandi perseverent; prohibere
etiam occasiones quae poterint[4] passionem in commemorationem
151 perducere, ut locutionis vel visus, ne aut eadem plurimis fabulis
revolvendo, aut inspiciendo quae exclusa sunt, viso admoniti
commoveantur. convenit denique etiam sanguineos colores parietum vel straminum sive operimentorum declinare.

adhibenda praeterea cibi abstinentia, permittentibus viribus,
usque ad tertium diem, non ob relaxanda corpora sed quo altiora, quorum est officium accepta digerere, immobilia perseverent. omnis etenim ciborum appropriatio motu quodam necessario perspicitur,[5] quo fiet ut ea quae sunt aptissime congluti-
nanda[6] motu resoluta differantur. quapropter ob acceptorum
digestionem cibum[7] sumi prohibemus, et abstinentiam utilissi-
152 mam iudicamus. prohibendi denique aegrotantes ab officio locutionis, ut si quid voluerint usi nutibus[8] vel scriptura dari sig-
nificent, magis quando ex pulmonis cannula, quam Graeci arteriam vocant, vel ipso pulmone aut thorace sanguinis nascitur
fluor.

convenit etiam articulorum tenacior ligatura, si vehemens
fuerit: densitati etenim articulorum patientes consentiunt partes. item spongiarum mollium ac limpidarum et levium, ex aqua
frigida vel aqua et aceto vel decoctione mali punici vel rubi aut
lentisci aut myrtae, patientibus partibus appositio, hoc est ex
153 quibus sanguinem ferri agnoverimus. et erunt haec iugiter commutanda ne naturali corporis vapore tepescant. ac si spongiae
visae fuerint aegrotantibus graves, erunt apponenda ptygmata
ex supradictis liquoribus infusa, aut suco plantaginis vel intybi
aut herbae calicularis aut uvae lupinae, quam Graeci strychnon
vocant, vel sempervivae, quam aizoon appellant, aut polygoniae
et acaciae ex aceto solutae.

---

[4] poterunt *Rm*

[5] perficitur *Rm*

[6] conglutinata *Rm*

[7] cibum *Rm*: ciborum *S*

[8] usibus nutus *S*: corr. *A*: fort. nutibus usi

ever small, and with its gentle condensing action causes the flow to stop.

Moreover, it is well to have the foot of the bed somewhat lower, the patient so reclining as to avoid all movement. And do not give him any occasion to speak or to see any object which 51 might cause a recurrence of the bleeding. Otherwise, by talking repeatedly about these matters[1] or by observing the bloody matter which has been discharged, he may suffer a relapse. It is also important to avoid red colors in walls, bedclothes, and covers.

Give the patient no food, if his strength permits, until the third day. The purpose of this measure is not to relax the body but to enable the inner organs, whose function it is to digest and distribute the food taken in, to remain at rest. For all distribution and assimilation of food must evidently involve some motion, and this motion may cause the parts, which should be firmly united, to become loose and break their connection. It is, then, because of the movement involved in digesting and distributing what he eats, that we require the patient to fast. And 52 we consider such fasting most advantageous. Also have the patient avoid talking, and if he wishes something let him indicate it by gesture or writing. This is especially important where the bleeding originates in the windpipe (Greek *artēria*), the lung, or the chest.

If the bleeding is severe, a tight bandaging of the limbs is helpful, for the parts affected by the bleeding will be sympathetically aided by the constriction of the limbs. Also apply soft, clean, and light sponges soaked in cold water, or water and vinegar, or a decoction of pomegranate, bramble, mastic, or myrtle; these applications should be made to the affected parts, that is, to the parts from which we decide that the bleeding comes.[2] 53 Keep renewing the sponges to prevent them from becoming warm by reason of the natural heat of the body. And if sponges are too heavy for the patient, use folded pledgets dipped in any of the aforesaid fluids, or in juice of plantain, endive, pellitory, uva lupina (Greek *strychnos*), houseleek (Greek *aeizōon*), knotgrass, or acacia dissolved in vinegar.

1. Presumably matters pertaining to his illness.

2. The reference is to the region where the bleeding seems to originate rather than the parts from which the blood is seen to issue.

ac si ex capite fuerit sanguinis fluor, erit psilothro expoliandum. tunc fomenta adhibenda ex oleo viridi aut roseo aut lentiscino aut melino aut murtino. sin vero plurimus fuerit fluoris lapsus, radendum caput atque gypso illiniendum vel acacia ex 154 aceto, magis frontis atque temporum partes. perseverante fluore cucurbita quoque apponenda subiecta flamma plurima occipitio.

si autem etiam per nares ferri videatur, erit[9] stypteria immittenda sicca, vel aceto infusa vel alio quolibet[10] ex liquoribus supradictis. ora quoque spongia ex aqua frigida expressa iugi tactu detergenda. tunc etiam cataplasmatum adhibendus est usus ex rebus constrictivis atque epithematibus, quae paulo post cum suis nominibus ordinabimus.

danda etiam aqua frigida vel pusca frigida aut gargarismus sine ullo percussu, quoties ex proximis partibus gutturis sanguinem ferri viderimus. ac si per inferiora vel altiora ferri sanguinem viderimus, sorbendos dabimus cyathos duos vel tres. 155 quod si minime mederi valuerint, etiam sucus plantaginis aut intybi vel uvae lupinae aut polypodii[11] aut herbae calicularis aut rosae erit offerendus. et neque plurimus iugiter, ne percussu partes noceantur, aut liquidorum influxione, quae quidem sint constrictivae virtutis, redundantia tamen laxare videantur; neque rursum longioribus intervallis, sic enim frigus a nobis illatum naturali vapore obtusum parvi temporis medelam[12] dabit vitiatam.

tunc tertia die transacta hora accessionis solitae articulos leviter ungemus frigido atque viridi oleo. dehinc detergemus faciem 156 quoque, spongia aqua frigida expressa retangentes. cibum dabimus parvum constrictivum, ut panem ex aqua frigida vel pusca, aut alicam[13] similiter, vel oryzam[14] decoctione thebaicarum palmularum confectam,[15] vel easdem ex aqua recenti confectas, aut si plurimum valere haec voluerimus, aqua caelesti, donec liquor mellis habeat crassitudinem, aut ex malis cydoniis. tunc etiam danda ova tremula ex pusca aut rore syriaco aspersa. dandus

[9] erit *Rm*: erunt *S*

[10] alia qualibet *S*: *corr. Rm*   [13] alica *S*: *corr. R*

[11] polygoniae *Rm, coll. 153*   [14] oryza *S*: *corr. R*

[12] medullam *S*: *corr. Rm*   [15] confecta *S*: *corr. R*

3. Possibly 'the parts near the throat.'

If the bleeding originates in the head, remove the hair with a depilatory and make applications of green olive oil, or rose, mastic, quince, or myrtle oil. If there is a considerable flow, shave the head and daub it with a gypsum plaster or a mixture of acacia and vinegar, covering especially the forehead and the temples. If the flow persists, also apply cupping to the occiput, using considerable flame.

If the bleeding is observed to come through the nostrils, insert alum, dry or soaked in vinegar or in any of the other fluids mentioned above. Also keep constantly wiping the patient's face with a sponge wrung out of cold water. Then employ plasters made of astringent substances and such applications as we shall name and describe shortly.

Whenever the bleeding is observed to come from the upper parts of the throat,[3] let the patient gargle with cold water or a cold mixture of vinegar and water or some other gargle that is free from pungency. And if the bleeding originates in the lower or deeper parts, have him swallow two or three cyathi of these substances. But if these measures do not relieve the condition, give him juice of plaintain, endive, strychnos, polypody, pellitory, or rose. But he should not continually take large quantities of such substances. For otherwise their pungency may irritate the affected parts; or the parts may be harmed by the influx of substances which, though astringent, seem to have a relaxing effect when taken in excessive amount. But, on the other hand, the drugs should not be taken at too long intervals; for in that case the cooling effect we have sought to produce is weakened by the normal bodily heat, and, as a consequence, the healing power of the remedy is dissipated after a short time.

Then at the end of the third day, at the hour at which the usual exacerbation is expected, gently rub the patient's limbs with cold green olive oil. Then keep wiping his face, too, with continual applications of a sponge wrung out of cold water. Give him a small amount of binding food, e.g., bread in cold water or in diluted vinegar, spelt groats similarly prepared, rice mixed with a decoction of Theban dates, or these dates prepared in fresh water. But if the most effective preparation of these foods is desired, [cook] in rain water until the liquid has the consistency of honey; quince may also be added. And give the patient soft eggs mixed with vinegar or moistened with the juice of

etiam panis simplex aut infusus. tunc interposito spatio temporis dandus potus aquae frigidae parvae.

    dehinc permittentibus viribus alternis diebus aeger nutrien-
dus, etiamsi nondum repressus fluor videatur, usque ad id tem-
157 pus quo cicatricem firmatam senserimus. quod quidem Themisonis atque Thessali sectatores usque ad septimum diem servari
dixerunt, hoc est trium diatritorum spatium. ut enim Antipater
ait tertio Epistolarum libro ad Gallum scribens, naturalis est
ratio trini numeri, non solum in diebus, sed etiam in omnibus
diatritis. sed est melius ut Soranus ait, quoniam non aequali
tempore nec dierum numero cunctis poterit cicatricis firmari
soliditas, ob alias causas et ob fortitudinem corporis ac debilitatem pro differentia naturali variatam, neque nos unum atque
eundem signare poterimus finem.

158   dehinc sequentibus diebus aliqua erunt emplastrorum apponenda aut epithematum constringentium atque frigidantium,
quae sunt plurima particulariter. etenim thebaicae palmulae
vino acriori infusae vel aceto contritae, admixtis malis cydoniis
decoctis aut mali punici corticibus aut alumine vel acacia aut
hypocistide aut galla aut oenanthe aut aloe, aut cerotario[16] ex
oleo roseo confecto vel melino aut myrtino aut lentiscino aut
oenanthino, admixta[17] etiam mastiche trita,[18] aut melle decocto,
galla contrita et aspersa,[19] aut pulvere mali punici vel mannae
thuris, admixto alumine liparo, quo malagmatis sumant omnia
qualitatem. tum linteo vel panno illinita patientibus partibus
159 apponenda. vel illud medicamen quod libris Celerum passionum
memoravimus, de cardiacis scribentes, et appellavimus diaroos,
vel ex polento et virgultis rubi vel arnoglossae aut herbae sideritis vel uvae lupinae aut caliculariae aut anulorum vitis aut sempervivae. item intyba cum pane ex aceto, aut palmulis, aut
murtae mollibus foliis, aut eiusdem semine viridi, ante cibum

[16] *fort.* cerotarium (*et* confectum)

[17] admixta *scripsi*: aut mixto S

[18] trito S: *corr.* R

[19] et aspersa Rm: aut aspera S: *cf. 165, 168*

---

4. The periods are composed of days 1–3, 3–5, and 5–7, respectively.

5. I.e., to continue the regimen until the scar is fully formed.

6. Or, following the reading of S, 'oak gall finely powdered or coarse.'

Syrian sumach. Bread, too, may be given, either plain or soaked [in these substances]. And after an interval of time the patient may drink a small quantity of cold water.

Thereafter, if his strength permits, give him nourishment on alternate days, even if the bleeding does not yet appear to be stopped. Nourishment on alternate days should be continued until we see that a strong scar has formed. Now the followers of Themison and Thessalus declare that this schedule of nourishment should be continued until the seventh day, that is, for an interval of three three-day periods.[4] And Antipater says in a letter to Gallus, contained in Book III of Antipater's *Letters*, that reckoning by triads is natural, not merely in connection with days, but in all other connections as well. But it is better to follow Soranus' rule,[5] since the formation of a firm scar does not in all cases require the same time or the same number of days. Among other reasons for this disparity are the natural differences between patients in respect to strength or weakness of body; and so we cannot say that the time required in each case will be the same.

On the following days apply any of the astringent and cooling plasters or epithems, of which there is a large number. For example, use Theban dates soaked in a dry wine or pounded up in vinegar, with an admixture of boiled quinces, pomegranate rind, alum, acacia, hypocist, oak gall, oenanthe, or aloes, or a cerate prepared with rose, quince, myrtle, mastic, or oenanthe oil. Ground-up mastic, cooked honey, with a sprinkling of[6] powdered oak gall, powdered pomegranate, or powdered frankincense, may also be added. Add also alum of Lipara,[7] so that the entire mixture may take on the properties of an emollient plaster; spread the mixture upon a linen cloth, and apply it to the affected parts. Or employ the so-called 'plaster of sumach,' which we mentioned in the chapter on the cardiac disease in our treatise *On Acute Diseases*;[8] or pearl barley, bramble, plantain, ironwort, strychnos, pellitory, vine tendrils, or houseleek. Before the patient takes food, give him endive with bread and vinegar, or with dates, soft myrtle leaves, or the green seeds of

7. Perhaps a kind of 'liquid alum.' Cf. Pliny *NH* xxxv. 184; Gloss. III, 568. 27, 597. 45, 602. 43; Cass. Fel., pp. 12. 6, 18. 10.

8. *Ac.* ii. 200. On the general treatment of hemorrhage cf. Sor. *Gyn.* iii. 41.

offerenda; vel ante cibum elixum aut non coctum panem et plantaginem ex aceto coctam[20] et viridi oleo, asperso rore syriaco.
item bulbi ex aqua et aceto et rore syriaco confecti dari pote-
160 rint[20a] cibo. non aliter etiam cochleae erunt offerendae: habent
enim quiddam glutinis naturalis utraque et compaginandi virtutem.

cum[21] proficiente curatione danda etiam pomorum quaedam,
ut mala cydonia cocta recenti mulso, vel torrida praesumpto
tegmine farina conspersa, aut sorba aut mali punici grana, aut
fabrilium uvarum;[22] item volantium non pinguia, ut sunt pectora
turdorum, vel pullorum matrem sequentium, item columbarum
aut phasianorum aut attagenarum aut perdicum, quarum erunt
murta pectora penetranda; tunc etiam porcinae carnes, cerebrum, pedes, auriculae, ora, vel auricularum summitates, quaeque vel fuerint nutribilia nec tamen difficilia digestione.

161 dandum etiam catapotium ex melle decocto[23] sub lingua de-
tinendum, singulare aut admixto gummi vel draganto. etenim
sufficienter decoctum mel, sicut in externis corporum glutinat
divisuras, non aliter etiam interioribus mederi necesse est atque
iam glutinata solidare. proficiente curatione dabimus etiam
vinum, et magis illud quod fuerit mordicantis virtutis, hoc est
quodam sensu linguam remordentis.

tunc ad summam paulatim erunt aegrotantes resumendi, cum
praecautione vehementium commotionum. sunt enim leviter
atque sensim movendi, portatoria scilicet vel cathedra longiore;
162 et firmato corpore lavandi. etenim lavacra fervoris causa atque
motus illati, quod corpora celerato spiritu agitantur, recentium
glutinationum atque mollium vulnerum redulcerantia probantur. cum enim oporteat coerceri atque densari patientia loca
contraria qualitate, necessario vexantur fervoris illati causa. inflata etenim parva ex occasione atque turgentia redulcerantur.
praecavenda denique etiam vehementia exercitia, et magis retento spiritu peracta.

tunc utendum peregrinatione terrena atque maritima. et si
corpus viderimus non attestante fortitudine augmenta carnis
accepisse, erit abstinentia cibi imperanda. tunc sequentibus

[20] *fort.* panis et plantago ex aceto cocta [20a] poterunt *R* [21] cum *fort. del.* (*cf. 161*)
[22] fabriles uvas *Rm: an* fabriles uvae? [23] decoctum *edd.: corr. Schmid RPh 53*

8a. Or perhaps: 'before giving him food, either boiled or uncooked, let him have bread, etc.'

the latter; or else before giving him food let him have bread [dough] boiled or uncooked,[8a] and plaintain cooked in vinegar and green olive oil with a sprinkling of Syrian sumach. Bulbs prepared with water, vinegar, and Syrian sumach may be given 50 as part of the food. Also give him snails to eat, for both kinds of snail[9] have a natural stickiness and an agglutinative property.

As the treatment proceeds, the patient should also be given certain fruits, e.g., quinces cooked in fresh mead or skinned, sprinkled with flour, and toasted; or sorb apples, pomegranate kernels, and some smoke-dried raisins. He may be given fowl, provided that it is not fat, e.g., breast of thrush, of chickens that still follow the mother hen, and of pigeons, pheasants, francolins, or partridges; use myrtle in seasoning the breast. Also use the meat, brains, feet, ears, snout, or ear tops of the pig, that is, whatever parts are nutritious but not hard to digest.

51 And have the patient hold under his tongue a pill made with boiled honey, alone or with the addition of gum or tragacanth. For, just as the boiled honey helps to close up wounds on the surface of the body, so it has a healing effect within the body and tends to strengthen the parts that have already healed together. As the cure progresses, prescribe wine, too, especially the kind which is sharp, i.e., affects the tongue with a biting sensation.

Then little by little restore the patient to a complete state of health, carefully avoiding any violent disturbances. Thus give him mild and gentle passive exercise in a sedan chair or couch. 62 And have him bathe only when the body has become strong. For the heat and motion involved in bathing accelerate the respiration and cause bodily agitation; the result is that newly healed and tender wounds are likely to open again. That is, since the affected parts require treatment of the opposite kind, i.e., confining and condensing treatment, they are necessarily harmed by introducing heat. In fact, if the parts are given even a small opportunity to become puffed up and swollen, the wound will open again. Thus violent exercises should be avoided, and particularly those which involve holding the breath.

Have the patient take a trip abroad, by land or sea. And if his body is found to have grown fat without any increase in strength, first prescribe fasting; then on succeeding days give

9. The reference may be to land and sea snails.

163 diebus parvus dandus est cibus vino detracto. etenim cicatricis
novitas, quippe ex venarum vasculis confecta atque nondum
fortificata, si carnis pondere fuerit praegravata, necessario rum-
petur. semper autem oportet ventrem mitius emollire: acriores
etenim clysteres incongruis motibus lacerant cicatrices atque
recursum faciunt passionis.

ac si vehemens atque plurimus fuerit sanguinis fluor, erunt
extendendae adiutorii virtutes. acetum denique sincere[24] dabimus ore retinendum vel gargarizandum aut sorbendum, spreto
quorundam iudicio qui asperum vel tussiculam commovens atque fluorem provocans acetum dixerunt, siquidem etiam gela-
164 tum sanguinem solvat. etenim asperat vel tussiculam commovet, si iugiter atque immodice fuerit datum. solvit autem eius
percussibilem virtutem distantia temporum oblatione variata,
quae non sensibili tactu, sed remissibili quadam digestione longioribus actibus immoratur. item quod fluorem non provocet
demonstrandum non est, siquidem sit manifestum in externis
corporibus vulneribus constitutis necessario fecisse densitatem;
et propterea conducibilis atque glutinantis virtutis fuerit ap-
probatum.

165 danda etiam acacia aceto soluta aut pusca aut ex supradictis
liquoribus, non aliter etiam hypocystis vel licium indicum aut
omphacium vel balaustium aut oenanthe aut polium[25] herba aut
gentiana aut macir aut ponticum[26] vel aegyptia spina, quam
acanthan vocant. quarum nunc sunt radices infundendae vel
decoquendae, nunc earum suci vel lacrimae admiscendae, siquidem sint frigidae atque constrictivae virtutis convenientia ob-
turamenta. item corticis vasculi vetustissimi vini exusti ⟨et⟩[27]
triti pulverem aspersum[28] tribus cyathis puscae frigidae aut decoctionis de qua supra diximus bibendum dari in modum cochleariorum duorum. etenim constringit cortex inveteratus, et
magis antiquissimi vini, commutatus tarditate temporis aucta
166 virtute. utendum etiam trochiscis confectis ex supradictis spe-

---

[24] sincerum *Rm, sed cf. Neue-Wagener Formenl. II. 166*

[25] polium *Am*: polios *S*

[26] rhaponticum *Rm*

[27] add. *R*

[28] asperum *edd. (cf. 158, 168)*

3 him a small amount of food and withhold wine entirely. For a
new scar, formed as it is from the blood vessels and not yet
strengthened, will inevitably be broken if it is prematurely
weighed down by heavy flesh. Again, the bowels should be kept
soft, but always by gentle means. For sharp clysters give rise to
harmful agitation, tear open the scars, and cause a recurrence
of the bleeding.

And if the bleeding is violent and copious, it will be necessary
to strengthen the remedies employed. Thus give the patient pure
vinegar to keep in his mouth, or gargle, or even swallow. We
reject the opinion of those who say that vinegar is irritating,
causes coughing, and, since it dissolves clotted blood, will pro-
4 voke a recurrence of bleeding. To be sure, vinegar aggravates or
irritates a cough if it is used constantly and in excess. But if it
is administered at suitable intervals, the lapse of time will overcome its pungency; for this pungency persists over a long period,
not by reason of any observable contact between the fluid and
the body, but through a kind of gentle diffusion. And it is not
necessary to point out that vinegar does not provoke bleeding,
for it is clear that vinegar always has an astringent effect in
cases of wounds on the surface of the body and is therefore
rightly considered beneficial for the healing of wounds.

5 And in these cases give the patient acacia dissolved in pure
vinegar, diluted vinegar, or any of the other fluids suggested
above. Similar use may be made of hypocist, Indian lycium,
omphacium, wild pomegranate flower, oenanthe, hulwort, gentian, muttee-pal, rhubarb, or the Egyptian thorn (Greek *acantha*); sometimes their roots may be steeped or boiled in the
fluid, at other times their juices or gum may be added to the
fluid, for these mixtures form useful plugs with cooling and
astringent properties. Also take the incrustation from a jar of
very old wine,[10] burn it, pound it to a powder, and have the patient take two spoonfuls of this powder mixed with three cyathi
of cold diluted vinegar, or of one of the decoctions mentioned
above. For the incrustation when old has an astringent property, particularly when the wine is very old; that is, the properties of the deposit change with the passage of time, its strength
6 increasing. Also employ troches made with the various sub-

10. Probably *cortex* denotes incrusted lees. Cf. Soranus *Gyn.*, p. 120. 28. But the
reference may be merely to the cork of wine jars.

ciebus; item ex rosis ⟨et ex⟩²⁹ seminibus trochiscos,³⁰ quorum
compositionem Responsionum libris De medicaminibus dicentes
tradidimus; item quod appellatur dielectru,³¹ item oenocraton
et alia similia quorum compositionem, ut supra dictum est,
Medicaminum libris tradidimus.

ac si coacervatus perseveraverit sanguinis fluor, utendum
etiam vehementioribus quibus obturentur altiora suae teneritudinis causa.³² tamen erunt ocius adhibenda, ne passionis ipsius impetu in manibus nostris vitam linquere cogantur aegro-
167 tantes. praedicto igitur periculo eorum proximis aut ministris,
vel quod producta vita spem saepe dederint sanitatis, erunt haec
|adhibenda: supradicti corticis cinis exustus cum liquida pice
spongiae impressus, decoctio lentisci et roris syriaci, et eligma-
tium supradictorum sucorum.³³

nam haec conficiuntur hoc modo. agmine vitis ustis virgultis, atque ex eorum cinere confecto liquamine, scilicet aqua
imbriali admixta, quam vulgo cisterninam vocant, dabimus ex
ipsa bibendos cyathos tres vel quatuor, nullis aliis speciebus admixtis. nam quidam in his, si febribus adficiantur, etiam vinum
immiscuerunt vividum,³⁴ vel spongiae ustae cinerem, qui con-
168 ficitur hoc modo. spongia expressa aceto atque pice liquida
|madefacta vasculo novo includitur testeo; tunc circumtegitur
luto et usque eo inuritur donec carbonescat; dehinc trita in pulverem ex quo cochlearis unius quantitas aquae vel puscae frigidae mixta datur bibenda. vel si virtutem medicaminis augere
voluerimus, tinctam, ut supra diximus, spongiam liquida pice³⁵
pulvere bituminis aspergimus.

decoctio autem lentisci conficitur hoc modo. eius virgultorum
sumentes sufficientem modum aquae imbrialis infundimus sextariis duobus, tunc decoquimus; et cum semel vel secundo sca-
169 tere viderimus, expressas detrahimus lentisci comas. tunc li-

²⁹ ex rosae seminibus *S*: *corr. Rm, coll. Paul. Aeg. vii. 12. 4, 6*
³⁰ trochiscis *Rm*
³¹ dielectrū *S*
³² sua et teneritudinis causae *S*: *corr. Friedel 28*
³³ suorum *S*: *corr. Rm*
³⁴ *cf. Chr. iv. 70*: uvidum *Rm*: *fort.* viscidum
³⁵ liquida pice *Rm*: liquidae picis *S*

11. Wine is a common ingredient of troches, but I do not know to what sort of troche
or other remedy the 'wine mixture' here mentioned refers.

stances mentioned above, as well as those made from roses and from seeds, preparations which we have described in the section on drugs of the treatise entitled *Answers;* and also the so-called 'troche of amber,' and *oenocraton,*[11] and other similar remedies whose preparation we have also described in the section on drugs.

Now, if copious bleeding continues, even stronger remedies must be used to stop the flow from the inner organs because of the frail state of these parts. But the remedies must be applied quickly, for by reason of the severity of the bleeding the patient 167 may die in our hands. First, therefore, inform his kinsmen or servants of the danger involved, but indicate that, if his life can be prolonged, there is often hope of a restoration of health. Then make use of the following preparations: burnt ashes obtained from the incrusted wine dregs mentioned above, mixed with liquid pitch and absorbed into a sponge; decoctions of mastic and Syrian sumach; and electuaries prepared from the juices named above.

These preparations are made as follows: Burn a number of vine cuttings together and prepare a fluid by mixing rain water, commonly known as 'cistern water,' with the ashes;[12] give the patient three or four cyathi of this mixture to drink, adding no other substances. Some physicians, however, where the patients have fever, add strong wine or the ash of burnt sponge. The 168 latter is prepared in the following way:[13] A sponge is wrung out of vinegar, soaked in liquid pitch, and placed in a new earthen vessel; the vessel is luted, and heat is applied until the sponge is charred. The sponge is then rubbed down to a powder. A spoonful of the powder, mixed with cold water or cold diluted vinegar, is given to the patient to drink. If it is desired to increase the strength of the preparation, after soaking the sponge in liquid pitch, as stated, sprinkle it with powdered bitumen.[14]

The decoction of mastic is made as follows: Take a sufficient quantity of cuttings of mastic; place them in two sextarii of rain water and boil them. When the slips are observed to bubble up at the surface once or twice, press them out and remove them. 169 Then boil down the remaining fluid until it is reduced to a third

12. I.e., letting the rain water drip through the ashes, forming a kind of lye.

13. Cf. Sor. Lat., p. 70. 5–9 (Rose).

14. We should expect mention here of the powdered lees (or cork). Cf. 165, 167.

quorem decoquimus donec ad tertiam partem deducatur, cuius cyathum admixtum duobus cyathis aquae bibendum propinamus.

non aliter etiam electariorum decoctio conficitur. ob electarium autem conficiendum erunt sumenda mala punica recentia, vel infusa nisi fuerint mollia. quibus contusis atque compressis, aliquantum detrahimus sucum atque decoquimus donec mellis crassitudinem sumat. et quantum medicaminis virtutem tendere voluerimus, tanto valentius mala exsucamus, quo expressa ultimum atque crassiorem sucum dimittant, ut etiam eorum cortex si quid humoris habuerit, sudet.

170 convenit etiam medicamen quod Themison ordinavit hoc modo: mali punici partibus duabus aloe admixta parvi cochlearis quantitate, cum aqua frigida offerendum.[36]

ac si solutio perseveraverit, addenda etiam constrictiva cucurbita patientibus partibus; tum diaiteon[37] emplastrum quod vehementer astringit, superimpositis spongiis aqua pusca infusis, ut supra scriptum, ciborum qualitate permanente. dandum etiam noctis initio medicamen quod dioporon[38] appellant, vel diasycaminon, sive catapotia quae Medicaminum libris praediximus, nunc autem perficienda conscripsimus hoc modo. gummi et acacia aequis ponderibus, admixto alumine scisso ad duplex pondus, quae sunt colligenda decoctione papaveris et danda quibusdam in duplicem modum.

171

at si quisquam non plurimum sanguinem fluxerit, nec tamen materia ferri cessaverit, convenit etiam tertia die phlebotomiam adhibere. etenim ex eo quod sanguis ferri non quieverit, manifeste conicimus glutinationem partium non fuisse perfectam divisurae sive vulneris, et propterea in tumorem venisse perspicimus. omne etenim vulnus quod usque in tertium diem glutinari non potuerit necessario tumescit. Thessalum denique indigna accusatione appetitum Sorani sententia recte purgavit. tertia etenim die phlebotomandos sanguinem[39] fluentes constituit, nutriens constrictivo cibo, non inconsequentia ordinans adiutoria,

172

---

[36] offerenda *R*

[37] diaeteon *edd.*

[38] diaporon *edd., sed cf. Ac. iii. 18*

[39] sanguine *edd.*

of the original amount. Have the patient drink a cyathus of it mixed with two cyathi of water.[15]

The electuaries are prepared by a similar process of boiling. For this purpose take fresh pomegranates and, if they are not already soft, soak them. Pound and press them, extracting a quantity of juice; and then boil down this juice until it attains the consistency of honey. If we desire to strengthen the drug, we must subject the fruit to proportionally greater pressure and extract the thicker juice which the fruit finally gives up, and also whatever liquid can be squeezed from the rind.

170   A drug which Themison prescribes is also helpful. It is prepared by mixing a small spoonful of aloes with two parts of pomegranate and is given to the patient to drink with cold water.

If the bleeding persists, astringent cupping should be applied to the affected parts. And one should use the willow plaster with its strong astringent properties, applying over it sponges soaked in diluted vinegar, as described above. Have the patient continue to take the same type of food. At nightfall give him the plaster of fruits (Greek *dioporōn*), or the mulberry plaster (Greek *diasycaminōn*), or the pills which we described in the section on drugs.[16] As indicated there, the pills to be used in the 171   present cases are prepared as follows: Equal weights of gum and acacia and a double weight of fissile alum are mixed in a decoction of poppy. This should in some cases be given the patient in double dose.

If the bleeding is not copious and yet does not cease, it is well to employ venesection on the third day. For from the fact that the blood does not cease flowing we may obviously conclude that there has been no complete healing of the break or wound in the vessel and that an inflammation has therefore arisen. In fact, every wound that fails to heal by the third day necessarily becomes inflamed. And this principle, enunciated by Soranus, has justly cleared Thessalus of the undeserved criticism 172   leveled against him. For Thessalus prescribes venesection on the third day in cases of unchecked bleeding, at the same time continuing to nourish the patient with binding food. Now these prescriptions are not illogical but are quite in keeping with the

15. No mention is made of the decoction of sumach.
16. Of the treatise *Answers*.

sed tamquam complexis passionibus apta, ut contrariis contraria
obicere videantur.

ac si etiam intra diatriti tempus fuerit attestata partium gravedo vel dolor aut spiratio difficilis vel tussicula sicca, phlebotomare convenit. atque aerem loci parvissime[40] tepidare,[41] et
iisdem partibus lanas oleo calido viridi expressas apponere, vel
ob sanguinis fluorem ea ordinare quae glutinare valent, sed virtutis frigidae non sint neque transvorationis asperent loca nec
173 tumorem commoveant. plurimum[42] dabimus etiam samiae terrae, quam ges astera vocant, unciae partem tertiam cum duobus
vel tribus cyathis aquae tepidae; non aliter etiam amylum vel
argallici radicem atque foliorum eius sucum. convenit denique
sub lingua retenta eius radicis particula sive amyli sive terrae
supradictae. danda etiam ex gummi sive draganto et thure et
opio et his similibus confecta electaria.

tunc tertia die accepta diatriti temporis observatione non
solius fluoris, sed etiam febrium, erunt aegrotantes oleo calido
atque plurimo et viridi perungendi. facies quoque aqua tepida
174 fovenda. cibus dandus complexioni passionis aptus, et pultes ex
oryza vel alica, frixa sive simplici, vel milio [et] decocto,[43] calidae
sed non oleosae, ac potius siccae vel ex oleo viridi confectae aut
cum palmulis vel amylo, admixto ges astere[44] aut argallici radice
incocta.[45] ceteris vero diatritis, hoc est intervallis dierum trino
numero servatis, cogentibus doloribus erit utendum fomentis atque cataplasmatibus laxativis, nunc etiam cum scarificatione cucurbitis sive hirudinum appositione, quas sanguisugas vocant.
tum vaporatio spongiarum apponenda.

sin vero etiam fluor periculosus fuerit sanguinis cum tussicula
175 vel asperitate gutturis, erit utendum quidem constrictivis epithematibus, sed calidis. dandum etiam sorbendum mulsum ex
melle decocto, et a vino abstinendum. danda denique aqua po-

---

[40] parvissimi edd.   [41] trepidare S: corr. Rm

[42] plurima S (cf. Neue-Wagener Formenl. II. 599): plurimis Rm

[43] milio et decoctio S: milio et decoctio ⟨ptissanae⟩ R

[44] ges asteros S: cf. 105   [45] radicem incoctam S: corr. R

apparently mixed character of the disease, for they involve the application of contrary measures when contrary conditions are present.[17]

Venesection should also be performed if before the end of the three-day period there is a feeling of heaviness or pain in the affected parts, difficulty in breathing, or a dry cough. Also warm the air of the room a little in these cases and apply to the parts in question wool wrung out of warm green olive oil. Or, because of the bleeding, continue to prescribe remedies which have the power of healing wounds, but avoid those that have cooling properties or irritate the parts used in swallowing or aggravate

3 the inflammation. Generally, a third of an ounce of Samian earth (Greek *gēs astēr*) mixed with two or three cyathi of warm water may also be given; so, too, starch or the root of comfrey and the juice of its leaves. The patient should keep a small part of the root, starch, or Samian earth under his tongue. Also give him electuaries made from gum, tragacanth, frankincense, poppy juice, or other similar substances.

Then on the third day, i.e., at the end of the three-day period, if the examination shows not only bleeding but also fever, anoint the patient with a great deal of warm green olive oil. And fo-

4 ment the face, too, with warm water. Prescribe food that is suitable in view of the mixed character of the illness, e.g., porridges of rice or spelt groats, roasted or raw, or of boiled millet, the porridges to be warm and not very rich, or, even better, dry or prepared with green olive oil, dates, starch, an admixture of Samian earth, or uncooked comfrey root. At the end of subsequent three-day periods (for we must continue to observe these three-day intervals), employ relaxing fomentations and poultices, if the pains require it; and in these cases also apply cupping with scarification, or leeches, called *sanguisugae* ['bloodsuckers']. Then prescribe applications of heat with sponges.

But if the bleeding also involves danger and is accompanied

5 by coughing or roughness of the throat, use astringent, but warm, applications. And let the patient sip some mead made with boiled honey; but do not let him have wine. He may be

17. The phrase *contraria contrariis* generally refers to the principle of treating diseases by remedies having properties opposed to those of the disease. Though this idea is included in the present passage, there is the further point that in the *status mixtus*, which combines contrary elements (both *strictura* and *solutio*), contrary measures may be employed.

tanda calida sed parvo modo; tum sorbilia quae passioni virtute
apta mederi possunt, ut est amygdala expoliata[46] in mulso decocta, quae abicienda, et admittendum amyli quantum valeat
mulsum in quandam crassitudinem redigere.

deinde similibus electariis atque sub lingua continendis medicaminibus utemur tempore amissionis, ut est mel atticum admixto gummi vel dracanto decoctum, aut glycyrriza vel eius suco,
176 nisi quisquam aegrotantium hoc improbaverit nausea commotus, quo eius stomachus facile moveatur. item ex lini semine
trito et tracanto drachmis duabus et amygdalis expoliatis xxv
et strobilorum granis xxx et ovi unius tosti vitello et amyli drachmis duabus, infuso passo sufficientis quantitatis, quo medicamen
electarii crassitudinem sumat.

sin vero etiam rauci fuerint aegrotantes, erit mel decoquendum cum ceteris speciebus singulatim resolutum[47] tracanto ex
infusione passi confecto. terminatur etenim asperitas faucium,
et[48] transvorationis partes leniuntur, et tussicula mitigatur, spu-
177 ta sanguinolenta reprimuntur. danda[49] etiam noctis initio, nisi
febrium obstiterit accessio, simplex diacodion. continuum vero
medicaminum usum quae tussicularia sunt appellata sive eorum
immodicam quantitatem necessario fugiendam mandamus. est
enim melius simplicibus atque consuetis mederi rebus. illa enim
temporaliter quidem mitigare videntur tussientium motum, sed
passionem totam faciunt deteriorem.

ac si attestante tumore fluor perseverans produxerit tempus,
in iisdem perseverare convenit quae supra memoravimus, admixto etiam lacte. si minui tumorem viderimus, dandum quoque lac amylatum et panis laganum pultibus infusum, sed ex fer-
mento confectum quo panis habeat qualitatem, faciat etiam me-
178 delam meliorem: strobilus denique cum suis fructibus, quod in
semet habeat resinale, ptisana decoctus. dehinc profectu cedente erit panis cum malva decoquendus, sed non exquisite con-

---

[46] expoliata *Rm, coll. 176*: ex pusca *S*: expolita *Sm*
[47] resoluto *edd.*   [48] vel *S: corr. R*
[49] *dubitanter retineo, fort. subintell.* antidotus: dandum *Rm*

given warm water to drink, but only in small quantity, and also soft foods of such qualities as will promote the cure of the disease. For example, boil blanched[18] almonds in mead; remove the almonds and add to the mead sufficient starch to give it some thickness.

Then at the time of a remission employ similar electuaries and other preparations to be held under the tongue, e.g., Attic honey boiled down with an admixture of gum, tragacanth, sweetroot, or the juice of the latter. But such a preparation should not be given if the patient objects to it and is so nauseated by it that he is ready to gag. Another electuary may be made with two drachms of flaxseed and tragacanth, twenty-five blanched almonds, thirty pine kernels, the yolk of one fried egg, and two drachms of starch, all soaked in a sufficient quantity of raisin wine to give the compound the consistency required for an electuary.

But if the patient is also hoarse, boil down honey with any one of the other substances and soften the preparation with a mixture of tragacanth and raisin wine. For thus the irritation of the throat will be eased, the parts used in swallowing relaxed, coughing relieved, and bloody sputa checked. And unless an attack of fever prevents it, the simple drug from poppy capsules may be given at nightfall. But we hold that the constant use of cough medicines or their use in excessive quantity must be avoided; and, in fact, it is better to treat the patient with the simple and customary remedies. For, while the cough medicines seem to relieve coughing temporarily, they actually render the disease as a whole worse.

Now if the bleeding, attended by inflammation, keeps breaking out over a period of time, keep the patient on the same foods as those mentioned above, adding milk to the diet. If the inflammation is reduced, give the patient milk mixed with starch. A cake made with bread crumbs and porridge may also be used; this should be leavened to give it the quality of bread and to improve its effectiveness as a remedy. Because of its resinous content, one may also use a pine cone together with its kernels cooked with pearl barley. Then, if the patient's condition improves, give him bread cooked with mallow, but not highly sea-

18. Or reading *ex pusca* (S): 'soak almonds in vinegar water; then boil them in diluted honey, etc.'

ditus. danda etiam ptisana cum lenticula, quam Graeci phacoptisanen[50] vocant. et apponenda extrinsecus cerotaria ex
murtino vel lentiscino aut melino oleo confecta. tum urgentius
augenda resumptio, ut supra demonstravimus, atque ita abstento sanguine, quoad fiet[51] glutinatio[52] perfecta.

179 at irruente tumore erit coniciendum vel advertendum utrum
glutinatio fecerit retentionem, cum neque gravedo neque dolor
aut punctio vel pulsatio vel saltus partium aut extentio vel febris cum arida tussicula aut stridor aut singultus vel quaepiam
sanitati impedita saucietas aegrum sequi videbitur, sed sit[53]
aequalis atque ordinata spiratio perseverans. tum si tumoris
causa fuerit retentio sanguinis temporaliter effecta, quae necessario sordidum atque humectum vulnus efficiat, phthisicorum
fluorem pronuntiamus.

tum cum producto tempore sanguinis fuerit ruptio variata,
erit curatio pro motibus temporum varianda, ut superpositionem
emergentem eadem curatione curemus. in lenimento vero leves
atque quietos adhibemus motus sub magisterio aliptae vel mu-
sici, quo etiam vocis exercitium artificis praecepta moderentur.
180 cibus dandus ex mediae qualitatis materia, adhibitis resumptivis
cyclis in quibus non erunt repentinae mutationes faciendae, sed
nunc ex mediae qualitatis materia primus ordinandus est cyclus,
dehinc ex volantum secundus, tunc ex agrestium tertius, atque
ex porcinis carnibus ultimus, et coniunctis deinde duobus contiguis ordo dirigendus, atque ita omnibus. sed ⟨in⟩[54] singulis
materiarum speciebus erunt magis constringentia procuranda,
ut in oleribus intybum, plantago; in marinis squillae, mulli; in
volantibus perdices, phasiani, attagenae; in agrestibus lepores,
capreae. et si celeriter aegros crassificari viderimus, erit absti-
181 nentia intercalanda; tum venter emolliendus. utendum praeterea partiliter nunc aquae potu, nunc vini leviter remordentis.

deinde veniendum ad recorporativae curationis materiam, la-
tenti motu adhibita drimyphagia ex pisce gobione, admixto

[50] phacoptisanen *Am*: psysanaeon *S*: ptissanophacen *Rm*
[51] fiat *Rm*
[52] glutinatione *S*: *corr. R*
[53] *fort.* fit
[54] *addidi*

19. Or, as is more likely, to the constrictive condition arising from the inflammation.

soned. Let him also have a mixture of pearl barley and lentils (Greek *phacoptisanē*). And apply externally cerates made with myrtle, mastic, or quince oil. Then employ restorative treatments more extensively, as we have indicated above. And restrain the flow of blood until the healing of the break is completed.

But if inflammation supervenes, we must consider and determine whether a stoppage of the flow is really due to healing of the break.[19] This is the case when there is no sensation of heaviness, pain, pricking, throbbing, pulsation, or tension of the parts, and when the patient does not show fever, dry coughing, stridor, hiccoughs, or any general impairment of health, but continues to breathe evenly and regularly. But if it is because of the inflammation that the bleeding is temporarily arrested and the wound, as a consequence, becomes unclean and festering, we may conclude that the bleeding will be connected with phthisis.

When, with the passage of time, a case of bleeding becomes chronic, the treatment must vary with the state of the ailment at a given time. That is, any subsequent attack must be treated in the manner described above for the first attack. But during the intervals of remission prescribe mild and gentle exercise under the direction of a trainer, preferably one who is a musician, so that the patient's vocal exercise may also be subject to professional direction. And [in these remissions] give the patient food of the middle class, and then apply the regular restorative cycles, but in such a way as to avoid the necessity of sudden changes. That is, in the first cycle let the patient take food of the middle class, in the second fowl, in the third the flesh of field animals, and in the last pork. In the next stage two successive cycles may be joined together and finally all. But in each class of food the more astringent varieties are to be chosen, e.g., among vegetables, endive and plantain; as sea food, squill and red mullet; among fowls, partridge, pheasant, and francolin; among field animals, hare and roe. If you observe that the patient quickly takes on fat, intersperse a period of fasting and also soften the bowels. Moreover, have the patient at times drink water and at other times a moderately sour wine.

Then change over to the food required for the metasyncritic treatment, gradually introducing the acrid diet with gudgeon

melle. dandi etiam pisces et cerebrum, una tantummodo die, atque[55] intervallatis diebus adhibitis localibus adiutoriis recorporativis, ut dropace, partibus primo quae fuerint remotae ⟨a⟩[56] patientibus, tunc vicinis, ac deinde ipsis. addendus etiam ex sinapismo rubor, quem Graeci phoenigmon vocant, atque sicca fricatio. tunc torrendum corpus sole, quod Graeci heliosin vocant. adhibenda quoque paroptesis. et aliquando sicca cibatio,

182 aliquando cum pane palmulae offerendae. et initianda[57] consuetudo frigidi[58] lavacri atque potus parvus scilicet primo, ac deinde auctus suggestione, quo possint etiam his aegrotantes uti partiliter. facit enim duriora corpora atque valentia acceptorum vel gestorum differentia,[59] contrariorum mutatione variata, quamquam sint ex eodem genere venientia. utilis praeterea navigatio approbatur et peregrinatio comprobatur: inde enim res salutares venient. praecavenda etiam venus, facile autem[60] haec passio refricatur. haec est secundum Methodicos ordinata curatio.

183 apud veteres vero dissonantia sunt ordinata. etenim de schemate iacendi atque phlebotomia et ligatione et constrictivis vel frigidis cataplasmatibus et aceto bibendo varia disceptatione pugnatum est.

de schemate inquam iacendi, siquidem alii supinos iubeant aegrotantes iacere, vel super eas partes quae non patiuntur. item Asclepiades consequenter[61] approbat supra partes quae patiuntur esse locandos aegrotantes, siquidem cum scriberet necessarias curationes adprehensa causa sic fuerit elocutus, etiam sanguinem inquit fluentes ita esse locandos.

⟨item de phlebotomia inquam,⟩[62] siquidem Erasistratus phlebotomari praeceperit patientes, alii vero eius sectatores etiam

---

[55] atque *om. R*

[56] *add. R*

[57] initianda *scripsi*: imitanda *S*: ineunda *Rm*

[58] frigidi *Am*: frigida *S*   [60] *an enim?*

[59] differentiae *S: corr. Rm*   [61] inconsequenter *Rm*

[62] *supplevi. sed fort. plura desunt, ut existimat Schmid RPh 55*

---

20. E.g., astringent. But the text, as it stands, is not entirely clear, and the version given is quite tentative.

21. I.e., on the parts affected, presumably because such a position would help to constrict the state of flow. But the argument is refuted below (189). And bleeding does

fish to which honey is added. Give the patient fish and brain, but only for one day. Then after the lapse of some days apply local metasyncritic treatments, such as pitch plasters, first to the parts far removed from the affected parts, then to those nearer, and finally to the affected parts themselves. Also irritate the skin to redness, a treatment which the Greeks call *phoenigmos;* for this purpose a mustard blister and dry massaging may be employed. Also prescribe sun-bathing (Greek *hēliōsis*) and the use of intense heat for baking the body. Sometimes meals may be given entirely dry, and sometimes a dish of dates and
82 bread may be given. Afterward have the patient begin bathing regularly in cold water, and have him also resume drinking [cold water], at first in small quantity, but subsequently in increased amounts so that he may alternate the bathing with the drinking. For variations in the patient's food and drink, as well as in his activity, help to make the body strong and healthy; and outwardly the treatments may be so varied that they seem completely different, even though they are all basically of the same kind.[20] Again, a sea trip and a change of climate will be advantageous, for they are followed by improvement in health. But venery should be avoided, for this ailment may easily break out anew. This concludes the account of the treatment of bleeding as given by the Methodists.

As for the physicians of the past, their prescriptions are quite
83 conflicting. Indeed, they hold varied and divergent views about the position in which the patient should lie; on the use of venesection, bandaging, and astringent or cooling plasters; and on the drinking of vinegar.

Thus with regard to the position of the patient, some hold that he should lie on his back or on the parts that are not affected. Asclepiades, however, comes to the conclusion that the patient should lie on the parts affected. For, having asserted that if the cause of an ailment is understood its proper treatment necessarily follows, he made the declaration that in cases of bleeding the patient should lie in this way.[21]

And there is conflict of opinion with regard to venesection: Erasistratus prescribes that remedy in these cases, but some of his own followers condemn it chiefly on the ground that it im-

not necessarily imply a basic *solutio* (190). It may be that more has dropped out of the text at this point than the mere transition to the next subject.

fieri principaliter damnaverunt[63] adiutorii genus, tamquam
virium vexabile; item plurimi nostrorum, tamquam laxativum
et propterea inconveniens fluori sanguinis ex solutione venienti
184 et indignum ad constrictionem. alii adhibendum probaverunt,
ut Hippocrates De morbis scribens, Diocles libro quo De passionibus,[64] causis et curationibus scripsit, Praxagoras libro tertio De curationibus, item Asclepiades libro quo De clysteribus
scripsit, dehinc Themison secundo libro Tardarum passionum,
et Thessalus secundo libro Regulari, sed adiecta discretione.
etenim si tertia inquit die rursum sanguinem fluxerint aegrotantes atque plurimum, quod intelligitur tamquam in complexis
passionibus, hoc est strictura obtinente, faciendum approbasse.
185 alii vero omnes statim atque sine ulla dilatione phlebotomandos
dixerunt, et magis si ex thorace vel pulmone sanguis fluxerit, vel
plurimus, avertendae materiae causa, quo patientibus partibus
derelictis aliorsum feratur, hoc est ad eas quae non patiuntur,
vel ob educendam materiae multitudinem. denique saepe inquiunt faciendam consuetudinem, si oportuerit, semel et secundo vel tertio, quo recurrens ex brachio post abstinentiam sanguis iterum avocetur; velut[65] Themison ait secundum se[66] et
186 laxamenti esse et minutionis ne initium tumoris[67] efficiat.[68] item
ut alii, ob evacuandas venas, quo exantlatae[69] celerius concedant
atque coeant divisurae; velut[70] Asclepiades, ad minuendum
⟨sanguinis⟩[71] cursum sive spirationem quibus passio adiuvatur.

item de ligationibus pugnaverunt, siquidem Xenophon et
Dionysius et Herophilus primo libro Curationum et Erasistratus
probent articulorum faciendam constrictionem: Herophilus vero

---

[63] damnaverunt ⟨hoc⟩ R
[64] passionibus ⟨atque⟩ Wellmann
[65] fort. divisim scrib. cum Bendz 101
[66] secundum se] secandam venam esse Rm
[67] tumoris Rm: toris S
[68] fiat Rm: an efficiatur?
[69] exeant late S: corr. Bendz 100
[70] vid. adn. 65 supra   [71] add. R

pairs the strength. And many of our own sect reject venesection
on the ground that it is a relaxing measure without any astringent effect and therefore improper as a treatment for bleeding,
4 which involves a state of looseness. But others declare that venesection should be employed, e.g., Hippocrates *On Diseases;*
Diocles *On Diseases and Their Causes and Treatment;* Praxagoras
On Treatments, Book III; Asclepiades *On Clysters;* and later
Themison *On Chronic Diseases,* Book II; and Thessalus *On
Regimen,* Book II. But Thessalus makes a distinction in the
cases and prescribes venesection [only] in cases where, on the
third day, copious bleeding takes place again; for he concludes
that these cases involve a complex condition[22] in which the state
5 of stricture predominates. But others declare that venesection
should be used immediately and without delay in all cases of
hemorrhage, and especially when the flow of blood is from the
chest or lung or when the bleeding is copious. In prescribing
venesection they seek to deflect the course of the blood, so that
it leaves the affected parts and flows elsewhere, that is, to parts
which are not affected; venesection may also serve to withdraw
excessive blood. Thus these writers state that in many cases
venesection should be repeated, that is, it should be performed
not merely once but twice or three times, if necessary. The purpose of such repetition is that when the blood flows back from
the arm[23] to the affected parts (from which the blood has ceased
to flow by reason of the venesection) it might once more be
deflected away from these parts. Thus Themison declares that
in his opinion venesection is both a relaxing measure and a
measure to lessen [the amount of blood] and thus avoid an out-
6 break of inflammation. Again, in the opinion of others the purpose of venesection is to open the veins so that the wounds,
drained of blood, may close and heal more quickly. And, according to Asclepiades, the purpose of venesection is to lessen the
movement of blood and the movement involved in respiration;
for these movements aggravate the disease.

There is also a conflict of opinion on bandaging. Xenophon,
Dionysius, Herophilus in Book I of his *Treatments,* and Erasistratus all prescribe the bandaging of external parts. But, according to Herophilus, the head, arms, and thighs should be band-

22. I.e., *status mixtus.*
23. I.e., after the first venesection.

capitis et brachiorum et femorum, Erasistratus magis inguinum
et alarum, etenim laxatione[72] sensus sanguinis approbat fieri retentionem. Asclepiades vero ad ipsum scribens libros Parasceu-
asticos ligationem excludit, eamque neque Erasistrato congruam: dicens osculari non posse sub discrimine venulas, quod
Graeci diaphragma vocant, vel misceri eas quae supra dia-
187 phragma esse videntur. omnes etiam nostrae sectae principes
id approbasse videntur. impressa etenim, inquiunt, ligatura[73]
vexat, non impressa inutilis esse perspicitur. item Antipater
tertio libro Epistolarum ait teneri materiam quidem ligatione,
sed cum fuerit indulta vel relaxata, in repentinum atque immodicum fluorem veniat,[74] siquidem abstinentiae causa altiora pen-
dendo latere potius quam teneri videantur.

item de constrictivis[75] cataplasmatibus plurimi dissenserunt.
nam si Erasistratus haec approbat, Asclepiades excludit tamquam materiam imprimentia vel coercendo in altum[76] revocan-
tia. item acetum alii tamquam tussiculam vel fluorem commo-
188 vens expulerunt, vel quod duras partes densando faciat. Themison vero his repugnans adhibendum iudicavit, attestante etiam
Thessalo. alii aiunt eius acrimoniam vel nimietatem temperan-
dam admixtione aquae.

plurimi vero contrariarum sectarum etiam clysteres atque urinales aiunt virtutes adhibendas. item Diocles taurinum gluten
bibendum dicit farinae concoctum et rubo, vel cum nepita amylum vel marrubium vel rosmarinum in aqua pusca dandum.
motus vero alii adhibuerunt, non solum fricantes, sed etiam
deambulationem imperantes post cibum, ut Erasistratus. Asclepiades vero De communibus adiutoriis scribens gestationem
189 in haemopticis[77] prohibet. utuntur quidam praeterea etiam
purgativis medicaminibus ex papavere vel helleboro aut diagri-

[72] laxationem *S*: corr. *Rm*
[73] ligaturae *S*: corr. *R*
[74] venire *Rm*
[75] constrictis *S*: corr. *Rm*
[76] altum *Rm*: latum *S*
[77] haemoptyicis *A*

24. And therefore that the head should not be bandaged, as Herophilus had suggested.

aged; according to Erasistratus it is preferable to bandage the groin and armpits. Indeed, Erasistratus holds that the flow of blood is arrested when the senses are relaxed.[24] Asclepiades, on the other hand, in his work *On Preparations*, written in opposition to Erasistratus, rejects the use of bandaging and declares that the measure is inconsistent with the latter's own system. For, as Asclepiades says, the small veins below the dividing membrane (Greek *diaphragma*) cannot open, and those above

87 this membrane are not connected with one another.[25] And all the leaders of our own sect seem to approve of Asclepiades' view. For tight bandaging, they say, is injurious, and bandaging which is not tight is of no use. Antipater in Book III of his *Letters* declares that, while bandaging arrests the flow of blood, the relaxing or loosening of the bandage is followed by a sudden and copious flow. For when the flow is arrested by bandaging, the blood apparently lies suspended within and its outflow is not permanently checked.

So, too, there is widespread disagreement about the use of astringent plasters. Thus, while Erasistratus approves of them, Asclepiades rejects them on the ground that, in preventing the egress of matter, these plasters compress or force it toward the inner parts. Again, some reject the use of vinegar on the ground that it provokes coughing and consequently the flow of blood,

88 or that its astringent action renders the parts hard. But Themison rejects this view and approves of the use of vinegar, as does Thessalus. Others declare that the sharpness and great strength of the vinegar should be reduced by dilution with water.

Again, many physicians belonging to diverse sects favor the use of clysters and also the taking of diuretic drugs. Diocles has the patient drink ox glue cooked with meal and bramble; or a mixture of starch and catnip, or horehound, or rosemary in diluted vinegar. Some physicians, e.g., Erasistratus, prescribe exercise; not merely do they massage the patient, but they order him to take a walk after eating. Asclepiades, on the other hand, in his work *On Common Remedies* rejects even passive exercise

89 in cases of blood-spitting. Again, some, e.g., Diocles, employ purgative drugs made with poppy, hellebore, or diagridium

25. The point seems to be that binding would accomplish no useful purpose. But it is not clear how this follows from Erasistratus' system (cf. 190).

dio, quod Graeci scammonian vocant, ut Diocles; item sudorem
moventibus et vomitum, ut Praxagoras, qui etiam plurima urinalia ordinavit.

sed haec facile iudicantur ex his quae secundum Methodicos
tradidimus. demonstranda tamen eorum contradictio et brevi
ratione formanda.

peccaverunt igitur qui supra patientes partes aegros iacere
voluerunt. omnis enim impressio sive affectio incongrua gluti-
nationibus approbatur. ceciderunt etiam falsa intentione decepti, qui non addita discretione phlebotomiae memoraverunt
190 usum. non enim in omnibus oportuit prohiberi, cum fluorem
saepe fuerit vehemens strictura complexa. et si secundum
Erasistratum osculatio venarum ex redundantia materiae veniens fluorem faciat, convenit uti detractione. facile enim corrigi vel reparari parva virium vexatio potest, plurima tamen ex
adiutorio patientibus utilitas fuerit. neque item in omnibus
erit approbanda phlebotomia, nam nullo tumore apparente
vexabilis iudicatur. etenim corporis fortitudo necessario depur-
gatur, et stomachus vitiatur, atque debilitate irruente difficile
coeunt divisurae, et eadem patienti videbimur ingerere quae
191 prohibenda suscepimus, quippe cum non aversio, sed potius partitio sanguinis fieri intelligatur, et duplici egestione celerata nullam mortis habeat dilationem. dehinc erit anceps utrum irruente rursum tumore phlebotomandi necne sint aegrotantes. sed
phlebotomati apertissime interficiuntur, non phlebotomati magno adiutorio privantur.

ligationes vero non tantum ad divertendam materiam adhibendae sunt, ut supra memoravimus, quantum ad densitatem
vero[78] faciendam adhibendas adprobamus,[79] siquidem impri-
mendo coerceant, sed mediocriter adhibere, ne moderatione cessante vexare potius quam curare videantur.

192　　peccat etiam Asclepiades frigida vel constrictiva epithemata
recusando. sunt enim[80] inconsequentia Erasistrati placitis, sed

---

[78] vero *om. R*　　[79] probamus *R: cf. 195, 216*　　[80] enim *Rm*: etiam *S*

(Greek *scammōnia,* 'scammony juice'). And some, e.g., Praxagoras, make use of sudorifics and vomitives; Praxagoras also
prescribes numerous diuretics.

Now the value of all these prescriptions can readily be esti-
mated by comparing the Methodist treatment, which we have
already described. Let us, however, here briefly set forth our
refutation of these other views.

In the first place, those who order the patient to lie on the
affected parts are mistaken. For all pressure on these parts or
burdening of them interferes with healing. Again, those who
speak of venesection without properly distinguishing the cases
are led astray by their improper understanding of the matter
and fail in their treatment. For venesection should not always
be rejected, since bleeding is often involved in cases where a
strong state of stricture obtains. And if, as Erasistratus holds,
anastomosis due to a plethora of blood may cause bleeding from
a vein, it is proper in such cases to employ venesection. For the
small loss of strength [involved in this treatment] can readily be
remedied or repaired, while the treatment itself is extremely
valuable to the patient. At the same time, venesection should
not be prescribed in all cases. For this treatment is harmful when
there is no obvious inflammation; the body is inevitably deprived of its strength, the appetite is impaired, and, as weakness
spreads, the wounds are scarcely able to heal. That is, this treatment obviously brings about the very conditions we have said
must be avoided. For the bleeding is not stopped; rather it is
divided, and, since there are now two outlets, the speed of its
discharge is increased, and death is not long delayed. And if
inflammation later supervenes in such cases, it will be hard to
decide whether to perform venesection or not; for, clearly, venesection may result in death, while the refusal to use this treatment will deprive the patient of an important remedy.

As for bandages, we approve of their use, as we have indicated,
not for the purpose of deflecting the blood but for their constrictive effect; for they confine the parts by their pressure. But
they should not be tightened excessively, for, unless there is
moderation in this regard, the bandages will harm rather than
help the patient.

Again, Asclepiades errs when he rejects cooling or astringent
applications. For, while their use is not consistent with the

officio congruae curationis efficacia. nam solutionem constringunt, divisuras conglutinant, quod ex vulneribus in superficie
constitutis et sub visum venientibus usu approbatur, quibus apposita apertissime profuerunt.

peccant etiam non aliter qui bibendum acetum negant. non
enim in omnibus fluoribus sanguinis dandum probatur, sed in his
qui approbato atque largissimo fluore vexantur. in parvis enim
193 aqua frigida sufficere potest, aut admixto parvissimo aceto. ac
si tumor fuerit attestatus, ut complexam passionem demonstret,
procul dubio constringentia fugienda quantum res pati vel admittere possunt. est igitur improprium, uti ea quae incongrue
adhibita nocere demonstrentur, etiam cum necessario convenire
fuerint visa prohibenda existimentur. etenim adversantia solutioni tussiculam ex fluore venientem mitigant, atque ipsum
fluorem constringunt, et sanguinem retinent cohibendo; et neque inurunt, siquidem superaddita[81] per digestionis vias patientibus partibus adveniant temperata atque admixta liquidis in
alto constitutis, et propterea obtusa virtutis violentia perdurant.
194 sunt etiam clysteres contrarii, siquidem commoveant corpus,
eo tempore praeterea quo conglutinationem faciendam nitimur.
hac ratione etiam urinalia medicamina atque ventriflua magis
noxia iudicantur, siquidem turbent atque vexent et vertant stomachum. item protervus omnibus vomitus et propterea contrarius iudicatur. rescindit enim vulnera, nisi quis eum iam
solidatis cicatricibus ob recorporationem adhibendum probaverit. est propterea affectatio sudorum, quam Graeci aphidro-
sin vocant, contraria. cum enim superflua atque redundantia
195 tollere videtur laxativae virtutis causa coeuntia disiungit. item
taurinum gluten tensionem atque duritiam facit.

motus vero corporis neque excludendos generaliter approbamus[82] neque approbandos, siquidem prius quam passio declina-

---

[81] superaddita *Friedel 31, n. 3*: saepe reddita S   [82] probamus *R, sed cf. 191, 216*

---

26. In arguing against Erasistratus' approval of these remedies, Asclepiades showed
that their use was inconsistent with Erasistratus' own system (cf. 187). Caelius (Soranus)
points out that the remedies cannot properly be rejected on these grounds.

system of Erasistratus,[26] they do serve as suitable and effective treatments. For they astringe a state of looseness and help to heal openings. In fact, in the case of wounds that are on the surface of the body and hence actually observable, the application of such treatments has clearly proved helpful.

Those who refuse to permit the drinking of vinegar are similarly mistaken. For, while vinegar should not be given in all cases of bleeding, it is necessary where there is obviously a copious flow. In minor cases, to be sure, cold water or water mixed with a very little vinegar may prove sufficient. Again, if inflammation is present and a complex condition [*status mixtus*] is thus indicated, astringent treatments should doubtless be avoided so far as circumstances permit. But, while a treatment may be obviously harmful when wrongly prescribed, it is a mistake to reject this treatment in the type of case where it has always proved helpful. Indeed, substances [like vinegar] which counteract a state of looseness will relieve a cough resulting from the flow of blood and will serve to restrain the flow itself, that is to say, will stop the bleeding through astringent action. And there will be no burning sensation, for the substances are taken in through the digestive tract and so reach the affected parts in a diluted state, i.e., mixed with the fluids within the body. The sharpness of the astringent substance is therefore tempered and remains so.

Clysters, however, should not be prescribed, for they agitate the body at the very time when we are trying to effect a joining-together of the parts. For the same reason we also consider diuretics and purgatives harmful, for they agitate and irritate the gullet and stomach and cause gagging. Again, we consider vomitives harmful in all these cases and therefore reject their use. For vomiting causes wounds to open again, and drugs that provoke vomiting should not be prescribed unless the scars have completely healed in the metasyncritic process. For the same reason the use of substances that provoke sweating (Greek *aphidrōsis*) is harmful; for, in removing superfluous and excess matter by the operation of their relaxing powers, these substances cause healing tissues to separate again. Furthermore, ox glue brings about tension and stiffness of the parts.

As for bodily exercise, we must neither prescribe nor reject it indiscriminately in all cases. For, while the patient must

verit, requiescere debeant aegrotantes, in declinatione vero sint movendi. sed non post cibum, tunc enim ob digestionem celebrandam[83] tempus est quiescendi. quo fiet ut prius quam cibum sumpserint aegrotantes gestatione sint movendi, secundo[84] etiam deambulatione. etenim parva adiectione neque ulcera refricantur, et in resumptione[85] virtus corporis excitatur.

196 ## XIV. DE PHTHISICA PASSIONE

PHTHISIS, sive ut plerique appellant phthoe,[1] quod corporis faciat defluxionem sive corruptionem, fit frequentius antecedente sanguinis fluore, aliquando etiam longi temporis tussicula sive catarrho thoracis cum altiora lacerantur, et primo levius, tunc ulcerata, facientia collectionem intrinsecus, quae cum siccata non fuerint, citius sumat passio[2] initium. sed non secundum has differentias erit efficacia curationis mutanda, siquidem antecedentes causae, quamquam diversae, unam facere passionem videantur.

197 sequitur autem aegrotantes febricula latens et saepe quae initium declinante accipiat die, atque veniente luce levigetur, attestante tussicula plurima initio noctis atque fine cum sputis saniosis, ac parvulis primo in his qui non ante sanguinis fluore vexantur, quae quidem admixta saliva latere videantur,[3] secundo etiam plurima ferri videantur. his vero qui ex fluore sanguinis in istam veniunt passionem primo sanguinolenta sputa efficiuntur, hoc est cruenta, quae Graeci haemalopa vocaverunt, tunc feculenta, dehinc livida vel prasina, et in ultimo alba atque purulenta, dulcia vel salsa, cum voce rauca aut acuta, et difficultate inspirationis, atque genarum rubore, et ceteri corporis ci198 nereo colore. item sequitur oculos exoletus aspectus et corporis tenuitas, quae nudatis membris proditur magis quam ex aspectu vultus. quosdam etiam sibilatio vel stridor thoracis sequitur;

---

[83] celebrandum S: corr. R

[84] secundo Rm: secunda S

[85] fort. resumptionem

[1] fort. suppl. ⟨nomen sumpsit ab accidenti⟩ vel tale quid

[2] passionis S: corr. R

[3] videantur om. R

remain quiet before the disease reaches the declining phase, in the period of decline he should have exercise. Yet this exercise should not be taken directly after eating, for that is the time for digestion and therefore for rest. And so before the patient takes food he should be given passive exercise, and later may also take a walk. For the little additional motion cannot cause the wound to open again; on the contrary, it will aid in building up the patient's strength during the period of recovery.

6   ## XIV. PHTHISIS

PHTHISIS or, as many call it, 'phthoë' gets its name from the fact that it involves a dissolution or decay of the body.[1] Bleeding is frequently a predisposing factor. And sometimes the disease is preceded by a protracted cough or a catarrh of the chest involving injury to the parts within. These parts are only mildly affected at first, but later become ulcerated; an internal abscess is produced, and, if this does not dry up, the disease of phthisis quickly takes hold. But the curative procedure need not be altered by reason of differences in the antecedent conditions. For these predisposing factors, however diverse they may be, evidently give rise to one and the same disease.

7   The symptoms of the disease are as follows: There is a latent fever, which generally begins toward the end of the day and is relieved with the coming of the new day; this is accompanied by much coughing at the beginning and the end of the night, with the discharge of sanious sputa. In cases in which bleeding did not precede phthisis, these sanious sputa occur at first in small amount, and, indeed, may not be noticeable, since they are mixed with saliva; later they appear in profusion. But in cases in which phthisis was preceded by bleeding, the sputa are at first bright red, that is to say, bloodshot (Greek *haemalōps*), then muddy, then bluish or greenish, and finally white and purulent, and either sweet or salt. The voice is either hoarse or high pitched, breathing difficult, cheeks flushed, and the rest of

8 the body ashen colored. The eyes have a worn appearance, and the patient is emaciated, a fact more obvious from the appearance of his naked body than from his countenance. In some cases there is a hissing sound or wheezing in the chest; and, as

1. Both words are connected with Greek *phthiō*, 'decay,' 'wane,' 'be wasted.'

crescente passione sudor superiorum partium usque ad pectoris
finem, cibi fastidium, vel[4] maior appetitus, sitis, et quibusdam
gravedo vulnerati pulmonis, ut etiam eius expuant fibras, quibusdam punctio ulcerato[5] thorace, pulsus debilis, densus, ac
deinde formicalis,[6] quem Graeci myrmecizonta[7] vocant. digitorum summitates crassescunt obuncatis unguibus, quod Graeci
gryposin vocant. sequitur praeterea inflatio pedum, et nunc
frigus, nunc fervor articulorum; nasi summitas pallescit, atque
aurium laminae frigescunt.

199   tunc peiorante passione ventris efficitur fluor albidarum egestionum et indigestarum, debilitatis naturalibus digestionis officiis. discernunt praeterea plurimi purulentum liquorem phlegmata carbonibus imponentes, quo exusta probentur. nam tetri
odoris esse necesse est omne quod natura fuerit mutatum, velut
ex defluxione carnis veniens. item in aquam mittunt aegrotantium sputamina. etenim naturalia facile solvuntur; vitiata vero
atque mutata perseverant, quadam continuitate[8] coacta subsidunt, siquidem sint gravia, et contra naturam ex defluxione
carnis venientia.

200   vicinae atque similes passiones sunt phthisicae: syntexis,
quam nos defluxionem dicere poterimus, atrophia,[9] quam nos
nutrimenti cessationem vocamus, item empyica passio[10] sive
anaphoretica, quam nos purulentam sive vomicofluam[11] dicere
poterimus, quod ex vomica interioris collectionis purulenta per
tussiculam excludunt sputa. sed haec discernuntur, siquidem
ex his atrophia longo tempore faciat tenuari, nullis etiam attestantibus sputis, saepe etiam sine ulla tussicula. etenim longo
tempore febricitantes atque tussientes, limpidis adhuc sputis
affecti, necdum phthisici iudicantur, in phthisicam vero passionem proni ac declives esse noscuntur.

201   item empyica passio, sive ut supra diximus anaphoretica, discernitur a phthisica, non aliter quam ulcerum collectione, quippe

---

[4] vel *scripsi, coll. Chr. iii. 15*: et *edd.*

[5] ulcera *S*: corr. *Rm*

[6] *fort.* formicabilis. *cf. Ac. ii. 145 n.*

[7] myrmezonta *S*: corr. *Rm, sed cf. Ac. ii. 145 n.*

[8] continuitate *conieci*: tenuitate *S*: tenacitate *Am, fort. recte*

[9] atrophian *S*: corr. *R*

[10] passione *S*: corr. *R*   [11] vomicofluam *Rm*: vomifluam *S*

the disease spreads, there is sweating in the upper parts down
to the end of the chest. There is loss of appetite for food, or else
a considerable appetite; the patient also suffers thirst. Sometimes there is a feeling of heaviness in the ravaged lung and the
patient spits up fibers of it; sometimes there is a stabbing pain
due to ulceration within the chest. The pulse is weak and thick,
and later antlike (Greek *myrmēcizōn*). The tops of the fingers become thick, and there is a hooking of the nails (Greek *grypōsis*).
The feet swell up, and the limbs are now cold and now hot; the
tip of the nose tends to be pale and the ears cold.

99   Then, as the disease becomes worse, there is a flow of white,
undigested matter from the bowels, the normal functioning of
digestion having been impaired. Many subject the purulent
sputa to diagnostic tests. Thus they place the phlegm over hot
coals and note its odor when it has burned;[2] for a foul odor
always characterizes the product of physical decomposition, as
would be the case if the sputa came from a dissolution of flesh.
Again, some place the sputa of the patient in water. Now normal sputa are readily dissolved. But those which are diseased
and abnormal remain coagulated and undissolved and sink to
the bottom; for they are heavy and are the morbid product of a
dissolution of the flesh.

00   The following diseases are similar and related to phthisis:
syntēxis, which in Latin we may call *defluxio* ['dissolution'];
atrophia (Latin *nutrimenti cessatio*, 'failure of the nutritive process'); and *empyēma* or the 'anaphoretic disease' [i.e., involving
the bringing-up of matter], a disease to which we may apply
the Latin terms *purulenta* and *vomicoflua* ['purulent,' 'suppurat-
ing'], because the patient in coughing gives up purulent sputa
from an internal abscess [*vomica*] or gathering. But these diseases may be distinguished from phthisis. Thus atrophy causes
the patient to grow progressively thinner over a long period of
time without any abnormal sputa and often without any coughing. Now even where prolonged fever and coughing occur, so
long as the sputa remain clear, the case cannot be diagnosed as
phthisis, though the patient may obviously be on the verge of
phthisis.

01   Empyema or, as we called it above, the anaphoretic disease
may be distinguished from phthisis and also generally from

2. Hipp. *Aph*. v. 11; Celsus iii. 22. 3.

cum empyicos saepe antecedat pleuritis vel peripleumonia et tumor immensus et febres vehementes cum horroribus frigidis et inordinatis; dehinc quod saepe coacervatam[11a] puris copiam excludant repente, ac deinde egestione facta febribus atque horroribus praeteritis liberentur, ut aut omnino his careant aut ex parte afficiantur: in phthisicis ea quae supra diximus antecedant, et liquida paulatim non coacervata excludantur, et pro modo auctae passionis etiam febres augeantur.

202 communiter autem haec passio stricturae atque solutioni erit adscribenda et subiacentibus passioni temporalibus coenotetis. in quibus[12] etiam ulcerum differentias monuimus promovendas. sunt enim necessario intuendae, siquidem complexa sit regulae, quam diaetan vocant,[13] medicaminum ratio, quam pharmacian appellant. denique si tumens ulcus fuerit, quod intelligitur ex dolore consequenti et ceteris tumoris signis, convenit aegrotanti calidus locus et abstinentia unius diei; tunc fomentatio laxativa atque cataplasmata et cucurbitae appositio cum scarificatione et

203 vaporationibus spongiarum et totius corporis perunctione; cibus quoque sorbilis, calidus, et magis panosus, observatis temporibus singulorum adiutoriorum, ut saepe docuimus.

ac si tumens non fuerit ulcus, ob purgationem sordis erunt aquae mulsae cyathi duo vel tres offerendi ante cibum, vel faenigraeci saepe torti decoctus sucus, sed non ita ut viscosus fiat quod servabitur. si secundo vel tertio mollius scatere coeperit, deponatur quoad[14] sit colore vinosus, ac deinde uni cyatho liquato admiscemus mellis cochleare: habet enim virtutem faenigraeci semen mitissimae detersionis. vel certe mulsum dabimus ex lini semine fricto atque trito admixto pulvere, aut ligato[15]

204 linteolo limpido †vel farina meregmi.†[16] si autem maior purga-

---

[11a] coadcervata S: corr. A
[12] quibusdam edd.
[13] vocant ⟨tum⟩ R: fort. vocant ⟨et⟩
[14] quoad Rm: quod S
[15] ligato Rm (cf. 208): liquato S
[16] vel farina immersa Rm: fort. vel farina marrubi: aliter [vel] facimus immergi

---

3. 196.
4. I.e., by the special requirements of a status mixtus.

abscesses due to wounds or sores. For empyema is often preceded by pleurisy or pneumonia, with intense inflammation,
acute fever, and irregular chills. Again, in many cases of empyema the patient all at once brings up a large mass of pus and
then, having discharged this matter, is relieved of his former
fever and chills, that is to say, there is either a complete or a
partial abatement. In phthisis, on the other hand, the antecedent conditions are those we indicated above,[3] and fluid is
given up a little at a time, not in a mass; again, as the disease
spreads, the fever, too, increases.

2   In general, phthisis is a disease involving both a state of stricture and a state of looseness and at each stage exhibits a certain
disease type. In these cases we advise giving special consideration to the different kinds of ulceration. These differences must
be observed, since the determination of a suitable regimen
(Greek *diaeta*) and of suitable drugs (Greek *pharmacia*) is complicated.[4] Thus if inflammation is present along with the ulceration, a condition which may be recognized by the ensuing pain
and the other signs of inflammation, have the patient lie in a
warm room and withhold food for a day. Use relaxing fomentations and poultices, cupping with scarification, and hot applica-
3   tions with sponges; anoint the whole body, and give the patient
soft, warm food, especially of the bready kind. In the case of
each remedy pay careful attention to the time element, as we
have often indicated.

But if the ulceration is not accompanied by inflammation,
give the patient two or three cyathi of hydromel to drink in
order to clear away the foul matter before he takes food; or
subject fenugreek seed to frequent pressing and give the patient
the cooked juice, but watch to see that it does not become too
sticky in cooking. If twice or three times it begins to bubble up
a bit, let it settle until it becomes the color of wine. Then mix a
spoonful of honey with one cyathus of this juice, for the fenugreek seed has a mild, detergent property. Or let the patient
have a mixture of mead and finely powdered and triturated
flaxseed. Either sprinkle the flaxseed powder directly over the
4   mead or tie it up in a small bag of clean linen[5]. . . . If, however,

5. *Sc.* 'and immerse it in the drink.' This, in fact, may have been the meaning of the
next phrase before the text was corrupted. More probably there was a reference to the
addition of another substance, e.g., powdered horehound.

tio fuerit facienda, irin illyricam atque herbum dandum probamus. oportet etiam herbum rubrum aquae infundere donec
infletur; tunc testa calefacta atque ignita molere, terere, ac
deinde tum[17] tenuissimo cribello eius pollinem mulso aspergere
in cochlearii quantitatem; vel ex melle decocto electarium facere, admixto scilicet polline supradicto. sed propter vehementiam herbi, erit conicienda sordis magnitudo, ut si fuerit putru-
osa, quam Graeci dysoden appellant, tunc solo herbi polline utemur;[18] sin vero non ita fuerit cogens causa, admixto sesamo iri
illyricae aequalis ponderis aut superantis, pro passionis magni-
205 tudine. ac si plurimum putruosum apparuerit ulcus ex his
quae feruntur, non solum per os convenit herbi pollinem dari,
sed ex ipso confectum etiam cataplasma ⟨cum⟩[19] aceto atque
melle extrinsecus apponere. tunc etiam lenticula simili usu adhibenda probatur, et praeterea purgativae virtutis aristolochia
et dracontia herba, sive quae appellatur aron. eius generis etiam
marrubium approbatur, quamquam sit stomachi vexabile, purgativae tamen virtutis. oportet autem eius manipulum tribus
aquae sextariis decoquere donec ad partem[20] redeant; tunc marrubium detractum proicere atque admiscere mellis boni libram,
206 et rursum decoquere donec ad suam veniat crassitudinem. ac si
marrubium viridius fuerit, tundendum atque exsucandum et in
unum cyathum suci libra mellis miscenda, et ita decoquenda.
aut aquae sextarii tres decoquendi sive admiscendi donec crassitudinem[21] sumant. faciunt etiam ex strobilis et amygdalis et
lini semine vel supradictis electaria confecta: item ex amygdalis
et ptisana cum melle et lacte sorbile medicamen, et primo cum
pane acceptum infuso melle, tunc etiam singulare sorbendum
parvissime, ad modum unius cyathi vel duorum, dehinc plurimum, longe ante tempus alterius cibi, quamquam sit in quibus-
207 dam hoc solum cibo sufficiens. etenim corpus nutriet et vulnera
reterget et cruentos vel purulentos **[22]

dehinc cum tenuia sputa ferri viderimus, facit etiam strobili
decoctio, quae conficitur hoc modo. viridem strobilum su-

---

[17] *fort.* erat cum   [19] *add.* R
[18] utamur *Rm*   [20] ⟨tertiam⟩ partem *R, sed cf. 207*
[21] ⟨mellis⟩ crassitudinem *R, ut saepe apud Caelium, sed cf. 207*
[22] *lacunam indicavi:* ⟨iuvat⟩ *R: fort. suppl.* ⟨locos mitigabit⟩ *vel sim.*

---

6. I.e., in preparations both for external and for internal use.

an extensive clearing-out of matter is required, give the patient Illyrian iris and vetch. Place red vetch in water and let it remain until it becomes puffed up; then warm it over the fire in an earthen vessel and grind and pound it down. Then with a fine sieve sprinkle a spoonful of the powder over the honey drink. Or make an electuary, using boiled honey with the addition of this same powder. But by reason of the strength of the vetch one must consider the character of the matter to be cleared away. Thus if this matter is rotten (Greek *dysōdēs*, 'foul-smelling'), add only the powdered vetch. But if the case is not so urgent, use sesame mixed with an equal or greater weight of Illyrian iris, depending on the extent of the disease. But if from the sputa it appears that the ulcerated parts are quite rotten, the powdered vetch not only should be given by mouth but should also be applied externally in a poultice with vinegar and honey. Lentil, too, may be similarly used;[6] so also may birthwort, because of its cleansing properties, as well as dragonwort or *aron*, as it is called. Horehound is of the same type, and, though it has an irritant effect on the esophagus, it has good cleansing properties. Place a handful of it in three sextarii of water and boil down to one-half. Then remove the horehound and discard it. Add a pound of good honey to the liquid and boil again until the whole attains the consistency of honey. But if the horehound is quite green, first pound it down and press out the juice; then add a pound of honey to one cyathus of the juice, and boil; or add three sextarii of water [to the mixture of honey and horehound] and boil until the mixture becomes thick. Electuaries compounded of pine cones and almonds together with flaxseed or any of the other ingredients mentioned above are also beneficial. And there is a preparation of gruel-like consistency, made with almonds, pearl barley, honey, and milk. This should first be taken with bread soaked in honey; later let the patient have a very little, say up to one or two cyathi, without bread; finally, let him take a large quantity, but see that he does so a considerable time before the hour when he is to take the rest of his food. Indeed, in some cases this preparation alone will suffice for the patient's food. For it will nourish the body, cleanse the ulcerations, and . . . the bloody or purulent. . . .

Then when it is observed that the sputa have become thin, a decoction of pine cone, made in the following way, is helpful.

mentes fructuosum, qui in semet habeat quaedam resinalia, aquae[23] tribus sextariis immixtum decoquimus donec pars liquoris insumatur. tunc detracto strobilo erit residuae parti liquoris miscenda mellis libra vel glycyrrhizae,[23a] tunc decoquenda[24] donec crassitudinem sumat. convenit etiam ex squillitico vino electarium confectum, ex quo erit sextarius unus librae mellis admiscendus, et gummi vino perfusi selibra. tunc deco-

208 quendum mel donec vinum insumatur. potest praeterea etiam melilotum linteolo ligatum tempore decoctionis immitti. item sucus glycyrrhizae simili modo atque eodem tempore misceri probatur. convenit etiam diacodion medicamen cochlearis quantitate sumptum, vel butyrum cum melle electario datum. et praeterea purgativae virtutis atque siccativae hoc medicaminis genus: marrubii suci viridis sextarii tres, mellis libra una, quae cum fuerint coctione crassificata, iris illyricae immittendae sunt drachmae duae. sed oportet neque semel atque eodem

209 tempore omnia haec aegrotantibus dari. varias etenim materias posuimus, siquidem iugis speciei unius oblatio satiat[25] aegrotantes et propterea recusetur. neque accessionis tempore haec danda mandamus.

quapropter una[26] etiam cetera in curationibus monemus intuenda, quo purgato ulcere humanioribus cibis utamur, hoc est ex mediae materiae qualitate. convenit interea motus latens pensili primo lectulo ⟨vel⟩[27] cathedra longiore atque in vicina porticu, adhibita etiam perunctione primo sedenti, ac deinde recepta fortitudine stanti. purgato ulcere dabimus vinum album atque lene mediocriter remordens. tum lavacrum adhibendum, quando etiam sicca conveniat cibatio singularis, vel

210 cum palmulis thebaicis et pulmento[28] in cibum dato,[29] vel arnoglossa herba et volantum non pinguia. item sub lingua amylum datum quod retentum in defluxionem veniens subiectis partibus patientibus irruat et paulatim adiuvet cicatricem; vel mel decoctum simili modo datum aut parvo ex[30] amylo admixto; tum etiam trochiscus[31] qui appellatur trigonos, vel mel vino remor-

[23] aquae *Rm*: quem *S*

[23a] glycyrrhiza *S*: *corr. R*

[24] decoquendo *S*: decoquendum *Rm*

[25] *fort.* satiet

[26] uni *S*

[27] *add. R*

[28] pulmentum *R*

[29] datum *Rm*

[30] ex *om. R*

[31] trochiscum *S*: *corr. R*

Take a green pine cone which is full of kernels and is resinous; place it in three sextarii of water and cook it until half the fluid has boiled off. Then remove it, and add to the remaining fluid a pound of honey or of sweetroot. Then cook again until the mixture becomes thick. An electuary made of wine of squills is also helpful. To a sextarius of this wine is added a pound of honey, and also half a pound of gum soaked in the wine. The honey is 8 then boiled down until the wine is consumed. During this cooking process melilot tied in a small linen bag may also be immersed in the fluid; sweetroot juice may also be added in the same manner and at the same time. A spoonful of the drug that is made from poppy capsules or an electuary made of butter and honey may also be taken with advantage. The patient may also take a drug with detergent and desiccant properties, prepared as follows: Take three sextarii of the juice of green horehound[7] and one pound of honey; boil them together until the proper consistency is attained, and then add two drachms of Illyrian iris. Now these remedies should not all be given the patient at 9 one and the same time. We have purposely set forth various preparations, since the continual offering of one kind cloys the patient and causes him to refuse it. We may add that these remedies should not be given at the time of an attack.

Also see to it that the other aspects of the treatment are not neglected. Thus, having cleared up the ulceration, employ a more liberal diet of food of the middle class. At the same time give the patient gentle passive exercise, first using a hammock or suspended couch in a near-by portico. Also anoint the patient, letting him sit at first, but later having him stand when he has recovered his strength. And with the clearing-up of the ulceration prescribe a mild white wine, moderately sour. Also prescribe bathing and at the same time a diet of dry food, plain or with o the addition of Theban dates or other soft fare. Plantain and lean fowl may also be given. And it is helpful to give the patient starch to hold under his tongue; the starch dissolves and passes down to the affected parts, gradually aiding the process of cicatrization. Cooked honey with the addition of a little starch, if desired, may be given in the same way. The following may also be employed: the so-called '*trigonos* lozenge'; a preparation of

7. The juice should probably be considered not pure but diluted, most of the three sextarii being water.

denti admixtum pari[32] suae quantitati et decoctum donec incoquatur vinum; tunc etiam antidotum quod appellatur theriaca mithridatios, quae in semet habet siccandi atque recorporandi virtutem. item zopirios, et dierisimu.[33]

211   apponenda praeterea extrinsecus emplastra quae in cicatricem ducere valeant, ut est melinon, ac deinde siccantia magis. tum cum firmum apparuerit lenimentum, erit amithaonion imponendum vel polyarchion malagma, admixto cerotario ex oleo cyprino confecto parte tertia, siquidem haec singularia primo tempore aegrotantes ferre minime possint.

tunc cyclica regula adhibenda, sed quae non repentinas habeat ordinum mutationes. denique nunc vinum, nunc aquam potare permittimus, iuxta cycli rigorem. danda etiam drimyphagia,
212 quam despuentibus sanguinem memoravimus. adhibenda etiam localia adiutoria, similiter cucurbita, dropaces et sympasmata et paroptesis et sinapismus; et bibendum medicamen quod diapipereon appellatur, valet enim callositatem ulceris tenuare atque siccare. fugienda praeterea bibendi medicaminis satietas, et eligendus consuetorum usus, magis siquidem insueta materia vexatus stomachus atque fastidio supinatus prodat aegrotantes. est praeterea[34] vehementer utilis navalis gestatio, atque longa navigatio, lectio, vocis exercitatio, et omne quod dare corpori fortitudinem potest.

213   veteres autem medici alii nihil de ista passione memoraverunt. sed Diocles, libris quibus De passionibus atque causis et curationibus scripsit, iubet initio cibos detrahi, nihil de fine abstinentiae significans, quousque sint aegrotantes retinendi. tunc sudores commovendos, quibus necessario vires auferantur, et neque hoc quemadmodum faciendum sit ordinavit. utitur etiam anacoeliasmis, quorum qualitates non memoravit, adiciens ver-

[32] pari *Rm*: parti *S*

[33] dierisimu (-um *Rm*) *scripsi* (= δι' ἐρυσίμου): dierisimus *S*: diaeresimus (= διαιρέσιμος) *perperam TLL*

[34] est praeterea *Rm*: et propterea *S*

---

8. Or perhaps the meaning is: 'And a cerate in which henna oil is a third part.'

honey and sour wine in equal parts cooked until the wine is boiled away; the so-called 'theriac of Mithridates,' which possesses a desiccant and a restorative property; the antidote of Zopyrus and that made with hedge-mustard.

11 In addition, apply plasters externally that can help the damaged parts to form a scar, e.g., a quince plaster, and later those with stronger desiccant properties. Then, when it is ascertained that the disease has entered an interval of remission, apply the emollient plaster of Amythaon or that of Polyarchus; but add a cerate made with henna oil, this cerate constituting a fourth part of the whole preparation.[8] The reason for the addition is that at first the patient is unable to endure the application of the unmixed emollient plasters.

Then use a cyclical regimen, but avoid sudden changes in passing from one treatment to the next. The patient may be permitted to alternate the drinking of wine and water, in keeping with the strict rules of the cycle. Also prescribe an acrid diet,

12 as we indicated above for cases of the spitting of blood. In addition, use local remedies, including cupping, pitch plasters, dusting powders, baking, and mustard plasters. Also prescribe the drinking of the so-called 'pepper drug,' for this has the property of attenuating and drying up the hardness caused by the ulceration. But have the patient avoid drinking drugs that will cause loathing; prescribe rather the customary preparations. For the gullet is unsettled by strange substances, and, overcome by disgust, it betrays the patient.[9] Again, it is extremely helpful for the patient to be on board ship and to take a long sea voyage; reading aloud, vocal exercise, and all other measures which can help build up the body's strength are also suitable.

13 The ancient physicians, with the exception of Diocles, have nothing to say about this disease. Diocles in his work *On Diseases and Their Causes and Treatment* orders the patient to fast at the beginning of the disease; but he does not indicate anything about ending the fast, i.e., how long food should be withheld. He says that sweating should be induced; but such a measure necessarily impairs the patient's strength. Moreover, Diocles does not set forth the method to be employed. He also prescribes purgatives but does not explain their nature. He pre-

9. I.e., ceases to function. The emphasis seems to be on the loss of appetite.

rendum sive deducendum a pulmonibus humorem, quando
fuerat mitigandum potius ulcus quam depurgandum. item
vomitum ex oxymelle adhibendum, quo corpus disiciendo[35] ul-
214 ceratas lacerat partes, atque hoc iugiter et post cenam faciendum
probat. dehinc proterva mentis caecitate deceptus etiam psichrolusian imperat adhibendam et allium dandum, quod necessario vexet aegrotantes inflando; tum vino flavo utendum sive
nigro et praeterea[36] duro. atque post prandium deambulatione
vexandos imperat aegrotantes. et nulli adiutorio sua tempora reddenda perspexit.

item Praxagoras secundo libro Curationum his qui pulmonis
ulcere afficiuntur initio helleborum probat atque sitim facien-
215 dam, tum resumendos, non advertens primo resumptione, tunc
helleboro utendum, quo possint eius laborem perferre aegrotantes. ad summam, non resumpto[37] viribus deficienti helleborum non convenit; resumpto autem vel fortificato exclusa
phthisica passione comprobatur. et propterea usus hellebori
recte prohibetur.

at Themison secundo libro Tardarum passionum quaedam
recte, quaedam caduca protervitate composuit. ex quibus est
etiam pendentis tori gestatio, quo plurima parte diei ac noctis
motu exerceantur aegrotantes, cum necessario accessio vesper-
216 tino tempore asperetur atque luce surgente levigetur. quo non
solum laboriosus, verum etiam intemporalis et inordinatus motus ab eodem adhibitus approbatur.[38] etenim initio lucis et dimissionis tempore nutriri cibo convenit aegrotantes.

est etiam noxium allium quod imperat dare, siquidem inflationem maximam faciat. unctio item ex ferventibus adhibita
virtutibus, quam circa vesperam probat adhibendam, cruribus
atque brachiis contraria iudicatur. tunc enim febres ardescunt.
217 imperat praeterea inter duos vel tres[39] aegros lavandos, cum
corpus elimatis viribus debilitet lavacri frequentia et sordidet

[35] *fort.* dissecando   [36] praeterea *Rm*: propterea *S*   [37] resumpto ⟨et⟩ *A*
[38] probatur *R*   [39] tres ⟨dies⟩ *R, sed cf. Ac. ii. 112*

scribes the cleaning-out or removal of fluid from the lungs at a time when the ulceration should be soothed rather than cleaned out. He induces vomiting with oxymel, though this measure agi-
4 tates the body and tears open the ulcerated parts; moreover, he recommends the continued use of this treatment after meal-time. Again, misled by his abject lack of understanding, Diocles also prescribes cold baths and has the patient take garlic, which is always harmful, since it causes flatus. Again, he employs wine that is yellow or dark, and also harsh. And he prescribes walking after eating, a harmful measure. In fact, he fails to prescribe any remedy at its proper time.

Praxagoras in Book II of his *Treatments* recommends hellebore at the beginning of cases of pulmonary ulceration; he induces thirst and then prescribes treatment to restore the patient's
5 strength. He is not aware that such restorative treatment should precede the use of hellebore, so that the patient may be able to endure the strong action of the drug. In general, hellebore is harmful where the patient's strength has not been built up, that is, is still impaired; the drug may be employed, however, where his strength has been built up and restored, but only after the disease of phthisis has been overcome. We are right, therefore, in rejecting the use of hellebore [while the disease is present].

In Book II of his *Chronic Diseases* Themison sets forth certain sound prescriptions and others that are reckless and without foundation. Among the latter is his prescription of passive exercise on a suspended couch, the patient being rocked for the greater part of the day and night. But in this disease the attack always increases in intensity at evening and is relieved in the
16 early morning. Therefore, the exercise prescribed by Themison is not only burdensome but poorly timed and irregular; for dawn and any other period of remission is the proper time for nourishing the patient with food.

Again, it is harmful to give the patient garlic, as Themison prescribes, for this causes extreme flatulence. Likewise, the anointing of the patient with heat-producing substances, which Themison declares should be done in the evening, is harmful for the arms and legs; for at that time there is a burning fever.
17 Again, Themison prescribes bathing at intervals of two or three days, despite the fact that such frequent bathing impairs the strength, weakens the body, and defiles and moistens the ulcera-

atque humectet ulcera. praeterea herbum, dehinc intybum et
plantaginem, cum sit horum usus differentia temporum separa-
tus. herbum enim purgationis adhibetur causa, frigerantia vero
cicatricis obducendae.

   item imperat ulcera facienda extrinsecus iisdem quibus intus
inesse senserimus, quod est perniciosum. putat enim aversione
humoris facta ad exteriores partes altiora ulcera praesiccari, et
propterea diutissime differendam sanitatem exteriorum ulcerum,
218 donec illa clauduntur.[40] imponenda namque ait emplastra quae
humoris provocant defluxionem, cum humoris defluxio iuxta sa-
pientia[41] placita nullius commodi teneat fidem. sic etiam plurima localia adiutoria adhibenda conscripsit, quae tamen multo
tempore manificas[42] ulcerationes, hoc est quas nos extrinsecus
infiximus, in cicatricem venire cohibeant: impediens plurima
quae congrue adhiberi possunt, ut defricationes, dropaces, cucurbitae, sinapismi,[43] paropteses, et alia quae cum vehementissime prosint, ulceratione cutis praefecta adhiberi non possint.

[40] clauduntur *Rm*

[41] sapientium *Rm*

[42] magnificas *S*: *corr. Rm, sed fort. scrib.* manu factas

[43] cucurbitas, sinapismos *R*

tion. In addition, he prescribes bitter vetch, endive, and plantain, though these substances should be employed at different
times. Thus the bitter vetch serves as a detergent, while the substances with cooling properties aid the formation of a scar.

Themison recommends inflicting wounds externally in cases in
which the patient clearly is suffering from internal ulceration;
but this is a most dangerous practice. He holds that, if the fluids
are diverted to the external parts, the internal wounds will dry
up; and that therefore the healing of the external wounds should
be delayed for a long time, that is to say, until the internal
wounds are healed. Thus he recommends the use of plasters that
will induce the continued flow of liquid matter [from these external wounds], though, according to expert opinion, such a procedure is of no advantage. In accordance with his plan, Themison also prescribes numerous local remedies. But these prevent
for a long time the cicatrization of the hand-inflicted wounds,
that is, those which he himself inflicted externally. And he makes
it impossible to use many local remedies that might be employed
to advantage, e.g., massages, pitch plasters, cupping, mustard
plasters, and baking, as well as others. Though these remedies
are extremely beneficial, they cannot be employed if the skin has
previously been wounded.

LIBER TERTIUS

SECUNDO libro Tardarum passionum [quo] paralyticae passionis, et canini raptus, et auriculae doloris atque fluentis humoris, ⟨et dentium doloris,⟩ et apprehensionis sensus, quam Graeci catalepsin appellant, et vocis amputationis, et influxionis, quam catarrhon vocant, et tussiculae, et sanguinis fluoris, et phthisicae passionis tradidimus curationem. nunc ceterarum prosequimur ex ordine disciplinam.[1]

I. DE SUSPIRIO SIVE ANHELITU, QUEM GRAECI ASTHMA VOCANT

ANHELATIO sive suspirium ab accidenti nomen sumpsit. vocatur praeterea secundum aliquos spirationis difficultas, quam Graeci dyspnoean vocant, sive orthopnoean, siquidem sese praefocari sentiant cum iacuerint aegrotantes, atque erecti facilius spirent. item ut alii dicunt, contrario vocabulo suae virtutis[1] nomen accepit. nam cum spirationem[2] convertat ac depravet, tamquam corrigat orthopnoea nuncupatur, quam nos spirandi dicere correctionem poterimus. multa enim contrariae interpretationis vocabulum sumpserunt, ut fella, quae Graeci glycea vocant, velut dulcia, cum sint amarissima.

gravat autem atque premit haec passio magis mulieribus viros, et iuvenibus senes atque pueros, et durioribus natura corporibus teneriora, hiberno atque nocte magis quam die vel aestate. in quibusdam ex initio generatur, in quibusdam perfectis[3] irruit passionibus, sed magis ex profundo frigore.

sequitur[4] patientes spirationis difficultas, et frequenter natura celerior magis quam tarda, item praefocationis sensus secundum

---

[1] *praef. om. edd. praeter S. cf. Chr. ii, init.*

[1] virtuti *R*

[2] spirationem *Rm*: sui ratione *S* (= *sua natura?*)

[3] *an* praefectis?

[4] frigore sequitur *edd. sine interpunct.*

BOOK III

IN BOOK II of *Chronic Diseases* we set forth the treatment of paralysis, cynic spasm, earache and running ear, toothache, seizure of the senses (Greek *catalēpsis*), loss of voice, flux (Greek *catarrhos*), cough, hemorrhage, and phthisis. We now consider the other chronic diseases in order.

I. SHORTNESS OF BREATH OR PANTING
(GREEK *ASTHMA*)

THE disease called *anhelatio* or *suspirium* ['shortness of breath,' 'panting,' Greek *asthma*] gets its name from its characteristic symptom. It is also called by some *spirationis difficultas*, corresponding to the Greek *dyspnoea*, 'difficulty of breathing,' or *orthopnoea*, 'straight breathing,' the latter term referring to the fact that the patient has a choking sensation when he is lying down but breathes more easily when he sits or stands up straight. But, according to others, the term *orthopnoea* is used to denote a property opposite to that present in the disease; that is to say, though the disease actually involves an abnormality and distortion of breathing, it is called *orthopnoea*, they say, as if it involved straight or correct breathing.[1] In that sense the term may be translated *spirandi correctio*, 'correction of breathing.' For many objects are given a name of contrary significance, e.g., bile, which the Greeks call *glycys*, 'sweet,' though it is actually very bitter.[2]

Men are more subject to attacks of asthma than are women; old men and boys more so than young men, and soft bodies more so than those of a hardy nature. The attacks come more often in the winter and at night than in the summer and during the day. In some cases asthma arises spontaneously, in others it supervenes upon a previous disease, often coming after a severe chill.

In asthma there is difficulty in breathing, frequently of short rather than long duration, and a choking sensation in the chest,

1. Perhaps 'as if the name might help to correct the breathing.'
2. Cf. such names as Euxinus and Eumenides.

3 thoracem, atque gravedo, et fervor igneus, item laterum⁵ ad superiora conductio. et cum passio vehementescere coeperit, stridor atque sibilatio pectoris cum vocis debilitate, tum extensio
colli atque vultus cum rubore et oculorum suspenso attentu, et
iacendi ⟨nulla⟩⁶ potestas schemate supino, tussicula nunc arida,
nunc uvida, cum sputis tenuibus et spumosis aut crassis et viscosis, et sudoribus et colore morbido atque pulsu humili. at si
gravior impetus superpositionis fuerit, ora aegrotantium lives-
cunt, et quidem excluso per nares humore mucilento relevantur
atque praefocationis carent metu. quod non aliter cedit etiamsi
super⁷ oculos lacrimarum fuerit fluor.

4   variantur autem tempora passionis superpositionibus et lenimentis, et nunc limpidis atque sinceris, nunc sordidis et passionis
tractibus implicatis, ut etiam tunc levis difficultas inspirationis
inesse videatur, quae facile prodetur si aegrotantes itinere ascen-
sibili gradiantur, aut ocius pergant, vel indigestione aut usu venereo affecti, vel frigore atque pulvere sive fumo graventur.

differt autem haec passio a peripleumonia, quod neque cum
febribus necessario fiat, et semper tarda esse videatur. item se-
5 cundum aliquos discernitur ab orthopnoea, siquidem haec cum
stridore atque praefocatione asperetur, orthopnoea vero cum
thoracis⁸ eversione atque singultu, aliquando etiam cum sanguinis fluore. item secundum aliquos magnitudine discernitur,
vehementiorem⁹ enim dicunt orthopnoean¹⁰ supradictis passionibus. sed est melius, ut uno atque generali concursu passionum
potentiam iudicemus, ut nunc vehementem passionem dicamus
et magis accessionis tempore, nunc leniorem et magis dimissionis
tempore.

est autem passio stricturae, quapropter convenit, ut mox corpus invaserit, sive cum repetendo superpositionem asperaverit,
iacere aegrotantes altioribus stramentis, thorace atque capite
6 sublevato, loco lucido atque calido mediocriter, adhibita requie,
et abstinentia cibi usque ad tertium diem, [et]¹¹ si vires permiserint. pectus tegendum lana atque fovendum oleo dulci calido,
adhibita quoque articulorum blanda calidarum manuum frica-

---

⁵ laterum *scripsi, coll. Escul. 20*: enteron *edd.*

⁶ *addidi*   ⁹ vehementem *S: corr. Rm*

⁷ per *R*   ¹⁰ *fort.* orthopnoean ⟨a⟩

⁸ stomachi *Rm*   ¹¹ *om.* R

3 together with a feeling of heaviness and burning heat. There is a drawing upward at the sides. As the disease begins to grow more intense, there occur wheezing and hissing sounds in the chest; the voice is weak, neck stretched, face distended and flushed, eyes open wide and staring. The patient is unable to lie on his back. Sometimes there is a dry cough, at other times a cough accompanied by sputa, either thin and frothy or thick and sticky. There is sweating, abnormal complexion, and a low pulse. But if the violence of the attack increases, the patient's face becomes blue; and relief is obtained with the discharge of mucous fluid through the nostrils. Only with such a discharge is the danger of choking averted; for even the flow of tears over the eyes will not produce the same result.

4 The disease is marked by alternate periods of attack and remission. The latter intervals are sometimes completely free and clear of symptoms of disease, but at other times are marred by the presence of traces of the ailment. That is, even in the intervals of remission the patient may still suffer from shortness of breath, a condition which becomes quite obvious when he does any climbing or hurrying or is distressed by indigestion, fatigued by venery, or troubled by cold, dust, or smoke.

Asthma may be distinguished from pneumonia, for it is not necessarily accompanied by fever and is always found to be a chronic disease. Some also distinguish asthma from orthopnoea,
5 on the ground that an attack of asthma is marked by stridor and choking, while an attack of orthopnoea is marked by heaving of the chest, hiccoughs, and sometimes even a flow of blood. Others also make a distinction on the ground of severity, declaring that orthopnoea is more violent than the other diseases mentioned. But it is better to base our judgment of the severity of the diseases solely upon the general clinical picture, and to hold that a disease is sometimes severe, especially during an attack, and at other times mild, especially during a remission.

Asthma is a disease involving a state of stricture. Consequently, at the beginning of the first attack or of subsequent attacks the patient should lie on deep bedding, with chest and head
6 elevated, in a moderately light and warm room. Have him remain quiet and, if his strength permits, withhold food until the third day. Cover the chest with wool and employ fomentations of warm sweet olive oil. Massage the patient's limbs gently with

tione, ut etiam tenendo medeamur teporibus admotis tempore quo accessio vehementescit; et cucurbitae lenissimis raptibus detrahendae. at si praefocatio coegerit, et vires permiserint aegrotantis, adhibenda phlebotomia, et diatriti tempore unctione antecedente. sorbilis atque calidus et varius in dimissione offeren-

7 dus cibus, atque alternis diebus donec passio declinet. sin vero imbecilles viribus fuerint aegrotantes, diurnis diebus dabimus cibum, sed ea die qua abstinere oportuerat, parvum, ea vero qua dare licebat, paulo plurimum. sin vero ⟨venter⟩[12] officium non agnoverit, simplex clyster adhibendus, et ante cibum mulsae ex melle despumato duo vel tres cyathi praebibendi. tunc cataplasma laxativum atque cucurbita cum scarificatione adhibenda thoraci et inter[13] utrasque scapulas, ac magis paulo inferioribus locis, quo sine ulla quassatione partium eius raptus efficiatur. tum vaporatio spongiarum atque cerotarium et malagma quod

8 diachylon appellant, vel Mnaseu,[14] atque ita lavacrum et vinum et varius reddendus cibus.

in lenimento vero si corpus[15] passio tardaverit, erit adhibenda resumptio gestatione, vocis exercitio, deambulatione, unctione, fricatione corporis retentu spiritu, tum lavacro atque cibo[16] ex pulmentis mediae qualitatis. dehinc ad recorporativam curationem transeundum. adhibenda drimyphagia atque ceterarum transitus mutationum, quas saepe cyclos ordinantes docuimus; tum etiam ex radicibus vomitus, vel si passio coegerit etiam helleboro provocatus. iubemus praeterea acetum scilliticum

9 aegrotantes ante cibum sorbere, vel cum aceto nitrum sive laser, aut hyssopi decoctionem cum fico contriti[17] vel nucleo pineo, quem Graeci pityda[18] vocaverunt, admixto mulso; item abrotanum tritum cum sulphure atque aceto ex mulso confecto, vel urticae semine aut radicum, et horum similium electariorum,[19] ut est melli admixta resina terebinthina aut cardamum, quod nasturtium vocamus, aut sesamum cum aloe et amygdalis ama-

[12] add. Rm (omisso vero): contra Bendz 52
[13] inter Rm (deleto tamen utrasque): in S
[14] mnaseum edd.
[15] corpus om. R (sed. cf. Chr. i. 167):fort. in corpore vel sim. (cf. Chr. iii. 13, v. 90)
[16] lavacro atque cibo R: lavacrum atque cibum S
[17] contritum S: corr. R
[18] pityida Rm
[19] similia electaria Rm (sed cf. materiarum Chr. iii. 22): fort. ante electariorum interpung.

warm hands, and when the attack grows severe help the patient
by holding him and thus inducing warmth. Also apply cupping
instruments and remove them with a very gentle pull.[3] If the
patient's attacks of choking require it, and his strength permits,
perform venesection at the end of the three-day period, after
anointing him. Let him take soft, warm, and varied food when
the attack abates; this food should be given on alternate days
7 until the disease as a whole declines. If, however, the patient's
strength is impaired, give him food each day, but in small
amount on the days on which he would otherwise have fasted,
and somewhat more liberally on the days when food would have
been allowed him in any case. If the bowels do not function, use
a simple clyster; and let the patient drink two or three cyathi of
hydromel made with skimmed honey, before he takes his food.
Then apply relaxing poultices and cupping with scarification to
the chest and between the shoulder blades. Cupping should especially be applied to the parts a little below, so that the drawing
effect may be accomplished without agitating the parts affected
by the disease. Then apply heat with sponges, a cerate, and the
8 so-called 'emollient plaster of juices,' or Mnaseas' plaster. Thereafter prescribe bathing and permit the patient to have wine and
varied food again.

Now if the disease becomes chronic, apply the restorative
treatment during the interval of remission, prescribing passive
exercise, vocal exercise, walking, anointing, massage of the body
while holding the breath, bathing, and meals consisting of food
of the middle class. Then pass to the metasyncritic treatment.
Employ the acrid diet and proceed with the various changes as
we have often described them in setting forth the series of treatments. Also induce vomiting with radishes or, if the disease
requires, with hellebore. In addition, have the patient, before he
9 takes his food, drink vinegar of squills, nitrum with vinegar, silphium juice, or a decoction of hyssop ground up with figs or pine
seed (Greek *pityis*) and with the addition of mead. Or he may be
given southernwood ground down with sulphur, nettle seed, or
radish seed, in a mixture of vinegar and honey; also similar electuaries may be given, e.g., a mixture of honey with resin of the
terebinth tree, or with nosesmart (Latin *nasturtium*), or with
sesame, aloes, and bitter almonds, and sometimes with the addi-

3. I.e., the cups should be permitted to exert only mild suction.

ris, aliquando etiam pipere vel ovi vitello, vel illud electarium
quod diascylles appellamus, cuius confectionem De medicamini-
10 bus scribentes tradidimus. tum etiam cucurbitae recorporativae
adhibendae thoraci atque interscapulo; dehinc dropax, paroptesis, heliosis, sinapismus,[20] acopa, recorporativa malagmata, ut
est diadaphnidon vel dialoae[21] vel diaeuphorbiu;[22] dehinc navigatio atque peregrinatio terrena, et potio theriacae antidoti, et
aquarum naturalium usus, quarum praestant in Italia cotiliae
appellatae sive albae vel nepesinae, tum etiam cataclysmus, hoc
est aquarum illisio superne iisdem locis qui patiuntur; utilis denique maritima et plurima mare tenus conversatio, atque consuetudo frigidi lavacri, quam psichrolusian appellant.

11   aliqui autem adversarum sectarum principes etiam dauco cum
aceto et melle aegros potaverunt sive iri cum mulso. et ventrem
plurimum deduxerunt, dando de diagridio, quod scammonian
Graeci appellant, obolos tres, cum duplici pondere aloes sive
hierae, quam catharticam vocant, vel ammoniaci salis obolum,
sive opoponacis[23] simile pondus, vel cneoron aut polion herbam
vel peplion aut calchanthum vel tapsian aut asininum lac et
castoreum, non solum lenimenti tempore, sed etiam in augmento
sive superpositione passionis. alii vero etiam urendum thoracem
vel caput crediderunt.

12   Themison quoque secundo libro Tardarum passionum in quibusdam eisdem compeccasse videtur, cum plurimum ventrem
depurgandum credidit ex diagridio, atque in ipsa accessione.
utitur praeterea constrictivis, atque his acrioribus, et imperat
dari tapsiae sucum cum opoponace[24] aut sagapeno, ex quibus
stomachus necessario vexatur. hic denique erit memorandum
quia potis medicaminibus non sine cautionibus utendum est,
ut[25] neque eorum plurima satietate vexandi aegrotantes. item
in impetu vel asperitate passionis recorporativa adiutoria prohibenda. erit enim coenoteta consideranda, qua facile medicamina qualitatis ratione accedente correctius approbamus.

[20] sinapismū S: corr. R

[21] dialoē edd.

[22] diaeuphorbio S: -ium Rm

[23] opopanacis R

[24] opoponace R: cf. supra

[25] fort. et: cf. Schmid RPh 131

tion of pepper or the yolk of an egg. The so-called 'electuary of squills,' whose composition we described in the section on drugs,[4] may also be used. In addition, apply metasyncritic cupping to the chest and between the shoulder blades; and prescribe pitch plasters, applications of intense heat, sun-bathing, mustard plasters, restorative ointments, and such metasyncritic emollient plasters as the so-called plasters of bayberries, aloes, or spurge. The following prescriptions are also beneficial: a trip by land or water; the drinking of the theriac antidote; the use of natural waters, of which the best in Italy are the Cutilian, Alban, and Nepesine springs; and the shower bath, i.e., the playing of a stream of water from above upon the affected parts. Finally, frequent sea trips and sojourning at the seashore, as well as the habit of taking cold baths (Greek *psychrolusia*), will prove beneficial.

11   The leaders of some of the other sects have the patient drink wild carrot with vinegar and honey, or iris with mead. They purge the bowels violently, prescribing three obols of diagridium (Greek *scammōnia*, 'scammony juice') with twice that weight of aloes or of a hiera purgative, which the Greeks call cathartic, or an obol of rock salt, or the same weight of opopanax; or such substances as Cnidian berry, hulwort, wild purslane, chalcanthum, thapsia, ass's milk, and castor. They employ these substances not only during the interval of remission between attacks but in the increasing phase of the attack itself. And some even prescribe the application of a cautery to the chest or head.

12   In Book II of his *Chronic Diseases* Themison, too, makes some of the same errors. Thus he prescribes a strong purge of the bowels with scammony juice, even during the attack itself. Besides, he employs astringent substances, and indeed the more acrid kinds, and he has the patient take thapsia juice with opopanax or sagapenon. But the gullet is necessarily irritated by all these juices. Note, moreover, that the drinking of drugs should be prescribed with care, to avoid the harm which may be occasioned by their excessive use. And do not prescribe metasyncritic remedies during the attack or exacerbation of the disease. For we must consider the general type of the disease, so that we may best prescribe the proper drugs with due regard for their qualities.

4. Of the treatise *Answers.*

13 ## II. DE STOMACHICIS

A PARTE corporis quae patitur stomachica passio nomen accepit. sed non omnis stomachi querela ilico passio nuncupatur, nisi fuerit ex multorum concursu signorum et perseverantia confecta, atque corporibus tardans, repetendo superpositionibus lenimenta.[1] plurimi igitur singulatim speciales curationes eius tradiderunt, nunc de stomachi duritia dicentes, nunc de ventositate, de reumatismo et debilitate, et horrore ciborum et fastidio.

14 Themison quoque primo libro Tardarum passionum solutionem circa stomachum, quam[2] appellavit reumatismum, secundo libro ventositatem. item Thessalus secundo libro Regulari curationem separavit soluti stomachi atque inflati. nos vero communiter sub una propositione de omnibus dicere curabimus, qua ventositatem vel ex tumore duritiam confectam stricturae iungimus, fastidium vero sive horrorem ciborum et corruptionem ambiguam, utrisque principalibus passionibus subicientes.

antecedentes causae quae stomachi passionem faciunt ceteris quoque passionibus generandis communes esse probantur, sed 15 magis istam[3] iugis indigestio parit, sive post cibum vomitus,[4] et perfrictio profunda, item maestitudo, et medicaminis insueti potatio.

sequitur autem in passione constitutos accessionis tempore animi defectio, articulorum frigidus torpor, aut variatus per membra acrior naturali fervor, qui magis medias teneat manus; tum roscidus sudor, et animi angustia, iactatio, anxietas sive concatenatio mentis, et desponsio, coloris mutatio, pulsus parvus celer imbecillus, corporis tabes, cibi fastidium, vel maior ci- 16 borum appetitus; tum corruptio acceptorum cum acore in bromosam vel fumosam transeuntium qualitatem; quibusdam etiam vocis amputatio, et dentium confixio[5] sive concubitus[6] inseparabilis, capitis gravedo, aurium tinnitus, et quibusdam sitis in-

---

[1] ⟨et⟩ lenimenta R: superpositionibus ⟨et⟩ lenimentis Rm

[2] quam om. R

[3] istam Rm: ista S

[4] vomitus Rm: gemitus S

[5] confixio Haller; cf. Ac. ii. 18, 70; iii. 67; Cass. Fel., p. 187. 13: confrictio S: conflictio TLL: contritio Rm: constrictio Reinesius 667

[6] hic, non post inseparabilis, interpunxerunt edd.

II. DISEASE OF THE ESOPHAGUS

3

THE disease of the esophagus takes its name from the affected
part of the body. But not every affection of this part is to be
called by this name. The affection must show the various signs
that make up the general picture of the disease of the esophagus,
and the condition must persist and become chronic, that is to
say, marked by intervals of remission after periods of attack.
Now many writers have set forth special treatments for the several ailments of the esophagus and have spoken of hardness,
gas, flux, or weakness of this part, and of loathing or distaste for
food.

14   Thus in Book I of his *Chronic Diseases* Themison takes up the
condition of looseness (which he calls *rheumatismos*) in the
esophagus; and in Book II he discusses gas in the esophagus.
So, too, Thessalus in Book II of his work *On Regimen* separates
the treatment of looseness from that of gas in the esophagus.
But we shall try to take up all these conditions under a single
general heading.[1] We shall consider under the state of stricture
a gaseous condition of the esophagus or hardness resulting from
inflammation; and we shall consider as not due exclusively to
one state, but as involving a combination of both principal states
of disease [i.e., *status mixtus*], a distaste or loathing for food, as
well as the turning sour of food that is eaten.

The antecedent causes of the disease of the esophagus are the
same as those that precede other diseases, too. The more com-
15 mon, however, are continual indigestion, vomiting after eating,
a severe cold, grief, and the drinking of drugs to which the patient is unaccustomed.

The signs of the disease at the time of an attack are: fainting;
cold numbness of the limbs or else an abnormal degree of heat in
various parts, especially in the middle of the hands; dewlike
perspiration, mental distress, tossing, mental anguish or a feeling of constraint, despondency, change of complexion; pulse
small, rapid, and weak, a wasting-away of the body, aversion for
16 food or else an increased desire for it; and decomposition of the
food eaten, the latter becoming sour and then foul-smelling and
fumy. In some cases there is loss of voice, grinding or firm
clenching of the teeth, heaviness of the head, and ringing in the

1. I.e., disease of the esophagus.

satiabilis; cum in accessu tumor maior fuerit excitatus, oris siccitas et saltus sub praecordiorum partibus; tum dolor in eadem
parte aut etiam inter palas tenens, sive latius, cum se tumor
uberior infuderit; dehinc transvorandi difficultas cum praefocabili sensu, quo denique commoti quidam nostrae sectae principes
Epistolarum libris hoc accidentiae genus stomachicam[7] synanchen vocaverunt.

17   durescente autem stomacho sine ullo fervore atque dolore,
cetera communia signa sequentur; tunc ligneus[8] earundem partium sensus, et magis inter palas, si omnis aruerit stomachus.
sin vero in superioribus, erit transvorandi difficultas donec ad
eius fundum accepta perveniant. aut si in eodem fundo, quem
Graeci basin appellant, fuerit durities, erit transvoratio facilis,
sed post eius perfectionem gravatio sequetur; tum durities atque
extantia in interioribus praecordiorum.

    ac si ventositas fuerit stomachi, tensio sequetur inflatione con-
18 iuncta, tunc capitis plenitudo cum oppressis atque iugibus ructationibus, testante gravedine quae magis accepto cibo sentiatur; tum sonus in interioribus liquidorum, tamquam semipleni
folliculi, errante vento per inania, atque ita tensione laxata erunt
ructatione relevandi. et si etiam intestina fuerint conflata,
rugitus interiorum sequetur, quem Graeci borborigmon appellant.

    ac si solutio fuerit stomachi, quam reumatismum vocaverunt,
sequitur salivarum fluor et quibusdam iugis sputus et oris hu-
19 mectatio nauseabilis cum mordicatione interiorum, quibusdam
plurimus vomitus crassioris vel tenacis[9] aut fellei et prasini humoris vel alterius cuiuslibet substantiae circa supradictos colores.

    sin vero occulta fuerit solutio, quam Graeci adelon appellant,
aut mente sensa[10] signa videantur,[11] quae Graeci logotheoreta

---

7 stomaticam *S*: *corr. Rm*

8 igneus *R*

9 tenuis *Bendz Eran 43. 49*

10 mente sensa *Ilberg (TLL 7. 450. 55), coll. Ac. ii. 98*: immensa *S*

11 *fort. om.* signa *et scrib.* videatur, quam Graeci logotheoreton *etc.*

---

2. Presumably, the chest and upper abdominal cavities.

3. Or 'thin' (reading *tenuis*).

ears; and sometimes there is unquenchable thirst, and, when considerable inflammation is present during an attack, the mouth is dry, and there is throbbing under the precordial region. Again, pain occurs in this region and extends between the shoulder blades or even further when the inflammation is more widespread. There is also difficulty in swallowing, together with a sensation of choking. For this reason some leading authorities of our sect in their books of *Letters* call a condition of this kind 'stomachic synanche.'

7   But hardening of the esophagus in the absence of any heat or pain due to inflammation is indicated by other general signs. There is a sensation of stiffness in the parts mentioned above, especially between the shoulder blades, if the esophagus as a whole has become dry; but, if only the upper parts are affected, there will be difficulty in swallowing and getting the food down until it reaches the lower end of the esophagus [i.e., the cardia]. But if the hardness is present only in this lower end (Greek *basis*), swallowing will be easy; but after its completion there will be heaviness and then hardness and distention under the precordia.

8   A gaseous condition of the esophagus is indicated by a puffing-up and swelling; the head feels clogged, and there is continual stifled belching, with a sensation of heaviness, especially when food has been taken. In addition, there is a sound of fluids in the inner parts[2] like the sound of a half-filled bladder; this is caused by the gas as it moves through the empty parts. The distention is relaxed and relief is obtained by the patient when he belches. And if flatus affects the intestines, too, a rumbling sound (Greek *borborygmos*) is heard within them.

   In the event of looseness or flux (Greek *rheumatismos*) in the esophagus, there is a flow of saliva, and in some cases continual spitting and nausea resulting from the collection of fluid in the

19   mouth; there are also sharp internal pains. In some cases there is considerable vomiting of thick or viscous[3] fluid matter, yellow or leek-green in color, or of matter in other forms but having these colors.

   But if the actual flux is hidden from view (Greek *adēlos*) and if the signs thereof can be apprehended only by the reason[4]

4. Or omitting *signa* and making alterations thus necessitated: 'and it [i.e., *solutio*] can be apprehended only by the reason, etc.'

vocaverunt, sequitur debilitas pulsus aegrotantis, et veluti stomachi pendentis atque trementis sensus, marcor ac defectio animi, quam Graeci lipothymian vocant; quae sumpto cibo temporaliter depellatur, resumptione suffecta, nec tamen perseverabili. sed rursum in eandem relabent defectionem in imagine
20 ultimae passionis. quo fit ut nisi quis celerius sumpserit cibum,
summa defectione iactetur. sic denique plurimi impausabiliter
tota die atque nocte cibum sumpsisse veteribus traduntur.
namque Asclepiades memorat Praxagorae famulum ternos bili-
bres panes per singulos dies accepisse, quibus comestis non aliter
passione afficeretur, quam si nihil acciperet. sed ab ista passione phagedaena discernitur, siquidem in ipsa non insumantur
vel digestioni tradantur accepta, sed gravatione sequente evomantur. haec sunt quae stomachi reumatismo occurrunt.
21   sed circa regulam methodicam discernentes superpositionis
tempore contrariarum adiutoria passionum stricturae ac solutionis, quae suis specialibus[12] signis approbantur, in lenimento
communi saepissime curatione utemur quam recorporativam
dicere poterimus, a Graecis metasyncriticam appellatam.
cum igitur primo stricturae passio corpus invaserit, atque
nova temporis[13] causa fuerit aegrotantis, sive in superpositione
constituta turbando aut dolore aut ventositate affecerit patientem, convenit eum iacere loco lucido atque calido mediocriter,
22 adhibito straminum atque operimentorum calidorum usu, et, si
vires permiserint, adiuncta abstinentia usque ad tertium diem,
et accessionis tempore omnifariam requie.[14] tum articulorum
blanda convenit defricatio cum quodam calidarum manuum amplexu, ut etiam tenendo medeamur; dehinc vaporationes inter
scapulas sive palas adhibendae, pectori quoque saccelli calidi ex
cantabro confecti sive polline (nam Graeci omelysin[15] vocant),
et harum similium[16] materiarum. convenit etiam multiplicati

---

[12] specialibus *scripsi, coll. Ac. ii. 187, Chr. v. 102*: speciebus *S*: speciebus ⟨et⟩ *R*

[13] tempore *R*

[14] requiem *S*: *corr. R*

[15] omelysin *scripsi*: omphacomeli *edd. cf. 63*

[16] *fort.* similibus (materiis?). *cf. Cael. Aur. Gyn. ii. 14, 22, sed* electariorum *Chr. iii. 9*

---

5. Cf. *temporaliter . . . nec tamen perseverabili* (19).

(Greek *logotheōrēta*), the patient will nevertheless have a weak pulse and a feeling that the esophagus is suspended and trembling; profound weakness and fainting (Greek *leipothymia*) also occur. These last symptoms may be relieved for a while by the taking of food, for the patient's strength is thereby restored; but the relief does not last long, and the patient slips back again into 20 a faint, as before. That is, unless he takes food in time, he will be completely overcome. Thus the physicians of the past report many cases where the patient took food all day and night without interruption. For example, Asclepiades tells us that a servant of Praxagoras ate three two-pound breads every day for a number of days, though his having done so had no more effect on the subsequent course of the disease than if he had eaten nothing.[5] But we must distinguish phagedaena ['morbid hunger and gluttony'] from the illness under discussion; for in phagedaena the food is not actually consumed or subjected to the digestive process but, by reason of its oppressive heaviness, is vomited out. This concludes our account of the signs attending looseness or flux of the esophagus.

21   Now in accordance with Methodist principles it is necessary, at the time of an attack, to use wholly different remedies, depending on whether the case in question involves a state of stricture or a state of looseness; the state may be determined from the particular symptoms in each case. In the intervals of remission, however, the treatment is usually the same in all cases, namely, the treatment called *metasyncriticē* by the Greeks, a term we may translate by *recorporativa* [i.e., bringing about a change in the bodily condition].

Let us first consider the cases in which the disease involves a state of stricture. Whether the attack is the first that the patient has experienced or is an attack in a chronic disease, causing distress, pain, and gas, he should lie in a moderately light 22 and warm room. Give him warm bedding and covers; if his strength permits let him fast until the third day, and while the attack is in progress have him remain perfectly quiet. It is also beneficial to rub the patient's limbs gently, taking hold of them with warm hands; and even holding the parts has a good effect. Also apply heat between the shoulder blades, and also use small bags containing hot bran or raw flour (Greek *ōmēlysis*) to warm the chest. Or use other substances like these. Applications of

linteaminis vaporatio sive pannorum vel plagellarum, quae
Graeci ptygmata vocant, oleo tinctarum; cucurbitae igni externo
vaporatae atque leniter appositae, iugi atque frequenti muta-
23 tione; aliquando etiam testea vascula, quae Graeci amphoras[17]
vocant, sive vitrea. tum fomentatio studiosa ac iugis ex oleo
calido atque dulci, vel in quo malvae agrestis radices decoctae
sunt; si singultus fuerit, sicyonio, si inflatio, ruta[18] vel anetho.
ac si vocis fuerit amputatio in accessionis affectu decumbentibus,[19] erunt spongiis aqua calida expressis ora vaporanda, et distinctio dentium facienda digitis immissis, quibus lenius gingivas
deprimamus. tum capitis fomentatio et resumptionum modera-
menta adhibenda, ut panis calidus vel cucumis aut melo, vel terrae gleba aqua calida infusa, et oris collutio ex aqua calida, et
accessione vergente parva potatio.

24 ac si in vehementiam passio venerit, adhibenda phlebotomia,
qua perfecta, si tertia fuerit dies, quam Graeci diatriton vocant,
erit aegrotans unctione curandus, calido scilicet ac dulci oleo.
tunc oris adhibenda collutio; cibus offerendus parvus, levis, calidus, sumptione facilis, ut sorbile quidquam ex pane atque melle
et sale et anetho confectum, sive pulticula mollis,[20] velut ex pane
aut alica, et ova sorbilia. tum alternis diebus permittentibus
viribus aeger nutriendus donec passio declinet. potus praeterea
dandus est plurimus, sed neque maioribus haustibus hauriendus,
neque coacervatim atque eodem tempore, quo potius aegrotos[21]
25 impleri quam relaxari faciamus. his autem partibus quae fuerint in tensione constitutae cataplasmata conveniunt laxativa,
ut est prae ceteris ex[22] faenigraeci pollinibus et semine malvae,
ex solo melle et parvo oleo admixto confectum, quod[23] plurimo
tempore corpori[24] possit sine ulla gravatione immorari. tunc
cucurbita adiuncta scarificatione, sive hirudinum appositio, quas
vulgo sanguisugas appellant; deinde cataplasma et vaporatio
spongiarum expressarum liquoribus saepe memoratis.

declinante passione, si ulla durities fuerit consecuta, erunt

[17] ambicas *Reinesius 668, coll. Chr. iv. 94, sed cf. Ac. iii. 150*
[18] ⟨cum⟩ ruta *R*
[19] *fort. ponenda virgula ante* decumbentibus, *non post*
[20] mollis *Rm*: molli *S*
[21] ignotos *S*: *corr. Haller*
[22] ex ⟨lini et⟩ *R, ut frequenter ap. Cael.*
[23] quo *R, fort. recte. cf. 56 fin.*   [24] corpori *R*: corporis *S*

heat with many layers of linen or cloth (Greek *ptygmata*) dipped in olive oil are also helpful. Cupping instruments heated externally with fire may also be lightly applied; these should be

3 continually and frequently renewed. Sometimes earthen or glass vessels, called *amphorae* by the Greeks, may be employed. Again, one should foment the patient carefully and continually with warm sweet olive oil, containing, if desired, a decoction of marsh mallow roots. If there are hiccoughs, use Sicyonian oil; if there is flatus, add rue or dill. If under the stress of the attack the patient loses his voice, apply heat to his mouth, using sponges wrung out of hot water; and pry the teeth apart by inserting the fingers so that the sponges may be gently pressed upon the gums. Also foment the head; and employ measures to restore the patient's strength. Thus give him warm bread, cucumber, melon, or a piece of [medicinal?][6] earth soaked in hot water. Have him wash his mouth with warm water, and, as the attack declines, let him drink a little.

4 But if the attack becomes more severe, perform venesection; and if this operation is performed on the third day, i.e., the end of the period which the Greeks call *diatritos*, follow it by anointing the patient with warm sweet olive oil. Then have him wash his mouth. Let him take a small quantity of light, warm food that is easy to swallow, e.g., a gruel-like preparation of bread, honey, salt, and dill, or soft porridge made with bread or groats, or soft eggs. Give the patient nourishment on alternate days, if his strength permits, until the disease declines. In addition, give him a great deal to drink, but have him sip only a little at a time and not take a large amount at any one time, for otherwise the

5 drinking will congest rather than relax the patient. Also apply relaxing poultices to the distended parts. The most suitable poultice is that prepared with fenugreek seed and mallow seed, with the addition merely of honey and a small amount of olive oil; such a poultice may remain on the body for a long time without causing any feeling of heaviness. And apply cupping with scarification, or leeches, which are commonly called 'blood-suckers' [*sanguisugae*]; in addition, use poultices and apply heat with sponges wrung out of fluids of the kind frequently mentioned above.

If there is any hardness of the parts during the declining phase

6. E.g., Samian earth.

cataplasmata apponenda, ut nuper docuimus, admixta resina
26 sive in olei vicem liquida pice, vel ex radice hibisci et adipe porcino, recenti primo tum veterato, confecta, sive ex hordei pollinibus aut lolii semine et arido fico et hibisco. tum etiam ex oleo
calido embasis sive ex varietate eiusdem per diversa virtutis,[25]
faenograeci decoctione vel radicis malvarum aut lini seminis.[26]
dehinc cibus varius dandus, sed qui nullam faciat inflationem
neque digestione tardus[27] approbetur,[28] sed omni facilitate conveniens, ut cerebrum porcinum, pisces teneri, atque olera quae
ventrem mollire valeant. tum lavacra convenit adhibere atque
vino aegrotantem resumere leni. utendum etiam malagmate
27 quod diachylon appellamus, sive Mnaseu, vel diamelilotu.[29] et
si ventositate fuerit stomachus affectus, adhibendum diasamsucu[30] sive diaspermaton, quorum compositiones de medicaminibus Responsionum tradidimus libris.

si reumatismus fuerit, quem nihil aliud quam solutionem accipimus, convenit aegrotantem iacere loco mediocriter frigido,
supino schemate, attritis ac teneribus stramentis utentem, adhibita requie et abstinentia, sicut superius diximus, permittentibus viribus. tum tenacior ligatio articulorum vel, si causa coegerit, constrictio facienda, apposita cucurbita stomacho plurima
28 flamma subiecta: dehinc solutione cogente[30a] spongia frigida
atque odoramenta quae percutere minus valeant caput, ut exhalatione sui frigus ingerant aegrotanti, ut mala cydonia, pira,
sorba, mala punica, murta, lentiscum, rosa, vel pulentum infusum, et his similia; oris collutio ex aqua frigida sive pusca.

ac si plurimus fuerit salivarum fluor, expuere iubemus aegrotantem siquidem retentus stomachum solvat, transvoratus autem humectet atque obducat et propterea geminet solutionem.
sed hoc convenit facere urgenti tempore, ne meditatio potius
expuendi fiat atque exinde provocatio fluoris augeatur. perseverante passione gargarismata sunt adhibenda ex supradictis vel

---

[25] virtutis ⟨ut⟩ R

[26] semine edd.

[27] tardus Am: tardius S: tardior R

[28] approprietur (tardius retento) Triller Clinotechnia 127, coll. Ac. i. 150, Chr. iv. 22, 70

[29] mnaseum vel diamelilotum S

[30] diasamsucū S   [30a] cogentes S: corr. R

---

7. Cf. 22.

of the disease, apply poultices, as indicated above, but add resin
26 or liquid pitch in place of the olive oil. Or use poultices made
with marsh mallow root and pork suet, at first fresh and later
aged; or with barley flour or darnel seed, dried fig, and marsh
mallow. In addition, bathe the patient in warm olive oil or, for
variety, in other substances of similar properties, e.g., a decoction of fenugreek seed, mallow root, or flaxseed. Then give the
patient varied food of the kind that does not produce flatus and
is not slow of digestion but, on the contrary, very easily digested
and therefore suitable, e.g., hog's brain, tender fish, and such
vegetables as will keep the bowels soft. And at this time prescribe bathing and use mild wine to help rebuild the patient's
strength. Also apply an emollient plaster, such as the so-called
27 'plaster of juices,' or that of Mnaseas, or the melilot plaster. And
if the esophagus is distended by gas, use the marjoram plaster or
the plaster of seeds, the composition of which we have set forth
in the section on drugs in our work entitled *Answers*.

Now if the disease of the esophagus involves a state of flow
(*rheumatismos*), which we consider identical with a state of looseness (*solutio*), the patient should lie on his back in a moderately
cold room; his bedding should be well worn and thin. See that
he remains quiet, and, if his strength permits, have him go without food, as in the former case.[7] Bind the limbs tightly and, if
the case requires, increase the astringent effect by applying a
medical cup to the upper abdominal region with considerable
28 flame. Then, if the state of looseness still makes it necessary, use
a sponge dipped in cold water, and also aromatics that are not
pungent enough to injure the patient's head, but whose emanations will produce a cooling effect, e.g., quinces, pears, sorb
apples, pomegranates, myrtle, mastic, roses, soaked pearl barley, and the like. Also have the patient wash his mouth with
cold water or diluted vinegar.

If there is a copious flow of saliva, have the patient spit it out,
for, if kept in the mouth, it causes further looseness in the
esophagus, and, if swallowed, it covers these parts with moisture,
thereby also aggravating the state of looseness. But the patient
should be made to expectorate only when the occasion requires,
for otherwise he will make a habit of spitting, and, as a consequence, an increased flow of saliva will be stimulated. If the disease persists, the patient should gargle with one of the liquids

29 ex aliquo suco ad fluorem sanguinis praescripto qui valeat frigore atque propria virtute mederi; vel si res coegerint,[31] ex iisdem
spongiae expressae, sicut in aliis docuimus, gutturi admovendae
sive pectori et interscapulo. lenius autem atque idem faciunt
ptygmata ex supradictis expressa liquoribus. constringunt enim
salivarum fluorem et nauseam relevant, quod non minus etiam
masticata conyza atque exputa, sive mastiche contrita, et lactucae albae semen facere valent. possunt etiam poto dari ea
quae congrue medeantur, ut duobus aquae frigidae cyathis seminis aspergantur cochlearia duo, sive mastichis cochleare unum,

30 vel plantaginis sive mali punici dulcis vel acidi sucus cum particula menthae parvissima vel cucumeris semine contrito. dandum quoque medicamen confectum quod dioporon appellamus,
item diamoron[32] sive diarhoos et his similia, quorum compositionem Medicaminum docuimus libris. cavendae praeterea hor-
rentium materiarum fabulae quae quadam commemoratione
vomitum commovere videantur. utendum cataplasmatibus
quae nuper de fluore sanguinis scribentes docuimus. et diatriti
tempore adhibenda perunctio ex oleo hispano sive lentiscino vel
murtino, qua praecuratus aegrotans, ora fovenda aqua frigida

31 vel spongiis ex ea expressis detergi.[33] tunc cibo reficiendi constrictivo, sicut de fluore sanguinis conscripsimus, atque ita parva
interposita dilatione frigidae parum aquae paulatim bibant.[34]
quod si quisquam non valuerit sustinere, calidam dabimus ut
nimio fervore constringat. imitatione enim velut usturae partium perficit densitatem.

ac si cibum sibi in stomacho natare senserint aegrotantes, convenit articulorum impressam ligationem facere, ita [ut][35] in
aquam ferventem manus aegrotantium mittere, vel si maiora
cogunt, etiam constrictivam adhibere cucurbitam, et primo ori
ventris, dehinc inter scapulas sive palas, quod metaphrenon
Graeci vocant; et aliquando tertiam inferius a prima convenit
adhibere.

32 ac si cibus fuerit reiectus, secundo nutriendi sunt aegrotantes.

[31] coegerit R

[32] diomoron S: corr. R

[33] detergenda Rm

[34] bibat S: corr. R

[35] seclusi

just mentioned; or he may use one of those prescribed for cases

29 of bleeding,[8] provided that its cooling powers and special properties make it a suitable remedy in the present type of case. Or if conditions require, apply sponges wrung out of these same liquids to the throat, chest, or the region between the shoulder blades, as we have described in other connections. The same result will be achieved even more gently with folded compresses dipped in the same liquids and wrung out. For these substances constrict the flow of saliva and relieve nausea; equally effective, moreover, are fleabane, which the patient may chew and then spit out, triturated mastic, and seeds of white lettuce. Substances that have a suitable curative property may also be given the patient to drink, e.g., two spoonfuls of [white lettuce] seed

30 or one spoonful of mastic added to two cyathi of cold water; use may also be made of plantain juice or the juice of sweet or bitter pomegranate, together with a very little mint or triturated cucumber seed. And one may also prescribe the so-called 'fruit' drug, the mulberry drug, the sumach drug, and others like them, whose composition we have described in the section on drugs;[9] but avoid all reference to disgusting substances, for such reference may provoke vomiting. Employ plasters such as we described in the recent chapter on bleeding. And at the end of the three-day period anoint the patient with Spanish oil, mastic oil, or myrtle oil, and at the conclusion of this treatment wash his face with cold water or use sponges wrung out of cold water.

31 Then restore the patient's strength with binding food of the kind we prescribed for cases of bleeding; and after a short interval let the patient slowly drink a little cold water. If he cannot take the cold water, give him water so hot that its intense heat will produce an astringent effect. For very hot water has a kind of burning action which causes a condensation of the parts.

And if the patient has the feeling that his food is floating in the esophagus, bind his limbs tightly, and plunge his hands into very hot water. If the seriousness of the condition requires it, also apply astringent cupping, first over the cardia, then between the shoulder blades (Greek *metaphrenon*). In some cases it is well to apply a third cup below the first.

32 If the patient vomits his food, give him a second feeding. If

8. E.g., *Chr.* ii. 155.
9. Of the treatise *Answers*.

et si ⟨vires non⟩ permiserint[36] ut diatriti rigorem servemus, erit alternis plurimis parvus cibus offerendus, quo quidem diurnis diebus sed non simili modo aegri nutriri videantur.[37] sin vero stomacho collectus humoris fluor mordicationem fecerit, ilico excludendus si plurimum superare fuerit visus, non quidem digitis immissis quo vomitum provocemus, ne magis influant acriora, et ex partibus sanis vel quae passione contaminatae non fuerint patientibus advenire liquida faciamus, quippe cum consuetudo

33 saepissime transeat in naturam. ac si plurimum edax fuerit humor, nec tamen ita superfluus ut ex sua sponte per vomitum excludi videatur ob facultatem reiciendi, quo minus eversio fiat stomachi dabimus potum, et perseverante solutione cataplasmatum sive medicaminum virtutes augemus.

tum si orexis sive appetitio cibi fuerit impedita, dabimus ea quae naturam[38] valeant excitare, ut intybi thirsum vel lactucae, et magis albae atque aceto tinctae, tunc albas olivas et panem pusca infusum cum parvo pulegio et sale et hispano oleo, item pultem ex pane vel tragoptisana atque pusca et oleo et sale parvo confectam et anetho vel porro capitato, vel tragoptisana,[39] quae ex lenticula atque alica conficitur. sed erit assanda lenti-

34 cula. tunc immittenda mala cydonia vel orbiculata sive scaudiana,[40] ut plerique vocant, vel mala pira aut sorba aut pira duracina, quae crustumina vocant, vel folia plantaginis mollia aut intybi. aspergenda etiam alicae sive oryzae grana mali punici vel uvae fabriles; dehinc etiam vina quaedam infundenda, ut murtinum, malinum, vel ex malo punico confectum, aut hydromel inveteratum vel quod melimelon[41] appellant aut hydromelon. danda etiam damascena et malum assum vel elixum vel

35 quidquam ex supradictis. sic etiam volantum quae nulla pinguedine accipientem gravent, ut passerum pectora vel perdicum

[36] ⟨vires non⟩ permiserint *scripsi*: ⟨vires⟩ permiserint *Rm*: permiserit *S*

[37] videntur *S*: *corr. Rm*

[38] *fort.* natura

[39] tragophacoptisana *Rm*: *an* phacoptisana?

[40] scandiana *Rm*   [41] *fort.* melomeli

10. I.e., to feed the patient only on alternate days (cf. 7). But the text here is doubtful.

11. Perhaps *tragoptisana* = 'a mixture of spelt groats and pearl barley.'

12. Or 'tart.' Cf. *Ac.* ii. 206.

his strength does not permit us to adhere rigorously to the three-day periods,[10] give him a large quantity of food on alternate days and a small quantity on the other days, i.e., give him food every day but not in the same amount. But if fluid matter gathers in the esophagus because of the state of flux and causes griping pains, it should be vomited at once, if there is a superabundance of it. But do not in that case [have the patient] insert the fingers to induce vomiting, for an even more copious flow of acrid matter will thus be provoked; that is to say, fluids from healthy parts, parts not touched by the disease, will be stimulated to flow regularly toward the diseased parts. For what begins as a habitual practice generally becomes in time a natural 33 process. If, however, there is a considerable amount of this irritant fluid, but not such an excess as to give rise to spontaneous vomiting, give the patient a potion to facilitate the vomiting of the fluid without violent gagging. And if the state of looseness persists, increase the strength of the plasters or drugs employed.

If the patient then loses his appetite for food (Greek *orexis*), give him substances that will stimulate his normal appetite, e.g., a stalk of endive, or heart of lettuce, especially the white variety, dipped in vinegar; white olives; or bread soaked in diluted vinegar with a little pennyroyal, salt, and Spanish oil. A porridge made with bread or spelt groats,[11] diluted vinegar, olive oil, a little salt, and dill or scallion, or a spelt gruel made with lentils and spelt groats may also be used. But in the latter case 34 the lentils should be roasted. Also add to the dish quinces, round apples (i.e., Scaudians, as some call them), ordinary apples and pears, sorbs, hard[12] pears (i.e., the so-called 'Crustumerians'), or soft leaves of plantain or endive. Pomegranate kernels or smoke-dried raisins may also be sprinkled over a dish of spelt groats or rice, and then a wine may be added, e.g., myrtle, apple, or pomegranate wine, or else well-aged hydromel, or the so-called 'melimelon' or 'hydromelon' preparations.[13] Also give the patient damsons, baked or cooked apple, or any of the other fruits mentioned above. The flesh of birds may also be prescribed, provided that it is free from fat and will not cause the patient dis-

---

13. *Melimelon* is a drink prepared with summer-apples; *hydromelon* contains honey, quince, and water. It is tempting to read *melomeli* (a drink containing quince and honey), which is juxtaposed with *hydromelon* in Dioscorides (*Mat. med.* v. 21, 22) and is presumably different from *melimelon* (*ibid.* i. 115). But see Orib. *Coll. med.* v. 29. 8 and *Rhein. Mus.*, LVIII (1903), 98.

aut attagenarum, tunc etiam quadrupedum levia, deinde porcina crura, item maritima quae non sint contraria solutioni, ut
squillae, mulli, carabi, bucini, spondylia, conchylia.

ac si cibus in acorem transierit, iisdem erit perseverandum atque eodem potu, cui erunt aspergendae coriandri seminis drachmae duae. tunc etiam asperiori vino utendum quod Graeci
hypausteron vocant. perseverante fluore erit etiam trochiscis
utendum quos haemoptycis[42] et coeliacis potandos scripsimus.

36 lavacrum interea tardius ac serius ordinandum. et multo atque
longo tempore prohibendi aegrotantes bibere priusquam cibum
sumpserint, nisi aliqua forte maior necessitas intolerandae sitis
occurrerit. erunt namque dandi cogentibus rebus ex vino aspe-
riore aqua commixti duo vel tres cyathi.

sed si forte complexionis passionum aliqua fuerint signa perspecta, erunt urgentiora conicienda quibus ordo magis serviat
curationum. plurimi vero medici stomachicos potant[43] eos qui
duritia laboraverunt[44] et singultu castoreum ex aqua mulsa solutum, quantitatem[45] pleni cochlearis tribus cyathis aquae mis-

37 centes. eos autem qui fluore stomachi, hoc est reumatismo laboraverint, aquam[46] potant, miscentes aloes cochlearis pleni
quantitatem, vel infusione vel decoctione aut suco.[47] sed erit
praecavenda medicaminum dandorum satietas, ac magis inio-
cundae[48] qualitatis, quam non solum aegre perferant aegrotantes, verum etiam officio appetendi cibi deserantur, et propterea passionis augeatur pernicies. haec etiam de illo potando
medicamine sive antidoto, quod hieran appellant, dixerimus.
†facienda etiam†[49] laboriosa atque dolore gravissima ignis
ustura.

38   sed in lenimento oportebit[50] aegrotantium fortificare corpora
atque resumere varia gestatione, et pro modo virium sub divo

---

[42] haemoptyicis *A*

[43] putant *edd*.: *corr. Bendz 39*

[44] *fort*. laboraverint (*cf. 37*)

[45] quantitate *edd*.

[46] aqua *R*

[47] *fort*. infusionem vel decoctionem aut sucum

[48] inlocandae *S*: iniucundae *Rm*: iniocondae *Almeloveen*

[49] *fort*. facit enim idem quod *vel sim*.; *an* facienda = *aestimanda?*

[50] oportebat *S*: *corr. Rm*

tress, e.g., breast of sparrow, partridge, or francolin; and then the lighter parts of four-legged animals, then pig's trotters, and such seafood as will not be unsuitable in a state of looseness, e.g., squill, red mullet, crayfish, trumpet shell, and various kinds of mussels or oysters.[14]

Now if the food the patient eats turns sour, keep him on the same diet of food and drink but add two drachms of coriander seed to the latter; and in this case also give him a somewhat sour wine (Greek *hypausteron*). If the state of looseness continues, prescribe troches such as those we have said should be employed for cases of blood-spitting[15] and for the coeliac disease. But do not prescribe bathing until much later; and for a considerable time forbid the patient to drink before taking food, unless there happens to be some compelling reason why he should be permitted to quench his thirst. And if circumstances do make it necessary, give him two or three cyathi of the tart wine mixed with water.

If, as it happens, there are signs which indicate a mixed state of disease [*status mixtus*], one must give heed to the more pressing conditions[16] and direct the treatment [in the first instance] to those conditions. Now many physicians prescribe potions for the disease of the esophagus. In cases of hardness of the esophagus or hiccoughs, they give the patient a solution of castor in honey water, mixing a spoonful of castor with three cyathi of water; and in cases of flux (*rheumatismos*) in the esophagus they have the patient drink water containing a spoonful of aloes, in the form of infusion, decoction, or merely juice. But one should avoid the excessive prescription of such drugs, especially those unpleasant to take; for not only is it hard for the patient to endure them, but he loses his desire for food and the ravages of the disease are thereby increased. The same may also be said of prescriptions of the drug or antidote called *hiera*. . . . an exhausting and painful cautery.[17]

In the intervals of remission, however, build up and strengthen the patient's body with varied passive exercise; and, depending

14. Cf. Sor. *Gyn.*, p. 37. 19.   15. E.g., *Chr.* ii. 175–76.

16. I.e., to those manifesting *strictura* or *solutio*, whichever preponderates in a given case where both are present.

17. The text and meaning are uncertain. Possibly the original text compared the drastic purge to a cautery.

deambulationes adhibere, sive lectionis exercitium, si fuerit li-
teratus aegrotans, vel ut communiter dixerim vocis; tum unctionem ac defricationem et eos motus qui magis humeros valeant
exercere, retento spiritu; et nunc palaestra corpus agitare, tum
lavacro rarissimo in his qui fluore vexantur stomachi, iugi autem
ac frequenti in his qui strictura laborare videntur. vinum vero
atque varium cibum constrictivum prioribus, laxativum sequentibus ordinamus, ut pisces teneros, echinos, ostrea, et olera
mollia, accedente regula methodicae disciplinae minuendae au-
gendaeque quantitatis.

39   dehinc adhibenda recorporatio, quam Graeci metasyncriticam
vocant, ex acriori cibo, quem Graeci drimyphagian appellant,
ex aqua capparis confecto et aceto et sale et cepe, sed ex depositis quae temporis requie ⟨nullo⟩[51] accepto marcore inflabilis virtutis careant qualitate. dandae etiam rapae sinapi madidatae
atque salsum[52] ex aceto et oleo conditum, vel aceto et mulso et
sinapi, aut mulso ex vino confecto, quae quidem erunt varianda.
admiscendum etiam piper pro ratione virium atque passionis
magnitudine, ut nunc uno nunc duobus nunc tribus acribus pulmentis utamur.

40   convenit etiam sicca fricatio cum aspergine corporea facta,
tunc frigidi consuetudo lavacri, quam psichrolusiam appellant,
et cibi sicciores, magis in his qui fluore, hoc est reumatismo laboraverunt.[53] tum rubor cutis faciendus inter scapulas et in
thorace usque ad ventrem, nunc ex ferventis resinae lenimento,[54]
nunc ex picis, nunc ex dropacis, primo communis ac lenioris,
deinde compositi ac vehementioris. atque ita nitri fricamento
utendum et sole torrendum corpus, quod Graeci heliosin appellant, aut paroptesis adhibenda ex carbonibus vel parietibus ignitis et ceromate, aliquando etiam ex fico calefacto; tunc defri-

---

[51] *add.* R
[52] salsamentum *Almeloveen, coll. 41*

[53] *fort.* laboraverint (*cf. 37*)
[54] linimento *Rm*

---

18. Presumably terebinth resin.
19. Cf. *Chr.* ii. 34 and n.

on the state of his strength, prescribe walking in the open air, or the exercise of reading aloud, if the patient is educated, or, to put it generally, vocal exercise; in addition, prescribe anointing and massage, and those movements which especially serve to exercise the upper arms and shoulders, the patient holding his breath. At this time exercise in the palaestra is also suitable. Bathing should be ordered at long intervals in cases of a state of flow in the esophagus, but regularly and frequently in cases where a state of stricture is involved. Prescribe wine and varied food. The food in the former cases [*solutio*] should be binding; but in the latter cases [*strictura*] laxative foods should be given, e.g., tender fish, sea urchins, oysters, and soft vegetables. In either event the principles of the Methodist Sect with regard to increasing and diminishing the quantity of food should be adhered to.

9   Then prescribe the alterative treatment (Greek *metasyncriticē*). Employ the acrid diet (Greek *drimyphagia*) prepared with water of capers, and with vinegar, salt, and onion. Of preserved foods those should be used which, though long stored, have remained unspoiled and will not cause gas. Also give the patient turnips dipped in mustard, and salted fare prepared with vinegar and olive oil, or with vinegar, honey, and mustard, or with a mixture of honey and wine; and keep varying these dressings. Add pepper to the food with due regard to the patient's strength and the severity of the disease, so that at times one sharply flavored food is employed, and at other times two or even three.

0   Dry massage may also be used, together with dusting powders for the body. In addition, have the patient bathe regularly in cold water (Greek *psychrolusia*). And prescribe the drier types of food, particularly in cases of looseness or flux (*rheumatismos*). Then, too, irritate the skin between the shoulder blades until it becomes red. Do the same on the chest and as far down as the epigastric region. Use as rubefacients now an ointment of hot resin,[18] now one of pitch, and now a pitch plaster, i.e., the simple mild plaster at first, and afterward the powerful one with many ingredients. Also have the body rubbed with nitrum. And prescribe sun-bathing (Greek *hēliōsis*), or the application of intense heat from burning coals, heated walls, a wax ointment,[19] or in some cases a hot poultice of figs. Follow this treatment by having the patient rubbed down with nitrum, olive oil, and adarce.

41 catio ex nitro atque oleo et adarce. adhibenda quoque acopa ex
euphorbio et diagridio et piretro et pipere et sinapi vel suco ferulaginis, quam[55] Graeci tapsian vocant. ungenda corpora vel admixta cera imponenda, donec sufficienter inflari vi medicaminis
partes videantur.

convenit etiam vomitus arte affectatus quo corpora dissecentur, et primo ex aqua mulsa vel ex aceto squillitico melli admixto, singulari vel adiuncto semine erucae aut cardami aut urticae
aut sinapi, aut salsamento[56] multo ex aceto et melle, tum etiam
ex radicibus, ultimo quoque helleboro lenticulae admixto vel
oryzae in his qui reumatismo fuerint affecti, cum sorbilibus vero
sucis[57] qui strictura.

42 adhibenda etiam ptarmica quibus stomachus commotione
capitis contremiscat. item sorbendus aut infundendus rhinen-
chyto ferramento naribus sucus cyclaminis aut erucae aut anagallidis herbae. gargarizandum sinapi ex aceto et melle, decoctio thymi aut origani vel pulegii aut hyssopi, aut squillae sucus
cum aqua mulsa, et cetera similia eius generis quae fuerint, et
magis cum initia atque summitas stomachi callosa videbuntur,
vehementiore modo curationis indigentia. tunc etiam adhibemus quaedam acriora, vel horum exhalationem[58] aegrotantes
haustu suo hortabimur adducto spiritu recipere, quo etiam alti-

43 ora agitatione medicaminis demutentur. sumpto igitur fictili
vasculo immittimus puscam, tum admixto nitro, origano, cardamomo, mastiche chia, carbonibus subiectis decoquimus. sed
erit primo os vasculi praegypsandum, immisso ⟨calamo⟩[59] utraque ex parte forato cuius summitati ovi vacuati imponimus testam ex utroque suo vertice perforatam: cuius altera caverna calamo inseratur, altera vaporem fumet acceptum. tum aegrotantem iubemus ore aperto supradictam cavernam labiis am-
plecti sive ovi ut supra diximus verticem, atque ita eius exhala-

44 tionem excipere. cuius quidem fervor erit moderandus ne nimietate partes exurat.

[55] quem S: corr. Rm (cf. Chr. i. 124, ii. 35)

[56] salsamenti multi S: corr. Rm

[57] succis ⟨in iis⟩ R

[58] exhalatione S: corr. R

[59] add. R

41 Also employ restorative ointments of spurge, scammony juice, pellitory, pepper, mustard, or the juice of deadly carrot (Greek *thapsia*). Anoint the body or, adding wax [to the ointments], make applications,[20] continuing the treatment until the parts appear to be quite swollen through the action of the drug.

It is also beneficial to induce vomiting artificially in order to agitate the body. For this purpose first use hydromel or vinegar of squills, together with an admixture of plain honey or honey to which seeds of rocket, nosesmart, nettle, or mustard have been added; or else employ a considerable amount of brine with vinegar and honey. Later induce vomiting with radishes, and finally with hellebore. In cases involving a state of looseness the hellebore should be mixed with a dish of lentils or rice; but in cases involving a state of stricture it should be given with gruels.

42 Also prescribe sternutatories, since the agitation of the head will produce a concomitant trembling of the esophagus. Have the patient swallow the juice of cyclamen, rocket, or pimpernel, or inject the same into his nostrils with the instrument used for such nasal injections. Also let him gargle with a mixture of mustard, honey, and vinegar, or with a decoction of thyme, marjoram, pennyroyal, or hyssop, or with squill juice and hydromel, or with other substances of a similar kind. Such gargling is especially necessary when the upper esophagus appears to be stiff and requires a stronger type of treatment. In that case use should also be made of certain pungent substances, the patient being directed to draw deep breaths and inhale the vapors from these substances; the agitation caused by the drugs will also

43 alter the state of the deeper parts. Thus take an earthen vessel and pour vinegar into it; then add nitrum, marjoram, cardamon, and Chian mastic, and boil over coals. But first plaster the mouth of the vessel with gypsum after inserting into it a reed pipe open at both ends. Over the top of this pipe place an empty egg shell, also perforated at both ends. Let one opening of this shell fit over the reed pipe and let the vapor steam out by the upper opening. Then have the patient open his mouth and with his lips encompass this upper opening, that is, the opening at the

44 summit of the egg; and thus have him draw in the vapor. But do not let the vapor become too hot, for excessive heat will cause burns.

20. I.e., of the cerates thus formed.

atque ita si plurima et perseverans mordicatio affecerit aegrotantem, erit mitiganda simplicibus gargarismatibus, ut aqua calida et oleo sive lacte aut decoctione cantabri aut suco ptisanae vel mixarum[60] decoctione aut amyli[61] cum aqua. oportet praeterea etiam partibus in passione constitutis apponere medicamen quod polyarchion appellamus vel diadaphnidon[62] et horum similium,[63] quorum compositionem Medicaminum tradidimus libris. dandum quoque medicamen theriacum bibendum quod diechidnon appellamus, cuius quoque compositionem Responsionum dedimus libris.

45   tunc aegrotantes maritima natatione exercendi atque cataclysmo curandi, hoc est aquarum illisione, suppositis partibus patientibus. animo praeterea securo atque facili esse convenit curandos, et aquarum naturalium usum adhibere, ut sunt in Italia quae cotiliae appellatae et nepesinae. lavacro atque potu aptissimo[64] utendum, adhibita aeris mutatione longa, terrena,[65] maritima. exercitationibus variis palaestrarum adhibito praeceptore utendum, atque ita iisdem resumptionibus corpus convenit recurare. sic enim perseveratione et ventositas excludetur stomachi et aliae quoque supradictae passiones depelluntur.[66]

46   III. DE PHAGEDAENA

EST etiam phagedaena ex stomachi passionibus qua affectos[1] sequetur cibi vehemens appetentia, quam Graeci orexin appellant, et coacervati accipiendi cupiditas et immasticata transvoratio, tunc gravedo atque tensio et propterea vomitus quem sibi coacti atque oppressi provocent aegrotantes, corporis macies, pallor, aliquando etiam vultus inflatio, oris pedor,[2] quibusdam etiam gingivarum putredo cum scabro dentium detrimento ⟨et⟩[3] tritu,[4] visus obtusio **[5] †sed passioni genus philonii in problematicis non daturos nos iterum pollicemur.† interposito

---

[60] mixarum *Rm*: noxarum *S*

[61] amylo *Rm, fort. recte*

[62] diadaphnion *S: corr. Rm*

[63] *fort.* similia: *cf. Cael. Aur. Gyn. ii. 14, 22; vid. Bendz 19*

[64] aptissime *Rm*

[65] terrena ⟨et⟩ *R*

[66] depellentur *R, fort. recte*

[1] affecto *S: corr. R*

[2] fetor *coni. Almeloveen, coll. 52*

[3] *add. Rm*

[4] tritus *S*: attritu *Rm*

[5] *lacunam statuit Rm*

Again, if the patient suffers severe and persistent griping pains, let him obtain relief with simple gargles, e.g., warm water and olive oil, milk, a decoction of bran, pearl barley water, and a decoction of sebesten plums or of starch with water added. Also apply to the affected parts the so-called 'plaster of Polyarchus,' the bayberry plaster, or others like these. We have described their preparation in the section on drugs.[21] Prescribe, too, the drinking of the theriac called *diechidnon* [the theriac of vipers], whose composition we have also set forth in the treatise entitled *Answers*.

45   Then have the patient take the exercise afforded by swimming in the sea. And prescribe the use of a shower, i.e., the playing of a stream of water over the affected parts. The patient should be kept unworried and calm. And it is well also to prescribe the use of natural springs, for instance, the Cutilian and the Nepesine in Italy; have the patient bathe in these waters and drink them, for this will be most beneficial. Again, have him take a long trip abroad by land or sea to obtain a change of climate. Also prescribe varied exercises in the palaestra under the direction of a trainer, and keep building up the bodily strength by these same restorative measures. For continual treatment of this kind will put an end to gas in the esophagus and will also overcome the other ailments mentioned above.

46   III. MORBID HUNGER

O NE of the diseases of the gullet is morbid hunger. Those affected by it have a ravenous appetite for food (Greek *orexis*) and a desire to take a great deal at one time, so that they swallow their food without chewing. This is followed by heaviness, distention, and, as a consequence, vomiting, which the patient himself is forced to induce because of his distress. The body is emaciated and pallid, face sometimes swollen, breath foulsmelling, gums in some cases festering, teeth scabrous and decayed, and vision blurred. . . .[1]

21. I.e., of the treatise *Answers*.

1. The rest of the symptoms, all the discussion before the account of the treatment, and the first part of the treatment are lost. I have not attempted to translate the obscure phrase *sed . . . pollicemur*, which is probably out of place. The reference seems to be to a decision not to employ Philo's drug in certain cases. See Friedel, p. 50; Kind, *RE*, s.v. 'Soranos,' 1130; Wellmann, *Neue Jahrb.*, XXI, 697.

enim tempore digestionis rapiuntur accepta atque repletis viis,
47 quos Graeci poros appellant, obtunditur appetitus. erit praeterea curandum tempore quo cibamus ea ministrare quae parum
nutriant, sed quanta vi queant appetentiam obtundant, ut sunt
olera quae non relaxent, ne vomitum moveant sed constringant
potius. sic enim sui quantitate famem leniunt[6] atque virtute
propria digestionem[7] non gravando perficiunt. bibere autem
[non][8] prius quam solidus sumitur cibus his qui fame urgentur
utilissimum iudicamus, siquidem potu impleti minus solidos ap-
petunt cibos. phagedaenicis vero hoc convenire negamus, hu-
mectatus etenim stomachus in vomitum facile provocatur, et li-
quefactus atque supernatans cibus facilius nauseam provocat
aegrotanti.

48   erit igitur sensim vomitus differendus atque eius consuetudo
mutanda, ut interpositis diebus parum demus aliquando cibum
et appositione cucurbitarum eius adiuvemus descensum, qui solitis suis locis insertus teneatur. alia vero vomitum permitta-
mus, ac deinde paucis interpositis diebus prohibeamus vel iterum
adhibeamus, sed in adiutorii vicem, hoc est ex radicibus, tum
etiam ex helleboro, quo regulae curationis adiutoria localia concurrant recorporativa virtute medentia, et partes ad fortitudinem naturalem ducant. quorum usum[9] ex supradictis atque in
aliis passionibus ordinatis accipiendum ducimus.

49 ## IV. DE IECOROSIS, QUOS GRAECI EPATICOS VOCANT, ET LIENOSIS, QUOS SPLENICOS DICUNT

Utraque passio a locis patientibus nomen accepit siquidem
sit in iecore vel in liene constituta, tumore scilicet effecta
sive collectione vel duritia atque saxitate,[1] quam scirrhosin vocant. sed de tumoribus libris Febrium docuimus; de collectioni-

[6] leniunt *Almeloveen*: sentiunt *S*: satiant *Rm*

[7] virtutem propria digestione *S*: *corr. R*

[8] *om. A*

[9] usu *S*: *corr. Rm*

[1] *sed* saxietate *ap. Cass. Fel. vid. ind., p. 252 Rose*

---

2. Possibly 'at intervals of several days,' or 'on alternate days.'

For when the time required for digestion has elapsed, what has been taken in is quickly distributed and fills the channels (Greek
47 *poroe*); thus the appetite is dulled. In addition, be careful, when feeding the patient, to give him food which has little nutritive quality but can to a considerable degree overcome the appetite, e.g., vegetables. But do not give him vegetables with laxative properties, for they might provoke vomiting; rather give him those with binding properties. For this food will by its bulk relieve the patient's hunger, and by reason of its specific qualities will bring about complete digestion without any feeling of heaviness. [In general] we consider it very advantageous for patients troubled by hunger to drink before they take solid food, for when they are filled with drink their desire for solid food is lessened. But in cases of morbid hunger (*phagedaena*) we hold that such a procedure is not suitable. For in these cases, when fluids enter the esophagus, the patient is prone to vomit; and the food, as it floats about, dissolves and is apt to cause nausea.

48 Now it will be necessary gradually to overcome the patient's tendency to vomit. This habit may be altered in the following way. For a period of several days² give the patient a little food from time to time, applying medical cups to help the food down until it reaches its proper place and is firmly held there. The next day let the patient vomit, and then for the ensuing period of a few days have him avoid vomiting as before. Then let him vomit again, but only as part of the treatment, employing radishes and then hellebore, too, for this purpose. Thus the local remedies, which by reason of their metasyncritic properties have a beneficial effect, will fit in with the basic system of treatment and will help restore the parts to their normal strength. The proper use of these local remedies may be gathered, we believe, from what has been said above and from the prescriptions given in dealing with other diseases.

49 ## IV. DISEASE OF THE LIVER (GREEK *HĒPAR*) AND OF THE SPLEEN (GREEK *SPLĒN*)

EACH of these diseases takes its name from the part affected, for it occurs in the liver or the spleen and manifests itself in inflammation, abscess, or hardness and stoniness (Greek *scirrhōsis*). Now we have already discussed inflammations in the

bus vero sive vomicis specialiter docemus.[2]   de duritia vero aut
saxitate quae cedente tumore efficiuntur nunc prosequemur.

sequentur enim quaedam communia iecorosis atque lienosis,
50 quaedam specialiter propria. sed communia: gravedo, spirationis difficultas, et magis in itinere[2a] ambulationibus clivosis,
tum piger motus atque anhelatio et sitis et oris siccitas, coloris
mutatio, pedum inflatio, aliquando etiam febricula latens et hy-
dropismi suffusio cum continua cibi corruptione.

propria autem vel specialia iecorosos haec sequentur: extans
durities sive scirrhosis in dextra parte praecordiorum, schemate
rotundo, costis ex aliqua parte subiecta et propterea veluti decisa, ex alia vero parte circumscripta atque rotunditate terminata; color saepissime aeruginosus sive arquati similis, quem
Graeci icteron appellant, urina turbata velut sandarachae colore,
51 et accessionis tempore dolor tendens usque ad dexterum iugulum
atque palam; et difficilis supra latus sinistrum iacendi copia, siquidem adducantur dexterae partes suo pondere pendentes et
propterea gravedine atque doloris punctione aegrotantes afficiant; tum fellosa stercorum egestio.

lienosis vero extans duritia atque saxea sub sinistra parte praecordiorum invenitur, schemate longo porrecta et veluti pectus
invadens, vel umbilici saepissime transgrediens finem atque latitudine superans, nunc minime, nunc vehementer, ut omnia con-
52 nata[3] videantur, et inspicientes eo falluntur ut membranam tumere sive extare putent quam Graeci peritoneon vocant; color
plumbeus, atque accessionis tempore dolor tendens ad iugulum
sinistrum et palam, et difficilis supra dextrum latus iacendi copia. memorant plerique etiam multitudine pediculorum aegrotantes affici et graviore per somnum sudore, attestante veretri
in officio[4] ventris erectione et assidue[5] e naribus sanguinis fluore.
praeterea oris foetor aegrotantes afficit cum gingivarum putre-
factione et defluxione. sectarum principes meminerunt tenuari

[2] docebimus Rm

[2a] et add. R

[3] connata Rm: conata S: an counata?

[4] officiū S: corr. R

[5] assiduo R

---

1. *Chr.* v. 91 ff.

2. I.e., beginning on the left side, it sometimes reaches to the right of the umbilicus.

treatise *On Fevers;* and we shall discuss gatherings or abscesses in a special chapter.[1] We shall now, however, speak of the hardness or stoniness which results from an inflammation.

In this disease some of the signs are the same whether the organ involved is the liver or the spleen; but there are, in addition, special signs characteristic of one or the other form of the disease. The signs common to both forms are a feeling of heaviness, difficulty in breathing, especially when walking uphill, sluggishness, panting, thirst, dryness in the mouth, abnormal complexion, swollen feet, sometimes a hardly perceptible fever, dropsical suffusion, and continual indigestion.

The special signs which characterize disease of the liver are as follows. There is a bulging hardness (*scirrhōsis*), round in form, at the right of the precordial region. Part of it lies under the ribs and thus appears to be cut off; the rest of it is definitely circumscribed and rounded off. The patient's complexion is frequently rust-colored or like that found in jaundice (Greek *icteros*). The urine is murky and in color somewhat like sandarach. At the time of an attack the pain extends as far as the right collarbone and shoulder blade. The patient finds it hard to lie upon his left side, for the parts on the right are drawn down by their own weight and consequently produce a feeling of heaviness, as well as a stabbing pain. And the feces discharged are yellowish.

On the other hand, in disease of the spleen the stony hardness occurs at the left of the precordial region and is of elongated shape; it just about reaches the chest and generally passes [downward] beyond the level of the umbilicus. Again, it sometimes passes a little beyond [the umbilicus] latitudinally;[2] and sometimes it goes considerably beyond, so that the whole region seems one solid mass, and persons examining the patient make the mistake of believing that the membrane which the Greeks call *peritonaeon* is swollen or distended. The complexion is leaden, and at the time of an attack the pain extends as far as the left collarbone and shoulder blade. The patient finds it hard to lie upon his right side. Many writers also report patients infested with lice, and experiencing copious sweating during sleep, erection of the penis during the evacuation of the bowels, and continual bleeding from the nose. Moreover, there is a foul smell from the mouth and, in addition, decomposition and dissolution of the gums. The leaders of the sects also say that the skin over

etiam cutem ventris et venas nigras apparere atque crassiores et
in cruribus ulcera difficile in cicatricem vel indecenter venientia.

53   in his igitur communiter oportet superpositionum tempore,
tamquam in tumore curando, calidum iacentibus providere locum. tum fomentis et cataplasmatibus et cibis laxativis uti tempore quo saepissime docuimus, sed tenuibus ac sorbilibus. tunc
cucurbitae atque scarificationes et sanguisugarum convenit appositio, quas hirudines appellant, et vaporationes. ac si vehemens fuerit, adhibenda phlebotomia his omnibus anteposita;
tunc clyster, si venter officium non agnoverit, sed ex decoctione
fici singularis **[6] impressi patientibus locis. flectetur enim et
exercitio quodam durities resolvetur.

54   conveniunt etiam frequentes cyclorum mutationes. denique
inter paucos dies adhibenda drimyphagia, tum radicum vomitus
cum aceto squilletico, vel certe helleboro erunt disiciendi.[7] tum
alia mutatione resumendi aegrotantes, adhibito usu aquarum
naturalium atque natatione maritima et vaporatione locorum
natura spirantium, quo[8] etiam sudores moveantur, non ob virium fatigationem, sed quo possit calida spiratione ac naturali
corporatio[9] fieri patientium partium. convenit praeterea etiam
in littore sicco ex harena sole ignita paroptesis; tunc malagmata

55 quae corpus valeant papulare, et primo leviora, ut est polyarchion[10] et Caphisophontos[11] et salibus[12] confectum, quod diahalon[13] appellant, item ex tribus resinis, quod diaretinon[14] vocant, tum etiam ut est quod appellant diamyrepsices balanu,[15]
item diaoriganu[16] et diacardamu vel diatapsias et diasbestu,[17]
quorum omnium compositiones Responsionum libris explicavimus. sed his quae sunt vehementia, ut est diatapsias, ita erit
utendum tamquam sinapismo uti solemus. haec est secundum
nos curatio eorum qui duritiam sive scirrhosin in iecore vel in
liene habuerint.

[6] *lacunam statui*   [7] *fort.* dissecandi   [8] qua *Rm*

[9] recorporatio *Rm, sed cf. Ac. iii. 134, Chr. i. 183*

[10] polyarthion *S: corr. Rm*

[11] ex caphiso fonte *S: corr. Schmid RPh 133, coll. Chr. ii. 34, nisi scrib. -is*

[12] ⟨ex⟩ salibus *Schmid RPh 133*

[13] diahalos *S*

[14] diaretismum *S*

[15] diamyrepsicen balanum *S*

[16] *fort.* dioriganu(m)

[17] diaoriganum, et diacardamum, vel diatapsias, et diasbestum *S*

the abdomen is stretched thin, that thick dark veins appear, and that sores form on the legs and produce ugly scars, if they cicatrize at all.

Now in all these cases at the time of the attacks give the patient a warm room to lie in, as in treating any case involving inflammation. Then apply fomentations and poultices and at the proper time, as we have often indicated, give the patient laxative food, but see that it is thin and gruel-like. Then employ cupping in conjunction with scarification, and leeches (*sanguisugae*, 'bloodsuckers,' also called *hirudines*). And apply vapor heat. If the disease is severe, perform venesection before applying any of the other remedies; and if the bowels do not function, prescribe a clyster, using a decoction of plain fig[3] . . . and apply to the affected parts with pressure, for the hardness will be relieved and overcome by such movement.

Frequent changes in the series of treatments are also beneficial. Thus employ the acrid diet for an interval of a few days; then provoke vomiting by the use of radishes and vinegar of squills, or apply the more drastic treatment with hellebore. Then make another change and apply restorative measures, having the patient use natural springs and also swim in the sea. And let him make use of the vapors from places having natural emanations. These warm, natural emanations will induce sweating and will have the effect, not of fatiguing the patient, but of promoting the metasyncrisis of the affected parts. The application of intense heat will also be beneficial; this treatment may be given on a dry shore with sand heated by the sun. Also apply emollient plasters that will cause the body to blister. First employ the milder kinds, e.g., the plaster of Polyarchus or of Cephisophon, the plaster of salts (Greek *diahalōn*), that which uses three resins (Greek *diarētinōn*), and that made from the fruit of the bito tree (Greek *balanos myrepsicē*); then also use plasters made, respectively, with marjoram, nosesmart, thapsia, and quicklime. We have set forth the composition of all these drugs in the treatise entitled *Answers*. The plasters of strong action, such as that made with thapsia, are to be used in the same way as mustard plasters are customarily employed. This concludes the Methodists' account of the treatment of hardness or scirrhosis of the liver or the spleen.

3. Or, as frequently, 'fig, either plain [or with the admixture of]. . . .'

56   apud veteres autem medicos plura, atque[18] dissonans et turbulenta curationis ordinatio invenitur. alii enim phlebotomiam
recusarunt in lienicis, ut Apollonius Citiensis, alii probaverunt.
atque horum alii ex dextro brachio iecorosos et ex sinistro lienosos phlebotomandos dicunt, alii ex talo eius partis quae patitur,
alii ex medio digitorum, omnifariam variis extimationibus[19] tentati. sumunt enim atque deposcunt[20] ex his partibus quae facile dividi possint phlebotomiam faciendam, hoc est brachiorum
venis, nisi forte ipsae tumuerint, et ob hoc oporteat longe a patientibus partibus phlebotomiam adhibere, quo[21] iniuria lateat
adiutorii.

57   item alii de ustionibus adhibendis certaverunt. et quidam
solis aiunt lienosis convenire, quidam autem iecorosis[22] ex medicaminibus scaroticis adhibitis sive cauteribus. et horum alii
urenda, alii superurenda[23] probaverunt, atque altius in lienicis
cauteres infigendos: quorum quidam simplices, quidam trisulcos,
quidam serratos approbant figendos.[24] tum ustionis ulcera hu-
mectantes atque in fluorem[25] humoris longo tempore provo-
cantes, scirrhosin defluxionibus auferendam crediderunt, ex quibus tumores atque indignationes et consensus cum vehementibus febribus necessario sequentur, siquidem peritoneos mem-
58 brana, quae est natura nervosa, ignis ustione vexetur. fiet etiam
secundo impossibile plurimis atque vehementibus adiutoriis uti
medicantem, ut sinapismo, cucurbitis rapidis[26] forti raptu remotis,[27] fricationibus, dropace, et his similibus, cum cicatrices caecitate viae et hebetudine torpentes, tamquam mortuae vim nullam
medicaminum accipiunt.[28]

[18] plura, atque] *fort.* plerumque

[19] *fort.* existimationibus (*Almeloveen*) *vel* aestimationibus

[20] sumit enim atque deposcit S: *corr.* R, *nisi nomen proprium excidit*

[21] quo R: quod S: *cf. 25*

[22] iecorosis R: iecorosos S, *Friedel 33*   [23] perurenda R

[24] figendos Rm: frigidos S: rigidos Rm: *de cautere frigido (medicamento caustico: cf. Theo. Prisc., p. 63. 14 Rose) agi vix probabile videtur*

[25] fluore S: *corr.* R   [26] rapidis ⟨hoc est⟩ *Almeloveen*

[27] raptu remotis *scripsi, coll. Chr. i. 36*: raptura motis *edd.*

[28] accipiant R

4. Perhaps 'between the fingers.' In any case, the hand corresponding to the affected side is referred to. Cf. Galen XIX. 521 K.

6   In the writings of the physicians of old there is a great deal on the treatment of this disease, but the prescriptions are conflicting and confused. Thus some physicians, among them Apollonius of Citium, reject venesection in cases of disease of the spleen; others approve of it. And of those who approve, some say venesection should be performed on the right arm in disease of the liver and on the left arm in disease of the spleen; others perform the operation on the ankle, left or right corresponding to the side affected; and still others on the middle finger.[4] Thus they are beset by viewpoints that are entirely conflicting. And, in fact, they begin by requiring that venesection be performed on parts that can easily be cut open, e.g., the veins of the arms; but they make an exception of the case where these veins are swollen, and hold that it is then necessary to perform venesection far from the affected parts, so that the wound involved in the operation may have no ill effect.

7   Again, there is disagreement on administering treatments that involve burning. Some say that these treatments are suitable only in disease of the spleen; others that they are suitable also in disease of the liver, and they employ caustic drugs and cauteries for the purpose. And of this group some prescribe superficial application, others deep burning; and the latter would apply the cautery more deeply in cases of disease of the spleen. Again, some apply the simple cautery, others the three-pronged, and still others the serrated type.[5] And these physicians keep the wounds caused by cauterization moist; they induce prolonged draining of fluid matter from them, and hold that the induration will be removed by these discharges. But inflammation, unsightly sores, and sympathetic affections with severe fever are the inevitable result of such measures, for the peritoneal membrane, which is naturally fibrous, is injured by the process of cauterization.

8   Moreover, this treatment makes it impossible for the physician to use a number of strong remedies, e.g., mustard plasters, drastic cupping, i.e., that in which the cup is removed with a strong pull, vigorous massage, pitch plasters, and the like. For the scars caused by the cauterization are impervious and devoid of sensation and, like dead tissue, are unable to absorb any of the healing powers of these remedies.

5. The text and meaning are uncertain.

diviserunt praeterea plerique etiam curationis officium, et alia
iecorosis, alia lienosis convenire probarunt. hinc denique ⟨quae-
dam hepatica⟩²⁹ quaedam³⁰ lienica³¹ vocaverunt. iecori etenim
cataplasmata aiunt adhibenda ex abrotano et sesamo; item bibenda medicamina, ut theriacam quam diascordion³² voca-
59 verunt, dieupatoriu³³ vel zopyrion;³⁴ item anodyna, quae nos indoloria dicere poterimus, ut ea quae scribunt diadion pipereon
et lexipyreton et chamaepityn, vel viridis pini decoctionem sin-
gulatim³⁵ vel cum melle; item urinalia medicamina, quae diuretica vocant, ut est mulsum cum dauci decoctione vel feniculi ra-
dicis³⁶ aut petroselini aut absinthii aut mali cydonii cum oenanthe. utuntur etiam oleribus, ut lactucae coctae vel incoctae,³⁷
asparago, radicibus olusatri, ventrem quoque deducentes antidoto quod hieran vocaverunt.

in lienicis vero epithema aiunt specialiter convenire ex cappare et myrobalano et aceto sale admixto, quod oxyalmen³⁸ vo-
60 caverunt, et herba cui nomen asplenos. dant etiam bibendam
aquam. dicunt³⁹ specialiter lienem deducere vel defluxionem⁴⁰
purgare, †ex quibus est ad nutriendum noxiae cuticulae†⁴¹ et
aquam⁴² ex lacu in quo saepissime candens ferrum fabricatores tin-
gunt, de qua iubent dari cyathos tres cum aceti cyatho uno; item
polion herbam aut hormini⁴³ semen in cotylae quantitatem, aut
capparis radicem cum squillae drachma dimidia, aut chamae-
dryos vel herpylli acetabulum ex aceto mulso cyathis tribus, vel
hipposelini semen cotylas duas cum vini cyathis tribus, aut
libanotida herbam, quam nos rosmarinum vocamus, cum feni-
61 culi semine in cotylae quantitate⁴⁴ ex vino mixto; item ammoniaci guttae drachmam unam cum mulso ex aceto confecto cyathis tribus [vel tamarisci ligno].⁴⁶ item cibum vel potum sumere
iubent aegrotantes in vasculis⁴⁷ tamarisci ligno confectis.

²⁹ *supplevi* (*fort. suppl.* ⟨quaedam iecoralia⟩) ³⁰ quasdam *S: corr. Rm*
³¹ lienicas *S: corr. R*
³² diascordion *scripsi* (*cf. Chr. v. 41*): dioscoridian *S:* diascorodon *Rm*
³³ diapatorion *S:* dieupatorion *Rm*   ³⁷ lactuca cocta vel incocta *R*
³⁴ Zopyrion *Rm:* diapyrion *S*   ³⁸ oxyalmon *S: fort.* oxalmen
³⁵ *fort.* singularem   ³⁹ bibendam aquam ⟨quas⟩ dicunt *Rm*
³⁶ radicis *scripsi*: radices *S:* radice *R*   ⁴⁰ defluxione *R*
⁴¹ ex quibus est et retrimentum Naxiae coticulae *Reinesius 669, coll. Diosc. Mat. med.
v. 149: fort.* scobem detritam (*vel* scobis detrimentum) Naxiae coticulae
⁴² aquae *edd.*   ⁴⁴ quantitatem *R*
⁴³ tormini *S: corr. R*   ⁴⁶ *seclusi*   ⁴⁷ vasculis ⟨ex⟩ *R*

Furthermore, many physicians separate the treatment of the two diseases, holding that some measures are suitable for disease of the liver, and others for disease of the spleen. Thus they call the former 'hepatic' remedies and the latter 'splenic.' Now for disease of the liver they prescribe the application of plasters of southernwood and sesame, as well as the drinking of such drugs as the antidote made from germander,[6] that made from agri-
59 mony, and that of Zopyrus. They also prescribe anodynes, which in Latin we may call *indoloria* ('pain-relieving'), such as that known as the anodyne of two peppers as well as the fever-allaying anodyne, and ground pine, i.e., a decoction of the green pine, either alone or with honey. They also use for disease of the liver preparations that promote urination (Greek *diurētica*), e.g., mead with a decoction of Cretan carrot, fennel root, parsley, wormwood, or quince and oenanthe; and, in addition, they prescribe such vegetables as lettuce, cooked or raw, asparagus, and alexanders roots. They purge the bowels with one of the antidotes called *hiera*.

But in cases of disease of the spleen they consider especially beneficial an external application of capers and ben nut in the mixture of vinegar and salt (Greek *oxyalmē*); they also use the
60 plant called *asplenos* ['miltwaste'] in these applications. And they prescribe the drinking of water. They hold that the spleen is specifically reduced and the discharge[7] cleared up by . . .[8] and by water from a tub in which smiths have often dipped their glowing hot irons; three cyathi of this water with one cyathus of vinegar is the dose they order. Again, they give the patient a cotyle[9] of hulwort, clary seed, or caper root with half a drachm of squill; or an acetabulum[10] of germander or thyme in three cyathi of oxymel; or two cotylae of alexanders seed with three cyathi of wine; or a cotyle of fennel seed and libanotis (Latin *rosmari-*
61 *num*, 'rosemary') mixed with wine; or a drachm of gum ammoniac with three cyathi of oxymel. They also order the patient to take his food and drink in dishes made of tamarisk wood.

6. Perhaps 'from garlic.' The text is uncertain.

7. The reference may be to a discharge such as that mentioned above (52), but the text is doubtful.

8. The text is corrupt. There may have been a reference to iron filings from a Naxian whetstone, or possibly to Cutilian waters.

9. I.e., 6 cyathi, or about half a pint.

10. About one-eighth of a pint.

quidam etiam decidendum vel auferendum lienem ordinare ausi sunt, quod quidem voce dictum, non officio completum accipimus. sequentibus autem atque diversis sese implicantibus potionibus medicaminum variorum stomachum vexant, vesicam commovent, atque totum corpus communiter in cachexiam mittunt, nescii quod quaedam ob acrimoniam propriae virtutis laceratione quadam communi potentia medeantur, et non[48] per

62 quasdam inerrabiles[49] proprietates; et neque alia iecoris alia lienis[50] esse medicamina recte senserint, omnia etenim omnium corporis partium sunt communia, quando simili fuerint affectae passione. regulantur enim sive diriguntur eorum virtutes non natura patientis loci, ⟨sed⟩[51] genere passionis, extentae atque indultae[52] pro modo morborum.

hoc est peccantium iudicium sed eorum causa qui rerum magis historias amant. cetera quoque a quibusdam probata brevi atque concinna oratione subiciam.

Diocles igitur libro quo De passionibus atque causis et curationibus scripsit phlebotomat iecorosos ex[53] dextero brachio,

63 tunc ventrem resolvit helleboro nigro atque papaveris suco. dat etiam cum mulso rosmarinum, quem Graeci libanotida vocant, et murram et pini folia; adhibenda quoque cataplasmata ex phoenicobalanis cum vino atque lini semine et sesamo et pollinibus, quos omelysin[54] appellant. dat praeterea aquam bibendam in qua sit cantabrum praelotum et ptisana[55] ex tritico, quae omnia sunt inflantia atque stomachi vexativa et digestione difficilia. lienosos vero, quorum gingivae sudaverint sanguinem, phlebotomat. et similiter vexat medicaminibus felliducis, quae cholagoga vocant, atque urinalibus, quae diuretica appellant.

64 Item Praxagoras primo libro Curationum iecorosis adhibet vomitum et ventriflua medicamina et sudorem moventia et uri-

---

[48] non *Rm*: nos *S*

[49] inenarrabiles *Rm*

[50] lienis *Rm*: venis *S*

[51] *add. R*

[52] extenta atque indulta *S*: *corr. R*

[53] ex *Rm*: et *S*

[54] quos omelysin *conieci*: quos omphacomeli *S*: ⟨et eo⟩ quod omphacomeli *Rm*, *Wellmann*: *cf. etiam 22*

[55] ptisanam *Am*

Some have even gone so far as to prescribe the excision and removal of the spleen; but we take it that this was mere talk and never actually practiced. In any case, with their succession of potions compounded from various drugs and mingled all together, these physicians irritate the patient's gullet, disturb his bladder, and bring his whole body into a general state of malaise. They are unaware that these drugs have general healing powers that they exert through a sort of rending action made possible by their characteristic sharpness, and not by virtue of any unerring powers.[11] Again, they are mistaken in holding that some drugs are suitable for the liver and others for the spleen; indeed, every drug taken has a general effect throughout all the parts of the body, since these parts are affected by the same disease. For the action of drugs should be controlled and directed not by the nature of the affected part but by the nature of the disease, and these remedies should be strengthened or weakened in keeping with the extent of the ailment.[12]

62

So much for the views of physicians whom we hold to be mistaken, though [this discussion is] only for the sake of students of the history of the subject. I shall next take up briefly in order the other treatments prescribed by various physicians.

Diocles in his book *On Diseases and Their Causes and Treatment* prescribes venesection on the right arm in cases of disease of the liver; he then purges the stomach with black hellebore and poppy juice. He also gives the patient rosemary (Greek *libanōtis*), myrrh, and pine foliage, with mead. Further, he prescribes the application of plasters made of dates, wine, flaxseed, sesame, and flour (Greek *ōmēlysis*). And he has the patient drink water in which bran has been soaked, or a mixture[13] of pearl barley and wheat, all of which cause flatulence, irritate the gullet, and are hard to digest. In disease of the spleen, if the gums bleed, Diocles performs venesection and again causes the patient distress by using drugs that carry off bile (Greek *cholagōga*) and those that promote urination (Greek *diurētica*).

63

64

Praxagoras in Book I of his *Treatments* prescribes emetic, purgative, sudorific, and diuretic drugs, as well as venesection and

---

11. The point seems to be that these drugs are not foolproof and will do harm if misused as they are by these physicians. An alternative reading, *inenarrabiles*, would mean: 'their healing properties are not due to any mysterious powers '

12. Cf. 66.   13. Perhaps simply 'or a gruel made from wheat.'

nalia et phlebotomiam atque fricationem. utitur etiam vino
non aquato et ustione cauterum[56] et his similibus. lienicos vero
phlebotomat et cataplasmatibus curat, utens digestibilibus cibis, et vino potat redolenti et aceto, adhibita fricatione atque
unctione et lavacro. dat praeterea bibendam mulsam aceto admixto ⟨cum⟩[57] daucio[58] aut hyssopo vel thymo aut capparis radice vel foliis aut semine aut aetheriae[59] herbae semine, quam
eryngion appellant, aut chamelaeae vel chamaepitys aut absinthii aut marrubii, adhibens etiam vomitum.

65   Erasistratus autem in iecorosis praecidens superpositas iecori[60]
cutes atque membranam, utitur medicaminibus quae ipsum
iecur late amplecantur. tunc ventrem deducit audaciter partem
patientem nudans.

Item aliqui Asclepiadis sectatores gestationes et lavacra et
vaporationes cataplasmatum atque malagmatum excluserunt in
iecorosis, suspicantes tenuissimorum corpusculorum fore consensum, hoc est spiritus, quem leptomerian eorum princeps appellavit, atque in egestorum constrictione falsitate causarum adiutoria magna recusantes.

Themison vero secundo libro Tardarum passionum plurima in
his methodico rigore ordinavit, sed proterva atque caduca in-
66 tentione. etiam[61] ex talo eiusdem partis phlebotomari iubet
aegrotantes, atque alternis vel interpositis duobus diebus sanguinis interea[62] fieri detractionem. vulnerandam quoque iecoris
partem ex superficie medicamine vel cauteribus existimat. et
concedit[63] esse quaedam propria lienis adiutoria ob eius firmitatem, hoc est quae fuerint vehementia, ut cataplasmata vel ustiones: eo concedens ut etiam ipsum quoque lienem igneo cautere transpungendum probet tribus vel quatuor locis, non ad-

[56] cauterium S: corr. R, nisi fort. cauteriorum
[57] ⟨cum⟩ R: fort. mulsam ⟨ex⟩ aceto, admixto daucio, etc.
[58] dauco R
[59] atheriae (vel athereidos) Kühn 145, coll. Nic. Ther. 849
[60] iecoris S: corr. R   [62] iteratam Rm: fort. iterum
[61] etenim Rm   [63] contendit Schmid RPh 135

massage, in cases of disease of the liver. He also employs wine unmixed with water, cauterization, and the like. Again, in disease of the spleen he performs venesection and employs poultices; he gives the patient digestible food, has him drink aromatic wine and vinegar, and prescribes massage, anointing, and bathing. He also has him drink a mixture of honey water and vinegar with Cretan carrot, hyssop, thyme, caper root, tops, or seed, the seed of the plant aetheria[14] (Greek *ērryngion*), chamelaea, ground pine, wormwood, or horehound. Praxagoras also induces vomiting in these cases.

65   Erasistratus in cases of disease of the liver cuts into the skin and membrane over the liver and applies drugs to surround that organ completely; then, while boldly laying bare the affected part, he purges the bowels.

   Some followers of Asclepiades bar the use of passive exercise, bathing, and the application of warmth through poultices and emollient plasters in disease of the liver; for they fear that there will arise a sympathetic affection of the very thin corpuscles forming the pneuma, which the leader of their sect calls *leptomereia* ['that which consists of fine particles']. Thus, though the case involves congestion of matter that should be eliminated, these physicians, through their mistaken notion of causes, refuse to employ salutary remedies.

   In Book II of his *Chronic Diseases* Themison, to be sure, gives a large number of prescriptions for these diseases strictly in accordance with Methodist principles; but he betrays undisci-
66 plined and futile ideas in prescribing that venesection be performed on the ankle corresponding to the side affected,[15] and in having the withdrawals of blood made, for a time, on alternate days or after intervals of two full days. He also holds that wounds should be inflicted on the surface of the liver with drugs or cauteries. And he agrees that, because of the sturdiness[16] of the spleen, certain strong measures, such as strong plasters or cauterization, are especially appropriate for that organ. In fact, he goes so far as to prescribe puncturing the spleen itself in three or four places with a red-hot cautery, unaware that the use of

14. This name occurs nowhere else, so far as I know, and may be the result of textual corruption.

15. I.e., the right ankle if the liver is affected, the left if the spleen.

16. Or, in view of the sequel, 'its insensitivity to pain' (*Rm*).

vertens quia pro magnitudine passionis ac virium corporis extenduntur atque indulgentur adiutoria, et non pro specie patientis partis, siquidem quaedam quae natura difficilem habuerint sensum, et propterea non facile tactum accipiant, morbo
tentata sensibiliora ceteris fiant, ut est plantae cavum, quod
67 tumore dolidum atque omnino sensibile et attentum fiet. atque
rursum ea quae natura facile sentiunt difficilioris sensus passionis
efficiuntur causa. quo fiet ut sit iuxta regulam methodicam ex-
plosum, ut qui intentione coenotetarum ducitur ⟨partes⟩⁶⁴ cor-
poris⁶⁵ facilene aut difficile sentiant curet,⁶⁶ sicut latius De coenotetis scribentes docebimus.

　　Thessalus vero secundo Regulari libro omni ex parte immuta-
tam atque eandem iecorosis et lienosis formam tradidit curationis.

　　sed quia plurimae atque variae his visceribus irruunt speciales passiones, ut arquatus sive aurigo, quam Graeci icteron
vocant, et cachexia vel atrophia atque hydrops, de his nunc ordinare curabimus.

68　V. DE AURIGINE SIVE ARQUATO MORBO, QUEM
　　　VULGO MORBUM REGIUM VOCANT, GRAECI
　　　　　　ICTERON APPELLANT

Passio vocabulum sumpsit secundum Graecos ab animalis
　　nomine quod sit coloris fellei. fit autem ex antecedenti iugi
indigestione vel medicaminibus ventrifluis potu datis atque per-
manentibus et minime exclusis.

　　sequitur in passione constitutos¹ mutatio coloris in fellis qualitatem, quae primo appareat ac magis videatur in albidis partibus oculorum atque plantarum cavis² vel venis quae sub lingua
sunt, ventris quoque abstinentia vel egestio albida atque argil-
69 losa, urina etiam crassior et crocea, oris amaror,³ sitis, cibi fas-

⁶⁴ *addidi*

⁶⁵ corpora *Rm*

⁶⁶ curent *S: corr. R*

¹ constitutis *S: corr. R*

² cavis *Schmid RPh 136*: talis *edd.*　　　³ amarior *S: corr. R*

---

　　17. Or the point may be that Thessalus' treatments are identical with those of
Themison.

strong or mild remedies should depend on the severity of the disease and the strength of the patient, not on the nature of the affected part. For a part of the body that normally is almost entirely without feeling, that is to say, is hardly sensitive to touch, if attacked by disease becomes more sensitive than the other parts. An example would be the curved part of the sole of the foot, which when inflamed becomes painful and exceedingly ten-
7 der and sensitive. On the other hand, parts normally quite sensitive may by reason of disease lose that sensitivity. And so, in accordance with Methodist principles, we must reject the notion that the physician who is concerned with general types [*coenotētae*, 'communities'] must be guided by whether a part of the body is normally sensitive or insensitive. We shall demonstrate this point more fully in the work *On the General Types of Disease.*

Finally, Thessalus in Book II of his work *On Regimen* sets forth treatments which are in all respects identical for the disease of the liver and the disease of the spleen.[17]

But, since there are many other diseases of various kinds which attack these organs in particular, e.g., the yellow disease or jaundice (Greek *icteros*), cachexia, atrophy, and dropsy, we shall now give an account of them.

8   V. JAUNDICE OR THE RAINBOW–COLORED
DISEASE, COMMONLY CALLED IN LATIN
MORBUS REGIUS [THE 'ROYAL DISEASE']
AND IN GREEK *ICTEROS*

Aaccording to the Greeks, the disease of jaundice gets its name [*icteros*] from an animal of yellowish color.[1] The disease occurs after prolonged indigestion or after the drinking of purgative drugs that remain within the body without being driven off.

Symptomatic of jaundice is the change to a yellowish color, which first appears and is particularly noticeable in the whites of the eyes, the hollows of the soles, and the veins under the tongue. Moreover, the bowels fail to move, or whitish and clayey
9 stools occur; and the urine is thick and saffron-colored. There is

1. Perhaps *ictis*, a kind of marten (so Aretaeus *SD* i. 15). Another tradition connects the name with a bird *ictinus* ('kite,' Suidas) or *icterus* ('yellow oriole,' Pliny).

tidium, gravedo et piger atque segnis motus in solitos usus,[3a] animi difficultas, pruritus et ariditas corporis, et veluti ex ustione solis aspera cutis superficies, saepe etiam iecoris tumentis inflatio sive saxea durities, difficile autem ac rarissime splenis vel stomachi consensus etiam.

ex his enim plerisque visum est[4] istam fieri passionem, quae sit quidem facile sanabilis, ceterum[5] neque ita felleum faciat corpus. fit praeterea nunc cum febribus, nunc sine febribus; et nunc celeriter circumscripta, nunc corporibus intardans et propterea chronia appellata.

70 convenit igitur cum primum corpus invaserit, sive tardaverit et in superpositionem veniens fuerit apprehensa, eam adhibere curationem quam de tumoribus in [corporibus in] corpore[6] constitutis saepe memoravimus. denique si vehemens fuerit, etiam phlebotomiae usus non reprobatur.

in lenimento vero corporis exercitio atque cibis digestibilibus resumendos ducimus aegrotantes. tum ad recorporativam venimus curationem, providentes ut adiutoriis localibus si qua durities in visceribus fuerit, hoc est in iecore vel stomacho aut liene, sicut superius docuimus, destruatur. sic enim cum passionis genus fuerit amputatum, etiam color naturalis corpori reddetur.

71 conicienda sunt eius praeterea accidentia, quae Graeci symptomata vocant, cum generali congrua curatione, id est ut fel diffusum recorporatione adhibita detergentes varie deducamus, nunc clysteribus acerrimis, nunc absinthio poto dato vel intybi agrestis suco uno vel duobus cyathis singularibus. ac si declinationis tempus permiserit, etiam cum vino aliquando ipsa quoque intyba comedenda probamus cocta vel incocta, item asparagum vel daucum aut feniculum. et ob plurimam oculorum infectionem erit sternutatio commovenda, medicaminibus scilicet quae Graeci ptarmica vocaverunt.

72 item naribus infundendum priusquam in lavacrum veniant aegrotantes, ut quidam probant, struthium cum lacte, et ad speciem referentes, asinino vel humano; similiter etiam elaterium

---

[3a] motus in solitos usus *scripsi* (*cf. Chr. i. 66*): visus, insolitus motus *edd.*

[4] est *Rm*: et *S*

[5] *fort. leg.* cum *vel* quoties

[6] in corporibus in torpore *S*: in corporibus *R* (*om.* in torpore)

also a bitter taste in the mouth, thirst, loss of appetite, a feeling of heaviness, sluggishness and listlessness in customary activities, mental distress, and itching and dryness of the body, the surface of the skin becoming rough as from sunburn. Often the liver is swollen and puffed up or of a stonelike hardness; but the spleen and esophagus are rarely affected sympathetically, and, if so, only slightly.

Such are the signs which generally are observed in this disease. Now jaundice is easily cured and, in fact, does not suffuse the body with bile very extensively. Again, it occurs sometimes with fever and sometimes without; and in some cases it terminates swiftly, while in others it persists in the body and is consequently called 'chronic.'

o   When the disease first attacks the body or when an exacerbation is observed in cases of chronic jaundice, the treatment required is that which we have often set forth for bodily inflammations. And if the attack is severe, the use of venesection is not to be rejected.

In the intervals of remission, however, we hold that the patient's strength should be restored with physical exercise and digestible food. Then proceed to the metasyncritic treatment, taking care to overcome by local remedies, as described above, any hardness that may be present in the inner organs, i.e., the liver, esophagus, and spleen. For, once the source of the disease is removed, the patient's normal complexion will be restored.

1   Moreover, watch the concomitant characteristics of the disease (Greek *symptōmata*) while applying the proper general treatment. Thus, employing metasyncritic measures, remove the bile which suffuses the body. Draw it off in various ways, now with sharp clysters, now with a potion of wormwood or one or two cyathi of the unmixed juice of wild endive. And during the decline of the disease, when it is permissible, the endive itself should sometimes be eaten, either raw or cooked, with wine; so also asparagus, Cretan carrot, or fennel. Inasmuch as the eyes are copiously suffused with bile, induce sneezing with the drugs that the Greeks call *ptarmica*.

72   And, in accordance with the prescription of certain physicians, before the patient enters the bath pour into his nostrils soapwort with milk. With regard to the kind of milk, either that of asses or that of humans may be used. In the same way elaterium, as

quod appellant, hoc est cucumeris agrestis sucum,[7] item cycla-
mini cum eodem lacte. fertur enim statim per nares quae vultum tenuerat fellis infectio, et magis si aeger ingrediens calidas
cellas fervens descenderit solium atque requiescens diurno tempore aqua calida fuerit vaporatus, adhibitis aliquando etiam
73 apophlegmatismis quorum materiam saepe memoravimus, item
his quae superficiem corporis lacessendo osculare[8] videntur, quae
appellata sunt anastomotica.[9] et propterea[10] recorporativa in
sudorem provocantia[11] fellis infectionem, hoc est dropax iugiter
adhibitus vel solis fervor torridus, quem Graeci heliosin appellant, item naturalium aquarum exhalatio vel medicaminum sudorem moventium usus. aspergendum denique corpus struthio,
nitro, sulphure, et his aspersionibus quae ob pruritum corporis
adinventae sunt, a Graecis sympasmata appellata. ferventiore
aqua fovendi aegrotantes. sic enim servata regula generali
etiam accidentia passionis curabuntur, non enim haec solis in
acutis erunt passionibus observanda, verum etiam in tardis,
quas Graeci chronias vocant.

74   utendum etiam aeris mutatione et gestatione varia et littoraria moratione, animi quoque laxamento ac iucunditate et aquarum naturalium voluptate, natatione varia et assiduo vomitu
simplici atque radicibus commoto, item drimyphagia, in qua
prae ceteris capparis magis usus approbatur, et acetum squilliticum in quo sit infusa anchusa herba et bulbi et squilla igne torrida, id est subassata, cum melle[11a] electario data.

vinum praeterea tenue probamus. et[12] perseverante passione
helleboro decocto corpus agitandum, vel si oportuerit bibendum
75 damus medicamen ex herbo et cervino cornu, in cotylae quantitatem cum tribus cyathis mulsae in his qui adiuncta febre vexantur, vel conditi in his qui sine febre afficiuntur. sed vitandam
probamus frequentem et variam medicaminum potationem quae
fella deducere promittuntur, sive ventriflua sive urinalia. ete-

---

[7] succus *Rm*

[8] osculare *Rm* (*cf. Chr. ii. 123*): iaculare *S*

[9] anastomatica *S: corr. Rm graece* (*cf. Ac. iii. 40, Chr. iii. 123*)

[10] *fort.* praeterea

[11] provocant *R*

[11a] in *add. R*

[12] sed *Rm*: at *Almeloveen*

it is called, i.e., the juice of wild cucumber, or cyclamen juice
may be used with the same kind of milk. For the yellow bile
which had suffused itself over the face will thus be swiftly carried out through the nose, especially if the patient passes
through the steamrooms before descending into the hot bath,
and then remains in the bath a long while and is thus thoroughly
steamed by the hot water. In some cases drugs may be given to
promote the discharge of phlegm; we have often set forth the
73 substances used for this purpose. Use may also be made of those
drugs, called *anastomōtica*, which, by irritating the surface of the
body, open the pores. So, too, employ metasyncritic measures
that cause the bile suffused through the body to pass into sweat,
e.g., the continual application of pitch plasters, intense baking
in the heat of the sun (Greek *hēliōsis*), vapors from natural
spring waters, and the use of sudorific drugs. Also dust the body
with soapwort, soda, sulphur, and those powders, called *sympasmata* by the Greeks, which have been found to be suitable for an
itching condition. And foment the patient with hot water. Now
if the general therapeutic principles are adhered to in this way,
the concomitant symptoms of the disease will also be cured. And,
indeed, these symptoms must be watched, not merely in acute
diseases, but also in those of long duration (Greek *chroniae*).
74 Prescribe also a change of climate, varied passive exercise,
and sojourning at the seashore. See that the patient is mentally
relaxed and diverted, and have him enjoy the use of natural
springs and do various kinds of swimming.[2] Induce vomiting
regularly, both without emetics and with the help of radishes.
And prescribe an acrid diet in which the use of caper is relatively
extensive; and use vinegar of squills to which have been added
alkanet, bulbs, and squill warmed over a fire, i.e., slightly
roasted. This preparation may be given as an electuary with
honey.

In addition, give the patient a thin wine; and if the disease
persists, let him take cooked hellebore to produce bodily agitation. Or, if necessary, give him a cotyle of a preparation of bitter
75 vetch and stag's horn, mixed, in cases which involve fever, with
three cyathi of hydromel, and, in cases which do not involve
fever, with three cyathi of spiced wine. But avoid having the patient continually drink the various drugs, whether purgatives or

2. E.g., in the sea and at mineral springs.

nim sitis extenditur et solidioris cibi fastidium duplicatur et corporis fortitudo minuitur atque cibi accepti corrumpuntur et omnis corporis materia adulterio medicaminum deterior fit, cum
habitudo, ut supra diximus, omnis fuerit immutata. quod facere
videmus eos qui saepissime ac iugiter herpillum dari probaverunt et absinthium et aloen et diagridium et coloquintida,[13] vel ex

76 aloe et coloquintida hieram confectam, item ex amygdalis et
absinthio et aniso trochiscos confectos, et decoctiones recentis
mulsi ex vino confecti cum hyperico vel aristolochia longa vel
herba adianto, quam Latini capillum Veneris vocant, vel cicere
albo. aliquando etiam haec mandenda probaverunt, item ru-
beam,[14] quam Graeci erythrodanon vocant, vel struthium tritum cum fico arido vel palmulis aut sulphure in ovis sorbilibus in
parvi cochlearis quantitate,[15] aut certe cervini cornu elimatum
pulverem drachmam unam, cum cyatho vini[16] et aquae cyathis duobus, vel nepete[17] quam Graeci calaminten vocant, aut
radicibus pastinacae, quam staphylen[18] appellant, decoctis[19] in
vini heminam et dimidiam[20] donec ad tertiae partis liquor[21] ve-

77 niat quantitatem. ex quo dandum probant cyathum unum cum
aquae cyathis tribus aut quinque cum dauci semine, aut apium
aut zingiber, meum,[22] vel asarum aut radicem herbae brioniae,
item seseli et libani herbae infusionem vel decoctionem; et trochiscos ex herpillo vel feniculo confectos vel ex aristolochia, quos
diherpillu vel diamaratru et diaristolochias[23] appellant. horum
enim varia multitudo vel usus frequens causa saepe ipsius fuit
faciendae passionis. non enim quoniam fellis detractio facta
ilico curationis est causa, nisi totius quoque passionis fuerit de-

78 structio consecuta. sic igitur his utendum erit, ut supra demonstravimus.

item quidam veneris probaverunt adhibendum usum, laxationem carnis faciendam aestimantes, ex quibus est Titus Asclepiadis sectator et Themison. sed est hoc nervositatis vexabile
quippe cum fortitudinem corporis tollat, quae magis est aegrotantibus adquirenda. item alii aurum iugiter aspicere vel intueri aegrotos praeceperunt sive aureos colores. his denique

[13] *fort.* coloquintidam   [14] rubea *S*: rubiam *Rm*   [15] quantitatem *Rm*
[16] cyatho vini *scripsi*: cyatho uno *S*: ⟨vini⟩ cyatho uno *R*
[17] nepetam *Rm*   [19] radices . . . decoctas *R*   [21] liquoris *S*: *corr. R*
[18] staphylinum *Rm*   [20] hemina et dimidia *R*   [22] meu *S*: meon *Rm*
[23] diherpillum vel diamaratrū et diaristolochian *S*

diuretics, that will, it is claimed, draw off bile. For thirst increases, the distaste for solid food is augmented, bodily strength is diminished, the food taken decomposes, the entire substance of the body is corrupted by its mixture with foreign drugs, and the whole bodily condition, as we have already said, changes for the worse. In fact, these are the very conditions that we see brought about by physicians who prescribe frequent and regular doses of thyme, wormwood, aloes, scammony, bitter gourd, a

6 hiera drug compounded of aloes and bitter gourd, troches made of almonds, wormwood, and anise, and decoctions of St. John's wort, the long variety of birthwort, the plant maidenhair (Latin *capillus Veneris*, 'Venus' hair'), or white chickpea, in a mixture of fresh mead and wine. Sometimes these physicians have the patients eat these substances solid. And they also prescribe a small spoonful of madder (Greek *erythrodanon*) or soapwort pounded up with dry figs, dates, or sulphur and given in soft eggs; or else one drachm of powdered shavings of stag's horn with a cyathus of wine and two cyathi of water; or catnip (Greek *calaminthē*); or roots of parsnip (Greek *staphylē*), cooked in a hemina and a half of wine until only one-third of this original

7 amount is left, the dose they prescribe being one cyathus of the decoction mixed with three to five cyathi of water and wild carrot seed.[3] Again, they prescribe parsley, ginger, spicknel, hazelwort, bryony root, hartwort, or a solution or decoction of frankincense; or troches made with thyme, fennel, or birthwort, which preparations they call *dierpyllu, dia marathru,* and *diaristolochias,* respectively. Indeed, the frequent use of so many different drugs is often the cause of the disease itself. For the mere withdrawal of bile will not by itself bring about a cure unless the

8 whole disease has also been overcome; and that is why such drugs should be used only in the way we have indicated above.

Some physicians, e.g., Titus, a follower of Asclepiades, and Themison, recommend venery, for they hold that a relaxing of the flesh is required. But the fact is that venery injures the system of nerves and sinews, for it robs the patient of the very strength which his body requires. Again, some order the patient to fix his eyes constantly upon gold or gold colors, and they recommend the use of gold-colored bedclothes. They believe

3. Or perhaps: 'mixed either with three cyathi of water or with wild carrot seed and five cyathi of water.'

etiam operimentis utendum laudaverunt, siquidem similia ra-
piantur et propterea morbi sive colorum aut fellis migrantia in
alias possint[24] transire materias eorum[25] concordantes colores,[26]
non conicientes quod sit magis credibile externa in aegrotum fa-
79 cilius transire: quippe cum viarum densitate superficie corporis
clausa interiora teneantur, vel certe similitudo magis passionis
possit provocare virtutem, occultae suasionis admonitione asperatam.[27] semper enim memoratione passionum tristes ac maesti
necessario fiunt aegrotantes, quae maxima causa est augendae
passionis. est autem maximum adiutorium et magis utilis aegrotantibus animi purissima laxatio sive serenitas. erit praeterea
perseverante passione etiam longa navigatio curanda et unctio,
adhibito praeceptore, quo assidua defricatione et[28] plenissima
fieri resumptio possit.

80   VI. DE CACHEXIA

CACHEXIA nomen sumpsit a quodam corporis habitu malo:
cacian enim vitium vel vexationem Graeci vocaverunt,
hexin habitudinem. sed principaliter eius curationem ante
Themisonem nullus ordinavit. ipsam namque secundo libro
Tardarum passionum, itemque primo atque quarto Epistolarum memoravit; item Thessalus secundo libro Regulari.

fit autem sive nascitur haec passio intemperantia aegrotantis,
vel curatione mala medicantis, aut post aegritudinem tardae
resumptionis causa, item ex medicaminibus saepissime potatis,
81 vel ex saxea duritie iecoris aut lienis, haemorrhoidis longissimi
temporis, [aut vomitu][1] item ex febribus longo tempore corpore
affecto, aut collectionibus, aut vomitu post vespertinos cibos, et
his similibus. est autem ipsa quoque passio saepissime hydro-
pismi antecedens causa, aut macularum simul[2] in superficie corporis accidentium.

sequitur cachecticos pallor subalbidus, aliquando etiam plumbeus color, debilitate tardus ac piger corporis motus cum inflatione inani, aliquibus etiam ventris fluor cum febricula in plurimis latente, quae circa vesperam magis augeatur, pulsus creber

---

[24] possit *edd.*   [25] earum *edd.* (*fort.* cum auro concordantes colore *vel sim.*)   [26] colori *R*

[27] asperatam *conieci*: superata *S*: superatam *R*: superdata (*vel* suscitata) *Triller
Clinotechnia 133*

[28] et *om. R*   [1] *seclusi*   [2] simul*conieci*: simili *S*: *fort.* ⟨et⟩ similium

that, since like attracts like, particles of the disease or the colors
or the bile may pass from the patient and enter other substances
of corresponding colors.[4] But they do not realize that it is even
more likely that the passage from the external objects to the
patient will prove easier. For, by reason of the clogging of the
pores, what is within is blocked and held fast under the surface
of the body. And, indeed, the correspondence of colors may even
increase the severity of the disease, aggravating it by tacitly
reminding the patient of it. For patients always become downcast and dejected when reminded of their disease; and such a
feeling especially tends to aggravate the ailment. On the other
hand, the most beneficial and effective aid the patient can have
is complete mental relaxation and calm. In addition, if the disease persists, have him take a long sea trip; also prescribe massage under the direction of a trainer, for regular and complete
rubdowns will help bring about a restoration of strength.

VI. CACHEXIA

THE word 'cachexia' is derived from words denoting 'a poor
bodily condition'; for *cacia* is the Greek for 'defect' or 'impairment,' and *hexis* for 'state' or 'condition.' Before Themison,
however, no one discussed the treatment of cachexia as a separate disease. But Themison, in Book II of his *Chronic Diseases*
and in Books I and IV of his *Letters*, and Thessalus, in Book II
of his work *On Regimen*, speak of cachexia.

The disease arises from intemperate living, improper medical
treatment, retarded recovery after an illness, continual taking
of medicinal potions, stonelike hardness of the liver or spleen,
chronic hemorrhoids, long-standing bodily fever, abscesses,
vomiting after the evening meal, and similar causes. Again, this
disease is itself very often a predisposing cause of dropsy or of
the simultaneous appearance of discolorations on the surface of
the body.

The characteristic signs of cachexia are: whitish pallor and in
some cases a leaden complexion, slowness and listlessness of
bodily movement because of weakness, swollen and puffed-up
condition of the body, in some cases loose stomach, in many
cases a low fever, generally increasing toward evening, thick and

4. The translation gives the general thought, but the text is quite uncertain.

ac densus, cibi fastidium, et vini magis appetentia, urina fellea, et extensio[3] venarum.

82   est autem passio saepius stricturae, sicut ex supradictis conicimus, aliquando etiam complexa solutione ob plurimum ventris fluorem vel simili quolibet fluxu. quapropter convenit complexa passione laborantis primo abstinere fluentia et intemperantiam aegrotantis corrigere vel curationes malas aut medicaminum potationes prohibere; in iecore vero aut liene si qua fuerit durities sive saxositas destruere, ut nuper demonstravimus; aut si fluor sanguinis fuerit plurimus abstinere, haemorrhoidas vero auferre, febres quoque solvere, ut De febribus scribentes docuimus; collectiones congrua curatione, sicut de ipsis scribentes

83 monuimus, sanare; et consuetos eis post vespertinum cibum vomitus paulatim detrahere.

ac si horum nihil fuerit accidens et sola in corpore visa fuerit cachexia, erunt eius superpositiones ac lenimenta providenda, et vigilante sine ulla ratione aegroto aut cibum[4] corrumpente, animi attestante difficultate, cum pigro ac segni corporis motu superpositionem cognoscere, et propterea in requie retinere aegro-

84 tum cum abstinentia cibi quo turbatio corporis resolvatur. item ea quae fuerint extenta lanis contegenda atque oleo calido fovenda, ac si venter fuerit fluens, abstinendus. item si plurima fuerit corporis tensio cum gravedine, erit adhibenda phlebotomia ex brachio mediocriter, sed non necessario in his qui haemorrhoidarum causa inanes videntur, †ac deinde retentione facta constricti sed non in omnibus qui communiter tanta ac tali fuerint strictura possessi.† tunc perunctos convenit refici cibo digestibili ac levi usque ad declinationis tempus;[5] servato genere accidentium alia cataplasmatibus alia cucurbitis recurare. cum declinatio apparuerit, plurimus ac varius cibus erit adhibendus, et

85 similibus superpositionem vergentem adiuvare.

atque ita lenimento veniente, quod facile approbamus ex cedentibus[6] asperitatibus passionis supradictis, hoc est his quae

[3] *fort.* extantia

[4] cibo *S*: cibos *Rm*

[5] tempus ⟨et⟩ *R*

[6] ex cedentibus *scripsi*: exercentibus *S*: ex cessantibus *Rm*

1. In 53–55, above.

1a. The meaning of this passage is very doubtful, and the text is probably corrupt.

rapid pulse, loss of appetite for food, increased desire for wine, yellowish urine, and distention of the veins.

2 The disease generally involves a state of stricture, as we may conclude from the symptoms mentioned, but in some cases a sort of looseness is also involved and may be evidenced by copious flux from the bowels and any similar discharge. And so, when the patient is suffering from this type of complication [*status mixtus*], it is first necessary to repress the discharges. One must also correct any immoderate habits of the patient and any improper treatment that he may be receiving, and terminate any habitual taking of drugs. If the liver or spleen is hard or stonelike, reduce this condition in the manner we have recently described;[1] also correct any marked tendency to bleed, remove hemorrhoids, and reduce whatever fever may be present by the methods indicated in our treatise *On Fevers*. If there are abscesses, employ suitable treatments as outlined in our discussion of

3 them; and in cases where the patient habitually vomits after the evening meal, gradually overcome the condition.

But if none of these conditions occurs and only the disease of cachexia appears to be present in the body, carefully note the attacks and the intervals of remission. If the patient remains sleepless without apparent reason, fails to digest his food properly, shows mental distress, and is sluggish and listless in his bodily movements, we may conclude that there is an attack. In that case keep the patient quiet and have him fast in order to

4 overcome the bodily disturbance. Foment the swollen parts with warm olive oil and cover them with wool; and if there is looseness of the bowels, correct the condition. Again, in cases where there is considerable swelling of the body as well as a feeling of heaviness, draw a moderate amount of blood by performing venesection at the arm. But venesection need not be performed if the patient's blood supply is low by reason of hemorrhoids....[1a] After venesection anoint the patient and repair his strength with light and digestible food until the attack declines. And carefully observing the character of the several symptoms, treat some with poultices and others with cupping. When the attack first appears to wane, prescribe varied food in considerable quantity,

5 and by such means help along the decline of the attack.

And then, when the interval of remission is at hand (which may readily be recognized from the abatement of the aforesaid

superpositionem designant, erunt corpora resumenda atque for-
tificanda. tum recorporativis utendum curationibus, quo re-
formata corpora, vel ut ita dixerim resectis vitiosis carnibus ac
renascentibus novis,[7] reparata ad memoriam redeant sanitatis.

quapropter aeger somno discusso semet in lecto continere
iubendus, etiam iacere paulisper, tum etiam neque repente con-
surgere, sed praetentato motu discere utrum se levem ac diges-
86 tum sentiat. etenim si fuerit occurrens indigestio, erit requies
adhibenda plurimo temporis spatio donec gravedo digeratur.
dehinc mediocri gestatione atque parvo cibo utendum, si non ex
accessione sed ex aliqua causa manifesta temporalis acciderit
corporis displicentia, quam Graeci disarescesin[8] vocant.

ac si nulla fuerit aegrotantis querela, erit a lecto levandus, et
ob expugnandam frigoris iniuriam oleo leviter perungendus.
tunc gestatio adhibenda, et si vires permiserint vel aeris tem-
peries, sub divo et magis intra[9] muros motu vehiculi. si vero
aliqua fuerit obstans causa, erunt haec sub tecto adhibenda, et
pro virium modo aut vehiculo manuali aut sella aut cathedra
87 exercendus aegrotus. tum gestatione perfecta, parva deambulatio adhibenda vel vocis exercitium atque ad unctionem veniendum, sed praecalefacto intra vestes aegro quoties calidum habuerit corpus. tum deposita veste erit linteolis levi defricatione
tergendus atque statim oleo parvo ungendus et summo tactu
fricandus, primo ab alio, postea a semetipso, retento spiritu †ut
etiam alia[10] teneantur.† dehinc rursum ab aliis defricandus, te-
nacius quidem sed non impressius, quo possit carnis inflatio
coagulari. sed haec erunt adhibito unctionis praeceptore facienda, quo secundum proprias mutationes omnium partium motus aequaliter ac totius corporis integret exercitium.

[7] novis (*vel* bonis) *Rm*: nobis *S*

[8] diarescesin *S*: *fort. scrib.* disarestesin

[9] extra *Rm*   [10] *an* ilia?

2. The point seems to be that if there is such an exacerbation, no food should be given at this time.

3. The idea seems to be to avoid a sudden chill.

symptoms, i.e., those indicative of the attack), rebuild and restore the patient's strength. Then employ metasyncritic treatments so that the body may be transformed or, so to speak,
rebuilt by the removal of diseased flesh and the formation of
new flesh, and may thus be restored to its former state of health.

The patient should therefore be instructed to remain in bed
on awakening from sleep, and to lie there a while. Even then he
should not rise suddenly, but by a tentative movement should
see whether he has a feeling of lightness indicative of good digestion. For if there is indigestion, further rest should be prescribed
for a considerable time until the feeling of heaviness is dissipated. Then give him light passive exercise and have him take a
little food, but only if this temporary malaise (Greek *dysareste-
sis*) is due to some obvious cause other than the exacerbation of
the disease.[2]

Now if the patient is quite free from distress, let him get out
of bed; and, to avoid the danger of injury from cold, anoint him
gently with olive oil. Then have him take passive exercise in the
open air if his strength and the mildness of the weather permit;
let him take this exercise in a carriage along a course sheltered
by walls. But if for any reason the exercise cannot be taken in
the open air, let him take it under cover of a roof in a hand-drawn
carriage or a chair. In arranging this exercise give due consideration to the patient's strength. Then, after the conclusion of the
passive exercise, have him do a little walking or vocal exercise
and then come for anointing. If the body is overheated, have
the patient keep his clothes on [for a time] and thus keep warm.[3]
Then remove his clothing, and with gentle rubbing wipe his body
with linen cloths; then immediately have him anointed with
a little olive oil and rubbed with a light touch. At first, persons
other than the patient should perform this rubbing, but later the
patient should do so himself, holding his breath. . . .[4] Then have
others rub him again, this time holding the flesh more, without
increasing the pressure, in order to reduce the swollen parts. But
have in charge of this treatment an expert anointer who will see
to it that, in accordance with the required series of changes, the
movements of all the parts constitute a uniform and integrated
exercising of the entire body.

4. As the text stands, the meaning apparently is: 'So that the other (parts?) may
also be held.' But the text is almost certainly corrupt.

88 tunc permittentibus viribus etiam raptorio machinamento gestetur ac deinde recussabili[11] sphaera,[12] quam italicam vocant. aliquando etiam harena asperso corpore, quam ammon[13] appellant, defricetur per intervalla dierum adhibito lavacro. convenit etiam psichrolusia, nullis obstantibus causis quae eam prohiberi permittant. tum vinum dandum austerum album leve.[14] dehinc iubendus superbibere atque siccum sumere cibum, vel certe quartam partem panis siccam manducare, adhibito usu assorum pulmentorum et neque curiose conditorum, ut

89 pisces, clunes vel agrestium leviora, et his omnibus iuxta regulam methodicam auctis aut minutis, interiecta vini abstinentia et cibi parva sumptione. utendum etiam locorum atque aeris mutatione, tum heliosin,[15] quam nos corporis torrorem[16] dicimus. ita dropacis adhibendus usus et pulveris nitri fricatio et sinapismus specialiter et usus aquarum naturalium vel natatio maritima. item harena littoraria ignita circumtecto corpore torrendi sunt aegrotantes, nunc inter paucos, nunc inter plurimos dies, ut vires permiserint. tum naviculae exercitium atque peregrinatio quemadmodum in praecedentibus ordinavimus.

90 ## VII. DE NUTRIMENTI CESSATIONE, QUAM ATROPHIAN GRAECI VOCANT[1]

Nutrimenti cessatio, quam Graeci atrophian vocant, ab accidenti nomen sumpsit ** et contingit in passione constitutis plurimus cibi appetitus, tum corruptio, quibusdam fastidium. item tenues atque latentes tepores[2] sunt, neque[3] febricula iugiter[4] et quibusdam inter plurimos dies soluta. ducitur praeterea quaedam etiam per urinam corporis defluxio, quam syntexin vesicae vocaverunt, cum plurima fuerit poti liquoris egestio, atque corporis subinde per dies singulos extenuatio.

---

[11] repercussibili *Rm* (*cf. Senecae De benef. ii. 17. 4*)

[12] sphaera *Sm*: fera *S*

[13] amon *S*: *corr. A litteris graecis*

[14] lene *Rm*

[15] *an* heliosi?

[16] torporem *S*: *corr. Rm*

[1] '*deerat quoque principium capitis in exemplari, quod nos ut potuimus sarsimus*' *Sm*, *Rm* (!): *fort. etiam deesse nonnulla sub fin. praecedentis capitis coni. Schmid RPh 155*

[2] tepore *S*: *corr. Rm*   [3] atque *Rm*   [4] iugis *Rm*

38 Then, if the patient's strength permits, let him be drawn by the 'pulling' device; have him also exercise with the so-called 'Italian ball,' which may be hit back and forth. At times sprinkle his body with sand (Greek *ammos*) and give him a vigorous rubdown; prescribe bathing at intervals of some days. Cold bathing is also beneficial, if there are no circumstances which make this treatment inadvisable. The patient should then also be given a wine that is dry, white, and mild. And he should be instructed to drink it after taking food, and to eat his food dry, or at least to eat a fourth part of his bread dry. Let him have broiled food, not highly seasoned, e.g., fish, and the loin or other easily di-

89 gested parts of field animals. Increase or decrease the quantity of food in every case, following the rules of the Methodist system, with intervals in which no wine is given and only a little food. Also have the patient visit new places and change climate. And prescribe *hēliōsis* ['sun-bathing'], which we may call in Latin *corporis torror* ['baking of the body'], pitch plasters, rubbing with powdered nitrum, and especially mustard plaster. Also prescribe the use of natural springs and sea-bathing. Again, cover the patient with beach sand heated by the sun, and have him bake his body. This baking may be repeated at intervals of few or many days, depending on his strength. Finally, let him enjoy the exercise afforded by boating, and let him take a trip abroad, as we have recommended in previous chapters.

90 ## VII. FAILURE OF NUTRITION
(GREEK *ATROPHIA*)

FAILURE of nutrition (Greek *atrophia*) takes its name from a symptom. . . .[1] The disease is marked by a great appetite for food, followed by the spoiling of the food eaten and in some cases loss of appetite. There is a mild, subdued warmth and a fever, not continuous and in some cases completely overcome after a number of days. In addition, there is a melting-away of the body by way of the urine, i.e., a colliquescence (Greek *syntēxis*) of the bladder. Whatever fluids are drunk are copiously discharged, with consequent wasting-away of the body day by day.

1. The first part of this chapter was missing from the manuscript used by *S*, and the text as we have it is *S*'s attempted reconstruction. There is no indication at what point the text is again based on the manuscript.

91   etiam[5] nunc igitur convenit, sicut in cachecticis diximus, providere ne qua pars corporis principaliter patiatur; et oportet[6]
congrua eidem morbo localia adhiberi adiutoria, ut iecoris vel
lienis duritiei, vel fluori ventris aut intestinorum vel vesicae,
vel ulceri in interioribus constituto, aut collectioni quam specialiter vomicam diximus. ac si etiam febres fuerint consecutae,
iisdem quoque adhibenda medela.

si horum nihil in corpore viderimus sed sola fuerit atrophia
consecuta, convenit aegrotum fortificari rationabiliter atque re-
sumi gestatione, pro virium quantitate, scilicet quibus saepe
92 memoravimus generibus, et unctionibus ordinatis plurimo oleo
superfuso, adhibita fricatione, et ministris corpulentis et mollibus vel quales esse fricatores Salutaribus praeceptis docuimus,
quo contactu corporum laxiore aegrotantis exercitata membra
solvantur. tum temperato utendum lavacro atque vino tenui
et pane limpido fermentato et pulmentis ex media materia; atque iuxta cycli regulam eorum augmenta ac detractiones variare, non repetitis nec perfectis ilico cyclis, sed unius tantummodo
qualitatis, ut de cephalaea[7] scribentes docuimus. denique cum
ex volantibus solis adhibemus, initium ex parvulis ordinamus,
93 cum[8] autem ex agrestibus, ex teneribus, cum porcinam,[9] ex membrorum summitatibus.

convenit praeterea locorum atque aerum commutatio et aliquando drimyphagia vel simplex vomitus, tum etiam ex radicibus confectus. et localia aliis atque aliis locis adhibenda, et
magis medianis partibus. non enim sine plurima vexatione partium quibus digestio celebratur inesse corporibus atrophia potest. ipsis igitur frequentius adhibendus est dropax et cucurbitae vel paroptesis aut sinapismus et sympasmata acriora, quae a
nobis aspergines nuncupantur, item malagmata eiusdem quali-
94 tatis.[10] utilis praeterea littoraria navigatio atque natatio maritima vel naturalium aquarum; tum post cibum animi laxatio,

[5] hic, non post extenuatio, interpunxerunt edd.

[6] oporteat S: corr. R

[7] cephalaea scripsi, coll. Chr. i. 26–28: cataleptico edd.

[8] cum Schmid RPh 136: tum S

[9] porcina S: corr. Schmid RPh 137

[10] quantitatis S: corr. Rm

91   It is therefore necessary in cases of atrophy, just as we have indicated in cases of cachexia, to see to it that any special affection of a particular part of the body is overcome. That is, we must apply the local remedies required by any such affection, e.g., hardness of the liver or spleen; flux of the stomach, intestines, or bladder; an internal ulceration; or an [internal] gathering of matter to which we give the special name *vomica* ['abscess']. And fever, if present, must also be treated.

If, however, none of these special conditions is observed to be present in the body, but the atrophy occurs alone, the patient's strength should be built up by appropriate means. Thus employ restorative measures, such as passive exercise of the kinds we have often mentioned above, with due regard to the patient's 92 strength; also anointings with copious suffusion of olive oil; and massage administered by soft, fleshy attendants. (As we indicated in our *Precepts of Health*,[2] persons of this type make good masseurs; for the patient's body is exercised and relaxed by contact with their soft flesh.) Then prescribe bathing in moderation, mild wine, pure leavened bread, and food of the middle class, with increases and decreases in the quantity thereof in accordance with the standard cyclical procedure. But do not repeat the cycles or bring them to full strength immediately; and employ only one type of food at a time, as we have indicated in the chapter on cephalaea.[3] Thus in precribing an exclusive diet of fowl [after the diet of the middle class], begin with the small birds; 93 in the diet of game begin with the tender animals; and in the diet of pork begin with the extremities of the animal.

In addition, a change of locale and climate is beneficial. So also is an acrid diet from time to time. Vomiting may also be induced both directly and with the use of radishes. Also apply various local remedies to the various parts of the body, especially to the middle parts. For the presence of atrophy in the body is inevitably attended by severe injury to the parts that are concerned with digestion. Therefore, apply pitch plasters frequently to these parts; and likewise cupping treatments, intense heat, mustard plasters, sharp dusting powders (Greek *sympasmata*, Latin *aspergines*), and emollient plasters of similar proper-94 ties. Again, a boat trip along the shore and swimming in the sea

2. *Salut. praec.* 36 (p. 199 Rose).
3. Cf. *Chr.* i. 26–28.

quam diachysin vocant, et articulorum complexio, adhibitis
ministris qui mollibus hoc manibus efficiant.

Themison vero secundo libro Tardarum passionum plurima
recte ordinasse probatur, aliqua vero caduca intentione dixisse
intelligitur. iubet etenim aegros non aequaliter aegrotantes
duodecim stadiorum spatium gressu conficere, aequalem modum
cunctis definiens. item igneo in loco vel ferventi fricari iubet
praefatigatos sudoribus aegrotantes, item sole torreri,[11] atque ita
per intervalla leviter defricari, et in calida atque oleo calido
95 eorum manus infundi, ex quibus periculum perfrictionis[12] necessario sequetur.

item post interdianum[13] cibum deambulationem probat adhibendam atque fricationem et lavacrum; tum post vespertinum
cibum ungenda[14] crura atque brachia, quod est dormituris
anxiosum. praeterea post cenam imperat vomitum praedato
passo aut vino dulci vel suco ptisanae. tum frequentato vomitu
ova duo danda sorbilia cum panis unciis duabus, ex quo incensa
altiora,[15] atque exercitatis vomitu visceribus facile corrumpuntur accepta. haec igitur recusantes, alia quae recte ordinasse
perspicitur amplectenda iudicamus.

96   VIII. DE HYDROPE

Hydrops ab accidenti nomen sumpsit, siquidem aquosus humor hanc passionem necessario comitetur: nam Graeci
hydor aquam vocaverunt. generatur autem ex antecedentibus[1]
plurimis atque diversis causis, ut cachexia, febribus ⟨in⟩ corpore[2] tardantibus, item duritia vel saxea densitate iecoris vel
lienis aut stomachi vel peritonei membranae aut matricis, item
spirationis difficultate, quam Graeci dyspnoean vocant, vel ventositate stomachi aut coli aut ventris passione, quam Graeci
coeliacen diathesin vocant, item longi temporis dysenteria, vel
97 in feminis menstrualis fluoris retentione, item haemorrhoidarum
veterum repentina atque incondita curatione facta, abstinentia
vel coacervata bibentium transvoratione, et magis si salsa fuerit
aqua, item medicaminum frequentata potione, et horum similibus.

---

[11] torrenti S: corr. Rm   [14] iungenda S: inungenda Rm
[12] perfricationis S: corr. Rm   [15] incensis altioribus Rm
[13] meridianum Am   [1] antecedentibus scripsi: accidentibus edd.

or in natural springs are helpful; also mental diversion (Greek *diachysis*) after meals, and clasping of the patient's limbs by attendants with soft hands.

In Book II of his *Chronic Diseases* Themison gives a number of correct prescriptions, but some of his ideas are clearly unsound. Thus he orders these patients, who are not all equally sick, to walk a distance of twelve stades, and he prescribes the same distance for all. Again, he exhausts the patient by having him sweat in a hot steamroom, and then he prescribes a rubdown. He also has the patient bake himself in the sun, then take mild rubdowns from time to time, and plunge the hands in hot
95 water and hot olive oil. But such measures always involve the risk of a violent cold.

Themison also prescribes walking, massage, and bathing after the midday meal; and anointing of the legs and arms after the evening meal. But such a measure is upsetting, especially when the patient is about to go to sleep. Furthermore, Themison prescribes vomiting after dinner, the patient having previously been given raisin wine, sweet wine, or pearl barley gruel. Then, when the vomiting is over, Themison has the patient take two soft eggs with two ounces of bread; but the inner parts are thereby inflamed, and, with the agitation of the viscera by the vomiting, the substances taken in are easily spoiled. We therefore reject these prescriptions of Themison, though we consider worthy of adoption the sound recommendations that he made.

96 ## VIII. DROPSY

DROPSY (*hydrōps*) derives its name from a symptom; for a watery fluid is a necessary concomitant of the disease, and the Greek word for water is *hydōr*. Dropsy may arise from many different antecedent causes, e.g., cachexia; chronic fever; hardness or stonelike thickening of the liver, spleen, esophagus, peritoneum, or womb; difficulty in breathing (Greek *dyspnoea*); gas in the esophagus or colon; the coeliac disease (Greek *coeliacē diathesis*); chronic dysentery; suppression of menses in women;
97 a hasty or inept attempt to treat chronic hemorrhoids; fasting; swallowing of a great deal of water at once, especially salt water; frequent drinking of drugs; and other such causes.

---

[2] ⟨in⟩ corpore *Rm* (*cf. Chr. v. 90*): corpora *S*

Graeci igitur vel aliarum sectarum principes eius potestatem vel differentiam nominibus variandam crediderunt. vocant enim hanc passionem etiam hyderon vel parecchysin, origini locorum specialia nomina tribuentes. nam parecchysin appellant sensibilem et manifestam liquoris superfusionem quae fiet inter peritoneum[3] membranam et intestina;[4] hyderon autem dispersum sive infusum per viarum raritatem atque carnis spiramenta liquorem. item dicunt hyderon ex renibus generari, hydropem vero ex duritate iecoris.

98

quod quidem nos iuxta sectae regulam reprobamus. etenim infusio sive superfusio liquoris est passioni communis, et neque antecedentes causae passionis facere discretionem recte creduntur, siquidem etiam ex plurimis aliis partibus patientibus hydropes generantur. eius igitur differentiam Hippocrates et Diocles duplicem dixerunt. aliam enim hyposarca[5] vocaverunt, aliam asciten. item Heraclides Tarentinus secundo libro Internarum passionum totius corporis inflationem sive humoris infusi perforationem catasarca[6] vocavit,[7] inter peritoneum vero et intestina asciten vel tympaniten appellavit. item Demetrius Herophili sectator undecimo libro De passionibus scribens alium dixit hydropem constitui sine ulla humoris infusione, sed sola inflatione turgente, alium ex humore diffuso, et eum nunc per totum corpus nunc inter peritoneum et intestina. cuius differentiam nunc plurimo vento tradidit; et[8] est vanum atque intellectu carens sine ullo humore superfluo laborantem hydropem vocare.

99

item plurimi tres differentias tradiderunt: aliam enim catasarca, aliam asciten, aliam tympaniten vocaverunt. Asclepiades autem alium celerem dixit, ut eum qui repente constituitur, alium tardum, ut eum qui tarda passione vexet,[9] et alium cum febribus, alium sine febribus. hoc quidem communiter etiam aliis specialibus passionibus adscribens, non advertit quoniam proprio nomine celer dicitur passio non sola quae repente conficitur, verum etiam ea quae celeriter solvi posse monstratur.

100

[3] peritonei *S* (*cf. Chr. v. 127*)

[4] intestinae *S: corr. R*

[5] hyposarcan *S, fort. retin.* (-am?), *sed cf. Cels. iii. 21. 2*

[6] catasarcan *S* (*sic etiam 99 fin.*)

[7] vocant *S: corr. Rm*

[8] *fort.* at

[9] vexat *R*

Now the Greeks, that is, the leaders of other sects, hold that different types of the disease should be indicated by different names. Thus they also call the disease *hyderos* and *parenchysis*, assigning these special terms according to the place where the dropsy originates. They use the term *parenchysis* for a palpable and visible suffusion of fluid between the peritoneum and the intestines; and *hyderos* for fluid scattered and seeping through the

8 fine passages and pores of the flesh. And they say that *hyderos* originates in the kidneys, while *hydrōps* is caused by hardness of the liver.

But, in accordance with the principles of our sect, we Methodists reject these distinctions. For a flow or suffusion of fluid is the common element of this disease, and we consider it wrong to make distinctions on the basis of the various antecedent causes. Indeed, dropsy may originate in affections of many other parts [besides those mentioned]. Thus Hippocrates and Diocles speak of two kinds of dropsy, calling one *hypo sarca* ['under the flesh'] and the other *ascitēs*. And Heraclides of Tarentum in Book II of his *Internal Diseases* speaks of the swelling of the whole body and its penetration by a suffusion of fluid as *cata*

9 *sarca*, while he calls a suffusion between the peritoneum and the intestines *ascitēs* or *tympanitēs*. Demetrius, the follower of Herophilus, in Book XI of his treatise *On Diseases* declares that one form of dropsy occurs without any spreading of fluid but merely with a turgid swelling and that the other form involves a suffusion of fluid, this taking place sometimes through the whole body and at other times between the peritoneum and the intestines. Now Demetrius goes into a long-winded discussion of these differences, but it is meaningless and indicative of a lack of understanding to call a case dropsy when it involves no spreading of any fluid.

Again, most writers speak of three different forms, calling one

0 *cata sarca*, another *ascitēs*, and the third *tympanitēs*. Asclepiades, however, declares that one form of dropsy is acute, namely, that which arises suddenly; and another chronic, namely, that which afflicts the body over a long period; and, again, that one form occurs with fever, another without. He employs these general distinctions in referring to other special diseases, too; but he is not aware that, for a disease properly to be called 'acute,' it must not only arise suddenly but must be capable of being overcome

hydrops autem fit quisquam repente ex coacervata bibendi transvoratione vel salsi liquoris potu. celerem autem passionis solutionem nullus aegrotantium meruit. item Proculus[10] Themisonis sector secundum plurimos inquit hydropis differentias

101 temporibus passionis adscribendas: initium enim atque augmentum esse leucophlegmatian[11] cum adhuc secundum carnem fieri mutationem viderimus; statum vero tympaniten, cum summa tensio secundum ventrem fuerit facta; declinationem autem asciten, cum quadam indulgentia fuerit inflatio relaxata: non secutus veri regulam neque advertens quia omnis species passionis sua quaeque tempora percurrit. denique etiam catasarca usque ad statum vel declinationem perseverat, ac[12] tympanites et ascites ex initio facti in augmentum venerint et statu sumpto declinaverint.[13]

item Apollonius Memphites alium dixit fieri hydropem cum retentione, ⟨alium sine retentione,⟩[14] ut si quid biberit sine dila-

102 tione tamquam per fistulam transiens egeratur. eius autem quem cum retentione fieri dixit secundum plurimos tres esse differentias affirmat. sed melius Demetrius Apameus ab hydrope discrevit eum qui sine dilatione potum liquorem per urinam egerit, diabeten appellans, sicut specialiter de ipso scribentes docebimus.[15]

melius igitur quantum ad species hydropis, quamquam non generaliter mutemus curationem, alium dicere in toto corpore constitutum, tamquam in papyro vel spongia inter viarum raritatem insertum, a liquore vocari leucophlegmatiam, quam latino nomine etiam intercutem recte dicemus, alium in parte corporis inter peritoneum et intestina subiecto liquore solo, vel admixto vento plurimo, vocari alterum asciten, alterum tympaniten.

[10] fort. scrib. Proclus

[11] leucophlegmantian S, et sic pluries infra (alia exempla non afferam), ut saepe in codd. latinis

[12] ac scripsi: at S: et R

[13] veniunt et s. s. declinant R: fort. venerunt et s. s. declinaverunt

[14] suppl. Schmid RPh 137, qui maiorem lacunam statuit post retentione: ⟨alium cum fluore⟩ Rm

[15] docuimus S: corr. Rm

1. We expect Caelius to say, in refutation of Proclus, that tympanites and ascites may be present in the initial and increasing phases of dropsy as well as at the highest stage and in the decline. But he does not say precisely this.

2. Presumably cata sarea, ascitēs, and tympanitēs.

3. The chapter (the fifth of Book V) is lost.

quickly. Now a given case of dropsy may arise suddenly from the swallowing of a great quantity of water all at once, and particularly from the drinking of a salt fluid. But no patient has ever been cured of dropsy swiftly. Proclus, the follower of Themison, declares, in common with many other physicians, that there are different forms of dropsy corresponding to the different periods of the disease. Thus he calls the beginning and the increasing phase *leucophlegmatia*, when changes in the flesh are still observable; he calls the disease at its highest stage *tympanitēs*, when the tenseness of the abdomen is greatest; and he gives the name *ascitēs* to the declining phase, when the swelling has been eased and relaxed somewhat. But in this he departs from true principles and does not heed the fact that every form of the disease has its own temporal phases. Indeed, the form *cata sarca* continues to the highest stage or even to the declining phase in cases of dropsy; again, there are cases in which it is found that tympanites and ascites appear at the onset of the disease, then increase, and, when the disease has passed its highest stage, decline.[1]

Apollonius of Memphis declares that one form of dropsy is marked by retention of fluid, and another form by an inability to retain, so that whatever the patient drinks is immediately discharged as if it passed through a pipe. And he declares, in agreement with most physicians, that the type of dropsy which involves retention appears in the three different forms.[2] But Demetrius of Apamea more properly distinguishes from dropsy the disease in which any fluid that is drunk is immediately discharged as urine, and he calls this latter condition *diabētēs*. We shall discuss diabetes in a special chapter.[3]

And so, with regard to the various forms of dropsy, though the differences have no bearing on the general treatment, it seems best to put the case as follows. One form of dropsy involves the whole body, spreading through the fine pores as a fluid seeps through paper or through a sponge, and from the nature of the fluid this form may be called *leucophlegmatia*, for which we may use the Latin term *intercus* [i.e., intercutaneous (fluid)]; the second form of dropsy occurs in one part of the body, between the peritoneum and the intestines, and involves fluid alone or fluid mixed with a great deal of wind, being called in the former case *ascitēs*, and in the latter *tympanitēs*.

103   sequuntur quaedam cunctos praeterea communia, quaedam singulis propria: communia autem, ut inflatio vel extantia tumoris,[16] et piger aut difficilis corporis motus, spirationis difficultas, quam Graeci dyspnoean vocant, somnus difficilis vel anxiosus, et magis post cibum, sitis, et urina comparatione sumpti potus parvior, fastidium, et aliquando febricula latens in plurimis, item quibusdam etiam vesiculae vel fistulae quibus eruptus humor feratur, ac deinde vulnera difficilia sufficiantur,[17] vel quae in cicatricem ⟨difficile⟩[18] venire possint.

104   specialia vero vel propria singulos sequuntur, ut leucophlegmatian vel intercutem mollis atque humida inflatio ventris ac vultus et crurum et folliculi genitalis vel praeputii, relucente liquore per cutem albido colore; item cum oris vel spirationis[19] sive anhelitus fetore totius corporis gravedo et impressioni digitorum cedens tumor, ita ut paululum cava permaneant loca; aliquibus etiam alborum atque crassorum humorum vomitus vel per ventrem egestio. unde etiam nomen passio sumpsisse a graeca derivatione videtur: leucon enim albidum, phlegma humorem crassum vocaverunt, vel quod aegrotantis color albidi

105 humoris[20] imaginem ferat. alii vero tamquam ex superfluo humore generata passione penetrans humor singula quaeque spiramenta possederit; nos vero intercutem nominamus.

   asciten denique sequitur ventris inflatio vel extantia, et pro corporis motu liquoris conlisi sonitus vel ad concussum palmae resonus, tamquam semipleni utris, ex quo nomen sumpsit; item pro schematis mutatione vel digitorum impressione demersio vel resurrectio liquoris, et conclusio superiorum partium atque tenuitas tamquam extentae cutis secundum ora vel colla aut iugula vel pectora. iacentibus praeterea aegrotantibus diffusa atque latior[21] tumoris[22] extantia fiet, surgentium vero vel stan-

106 tium maior atque extenta. et increscente passione corporis fri-

[16] *fort.* humoris

[17] sufficiant *S*: *corr. Rm*

[18] *supplevi*: ⟨aegre⟩ *R*

[19] spiratione *S*: *corr. R*

[20] albidi humoris *scripsi*: albidioris *S*

[21] latior *A*: elatior *S*   [22] *fort.* humoris. *cf. 103*

4. *Tumoris* may mean 'caused by inflammation'; if *humoris* be read, the meaning is 'caused by an accumulation of fluid.'

3   There are some symptoms common to all these forms, and others that are peculiar to some one form. The common symptoms are a swelling or a bulging distention,[4] sluggishness or distress in bodily movement, difficulty in breathing (Greek *dyspnoea*), wakefulness or troubled sleep, especially after taking food,[5] thirst, relatively little urine in comparison with the amount of fluid drunk, loss of appetite, and in some cases a fever, generally low. There are also in some cases blisters or fistulas, through which the fluid is carried as it breaks out. This process gives rise to intractable wounds, which can be made to cicatrize only with difficulty.

4   We now enumerate the special symptoms that characterize each form of the disease. Thus leucophlegmatia or *intercus* is marked by a soft, moist swelling of the abdomen, face, legs, scrotum, and foreskin, the fluid appearing whitish through the skin. There is also an offensive smell from the mouth, i.e., bad breath, a feeling of heaviness throughout the body, and a swelling that gives way before the pressure of the fingers so that the parts remain somewhat depressed. In some cases thick white fluids are vomited or else discharged by way of the bowels; and it is from this circumstance that the disease seems to have derived its Greek name, for *leucon* is the Greek for 'white' and *phlegma* for 'thick fluid.' Or it may be so called because the patient's
5   color is like that of white fluid. Others [would have the disease called] from the fact that when the disease arises the fluid overflows and enters each and every pore; and, in fact, in Latin we call it *intercus*.

Now ascites is marked by abdominal swelling or distention. Again, when the body moves, there is a sound of fluids striking together; and when the abdomen is struck with the palm, there is a resonant sound as from a half-filled wineskin, whence the name of the disease.[6] With a change of the patient's position or pressure of the fingers, the fluid is depressed or rises. There is a drawing-together and tightening of the upper parts, the skin around the mouth, neck, throat, and chest somehow becoming taut. Again, while the patient is lying down, the swelling is more diffuse and spread out, but when he arises or stands up the bulge
6   is greater and more prominent. As the disease increases in se-

5. The phrase 'especially after taking food' may perhaps be construed with 'thirst.'
6. *Ascos,* 'wineskin.'

gus atque torpor accedit, aliquando etiam tussicula et stercorum
vel urinae abstinentia et per ventrem fluidior exitus, et apprehenso folliculo atque virili veretro extans inflatio reduplicata,[23]
et aliarum partium surgens tensio, sicut in leucophlegmatia.
vocatur autem hic hydropismus, ut Diocles, etiam hepatias aut
splenites a patientibus partibus nomen ducens, hoc est iecore vel
liene.

item tympaniten sequitur rotunda atque extans inflatio secundum gastera cum tensione plurima et ad percussum palmae
107 resonus velut tympani, unde etiam nomen accepit; item ructationes et aliquando intestinorum tormenta quae excluso[24] vento
per podicem digerantur atque gravedinis detrahant quicquam.

est autem passio communiter stricturae omnis hydropismus
sed complexa aliquando solutione ex aliis accedentibus, ut ventris fluore. praeterea est naturaliter tarda passio, siquidem numquam celeriter soluta vel emota corporibus videatur. item
generaliter magna, siquidem et difficultatem et indecentiam et
periculum inferat aegrotanti. denique semper difficilis curatione, nunc vehementer, nunc minime comprobatur. etenim
magnitudine vehemens et varietate accidentium et corruptione
108 virium magis incurabilis iudicatur. parva vero magnitudine
comprobatione supradicta atque paucis et simplicibus accidentibus, quae Graeci symptomata appellant, et sine nimia virium
laesione, minime curatione difficilis approbatur.

et quae secundum aliarum sectarum principes de effectis vel
exitibus passionum scripta sunt, ut[25] etiam secundum causas ex
quibus efficiuntur et patientes locos et naturas et aetates et annalia tempora, ut hiemis vel aestatis et eorum media tempora,
⟨et⟩ generationem[26] passionis, alii difficiles curatione alii faciles
[curatione alii faciles][27] hydropes approbantur. quae quidem
omnia magnitudini passionis adscribenda sunt, ne infinitus modus differentiarum videatur accidentium numero variatus.

---

[23] reduplicans *Rm: fort.* reduplicat
[24] excluso *Rm*: inclusae *S*
[25] ut *om. R*   [26] mediis temporibus generationes *S: corr. Rm*   [27] *del. R*

verity, there occur cold and numbness, in some cases coughing, retention of solid feces and urine, and the passage of a fluid discharge through the bowels; the swelling is so increased that it involves the scrotum and penis. And the other parts, too, are increasingly distended, as in leucophlegmatia. This condition is also called, e.g., by Diocles, 'hepatic' or 'splenic' dropsy, a name derived from the affected parts, namely, the liver or the spleen.

Finally, tympanites is marked by a prominent round swelling at the abdomen, with considerable tenseness. When the abdomen is struck with the palm of the hand, there is a resonant sound like that of a drum, whence the disease receives its name.[7] There is belching and sometimes also intestinal cramps. These cramps are dispelled by the passage of wind through the anus, with consequent partial relief of the feeling of heaviness.

In its general nature dropsy in all its forms is marked by a state of stricture; but in some cases a state of looseness is also involved, as is indicated by other symptoms, such as flux of the stomach and bowels. Again, dropsy is by nature a chronic disease, since it is never found to be dispelled or driven from the body swiftly. And, in general, it is a serious disease, involving unsightliness and causing the patient distress and danger. Again, the treatment always involves some difficulty, sometimes more, sometimes less. Thus a severe case marked by a variety of symptoms and impairment of strength is quite hard to treat successfully; while a case considered mild by these standards, that is to say, involving only a few simple concomitants of disease (Greek *symptōmata*) and no serious impairment of strength, offers very little difficulty of treatment.

Again, statements of leading physicians of other sects giving the probable result or outcome of these diseases, e.g., on the basis of the causes from which they arise, the parts affected, the sex of the persons affected, their ages, the seasonal incidence, i.e., whether the disease arises in winter, in summer, or in the intermediate seasons, and the form which the disease takes—all such statements merely indicate that some cases of dropsy are hard to cure and others easy. In fact, all the criteria they adduce ought to be combined under the heading of the severity or extent of the disease, to avoid the endless multiplication of distinctions based on variations in the number of symptoms.

7. *Tympanon*, 'drum.'

109   etenim secundum causas, difficiles aiunt curatione hydropes
qui ex saxitate magis atque[28] ex duritia fuerint facti, item eos qui
ex dysenteria vel coli passione, ab his qui ex coacervato haustu
bibendo vitium conceperunt. item secundum locos, difficiles
inquiunt eos qui ex iecore, faciles vero eos qui ex liene. item secundum naturam vel sexum, difficiliores inquiunt curatione semper feminas maribus. item secundum aetates, faciliores inquiunt curatione pueros vel pubentes, difficiles vero aetatis mediae
vel senes, non solum quod natura ⟨alii⟩[29] crescere vel augeri,
110 alii[30] minui vel declinare videantur, sed etiam quod alii prohi-
beantur[31] vel[32] cogantur, alii neque suaderi[32a] neque cogi posse
probentur. item secundum annalia tempora, quae Graeci horas
appellant, difficiles inquiunt curatione aestatis tempore laborantes, siquidem multa siti afficiantur. alii vero e contrario faciles inquiunt curatione, siquidem exitum liquorum fieri provocet fervor aestatis et corporis praeterea faciat siccitatem; difficiles vero hiemis tempore ob corporum densitatem vel frigus,
item verno tempore, siquidem humidiora atque liquorum redundantia fiant corpora. autumni vero prima similia aestati, ulti-
111 ma hiemi dixerunt. item secundum generationem sive fabrica-
tionem passionis, difficilem inquiunt curatione leucophlegmatian, facilem vero asciten, et horum medium tympaniten.
    dissenserunt praeterea etiam de patientibus partibus quae
principaliter afficiantur. Erasistratus namque iecur inquit pati,
in apertionibus enim saxeum semper inveniri confirmat; alii vero
colum, sed consentire iecur; alii splenem ac iecur et colum; alii
etiam peritoneum; alii renes quoque et matricem principaliter
pati dixerunt. et apparet omnia necessario praetangi, quod quidem etiamsi latuerit nullus timor curationis mutandae medican-
tibus accedat, neque etiam ob localium adiutoriorum ordinem
quicquam obesse monstretur, cum haec eadem **[33]

    [28] atque *scripsi*: quam *S*
    [29] ⟨alii⟩ *Schmid RPh 138*: ⟨illae⟩ *Rm*: *fort.* ⟨aliae⟩ (*sc.* aetates)
    [30] alii *Schmid RPh 138*: aliae *S*
    [31] persuadeantur *Rm*
    [32] vel *Schmid RPh 138*: alii *S*: *fort.* atque
    [32a] suadere *S*: *corr. R*
    [33] *lacunam statuit Rm post* monstretur: *fort. statuenda post* accedat

    8. The reference is probably to post mortem examinations rather than to a surgical
procedure of the kind described above, 65.

09   Thus with regard to causes, these physicians say that cases
of dropsy arising chiefly from stonelike hardness and those arising from dysentery or disease of the colon are harder to cure
than those caused by the drinking of a great deal of fluid at one
time. With regard to the parts affected, they say that cases of
dropsy involving the liver are hard to cure, while those affecting
the spleen are easy to cure. As for nature or sex, they consider it
always more difficult to treat women than men. In the matter of
age, they say that cases of boys or youths are easy to deal with,
while cases of middle-aged or old men are more difficult. For, in
the first place, they say, the former are by nature growing and
10 increasing, while the latter are shrinking and declining; and,
again, the former can be restrained and coerced, while the latter
can neither be persuaded nor coerced. As for the seasons of the
year (Greek *hōrae*), some of these physicians hold that successful
treatment is more difficult in summer because the patient is very
thirsty. But others, on the contrary, declare that the treatment
of dropsy is easier in summer because the heat of summer accel-
erates the discharge of fluids and, in fact, desiccates the body;
but that the treatment is difficult in winter because of the coldness and condensation of the body, and also in the spring, since
bodies then become more moist and more abundant in fluids.
As for fall, they say that the first part is comparable to summer
111 and the last part to winter. Finally, with reference to the form
which the disease takes or its structure, these physicians consider leucophlegmatia hard to cure, ascites easy, and tympanites
midway between these two.

    Again, there is disagreement as to which parts are chiefly af-
fected in dropsy. Thus Erasistratus declares that the liver is so
affected, and he says that, when patients with dropsy are
opened,[8] the liver is always found to have a stonelike hardness.
Some, again, assert that the colon is principally affected and the
liver sympathetically; others that the spleen, liver, and colon
are all affected; others add the peritoneum; and still others say
that the kidneys, too, and the womb are principally affected.
Now it would appear that all these parts are necessarily attacked; but even if this is beyond observation, physicians need
not trouble themselves to vary the treatment. Nor should there
be any difficulty on the score of the application of local remedies
since these very remedies. . . .

112　　** ⟨aegrotantem⟩[34] oportet[35] ceromate sole fervefacto iactari[36] vel pellibus sole ignitis involvi. adhibenda etiam acopa ferventia, et sudationes ex naturali materia provocare. habet enim recorporandi virtutem ex quacumque metallorum materia exhalatio naturalis. item ex harena littoris sole ignita torrenda corpora; hiemis vero tempore igne praetorrenda atque ita corpori admovenda, ut ex ipsa excepto capite cetera corporis omnia contegantur. item sinapismus usque ad cutis ruborem[37] adhibendus, qui maxime vehementem fortitudinem locis humore corruptis atque, ut ita dixerim, tabentibus[38] admovet ac minis-

113　trat. item locorum et aquarum mutatio adhibenda et peregrinatio magis maritima. est enim lacerantior atque corporis apertionibus efficax ob salsitatem maritimus aer. conveniunt etiam vaporationes spongiarum ex aqua maritima expressarum vel aqua salsa decocta.

in tympanicis vero specialia, ut plerique volunt, iuxta communem virtutem recorporativae curationis, etiam decoctio centaureae herbae et absinthii et origani et hyssopi et marrubii adhibenda, et similis virtutis epithema, ut est quod appellatur dianitru[39] ex fico atque nitro et absinthio confectum. tundendum igitur aridum ficum sed quod sit pingue ac sucidum, item singulatim absinthium et nitrum admiscendum duabus partibus

114　fici. et quarta pars origani, aliquando etiam rutae admiscenda particula. facit enim medicamen quod appellamus diahyssopu,[40] item uva passa cum cumino vel farre, cum adipe veteri et vino. hoc quidem plurimi magis intercutibus convenire probaverunt. item bubulo stercore ungendos cum aceto aegrotantes dixerunt. apponenda etiam malagmata quae fortificare ac recorporativa virtute mutare valeant corpora in meliorem habitudinem.

intercutes autem et ascitas his curandos probant quae siccare atque exiccare valeant corpus vel sudorem commovere. sed

[34] *addidi*

[35] oporteat *S*

[36] inungi *Rm*

[37] ruborem *Schmid RPh 151*: humorem *S*: tumorem *Rm*

[38] habentibus *S*: *corr. Rm*

[39] dianitrum *edd.*　　　　　　[40] diahyssopum *edd.*

9. The part of the chapter dealing with the first part of the treatment is lost.

12   ...⁹ Have the patient roll on a wrestling floor,¹⁰ that is, exposed to the hot sun, or have him rolled up in skins heated by
the sun. Also employ hot restorative ointments. And induce
sweating by means of natural substances;¹¹ for the vapors that
arise naturally from any mineral substance have a metasyncritic property. Also bake the patient's body with beach sand
heated by the sun; and in winter first heat the sand over a fire
and then apply it to the body, covering the whole body except
the head. Again, apply mustard plasters until the skin is red;
such a treatment will greatly strengthen the parts that are de-
13   caying and, so to speak, melting away because of the fluid. The
patient should also have a change of locale and of water, and a
trip abroad, preferably by sea. For, because of its saltness, the
sea air has a more penetrating quality and is more effective for
opening the pores of the body. Applications of heat with sponges
wrung out of boiled sea water or salt water are also beneficial.

But in cases of tympanites certain special remedies should be
employed, as many physicians recommend, in addition to the
general metasyncritic treatment. Thus give the patient a decoction of centaury, wormwood, marjoram, hyssop, and horehound;
and employ an epithem of similar properties, e.g., the so-called
'epithem of nitrum,' containing fig, nitrum, and wormwood.
Pound up a dried fig, one that is fat and juicy, however, and add
separately [one part each of] wormwood and nitrum to two parts
114   of fig; add also one-fourth part of marjoram, and sometimes a bit
of rue. The drug known as the 'hyssop remedy' is also beneficial;
so is an application of raisin, cumin or ground spelt, old fat, and
wine. Many, however, recommend this latter preparation rather
for cases of *intercus*. [In tympanites] physicians also prescribe
that the patient be anointed with a mixture of cattle dung and
vinegar. And they employ emollient plasters that will strengthen
the patient and, through metasyncritic properties, will change
his bodily state for the better.

In treating *intercus* and ascites, they recommend the use of
those plasters that will drain and desiccate the body or provoke

10. I.e., one covered with a mixture of earth or clay, wax, and oil. It is not possible
to interpret *ceromate* here in its usual sense of a wax ointment unless *iactari* is altered.
See *Chr.* ii. 34 and n.

11. The sequel makes it probable that the reference is to baths in hot mineral
springs.

erit cavendum ne immodico usu medicaminum corporis super-
115 ficies ulceretur. est autem nostrum medicamen quod ex herba
chamaeleonte nigra conficitur; item ex stercore caprino, quod
appellatur diacopraegias,[41] item diacentaureu[42] et diaoriganu,[43]
quae ab herbarum nominibus vocabula sumpserunt; item icesion
emplastrum, quod magis post humoris detractionem adhibendum probamus quo partes roborentur; item diaiteon emplastrum
et diadictamnu[44] et barbara et diasycaminu.[45] oportet autem
interpositis quinque diebus vel eo pluribus, detracto iamdudum
posito medicamine, perspicere profectum ac rursum imponere
omnibus locis ex anterioribus ac posterioribus corporis partibus.
116 singula enim medicamina erunt illinienda pellibus teneris atque
ita corpori addenda,[46] superposita lana molli cum levibus fas-
ciolis colliganda. et pro viribus corporis adhibenda gestatio atque unguenta congrua et defricatio.

tympaniten vero recorporativa curandum probamus curatione et conicienda etiam inflationis medela,[47] quam Graeci em-
pneumatosin vocant. adhibenda denique reflantia, ut est quod
appellamus diaspermaton vel polyarcion aut diaartymaton aut
diasamsucu[48] aut diamelilotu.[49] haec enim valent etiam ventositatem tollere. adhibenda praeterea in his ea quae superius
ordinavimus.

117 tum profectu accedente regula cyclorum adhibenda[50] natatio
maritima vel aquarum naturalium. alii vero non absurde etiam
aquae marinae vaporationem probant adhibendam, quo sudores
provocantur.[51] inquiunt enim implendum solium[51a] aqua marina
ferventi, tunc quadrangulam compaginem immittendam praeli-
gatam loris in quam erit includendus aegrotans. sed praeliganda
compago pelle ut aquae prohibeat[52] ingressum, quo exhalatione
vaporis calefactus aegrotans in sudorem venire cogatur. sed
erit aqua calefacienda innovatione frequenti ferri candentis im-
118 missione massarum. oportet autem semper aegrum adhibito
animi laxamento curari, quam Graeci diachysin vocant. quae-
renda denique animi desideria quae sine vexatione corporis prae-

---

[41] diacopraegeias (= διὰ κόπρου αἰγείας) *Reinesius 670*: diacapregias *S*: *fort. scrib.* dia
copru (a)egias (*cf. Schmid Mél. Niedermann 121*)

[42] diacentauream *S*

[43] diaoriganū *S*

[44] diadictamnum *S*

[45] diasycaminum *S*

[46] *fort.* addenda ⟨et⟩

[47] adiciendam etiam inflationis medelam *Rm*

[48] diasamsucum *S*

[49] diamelilotum *S*

sweating. But care must be taken not to injure the surface of the
5 body through the excessive use of these remedies. There is also
our own[12] preparation made with black chamaeleon; also that
which uses goat's dung and is called *diacapregias;* the plasters
that take their names from the plants centaury and origan; the
Hicesian plaster, which we believe should be applied preferably
after the removal of the fluid, in order to strengthen the parts;
and, finally, the plasters of willows, dittany, and mulberries, and
the so-called 'barbara' plasters.[13] After an interval of five days
or even longer from the time the plasters are applied, remove
them and examine their effect; then apply them once more at all
points, both on the anterior and the posterior parts of the body.
6 First smear each plaster on a thin skin and then apply it to the
body, placing soft wool over it and binding lightly with bandages. Also prescribe passive exercise, suitable anointing, and
massage in accordance with the patient's strength.

In cases of tympanites employ the metasyncritic treatment,
and also correct the inflated condition (Greek *empneumatōsis*).
Thus use resolvent drugs, e.g., Polyarchus' plaster, or those from
seeds, condiments, marjoram, or melilot; for they will remove
the inflated condition. In these cases use should also be made of
the remedies prescribed for the other forms of dropsy.
7 Then, as the patient improves, prescribe swimming in the sea
or in natural springs, in harmony with the standard cycle of
treatments. Some physicians, not without reason, recommend
a hot vapor bath with sea water to induce sweating. They have
the bathing pool filled with heated sea water, then place the patient in an oblong box and let this box down into the water with
the help of ropes. The box, however, is first covered with leather
to prevent water from seeping in, so that the patient may be
warmed by the hot vapors and thus made to sweat. But keep
renewing the heat of the water constantly by immersing masses
8 of red-hot iron. At all times see that the patient is in a relaxed
state of mind (Greek *diachysis*). And try to find mental diversions for him which, without harming his body, will afford him

12. Apparently a Methodist recipe.

13. I.e., 'foreign.' But why these plasters were so denominated was not clear even to
Galen (cf. XI. 126 Kühn).

50 *fort.* adhibenda ⟨et⟩
51 provocentur *Rm*
51a solum *S: corr. R*
52 prohibeant *S: corr. R*

beant voluptatem,[53] et amicorum convivia quae ciborum parcitate animi tamen lascivitate frequentent. utile etiam si longi
fuerint dies partiri modum sumendi cibi. facilius enim accepta
digeruntur duorum temporum oblatione divisa.

ac si iuxta ordinem datum levigati indulgentia passionis rursum fuerint accessionibus typicis aegrotantes affecti, quo iterum
impleri videantur, erit melius uti prius radicum vomitu, dehinc ante diem radicum usus album veratrum immittere; tunc
sequenti die hoc detracto radices dare vel certe hellebori decoc-
119 tionem. sed horum usum vel confectionem dexteram atque adhibendi modum Responsionum libris de adiutoriis scribentes
docuimus, et nunc exinde haec accipienda monemus.

haec est mundior atque vera hydropum curatio. etenim potui
medicamina danda cavere decet. alia enim vesicam commovent, alia intestina lacerando ulcerant vel dysentericam faciunt
passionem, alia stomachum vertunt et fastidium generant cibi
et sitim extendunt. quapropter si cogentibus rebus utendum
viderimus quibusdam aquiducis medicaminibus, quae Graeci
hydragoga vocaverunt, ea dabimus his qui plurimo humore in-
120 fusi aquoso corpore laborare videntur. habere etiam convenit
curam ne rursum corpora repleantur, ex quibus est euphorbium
mulso commixtum poto datum vel ovis sorbilibus aspersum,
duorum vel trium cochleariorum quantitate, vel decoctio radicum aut squillae.[54] oportet autem squillae libras duas omni
purgamento absolutas quo ad[55] unam libram redigatur,[56] con-
cisas in vas fictile novum praelitum mitti, tum adiectis vini sextariis tribus, quibus ad tertias[57] decoctis ex ipso liquore erunt ad
duo cochlearia aegrotanti danda, et proficiente curatione usque
121 ad unciae unius accedere modum. sed hoc erit post gestationem
adhibendum vel post perunctionem corporis et ante sumptionem
cibi,[58] plurimo interiecto tempore. ex decoctione autem radicum
duos vel tres cyathos dandos probamus. sin vero etiam urinam
quis voluerit commovere, erunt omnia aromatica[59] probanda[60]

[53] praebeant voluptatem *Rm*: praeveniant voluntatem *S*: cf. *Chr. v. 86, 135*

[54] squilli *S*: corr. *Rm*

[55] quod ad *S*: corr. *R, nisi fort.* quoad ad

[56] redigantur *Rm*

[57] *fort.* tertiam

[58] cibi *Rm*: cum *S*

[59] diuretica *Rm*

[60] probanda *scripsi: an* adhibenda? praebenda *Rm*: prohibenda ⟨et adhibenda⟩
Schmid RPh 139: prohibenda *S, quod si retineas, scribas fortasse* ⟨sed⟩ quae ... zinziberis,
haec *etc.*

pleasure. And let him take his meals in the company of friends, a practice that will keep him cheerful even though he is permitted little food. It is also beneficial, when the days are long, to have him take his meal in two parts, for the food is more easily digested if divided and thus given in two servings.

Now if the patient is relieved of the attack and experiences a regular interval of remission followed by another periodic attack, and is observed to be filled [with fluid] again, it will be best to employ radishes in the first instance to induce vomiting. The day before using them, however, insert white hellebore into them; and on the next day remove the hellebore and give the patient the radishes. Or else use a decoction of hellebore for this

9 purpose. We have described the proper use of these vomitives, that is, their preparation and the method of administering them, in the section on remedies of the treatise entitled *Answers*. For this information we now refer the reader to that treatise.

The above is the sound and proper method of treating dropsy. And one should try to avoid giving the patient drugs to drink, since some affect the bladder, others ulcerate and wound the intestines or cause dysentery, still others cause gagging, a loathing for food, and an increased desire for drink. And so, drugs for the purpose of drawing off water (Greek *hydragōga*) should be given only if circumstances obviously compel their use in cases where there is a great suffusion of fluid and the patient is suffering from

20 the watery condition of his body. Measures should also be taken to prevent the body from becoming filled again. For this purpose two or three spoonfuls of a mixture of spurge and mead may be used, with the addition, if desired, of soft eggs; a decoction of radishes or squill is also beneficial. In the case of squill, take two pounds, wash away all foreign matter and reduce the weight to about a pound, chop it up, and place it in a new earthen vessel thoroughly luted. Add three sextarii of wine, boil down to a third of the original amount, and give the patient about two spoonfuls of the liquid that remains. As the treatment pro-

21 gresses, gradually increase the amount up to one ounce. This medicine should be given after passive exercise or anointing of the body, and a long time before the taking of food. In the case of the decoction of radishes, let the patient take two or three cyathi. But if one wants to induce urination, give the patient any of the aromatic drugs, not those that are too potent, but rather

quae non curiosa sed magis simplicia esse videantur, ut est decoctio seminis cucumerum vel feniculi aut dauci aut apii, anesi,
petroselini, item mentae, asari, nardi, squinanti, zinziberis.
haec singula vel cum vino vel ex ipsis confecta erunt offerenda.
ac si ex his humor detrahi non potuerit, oportebit tamquam
alienum paracentesi[61] auferre.

122   sed nunc decet, prius quam ipsius officii usum doceamus, his
respondere qui istius[62] curationis adhibendae dissonantia iudicia
posuerunt. antiquorum igitur aliqui incongruam[63] paracentesin
dicunt, ut Euenor libro quinto Curationum, Erasistratus libro
quo De hydrope scripsit et eius sectatores, Thessalus secundo
libro Regulari. alii vero congruam laudaverunt, ut Asclepiades
libro quo De hydrope scripsit et Themison secundo libro Tardarum passionum, quibus etiam nos iuxta Sorani sententiam
consentimus.

    adsertores tamen primae sententiae, hoc est istius repro-
123 bandae curationis, haec dicunt: 'peritoneos[64] membrana [a][65]
natura nervosa esse perspicitur, et est omne quod nervosae fuerit
qualitatis punctionibus inimicum siquidem consensus ingerat.[66]
praeterea spirationis naturalis causa, qua nos aerem recipere atque reddere haustu potili necesse est, intestina quoque commoventur, quibus superficies corporis consequenter tangitur. et est
periculum haec[67] paracentesi[68] vulnerare[69] loca, quippe cum non
solum corruptus humor detrahi videatur, verum etiam naturalis
saepe spiritus excludatur: quod est vehementer corporibus
noxium. dehinc etiam post effectum punctionis aliqui aegri[70]
sua vulnera resolventes voto prius torporis deponendi[71] vitam
124 quoque liquerunt. item neque tempus sibi conveniens hoc genus
adiutorii habere videtur. etenim passione constituta vel superpositione sive lenimento, aliud tempus mitigationem demonstrat, at[72] aliud[73] resumptionem vel recorporationem. paracentesis vero conturbat atque vires corporis tollit, et non recorporativa virtute medetur, sed usum recorporativum impedit. ad
summam nemo, inquiunt, salvatus est eorum qui per paracentesin curati sunt. quapropter adhibenda negatur.'

[61] paracentesin S: corr. Rm   [62] iustius S: corr. R   [63] congruam S: corr. Rm
[64] peritonei S (cf. Chr. v. 127)   [65] seclusi   [66] an ingeratur?   [67] haec Rm: hanc S
[68] paracentesi R: paracentesin S   [69] vulnerari R   [70] aegris S: corr. R
[71] torporis deponendi] passionis deponendae Rm, coll. 127
[72] at scripsi: aut S: om. Rm   [73] aliud Rm: aliam S

the simple substances, e.g., a decoction of cucumber seed, fennel, Cretan carrot, celery, anise, parsley, mint, hazelwort, spikenard, rush, and ginger. These should be given alone or in wine, and mixtures of several of them may also be made. But if the fluid cannot be drawn off by these drugs, it will have to be removed as foreign matter by tapping.

22   But now, before we explain the procedure of tapping, we must reply to those who have held conflicting opinions on this treatment. Some of the physicians of the past declare that the use of tapping is improper; among them are Euenor in Book V of his *Treatments*, Erasistratus in his work *On Dropsy*, followers of Erasistratus, and Thessalus in Book II of his work *On Regimen*. Others, however, consider tapping a suitable remedy, e.g., Asclepiades in his book *On Dropsy* and Themison in Book II of his *Chronic Diseases*. We, too, on the authority of Soranus, agree with this latter group.

Now those who hold the former opinion and reject tapping
23   argue as follows: 'The peritoneal membrane is by nature fibrous, and anything of this character has a hostile reaction when pricked, because it gives rise to sympathetic pains. Again, in the normal process of breathing, in which air must be drawn in like a fluid and exhaled again, the intestines are also moved, and these in turn are in contact with the surface of the body. Now it is dangerous to puncture these parts by the process of tapping, for while the corrupted fluid is being withdrawn, normal pneuma, too, will often be driven out. This loss of pneuma is extremely harmful to the body. Moreover, even after the opening has been made, some patients, in their desire to be rid of the feeling of numbness as soon as possible, remove the bandage
24   from their wounds and as a result lose their life. Again, there is apparently no proper time for this kind of treatment. For the disease is either in a period of attack or in an interval of remission; in the former case a soothing treatment is required, in the latter a restorative or a metasyncritic treatment. Tapping, however, agitates the body and impairs its strength. Not only does it exert no metasyncritic curative powers, but it even impedes the use of metasyncritic measures. In short, of those patients treated by tapping, not one has been cured. Therefore its use is to be rejected.'

item Erasistratus ait quod iecore in duritia constituto obesse paracentesis videatur, siquidem gravatio iecoris tumentis toleretur humoris substantia sublevata atque natans in liquidis; quibus effusis omnis gravedo partium tumentium quae diaphrag-
125 mati sunt natura connexae atque venae maiori, [atque contendit][74] quam Graeci quilen appellant, adductione sui tumores ingerant vicinarum ac deinde celerem faciant mortem. item Ptolemaeus Erasistrati sectator ait causam passionis esse iecoris duritiam, supercreatam vero humoris infusionem. paracentesis igitur liquorem detrahens passionem minime detrahere agnoscitur, siquidem non auferat causam ex qua humor creatus esse videatur.

sed sunt haec omnia facile expugnabilia. tunc enim vulnerata nervositas in tumorem venire recte iudicatur, quoties naturali
126 habitu fuerit constituta. nunc autem morbo vitiata peritoneos[75] membrana contra naturam habere perspicitur, et non similia atque eadem sequentur naturaliter[76] vel contra naturam constituta. item intestinorum vulnerationem metuere inanis timoris est, etenim exercitatis atque prudentibus hoc genus officii committitur. dehinc plurimum peritoneos[77] membrana distabit interiecti[78] humoris causa submota. spiritus vero etiam phlebotomatis sanguini iunctus excluditur, nec ilico tamen reprobanda phlebotomia, cum sit ab omnibus rectissime adiutorium comprobatum. ferendum est enim leve damnum naturalis officii quoties maior utilitas excludendae passionis promittitur.
127 solvere vero ligationem aegrotantes, et immoderato fluore ac voto[79] deponendae passionis in mortem venire, simile quiddam est tamquam phlebotomatum ligaturam medici solvere ac deinde plurimo sanguinis fluore vitam finire. haec enim non adiutorii est accusatio[80] sed stultitiae aegrotantis.

[74] *del. R: fort. transp. post* ait *huius aut praecedentis paragraphi: an scrib.* atque cavae?

[75] peritonei *S*

[76] *fort.* innaturaliter

[77] peritonei *S*

[78] interiecta *S: corr. Rm*

[79] ac voto *Rm (cf. 123):* acuto *S*

[80] accusatio *conieci:* curatio *S:* culpatio *Rm: an* causatio?

14. In ascites or tympanites (cf. 102, above); for anasarca cf. 132, below.

Moreover, Erasistratus declares that tapping is evidently harmful in cases where the liver is hard. For the heaviness of the swollen liver can be endured by the body only when the organ is buoyed up by the fluid matter and floats in the liquid. But if this liquid is removed, the whole weight of the swollen
5 parts, which by nature are connected with the diaphragm and the great vein (Greek *coelē*, 'hollow'), bears down upon the neighboring parts, causing them to become inflamed and bringing about swift death. And Ptolemaeus, a follower of Erasistratus, holds that hardness of the liver is the cause of dropsy and that the spreading of the fluid appears later. Therefore, in his opinion, though tapping removes the fluid, it cannot be said to remove the disease, for it does not get rid of that which seems to generate the fluid.

Now all these arguments against tapping can be easily refuted. To be sure, it is correct to say that an injury to the fibrous structure of the peritoneum causes inflammation when this mem-
6 brane is in its normal state. But when the peritoneum is affected by disease, as in dropsy, it is obviously in an abnormal state; and it is not true that tissues in an abnormal state and those in a normal state have the same or similar reactions. Again, there is no ground for fearing that the intestines may be punctured. For a treatment like tapping is intrusted only to those who are experienced and careful. Furthermore, the peritoneum will be at a considerable distance [from the intestines],[14] its position being changed by reason of the interspersed fluid. In fact, pneuma is also lost[15] together with blood whenever venesection is performed, but one would not on that ground reject venesection, which is very properly esteemed by all as a remedy. For some small loss in normal functioning must be incurred as the price for any remedy that offers great effectiveness in driving out a disease.

7 Opponents of tapping speak of the possibility that the patient will, through a desire to be rid of the ailment, undo the bandage and thus cause an excessive flow and consequently death. But this is somewhat like the possibility that a patient after venesection will open the ligature made by the physician, and die through excessive loss of blood. For it is not the remedy but the stupidity of the patient that is to blame for this.

15. Apparently in answer to an argument that tapping would involve loss of pneuma.

habet praeterea paracentesis etiam aptissimum tempus, quod
illi inveniri negant, sicut cucurbita scarificatione adiuncta atque
hirudinum appositio, quae non in accessione aut lenimento sed
in dimissione superpositionis recte adhibenda probantur, sicut
in aliis docuimus[81] De adiutoriis specialibus scribentes. omnes
enim paracentesi curatos, ut aiunt, mori apertissime mentiun-
128 tur. nos enim quosdam vidimus evasisse. plurimi vero moriuntur siquidem medentium tardante consilio[82] serius paracentesis adhibeatur, utque[83] alii adhuc tumente[84] peritoneo[85] membrana et neque usu dextero operantes divisuram faciendo mortis periculum incurrunt. ex quibus est etiam Asclepiades qui
diviso loco fistulam relinquendam putavit, ex qua stirpis in modum impressa vel perpuncta[86] peritoneos[87] membrana[88] graves
consensus atque indignationes adferat, quippe cum saepe etiam
gelati sanguinis corpuscula irruentia vulnerum divisuris vel
quaeque externa magnos tumores atque indignationes commo-
verint.

129 Erasistrato vero causanti quod post detractionem humoris ex
iecoris duritia in passionem venerunt superiores partes, ac magis
salutares adductione quadam ponderis indignentur, erit respondendum quia plurimi hydropes sine ulla iecoris duritie in passionem venire probantur. etenim ex aliis causis fieri posse superius demonstravimus. plerisque etiam quamquam iecur du-
ruerit non necessario in hydropem venire contingit, ac saepe adductione partium vel indignatione superiorum vexari perspicimus, quo saepe tumor etiam perdiderit aegrotantes. omitto
quod iuxta eius sententiam oportebat supinis iacentibus aegrotis nullam querelam partium attestari, siquidem iecur nullo
pondere superiora distendat, hoc est discrimen, quod Graeci diaphragma appellant.

130 Asclepiades vero repentinam effusionem atque coacervatam

[81] docebimus S: corr. Friedel 45
[82] tardantes consilia S: corr. R
[83] cf. adn. ad Ac. i. 85
[84] tumentes S: corr. R
[85] peritonei S
[86] per puncta S: corr. A
[87] peritonei S
[88] membranae S: corr. R

Moreover, there is an appropriate time for tapping, despite the denials of those who reject the remedy, just as there is an appropriate time for cupping with scarification and for the application of leeches, namely, not during the attack proper nor in the interval between attacks, but in the declining phase of the attack. This we have shown in our work *On Special Remedies*. Again, the statement of these physicians that all patients who 28 are tapped for dropsy die is an obvious untruth, for we have seen some such patients who were cured. To be sure, most of them die, but that is generally because the doctors are slow in coming to a decision and tapping is administered too late. And in other cases the patient's life is endangered because the operation is performed when the peritoneum is still inflamed, or because those who make the opening are unskilful. To this latter class belongs Asclepiades, who thinks that after the opening is made a pipe should be left in it; but the pressure on the peritoneum or the piercing of it by this stemlike pipe causes severe pain and injuries. For particles of clotted blood or foreign matter often enter the open wounds and give rise to considerable inflammation and irritation.

29 Now Erasistratus argues that after the withdrawal of the fluid the hardness of the liver causes the parts above it to become diseased, that is, parts that are relatively healthy are injured because they are drawn down by the weight of the liver. Our answer to him is that most cases of dropsy arise without any hardness of the liver; for, as we have shown above, dropsy may develop from other causes. And, in fact, most cases of hardness of the liver are not followed by dropsy.[16] On the other hand, we generally observe that such patients [without incurring dropsy] are troubled by the weight of the affected parts and suffer a concomitant attack in the parts above the liver, the inflammation even resulting in death in many cases. I need not add that, according to Erasistratus' own views, if the patient[17] lies on his back, there should be no pain in the parts in question; for then the weight of the liver will not stretch the part above it, that is to say, the dividing membrane (Greek *diaphragma*).

30 Now Asclepiades holds that it is dangerous to withdraw the

16. If the text is sound, it might be best to consider this and the following sentence parenthetical and not relevant to the main argument.

17. E.g., a dropsical patient who has been tapped.

cum periculo fieri testatur, siquidem viae, quas Graeci poros
appellant, interiecto humore[89] blando se tactu contingant et
propterea illaesi maneant aegrotantes, detractione autem facta
liquorum aspero se tactu contingant atque concidentes angus-
tentur;[90] ac simili ratione etiam spiritus vehementer irruens car-
ni dolorem faciat atque inflationem et tormenta intestinorum **[91]

 est praeterea facile expugnabile Ptolomaei dictum, quod paracentesis humorem detrahens passionem non auferat. etenim
primo neque ex alio quolibet adiutorio singulari haec passio solvi
131 posse perspicitur, quippe cum sit magna atque perseverans. dehinc quaedam adiutoriorum ob relevanda accidentia passionum,
quae Graeci symptomata vocant, adhibenda probentur,[92] quamquam non totum solvere morbum videantur, ut phreneticis luce
commotis oculorum praetectio. item alia quaedam, quae[93] quamquam nihil per se medeantur, aliis tamen adiutoriis praeparent[94]
corpus vel patientem locum quo facile adiutorii beneficium su-
niat, ut[95] tonsura vel rasura capitis fluore quolibet adfectis, quo
detractis capillis illinienda medicamina constrictiva vel epithemata aut cucurbitae appositione nullis obstantibus medeantur,
quamquam sit detractio capillorum laxativa. at vero paracen-
132 tesis etiam per se plurimum medetur. relevat enim detractione
plenitudinem, tensionem[96] atque spirationis difficultatem, quam
dyspnoean vocant. et aliis adhibendis adiutoriis praeparat
partes. non enim potuerunt medicaminum illinimenta vel appositio sincera virtute ad viscera vel patientes partes pervenire,
cum interiecto humore peritoneos[97] membrana plurimum a cutibus distet. transeunt[98] autem facile ad ea ad quae destinata
erant, humoris interiecti ablatione permissa.

[89] interiecta mora S: corr. Rm

[90] augustentur S: corr. A

[91] *lacunam statui*

[92] probantur R

[93] quae *om.* R

[94] praeparant R

[95] ut R: ac S

[96] detractionem plenitudinis tensionis S: corr. R

[97] peritonei S

[98] transeant S: corr. R

18. We should expect here some refutation of Asclepiades' argument.

fluid all at once and in a single operation. For, so long as there is fluid interspersed among the channels (Greek *poroe*), the latter are in gentle contact with one another, and for that reason the patient suffers no injury; but when the fluid has all been withdrawn, they grate roughly against one another and are contracted and constricted. Similarly, says Asclepiades, a strong rush of pneuma also causes pain and swelling of the flesh and cramps of the intestines. . . .[18]

Again, we may easily demolish the argument of Ptolemaeus that, though tapping removes the fluid, it does not get rid of the disease. For, to begin with, it is obvious that dropsy cannot be overcome by any other single remedy, since it is a grave and persistent disease. Again, in treating a disease some remedies are administered to relieve the concomitant conditions (Greek *symptōmata*) of the disease, without being able to overcome the disease as a whole, e.g., covering the eyes in cases of phrenitis when the patient is disturbed by light. Furthermore, certain other treatments, though they possess no curative powers in themselves, are administered in order to prepare the body or the part affected for other remedies, so that the beneficial effect of the latter may be easily obtained, e.g., cutting or shaving off the hair of the head in cases involving any kind of flux. (The purpose of removing the hair is merely to make possible the rubbing-on of astringent liniments and epithems and the application of cupping instruments, so that these may exert their healing effect without any obstacles. And yet, the removal of hair in itself has a relaxing effect.[19]) But tapping, on the other hand, has a strong curative power in and of itself. In fact, by withdrawing fluid, it relieves congestion, distention, and difficulty in breathing (Greek *dyspnoea*). It also prepares the parts for the application of other remedies. For the drugs that are rubbed on the body or otherwise applied cannot reach the viscera or the affected parts with unimpaired potency so long as the peritoneum is kept at a considerable distance from the outer skin by the fluid interspersed between them.[20] But when the obstacle formed by this fluid is removed, the effect of the drugs is readily transmitted to the parts for which they are intended.

19. I.e., in contrast with a primary remedy, an ancillary remedy need not even have the general effect (relaxing or astringent) required by the nature of the disease.

20. As in anasarca (Caelius' *intercus*).

quapropter paracentesin adhibendam probamus, sed non his qui viribus fuerint fatigati aut adhuc in tumore peritonei membranae constituti, addentes etiam vel praedicentes periculum. plurimi enim quamquam alterius[99] superesse vitae potuerint et sine ullo dolore mortem capere, paracentesis cura celerem mortem pertulerunt.

133   **[100] usque ad inane penetrandus, sicut in phlebotomandis facimus, sed ab umbilico inferius his qui levius afficiuntur, praecaventes venarum divisuras. ac deinde muliebri cathetere liquorem detrahimus, qui saepe aquosus, saepe fulvus aut sanguinolentus vel spumosus excluditur. quod quidem etiam ante factam divisuram plerique futurum signis apprehendere voluerunt, quorum alii talem fore dixerunt qualis urina fuerit aegrotantis, alii qualis color apparuerit cutis, alii quolibet viscere patiente sanguinolentum, non patiente vero ex causa avidissimi potus hydropismo concepto vel salis potu, mundum atque perspicuum liquorem fore.

134   sed haec praeter quod falsissimae sunt opinionis etiam ad mutationem chirurgiae inutiliter quaesita videntur, nisi solum quod recte probamus per cathetera liquorem, si res[101] patiuntur, semel atque eodem tempore omnem auferendum. sin vero aliqua obstiterint, post primam detractionem motarium aqua infusum supra divisuram resimplicantes,[102] spongiam desuper mollem apponemus ac deinde levi fasciola amplexo loco paululum differimus, quo turbatio corporis resolvatur. ac deinde resumpto aegrotante eodem die residuum detrahimus humorem; sin minus, alia die, manibus comprimentes subiectas partes, congrue aegrotante locato, hoc est schemate competenti.

135   ac si forte rursum confluente humore fuerit repletus vel virium debilitas prohibuerit eodem tempore totum detrahi, tunc interiectis duobus diebus vel quantum vires permiserint residuum retrahimus,[103] sed alio in loco divisuram facientes, vel si rursum

---

[99] ulterius *Rm*

[100] *133–55* (paracentesin prohibet) *habet S ad Chr. v. 14* (*post* cathedra vel sella): *huc pertinere notavit Rm. suppleas* ⟨venter igitur est⟩ *vel sim. vide Ilberg Vorläufiges 8*

[101] vires *Rm* (*cf. 135*)

[102] res implicantes *S*: *corr. Bendz Eran 43. 52, coll. Chr. v. 20*

[103] detrahimus *R*

We therefore approve of the use of tapping, though not for patients whose strength is exhausted or whose peritoneum is still inflamed. But, in prescribing tapping, we must point out the danger in advance. For many a patient, though he might have survived his neighbor and subsequently died a painless death, has met a swift death because of treatment by tapping.

33 [In tapping for dropsy] cut [into the abdomen] as far as the cavity, as in venesection.[21] In mild cases make the incision below the umbilicus, and in all cases be careful not to cut any veins. Then withdraw the fluid, using a female catheter. The fluid as it comes out is sometimes watery and at other times yellowish, bloody, or frothy. Many physicians claim that even before the opening is made they can tell by certain signs what the color of the fluid will be. Thus some declare it will be the same color as the urine of the patient, others that it will be the same color as the skin. And still others hold that, if some vital organ is affected, the fluid will be bloody but that, if no vital organ is affected and the patient has incurred dropsy by drinking greedily or drinking salt water, the fluid will then be colorless and transparent.

34 But, apart from the fact that these views are untrue, they are quite useless as a basis for modifying the surgical procedure. With regard to this procedure we hold, and properly so, that, if circumstances permit, all the fluid should be removed by the catheter at one and the same time. But if there are any obstacles, after the first portion has been withdrawn, soak a linen cloth in water, spread it over the opening, and place a soft sponge over the cloth. Then bind the part with a loose bandage and postpone further withdrawal of fluid for a short while, so that the bodily shock may be overcome. And if the patient has recovered, withdraw the rest of the fluid on the same day, but otherwise on the next day [squeezing out the fluid] by manual pressure on the parts, placing the patient properly, i.e., in a suitable position.

35 If the patient's body happens to be filled again by another suffusion of fluid or if weakness prevents the removal of all the fluid at one time, then after an interval of two days withdraw as much of the remainder as the patient's strength will permit. But make the opening in another place, and if a third withdrawal is

21. The point of the comparison is that in venesection the incision is made through the walls of the vein and into its inner cavity.

oportuerit, tertio. etenim prima divisura servata distans aut
cohaerens soluta tumores vel consensus ingerit vehementes.

tum perfecta humoris detractione, neque abstinentia utemur,
ut Asclepiades, neque plurimum damus cibum, sed pro modo vi-
136 rium. etenim abstinentia omni ex parte adhibita vires vexat,
quippe post plurimam detractionem. multi item oblatio cibi
gravans opprimit corpus potius quam resumit. erunt autem
ante cibum sensim perungendi atque reficiendi facilibus et poto
sufficienti. ac si dolores aliqui emerserint, vaporationibus solvendi atque cataplasmatibus mitigandi; tunc indulgentia relaxatis vel forte non emergentibus, adhibemus ea quae tumorem
fieri non sinant, et superimpositis spongiis conligamus. transacto tumoris metu, magis ventris folliculum vel cutem intestinis
cogimur adserere, atque similiter cetera quae in tumore fuerant
constituta, ut nuper docuimus.

137　　aegrotantes praeterea navicula exerceri hortamur, et paulatim
recorporativae subicimus curationi. ac si neque ita fuerint reso-
luti, utemur helleboro iisdem curationibus insistentes, donec
corpus repetat fortitudo atque densior vel coacta ⟨caro⟩[104] noscatur attestante rubore. haec est secundum methodum hydropum curatio.

plurimi autem aliarum[105] sectarum principes atque nostrae
veteres nihil veri curantes ac magis contemptu quodam astruc-
tiones corporum aspernantes, solius detrahendi humoris inten-
138 tione traducti, quoquo modo id perficiendum crediderunt, immensa siti atque fame aegros afficientes, corpore concavo pectine
decurso. et mille praeterea urinalibus medicaminibus,[106] quae
diuretica vocant, vesicam commovendam probant, et ventrifluis
potionibus, quae catartica appellant, ventrem provocandum dicunt, cocco cnidio atque lepida cyprina et chamelaea[107] et hippo-
phaë herba et ex crotonibus confecto oleo cicino, item neoro,[108]
ex quibus cunctis stomachus vexatur atque cibi appetitum amit-

---

[104] add. R
[105] aliarum Am: earum S　　　　　[107] chamaeleae S
[106] medicaminum S: corr. R　　　[108] fort. scrib. cneoro (Rm)

required, in a third place. For, if the first incision is kept open or is reopened after being permitted to close, there will in either case be inflammation and severe pains.

Then when the withdrawal of fluid is completed, neither starve the patient, as Asclepiades does, nor give him a great deal of

36 food, but base the diet on his strength. For complete fasting impairs the strength, especially after the withdrawal of so much matter; on the other hand, a great deal of food weighs down and overwhelms the body instead of restoring its strength. Before giving food, anoint the patient gently; then refresh him with easily digestible food and sufficient drink. If any pains develop, use hot applications and poultices to relieve and overcome them. When these pains have been mitigated by the soothing treatment, or if, as it happens, they do not develop at all, apply treatment to prevent the occurrence of inflammation, place sponges over the parts, and bandage them. When the danger of inflammation is over, press the abdominal casing,[22] i.e., the skin, more closely to the intestines; and take similar measures in the case of the other parts which had previously been distended, as we have indicated.

137   In addition urge the patient to take passive exercise by sailing in a boat. And gradually institute the metasyncritic treatment. If the disease is not then overcome, employ hellebore and continue with the same treatments as before until the body is strong again and the flesh is firm and compact and of a ruddy complexion. This concludes the account of the treatment of dropsy according to the Methodists.

But many leaders of other sects and former leaders of our own sect, caring nothing for truth, or rather despising and disdaining the problem of rebuilding the body, are concerned solely with the withdrawal of the fluid. They believe that this may be done

138 in any way at all; they subject the patient to extreme thirst and hunger, stroke the body with a concave comb, and, in addition, excite the bladder with countless drugs to promote urination (Greek *diurētica*), and agitate the stomach and bowels with no end of purgative drugs (Greek *cathartica*). Among the latter they use Cnidian berry, flakes of copper, chamelaea, spurge, castor oil obtained from the castor-oil plant, and cneorum. But all these drugs adversely affect the gullet and cause loss of appetite,

22. Possibly the reference is to the peritoneum.

tit, sitis incenditur, corpus defluit, sanguis corrumpitur atque
humor detractus renascitur, vires auferuntur, siquidem neque
potestas moderandae detractionis sit in artificis manu. item
quidam tamquam siccabile[109] humoris ophiten lapidem ligave-
139 runt, experimentis[110] aegrorum salutem credentes. singulatim
denique nobilium medicorum historiam ordinamus.[111]

Herodicus igitur, ut Asclepiades memorat, ventris adhibet
purgationem atque post cenam vomitus, qui sint implebiles potius quam siccabiles. tunc vaporationibus tepidis aceti decocti
exhalatione confectis utitur, vel aquae marinae admixta thallia
herba atque hyssopo et his similibus. vesicis bubulis repletis
corpus vaporandum probat, vel aliis quibusque maioribus inflatis tumentia loca pulsari iubet. sic etiam antiquissimus Euryphon.

Hippocrates vero libris quos Ad sententias cnidias scripsit
magis utendum dicit egestate atque vaporatione et continentia
140 et danda sicca vel arida quaeque et acriora mandenda. sic[112]
enim †aequibilis†[113] aeger fiat, hoc est urina facilior. ac si spiratio difficilis fuerit, quam dyspnoean vocant, et tempus aestatis
et aetas[114] media, dicit ex brachio phlebotomandos, et post detractionem factam dat panem calidum vino infusum atque oleo
et carnem suillam ex aceto decoctam. dat etiam cantharidas
tres, detracto capite et pedibus et pinnis, in tribus cyathis aquae
contritas.

sed neque quo tempore exercitio utendum sit manifestans,
neque usque quo mandenda sint acriora vel quando vaporationes
adhibendae. dehinc si phlebotomare oportuerit, non solum
aestivo tempore ac media aetate,[115] sed etiam omni tempori at-
141 que aetati convenire probamus. est praeterea importunum
vinum ac repugnans eo tempore commodis phlebotomiae. item
cantharides humorem commovent. carnis quoque offerendae
tempus significare neglexit.

---

[109] siccabilem R

[110] experimentis *Haller*: expertis *edd.* (*ironice?*)

[111] ordinemus R

[112] sic R*m* (*coll. graec.*): si S

[113] *fort. latet vocabulum ab* aqua *derivatum quod* οὑρητικώτατος *vertat* (*v. TLL s.v.* 'aequibilis'). *an* aequabilis (*cf.* ob aequandum corpus, *154*), *magis si Sorani* (*Caelii?*) *textus Hippocraticus* ἰσχνός *pro* ἰσχύι *praebebat?*

[114] aestas *edd.*

[115] aestate *edd.*

thirst, dissolution of the body, decomposition of the blood, reappearance of fluid of the kind withdrawn, and loss of strength. For one who administers such purgatives is unable to control the amount of matter withdrawn. Some prescribe the use of a serpentine as an amulet, in the belief that the stone will dry up the fluid; in so doing they intrust the safety of the patient to blind experiments. We now give an account of the views of the famous physicians, one by one.

Herodicus, according to Asclepiades, purges the stomach and bowels and prescribes vomiting after eating, a procedure which causes an accumulation, rather than a draining, of fluid. He also applies heat, using the vapors from boiling vinegar or sea water with the addition of caper, hyssop, and similar substances. He fills ox skins with these substances and has the body steamed in this way. Or he inflates other large bladders and uses them to strike the swollen parts. The ancient physician, Euryphon, prescribes the same treatment

Hippocrates, in his work *Against the Cnidian Sentences*,[23] prescribes a regimen involving rigorous exercise, vapor baths, and temperance. He gives the patient all kinds of dry and sharp food to eat; for thus, he believes, . . . urination will be easier for the patient. If there is difficulty in breathing (Greek *dyspnoea*), then, provided that it is summer and the patient is in the prime of life, Hippocrates prescribes venesection at the arm, and after the withdrawal of blood gives the patient hot bread dipped in wine and olive oil and pork cooked in vinegar. He also prescribes[24] the taking of three blister beetles pounded up in three cyathi of water, the head, feet, and wings being removed.

But Hippocrates does not make clear when the patient is to exercise or how long he must take sharp food or when the vapor baths are to be given. Again, if venesection is necessary, we believe that it should be performed not only in the summer and in the prime of life but at every season and age. Furthermore, wine is harmful and is given at a time when it counteracts the advantages of venesection. Again, the blister beetles agitate the fluid. Finally, Hippocrates fails to indicate the time when pork is to be given.[25]

23. *Regimen in Acute Diseases* (Appendix), I. 172. 3 Kühlewein (= II. 498 Littré).

24. I. 175. 10 Kühlewein (= II. 512 Littré).

25. The time seems to be indicated broadly in the Latin, but this is not the case in the Greek.

Diocles libro quo De passionibus et causis et curationibus scripsit siccandos inquit ac mediocriter vaporandos et deambulationi tradendos aegrotantes, et plurimos sudores commovendos vel vomitum, et urinam provocandam[116] cardamomo[117] et apii semine resoluto suco herbae salviae; item diagridium[118] quantum ventrem valeat semel deducere, et in aceto panem solutum, et piscem salsum[119] vel pisces elixos et assos vel silurum piscem, olera, radices, allium, origanum, rutam, satureiam, vinum album

142 et non aquatum, et ferarum carnem. in deambulationibus ventrem iubet contineri, ceteras corporis partes defricari exceptis cruribus.

sed hic quoque communi ceterorum subicitur accessioni.[120] solum praedamnamus quod humorem detrahens purgativis atque urinalibus medicaminibus et vomitu et sudoribus provocatis, quibus ex rebus sudor movendus sit tacuerit vel vomitus. item deambulatio saepe laboriosa et piscis silurus bromosus et allium inflabile et plurima ferarum carnium malos habere sucos probantur. inde item quae sint olera deligenda memorare neglexit, et neque fortificari venter fricatione[121] vel crura aut totum corpus recte potest, cum nullum modum vel tempus memoravit.

143 Praxagoras secundo libro Curationum cataplasmatibus utitur et malagmatibus sudorem moventibus et urinalibus medicamentis aliis atque aliis et ventrem deducentibus, similiter cono et foliis hederae et semine coliculi agrestis aut nasturtii aut centaurea vel allio, pipere et pseudodictamno aut dauco et chamaepitys herbae[122] et petroselini semine vel graminis vel quolibet horum similium. et sudorum diurna provocatione corpus deducit. utitur vomitu non solum ieiuno verum etiam post vespertinum cibum, et aegros plurimum potat, ex quibus sensuales

144 viae implentur. utitur etiam cataplasmatibus aromaticis quorum species non designat sed solum cum †moromeli†[123] vel lini semine adhiberi iubet, vel malis cydoniis aut caricis vel adipe

---

[116] urinam provocandam: ⟨ac ventrem⟩ *Rm*: urinam ⟨et ventrem⟩ provocandum *Wellmann*

[117] cardamomo *scripsi*: diagridio *edd.*

[118] diagridium *scripsi*: cardamomum *edd.*: cardamomo *Wellmann*

[119] salsum ⟨dandum⟩ *R*

[120] accusationi *Rm*   [121] ventrificatione̅ *S*: corr. *Rm*

[122] chamaepity herba *R*: *fort. scrib.* chamaepityis herbae

[123] *an* meliloto (*vel* -i)?

Diocles, in discussing dropsy in his work *On Diseases and Their Causes and Treatment*, prescribes the draining-off of the fluid, mild applications of heat, walking exercises, profuse sweating, and vomiting. And he stimulates urination with cardamum and celery seed dissolved in the juice of sage plant. He also uses scammony juice,[26] in an amount which will effect a single purge of the stomach, bread soaked in vinegar, pickled fish, boiled or broiled fish such as sheatfish, vegetables, radishes, garlic, marjoram, rue, savory, white wine undiluted with water, and the flesh of game animals. In connection with the walking exercises he requires that the abdomen be held, and the other parts of the body, with the exception of the legs, massaged.

Now Diocles is open to the same general refutation as the other physicians; but we confine our criticism to the following points. In ordering the withdrawal of the fluid with purgatives and diuretics and through the stimulation of vomiting and sweating, he fails to indicate what substances are to be used to induce vomiting and sweating. Again, walking is often strenuous for the patient, sheatfish is foul-smelling, garlic produces gas, and the flesh of game animals generally contains unwholesome juices. Moreover, Diocles does not tell us which vegetables to use; nor can massage be properly applied to the strengthening of the abdomen, legs, and whole body, since he does not indicate the amount or the time of such massage.

Praxagoras, in Book II of his *Treatments*, employs poultices and emollient plasters that induce sweating, and also various diuretics and purgatives. Similarly, he employs pine cone, ivy foliage, wild cabbage seed, cress seed, centaury, garlic, pepper, false dittany, Cretan carrot, the seed of ground pine, parsley, or grass, or any other similar substance; and, by stimulating perspiration every day, he reduces the bodily swelling. He also stimulates vomiting not only on an empty stomach but even after the evening meal, and he gives the patient a great deal to drink; but both these procedures cause the sensory channels to be congested. Furthermore, he prescribes poultices of aromatic substances. But he fails to identify these substances and merely orders them to be applied with . . . flaxseed, quinces, dried fig,

26. I have transposed the position of scammony juice and cardamum as found in the earlier editions. Scammony juice is pre-eminently purgative; cardamum, diuretic. This transposition makes unnecessary further alteration in the Latin text of the preceding clause.

et aqua aut uvae lupinae vel apii suco, equidem virtutis repug-
natione omnia confundens, siquidem alia sint constrictiva, ut
mala, alia laxativa, ut plurima ceterarum specierum. deinde
post oris collutionem sorbiles dat cibos quibus ventrem facilem
se facere pollicetur. item potum repugnantem ordinat:[124] dat
enim acetum vel puscam vel his rursum contraria, ut mulsam.
quibus confusa regula etiam secundum ipsum approbatur.

145   Erasistratus libro quo De hydrope scripsit deambulationem
ordinat adhibendam prius quam aeris aestus ardescant, tamquam curans.[125] sed si ventris, inquit, facilitas non fuerit, prohibenda medicamina atque legumina et olera, cum sint plurima
olerum quae molliant ventrem sine ulla corporis vexatione. item
plurimo cibo aegros nutriendos probat cum sit ex parvo saepe
indigestionis metus. si neque, inquit, venter fuerit motus, adhibendum clysterem simplicem, hoc est qui nulla sit acriori materia confectus. cibum partitur cibo [vel cena],[126] et ante ves-
146 peram aegros deambulatione moveri iubet. tunc initio noctis
reficit, quando etiam sanis metus est digerendi. post cibum
praeterea perungit in lectulo et certo numero utitur fricationum.
dat catapotia medicaminum ante utramque cibi refectionem in
fabae[127] modo[128] pro viribus aegrotantis, neque plus decem neque
minus quinque numero, et eorum materiam tacet. solum memorat quod iecorosis haec catapotia congrua videantur atque ad
urinales partes venientia plurimum faciant mictum. tum post
catapotia dari iubet cibo panem ex farina sesami et sale[129] obdul-
catum ne sitim faciat, non discernens tempus drimyphagiae.
147 tum inquit dandos pisces atque carnem gallinarum vel ferarum
et agnorum et haedorum et sorbilia plurima cum melle vel lacte,
non advertens lactis et mellis qualitatem in corruptionem facile

[124] repugnantem ordinat *conieci*: repugnante mordicativo *S*

[125] ⟨in aestate solum⟩ curans *R*

[126] cibo vel coena *S*: prandio et coena *Rm, coll. 147*

[127] favi *S*: corr. *Sm*

[128] modum *R*

[129] sale *Rm, coll. Chr. iv. 12*: salsum *S*

---

27. Or if the reading of *R* is adopted: 'as if the disease had to be treated only in summer.'

or fat, and water or the juice of strychnos or celery. But in this prescription he mingles all sorts of substances of conflicting properties, some of them astringent, such as the quinces, and most of the others relaxing. Then, after having the patient wash his mouth, Praxagoras prescribes soft food; such food, he asserts, will ease the bowels. But he gives drinks of conflicting properties: on the one hand, vinegar or a mixture of vinegar and water, and, on the other hand, liquids that are the opposite of these, e.g., hydromel. Such are the confusions which are involved even in his own account of the treatment.

5   Erasistratus in his book *On Dropsy* prescribes walking as exercise in the hours before the air becomes too warm, as if that will cure dropsy.[27] If the bowels are not soft, he forbids the use of drugs, legumes, and other vegetables, though there are numerous vegetables which will soften the bowels without injuring the body in any way. Again, he gives the patient a great deal of food, though there is often reason to fear indigestion from only a little food. If the bowels do not move, he prescribes a simple clyster, that is, one which does not contain any sharp substance. He divides the patient's food into two meals,[28] prescribing a
6 walk as exercise before evening, and then giving the patient his dinner at nightfall. But one must feel concern about the digestion even of healthy persons who eat at that time. And after the meal Erasistratus has the patient anointed in bed and rubbed a certain number of times. Before each meal he prescribes medicine in the form of pills the size of a bean, having the patient take no less than five and no more than ten, depending on his strength. But he does not disclose the composition of these pills, merely stating that they seem to be beneficial for disease of the liver and that when they reach the urinary parts they stimulate profuse urination. Then after the pills he prescribes food, first giving the patient bread made out of sesame flour and seasoned with salt[29] to avoid causing thirst. But in this Erasistratus shows
7 that he does not know the proper time for the acrid diet. After the bread he gives the patient fish, poultry, game, lamb, or kid, as well as many soft preparations with milk or honey. But he is unaware that the character of milk and honey is such that they

28. This seems to be the idea, but the text is very doubtful.

29. This is a strange way of obviating thirst and makes one suspect the text. If *salsum* (S) be retained, the meaning may be 'both salted and sweetened, etc.'

venire. nunc dat potum parvum; et non post prandium sed post
vespertinum cibum hoc convenire dicit, ut etiam similiter memorat Philistionis frater. probat etiam ante alios cibos accipienda arida fica[130] pinguia duo vel tria mox contusa atque oleo
tincta. sed haec omnino digestione difficilia iudicantur. prohibet praeterea lavacrum vel plurimo temporis intervallo permittit, et non designat quod illud vel quantum sit tempus.

148   utitur etiam malagmatibus, cataplasmatibus[131] cum somno
cubaverint aegrotantes, non tamen designans ⟨ea. et est in-
ter⟩[132] eos qui coacervatam ac vehementem humoris detractionem reprobant, quam Graeci cenosin vocant, et propterea
etiam paracentesin, quod quidem incongrue[133] dictum superius
docuimus. item tumore in iecore constituto, attestantibus febribus, ob tumoris medelam cataplasmatibus utitur ex malis
cum vino, constringens ea quae laxamentum poscere videntur.
et ad digestionem faciendam[134] ex ficu atque chamelaea et cha-
149   maepity utitur cataplasmatibus. item ad eliciendum quicquam
in locis constitutum utitur diapeganu,[135] quod ex ruta conficitur,
et nihil de temporibus memorat adiutoriorum.

    Asclepiades etiam, libro quo De hydrope scripsit, parvo hu-
more collecto sive plurimo, necdum tamen pedibus aut cruribus
infuso, athletarum regulam adhibendam probat ex plurima deambulatione atque cursu et defricatione[136] retento spiritu; tunc
cibo dandum panem diligenter elaboratum atque exercitum cum
piscibus natura duris. ac si inferiores humor occupaverit partes,
plurimos prohibet motus et medicamina ventriflua atque uri-
150   nalia. utitur autem paracentesi sed omnino ex angusto atque
parvo foramine. in leucophlegmatia vero fricationes[137] et cataplasmata frigerantia ex malo cydonio et murra et vitis anulis,
quos helicas vocant, et malo punico et lenticula et herbo atque
pulento veteri et alumine vel ruta et bulbo et melle et origano et
thymo et nitro et caricis, et ex vesicis illisionem adhibendam
probat. laudat etiam punctionem quatuor digitis a talo dis-
tantem faciendam superius ab interiore parte, sicut in phlebotomia servatur, ut per eandem punctionem humore effuso cor-
151   pora releventur: si minus, scarificatione altiore utendum refe-

[130] arida fica *Rm, coll. 113:* aridi fici *S*
[131] ⟨et⟩ cataplasmatibus *R*   [132] *supplevi*   [133] congrue *S: corr. Rm*
[134] a digestione facienda *S:* ob digestionem faciendam *R*
[135] diapegano *S*   [136] defricatione *Rm:* refricatione *S*   [137] fricationes ⟨adhibet⟩ *R*

easily spoil. He then permits the patient to drink a little, holding this to be beneficial after the evening meal but not after lunch; the brother of Philistion also holds a similar view. Before the patient takes any other food at his meals Erasistratus has him eat two or three rich dried figs, freshly pounded up and dipped in olive oil, though figs are considered quite hard to digest. Again, he forbids bathing or permits it only at long intervals, but he does not state what kind of bathing or the length of the time interval.

48   Erasistratus also prescribes the application of emollient plasters and poultices when the patient goes to sleep, but he does not specify the drugs. And he is one of those who reject the forceful withdrawal of all the fluid at once (Greek *cenōsis*, 'evacuation'), and consequently he also rejects tapping, a view which, as we have shown above, is unsound. Again, when there is inflammation of the liver accompanied by fever, he employs poultices of quinces and wine to heal the inflammation; that is, he treats with astringents a condition that obviously requires relaxing measures. To aid digestion he uses poultices of fig, chamelaea, and

49 ground pine. And to draw out matter present in the affected parts he employs the plaster of rue (Greek *pēganon*). But he says nothing about the times when these remedies should be applied.

Asclepiades in his book *On Dropsy* holds that in cases where fluid has already gathered, whether in small or in large amount, but has not yet spread to the feet or the legs, an athlete's regimen should be prescribed, with considerable walking and running, as well as massage while the patient holds his breath. He then prescribes as food bread carefully kneaded and prepared and fish tough by nature. But if the fluid spreads to the lower parts, he forbids much exercise and also the use of purgatives

50 and diuretics. He does employ tapping, but from a small narrow opening. In leucophlegmatia he prescribes massage and cooling poultices of quince, myrrh, vine tendrils (Greek *helices*), pomegranate, lentil, bitter vetch, old pearl barley, alum, rue, bulbs, honey, marjoram, thyme, nitrum, or dried figs. And he recommends striking the parts with inflated skins. He also suggests making an opening four digits[30] above the heel on the inner side of the leg, as is done in venesection, in order that the fluid may

51 flow out of this opening and thus relieve the body. If this meas-

30. About three inches.

rens, scilicet vehementiore atque efficaci adiutorio, et neque declinans vulnerationes quae necessario in huiusmodi passionibus
difficiles curatione probantur.

Socrates chirurgus omni ex parte divisuras faciens easdem
adussit, extemplo corporis ingerens raptum, quem Graeci spasmon appellant.

Themison secundo libro Tardarum passionum utitur gestatione et defricatione atque exercitio vel communiter regula exer-
cibili, salibus ac nitro fricans corpus et frigida perfundens. ex
quibus non aequaliter adficit membra, quippe cum interpositis
tribus vel quatuor diebus aqua marina ferventi perfundat.

152 item iubet post gestationem tribus vel quatuor cyathis vino
mixto aegrotantes potari, ⟨sumptis nutrimentis digestione diffi-
cilibus⟩[138] in ordine, inquit, medicaminum, non designans quem
esse velit ordinem medicaminum aut[139] nutrimenta digestione
difficilia. in vespertino inquit cibo utendum mediocri potu, ut
nec sitis aegros afficiat neque plurima liquoris ingestio, sed vinum eligat[140] acrioris virtutis et neque[141] confusum. sed temperandi moderationem tacet, ut mediocriter quidem dicat, quod
est improprie dictum. etenim extenta[142] temperandi moderatio
nervos nocet et ingerit sitim.

153   prohibet praeterea idem ventriflua medicamina atque urinalia,
quae catartica atque diuretica vocant. et per singulos menses
ternos radicum ordinat vomitus. sed erat regulae medicinali
conveniens ad lenimentorum latitudinem sive spatium vomi-
tuum designare quantitatem. utitur etiam in utroque talo
scarificatione, ut Asclepiades. in ascite vero initium ex vomitu
sumit quem helleboro faciendum probat si, inquit, metuerit
quisquam radicum vomitum. et est praeceps atque, ut ita
dixerim, periculosum non medicatum corpus magno adiutorio
dissecare.[143] aliis[144] quoque regulam similem dicit ordinandam,
sed passionis initio neque ungentis tangi neque fricari ventrem

154 permittit. ceteras autem corporis partes si multa, inquit, fuerit
humoris infusio defricandas initio,[145] ex ventris finibus[146] augen-

138 add. R   140 fort. eligit
139 aut ⟨quae⟩ R   141 aqua Rm
142 extenta scripsi: extendit S
143 discere S: corr. Bendz 101, coll. Chr. iii. 41, iv. 3, 76: disicere Rm
144 aliis Rm: aliam S: ⟨in tympanite⟩ aliam Wellmann, Celsus 103
145 initium S: corr. Rm   146 fort. ⟨et⟩ initio ex ventris finibus ⟨sumpto⟩ etc.

ure is ineffective, he recommends the use of deep scarification, a strong and drastic remedy; and he does not hesitate to inflict wounds, which in diseases of this kind are always hard to treat.

The surgeon Socrates makes openings everywhere and cauterizes them, immediately causing bodily convulsion (Greek *spasmos*).

Themison in Book II of his *Chronic Diseases* prescribes passive exercise, rubdowns, and active exercise, that is to say, a general regimen of training. He rubs the body with salt and nitrum and bathes it with cold water. But he does not carry through this treatment consistently, for after three or four days have elapsed 2 he bathes the parts with hot sea water. And after the passive exercise he orders the patient to eat food that is hard to digest,[31] and then to drink three or four cyathi of diluted wine. These prescriptions are to fit in with a certain order of drugs, but he does not indicate what order of drugs he means, or what food hard to digest he has in mind. In the evening meal he advises the use of a little drink to avoid the adverse effect both of thirst and of the excessive taking-in of liquid; and he selects a clear wine of sharp properties. But he does not indicate the degree of dilution, and he speaks merely of a small amount [of wine]. In so doing he errs, for a very strong mixture injures the nerves and causes thirst.

3 Again, Themison prohibits the use of purgative drugs and those which stimulate urination (Greek *cathartica* and *diurētica*, respectively). And he prescribes that vomiting be induced with radishes on three occasions each month. But to indicate the number of vomitings is better suited, according to medical principles, to the interval or period of remission. Like Asclepiades, Themison scarifies both ankles. In cases of ascites, however, he begins by inducing vomiting, for which he says that hellebore should be employed, if one is afraid to use radishes. But it is rash and, if I may say so, dangerous to disrupt, with a powerful drug, a body which has not been treated previously. For other forms of dropsy Themison prescribes a similar system of treatment. At the beginning of the disease he does not permit the 4 abdomen to be touched or rubbed with ointments; but in case there is a widespread suffusion of fluid, he has the other parts of the body rubbed down at the beginning of the disease, the mas-

31. The text is very uncertain here.

dum[147] curationis modum. sed oportebat ob aequandum corpus totum fricatione curari. item interpositis quatuor vel quinque diebus, aqua calida et magis marina tribus vel quatuor vasculis foveri,[148] sed neque hoc aequaliter.

item ante unctionem utitur sinapismo. post singulas gestationes lambendam dicit scillam in electarii vicem. et si plurima fuerit humoris infusio, utitur paracentesi. sed primo die, si vires 155 patiuntur, abstinet cibo; quod si minime ferre potuerint aegrotantes, partem tertiam panis solitae quantitatis aqua infusam offerendam dicit. tum alia die articulos ungens atque ora lavans simili panis reficit modo cum pulmento volantum, ceteris quoque diebus omni aequalitate augens atque aegros resumens.

Thessalus autem secundo libro Regulari plurima Themisonis similiter probat, sed quinque vel tribus cyathis vini aqua temperati ante cibum potat aegrotantes, et paracentesin prohibet.[149] **

---

[147] coercendum *Wellmann, Celsus 103* (*virgula ante* initio, *non post, posita*)

[148] foveri ⟨ventrem iubet⟩ R

[149] tanquam Apollophanion aut Diaeuphorbium *huc addidit A*: pertinere ad Chr. v. 14 videntur (v. Chr. iii. 133 n.)

sage proceeding outward from the ends of the abdomen with increasing force. But, in order to bring the body back to normal, it is necessary to subject the whole of it to this treatment by massage. Again, after an interval of four or five days he prescribes heating the body with hot water, preferably sea water, in three or four vessels. But this treatment, too, lacks uniformity.[32]

Themison employs a mustard plaster before the anointing; and after each treatment with passive exercise he says that the patient should lick a squill, using it as a sort of electuary. If there is a great suffusion of fluid, he employs tapping. On the first day, if the patient's strength permits, he withholds food 5 entirely. But if the patient cannot endure this, he permits him to have a third of the amount of bread usually taken, the bread to be served soaked in water. Then on the following day, after anointing the patient's limbs and washing his face, he feeds him the same amount of bread and, in addition, some fowl, gradually and uniformly adding to the food on succeeding days, and thus restoring the patient's strength.

Thessalus in Book II of his work *On Regimen* for the most part employs the same system of treatment as Themison. However, he has the patient drink from three to five cyathi of wine diluted with water before taking food, and he forbids the use of tapping. . . .

32. Perhaps the meaning is 'fails to reduce the body uniformly,' but the interpretation is far from certain.

LIBER QUARTUS

I. DE ELEPHANTIASI

** heliosis, dropacismus et lixivii calidi perfusio et psichrolusia atque cataclysmus, hoc est aquarum e supernis illisio, natatio maritima et aquarum naturalium, et magis frigidarum quae aluminis naturam exhalent, quas stypterizusas[1] vocaverunt, sive ferrugineas, quas siderizusas[2] appellant. item adhibenda smegmata alia donec maculae albescant quas supra memoravimus, vel cimolia terra subassata cum hordei polline, et nitri quippiam 2 vel alia quae lacessere valeant magis ac levius, ut est cinis ustarum bucinarum vel halcyonium[3] aut cum eodem pumex assatus vel sulphur vivum vel sepiarum testa exusta cum pumice et nitro et cimolia subassata atque gummi et galla, aequi haec omnia ponderis. item acopa et malagmata mediocriter lacessentia praeter cutis ulcerationem et his unguenta similia, ut myrobalani cum aceto aut vinum cum ammoniaci gutta et alumine. ac si ulceratio fuerit locorum consecuta, erunt congrua pro differentia ulcerum adhibenda. quapropter ea quae serpere per corpus viderimus amputabimus,[4] tumentia vero mitigativis temperamus et laxativis virtutibus, item humecta atque fluida 3 densamus et sordida purgamus, cava replemus et aequalia in cicatricem ducimus, sicut Responsionum libris chirurgiam scribentes monuimus. ea autem quae in cicatricem venerunt sinapismis roboramus, praelatis metasyncriticis cyclis et radicum vomitu et ceteris quae sua[5] sunt. tum resumpto corpore vehementer utilis hellebori albi datio probatur quo corpora dissecentur. quae non semel adhibenda, sed etiam saepissime per intervalla praeroborato corpore. item navigatio et in aeres meliores

---

[1] stypteriazas *S*: stypteriazusas *Rm*: cf. *CGL III. 550. 21 (Schmid Mél. Niedermann 120)*

[2] siderizasas *S*: corr. *Rm*

[3] halcyonum *S*: corr. *R*

[4] amputamus *R*

[5] similia *Rm*

BOOK IV

I. ELEPHANTIASIS

. . .[1] [prescribe] sun-bathing, pitch plasters, a dousing with hot lye, cold baths, a shower bath, that is to say, a stream of water from above, and swimming in the sea or in mineral springs. Cold springs that give off vapors of alum (Greek *styptērizusae*) and chalybeate waters (Greek *sidērizusae*) are the best for this purpose. Also use cleansing powders until the spots referred to above clear up, e.g., partially roasted Cimolian earth with barley flour and some nitrum; and other substances which are more or less irritant, such as ash of burnt bucina with which bastard sponge or pumice has been roasted; virgin sulphur or burnt cuttlebone with pumice, nitrum, partially roasted Cimolian earth, gum, and oak gall, these ingredients all being of equal weight. And apply mildly irritant restorative ointments and emollient plasters, but do not permit them to ulcerate the skin;[2] use also ointments of similar properties, such as ben nut and vinegar, or wine, gum ammoniac, and alum. But if the parts are ulcerated, apply suitable remedies according to the type of ulceration. Thus when the kind of sore which moves slowly over the body is observed, use amputation; if the sores involve inflammation, relieve them with relaxing substances; if they are moist and running, use astringents; if defiled, cleanse them; if hollows are caused, fill them out; but if the sores are smooth, bring them to cicatrization, as we have pointed out in the section on surgery in the work entitled *Answers*. When sores have been brought to cicatrization, strengthen the tissues with mustard plasters; and apply metasyncritic measures, including the vomitive treatment with radishes and the other appropriate remedies. Then, when the bodily strength has been restored, a prescription of white hellebore is extremely beneficial for its lacerative effect. This drug should be administered not merely once, but at frequent intervals, the body having previously been strengthened. Boat

1. The description of the disease and the first part of the treatment are lost. The disease has been thought to be a form of leprosy.

2. In view of the sequel the phrase may possibly mean 'if there is no ulceration of the skin.'

transitus: sic enim passio solvetur, aut non ex ea deformatus aegrotans ad finem vitae perveniet.

4   veterum autem medicorum nullus istius passionis curationem ordinavit, excepto Themisone atque ex philosophis Democrito, si vere eius De elephantiacis conscriptus dicitur liber, quo sanguinis corruptionis causas conscribens phlebotomandos imperat aegrotantes et potandos[6] decoctione herbae quam in Syria memorat nasci et in Cilicia. sed neque hanc dicere possumus, neque passio tam difficilis his duobus adiutoriis solvi creditur posse.

Themison vero secundo libro Epistolarum ad Dimantem scribens phlebotomari iubet recte quidem, sed non stricturam considerans potius quam convivantem[7] causam sanguinis detrahen-
5   dam.[8]   quod est aestimabile atque ut ita dixerim dogmaticum, sicut secundo libro de Coenotetis scribens Soranus docuit. utitur praeterea vomitibus ieiunis,[9] itemque radicum, eorum confundens tempus. oportet enim superpositionis tempore adhibere phlebotomiam, in lenimento vero vomitum.

item ventrem inter paucos dies leviter deducendum iubet atque superficiem corporis constringendam unguento myrobalani cum aceto et oleo rosaceo parvo vel myrtino et ammoniaci gutta
6   cum alumine. deponit etiam aegrotantes in decoctione frigida ex herba perdicio[10] confecta vel plantagine aut murta aut rubo, bis in die, atque sufficienti tempore quadam tarditate aegrotantes imperat immorari. dat cibos facile reflabiles, et potu[11] magis aquam. quae sunt incongrua. phlebotomia enim similiter laxativum genus est, et cibus reflabilis; et[12] singula unguenta quae imperat adhiberi constringunt, item embasis quam fieri ex decoctione herbarum iubet supradictarum; item unguenta condensant corpora. sed hoc passus est cum nondum limpide methodicam perspiceret disciplinam, et Asclepiadis secta cir-

---

[6] dotandos *S*: *corr. Rm*

[7] continentem *Rm*, *Almeloveen qui etiam* coniuvantem *vel* comitantem *coniecit*

[8] detrahendi *Rm*

[9] vomitivis ieiunus *S*: *corr. Rm, coll. Chr. ii. 31*

[10] perdicia *S*: *corr. Rm*   [11] *fort.* potum   [12] *at R*

---

3. Or 'immediate,' reading *continentem* (Greek *synecticēn*). If *detrahendi* be read, the meaning might be: 'he considers the state of stricture no more than a subsidiary reason for withdrawing blood,' or possibly 'he gives more weight to a concomitant cause than to the state of stricture as a reason for withdrawing blood.'

trips and voyages to better climates are also beneficial. Thus the disease will be overcome, or at least will not permanently deform the patient.

4   Of the physicians of the past, only Themison has described a treatment for elephantiasis; and, of the philosophers, only Democritus, if, indeed, he is the author of the book on elephantiasis ascribed to him. In this book the author describes the causes of the unwholesome condition of the blood, prescribes venesection, and has the patient drink a decoction of a plant which he says is found in Syria and Cilicia. But we cannot say what this plant is; and in any case it is unlikely that so difficult a disease can be overcome by these two remedies.

   In Book II of his *Letters* Themison, writing to Deimas, prescribes venesection in cases of elephantiasis; in this he is correct, of course, but he is concerned not so much with the removal of the state of stricture as with the removal of the concomitant[3]

5   manifestation thereof, the blood. But such a viewpoint is based merely on opinion and is, so to speak, dogmatic, as Soranus showed in Book II of his work *On the General Types of Disease*. Moreover, Themison prescribes vomiting on an empty stomach and also uses radishes to induce vomiting. But he confuses the times of these remedies. For he should perform venesection during the time of the attack and induce vomiting during an interval of remission.

   In addition, he prescribes gentle purging of the bowels at intervals of a few days and has the surface of the patient's body rubbed with an astringent ointment of ben nut with vinegar and a little rose oil, or with myrtle oil, gum ammoniac, and alum.

6   And he immerses the patient in a cold decoction of pellitory, plantain, myrtle, or bramble twice a day, and orders him not to hurry but to remain there a sufficient length of time. Themison also prescribes foods that readily give off vapors and, for the most part, recommends water as drink. But these prescriptions are inconsistent. For venesection has relaxing properties, and the same is true of foods which give off vapors. But the ointments which he prescribes are in every case astringent, and so is the bath which he has the patient take in a decoction of one of the herbs mentioned above. Again, anointings have a condensing effect on the body. But Themison permits this treatment, since he has as yet no clear perception of the Methodist system

cumsaeptus passionis causam in enstasi[13] aestimaret quam prae-
7 stabat fieri[14] per faciem[15] sive cutem.[16] et ob hoc quaerebat
materiam a superficie ad altiora, velut latius patentia,[17] revocare. utitur denique constrictivis extrinsecus et rapit ad interiora ea quae fuerint appositorum virtute depulsa. provocat
etiam ventris fluorem et vomitum et utitur hellebori purgatione,
adhibito psilothro in tres vel quatuor dies, vel alio quolibet uren-
ti medicamine usque ad cutis ruborem, quo magis perseverantem
faciat passionem.

adhibet praeterea cataplasmata ex quibus etiam sucos adhibuit arnoglossae vel perdicii herbae. item malagmata adhibet
constrictiva, ex quibus nunc plurimi laudant arcagation[18] appel-
8 latum medicamen. item exercitium probat, et defricans cutem
declinat ungere. sed adhibet lavacrum,[19] non coniciens hoc quoque esse laxativae virtutis. adhibet etiam ammoniaci guttam
cum aceto vel vino aut quae sunt intra se contrariae qualitatis.
item post exercitium sudationem faciendam igne vicino, sed
aqua frigida fovendos imperat aegrotantes, et usum hellebori
geminum probat. quae sunt quidem vera adiutoria si tempora
quoque serventur, ut Responsionum docuimus libris.

item quidam Themisonis sectatores initia quoque passionis
praevisa coercentes, pronos ac declives vel venturos in eandem,
9 quos viderint, phlebotomant et helleboro purgant. eos autem
quos iam possessos acceperint iisdem negant curandos adiutoriis,
siquidem corruptione quadam vel laxatione extremae cutis in
corporibus haec passio generetur, et sit rarifica[20] carnis atque
mollifica corporis phlebotomia. quapropter inquiunt esse frigo-
randam[21] vel siccandam corporis superficiem, quo possit eius
humor ad intestina vel ventrem recurrere, ac deinde clysteribus
vel purgativis medicaminibus, quae catartica vocant, ⟨deduci⟩

---

[13] in enstasi] in extasin *S*: *corr. Bendz 69, coll. Ac. iii. 220 (cf. Gal. X. 101 K, Sor. Gyn., pp. 95. 26, 96. 16)*: intrinsecam *Sm*: in extis (exta *Wellmann, Hermes 57. 399*) sitam *vel* intus sitam *Reinesius 670*

[14] ferri ⟨ad⟩ *Wellmann l.c.*

[15] per faciem *scripsi (cf. Med. Plin., p. 33. 20 Rose)*: per ensem *S*: superficiem *Sm*: forensem *Reinesius l.c. (cf. ulceribus forensibus Antid. Brux. 42, p. 375 Rose): fort.* per superficiem

[16] cutalem *Reinesius l.c.*

[17] patentia *R*: patientia *S*

[18] argagation *S*

[19] lavacrum *conieci*: graecum *S*

[20] arifica *S*: *corr. Rm*

[21] *fort. scrib.* frigerandum (*R*)

and, trammeled by the sect of Asclepiades, he holds that the cause of the disease consists in an obstruction which, he asserts, 7 manifests itself at the face and the skin.[4] For this reason he seeks to direct matter from the surface to the deeper parts, believing the latter to be more open. Thus he applies astringent drugs externally and drives to the inner parts that which is dispersed by the strength of these drugs. He also stimulates flux of the bowels and vomiting, employs hellebore as a purge, and every three or four days applies a depilatory or some other caustic preparation as a rubefacient. But the effect is merely to prolong the disease.

Themison also applies poultices, among them those containing the juices of plantain or pellitory. And he employs emollient plasters that are astringent, among them the so-called 'plaster of Archagathus,' which is now recommended by many physi- 8 cians. In addition, he prescribes exercise and also massage of the skin; he does not anoint the patient but prescribes bathing, unaware that this, too, has relaxing properties. He also makes use of gum ammoniac with vinegar or wine, or prescriptions which themselves are of conflicting qualities. After exercise he induces sweating by keeping the patient near a fire; but he also prescribes applications of cold water and also the use of both kinds of hellebore. Now, to be sure, these are all sound remedies, provided that the proper time element is observed, as we have indicated in the work entitled *Answers*.

Some followers of Themison, in an effort to prevent the development of what they suspect to be an incipient case of elephantiasis, prescribe venesection and purging with hellebore for anyone whom they judge to be on the verge of incurring the 9 disease. But they forbid the use of these measures in the treatment of cases in which they judge that the patient is already in the grip of the disease. Their reason is that elephantiasis develops in the body from a state of decomposition or an atonic condition at the surface of the skin, and that venesection will further relax the flesh and soften the body. They hold, therefore, that the body's surface should be chilled and dried, so that its fluids may pass back to the intestines or stomach, and may from there be removed by clysters or purgative drugs (Greek *cathar-*

4. The text and meaning are very uncertain. With readings like Reinesius' or Wellmann's the meaning would be 'that the cause of the disease lies in the internal organs, though the disease breaks out externally through the skin.' Cf. Aretaeus *SD* ii. 13.

detrahendo[22] cibum. praeterea praepotandos probant aegrotantes suco nepetae, servata moderatione quantitatis, quae neque minuenda neque superanda sit,[23] tribus cyathis usque ad sex.
10 cibum etiam dandum frigidum atque constrictivum et parvum,
potum frigidum sed meracum ex vino vehementioris acrimoniae
atque albo vel veteri. et saepe tenendos aegrotantes; vel[24] siccandos abstinentia bibendi,[25] siccioribus reficiendos cibis. quae
sunt utraque incongrua ac dissonantia siccandae cuti,[26] secundum eorum intentionem. si[27] enim, ut aiunt, e superficie trans-
mittendus est humor ad altiora, atque eo provocandus ut clysteribus ac purgativis medicaminibus excludatur per ventrem,
erit [enim][28] contrarium siti atque siccioribus cibis et vino supradicto altiora siccare.
11 item aliqui humorum[29] multitudinem intuentes frequenter adhibendam phlebotomiam atque clysteres et ventriflua medicamina, quae catartica vocant, iubent et magis ⟨quod⟩[30] diaca-
melaeas[31] appellant. quibus necessario corrumpentes aegrotos
in peiorem habitudinem corporis vertunt, quem Graeci cachexian vocant.
item alii corruptione hoc fieri atque mutatione ex venenis effecta aestimantes, temperativis uti medicaminibus decreverunt.
ex quibus magis asinino lacte aegrotantes potandos imperant
simplici vel accurato, quod schiston appellant, item vino dulci et
cibis similibus: quibus foeda digestione corruptis maior efficitur
12 corporis corruptio. ordinant praeterea theriacam dandam,
quam cuncti mithridatium appellamus, quae quidem recorporativa virtute mederi posse perspicitur. dant etiam viperas man-
dendas, sed amputato capite atque cauda, mensura digitorum
quatuor; cetera coquentes atque obdulcantes sale et oleo aegris
offerunt comedenda.
alii etiam aqua ex labris quibus candens tingitur ab operanti-
bus ferrum potandos dicunt, cum sit haec passio secundum pluri-

---

[22] ⟨educi⟩ detrahendo R: *fort.* detrahendum (*sine add.*)
[23] sit ⟨a⟩ R
[24] ac R
[25] bibendi ⟨et⟩ R
[26] cuti R: cutis S
[27] si R: sic S
[28] *om.* R: *retin.* Bendz 62

[29] humorum *Rm*: horum S
[30] *add. Rm* (*aliter* appellatum *pro* appellant)
[31] diacameleos S

tica) in the process of removing [the waste products of] food.[5] In addition, they have the patient drink mint juice, carefully limiting the quantity to no less than three cyathi nor more than six.

o They prescribe a small amount of cold, binding food; and also a cold drink of unmixed white wine, quite sour and old. They often have the patient's limbs held fast. And they dry him out by withholding drink, and then restore his strength with dry foods. But both these measures are inconsistent and out of keeping with the application of drying remedies to the skin, according to the ideas of these very physicians. For if, as they say, we must move the fluid matter from the surface to the deeper parts of the body and must stimulate this transfer so that the fluid may be driven out by way of the bowels with the help of clysters and purgative drugs, it will be inconsistent to drain the deeper parts by restricting drink and by prescribing dry food and wine of the kind mentioned above.

11   Moreover, some physicians, noting the large quantity of fluids in this disease, prescribe the frequent use of venesection, clysters, purgative drugs (Greek *cathartica*), and especially the 'purgative of chamelaea,' as it is called—measures which inevitably harm the patient and bring about what the Greeks call *cachexia*, a change for the worse in his bodily condition.

Some physicians, considering that elephantiasis develops from a pollution and decomposition brought about by poisons, hold that soothing medicines should be employed. Thus they particularly prescribe the drinking of ass's milk, either ordinary or curdled (Greek *schiston*), and sweet wine, and the eating of foods of similar properties. But these drinks and foods will spoil because of the patient's impaired digestion and will aggravate the state

12 of the disease in the body. They also prescribe the antidote that we all call *mithridatium;* this has therapeutic value by reason of its metasyncritic properties.[6] And they also have the patient eat vipers four digits in length with the head and tail removed. They cook the rest of the snake, season it with salt and olive oil, and give it to the patient to eat.

Some physicians give water to drink from vessels in which workers have dipped red-hot iron. And this despite the fact

5. *Detrahendo cibum* may, however, refer to the withholding of food from the patient, i.e., at first, in contrast to the prescription at the beginning of 10.

6. The point of the criticism is that the drug cannot be used during an attack.

mos scriptores ex aqua gravi, quae aut natura aut aliqua corruptione foedata sit, saepius generata.

13 alii quoque etiam cutis vulnerationem affectandam probant,
qua corpus exhumoretur, neque cunctis commune iudicium[32] et
ignaris cognitum providentes, quod peiorante passione superficies corporis ulceretur.

item alii aegrotum in ea civitate quae numquam fuerit isto
morbo vexata, si fuerit peregrinus, cludendum[33] probant, civem
vero longius exulare aut locis mediterraneis et frigidis consistere,
ab hominibus separatum, exinde revocari si meliorem receperit
valetudinem, quo possint ceteri cives nulla istius passionis contagione sauciari. sed hi aegrotantem destituendum magis imperant quam curandum, quod a se alienum humanitas approbat
medicinae.

II. DE PHTHIRIASI

14

ANTECEDENTE cachexia etiam hoc symptoma generatur, quod
nos accidens dicere poterimus. sumpsit igitur nomen non
a genere sed a multitudine pediculorum. plurimi enim creantur
nunc per totum corpus, nunc per eas partes quae capillatura
contectae[1] sunt, et nunc consueti atque simplicis formae, nunc
ignoti, hoc est latiores et duri magis ac saevientes morsibus vehementer. quos quidam ferales appellant, nam saepe etiam sub
capillis inveniuntur corpora penetrasse.

15 sequuntur autem aegrotantes vigiliae et pruritus corporis atque pallor, cibi fastidium et stomachi debilitas et calvities. et
est passio solutionis, cholerae rubeae egestione plurima per
tenues vias emergente, qua haec animalia generantur.

---

[32] *fort.* indicium

[33] excludendum *Rm: an* caedendum?

[1] conceptae *S: corr. Schmid 65*

---

7. Or, reading *indicium:* 'a symptom common to all cases.'

8. The implication is that ulceration, whether natural or artificial, is of no benefit.

9. I.e., 'and left to die.' Or possibly: 'he should be [permanently] banished.' But
neither of these interpretations is quite satisfactory, and it may be preferable to read
caedendum: 'he should be killed.'

10. The language is reminiscent of Terence's *humani nil a me alienum puto.*

that, according to many writers, elephantiasis often arises from water that is naturally unwholesome and noxious or rendered so by some sort of pollution.

Again, some physicians recommend inflicting wounds on the skin in the effort to free the body of the harmful fluids. But they fail to note, what is a matter of universal agreement[7] and known even to the most inexperienced physicians, that the surface of the body becomes ulcerated as the disease grows worse.[8]

Some assert that if a case of elephantiasis occurs in a city in which the disease has never occurred before, if the patient is a foreigner he should be imprisoned;[9] if a citizen, he should be sent into distant exile or made to stay in cold, inland places away from other people, and should be brought back only if he regains his health. Their purpose is to protect the rest of the citizens from injury through contact with the disease. But their prescription for the patient amounts to abandonment rather than treatment, and such a view is foreign to the humanitarian principles of medicine.[10]

II. PHTHIRIASIS

AFTER a patient is in a run-down state, phthiriasis may develop as a concomitant condition (Greek *symptōma*, Latin *accidens*). The name refers not to the kind of lice but to the large number of them present.[1] For these lice develop in great numbers sometimes over the whole body and at other times over the parts covered with hair. And sometimes the lice are of the usual kind with simple shapes, but at other times there are strange types, broader and harder than the usual kind, and fierce-biting. Some writers call the latter 'wild,'[2] for one often finds that they even get under the hair and enter the body.

The signs of the disease are sleeplessness, itching of the body, pallor, loss of appetite, weakness of the esophagus, and loss of hair. The affection is one which involves a state of looseness. For a considerable discharge of reddish bile appears through the thin pores, and it is from this matter that the animals are generated.

1. Or perhaps 'it takes its name not from the basic nature of the disease, but from the large number of lice present.' Greek *phtheir*, 'louse.'

2. Cf. Aristotle *Hist. an.* 557a4.

denique superpositionis tempore iacere oportet aegrotos loco mediocriter frigido, atque cibis constrictivis et temporibus iam saepe demonstratis refici. fomenta vero et perunctiones et cataplasmata membratim erunt adhibenda, qualia Themison elephantiacos curans ordinavit. sed ea loca quae capillatura vestita sunt erunt praeterea radenda.[2]

16 ⟨post⟩ superpositionem[3] resumptio adhibenda atque recorporatio, sicut in cachecticis vel elephantiacis ordinavimus. sed iugia adhibenda smegmata, quae nos lacessentes atque purgativos pulveres nuncupamus, item unctiones, magis cum mox fuerit capillatura derasa, praefotis partibus aqua marina vel aceto salso. sunt haec denique plurima speciatim posita, ut bulbi cum nitro atque oleo contriti quo mellis faciat crassitudinem, ex quibus corpus erit illiniendum; item staphisagria cum aceto atque oleo trita, vel infusa aceto et oleo tunc contrita cum salis fluore, quem Graeci halos anthos vocant, donec liquidi

17 mellis similitudinem faciat, nunc etiam cum sulphure vivo atque aceto. vel ita[4] ponderibus composita medicamina: staphysagriae drachmas duas, sandaracae drachmas duas, nitri obolos duos, admixto oleo et aceto donec in mellis crassitudinem veniat; vel sandaraca cum oleo, et nunc staphisagria et abrotanum aequis ponderibus, admixta calce, quam Graeci conin vocant, et his similibus. palpebris autem erunt adhibendi sicci pulveres atque collyria, quae Graeci blepharica[5] vocant, nos palpebraria dicere poterimus, ex aere usto atque aneso asso, sed et lapide

18 scisso et pipere et staphisagria confecta. haec etiam in his qui praeter phthiriasin pruritu vexantur sunt adhibenda, adiectis magis ferventioribus aquis in usu lavacri et asperginibus pulveris ex thure et nitro et sulphure confecti.

item solicationes,[6] quas Graeci helioses vocant, adhibendae sunt; dropaces quoque et vomitus radicum et ea quae iam saepe de aliis memoravimus scribentes passionibus, quae corpus recorporativa virtute fortificare atque in meliorem habitudinem

[2] praeterea radenda] praeradenda *Triller Clinotechnia 268*

[3] ⟨post⟩ superpositionem *scripsi*: superpositione *S*

[4] istis *Rm*

[5] phlepharica *S*: *corr. Rm*

[6] solationes *Am* (*cf.* insolo, insolatio): *fort.* soli dationes (*cf.* B. *Junel, In Cass. Fel. studia 112; Cass. Fel., pp. 141. 1, 153. 14*)

Thus at the time of an attack have the patient lie in a moderately cold room and nourish him with binding foods at the times we have often indicated in previous chapters. Foment and anoint him, and to the various parts of the body apply plasters of the kind which Themison prescribes in his treatment of elephantiasis.[3] But first shave the parts that are covered with hair.

In the interval of remission apply the restorative and metasyncritic treatments as we have described them in the chapters on cachexia and elephantiasis;[4] but make continual use of irritant and cleansing powders (Greek *smēgmata*). Also anoint the patient, especially when the hair has just been shaved off, first, however, fomenting the parts with sea water or salted vinegar. Again, many specific remedies are recorded, e.g., bulbs rubbed up with nitrum and olive oil to the consistency of honey and used as a liniment for the body; stavesacre rubbed up with vinegar and olive oil, or soaked in vinegar and olive oil, and then rubbed up with the flower of salt (Greek *halos anthos*)[5] until it attains the consistency of liquid honey; or stavesacre with sulphur and vinegar. The following medicines may also be used, compounded according to these weights: stavesacre, two drachms; sandarac, two drachms; nitrum, two obols, with an admixture of olive oil and vinegar until the preparation attains the consistency of honey; or sandarac with olive oil, and, in addition, stavesacre and southernwood, all in equal weights, with an admixture of lime (Greek *conis*) and similar substances. And to the eyelids apply dry powders as well as eye salves (Greek *blepharica*, which we may in Latin call *palpebraria*) made of calcined copper, roasted anise, limonite, pepper, and stavesacre. These remedies should also be used when the patient, without having phthiriasis, suffers from itching. In addition, order bathing in very hot water and the application of dusting powders made of frankincense, nitrum, and sulphur.

Also prescribe sun baths (Greek *hēliōseis*), pitch plasters, the use of radishes as a vomitive, and those measures which we have often mentioned above in connection with other diseases, i.e., measures that by reason of their metasyncritic properties can strengthen the body and bring about a change to a better state.

3. *Chr.* iv. 7.
4. *Chr.* iii. 85–89; iv. 1–3.
5. See K. C. Bailey, *The Elder Pliny's Chapters on Chemical Subjects*, II, 667.

commutare valeant. sic enim detracta corporis cachexia, quam nos malam habitudinem dicere poterimus, eius quoque comitantia depellentur.

III. DE VENTRICULOSIS, QUOS GRAECI COELIACOS VOCANT, ET DE CETERIS DEFLUXIONIBUS

19

Ventriculosa passio, quam Graeci coeliacen vocant, a parte corporis quae patitur nomen accepit. generatur ex antecedenti indigestione continua vel tumore vehementi aut dysenteria.

sequitur in hac passione constitutos varia stercorum egestio qualitate atque colore, nunc tenuis ac soluta, nunc aspera et inaequalis vel constricta, et nunc alba, nunc similis urinae camelorum, nunc flava et spumosa, nunc prasina vel livida aut nigra 20 aut purulenta aut sanguinea, cum gravi fetore et rugitu intestinorum, quem Graeci borborismum[1] appellant, atque in exitu sonitu,[2] et post effusionem factam[3] velut scatentis stercoris vesiculae; et nunc iugiter nocte atque die, nunc coacervatim sed interiecto spatio, ut per diem bis vel semel, aut interpositis uno vel duobus diebus aut eo amplius; et nunc cum tensione atque ventositate et tormento vel dolore aut singultu, considente atque conducta cute quae ventrem circumtegit attestante siti et ipsius ventris fervore et levi in interioribus torpore frigido. sequuntur etiam vigiliae, fastidium cibi, et aliquibus plurimus appetitus, 21 virium debilitas, pallor subalbidus, et nunc febres, dehinc corporis odor teter plurimus, ut etiam quae suis manibus tetigerunt computrescant et difficile careant odore concepto, tum vultus inflatio atque pedum. quibusdam etiam dysenteria congenera-

[1] fort. scrib. borborigmon: cf. Chr. iii. 18; iv. 92

[2] sonitū S: fort. sonitus

[3] factae edd.

---

1. *Pathos coeliacon* in the first instance means 'disease of the stomach,' while *pathos stomachicon* is 'disease of the esophagus or of the cardia.' To avoid confusion of the two I have adopted 'the coeliac disease' as a translation of the former term. Of course, no identification with the specific modern disease of that name is involved.

Again, just as Greek *coelia* may refer not merely to the stomach but to the abdominal cavity generally and to the bowels, the coeliac disease has often been considered more generally than as an affection merely of the stomach. And the Methodists' lack of precision in anatomical matters makes it difficult for us to know what meaning they attach to *coelia* in a given context. In this connection it may be noted that Celsus locates the

For in this way cachexia (which we may render in Latin *mala habitudo*) will be overcome, and symptoms accompanying that condition will also be removed.

9   III. COELIAC DISEASE (GREEK *PATHOS COELIACON*)¹ AND OTHER FLUXES

Coeliac disease (Greek *pathos coeliacon*) takes its name from the affected part of the body [i.e., *coelia*]. It arises after a prolonged state of indigestion, severe inflammation, or dysentery.

In this disease the fecal discharges show great variation in quality and color, being now thin and loose, now rough, uneven, and compact, now white, now like camel's urine, now yellow and frothy, now green, blue, black, purulent, or bloody. The feces have a heavy odor, and there is a rumbling sound (Greek *borborismos*) in the intestines. As the feces leave the body and even after the outpouring, there is a sound as from a vessel that is boiling over with excrement. This effusion in some cases goes on continually night and day, and in other cases takes place in a mass at various intervals, e.g., twice a day, once a day, once every two or three days or even longer. The condition may be marked by abdominal distention, flatulence, cramps, pain, hiccoughs, a settling and tightening of the skin over the stomach, thirst, a burning sensation in the stomach itself, and a mild sensation of cold and numbness in the inner parts. There occur also sleeplessness, loss of appetite (though in some cases the appetite is very large), loss of strength, whitish pallor, fever in some cases, a heavy odor from the body so foul that whatever the patient touches with his hands is also tainted and can hardly be freed of the odor it receives, and, finally, a puffing-up of face and feet. In some cases dysentery develops along with the coe-

---

seat of the coeliac disease in the pylorus (iv. 19). Again, Alexander of Tralles treats the coeliac disease and dysentery together (ix. 3). The absence of a separate chapter on the coeliac disease in Alexander, as well as in such authors as Theodore Priscian and Cassius Felix, is probably due to a merging, if not identification, of the disease with dysentery. Indeed, the chapter on dysentery in our own author shows signs of having been confused, somewhere in the course of the tradition, with the chapter on coeliac disease. And there are ancient authors who locate the coeliac disease exclusively in the intestines. But it seems most probable that for Caelius (Soranus) the coeliac disease was primarily a chronic disorder of the digestive process in the stomach, even though the symptoms were to be observed in the bowels and their discharges.

tur cum facile fuerint intestina ulcerata ob defluentium acrimoniam.

est autem passio solutionis et aliquando stricturae[4] complexa,
siquidem aliqua eius videantur esse coniuncta, ut ex supradictis
conicitur. sed discernitur a speciali reumatismo ventris, siquidem plurimae in ipso fiant egestiones, sed non variatae supradictis concursibus.

22   quapropter cum adhuc nova vel emergens fuerit passio, vel[5]
plurimi temporis sed in superpositione constituta, quam Graeci
epitasin[6] vocant, erit eo tempore locandus aegrotans constrictiva
ratione, ut saepe docuimus, adhibita requie et quantum vires
permiserint abstinentia. etenim ad perferendum atque corpori
adpropriandum cibum sumptum nunc venter patiens indignatur,
tamquam oculi patientes visus officio inquietati.[7] somnus etiam
plurimus curandus atque sitis, et lanis mollibus venter
contegendus leviter oleo hispano praetinctis[8] vel melino aut ro-
23   saceo aut murtino aut lentiscino oleo. ac si ventositate quoque
vel tormento affecti fuerint aegrotantes, dulci oleo dimissionis
tempore lanae tingendae sunt. perunctio vero ex oleo viridi adhibenda, facies quoque aqua tepida relevanda.[9] tunc cibus
dandus, ut alica ex aqua frigida ita curata ut sua caruerit difficultate, quod fiet ex farris tepore,[10] aut decoctione palmularum
thebaicarum. dandus etiam panis solus aut cum eo ova hapala,
item pultes ex oryza vel alica aut farre aut milio, ex parvo hispano oleo confectae et parvo salis grano.

vel si dolor admonuerit, adhibenda cucurbita **

† ** [11] longior procurandum[12] tamen ut si quid partis spongia
24   ceperit solitae damnum moderationi non sit† tunc leviter oppresso folliculo quo liquoris[13] reflatio fiat, erit tentandum ne
clysteris caverna fuerit clausa. dehinc apponenda podici fistula
dextera manu usque ad eius verticulum, quem Graeci aspidiscon

[4] *fort.* strictura

[5] vel *Schmid RPh 139*: nec *edd.*

[6] *an* epit(h)esin? *cf. Rose, ind. in Cass. Fel., p. 205*

[7] inquietati *Rm*: in qua aetati *S*

[8] praetinctis *scripsi*: praetactus *S*: praeunctus *Rm*

[9] relavanda *Almeloveen*: lavanda *Rm*

[10] torrore *Rm*   [11] *lacunam indicavit Schmid RPh 142*

[12] *cf.* fistula longior procuranda, *Chr. iv. 25*

[13] liquore quo folliculi *edd.*

liac disease, since the intestines are easily ulcerated by the acrid matter flowing down through them.

The coeliac disease is a disease involving a state of looseness, but the latter is combined at times with a state of stricture, for some of the symptoms, as may be seen from the above account, involve such a state of stricture.[2] Again, this disease may be distinguished from the particular disease called 'flux' (*rheumatismos*) of the stomach; for, while the latter condition also produces copious discharges, these are not marked by the special symptoms described above.

2   And so, when the coeliac disease is still new and just developing, or, if chronic, is in a period of exacerbation (Greek *epitasis*), have the patient placed in the manner required for astringent effect, as we have often indicated, and prescribe rest. Also have him fast so far as his strength will permit, for the stomach is at this time affected by the disease and is not equal to the task of taking food and distributing it to the body. It is similar to the case of diseased eyes whose power of vision is impaired. See that the patient gets a great deal of sleep, and have him abstain from drink. Cover the abdomen with soft wool after dipping the

3   wool lightly in Spanish, quince, rose, myrtle, or mastic oil. If the patient also suffers from gas or cramps, dip the wool in sweet olive oil at times when the attack abates. Anoint the patient with green olive oil; also refresh his face with warm water. Then give him such food as spelt groats in cold water. This should be so prepared as to obviate the difficulty of digestion, that is to say, by warming the spelt. Or the latter may be served in a decoction of Theban dates. Also give the patient bread, either alone or with soft eggs, and porridges made of rice, spelt groats, ground spelt, or millet, together with a small amount of Spanish oil and a pinch of salt.

If the pain requires it, apply a cupping instrument. . . .

4   . . . Then by gentle pressure of the clyster bulb,[4] which should cause the liquid to emerge, test to be sure that the opening of the pipe is not obstructed. Next, with the right hand insert the pipe into the anus as far as the joint [where the bulb is attached]

2. Or perhaps 'involve such a combination.'

4. There was probably some mention of a clyster in a part of the text now lost. The text as we have it is manifestly corrupt, and it is possible that the part beginning *tunc leviter* belongs not to the discussion of the coeliac disease but to an account of the *ceterae defluxiones* referred to in the title, or even to the chapter on dysentery.

vocant, impulsu levi et neque recto ductu contra oppositas partes, neque superiora repentino vel cum plurimo conatu. tumores
etenim exinde atque collectiones efficiuntur. quapropter sensim
atque paulo inferius inclinato ductu iniectio fieri debet ad illam
partem in qua constitutum est os sacrum, quod Graeci quoque
25 vocant hieron osteon, [tunc][14] illic enim spatium latius longaonis.
tum[15] appositione facta erit digitus[16] detrahendus quo caverna
fuerat obstrusa, atque sinistra manu continenda immobilitate
servata clysteris fistula, et dextra comprimendus folliculus leniter ac moderate, quoties inferiora intestina ulcerata noscuntur.
erit denique parvae longitudinis atque latioris[17] cavernae fistula
procuranda, qua possit facili effusione patientibus locis medicamen tradere, ne suspensum [ab][18] his quae patiuntur non solum
nihil afferat commodi, verum etiam sanis irruens officiat. erit
autem folliculi impressio vehementius facienda atque fistula
longior procuranda in his quibus superiora intestina fuerint ul-
26 cerata, quo medicaminis liquores eo valeant pervenire. et hor-
tandus aegrotans ne retento spiritu quodam recursu referat[19]
medicamen. ac si magna fuerit putredo, quam nomen[20] appellant, non erit immodicum[21] etiam ex utraque parte clysteris fistulam cavernare, quam Graeci amphitreton vocant, quo possint
medicaminum liquida per utramque partem intestinorum lateribus advenire.

tum cum omnis fuerit folliculus complicatione vacuatus sive
oppressione manus refusus, quo medicamina pervenisse sentia-
mus, erit detrahenda fistula suspensa manu, et distentis cruribus
aegrotantis spongiae commodandae[22] podici expressae ex decoc-
27 tione calidi liquoris in quo praecocta sint mala punica, quo constrictione quadam virtutis herbarum, quam Graeci stypsin vocant, atque fervido tactu densatis partibus longaonis iniecta
teneantur. tum modico temporis spatio intermisso, erunt etiam
illa quae clunibus fuerant supposita detrahenda. et si fuerit
aeger in ventris officium provocatus, in inferioribus ulceratione
constituta, et magis si in longaone fuerit perspecta, erit hortan-
dus paulisper resistere et iniecta continere, tangentibus nobis

[14] om. R
[15] tum scripsi: cum S
[16] digitis S: corr. Am
[17] latioris Schmid RPh 142: altioris S
[18] om. R

[19] referiat edd.
[20] menomen S: corr. R (= νομήν)
[21] incommodum Rm, fort. recte
[22] accommodandae Almeloveen

(Greek *aspidiscon*). This insertion should be made with gentle impulses. It should not be made with direct pressure against the opposing parts or with a sudden or powerful effort to reach the higher parts; in that case inflammation and abscesses may result. And so, make the insertion slowly, and at a rather low angle, in
5 the direction of the *os sacrum* (Greek *hieron osteon*), for in that direction lies the broad part of the rectum. As the clyster enters the anus, remove the finger that blocked off the clyster's opening; then hold the pipe steadily in the left hand, and squeeze the clyster bulb with the right. This should be done gently and with moderate pressure in those cases where it is clear that only the lower parts of the intestines are ulcerated. In fact, in such cases the pipe used should be short and should have a broad opening in order to carry the drug to the diseased parts and spread it there without difficulty. For if carried up higher, the drug will not only bring no relief to these affected parts but, indeed, will injure the healthy tissues against which it impinges. In those cases, however, in which the higher parts of the intestines are ulcerated, it will be necessary to press more firmly on the clyster bulb and to use a longer pipe in order that the medicinal fluids
26 may reach the diseased parts. Also urge the patient by holding his breath to keep the drug from flowing back. And if the decay (Greek *nomē*) has spread extensively [in the intestines], it will not be out of place to use a clyster pipe with an opening on either side (Greek *amphitrētos*), so that the drugs may flow out of both openings and thus cover the sides of the intestines.

When the whole clyster bulb is completely pressed together and emptied, that is to say, has poured forth all its contents under manual pressure, and we may therefore be sure that the drug has reached its destination, remove the clyster pipe by gentle manipulation. Then spread the patient's legs and insert in the anus sponges wrung out of a hot decoction of pomegranates.
27 This plant's astringent property (Greek *stypsis*) and the heat of the application will condense the rectal parts and thus serve to keep the injected drugs within the intestines. Then after a short interval remove the props which had been placed under the patient's buttocks. And if he feels impelled to go to stool, then in the cases where the ulceration is in the lower parts of the intestines and especially in the rectum, urge him to resist the impulse for a little while and hold back the injected fluid, while you help

easdem partes quae pati noscuntur, quoties provocari aegrum in
egestionem medicaminis viderimus. ac si in superioribus fuerint
28 ulcera, erunt permittendi egerere cum volent. etenim medicamen iam recurrens atque defluens ad inferiora longaonem sanum
inutili virtute adficiendo exulcerat. nam quibus alienatae[23] sor-
des detrahuntur, iisdem non ulcerata vitiantur exusta, cum admotae[24] corporibus tardius fuerint immoratae. exclusis igitur
cum medicamine post sufficiens temporis intervallum muculentis
humoribus atque ramentis et variis defluxionibus intestinorum,
sufficienter operatum medicamen accipimus, quamquam non de
perfecta curatione tuto pronuntiare possimus, cum saepe ulcerationis particula in superioribus constituta minime valeat medicamen accipere, et propterea non omnibus commodata curatio
videatur.

29   vel si commixtum putredini medicamen cuncta purgaverit,
hoc adprehendimus cum solum praeter aliqua purgamenta fuerit
exclusum. at si hoc egestio secuta fuerit quaedam aliena, minus
quidem, purgata tamen accipimus ulcera et propterea sanitatis
spem pollicentia. item si nihil fuerit exclusum neque ipsius
iniectionis quidquam, erit credendum necessario medicamen inhaesisse quantum sua valuit potentia, et propterea sui operis in-
tegrasse virtutem, quamquam non perfecisse videatur. nec
recte culpanda virtus est quae una iniectione non dederit sanitatem, cum plenam fecerit futurae perfectionis fidem, persevera-
30 tionem sui persuadens. unde si omnino nullum fuerit redditum
medicamen,[25] erit impavide accipiendum. atque[26] e contrario si
eius nulla particula fuerit retenta, et statim effusum nullum sui
demonstraverit effectum, omnia desperanda. est enim plurimae
debilitatis atque alienatarum vel mortuarum partium signum.
coniciendum praeterea ne, ut saepe contigit, vetustate medicaminum efflata virtute nullus sequatur effectus, et propterea sicut

[23] alienae *Rm*

[24] admota (*et mox* immorata) *S*: *corr. R*

[25] *post* redditum, *non hic, virgulam ponunt edd.*

[26] *fort.* utque *Bendz 49* (*cf. adn. ad Ac. i. 85*)

5. I.e., barring the exceptional case just indicated.

6. This phrase may perhaps be construed with *accipiamus:* 'we may still, though with
less assurance, take it, etc.'

by taking hold of the affected parts. This must be done whenever the patient seems impelled to evacuate the bowels. But if
the ulceration is in the higher parts of the intestines, permit him
28 to go to stool whenever he wishes. For the drug in any case will
flow back and return to the lower parts, and [if not soon dis-
charged] will subject a healthy rectum to its harmful properties
and cause ulceration there. That is, as foul, corrupted matter
is carried down, it blights and consumes parts previously free
from ulceration, if it remains in contact with the body for too
long a time. And so, when a sufficient interval of time elapses
and slimy fluids, bits of matter, and various intestinal discharges
are passed off together with the injected drug, we may take it
that the drug has produced adequate effect. But it will not be
safe for us to declare that the treatment has been successfully
completed, for it often happens that the drug cannot reach
ulcerations in the higher parts of the intestines. This treatment,
therefore, is evidently not adapted to all cases.

29   Again, we may be sure[5] that the drug has commingled with
the corrupted parts and cleansed them all when we see the drug
ejected alone, i.e., no longer with any foreign matter. But if a
discharge of corrupted matter follows the ejection of the drug,
we may still take it that the ulcers have been cleansed, though
incompletely,[6] and that there is ground for expecting a return to
health. Furthermore, if nothing at all is discharged, not even any
of the drug, we must, of course, conclude that the drug has adhered to the diseased parts, so far as it could, and thus has continued to function, even though it seems not to have completed
its task. And it is wrong in such a case to blame the drug as
ineffective if a single injection does not produce a cure, for there
is every reason to be confident of an ultimate cure that will be
complete, and every indication that the same treatment should
30 be continued. Therefore, if no part of the drug is discharged at
all, there is no occasion for fear. On the contrary, if no part of it
is retained in the bowels, that is, if the drug by flowing out at
once gives evidence of being without effect, the case is quite
hopeless. For this is a sign that the patient is extremely weak and
that the parts in question are corrupted or dead. One must also
consider the possibility that the drug may fail to take effect because of its age and consequent loss of strength, and may therefore be discharged from the bowels in the same clear state in

iniecta sunt limpide[27] revocentur. quapropter etiam hoc intuendum esse mandamus.

tum post egestionem factam spongiis erit podex[28] detergendus,
vel si nihil fuerit exclusum interiecto spatio unius horae perunctum reficere aegrotantem cibis congruis atque stomacho aptissi-
31 mis, ut lactucae thyrso vel intybo cum aceto quod sit ex murta
confectum, aut olivis fractis vel natantibus, quas colymbadas
appellant, et ovis hapalis, et volantibus nuper memoratis quae
sint nutrita constrictivis, ut murta, rosa, lentisco. etenim
eorum pinguedo sic defluxit atque caro constrictiva sufficitur,
magis in eorum pectoribus, quorum plus ossibus vicina aptiora
probantur. sunt enim teneriora ceterorum.[29] danda etiam pomorum quaedam constringentia atque olerum cocta quorum
superius atque de aliis scribentes passionibus memoravimus.
32 potui dabimus aquam frigidam. quod si minime toleraverint
aegrotantes, dabimus ferventem plurimum aquam cisterninam.
et si sine febribus fuerit aegrotans, dabimus vinum exercitioris
paulo virtutis, ut supra docuimus. omnino enim invitantes ad-
petitum sive suscitantes, quem Graeci orexin vocant, stomachi
robur debemus custodire, nisi cum nausea etiam venter fuerit
resolutus. oportet etenim curare ne rursum plurimum cibum demus aut potum, vel priusquam solidum cibum sumpserint aegro-
33 tantes bibendum credant. nam convenit neque gravata neque
humecta intestina servari.

si igitur medicaminis iniectio aliquo fuerit peccato vitiata, ut
non omnibus adiutorii partibus informata videatur, mox medica-
menti monstrabit errorem. nam quidam iniectionem[30] aliqua
ex parte vomuerunt. aliqui stomachi ac ventris dolorem senserunt singultibus atque nausea affecti, cum anxietate ac siti et
immitigabili ardore et articulorum frigido torpore et pulsu ma-
ligno atque sudore vel defectu aut pressura capitis sive gravatione, quam carosin vocant, siquidem sit nimiae virtutis medicamen iniectum in febribus vel viribus vitiatis aut in alto tumori-
34 bus constitutis. vomitus autem medicaminis iniecti, si ex tumore ventris fuerit factus vel teneriorum intestinorum, tam-

[27] limpida *Rm*

[28] podex *Rm*: postea *S* (*retin. Bendz 52*)

[29] ceteris *Rm*

[30] iniectione *S*: *corr. Rm*

which it was injected. This circumstance occurs frequently; it must therefore be looked into as a possibility.

Now after the discharge takes place, wipe the anus clean with sponges; but if there is no discharge, after the lapse of an hour anoint the patient and refresh him with appropriate food suitable to the gullet, e.g., heart of lettuce or endive in vinegar which has been prepared with myrtle; crushed olives or swimming [i.e., pickled] olives (Greek *colymbades*); soft eggs, and the flesh of birds such as those lately mentioned,[7] provided that they have been fed binding food like myrtle, rose, and mastic. Birds so fed lose their fat, and their flesh, especially the breast, becomes binding. The parts of the breast nearer the bones are more suitable for the present purpose, being tenderer than the others. Also give the patient fruits and cooked vegetables that are binding; we have already noted examples of these in chapters on other diseases. Give the patient cold water to drink; but if he cannot endure this, let him take very hot rain water. And if he is without fever, give him rather strong wine, as we have indicated before. For we must by all means entice or arouse an appetite for food (Greek *orexis*) and thus maintain the strength of the esophagus, unless there is both nausea and looseness of the stomach and bowels. On the other hand, take care not to give a great deal of food or drink, and do not let the patient think that he must drink before he takes solid food. For the intestines must be kept neither weighed down nor moist.

Now if the injection of the drug is marred by some mistake, the remedy not having been properly devised in all respects, the error in the treatment will soon become apparent. For in some cases the patient vomits a part of the drug injected, and in some cases there is a sensation of pain in the gullet and stomach, with hiccoughs and nausea. Other symptoms may be restlessness, thirst, unrelieved heat, cold numbness of the extremities, abnormal pulse, sweating, fainting, and stupor or drowsiness (Greek *carōsis*). The cause of these conditions is the injection of too powerful a drug in cases where fever is present, or the patient's strength is severely impaired, or there is a deep-seated inflammation. And if the injected drug is vomited by reason of inflammation of the stomach or the small intestines, this is a fatal sign, as

7. The reference is not clear and furnishes additional evidence of the derangement which the chapters on the coeliac and related diseases have suffered.

quam in iliaca passione, saepius aegrotantibus intulit mortem.
si autem nullo tumore subiecto fuerit effectus, ingerit vexationem atque metum, aut ut saepe contigit passionis significat
depulsionem, siquidem nulla pars ulcerum in intestinis a medicaminis contactu videtur immunis.

tardante passione etiam recorporativis convenit uti rebus **[31]
quapropter oportet ea quae feruntur per ventris officium celeriter auferre, et ora aegrotantium spongiis ex pusca frigida sicca-
35 tis[32] reficere, articulos ligare et stomacho cataplasma constrictivum imponere quod diadaphnidon dicunt, vel similis virtutis;
odoramenta quoque resumptiva adhibere et frequentius cibo nutrire ex supradicta materia. ac si accepta non tenuerint, erunt
secundo offerenda, adhibita articulorum fricatione, cucurbita ori
ventris infixa, vel si potuerit etiam a tergo inter scapulas.

ac si dolor occurrerit et singultus ob ardorem atque sitim, fomentis utendum est et cataplasmatibus et spongiarum vaporatione et olei iniectione, quo possit medicaminis vexatio celerius
36 obtundi. perseverante incendio etiam calida et oleo et lacte sunt
iniciendi. et si nulla fuerit tumoris[33] significatio, eorum frigidus
adhibendus est usus. et ob mitigandam sitim iugis adhibenda
oris collutio; dandus interea potus. item propter articulorum
frigus adhibendi tepores cum blanda manuum tenacitate, quam
diacerisin[34] vocant, item unctio. sudores autem si ex pressura
fuerint apparentes, erunt detergendi; ⟨si⟩[35] ex diaphoresi, et
asperginibus cohibendi et congruo cibo et ceteris quae de cardiacis[36] scribentes docuimus.

quibus depulsis, hoc est[37] praesentibus periculis evadentibus
37 aegrotis, si forte rursum in priscam dysenteriam venerint, erit
tentandum multo tempore simplicibus uti iniectionibus, hoc est
his quae sine calce, quam asbeston vocant, vel auripigmento,
quod arsenicon appellant, conficiuntur. tum si perseveraverit

---

[31] *lacunam statui*

[32] expressis *Rm*: *fort.* insuccatis, ex(s)uccatis   [33] humoris *S*: *corr. Rm*

[34] diacerisin *scripsi* (= διαχείρισιν *vel* -ησιν): diacertosin *S*: diacerosin *Am* (*cf.* χείρωσις)

[35] *supplevi*   [36] cardiacis *Rm*: caroticis *S*   [37] est ⟨a⟩ *R*: *fort.* est ⟨e⟩

8. Cf. *Ac.* iii. 141.

9. The following passage (perhaps to the end of 44) may be out of place. It may belong in the lacuna indicated at 23, and possibly to the chapter on dysentery (cf. 37).

in ileus.[8] Even if such vomiting takes place without any underlying inflammation, there is still reason for concern and anxiety; but it often happens that this latter condition indicates the overcoming of the disease, for it is a sign that no part of the ulceration in the intestines has escaped contact with the drug.

When the disease becomes chronic, employ metasyncritic treatments. . . . [9]Thus having quickly removed the stools, refresh the patient by wiping his face with sponges wrung out of cold diluted vinegar, bind his limbs, and apply an astringent plaster over the chest, e.g., the so-called 'bayberry plaster' or another of similar properties. Also employ aromatic substances with restorative properties. And feed the patient frequently with food of the kind mentioned above.[10] If, having taken such food, he cannot retain it, massage his limbs and apply a cup over the upper orifice of the stomach and, if possible, also to the interscapular region of the back. And try giving him food a second time.

If pain and hiccoughs occur, with burning heat and dryness, employ fomentations and plasters, apply heat with sponges, and inject a clyster of olive oil in order to overcome quickly any painful effects of drugs. If the burning sensation persists, inject warm water, olive oil, and milk; but if there is no sign of inflammation, use these substances cold. To relieve dryness, wash the patient's mouth continually, and let him drink at times. To overcome the coldness of the limbs, apply warmth by a gentle clinging motion of the hands (Greek *diacheirisis*, 'manipulation'). Also anoint the patient; and wipe away the sweat which arises from stupor and exhaustion, and check the flow of perspiration by using dusting powders, appropriate food, and the other measures which we pointed out in the section on the cardiac disease.[11]

If, after overcoming all these symptoms and avoiding the immediate dangers, the patient happens to lapse back into the former condition of dysentery,[12] try to treat this condition by injecting clysters of simple substances, that is, those prepared without quicklime (Greek *asbestos*) or orpiment (Greek *arsenicon*). This treatment should be made over a considerable period of time. If, however, the disease still persists, change to stronger

10. 31.   11. Cf. *Ac.* ii. 191 ff.

12. This may possibly (though not necessarily: see 19, 21) indicate that we are dealing here with part of the original chapter on dysentery.

passio, ad vehementiora transeundum, sed ex simplicibus rebus confecta, sollicitam habentes calcis vel auripigmenti iniectionem. oportet enim putredini etiam cataplasmatibus occurrere, quorum sunt ervi pollines pusca decocti et lentiscinum oleum acacia immixta donec mellis sumat crassitudinem; item lenticula molita cum melle vel rosaceo vel lentiscino oleo decocta.

38   ac si putredinis causa sanguinis effusio fuerit consecuta, erunt spongiae expressae ex aceto calido pubetenus vel sub umbilico et coxarum summitatibus, quas Graeci ischia vocant, admovendae. dehinc iisdem locis etiam cucurbitae fervefactae adfigendae, articuli ligandi, dandus digestibilis cibus et qui facile corpori insinuetur, tunc vinum quod sit praecoctum in cortice mali punici. iniciendum autem acetum nunc solum, nunc cum thure masculo vel eius manna contrita, vel quod ex confectione superat diaiteon[38] emplastri cum sibi eius materiae miscentur. imponenda etiam similis virtutis emplastra, vel acacia aceto soluta,

39 tunc donec scatere tentet coquenda, aut in amplo mali punici cortice supra tepentem cinerem sensim calefacienda, et ex ipso liquore partes contegendae. dehinc cerotaria apponenda ex oleo murtino aut melino aut viridi, contrita acacia atque consoluta, vel ex omphacino aut oenanthino cum ruta[39] aut balaustio aut aliquando his omnibus. vel ut Themison composuit acaciae partem unam, rosae aridae partem unam, ammoniaci guttae partem dimidiam, cerae partes quatuor, et olei rosacei quod sit sufficiens: haec contrita in vino amineo et soluta cera cum rosaceo oleo miscenda.

ac[40] si sanguis fuerit retentus, quod fiet aliquando cum gelatur, aliquando densitate putrescentis venae, erunt discernendae

40 causae hoc modo. nam densatam intelligimus venulam quoties pulsus exurgit atque frigus corporis resumpto fervore mitescit, aegrotantis animus melior, atque spiratione corpus facillime relevatur. ac[40] si gelatus obstiterit sanguis, quod Graeci thrombosin vocant, et propterea fuerit fluor celatus,[41] supradictis contraria sequentur, ut pallor, iactatio, pulsus parvitas vel amputatio, quam Graeci asphyxian vocant, gravedo, inflatio, frigidus

---

[38] diatheon *edd.*

[39] murta *Rm*

[40] at *R*

[41] *fort.* gelatus

preparations, but continue to use simple substances and to distrust the use of quicklime or orpiment in clysters. As a measure against continued disintegration, use plasters such as powdered vetch seeds cooked in diluted vinegar; mastic oil, with enough acacia added to produce the consistency of honey; and also ground lentils and honey, cooked in rose or mastic oil.

38   And if an outpouring of blood takes place by reason of the decay of tissue, apply sponges wrung out of vinegar to the lower abdominal region, i.e., the region below the umbilicus, and to the ends of the hips (Greek *ischia*). Then apply cupping to the same parts, using considerable flame; and bind the limbs. Give the patient digestible food that the body will easily assimilate, and also wine previously cooked in pomegranate rind. And inject a clyster of vinegar, either alone or with male frankincense, i.e., its powdered dust, or what is left over in the composition of the plaster of willows when the ingredients are mixed together. And apply plasters of similar properties. For example, take aca-
39 cia dissolved in vinegar, and cook until it begins to boil; or heat it slowly over warm ashes in the rind of a large pomegranate. Cover the affected parts with the decoction. Then apply cerates made with myrtle oil, quince oil, or green olive oil in which acacia is rubbed up and dissolved, or with omphacium or oenanthe oil, with the addition of rue or wild pomegranate flower. Sometimes all these substances may be used together. Or use the cerate whose composition Themison gives as follows: one part of acacia, one part of dried rose, half a part of gum ammoniac, four parts of wax, and a sufficient amount of rose oil; the acacia, rose, and ammoniac are rubbed up in Aminaean wine together with the melted wax, and then mixed with the rose oil.

If, however, there is no outpouring of blood, the reason in some cases is the clotting of the blood, and in others the condensation of a decaying vein. These cases may be distinguished
40 as follows: We may conclude that the vein is condensed if the pulse becomes more prominent. The coldness of the body abates and its warmth returns, the patient is in better spirits, and his body breathes easily and feels relieved. But if the obstacle to the outpouring is clotted blood (Greek *thrombōsis*), and the flow of blood is therefore concealed [within the body], the opposite symptoms occur, namely, pallor, tossing, small pulse, or even a suspension of the pulse (Greek *asphyxia*), a feeling of heaviness,

torpor pubetenus ac paulo superius, tum defectio cum sudore.

quapropter erit aceti iniectio facienda tunc cum fluor fuerit
41 abstinendus; diurnis diebus cibo reficiendus aegrotans. si autem
plurima ex parte retenta putredine parva excluserint aegrotantes quae sint sanguinolenta et ramentosa, et propterea profectu apparente †melior esse curatione,†[42] adiuncto tamen metu
ne retenta solvantur, oportet etiam secunda vel tertia die eundem trochiscum inicere sed solutum,[43] vel certe sucum plantaginis aut acaciam cum aqua.

sin vero quibusdam diebus sine officio ventris fuerint aegrotantes ac rursum iniectionibus asperati,[44] conicimus in his non
cicatricem ulcerum[45] factam, sed medicaminum supraducto cortice fuisse obtrusa. et propterea post effectum ventris nuda
atque sordidata[46] rursum humore fluere. ordinabimus item[47]
tribus diebus lenticulae coctionem crassioris suci iniciendam.
42 etenim intestina vi propria medicaminis coercentur, quam
Graeci stypsin vocant, et ulcerum mitescit asperitas, et ex anterioribus medicaminibus facta conglobatio sive cortex in saniem
provocatus cadit, et subiecta ulcera in cicatricem venire coguntur.

ac si plurimo tempore ulceratio perseveraverit cum corporis
debilitate atque fastidio, erit frequentia medicaminum evitanda
sive iniectionum sive potionum. maior enim ex ipsis vexatio fiet
43 cum cibi appetitus extinguitur et in fastidium veniunt aegrotantes, nisi parva insuetorum multis fuerint consuetis admixta.
decoctionem autem lenticulae secundo vel tertio per singulos
iniciemus dies. ex ipsa enim sufficienter intestina coercentur et
latenter corpus nutritur, cum quadam[48] particula digestioni[49]
usurpata viribus profecerit aegrotantis.

tum cum limpida ulcera senserimus, erunt cohibenda ea quae
vehementius consiccare valeant, quae Graeci styphonta vocant,

---

[42] melior esse ⟨videatur⟩ curatio R: *fort.* meliores sint curatione

[43] solita S: *corr.* Rm

[44] asperandi *Am*   [45] ulceris *edd.*

[46] obtrusum e. p. p. e. v. nudum atque sordidatum Rm (ulceris *retento*)

[47] autem R   [48] quaedam Rm   [49] digestione R

---

13. Perhaps 'swelling.'

14. The absence of any previous reference to a troche confirms the suspicion of
lacunae in what precedes.

flatus,[13] cold numbness in the lower abdominal region and even a little higher, fainting, and diaphoresis.

Now whenever there is bleeding to be stopped, inject a clyster 41 of vinegar; and nourish the patient every day with food. But if most of the corrupted matter is retained, and only a small amount of blood containing bits of matter is discharged, and if, as a consequence, there appears to be an improvement . . . but there is still the fear that the retained matter may dissolve in a flux—in such a case, on the second or third day inject the same troche,[14] first, however, dissolving it. Or use, instead, plaintain juice or acacia with water.

But if there has been no discharge from the bowels for several days and if, further, the injection of clysters aggravates the patient's condition, we may conclude in such cases that the ulceration has not yet cicatrized, but is covered over with a sort of shell formed by the drugs; and that, as a consequence of the resumption of bowel action, this ulceration will once more be exposed and give up a foul discharge. After three days inject[15] a 42 thick decoction of lentil. In this way the intestines are contracted by the characteristic astringent action (Greek *stypsis*) of this remedy and the severity of the lesions abates. Again, the mass or shell formed by the drugs previously administered is attacked and dissolved into sanies, and cicatrization of the underlying sores is thus induced.

Now if the ulceration persists a long time, with consequent bodily weakness and loss of appetite, avoid the frequent use of drugs, whether in clysters or in potions. For these produce even 43 greater distress when the appetite for food is lost; and the patient is affected by nausea, unless a few new items[16] are added to the many which he has been taking regularly. Also inject the decoction of lentil a second or even a third time on successive days. For the intestines are adequately confined by this treatment and the body is imperceptibly nourished, since in some small part the injection is absorbed by digestion and thus enhances the patient's strength.

After you note that the ulceration has cleared up, avoid the use of intensely desiccant substances (Greek *styphonta*), and in-

15. I.e., as an enema.

16. It is not clear whether the reference is to food or drugs.

et inicienda mediocriter constringentia. ac si quisquam eorum non tulerit virtutem, erit diachylon medicamen oleo roseo sol-
44 vendum ac diligenter liquefactum iniciendum, vel plumbeo mortario plumbeo pistillo circumducto,[50] immisso oleo rosaceo conterendum donec in sucum veniat atque crassius fiat. horum quoque similibus utendum monemus. tunc vino leni atque carne volantum vel marinorum utendum, ut squillae, mulli, carabi;[51] et pro modo virium gestatione resumptionis causa. dehinc cum omnia tuta viderimus, lavacrum adhibemus, sed non properanter, et magis cum forte iniectio fuerit facta trochisci, nisi primo ventrem egesserint aegrotantes.

tardante passione superpositionis tempore iisdem uti convenit. in lenimento vero erit fortificatio adhibenda corporibus per variam gestationem et vocis atque corporis exercitium **[52]
45 post singulas egestiones adhibenda ⟨encathismata⟩[53] ex oleo et aqua calida et decoctione lini seminis aut faenigraeci aut malvae agrestis ⟨et⟩[54] iisdem partibus, hoc est sessioni, quam Graeci hedram vocant, [et][55] specialiter admovenda vaporatio ex pollinibus cataplasmate calido vel saccello. dehinc etiam radix agrestis malvae decocta atque contrita[56] et calida testa calefacta erit apponenda. ac si iugis fuerit dolor, immittendus digitus usque ad altiora praeunctus adipe anserino cum faenigraeci semine cocto atque contrito, aut aliquo medicamine ex his quae appellamus[57] lipara. ac si haec minime fuerint inventa, erit hoc cero-
46 tario faciendum simplici atque limpido. et cum tempus cibi dandi occurrerit, adhibenda perunctio stricturae congrua. tunc nutrimento dandus panis ex aqua calida aut alica lota aut pulticula ex melle confecta aut ova sorbilia cum pane. potui autem aqua calida offerenda.

perseverante autem tumore adhibenda cucurbita adiuncta scarificatione locis tumentibus et vaporatio spongiarum; declinatione occurrente, adhibenda cerotaria et resumptio cauta. sic enim sedantur iuges egerendi ventris delectationes, cum tumor mitigatione conquiescit atque ille qui putatur reumatismus indulgentia tumentium facilius abstinetur.

[50] circumductum *Rm*

[51] carani *S: corr. Rm*

[52] *lacunam statuit Schmid RPh 143*

[53] *add. Schmid RPh 144, coll. Chr. iv. 47:* ⟨spongia⟩ *R: fort.* ⟨expressa spongia⟩

[54] *addidi, coll. 47*   [55] *delevi*   [56] decoctae atque contritae *S*   [57] *fort.* appellant

ject, instead, those that are only mildly astringent. And if a patient cannot stand the strength of the latter, melt the preparation of juices (*diachylon*) in rose oil, and when it is completely
44 dissolved, inject it. Or with circular movements of a lead pestle in a lead mortar, pound up the preparation, adding rose oil until a rather thick juice is obtained. We also advise the use of other substances like these. Then let the patient drink mild wine and eat the flesh of birds or of sea animals like shrimps, red mullets, and crayfish. Also prescribe passive exercise, in accordance with his strength, for the purpose of restoring his vigor. And when it is completely safe, prescribe bathing; but do not hurry with this treatment, especially in the event that the troche has been injected. In this case wait until the patient first moves his bowels.

When the disease becomes chronic, use the treatment outlined above for the periods of exacerbation. In the intervals of remission, however, strengthen the body with varied passive movement, vocal exercise, and active bodily exercise. . . .

45 [17]After each discharge from the bowels prescribe sitz baths of olive oil, hot water, and a decoction of flaxseed, fenugreek seed, or marsh mallow. And to the same parts, i.e., particularly to the anus (Greek *hedra*), apply heat by means of flour, using either a warm poultice or a bag. Also apply marsh mallow root cooked and pounded down and heated in an earthen vessel. And if the pain is continual, insert the finger far within, first smearing it with goose fat and cooked, triturated fenugreek seed, or with some other substance among those we call *lipara* ['fatty']. If these substances are not available, use a simple and pure wax
46 plaster. And when the time for feeding the patient comes, anoint him in a manner suitable for a state of stricture. Then feed him bread or spelt groats in hot water; some porridge prepared with honey; or soft eggs with bread. And give him warm water to drink.

If the inflammation still persists, apply cupping, with scarification, to the inflamed parts; and also use sponges to apply heat. And when the attack declines, employ wax plasters and cautious restorative treatment. For in this way the continual desire to go to stool abates as the inflammation subsides under the influence of soothing treatment; and what is thought to be a flux is easily checked by relieving the inflamed parts.

17. The next pages do not seem to belong to the coeliac disease proper. See 48 n.

47　ac si aequalis tumori fluor occurrerit, utriusque erit conicienda curatio. quapropter si fomentum ex oleo hispano vel melino aut murtino aut lentiscino adhibuerimus, et cataplasmata erunt ex aceto atque melle vel stymmatibus praeinfusis coquenda. item praescriptis iamdudum iniectionibus concoquenda quaedam constrictiva, ut murta vel rosa aut mala punica, lacte[58] autem et ceteris admiscendum amylum; et encathismatibus[59] aliqua decoctio stymmatum adiungenda aut mali punici. et apponenda rursum sessioni vaporatio stymmatum aut cantabri conligati

48　vel in aceto decocti vel quam omelysin vocant, ex pollinibus panno conligatis atque ex stymmatibus confectis. perungenda etiam digito interiora longaonis ex cerotario oleo roseo confecto aut adipe cum oleo roseo. tunc post perunctionem ora lavanda aqua tepida. cibus dandus pulticula calida, ut de ventriculosis scripsimus, quos Graeci coeliacos vocant, ex alica vel farre aut oryza aut milio aut olyra aut pane alexandrino, haec singularia vel aliquando amylo admixto aut lacte aut melle ex favo expresso. potus parvus dandus sed calidus. tum effecta declinatione resumptio adhibenda.

49　ac si solutio fuerit urgentior vel sola, frigidus convenit locus aegrotanti et supina iacendi positio, paulo levatius[60] capite locato, et suppositione lanarum clunes vel inferiores longaonis partes sublevandae. adhibenda etiam requies et impressus articulis manuum amplexus vel ligatio paulo tenacior. deponenda etiam omnis animi intentio et magis cogitatio passionis avertenda. admonet enim egestionem ac provocat inquietudinem in memoriam reducta conscientia. erit denique persuadendum ne quoties fuerint aegri in egestionem[61] commoti ilico ventrem facere festinent, sed quantum potuerint resistendo differant

50　motum.[62] fit enim quaedam meditatio atque frequens egerendi consuetudo et oportet effugere laborem motus ac nudandi[63] corporis frigus, nisi forte acrior aut incendiosa fuerit defluxio.

[58] lacti *Rm, fort. recte*

[59] encathismatibus *Bendz 69, Schmid RPh 142*: enatis matibus *S*: enematibus *Rm*

[60] levatius *Rm, coll. Chr. i. 8*: levius *S*

[61] egestione *edd.*　　[62] motu *S: corr. Rm*　　[63] nutandi *S: corr. A*: nudati *Rm*

18. Cf. 23; note, however, the prescription of cold water there. The references to the coeliac disease here and in sections 51, 54, and 60, below, indicate that this whole section belongs either to the discussion of *ceterae defluxiones* (19) or to the chapter on dysentery.

47 Now if a state of looseness occurs equal in degree to the inflammation, the treatment should be directed toward both conditions. Thus we use fomentations of Spanish, quince, myrtle, or mastic oil, as well as plasters prepared by cooking vinegar and honey, with the addition of astringent bases (*stymmata*), if desired. Again, in preparing the clysters described above, it will be necessary to cook with them certain astringent substances, such as myrtle, rose, or pomegranate, also to mix milk and the like with starch. And for the sitz baths a decoction of astringent substances or of pomegranate should be added. Apply heat to the anus in these cases, too, using vapors from astringent substances

48 or from bran tied up in bags or cooked in vinegar, or from raw flour (Greek *ōmēlysis*) mixed with astringent bases and tied up in a cloth. And, using a finger, anoint the interior parts of the rectum either with a wax plaster prepared with rose oil or with fat and rose oil. Then, after the anointing, wash the patient's face with warm water. And feed him some warm porridge, as we prescribed above[18] for those suffering from the coeliac disease (Greek *coeliacoe*). The porridge may be prepared with spelt groats, ground spelt, rice, millet, rice wheat, or Alexandrian bread. These substances may be used plain or, on occasion, with an admixture of starch, milk, or honey obtained from the comb. Give only a little to drink, but see that it is hot. Then when the decline of the disease is accomplished, employ treatments to restore the patient's strength.

49 Now if the state of looseness predominates [over the state of stricture], or, indeed, occurs alone, the patient should have a cool room and should lie on his back with his head raised a little. Raise the loins and the parts containing the lower end of the rectum by placing wool beneath them. Keep the patient quiet. Take hold of his limbs and press them firmly with your hands; or employ somewhat tight binding. Have him avoid all mental strain, and especially all thought of the disease. For the conscious memory of it arouses the desire to evacuate the bowels and causes restlessness. Again, urge the patient, when this desire to evacuate is aroused, not to hurry immediately to move his bowels, but to resist the urge and postpone the movement as long as possible.

50 For otherwise there will develop the practice and habit of frequent evacuations. But the patient should avoid the exertion of these movements and the chill of exposing the body, unless it

retenta enim sessionis in locis, quam Graeci hedran vocant,
longaonem exurit. convenit denique, si possibile fuerit, aegros
ad sessionem egestionis deportari, aut humilius a[64] lecto scaphia
posita ad egestionem produci capiendam.[65] vel si plurima fuerit
corporis defectio qua iacentes non valeant fluentia retinere,
erunt egestiones spongiis suppositis excipiendae et mediis partibus apponendae lanae, nunc oleo constrictivo praetinctae vel
51 decoctione buxi vel murtae aut mali punici et horum similium
stymmatum vel sucorum constringentium, nunc asperso rhu
terginario[66] quem Graeci byrsodepsicon vocant, vel trita galla
erunt media siccanda. haec enim constrictionem sine ullo frigore fore promittunt. dehinc apponenda ex palmulis epithemata et malo cydonio et balaustio et alumine et horum similium,[67] sicut de coeliacis vel sanguinem spuentibus aut stomachicis scribentes docuimus. iniciendus etiam per clysterem
sucus plantaginis aut polygoni herbae vel intybi aut uvae lu-
52 pinae aut herbae caliclariae[68] vel sempervivae aut mespilae,
malvae aut orizae, aut decoctio mali punici vel eius caduci, quod
Graeci cytinon rhoas appellant, nos ampullagium.[69] et aliquando haec ipsa erunt conterenda, vel rosa aut rubus, quam Graeci
baton appellant, aut lentiscus aut galla aut thallia aut rubi vir-
gulta vel vitis anuli, quos helicas vocant, aut salicis folia [aut][70]
ex vino bunito his qui sine febri adficiuntur, ex aqua vero his qui
febricitant. item ros syriacus aut omphacium aut acaciae sucus
vel hypocistidos herbae aut balaustii drachmae duae in quatuor
vel quinque cyathis coniciendae. est enim ea quantitas iniectionis redundans, hoc est siquidem plurima gravedine quadam
provocet ventrem. item lenticulae decoctio aut licium indicum
53 cum lacte: sint autem amyli drachmae quatuor, licii drachmae
duae, lactis cyathi septem vel octo. extendenda enim haec singula atque minuenda sunt pro magnitudine solutionis[71] ac virium
aegrotantis.

ac si plurimus fuerit in ulceribus sensus ut medicaminum constrictione lacessita indignentur, erunt inicienda ea quae cum
dulcedine admota partes valeant praesiccare, quo neque ulcera-

---

[64] a *scripsi:* e *edd.*   [65] capiendam *scripsi:* faciendam *edd.*
[66] rutherginario *S: corr. Schmid RPh 145; cf. Mél. Niedermann 122:* rhoe coriario *Rm*
[67] similibus *Rm, fort. recte. cf. adn. ad Chr. iii. 22: contra Bendz 19*
[68] caricariae *S:* calycariae *Rm, fort. recte. cf.* calicaris (*S*) *55*
[69] *fort. scrib.* ampullacium (*vel* -ceum). *cf. Chr. v. 44; Schmid Mél. Niedermann 120*

happens that the flux is sharp and burning. For in that case the feces, if retained, inflame the rectum at the anus (Greek *hedra*). And so, if possible, carry the patient to stool or have pots placed beneath his bed and brought out for the purpose of receiving a bowel movement. Again, if the patient lies in a state of complete collapse and is therefore unable to control the flow of matter, catch the discharges with sponges placed beneath. And to the middle parts of the body apply wool dipped in an astringent oil

51 or in a decoction of box, myrtle, pomegranate, or similar astringent juices (Greek *stymmata*). Again, the middle parts may be dried by sprinkling over them some tanner's sumach, which the Greeks call *byrsodepsicē* [*sc. rhus*], or some pulverized oak gall, for these substances have an astringent effect without causing chill. In addition, apply epithems prepared with dates, quinces, wild pomegranate flower, alum, and the like, as we have already indicated in discussing the coeliac disease,[19] blood-spitting, and the disease of the esophagus. And inject a clyster of the juice of

52 plantain, knotgrass, endive, strychnos, pellitory, houseleek, medlar, mallow, or rice; or a decoction of pomegranate or its flower (Greek *cytinos rhoas*, Latin *ampullaceum*). In some cases these same substances or rose, bramble (Greek *batos*), mastic, oak gall, bramble foliage or slips, vine tendrils (Greek *helices*), or willow foliage may be rubbed up in earthnut wine for patients who do not have fever, and in water for those who have fever. And add two drachms of Syrian sumach, omphacium, or the juice of acacia, hypocist, or wild pomegranate flower to the four or five cyathi of the clyster. For a clyster of this volume is quite ample, since a large clyster would cause a feeling of heaviness in the abdomen. A clyster containing a decoction of lentils

53 or Indian lycium with milk may also be used, e.g., four drachms of starch, two drachms of lycium, and seven or eight cyathi of milk. Increase or diminish the several ingredients of these clysters to accord with the extent of the state of looseness and the patient's strength.

And if there is such great pain in the ulcerated parts that irritation and injury would result from the astringent action of the drugs, inject such substances as will have a drying effect through gentle action. In this way you will avoid irritating the sore parts

19. See 48 n.

tionem provocemus neque fluorem negligamus. ex quibus est in febricitantibus sucus ptisanae cum adipe caprino, contrito atque
54 commixto tracanto vel gummi aut argallici[72] radice (sed illa duo infusione praemollienda, radix autem coquenda), aut rosaceo oleo ovum commixtum aut lac coagulatum vel cum amylo concoctum ad tertiam partem. in his vero qui sine febribus fuerint, passum convenit creticum et vinum squilliticum[73] supradictis[74] speciebus.

tum refectionis tempore unctio adhibenda ex oleo hispano ac deinde ora lavanda pusca tepida. cibus autem specialiter, ut in coeliacis ordinavimus, dandus. similiter etiam potum convenit dare. lac quoque bibendum praecoctum, quod appellant diaco-
55 cleon,[75] sive singulare.[76] etenim fluores crassificando cohibet et ulcera deterget et acrimoniam humorum temperat et sine ullo labore corpora nutrit. est autem coctionis hic modus. lac sumendum ex agresti pastu perfectum. etenim in civitate nutritorum animalium reprobamus, siquidem caprae[77] e salsiore pascua sitientes plurimum atque coacervatim bibant, et multum lac sed aquatum faciant, quod est constrictioni ventris incongruum. quapropter magis ex capra[78] quae lentisci pascua vel murtae aut rubi aut vitis foliis vel quercus aut salicis vel hederae aut terebinthi aut herbae caliclaris[79] vel polygonii aut plantaginis et horum similibus fuerit nutrita, erit lac accipiendum. confluxit
56 enim constrictiva qualitas herbarum in lactis qualitatem. nam saepe diagridium vel helleborum mandentes purgativae virtutis efficiunt lactem,[80] sicut feniculum[81] comedentes lac generant quod visum praestet accipientibus abunde. denique erit primo probandum atque eligendum quod sit albidius atque sine ullo odore et neque globosum, hoc est frustis coagulatis variatum, quod Graeci thrombodes appellant, neque in urinae similitudinem mutatum, quod iidem uroides appellant, sed quod possit unguibus destillatum manere sua tenacitate collectum. boni

---

[72] argillirici *S*: *corr. Rm*   [73] Scybeliticum *Rm*
[74] *fort.* ⟨admixtis⟩ supradictis
[75] *exspectaveris* diacoc(h)lacon, *sed cf. Chr. iv. 57; Schmid Mél. Niedermann 122*
[76] silicare *Reinesius 671, sed cf.* sine his *58*
[77] *an* capreae?
[78] capra *R*: caprea *S*   [80] lac *Rm*
[79] caliclaris *scripsi*: calicaris *S*   [81] feniculum *Rm*: procicolium *S*

---

20. See 48 n.

without neglecting the state of flow. In cases where fever is present, a suitable preparation of this kind is pearl barley water with goat's fat together with which tragacanth, gum, or comfrey 54 root is rubbed up and mixed. Before using the tragacanth or gum, however, soften them by soaking; and cook the root. An egg mixed with rose oil, or else sour milk, or milk boiled down with starch to a third of the original quantity, may also be used in these cases. But in cases where there is no fever, Cretan raisin wine and wine of squills go well with the other substances mentioned above.

Then at mealtime anoint the patient with Spanish oil and wash his mouth and face with warm diluted vinegar. Give the special food we have prescribed for the coeliac disease;[20] and do likewise in prescribing drink. The patient should also drink precooked milk, taking either the kind called *diacochleōn* or the simple 55 ple variety. For cooked milk stops the discharges by its thickening action, cleanses the ulceration, moderates the acrid properties of the fluids, and nourishes the body without imposing any exertion. The method of cooking the milk is as follows. Take milk which is produced in rural pasture lands. We reject the milk of animals pastured in and near the [coastal] cities, for she-goats made thirsty by salty pasturage drink frequently and in great quantities. And so, while they produce a great deal of milk, it is watery and therefore unsuitable as an astringent for the stomach. Take milk, then, preferably from a she-goat whose nourishment has come from feeding on the foliage of mastic, myrtle, bramble, vine, oak, willow, ivy, terebinth, pellitory, knotgrass, plantain, or the like. For the astringent properties of 56 these herbs join in forming the character of the milk. So it is that mothers who have taken scammony or hellebore often produce milk of purgative qualities; so also those who have taken fennel produce milk that insures good vision for those receiving it.[21] And so, first test and select white, odorless milk that is not lumpy or clotty (Greek *thrombōdes*). At the same time it should not be so thin that it resembles urine (Greek *uroeides*), but when a drop of the milk is placed on the fingernail it should maintain its form by reason of its cohesiveness.[22] Take, then, four or five

21. Fennel was much used by the ancients in diseases of the eye. It was also thought to sharpen the vision (cf. Isidore *Origines* xvii. 11. 4).

22. Cf. Soranus *Gyn.*, p. 70. 1.

igitur, ut diximus, lactis quatuor vel quinque sextarios oportet in
57 vas fictile mittere sive aeneum; immittendae et cochleae, quas
nos lapides marinos vel fluminales accipimus, non marinae igitur
ob salsitatem, sed fluminales. inustae primo quo[82] sint igne pel-
lucidae, tum auferendae, et exsufflatis omnibus quae de se forte
dimiserint ac depurgatis, supradicto vasculo immittendae. ac
ferulis lac cum iisdem cochleis movendum donec ad mediam
veniat partem sive tertiam. dehinc refuso lacte proiciendae
priores cochleae atque aliae innovandae similiter exustae, sed per
profectum numero atque forma minores, longa per intervalla.
haec confectio lactis diacocleon appellatur.

58   sine his vero confectio erit longe simplicior, quam Graeci aperiergon vocant. vas enim lactis erit imponendum igni molliori,
et immissa ferula metienda mensura totius ac dimidiae et tertiae
quantitatis, quo non coniectura sed vera dimensione coctionis
quantitatem sumamus. tunc ex ipsa ferula circumlato ductu
movebimus coquentes, ne lateribus vel fundo iugi mansione in-
sidat.[83] dehinc ultimo coctionis tempore plurimus detrahendus
est ignis, et cum ad partem dimidiam vel tertiam venerit, erit in
aliud vas refundendum. exinde aegro dandum non frigidum sed
59 leviter egelatum,[84] quod galactodes appellant. ac si forte stomachi fuerit eversio commota cum accipere aegrotantes horrescunt, erit frigidum dandum, praetecto vasculo nivibus. ut
enim mel decoctum fit constrictivum, sic etiam lac deposito atque excocto tenuissimo liquore, quem Graeci orrhon appellant,
et vapore concepto constrictivum fieri necesse est. convenit
denique etiam supra dictus ex regula[85] motus. est enim virtute
constrictiva, et sui corporis raritate tenuitatem lactis vel aquatum a liquore ebibens.

accipere autem aegrotantes debent pro passionis magnitudine
et sumendi voluntate, quam Graeci orexin vocant, quidam pluri-
60 mum, quidam parvum: et primo ex ea decoctione quae sit ad

---

[82] quoad *Rm*

[83] insidāt *S: corr. Rm*

[84] gelatum *S: corr. Rm (cf. Chr. iv. 63; Ac. iii. 58)*   [85] *fort.* ferula

---

23. The word properly should be *cochlaces* (κόχλακες) or the Latinized *cochlacae*, but
there seems to have been a confusion with *cochlea* ('shell'). See Paul. Fest., p. 39;
CGL III. 538. 36, 559. 50.

24. The point seems to be that the temperature at which the milk is served does
not affect the astringent quality imparted to it by the boiling.

sextarii of good milk, as we have indicated, and put it in an
57 earthen or copper vessel. Also place pebbles [*cochleae*],²³ which
we call 'sea stones' or 'river stones,' into the vessel. In this case
use river pebbles rather than sea pebbles because of the salty
quality of the latter. Before immersing them, heat them until
the flame makes them transparent; then take them from the
fire, blow off and clean away any flaking that may have occurred, and place the pebbles in the aforesaid vessel. Using rods,
stir the milk together with these pebbles until the milk is reduced to half or even a third of the original amount. Then pour
off the milk [into another vessel], discard the pebbles previously
used, and replace them with others similarly heated. Repeat the
process at long intervals [with the milk that remains in each
case], gradually reducing the number of pebbles and choosing
smaller ones. This preparation of milk is called *diacochleōn* ['with
pebbles'].

58   But the following method, which dispenses with the use of
pebbles, is far simpler (Greek *aperiergon*). Place a pot of milk
over a gentle flame; insert a rod which will measure the whole,
half, and third parts so that the amount boiled away may be
ascertained by actual measurement rather than merely guessed
at. Then, as the milk cooks, stir it with the same rod, using a
circular motion to prevent it from remaining stationary and
consequently settling upon the sides or bottom of the vessel.
Then, toward the end of the cooking, remove most of the flame,
and, when the milk is reduced to a half or a third of the original
amount, pour it into another vessel. Then give it to the patient,
not cold but somewhat warm (Greek *galactōdes*, 'milk-warm').
59 But if it happens that the patient begins to gag and he shrinks
from taking the milk warm, give it to him cold, placing snow
around the vessel. Just as honey is astringent when boiled down,
so milk, too, must take on an astringent property when heat
has been imparted to it, and the thin fluid (Greek *oros*, 'whey')
is removed through boiling.²⁴ Moreover, the stirring with the
rod is also helpful; for it serves to thicken the milk, since the rod
absorbs within its loose structure the thin or watery part of the
milk and separates it from the rest.

Now the amount of milk taken by the patients should depend
on the severity of the disease and on the patient's desire (Greek
60 *orexis*); thus let some drink a great deal and others little. Have

dimidiam partem redacta, tum ex ea quae ad tertiam venerit
partem, siquidem sit paulo plus constrictivae virtutis. sed erit
eius usus comparatione prioris minuendus. tunc post bibitum
lac nullum potum sumere debent aegrotantes. est enim ratione
carens lac decoctione constrictum supermisso liquore in aquam
vertere. praeterea in his qui sufficienter vel quantum voluerimus sumpserint, nihil erit omnino superdandam. his vero qui
minus accepisse videbuntur, sicut de coeliacis ordinavimus, erit
superdanda pulticula ex lacte confecta, ut destinatus impleatur
61 modus. tunc post intermissionem mediocrem, si quisquam
nauseaverit, erunt danda mali punici grana vel acinae uvarum
siccarum, quas fabriles appellant, aut mespila vel sorba.

quidam igitur primam decoctionem probaverunt secundae
praeponendam, siquidem lac in semet velut calcis qualitatem
accepisse videatur, qua possint putredines ulcerum abstineri.
alii vero secundam magis probaverunt, quibus etiam nos consentimus: non enim admixta supradicta qualitas[86] causa est
abstinendae passionis. potest enim etiam quiddam calcis
62 vivae, quam Graeci asbeston appellant, lacti admisceri. sed est
incoctio sive insumptio aquosi liquoris, quo amisso sincerior lactis qualitas fiat; quae neque curiosa confectione[87] neque nidorosa
vel fumosa sufficitur, sed[88] simplici coctione fuerit procurata.
cum enim lac se a suo humore separaverit, quem[89] Graeci orrhon
appellant, crassius effectum ac viscosius,[90] insidens ventri atque
intestinis et multo tempore immoratum, liquida concrassat et
ulcera mitiganter amplectitur.

item alii tertiam partem aquae lacti miscentes decoquunt,
adserentes quod sit decoctio melior, ne ullo nidore sive fumo aut
63 ustione lactis natura vitietur ob aquae admixtionem. hi autem
si usque eo coquendum iubent donec ad modum praemixti red-

[86] admixtae supradictae qualitatis S: corr. R
[87] confectio edd.   [89] quam S: corr. Rm
[88] sed scripsi: si edd.   [90] viscosus S: corr. A (p. 708): viscosum Rm

25. See 48 n.

them drink first from the milk which has boiled down to half the original amount, and then from that which has boiled down to one-third, for the latter has a somewhat more binding quality. But in all cases have the patient take less of the latter decoction than he takes of the former. After he has drunk the milk, the patient should have no other drink. For it is illogical to thicken milk by boiling, and then to let the patient drink fluids over it and turn it to water. Again, after a patient has taken a sufficient amount of milk, i.e., as much as we want him to, he should be given no food at all. But if he takes less, give him, in addition, a porridge prepared with milk to fill out the required amount, in

61 accordance with our prescriptions for the coeliac disease.[25] Then after a short interval of time, if a patient becomes nauseated, give him pomegranate kernels, smoke-dried raisins (called *fa-briles*), medlars, or sorb apples.

Now some hold that the first method of boiling down milk[26] is preferable to the second, on the ground that in the first method the milk apparently absorbs something of the quality of lime, and the rotting of the sores can be checked by this means. But others consider the second method preferable, and we agree with this group. For the addition of the quality in question to the milk will not overcome the disease; and one could just as well

62 add some quicklime (Greek *asbestos*) to the milk. But the important thing is the boiling away and removal of the watery fluid. For when that is gone the quality of the milk becomes purer; and this quality cannot be obtained by any subtle procedure of steaming and smoking, but is gained by simple boiling. For when the milk proper is separated from its watery fluid (Greek *oros*, 'whey'), it becomes thicker and more viscous; it settles over the stomach and intestines and, when it has remained there for some time, causes the fluids to coagulate and forms a soothing protection for the ulcerated parts.

Some add a third part of water to the milk before boiling it, saying that this makes a better decoction; they hold that the addition of the water will prevent the quality of the milk from

63 being impaired by any steaming, fumes, or burning. But if these physicians prescribe that the mixture be boiled down merely to

26. I.e., with pebbles. The view (see *Rm*) that *prima decoctio* refers to the boiling down to half the original amount, *secunda decoctio* to the boiling down to a third, seems untenable.

eat lactis qui fuerat priusquam aqua misceretur, et liquidius
conficiunt et non sine suo naturali liquore, quem Graeci orrhon
appellant, aegrotantibus dabunt, prisca lactis quantitate servata. sin vero ad partem dimidiam vel tertiam decoquent, non
solum plurimum decoctionis tempus insumunt, verum etiam
tarditate coquendi diutina fumosum faciunt medicamen. haec
sunt quae in ipsorum erroribus respondemus.

eius autem datio erit discernenda. nam primo egelatum[91]
bibi debet sive tepens, quod Graeci galactodes appellant; tum
fervens, sed cum primo fuerit profectus aliquis ex ante dato.
hinc enim perfecta passionis fiet abstentio.

64 ac si quisquam aegrotantium lac sumere noluerit, aut horrido
visu aut stomachi supinatione recusans, erit aliis adiutoriis adiu-
vandus. et si ulcus fuerit in superioribus ac densioribus[92] intestinis, utendum medicaminibus potis, quae Graeci anoterica vocaverunt. etenim quae clystere iniciuntur, haec magis patientibus aptanda[93] sunt locis inferioribus.[94] et cum cibi fuerit adpetentia servata,[95] nec ullo fastidio aegri videbuntur adfecti, erit
medicaminum consueta magis eligenda materia; ac si fastidium fuerit, sola probanda. sed eorum compositionem atque
ordinem ex his quae de coeliacis ordinavimus sumi mandamus.
65 licet praeterea cum his etiam acaciae vel oenanthes ex aqua cisternina contritae[96] donec collyriorum faciat crassitudinem, rotun-
data frusta dare bibenda, aut resoluta cum vitello ovi assi in
quantitate[97] dimidii cochlearii, aut aqua resoluta, in his qui
febre afficiuntur tribus cyathis. in his vero qui sine febribus
sunt cum vino erit offerendum.

praeterea communiter etiam haec quae sanguinem expuenti-
bus dantur probamus, quorum est sucus plantaginis, vel una die

[91] gelatum S: corr. Rm (cf. 58)

[92] fort. tenerioribus; cf. tensiores (S) Chr. v. 54

[93] apta R

[94] inferioribus transp. R: habet S post etenim quae, illic fort. servandum addito ⟨his⟩ post magis

[95] cibi fuerit a. servata scripsi: cibi fuerint a. servati S: ⟨in⟩ cibi fuerint a. servati R

[96] contrita S: corr. R   [97] quantitatem Rm

the amount of the milk that was present before the water was added, the concoction they produce is thinner,[27] and, moreover, it is not free from the natural watery fluid (Greek *oros,* 'whey'). Such is the concoction they give the patient if they stop the boiling when the original quantity of milk is reached. But if they have the milk boiled down to one-half or one-third, not only do they use up more time in cooking, but, by reason of the slowness of cooking, they impart a smoky character to the remedy. Such is our answer to their erroneous views.

Again, the method of giving the remedy involves distinct stages. Thus the patient should first drink it lukewarm or tepid (Greek *galactōdes,* 'milk-warm'). Later he should take it hot, but only after he has shown some improvement from the milk previously taken. In this way the disease will be completely checked.

64 But if a patient does not wish to take milk, refusing it either because its appearance is repulsive to him or because of sluggishness of the gullet, he will have to be helped with other remedies. Thus, if the ulceration is in the upper and more closely packed intestines,[28] prescribe the drinking of drugs that the Greeks call *anōterica.*[29] For injections made by clyster are more suitable when the lower parts of the intestines are affected. And if the patient retains his desire for food and does not appear troubled by loss of appetite, the common drugs should be more generally chosen for him; but if there is loss of appetite, these simple drugs should be used exclusively. Determine their composition and the details of their use on the basis of the prescriptions we set forth in 65 dealing with the coeliac disease.[30] In addition, one may give the patient acacia or oenanthe rubbed up in rain water to the consistency of a salve and then divided into round pieces; these may be taken mixed with half a spoonful of the yolk of a fried egg, or dissolved in water. In cases where fever is present, use three cyathi of water, and in cases which are free from fever give the patient the medicine with wine.

In addition, we hold that, in general, the prescription used for cases of blood-spitting may be used in the present cases, viz.,

27. I.e., than the original milk. Or perhaps the meaning is merely 'too thin.'
28. I.e., the small intestines.
29. 'Upper,' i.e., 'given by mouth.'
30. See 48 n.

ac nocte rhus syriacus[98] infusus vino vehementiori, quo detracto
oryza immissa vino[99] coquemus; dehinc lenticulae pulmentum
decorticatae atque subassatae in pulticulae modum conficere;
66 item ova aceto cocta vel ovorum vitella quae sint carbonibus
assata; item decoctio ex plantagine aut agresta[100] et intybo, quod
cicorion Graeci vocant. sed haec singula erunt duplici coctione
curanda. nam post primam coctionem erunt in aliam aquam
transferenda cum aliis nondum coctis, quorum coctione perfecta
priorum secundum probamus effectum. erunt praeterea haec
condienda oleo viridi et aceto et parvo sale vel, quod est melius,
rhos.[101] et si sordidum tardaverit ulcus,[102] iniectione mulsi per-
67 severandum probamus, nisi solutio fuerit adiuncta, vel decoctione ⟨corticis⟩[103] mali punici etiam si crebrae temporaliter ventris egestiones, quae quidem erit terenda;[104] item corticis pini aut
subassatae interioris tunicae sive corticis glandis, quam sardia-
nam vocant, aut pulenti aut cuiuslibet materiae vehementius
astringentis. ac si quisquam harum virtutum recusaverit usum
horrens oblata, siquidem sensu torqueant acriore,[105] erunt haec
mellis decocti atque durati latitudine cingenda quo sub dulcedine lateant acriora, et nihil eorum virtuti derogetur, siquidem
etiam mel coctum constringat. item malorum punicorum trium
68 mediae magnitudinis corticem sumentes, admixto vino lym-
phato, hoc est aqua temperato, coquemus in his qui sine febribus
afficiuntur, vel declinante causa melius habere videntur; cum
cisternina vero heminis[106] sex, quas cotylas Graeci appellant, in
his qui etiam febribus afficiuntur, donec ad tertiam partem
liquor deveniat. tum ex ipso duos vel tres cyathos ante cibum
dabimus aegrotanti, vel eadem mala omnia contusa atque cola-

---

[98] syriaci S: corr. Rm

[99] oryza immissa vinum *vel* oryzam immissam vino Rm

[100] agresta *dubitanter retinui*

[101] rhoe Rm

[102] ulcus ⟨in⟩ R   [104] erunt terenda S: *fort.* erunt ferenda(e)

[103] *add.* R   [105] *fort.* sensum torqueant acore

[106] heminis *scripsi*: heminas S: ⟨ad⟩ heminas R

plantain juice; or an infusion of Syrian sumach in strong wine—
the sumach is removed after it soaks for a day and a night, and
rice is then added to the wine and cooked with it; or a dish of
lentils shelled, slightly warmed, and prepared as a porridge; or
66 eggs cooked in vinegar; or the yolks of eggs cooked over coals.
A decoction of plantain or sour grapes[31] and chicory (Greek
cichorion) may also be used; but these substances must in each
case be subjected to a double cooking. That is, after a portion
has been cooked once, place it in other water along with a part
not yet cooked. When the cooking of this part, too, is completed,
we know that the first part has been subjected to a double cooking. Furthermore, these substances should be seasoned with
green olive oil, vinegar, and a little salt, or preferably sumach.
But if the ulceration festers chronically, continue the injection of
67 mead unless a state of looseness is also present. And even if for
a time there are frequent discharges from the bowels, rub up
some pomegranate rind and have the patient drink[32] a decoction
of it. Or use a decoction of pine bark or of the inner coating[33]
or skin of the so-called 'Sardian acorns,'[34] roasted a little, or
pearl barley, or any other strongly astringent substance. And if
a patient refuses to use these substances and shudders when they
are served, because their acrid properties revolt him, cover them
over with a strip of cooked honey which has hardened. This will
hide the acrid parts under a cover of sweetness and at the same
time will not detract at all from their strength, for the cooked
honey also has astringent properties. Again, take the rind of
68 three medium-sized pomegranates, add diluted wine, i.e., wine
mixed with water, and cook. This decoction will be suitable for
cases that are free from fever or cases in which the disease is declining and the patient seems to be improving. But where fever
is present, use up to six heminae (Greek *cotylae*) of rain water
[instead of the wine], boiling until the fluid is reduced to a third
of the original amount. Then give the patient two or three cya-

31. The existence of the word *agresta* is doubtful; the meaning here assigned is
inferred from Romance (see *Thes. Ling. Lat.*). As an alternative, one may read *agresti*
and assume that the name of the wild plant in question has dropped out; or one may
read *plantagine ⟨aut lata⟩ aut angusta*, referring to the two varieties of plantain.

32. From the sequel it would seem that this preparation is to be drunk rather than
injected by clyster. But our text is quite uncertain here, and the meaning is at many
points obscure.

33. The coating may still refer to the pine bark, not to the acorns.

34. A type of chestnut. Cf. Diosc. *Mat. med.* i. 106.

ta, vino aut aqua immixta, erunt offerenda non plus cyathis duobus. item mala cydonia cum malis punicis decocta in vino dulci aut squillitico, tunc frixatione[107] siccata atque crassificata
69 cum lacte data conveniunt vel aquae cyathis sex; item ges aster cum aqua data[108] curationi convenit. alia quoque plurima simillimae virtutis infinita specie concurrunt.[109]

item cibo danda alica cum vino melino aut murtino aqua temperato. tunc plurimo profectu accedente dandi turdi atque pulli gallinacei vel columbarum atque volantum quaeque sicciora, ut phasiani pectora vel perdicis aut attagenae agrestis, quae singula erunt postea apte coquenda aut mediocriter assanda, ne lignosa fiant et digestioni officiant. aliquando etiam erunt haec animalia reclusis pectoribus virgultis murtae penetranda
70 aut eis magis replenda. tunc mediocriter coquenda ac deinde farina conspersa tegenda et cinere calido maturanda. item maritima quae sunt densioris carnis, agrestium quoque, hoc est leporis vel capreae, conveniunt pulmenta; vel pomorum quaeque vivida[110] virtute constringere valent, ut mala cydonia cocta vel assata, item pira, sorba, mespila quae nondum fuerint maturitate dulcia, pruna agrestia, mali punici grana cum exterioribus membranis exsiccata, item uva et magis fumi vapore siccata, quam fabrilem appellant. omnis praeterea cibus erit diligenter masticatione exercendus quo digestibilis fiat, ne venter debilitate segnior plurimo laboret nixu appropriando corpori quae sumpserit.

71 mediis[111] autem partibus erit apponendum diaiteon[112] medicamen et omne quod fuerit siccativum malagma, vel aceto confectum. tunc etiam vinum dandum quod fuerit natura plurimum constringens ac pro regionibus cognitum, ut in Italia praenestinum appellatum vel surrentinum, et magis signinum ac marsicum, ex quo oportet etiam alicam myrto[113] curatam dari. ac si forte hoc vini genus minime fuerit repertum, erit quiddam aquae calidae admiscendum quod eandem valeat imitari virtutem, ut rhaponticum, vel illud quod Graeci appellant ⟨hymenodes⟩[114]

---

[107] frixatione *scripsi, coll.* frixantes *Ac. i. 77*: fricatione *S*: frixione *Rm*
[108] data *scripsi*: ducta *S*: datus *Rm*
[109] occurrunt *Rm*
[110] *fort.* viscida, *sed cf. Chr. ii. 167*   [112] diatheon *S*
[111] mediis *Rm*: melius *S*   [113] mero, *alii* myrto *Rm*: myro *S*
[114] *addidi, coll.* Gal. XI. 865 (*Kühn*), Diosc. Mat. med. i. 106. 1

thi of the decoction before he takes food; or pound up and strain all three pomegranates, adding wine or water; and give the patient no more than two cyathi. Quinces and pomegranates cooked in sweet wine or in wine of squills and then dried and thickened by roasting are beneficial when given with milk or with six cyathi of water. Likewise, Samian earth with water contributes to a successful treatment. And there are many other substances with similar properties which may be employed in countless preparations.

As food, give the patient spelt groats with quince or myrtle wine diluted with water. Then, after he has shown considerable improvement, give him thrushes, young chickens, squabs, and any of the drier meats of birds, e.g., breast of pheasant, partridge, and wild francolin. After being chosen, these birds should in each case be properly cooked or moderately roasted to prevent their becoming woody and impairing digestion. Sometimes they may be opened at the breast and pierced, or preferably stuffed, with myrtle twigs. Then cook them moderately, cover them with a sprinkling of flour, and let them simmer over warm ashes. Meaty fish is also beneficial; so also are stews made from the meat of field animals such as hare or roe. And use may be made of any fruits which are astringent by reason of their sharp quality, e.g., quinces, either cooked or roasted, pears, sorb apples, medlars not yet ripe enough to be sweet, wild plums, pomegranate kernels dried with their outer skins, and raisins, preferably smoke-dried (*fabriles*). Furthermore, have the patient chew all his food thoroughly to aid its digestion and to make it unnecessary for the stomach, which is less active by reason of its weakness, to work laboriously in distributing to the body the food taken in.

And apply to the middle parts of the body the plaster of willows or any of the desiccant plasters, e.g., those made with vinegar. Then give the patient a very astringent wine, one known by the name of the region from which it comes, e.g., in Italy the so-called Praenestine or Surrentine wines, and, in fact, preferably the Signian and Marsian kinds. Spelt groats prepared with myrtle should be given in this wine. And if it happens that the proper kind of wine cannot be obtained, use a mixture of hot water with some substance which can match the properties of the wine, e.g., rhubarb, or the membranaceous film that adheres inside the

inter corticem quercus inhaerens, per tanta[115] nervorum fila te-
72 neriora.[116] item rhus linteo ligatus[117] vel galla viridis, quae appellata est omphacine, aut vitis anuli, quas[118] elicas appellant,
aut virga rubi aut cerasia aut mala punica aut fabae graecae
folia. non haec quidem erunt iugiter adhibenda, sed medicaminis vice.

tunc apparente magis profectu adhibendum lavacrum, et corporum motus per gestationem vel deambulationem insinuandus.
ac si passio perseveraverit transacta superpositione, erunt iisdem
quae supra memoravimus resumendi aegrotantes, adiecto vocis
exercitio cum corporis vehementi defricatione, et magis ventris
in locis.

item cyclus[119] iuxta regulam, quae aut qualitatis solius habeat
73 ductum, ut aequali quantitate servata descensus vel transitus
ad parvi nutrimenti mutationem veniat, ut a turdis[120] vel parvis
volantum animalibus ad palumbos vel perdices et his similia;
aliquando per quantitatem solam, ut eodem pulmento servato,
exempli causa perdicis, ex[121] parvo modo veniant ad plurimum.
tunc erunt utraque iungenda, ut etiam qualitate ac quantitate
variatus formetur cyclus, cum vires aegrotantis valentes viderimus. quomodo autem initium sumendum sit, vel panis fieri partitio, vel quia[122] in pulmentorum mutationibus vinum vel lavacrum detrahimus, ex iamdudum dictis accipiendum probamus.
74 sed lavacra rara atque calida magis invenimus aptissima.

tum confirmato corpore ac resumptis viribus, vomitum convenit adhibere, et primo ex simplici potu, secundo ex radicibus,
quo partiliter locale adiutorium ventri praestemus, et quodam
vehementi motu veluti purgatione per vomitum effecta, omni
impedimento digestionis officii liberetur.

tum transeundum ad mediae qualitatis pulmenta, et cetera
cyclorum ordine suo reddenda usque ad porcinae pulmenta.

---

[115] per tanta *scripsi*: pertetā *S*: *an scrib*. per tot?
[116] per tanta nervorum fila teneriora *fort. secl. ut gloss. ad* hymenodes
[117] ligato *S*: *corr. R*
[118] anuli quas *scripsi*: amyli quas *S*: annuli quos *Rm*
[119] *fort.* cyclus ⟨adhibendus⟩ *vel sim.*
[120] tardis *edd.*   [121] ex *Rm*: et *S*   [122] quo modo *Rm*

---

35. In all these cases it is understood that the juice is to be used.

2 bark of the oak tree (Greek *hymenōdes*). Also apply sumach, covering it with a linen bandage, or oak gall that is unripe (Greek *omphacinē*), vine tendrils (Greek *helices*), bramble twig, cherries, pomegranate, or tops of the Greek bean plant.[35] Do not apply these substances continually, but use them in alternation with[36] the plaster.

Then, when the patient's continued improvement is obvious, prescribe bathing and gradually introduce passive exercise or walking. And if the disease persists after the conclusion of the attack, treat the patient with the same restorative measures as we described above, adding vocal exercise and strong massage of the body, especially of the abdomen.

Employ the cycle of treatments in accordance with standard procedure. First make the series of changes with sole reference
3 to the quality of the food given. That is, keep the quantity equal, but arrange a cycle or series of changes in the quality of this small amount of nourishment. Thus have the patient pass from thrushes or other small birds to ringdoves, partridges, and the like. But sometimes the changes should be with reference to quantity alone. In this case the same food is given, let us say partridge, but the amount is increased from a little to a great deal. Then both kinds of variation should be combined so that the cycle involves changes both in quality and in quantity; let this be done when the strength of the patient appears adequate. For the method of beginning this procedure and of making the required division of the bread and the necessity of avoiding wine and bathing at the time of changing the food we may refer to
4 what we have already written.[37] And we have found it best for the patient to take very few baths, and those preferably hot.

Then, when his body has been built up and his strength restored, it is well to apply the vomitive treatment, first having the patient drink a simple vomitive. Later, radishes should be used in order to afford a partial local remedy for the stomach and to remove all obstacles to digestion. The radishes accomplish this purpose by the violence of their action, the vomiting having the effect of a sort of purge.

Then have the patient pass to food of the middle class; and prescribe the other elements of the cyclic treatment, each in its

36. Perhaps the meaning is 'instead of' or else 'in the same way as.'
37. E.g., *Chr.* i. 25–28.

itaque agrestium, hoc est leporum atque capreae, danda iamdudum docuimus; dehinc adiungenda drimyphagia quae sine vomitu erit adhibenda uno vel duobus diebus; ac deinde ceterae cycli
75 partes integrandae. convenit praeterea olivas nigras aceto decoctas cum mali punici cortice contritas, admixto pipere albo et
oleo hispano modico atque recenti, ieiuno aegrotanti dare, nunc
nulla addita alia specie, nunc adiuncto pane.

ordinanda etiam cetera resumptiva atque recorporativa virtute medentia, ut gestatio varia, deambulatio, vocis exercitium,
perunctio, defricatio, quae nunc[123] exercitii tempore atque uncto,
nunc arido vel sicco erit aptissima; item sicca cibatio et cucurbita recorporativae virtutis secundum medias partes, dropax
illitus usque ad ventris confinia atque vertebrorum, psilothra,
sinapismi et paroptesis usque ad cutis ruborem cum defricatione
76 ex oleo atque nitro; item arena sole ignita, acopa acriora, ut ex
euphorbio et opobalsamo et simili virtute medentibus confecta;
item malagma secundum ventrem, quod appellatur diatapsias
vel diacapareos[124] et diaeuphorbiu,[125] et aliquando parva sumptio medicaminis poti quod appellamus diatrion pipereon (et sunt
haec cuncta medicamina[126] libro[127] conscripta Responsionum);
item peregrinatio atque natatio maritima et naturalium
aquarum.[128]

ac si fortificatum corpus rursum fuerit humoris fluore tenta-
tum, quod Graeci reumatismum vocant, convenit hellebori
datio[129] decocti vel radicibus inserti, quod catapecton[130] appellant. dissecat enim corpus et quadam novitate confirmat.
77 culpandi praeterea etiam nunc veteres medicinae conditores.
Hippocrates enim libro quem Ad sententias cnidias scripsit,
helleborandos principio aegros ordinavit, ultimum adiutorium
ceteris anteponens. dat praeterea panem ita curatum ut neque

[123] nunc *transp. R post* atque *prox.*

[124] diacappareos *Reinesius 670:* diacapaneos *S*

[125] diaeuphorbium *S*

[126] medicamina *R:* -um *S*

[127] *fort.* libris. *an excidit numerus (cf. Friedel 35)?*

[128] *fort.* aquarum ⟨usus⟩

[129] dati *S: corr. Rm*

[130] catapecton *Rm:* catapaston *S*

proper order, through the pork diet. Thus, as we have already
indicated, give the meat of field animals, i.e., hare and roe. And
then employ acrid foods, administering them for one or two
days without attempting to provoke vomiting. Thereafter complete the other parts of the cycle. It will also be beneficial, when
the patient's stomach is empty, to give him black olives boiled
in vinegar and rubbed up with pomegranate rind, with the addition of white pepper and a small amount of fresh Spanish oil.
Sometimes this preparation should be given without the addition of any other food, at other times with bread.

Prescribe also the other remedies with restorative and metasyncritic powers, e.g., varied types of passive exercise, walking,
vocal exercise, anointing, and massage (the massage being most
suitable if given sometimes at exercise time, after the body is
anointed, and sometimes when the body is quite dry); also dry
food, metasyncritic cupping applied to the middle parts of the
body, the smearing-on of pitch plasters as far as the ends of the
abdominal region and the hips, depilatories,[38] mustard plasters,
the application of intense heat until the skin becomes red, massage with olive oil and nitrum, the use of sand heated in the sun,
and sharp restorative ointments such as those made with spurge,
balsam juice, and drugs of like properties. Also apply to the
abdomen such emollient plasters as the so-called 'thapsia,' 'caper,'
and 'spurge' plasters; at times have the patient drink a small
amount of the so-called 'potion of three peppers.' All these remedies are described in one of the books of the treatise entitled
Answers. A trip abroad and swimming in the sea and in natural
waters are also beneficial.

Now if, after the body is strengthened, it again shows a state
of flow (Greek *rheumatismos*), it is well to give a dose of hellebore
cooked or inserted into radishes (Greek *catapēcton*, 'implanted').
For such a preparation lacerates the body and, in renewing it,
gives it strength.

Let us now go on to refute what the ancient founders of medicine had to say on this subject. Hippocrates in his book *Against
the Cnidian Opinions*[39] prescribes hellebore as the first treatment, putting what should be the last treatment before all the
others. In addition, he gives the patient bread so prepared that

38. Not for the purpose of removing hair, but for irritant action.
39. *Reg. ac.*, Appendix, p. 172 Kühlewein (II. 500 Littré).

ab hominibus recte valentibus posse digeri facile videatur. item pulentum atque faenigraeci semina, cum sint haec qualitate contraria: alia enim astringunt, alia relaxant. et nulli adiutorio tempus adiunxit.

Diocles quoque libro quo De passionibus atque causis et curationibus scripsit, providens siccandum corpus urinalibus medicaminibus utendum iubet, quibus non solum humor ventris siccari minime posse perspicitur, verum etiam vesica in morbos cogi invenitur.

78   item Erasistratus tertio libro De ventre prohibet cibos digestibiles ac nutribiles aestimans haec facile posse corrumpi, non coniciens quoniam omni aegrotanti digestibilium rerum usus convenire perspicitur, quo minime [et]¹³¹ in laborem mediae partes, quibus digestionis celebrantur officia, cogi videantur [officia].¹³² prohibet praeterea specialiter lenticulam atque mala cydonia et si quae similis fuerint virtutis: quo una voce omnem congruam videatur recusare curationem. nutribilia etenim, quae ob resumendas vires principalem tenuerunt locum, superfluum est, ut aestimat, adhibere.

Lucius¹³³ etiam quarto libro Tardarum passionum principio adhibendum vomitum post cibum probat, sed cum nova ac
79 recens in corpore fuerit passio. sine dubio dupliciter nocens: primo quod intemporaliter, etenim novellae passiones suasu quodam et non agitatione vehementi sunt depellendae; dehinc quod incongrue,¹³⁴ siquidem sit vomitus post cibum gravabilis capiti. inquit praeterea, si humoris perseveraverit fluor atque longo tardaverit tempore et typico motu ventrem fecerit humectari, occursibus periodicis tribus vel quatuor interpositis diebus, ventrem convenit provocare. unde plurimi etiam lac offerendum probant quod schiston appellatur sive catarticum, quo in acutum potius ac periculosum veniant morbum, et exinde possit medicina tamquam celerem facilius curare passionem.

---

¹³¹ om. R   ¹³² om. R
¹³³ Lucius Rm: Lisius S: Lusius Sm: an Lysias? cf. Chr. ii. 59
¹³⁴ incongruae S: corr. R

it seems impossible even for healthy persons to digest it readily. He also uses pearl barley and fenugreek seed, though these substances have opposite qualities; for the former is binding, the latter relaxing. Moreover, he does not indicate the time for any of his remedies.

Again, Diocles in his book *On Diseases and Their Causes and Treatment* prescribes the use of diuretics in an effort to dry out the body. But not only are these clearly unable to dry up fluids in the stomach and bowels, but they actually subject the bladder to various diseases.

78 Erasistratus in the third book of his work *On the Abdomen*[40] bars the use of digestible and nutritious foods, holding that they are prone to spoil. But he does not realize the obvious necessity of using only digestible food in all illness, so that the middle parts, where digestion takes place, may be subjected to as little strain as possible. In addition, Erasistratus specifically forbids lentils, quinces, and substances of similar properties. But thereby he seems in a word to forbid every appropriate treatment. And, indeed, according to his views, it is unnecessary to use nutritious foods, though these are the principal means of building up the body's strength.

Lucius in Book IV of his *Chronic Diseases* holds, to begin with, that vomiting should be induced after eating, this treatment to be given when the disease is new, i.e., of recent origin, in the
79 body. But this prescription is doubly harmful, for, in the first place, the treatment is ill-timed, since diseases of recent origin should be overcome by a sort of gentle suasion and not by violent agitation. And, secondly, the treatment is inappropriate, for vomiting after eating causes heaviness of the head. Lucius goes on to say that if the discharge of fluid persists over a long period and becomes chronic, causing a looseness of the stomach at periodic intervals, with the onset appearing regularly every four or five days, the stomach should be stimulated. Hence many also recommend the milk called *schiston* ['separated,' i.e., curdled] or *catharticon* ['purgative'] in order to bring the disease into an acute and dangerous state, holding that a cure may then be more easily effected, the disease having become virtually acute.[41]

40. I.e., *On Abdominal Diseases*. Cf. Galen XI. 192 Kühn.
41. A lacuna should perhaps be indicated at this point.

80   IV. DE VENTRIS DEBILITATE

E TIAM hoc quidam symptomatis genus, quod nos accidens ap-
    pellare poterimus scripserunt. et aiunt debilitate ventris
acceptum cibum plurimo tempore in eodem permanere, aliquando corrumpi, et magis cum intestinum quod Graeci nestin vocant fuerit quoque debilitate vitiatum. fieri[1] etiam inflatione
secundum ventrem existente, attestante parvo dolore et rugitu
intestinorum, quem borborismon[2] vocant, cum plurimo sputu ac
ructatione iugi. sed erit accipienda curatio ex his quae cum dolore atque intestinorum tormento aegrotantibus adhibenda
scripsimus.

81   V. DE VENTRIS TUMORE AC DURITIA ET
               VENTOSITATE, INFLATIONE AC SALTU

T UMOREM ventris extantia sequetur secundum praecordiorum
    media, resistens atque dolorosa, attestante fervore et iugi
saltu et aliquando febricula, cum fastidio et siti, anxietate et
iactatione. sequentur etiam vigiliae et cibi corruptio. sed discernitur a superiorum tumore, hoc est peritonei sive cutis superpositae: primo quod transvoratus cibus velut percussum praestet
82 circa stomachi finem vel ventris initium; secundo quod adducta
cutis digitis conduplicata sequatur.

    duritiam vero ventris sequetur extantia plurimum resistens,
sine ullo fervore atque pulsu vel dolore, sed sola spiratione difficili et digestionis impedimento parvissimo.

    item ventositatem sequitur tensio cum rugitu intestinorum,
quae facile relaxetur[1] ac rursus colligatur. et si palma fuerint
partes pulsatae, ut tympani resonum fingant, impressae vero

      [1] *fort.* fiet
      [2] *fort. scrib.* borborigmon. *cf. Chr. iv. 20 adn.*
      [1] relaxatur (*et mox* colligitur, fingunt, faciunt, replent) *R*

      1. See *Chr.* iv. 19 n.
      2. *In eodem* may possibly mean 'undigested.'

IV. WEAKNESS OF THE STOMACH[1]

80

SOME writers have also described the following symptom (a term which we may in Latin translate *accidens*). They declare that because of weakness of the stomach food taken in may remain there[2] for a long period of time; and that in some cases the food decomposes, particularly when that intestine which the Greeks call *nēstis* [the jejunum] is also affected by weakness. Weakness of the stomach is attended by abdominal swelling, a little pain and a rumbling sound in the intestines (Greek *borborygmos*), copious sputa, and continual belching. The treatment will have to be based on the prescriptions we have given for cases of intestinal pains and cramps.

81 ## V. INFLAMMATION, HARDNESS, GAS, SWELLING, AND THROBBING OF THE STOMACH

IN A case of inflammation of the stomach there is a swelling at about the middle of the precordial region. This swelling is resistant to pressure and is painful; the region is intensely hot and affected with continual throbbing. In some cases there is fever, loss of appetite, thirst, a feeling of uneasiness, tossing, sleeplessness, and the turning sour of food. This type of inflammation may be distinguished from that of the more external parts, e.g., of the peritoneum or of the skin over it. For, in the first place, in inflammation of the stomach there is a piercing sensation when the food that is swallowed reaches the end of the

82 esophagus or entrance to the stomach. Secondly, when the skin is drawn together with the fingers, it can be folded over.[1]

In cases of hardness of the stomach there is a swelling which is extremely resistant to pressure, but without any heat, throbbing, or pain. The hardness is accompanied merely by difficulty of respiration and a very little interference with digestion.

The presence of gas is indicated by distention and rumbling of the intestines. This condition is such that it is easily relieved, but the gas gathers again; and if the parts are struck with the flat palm they resound like a drum, but if pressed they give way

1. This is not possible, according to Caelius (Soranus), in inflammation of the more external parts.

recessum faciant tardum, et detracta manu facilius surgendo concava repleant loca.

83   inflationem vero, quam Graeci oedema vocant, sequetur extantia partium, sed facile atque plurimum impressioni cedens, et neque tympani resonum fingens, neque fervoris ingerens sensum.

item saltus commotio iugis[2] sequetur, sicut etiam cor salire perspicimus cum nimio vel timore vel gaudio afficimur. sequitur etiam sensus tamquam volantis interioribus[3] omnibus, attestante inani tussicula longa per intervalla et thoracis pungente tensione.

sed erit accipienda curatio ex his quae de strictura stomachi conscripsimus.

84   VI. DE DYSENTERIA

A DIFFICULTATE[1] officii passio nomen accepit dysenteria. est autem intestinorum reumatismus cum ulceratione. sed fit antecedente fluore, quem Graeci diarrhoean vocant, aut cholera aut tumore ventris. et est difficile celer, frequentius tamen tardans passio.

sequitur in passione constitutos muculenta ventris egestio, atque e ramentis innexa et humore crasso, primo cum naturalis intestinorum defluit corpulenta soliditas, dehinc varia atque sanguinolenta et fellosa aut saniosa atque faeculenta, aut cum
85 gelati sanguinis corpusculis, quae thrombos appellant, et livida aut carnosa et membranis plurimae longitudinis innexa, attestante gravi fetore cum dolore ulcerum et fastidio et siti atque interiorum ardore. sequentur etiam vigiliae et aliquando febricula, anxietas, iactatio, hebetudo, et aliquibus intestinorum rugitus et tensio cum ventositate et impedimento urinae reddendae; in quibusdam etiam vomitus et saltus praecordiorum, aut torpor frigidus, lingua humecta aut plurimum sicca aut aspera,

----

[2] saltus (an saltum?) commotio iugis *conieci*: saltus commotos iugis *S*: *fort. scrib.* saltu commotos iugis ⟨saltus⟩ (*vel* ⟨palpitatio⟩)

[3] interioribus *scripsi*: interius ab his *edd.*

[1] *fort.* difficultate ⟨intestinorum⟩

----

2. Both the text and the meaning are very doubtful here.

slowly, and when the hand is removed they quickly rise to fill
out the depressed places.

83   In cases of swelling (Greek *oedēma*) there is a bulging-out of
the parts, but the swelling yields readily and completely to pressure. It does not produce a sound like that of a drum, nor does
it give rise to a sensation of heat.

Finally, in cases of throbbing there is continual excitement,
like the palpitation of the heart which we feel when we experience great fear or great joy. And inside his whole body the
patient has a feeling as if of flying;[2] there is also a dry cough at
long intervals and distention of the chest with a piercing sensation.

The treatment will have to be based on what we have prescribed for cases of a state of stricture of the esophagus.[3]

84   VI. DYSENTERY

D YSENTERY takes its name from its interference with the
functioning [of the intestines].[1] It is an intestinal flux accompanied by ulceration, and arises after an antecedent flux
(Greek *diarrhoea*), or after cholera or inflammation of the
stomach. It is hardly ever an acute disease, being generally
chronic.

The signs of the disease are a slimy discharge from the bowels
made up of small particles and a thick fluid. At first the fluid is
the natural solid matter within the intestines reduced to a
liquid state; but later there are various bloody and bilious, and
sometimes sanious, and feculent discharges, with particles of
85 clotted blood (Greek *thromboe*). There may also be livid discharges and some containing pieces of flesh adhering to long
membranes. The discharges have a heavy odor, and the ulceration is painful; there is also loss of appetite, thirst, and a burning
sensation in the inner parts. Other symptoms are sleeplessness,
in some cases fever, uneasiness, tossing, dulness of the senses,
sometimes a rumbling in the intestines, abdominal distention
and gas, difficulty in urination, sometimes vomiting, throbbing
in the precordial region, cold numbness, tongue moist or very

3. *Chr.* iii. 21 ff.

1. Greek *entera*, 'intestines.'

colore cinereo aut livido; item corporis defluxio et accepti corruptio cibi fervens, cum iugi atque incessabili egerendi ventris
86 desiderio, et in eadem admonitione mordicatio intestinorum
omnium vel podicis aut vicinarum partium. fit autem ulceratio
aut in tenuissimis intestinis, ut pyloro, nestidi, typhlotero,[2] aut
in crassioribus, ut in colo vel longaone. in omnibus enim eodem
tempore fieri vel esse ulcerationem minime posse accipimus,
siquidem mors praeveniat aegrotantes.

in tenerioribus[3] igitur intestinis factam ulcerationem adprehendimus ex doloris sensu supra umbilicum constituto sive ex
eodem loco initium sumente,[4] et egestionibus ventris semper
tenuissimis. ac[5] si in crassioribus intestinis fuerit ulceratio con-
87 stituta, sensus doloris secundum umbilicum efficitur et egestiones ventris carnosae apparebunt, et frequenter coagulata magis atque coacta stercora egeruntur cum solus fuerit passione
longao vexatus, et magis eius inferiora. praevenit enim ⟨teneri-
orum ulceratio⟩[6] atque non sinit cibi digestionem in stercoris
venire qualitatem. aliquando denique ultimo egestionis tempore ulcerum tactu sanguinatio fiet, ut guttarum distillatio appareat et insignia tenesmi demonstret, quo[7] iuxta sessionis finem,
quam Graeci hedran appellant, longaonis pars ulcerata intelligatur, manifestis atque promptis concurrentibus signis. nam
delectatione frequenti aegrotantes afficiuntur ventris egerendi,
atque ipsa egestio cum quadam voluntate et labore nimio effici-
88 tur; tensio clunium et pectinis pubetenus, cum sensu tamquam
quiddam corporis solidioris inesse putetur. ipsa quoque stercora
vel eorum egestio parva atque leviter muculenta videtur[8] et humore crassiore confecta. excluduntur enim primo pinguia, dehinc sanguinolenta cum stercore coagulato. nos denique tenesmon dysenteriae adiungendum[9] probamus, siquidem sit ulceratio partis intestini (nisi quis voluerit ante ulcerationem solum
tumorem appellare tenesmon: quod est quidem inconsequens

---

[2] *fort. scrib.* typ(h)lo entero. *cf. Mulomed. Chir. 209*

[3] in tenerioribus *Schmid RPh 146*: interioribus *S*: in tenuioribus *Rm*

[4] sumentem *S*: *corr. R*

[5] at *R*

[6] *supplevi*: ⟨tenuium ulceratio⟩ *R*

[7] quo *R*: quod *S*

[8] videtur *R*: videatur *S*: *fort.* videntur

[9] adiungendam *S*: *corr. Rm*

dry and rough, complexion[2] ashen or bluish, colliquescence of
the body, decomposition of food accompanied by a burning
sensation, continual and unabating desire to empty the bowels
36 and, in connection with that feeling, an irritation throughout
all the intestines or in the anus or neighboring parts. There is
inflammation either in the small intestines, e.g., in the pylorus,
jejunum, or caecum,[3] or in the large intestines, e.g., in the colon
or the rectum. For we hold that it is hardly possible for the
ulceration to be present at one and the same time throughout all
the intestines, since death would come first.

Now we may infer that the ulceration is in the small intestines
if there is a sensation of pain above the umbilicus or beginning
at that point [and extending upward], and if the discharges from
the bowels are always very thin. But if the ulceration is in the
large intestines, the sensation of pain is then below the umbili-
37 cus, and the discharges from the bowels contain fleshy matter;
and, in fact, the feces are frequently compact and solid when
only the rectum is affected by the disease, and especially the
lower parts of the rectum. That is to say, ulceration of the small
intestines prevents the digested food from taking the usual form
of fecal matter. In some cases there is bleeding at the end of the
bowel movement because of the irritation of the sores, drops of
blood appearing. The patient also shows the characteristic signs
of tenesmus, which, together with the other clear and obvious
signs that are present, indicate that the ulceration is in the portion of the rectum near the fundament itself (Greek *hedra*). For
the patient experiences frequent desire to move the bowels, and
the movement itself is accompanied by straining and intense
38 effort. There is also tension in the loins and at the pubic region,
and a feeling that something solid is present within. The fecal
matter itself, or rather what is discharged of it, seems small in
amount, somewhat slimy, and composed of thick fluid. For first
the fatty parts are passed and then the bloody along with the
solid feces. And so we hold tenesmus to be a concomitant of
dysentery, for it is an ulceration of part of the intestines (unless
one wishes to refer the term 'tenesmus' to mere inflammation

2. The reference may be to the color of the tongue.

3. The inclusion of the caecum among the small intestines may possibly be the
result of textual derangement, but seems more probably to be due to a carelessness not
uncommon among the Methodists in anatomical matters. Rufus (*Anatomical Nomenclature* 170) is more accurate.

omnium scribentium dictis, quibus tenesmus necessario fuit pro-
videndus) **[10]

89 ** ut sola[11] protervitate medicamina pota danda alacri temeri-
tate confingant. sed etiam nobilium multi, ut Diocles libris
quos De passionibus atque causis et curationibus scripsit, lac
ordinat cum melle bibendum, ventrem provocans in fluorem.
item murrham cum ovis atque vino, cum necessario stomachum
murrha evertere videatur. item utitur ptisana cum adipe sorbenda, item galla cum opio, neque discretionem qualitatum neque temporum memorans usum.

Praxagoras libro primo Curationum statuit ventrem deducendum peplio et lacte plurimo cum mulso, potans et aqua salsa et
suco betae et oleo cum mulso, hoc condimento iniciens et oleo et
90 liquido cerotario cum aqua: quibus venter magis in fluorem provocatur. item nutrit bis cocto pane, qui sit necessario digestione
difficilis cum plurimum torretur,[12] item piscibus saxatilibus et
carnibus teneris, cum debuerit densioribus magis ob stringendam
solutionem. dat aquam bibendam et vinum dulce, quod etiam
sanos inflare perspicitur. offert farinam cum lacte coctam, quae
indigestibilis probatur; sic etiam tritici ptisanam[13] cum cantabro. ordinat etiam secundam et tertiam curationem, nullam
adiciens discretionem.

item Erasistratus secundo libro De ventre plurima recte com-
ponens solis utitur constrictivis, cum sint plurimi dysenterici
laxatione indigentes.

Themison primo libro Tardarum passionum plurima recte
91 memoravit, aliqua vero correctione indigentia. laxamenti enim
causa atque lapsus faciendi aquae[14] et arnoglossae suco iniectionem faciendam probat, et hoc aptum etiam tumoribus memorat, quod ob constrictionem siccare perspicitur. adhibet

[10] *lacunam indicavit Rm*

[11] solita *Rm*

[12] *an* torreatur?

[13] ptisanam *R*: -a *S*

[14] *fort.* aqua (⟨ex⟩ aqua *Rm*)

---

4. The restorative and the metasyncritic treatments, respectively.

5. Cf. 78.

before ulceration; but such a definition would be inconsistent with the views of all writers who have had to deal with tenesmus). . . .

. . . so that with sheer nerve they brazenly and rashly concoct
medicines for patients to drink. Furthermore, in common with many well-known physicians, Diocles in his work *On Diseases and Their Causes and Treatment* prescribes the drinking of milk with honey, thus causing looseness of the stomach. He also has the patient take myrrh mixed with eggs and wine, though myrrh seems always to cause gagging; and he prescribes the drinking of pearl barley with fat, or oak gall with poppy juice. But he makes no distinction between these different substances and does not indicate the time for their use.

Praxagoras in Book I of his *Treatments* prescribes purging the stomach with a large dose of wild purslane and milk, together with mead; he also has the patient drink salt water, beet juice, and olive oil with mead. And he employs this sharp preparation as a clyster, adding olive oil, a liquid cerate, and water to the
mixture. But the flux of the stomach and bowels is intensified by these substances. Again, he nourishes the patient with twice-cooked bread, though this is always hard to digest, since it is subjected to excessive heat. And he recommends rockfish and tender meats, though he ought preferably to employ the denser kinds to overcome the state of looseness. He gives the patient water to drink and also sweet wine, though the latter produces gas even in the case of healthy persons. And he prescribes spelt meal cooked with milk, an indigestible mixture; also a gruel made with wheat and bran. He goes on to prescribe the second and third treatments[4] but fails to distinguish between them.

Erasistratus in Book II of his work *On the Abdomen*[5] correctly prescribes a large number of remedies; but he limits himself exclusively to astringent preparations, though many cases of dysentery require relaxing treatment.

Themison in Book I of his *Chronic Diseases* is generally sound, but some of his prescriptions need correction. Thus, in order to loosen the bowels and lubricate them, he recommends the injection of a clyster of water and plantain juice, and asserts that this is a suitable treatment also in cases of inflammation. But it is obvious that, because of its astringent property, plantain has a desiccant effect. He also prescribes bloodletting at the nostrils,

etiam naribus atque auribus et angulis oculorum sanguinis detractionem, nihil propositis profuturam; et post cibum unctionem, quo tempore quies est adhibenda ob digestionis perficiendae facilitatem. dat etiam vinum asperius, cum fluorem vehementescere viderit atque febrem. et meracum probat offerendum, quo tempore ob augmentum passionis aqua vino infecta
conveniat, maxime cum meraca potio vexare nervos approbetur,
quos Graeci cremasteras vocaverunt.[15]

VII. DE COLICIS PASSIONIBUS

92

** concurrit praeterea gravedo, sitis, fastidium, et incessente[1]
passione sive accessionis tempore articulorum frigidus torpor et
livor, attestante sudore, et mentis hebetudo cum pulsus parvitate ac densitate. item sequitur singultus et ventris abstinentia
aut cum dolore egestio, urinae reddendae difficultas, capitis
gravedo, intestinorum rugitus scatens, quem Graeci borborigmon vocant. et augmento passionis vomitus humorum cras-
93 sorum, quos Graeci phlegmata vocant, tum felineorum,[2] cum
tensione membranae quae ventrem intra[3] cutem circumtegit et
appellata est peritoneos,[4] quae perseverans faciat inflationis
causa resonum tympani, cum palma fuerint loca pulsata. tum
extantia cum rugitu plurimo, et dimissionis tempore venti per
podicem egestio cum magno sonitu.

ac si tumor fuerit insidens atque roboratus, erit extantia du-
rior ac pulsuosa,[5] attestante fervore. cuius circumscriptio[6] simplex sed inaequalis esse videbitur, quo discernitur a iecoris ac
splenis vel peritonei tumoribus, qui[7] in peritoneo sunt aequales,
in iecore vero ac liene quadam circumscriptione[8] finiti. est au-

---

[15] *fort. deesse finem capitis coni. Schmid RPh 156*

[1] incessante *S: corr. Rm*

[2] felleorum (*ut freq. ap. Cael.*) *Rm, sed cf.* colorem fellineum *Gloss. Med., p. 92. I*
(*Heiberg*)

[3] infra *Rm*

[4] peritoneos *R:* peritoneon *S, sed cf. Chr. v. 127*

[5] pulsuosa *scripsi:* pulsuoso *Am:* pulvoso *S*

[6] circunspectio *edd.*   [7] *fort.* quia   [8] circunspectione *edd.*

---

6. Perhaps 'when he observes an aggravation of the flux and fever.'

ears, and the corners of the eyes, though this measure is of no benefit in the cases in question. And he has the patient anointed after eating, though rest is required at that time in order to help complete the process of digestion. Themison also prescribes a tart wine, though he can observe that the flux and the fever are thereby aggravated.[6] And he prescribes this wine undiluted,[7] though at this time, because of the exacerbation of the disease, the proper drink is water mixed with a little wine. This is particularly true, since undiluted wine injures the muscles that the Greeks call *cremastēres*.[8]

VII. DISEASES OF THE COLON

92

... [1]Additional symptoms include a feeling of heaviness, thirst, loss of appetite, and, during an attack or exacerbation of the disease, cold numbness and leaden color of the limbs, sweating, dulness of the mind, and small, thick pulse. There are also hiccoughs, suppression of bowel movements or else painful evacuation, difficulty of urination, heaviness of the head, and intestinal churning and rumbling (Greek *borborygmos*). In the increasing phase of the disease the patient vomits thick fluids 93 (Greek *phlegmata*), then bilious matter. And there is distention of the membrane, called *peritonaeos*, which is situated underneath the skin and incloses the abdominal cavity. If this distention persists, the parts when struck with the palm of the hand resound like a drum; this is due to the puffing-up of the membrane. Again, there is abdominal swelling and much rumbling; during the remission wind is passed noisily through the anus.

If the inflammation persists and becomes deeply rooted, the swelling grows harder and pulsates, the region in question becoming hot. There will be only one swollen area, but the swelling will not be uniform. In this way we may distinguish inflammation of the liver, spleen, or peritoneum from that of the colon. For inflammation of the peritoneum shows a uniform swelling, and in inflammation of the liver or the spleen the swelling is confined to a definite area. Now this disease of the colon is some-

7. Or 'in a strong mixture.'

8. I.e., 'suspenders,' supporting the testicles and supposed also to support the ovaries.

1. The beginning of the chapter is lost.

tem passio aliquando continua, ut plerosque tamquam ileicos[9]
interficiat, aliquando deficiens, ut saepe tarditate perseverans
difficile curabilis fiat.

94   sed eius curatio etiam nunc stricturae conveniens probatur.
quapropter si acuta vel celer fuerit passio vel in superpositione
constituta, convenit aegrum iacere loco calido, contectis partibus in passione constitutis lana limpida atque calida. adhibendus etiam fotus olei dulcis calidi et saepe memoratae vaporationes. cucurbitae apponendae leves, quas Graeci cuphas appellant, item vascula quae ambicas[10] vocant et sunt materia testea
vel vitrea confecta. tum requies atque abstinentia cibi usque ad
tertium diem, et si causae poposcerint adhibenda phlebotomia.
95 ac si sumpto cibo quisquam dolore fuerit affectus vel nausea,
erit vomitus provocandus sumpta primo aqua tepida vel aqua
et oleo, quibus potis immissis digitis accepta reddantur. vexatione[11] enim vomitus sumptorum perseverans pondus atque tensio et mordicatio tumentium gravior vexatio iudicatur.

adhibenda etiam clysteris iniectio ex olei calidi cyathis quatuor, admixto et consoluto adipe anserino vel gallinaceo vel ovorum vitellis aut decoctione lini seminis vel hibisci radicis aut
malvae usualis aut faenigraeci suco. iniciunt autem aliarum
sectarum principes etiam rutacium[12] aut anethinum aut panaci-
num, vel ex cymino atque castoreo et bitumine, secundum
96 Themisonem vero etiam cum absinthio. castorei namque vel
bituminis duae drachmae cyathis olei quatuor miscentur. ruta
vero et anethum et absinthium et cyminum linteolo illigata oleo
coquentur. sed sunt haec acerrima et propterea tardis passionibus congrua, quas Graeci chronias vocant, vel ventositate laborantibus et non causa tumoris dolentibus. bitumen autem
saepe etiam fastidium ingessit everso appetitu, quem Graeci
orexin vocant.

cibus dandus conveniens dimissionis tempore atque alternis
97 diebus donec passio declinet, et sorbilis levis calidus. dandus
etiam potus non plurimus, ne intestina graventur, etiam ipse

---

[9] *fort. scrib.* iliacos (*Rm*). *v. TLL*

[10] ambigas *S*: *corr. A* (*litt. graec.*): *cf. Ac. iii. 150, Chr. iii. 23*

[11] vexationem *S*: *corr. R*

[12] rutatium *S* (*sed* rutacii *S, 104*): rutaceum *Rm*

times unremitting and then generally results in death in the same manner as ileus. But at other times the disease shows remissions, and then often becomes a persistent chronic disease that is curable only with difficulty.

94 But then, too,[2] the treatment aims at overcoming a state of stricture. Thus, if the case is acute (i.e., swift) or [if chronic] is in the period of an attack, the patient should lie in a warm room and the affected parts should be covered with warm scoured wool. Foment with warm sweet olive oil and employ the hot applications often described above. Apply mild cups (Greek *cuphae*, 'light'); for this purpose use earthen or glass vessels called *ambices*. Then have the patient rest, withhold food until the third day, and, if the case requires it, perform venesection.

95 If a patient, having taken food, suffers pain or nausea, induce vomiting. For this purpose have the patient first take warm water, or water and olive oil; when he has drunk this, let him insert his finger and give up the food taken in. For the heaviness and distention caused by the continued presence of the food and the consequent irritation of the inflamed parts constitute a more serious form of injury than the discomfort of vomiting.

Also inject a clyster consisting of four cyathi of warm olive oil with the addition of melted goose fat or chicken fat, egg yolks, a decoction of flaxseed, marsh mallow root, or the juice of common mallow or fenugreek. Now leading physicians of other sects actually employ clysters containing the juice of rue, dill, or allheal. They also use cumin, castor, or bitumen in clysters; and Themison prescribes the use of wormwood in this connec-

96 tion. In the case of castor or bitumen two drachms of the substance are mixed with four cyathi of olive oil, while the rue, dill, wormwood, and cumin are tied up in a small bag and thus cooked in the olive oil. But these substances are all acrid and, while suitable for chronic cases[3] (Greek *chroniae*) or for cases of gas, are unsuitable for inflammation. Moreover, bitumen often spoils the appetite (Greek *orexis*) and produces a distaste for food.

When the remission begins, give the patient suitable food on alternate days until the disease declines; this food should be

97 soft, light, and warm. And give him some drink, also warm, but in small amount, to keep the intestines from being weighed

2. As in ileus or in any acute disease of the colon.

3. I.e., for the interval of remission in chronic cases.

calidus. tum post fomenta cataplasma adhibendum ex lini atque faenigraeci seminibus et polline, quod Graeci macton[13] appellant, aqua mulsa coctum vel[14] decoctione fici pinguis et hibisci
radicis et malvae usualis vel horum similium. cucurbita apponenda adiuncta scarificatione; vel hirudines admovendae omnibus partibus in tensione constitutis, ac deinde vaporatio spongiarum expressarum in[15] aqua calida et oleo et decoctione faenigraeci et malvae. tunc post unctionem ex iisdem etiam encathismata adhibenda.[16]

98   quidam medici in his qui vento fuerint inflati ex decoctione
stercorum cum aromatibus coctorum vaporationem adhibendam
probaverunt, ex quo liquorem etiam oxymelitos miscuerunt,
cataplasma conficientes admixtis etiam tunc aromatibus vel nepeta herba aut pulegio aut hyssopo aut cymino. sed haec in
tardis passionibus, adiuncta ratione, locum sumunt.

   perseverante morbo, convenit in accessionis statu aquam
bibere[17] cyathos duos vel tres, calido oleo diligenter admixto. etenim incendia levigat et ventrem mollit et tumorem mitigat.
quapropter magis hoc melius mulso probamus, siquidem saepe

99 conflammet atque inflet. dantur etiam plurima alia bibenda
composita vel simplicia, ut est Zenonis, diasticados[18] appellatum, colicum[19] medicamen, item Cassii ex gingibere confectum,
quod diagingibereos appellant, et mille praeterea quae concurrenti tempore lacessendo medeantur, praeter tempus vero gravationem ingerentia aliquos in periculum graviter mittant, aliquos
errore relevationis fallant, ob praesentis temporis perditum sensum, quod Graeci anaesthesian appellant, hebetudine partium
suffecta. item simplicia, ut decoctio apii vel nardi celtiberici

100 aut herbae salviae aut polii aut cymini aegyptii vel rutae aut
dauci, magis cretici, aut petroselini, tribus cyathis aquae calidae
admixto cochleari vel asperso suco polii aut cymini aegyptii aut
petroselini aut cochleari castorei, itemque feniculi. sed est sem-

---

[13] magton S: corr. A (litt. graec., ut 94)

[14] vel R: mel S

[15] fort. ex

[16] adhibent S: corr. Rm

[17] aquam bibere scripsi: etiam bibere S: etiam bibere ⟨aquae tepidae⟩ R

[18] diasticon S: dia stoechados Rm   [19] codicum S: corr. Rm

---

4. Or perhaps 'from the flour of flaxseed and fenugreek seed.'

down. Then after fomenting, apply a poultice of flaxseed, fenu-greek seed, and flour,[4] kneaded (Greek *macton*) and cooked in hydromel or in a decoction of juicy fig, marsh mallow root, common mallow root, or the like. Employ cupping with scarification. Or apply leeches to all distended parts. Then steam the parts with sponges wrung out of hot water, olive oil, and a decoction of fenugreek and mallow. After anointing the patient, prescribe sitz baths of the same substances.

98 Some physicians hold that, in cases of distention due to gas, steaming should be administered from a preparation of feces boiled with aromatic substances. These physicians also add a decoction of oxymel to make a poultice, and they add at this stage, too, such aromatic substances as mint, pennyroyal, hyssop, and cumin. But preparations of this kind can reasonably be used only in chronic cases.

If the disease persists,[5] the drinking of two or three cyathi of water carefully mixed with warm olive oil is beneficial at the highest stage of an attack. For it relieves the burning sensation, softens the stomach and bowels, and soothes the inflammation.
99 We therefore consider this remedy preferable to mead; for mead often adds to the inflammation and distention. Many other drugs, simple or compound, may also be given the patient to drink, e.g., Zeno's preparation, the so-called 'cassidony remedy,' for diseases of the colon; also Cassius' preparation made with ginger (Greek *dia zingibereōs*). And there are countless other drugs which, if given at the proper time, exert a therapeutic influence by their irritant action. But if these drugs are given at the wrong time, they cause an oppressive heaviness, in some cases seriously endangering the life of the patient, and in other cases merely giving a deceptive appearance of relief through the temporary loss of sensation (Greek *anaesthēsia*), the parts becoming numb. Simple drugs often prescribed include a decoction
100 of celery, Celtiberian nard, sage, hulwort, Egyptian cumin, rue, wild carrot, especially the Cretan variety, or parsley. Thus a spoonful of the juice of hulwort, Egyptian cumin, parsley, castor, or fennel is added to, or poured into, three cyathi of hot water. But the prescription of such substances is always to be

5. Cf. 96 n. *Perseverante morbo* may possibly be construed with the preceding sentence (as an explanation of *tardis passionibus*); this is the interpretation of the previous editors.

per horum datio in tumoribus vitanda, siquidem sint acria vel
lacessentia virtute.

convenit praeterea cum totius passionis fuerit status, solio
oleo calido pleno aegros dare. et firmata declinatione gestationem adhibere, aucta moderatione ciborum, tum vinum atque
communiter resumptionem, et mediis partibus cerotaria ex oleo
sabino vel cyprino aut sicyonio vel glaucino aut amaracino aut
101 laurino aut panacino aut rutino aut anethino,[20] samsucino, vel
quod diatessaron appellatur, resina terebinthina, cera, iri illyrica, hyssopo, omnibus aequalibus, sive quod diapente vocant,
pice, nitro, alumine, sulphure, cera. sumendae denique picis
liquidae heminae duae et cerae libra, quibus solutis atque leviter
refrigeratis aspergendum nitrum rubrum tritum et alumen scissum et sulphur vivum, singulae selibrae.

cum autem in lenimento tardaverit passio, conveniunt ea
quae fortificare valeant corpus sive[21] recorporatione demutare,
ut varia gestatio et deambulatio, vocis exercitium atque perunctio, adhibito monitore, sive fricatio cum retentione spiritus et
102 sphaerae lusus vel cursus et humerorum additus motus; item
cibus qui inflare minime possit ex mediae materiae qualitate, et
tenue vinum; atque lavacrum longa per intervalla, hinc enim
facile corpora perfrigescunt. item rubor faciendus ventris in
partibus atque inter scapulas et clunes,[22] ex dropace vel sole et
flammae paroptesi vel parietibus vel ceromate aut pellibus vel
arena littoris sole ignita. item strigilis rasio adhibenda corporibus et sicca defricatio ex asperis pannis et cucurbita recorporativa apponenda; item unctio acoporum ferventium acriorum, ut
103 sunt diaeuphorbiu[22a] aut cacri; tum[23] nitri fricatio et sinapismus
et vaporatio fervens ex aqua marina vel salsa vel supradictarum
acriorum virtutum decoctionibus vel saccellis sale repletis, qui-

---

[20] *fort.* anethino ⟨aut⟩

[21] sine *S*: *corr. Rm*   [22] *fort.* clunibus

[22a] diaeuphorbium *S* (*sic etiam 103 fin.*)

[23] cacri; tum *scripsi*: cacritum *S*: *fort.* cacri; item *scrib.*: cachryos et *vel* diacachryos
et *Rm*

avoided in cases of inflammation, for they are acrid and cause irritation.

When the entire disease reaches its highest stage, it is well to put the patient into a tub filled with hot olive oil. And when the decline of the disease is corroborated, prescribe passive exercise and increase the amount of food. Then prescribe wine and the general restorative treatment. Apply to the middle parts cerates made with Sabine or Sicyonian oil, or oil of henna, glaucium, amaracus, laurel, allheal, rue, dill, or sampsuchon.[6] Or use the so-called 'four-drug remedy,' made of equal parts of resin of the terebinth tree, wax, Illyrian iris, and hyssop; or the so-called 'five-drug remedy,' made of pitch, nitrum, alum, sulphur, and wax. To compound this latter drug, take two heminae of liquid pitch and a pound of wax; melt them, let them cool somewhat, and add a half-pound each of triturated red nitrum,[7] fissile alum, and virgin sulphur.

When the disease becomes chronic and enters a period of remission, measures should be taken which will strengthen the body or change its nature by metasyncrisis, e.g., varied passive exercise, walking, vocal exercise, anointing under professional supervision, massage while the breath is held, ball playing or running, with additional motion of the upper arms and shoulders. Give such food as will not cause flatulence; this food should be of the middle class. Also prescribe mild wine; and baths, too, but only at long intervals, for the body may easily become chilled by them. Again, let the abdomen, the interscapular region, and the loins be irritated to redness with pitch plasters, sun baths, or applications of intense heat with flame, heated walls, wax ointments,[8] skins, or sun-baked beach sand. And scrape the body with a strigil; employ also dry massage with rough cloths, and apply metasyncritic cupping. Anoint the body with sharp and burning restorative ointments, such as those prepared from spurge or cachry; then rub the body with nitrum, and use mustard plasters, hot applications of sea water or salt water, decoctions of the sharp substances already mentioned, or bags filled with salt. In some cases after these applications it will be well to

6. Amaracus and sampsuchon (marjoram) are usually identified (see, e.g., Diosc. *Mat. med.* iii. 39), but the oils amaracinum and sampsuchinum seem to be quite different (*ibid.* i. 48, 58).

7. *Ibid.* v. 113. 1.   8. Cf. *Chr.* ii. 34 and n.

bus praestitis vel corpori admotis erunt aliquando cauteres su-
perponendi et circuminvolvendi.[24] item farina circumclauden-
dus locus in passione constitutus et implendus item[25] [cauliculis
et][26] oleo. tum immittendi cauteres igniti sensim, non usque ad
loci scarificationem sive ustionis effectum, sed usque ad ruborem
faciendum. tum malagma quod appellatur diaspermaton vel
polyarchion aut diadaphnidon, diachylon aut diaeuphorbiu.
104 item aquarum illisio patientibus locis, quam cataclysmon Graeci
vocaverunt, et iniectio clysteris rutacii aut anethini aut pana-
cini olei vel extenta virtute aquae salsae. et cum olim futuram
superpositionem viderimus, vomitus ieiunus[27] adhibendus ex[28]
radicibus; tum perseverante passione etiam ex helleboro radicibus inserto, tum infuso ac deinde conciso iuxta ordinem cycli
partium ceterarum. dandum etiam potui medicamen quod
Graeci theriacen antidotum vocant, vel diagingibereos.

peregrinatio quoque adhibenda et longa navigatio, et usus
aquarum naturali virtute medentium, et magis sulphuris ac medicaminis[29] virtutem redolentium, item maritimarum, et primo
105 ferventium tum frigidarum. ac si retentio ventris fuerit, ob
egestionem faciendam adhibenda iniectio ex melle atque sale.
quae si minime compleverit effectum, etiam ex aloe admixto
suco coliculi agrestis vel usualis vel lapatii: ex quibus erunt catapotia facienda in ervi magnitudinem, quorum quatuor vel quinque dabimus transbibenda. item marini coliculi offerendi.
erunt praeterea praecavenda magis quae passionem valeant refricare, ut frigus, indigestio, libido, vel quae inflare valeant cum
sumuntur, item frigida plurimo scilicet tempore.

veteres autem, et magis Erasistrati sectatores, ventrem movere medicaminibus certaverunt ventrifluis, quae catartica vocant, vel pessulis, quos balanismos dixerunt. item alii ad acriores clysteres confugerunt ex initio adhibendos velut Asclepiades[30] **

---

[24] circumvolvendi *R*   [26] *om. R (fort. adnotatio marginalis erat ad 105)*

[25] item *fort. secl.*   [27] ieiunio *S: corr. Schmid RPh 147*

[28] ⟨et⟩ ex *Schmid ibid.*

[29] bituminis *vel* aluminis *Rm: an* dicaminis (= resinae dicaminis)?

[30] item . . . Asclepiades *ad initium capitis proximi perperam posuerunt editores: cf.
Schmid RPh 148*

---

9. Or perhaps merely 'to move the cauteries about the part in question.'

wrap cauteries [in cloths][9] and hold them over the places in question. Again, wall in the affected part with meal and fill with olive oil; then insert heated cauteries for a short time, not to the point of opening or burning the skin, but only until it becomes red. Then apply an emollient plaster, e.g., the so-called 'plaster from seeds,' Polyarchus' plaster, and those from bayberries, juices, or spurge. And direct a stream of water (Greek *cataclysmos*) over the affected parts. Also inject a clyster of rue, dill, or allheal oil, or, increasing the strength of the treatment, a clyster of salt water. And when an attack is observed to be approaching, provoke vomiting on an empty stomach by the use of radishes; later, if the disease persists, use hellebore inserted in radishes, then soaked [in vinegar], and later cut up.[10] Let this treatment depend on the order of the other parts of the cycle. Also have the patient drink the preparation that the Greeks call the 'theriac andidote,' or else the antidote prepared from ginger.

And let him take a trip abroad or a long sail, and make use of waters having natural therapeutic properties, preferably those with a sulphurous and medicinal odor.[11] Sea water should also be used for bathing, first hot and then cold. And if there is no evacuation of the bowels, inject a clyster of honey and salt in order to produce a discharge. But if this has no effect, employ aloes with the addition of the juice of wild or common cabbage, or dock; also use these ingredients to make pills the size of vetch seeds,[12] and give the patient four or five of these pills to swallow. Also give him sea cabbage. Furthermore, see to it that the patient especially avoids anything that can cause a recurrence of the disease, e.g., cold, indigestion, sexual desire, or any food or drink which if taken will produce gas; and in particular let him avoid all cold things for a considerable length of time.

The physicians of old, however, and especially the followers of Erasistratus, tried to bring about bowel movements by using purgative drugs (*cathartica*) or applications of suppositories (*balanismoe*). And others, among them Asclepiades, had recourse, from the very first, to sharp clysters. . . .

10. But cf. *Chr.* ii. 31, where the hellebore is first removed and the radishes then cut up. Perhaps the same procedure is referred to here, but in that case either our text is unsound or the language is loosely used.

11. The text is uncertain. Possibly the reference is to a kind of resinous or pitchy odor.

12. A common standard of measure in the medical writers.

106   VIII. DE LUMBRICIS

**¹ et aliquibus etiam fluor ventris efficitur sine lumbricorum exclusione, aliquando attestante fastidio et debilitate et pallore cum tenuitate² corporis, et nunc tussicula arida levi ex occasione commota, nunc solutione atque defectu³ corporis et animae, quem lipothymian appellant. pueris⁴ vero dormientibus turbatio membrorum efficitur, gemitu attestante cum iactatione et stridore dentium, et saepe contra solitum morem prona positio iacendi, tum clamatio sine manifesta ratione,⁵ exiliente cum
107 vocibus aegrotante. quibusdam etiam repentinus casus occurrit ut oppressi obmutescant, numquam similiter affecti. item aliquando conductione vel contractu membrorum rapiuntur, et quidam per intervalla conticescunt et in febribus demersione lethargorum simili premuntur. item totius vultus paulatim nimia insinuatio; nunc detracto rubore mutantur,⁶ et aliquando articulorum frigore; cum difficili responsione si quid⁷ interrogentur, manibus elatis iactantur attestante sudore. in pueris vero lumbricorum conversio sive connexio saepe occurrit, ut etiam tactu sentiatur durities in ea intestini parte quae fuerit magis in ulti-
108 ma tenuitate. tum denique eorum eversione⁸ aegrotantes interficiuntur. pulsus vero, ut etiam Themison libro nono Epistolarum designat, est inaequalis ac plurimum deficiens.

excluduntur autem nunc per ventrem, nunc per stomachum atque os vel nares, et aliquando sponte connexi in sphaerae similitudinem, plurimi amplexu mutuo vinculati, aliquando singulares. item sanguinolenti vel fellosi, aut cum stercore per podicem vel humore felleo, vivi aut mortui, pleni aut inanes, et omnes aut ex parte albi vel fulvi. alia denique plurima sequen-

¹ *lacunam indicavit Rm*: cf. *Diaet. pass. 117–18* (= *Esc. 29*); *Schmid RPh 148*

² tenacitate *S*: *corr. Rm, nisi fort.* teneritate

³ solutio atque defectus *R*

⁴ *fort.* plurimis, *sed cf. 107*

⁵ manifesta ratione *R, coll. 110*: manifestatione *S*

⁶ mutatio *R*

⁷ si quid *scripsi*: siquidem *S*: si quidem *R*

⁸ conversione *Rm* (*ut supra*)

---

1. The reference may now be to patients generally (cf. 110).

2. The meaning may be merely 'where the intestines are thinnest.'

VIII. WORMS

... In some cases there is looseness of the bowels without the expulsion of the worms; and sometimes there occur loss of appetite, weakness, pallor, and emaciation. In some cases a light, dry cough occurs from time to time; and sometimes there may be collapse of body and loss of consciousness (Greek *leipothymia*). In the case of children there is a restless movement of the parts of the body during sleep, accompanied by sighing, tossing, and gnashing of teeth; often the child[1] lies in a prone position contrary to his usual custom. Again, he cries out apparently without reason, leaping up as he cries. In some cases the seizure occurs suddenly, the patient being overcome and speechless without ever having been so affected before. And sometimes the parts of the body are seized with convulsion or spasm. Some patients become speechless at intervals, and are overcome by fever and drowsiness as in lethargy. Gradually the whole countenance is affected; at times the patient loses color and appears changed. Sometimes the limbs are chilled. And it is hard to get the patient to answer questions. He tosses about with outstretched hands, all the while sweating. In the case of children there often occurs a massing together or entangling of the worms, so that the part of the intestines which is most severely emaciated[2] feels hard to the touch. Then finally, with the discharge[3] of the worms, the patient dies. In this disease the pulse is uneven and often interrupted, as is also attested by Themison in Book IX of his *Letters*.

The expulsion of the worms takes place sometimes through the bowels, and at other times through the esophagus and the mouth or nostrils; sometimes, as it happens, they are massed together and form a sphere, a large number of them being intertwined, and at other times they are driven out one at a time. Again, they are covered with blood or bile, or they emerge from the anus covered with feces or with a yellowish fluid. The worms when expelled may be alive or dead, full or empty, and either all or in part[4] white or yellow. In addition, there are many other signs

3. Or 'massing together' (*Rm*). But the reference may originally have been to a bursting of the intestines by the mass of worms. Cf. also 112–16.

4. This phrase may be otherwise interpreted (1) to refer to the complete or partial expulsion of the worms, (2) to refer to the expulsion of whole worms or parts of worms.

tur aegrotantes, quibus designari supra memorata necesse est:
et nunc parva, nunc plurima pro quantitate animalium ac forma;
109 vel quod nunc plurimum, nunc parum noceant; locorum differentia variante, cum nunc ad stomachum ascendunt, nunc in
intestinis perseverant; et aegrotantium vires nunc debilitate,
nunc fortitudine habituantur; et nunc cum febribus, nunc sine
febre.

sed quoniam multa ex accidentibus aliis quoque similia passionibus inveniuntur, ut alienatio mentis furori atque phrene-
tidi, vocis amputatio lethargo et praefocationi matricis et apoplexiae et epilepsiae atque apprehensioni sensuum,[9] qui autem
ex lumbricis patiuntur numquam spumas excludunt. at vero
praefocatio ex matrice cum ascensu matricis efficitur, quem
110 Graeci anadromen vocant, et magis in aetatibus perfectis, antecedente matricis aegritudine. ex lumbricis vero facta vocis oppressio magis aetatibus imperfectis adscribitur, antecedente ventris atque intestinorum querela. item a catalepticis discernuntur lumbricis laborantes, siquidem illi in febribus obmutescant,
maiore atque percussibili pulsu testante.[10] qui autem a lumbricis id patiuntur etiam sine febribus vocis amputationem sustinent, cum pulsu parvo atque crebro. item ab ileicis[11] discernuntur qui lumbricorum tormento vexantur, siquidem neque
ventris officium in his abstineatur vel[12] pallor antecedat aut contra consuetudinem iaceant proni vel dormiant cum gemitu et
111 irrationabili exclamatione. item a stomachicis discernuntur,
cum nullus fuerit tumor[13] in stomachi partibus inventus et[14] intestinorum tormenta sustineant. a syntecticis vero discernuntur, quod nulla querela tormentorum vel conversionis aut doloris
in intestinis vel ventre afficiantur, quod necessario lumbricis
laborantes sequetur. item ab his qui naturaliter, vel ex multitudine cibi, per somnum labia conducunt in similitudinem sor-
bentium, vel sine ulla ratione [aut][15] exiliunt, quod moderatione

[9] *lacunam hic statuit Schmid RPh 149, fort. recte*

[10] testantes *S: corr. R, nisi fort.* attestante

[11] iliacis *Rm. cf. 93*

[12] et *R*

[13] tumor *Schmid RPh 151, coll. Diaet. pass. 128 (= Esc. 29):* humor *edd.*

[14] *fort.* sed

[15] *om. R (sed fort. scrib.* ⟨clamant⟩ aut)

by which the various cases are to be characterized. Thus the effects are small or large depending on the quantity and shape

9 of the worms. Again, the worms sometimes do considerable harm and sometimes very little. The places affected may also vary, the worms sometimes rising as far as the esophagus and at other times remaining in the intestines. Sometimes the patient is weakened by the attack, but in other cases the patient's strength is unimpaired. Furthermore, the attack of worms occurs sometimes with fever and sometimes without.

Now many of the symptoms here found are similar to those found in other diseases. Thus loss of reason also occurs in mania and phrenitis, loss of voice in lethargy, hysterical suffocation, apoplexy, epilepsy, and catalepsy. But those who suffer from worms never foam at the mouth.[5] On the other hand, hysterical suffocation always involves an ascent (Greek *anadromē*) of the

10 uterus, and usually occurs in adult life after an affection of the uterus. But loss of voice resulting from worms is more likely to occur before adult life and after an affection of the stomach and the intestines. Again, patients suffering from worms may be distinguished from cataleptics. For the latter lose their voice during feverish attacks, and they have a large and strong pulse; but patients with worms may also become speechless without any fever, and they show a small, rapid pulse. Cases of worms are likewise distinguishable from cases of ileus. For in cases of worms the functioning of the bowels is not suppressed; moreover, the patient shows an antecedent pallor, or contrary to his usual custom he lies in a prone position, or sighs and cries out

11 irrationally in his sleep. So, too, cases of worms are distinguishable from cases of the disease of the esophagus, for in the former disease no inflammation is found in the gullet, but intestinal cramps are present. Again, cases of worms are to be distinguished from cases of wasting disease, for in the latter the patients do not suffer cramps, twisting pains, or tenderness in the intestines or stomach, whereas these symptoms always occur in cases of worms. Finally, we must distinguish cases of worms from cases in which a person naturally or through excess of food contracts his lips in his sleep and seems to be sucking or jumps up without any reason. In these latter cases moderation and

5. As do epileptics. But there is reason to suppose that the comparison was expressed rather than implied and that a portion of the text is lost.

accedente atque cibi facta deductione relevantur. hi vero qui
lumbricis afficiuntur magis vexentur[16] parcitate ciborum. haec
est similium discretio passionum.

112   de exclusione vero sive egestione lumbricorum veteres medici
praesciam significationem posuerunt, et appellaverunt progno-
sin, in quo diversa senserunt. nam Hippocrates libro Prognostico significare inquit lumbricos interfectionem aegrotantis quoties mortui fuerint exclusi omnibus in morbis. item quidam
communiter mortuos lumbricos aiunt gravia denuntiare, siquidem ostendant inesse corpori corruptionem.[17]

Diocles libro Prognostico evomitos inquit lumbricos nihil
alienum significare nec esse absurdum; per inferiora vero excludi
113 quoque lumbricos non admirandum, sed mortuos et inanes esse
melius ac salutare, vivos vero atque plenos et sanguinolentos perniciosum. item libro De egestionibus scripto vivos vel plenos ac
sanguinolentos febribiles dixit.

Herophilus vero libro quem ad Hippocratis Prognosticum
scripsit sive vivos sive mortuos excludi negat incongruum.

Apollonius Glaucus libris quos De interioribus scripsit reiectos
rotundos lumbricos initio significare indigestionum frequentiam,
ultimo vero aegritudinis properare iudicium, quod crisin appellant; item vivos ac plenos et sanguinolentos non recta portendere.

114   Apollonius Memphites percunctativo sive universali modo,
quem Graeci catholicon vocant, omnia inquit in intestinis animalia nata in morbis gravia significare, et magis mortua quam si
viva excludantur.

item Antiphanes libro quem Panopten appellavit melius esse
per inferiora quam per vomitum lumbricos excludere, et solos
magis quam cum stercoribus.

Chrysippus Asclepiadis sector libro tertio de lumbricis solis
in celeribus causis sive periculosis mortuos inquit lumbricos
egestos interfectionem aegro portendere: ostendunt enim mortui

---

[16] vexantur R, fort. recte

[17] ruptionem S: corr. Rm (cf. 115)

---

6. From the subsequent discussion the expulsion must be assumed to take place
during the attack. But our text of the *Prognostic* does not contain this statement; nor
do I find it elsewhere in the Hippocratic Corpus. See 115 n.

the withholding of food bring relief; but cases of worms may be aggravated when food is withheld. So much for the method of distinguishing cases of worms from similar diseases.

2   On the basis of how the worms are expelled or discharged the ancient physicians announce the future course of the disease (Greek *prognōsis*). In this connection, however, they hold conflicting views. Thus Hippocrates in his *Prognostic* holds that in every disease the expulsion of dead worms portends the death of the patient.[6] And some hold that dead worms generally indicate grave consequences, since they show that a decomposition is present in the body.

On the other hand, Diocles in his *Prognostic* holds that the vomiting of worms does not indicate anything untoward and is not unusual; and, furthermore, that the expulsion of worms 3   through the anus is in itself without significance. He declares, however, that it is a good sign indicative of recovery if the worms are dead and empty, but a deadly sign if the worms are alive, full, and bloody. In his book *On Evacuations* Diocles speaks of live, full, and bloody worms as indicative of fever.

Herophilus, however, in his book written in opposition to the *Prognostic* of Hippocrates, holds that the expulsion of the worms, whether dead or alive, is not a bad sign.

Apollonius Glaucus in his work *On Internal Diseases* declares that the expulsion of round worms is, in the beginning, a sign of frequent indigestion, but in the last stage indicates that a determination of the disease (Greek *crisis*) is approaching. He holds that it is not a good sign if the worms are alive, full, and bloody.

4   Apollonius of Memphis holds it as a general and universal proposition (Greek *catholicon*) that in any disease the generation of worms in the intestines is a dangerous sign; and more dangerous if they are dead when expelled than if they are alive.

Antiphanes, in the book he entitles *Panoptēs* ['All-seeing'], holds that it is a better sign if the worms are expelled through the anus than if they are vomited out; also that it is better if they are evacuated alone than if covered with excrement.

Chrysippus, a follower of Asclepiades, writing on worms in Book III[7] declares that the expulsion of dead worms is a deadly sign only in acute or dangerous cases; for in his opinion it is only

7. Possibly 'in Book III of his treatise *On Worms*.'

maciem[18] vehementem inesse, quando magis aegri periclitantur.
115 sic inquit denique Hippocratem ferri[19] dicentem suo libro eos qui
in aegritudinis declinatione cum stercoribus egeruntur nihil
grave significare. sed neque inquit Dioclem Hippocrati contrariam protulisse sententiam dicendo mortuos vel inanes esse
meliores, siquidem hic in febribus solutionum hoc dixisse videatur, Hippocrates autem mortem significare, sed in febribus
stricturae.

nos vero communiter significari aliquam ex lumbricis dicimus
corruptionem, quam lientericis irruentem bonum quicquam portendere iudicamus, ⟨ut⟩[20] de ipsis scribentes docuimus, in omni-
116 bus vero ceteris noxiam. item sanguinolentorum exclusio etiam
debilitatem significat. albi etenim ex[21] nondum mutata aut
corrupta materia nutriuntur, sanguinolenti vero vellendo ex ipso
sanguine nutriuntur. item in augmento accessionis febrium
exclusi turborem altiorum partium ostendunt, et magis si fuerint
sanguinolenti; declinatione[22] vero laxamentum, sicut cetera, hoc
est stercorum vel urinae vel quorumlibet officiorum egestio.
etenim laxatis corporibus reddi videntur, quippe cum quorum
117 adiectio gravet, eorum detractio necessario relevet. haec est
lumbricorum significatio.

sed ob curationem, in his quos ascaridas vocavimus, si tumor
in longaone fuerit constitutus oportet iniectionem olei adhibere,
quae cum fuerit reddita, erit infusio aut decoctio centaureae vel
absinthii inicienda. ac si ramenta fuerint exclusa sanguinolenti
coloris, decoctio mali punici corticis vel gallae convenit iniec-
tioni, aut[23] si perseveraverit, chartae exustae et auripigmenti,
quod Graeci arsenicon vocant, aequali pondere,[24] quod sit in

---

[18] aciem *S*: *corr. Rm*

[19] fari *Rm*   [22] ⟨in⟩ declinatione *R*

[20] *add. R*   [23] ac *R*

[21] ex *Rm*: et *S*   [24] aequale pondus *Rm*

---

8. *Prognostic* 11 (p. 88 Kühlewein; II. 136 Littré): 'when a disease is approaching
a crisis, the passage of round worms with the discharges is a good sign.' Cf. *Coan Prenotions* 589 (V. 720 Littré). Chrysippus took this Hippocratic passage to refer to dead
worms.

9. Now the view ascribed to Hippocrates in 112 seems to be referred to.

10. The treatise *On Chronic Diseases*, as we have it, contains no separate chapter
on lientery, the disease in which the digestive process fails and the food is discharged
through the bowels imperfectly digested. It is possible that Caelius is referring to an-

in these dangerous cases that the presence of dead worms is in-
5 dicative of extreme weakness. And so, according to Chrysippus,
this is what Hippocrates refers to when he declares in his treatise
that in the decline of a disease the discharge of worms covered
with feces has no alarming significance.[8] At the same time Chrysippus points out that when Diocles declares that the presence
of dead or empty worms is a more favorable sign, he is not ex-
pressing a view contrary to that of Hippocrates.[9] For in Chrysippus' opinion Diocles makes the statement in connection with
cases of fever accompanied by a state of looseness, while Hippocrates holds that the presence of such worms is a deadly sign,
but only in cases of fever accompanied by a state of stricture.

We, however, hold that the presence of worms, in all diseases
except lientery, is a general indication of decomposition, which
is a sign of danger; but in the case of lientery we consider the
appearance of worms a good sign, as we have indicated in our
6 discussion of this disease.[10] And we hold that the passing of
worms that are full of blood is a sign of weakness. For the whitish worms are nourished by food matter before it is altered or
decomposed; the blood-gorged worms, on the other hand, are
nourished by drawing upon the blood itself. Again, the expulsion
of worms during the increasing phase of an attack of fever is indicative of a disturbance in the inner parts, especially if the
worms are full of blood. But in the declining phase the expulsion
of worms indicates a relaxing, just as does every other discharge,
e.g., of feces, urine, or any other matter. For it is evident that
the discharge of the worms is accompanied by a relaxing of the
body, since the body is necessarily lightened by the removal of
7 that which, when present, weighs it down. So much for symptomatology in the disease of worms.

As for the treatment, in the case of the worms we call 'ascarides,' if the inflammation is located in the rectum, inject a clyster of olive oil. When this is discharged, inject an infusion or
decoction of centaury or wormwood. If bits of blood-colored
matter are discharged, a decoction of pomegranate rind or oak
gall should be added to the clyster; or, if the condition persists,
equal weights, i.e., six drachms, of burnt paper and orpiment

---

other treatise or to a lost chapter of our treatise. Yet another possibility is that some
part of iv. 27–77 belongs to a discussion of lientery. But those sections contain no reference to worms.

quantitate drachmarum sex, cum suco arnoglossae. ac si putredo apparuerit, quam Graeci nomen[25] appellant, erit aqua salsa
incienda atque congrua medicamina, sicut nuper docuimus. ex
his enim et animalia interficiuntur et alia pronasci[26] prohibentur
et ulcera cicatricantur.

118   ac si rotundi fuerint lumbrici, qui nunc stricturae accidunt,
nunc solutioni, nunc ulceribus intestinorum, et nunc in celeribus
passionibus, nunc in tardis, quas chronias vocant, ⟨nunc⟩ non[27]
ex supradictis sed[28] sua in corpore alienitate nascentes[29] ex corruptione ciborum effecta,[30] oportebit curationem pro supradicta
curari[31] differentia. et si ipsa animalia corrumpenda[32] viderimus, erunt medicamina adhibenda ut[33] tamquam aliena atque
indigentia detractione auferantur. ac si passionibus fuerint
appendicia, quae saepe generandorum animalium fuerunt cau-
119 sae, erunt congrua iisdem passionibus adhibenda. his enim con-
victis etiam animalia interficiuntur.

    quapropter si strictura fuerit in corpore, fomentatio compe-
tens est adhibenda atque cataplasma laxativum et, si ratio
coegerit, phlebotomia: quae singula suis temporibus aptanda
probamus. tum cucurbita adiuncta scarificatione medianis partibus admovenda. his enim laxatis sine ulla medicaminum virtute atque[34] facile animalia decidunt, oleo poto aut aqua calida
et oleo vel decoctione mixarum[35] aut glycyrrhizae, cuius libra
infusa in aquae heminas sex usque ad tertiam partem erit deco-
120 quenda. et his praeterea cibi tempore dari potest sorbile quicquam, ut illud quod Graeci appellant oleoptisanon.[36] ex his
enim et tumentia relaxantur, et animalia quae inesse videntur
lapsu quodam ac desertione tumentium dimissa fundentur.

    at si solutio fuerit in corpore, erunt constringentia adhibenda
et exercitatius[37] cataplasma, sed ex lupini pollinibus confectum

---

[25] menomen S: corr. R (cf. 26)   [27] ⟨nunc⟩ non scripsi: non S: nunc R

[26] alia pronasci Rm: alii trochisci S   [28] nunc R

[29] nascentes conieci: vacantes S: vagantes Rm: fort. natantes

[30] effecti Rm

[31] mutari Schmid RPh 148, fort. recte   [33] ut R: aut S

[32] corruptione ⟨ciborum genita⟩ Rm   [34] aeque Sm

[35] mixarum Rm (my-): noxarum S. cf. 124, 125

[36] fort. scrib. elaeoptisanen (elaeoptissanon Rm)

[37] fort. scrib. exercitius (cf. Chr. iv. 32)

(Greek *arsenicon*) together with plantain juice should be used in the clyster. But if there is any indication of progressive decomposition (Greek *nomē*), inject salt water and such suitable drugs as we have just referred to. For the worms will be killed by these means, others will be prevented from developing, and the ulceration will cicatrize.

8   Round worms, however, may appear during a state of stricture, or a state of looseness, or in conjunction with intestinal ulceration, sometimes in acute diseases, and sometimes in chronic diseases (Greek *chroniae*); and sometimes they do not arise from one of the aforementioned conditions, but from waste matter present in the body by reason of the decomposition of food. Now the treatment must depend on the particular type of case.[11] And if it appears that the worms have decomposed,[12] apply drugs in order to get rid of them as foreign bodies requiring removal. But if they are directly connected with actual diseases, which often cause these animals to be generated, apply

9   the measures required by these diseases. For if the diseases are overcome, the animals will also be killed off.

Hence, if a state of stricture is present in the body, apply a suitable fomentation and a relaxing poultice and, if necessary, venesection. Employ each of these measures at its proper time. Then apply cupping with scarification to the middle parts. For when these parts are relaxed, no powerful drugs are needed, but the worms are expelled if the patient takes a drink of olive oil, or hot water and olive oil, or a decoction of sebesten or sweetroot, a pound of the root being placed in six heminae of water and boiled down until only a third of the original amount of water

20   is left. In addition, some gruel-like food may be given at mealtime, e.g., what the Greeks call *elaeoptisanē* [pearl barley and olive oil]. For the inflamed parts will be further relaxed by these foods, and such worms as are present will be discharged from below, slipping away from and, as it were, deserting these inflamed parts.

If, however, there is a state of looseness in the body, use astringent substances and apply a strong plaster, this time made with ground lupines; use vinegar and honey with an admixture

11. This sentence may possibly mean: 'In such cases [of round worms] the treatment must be of the type discussed above.'

12. Or, with some such reading as that of *Rm:* 'that the worms are the product of the decomposition of food.'

et aceto cum melle, tribus vel quatuor cyathis aquae commixtis,
cum cervini cornu serragine aspersa, quam Graeci rhinema[38] vocant, in cochlearis pleni quantitatem, si tarda fuerit passio,
quam Graeci chronian vocant, quoniam indiget recorporatione
atque lacessentium medicaminum virtute. sed in lenimento
constituta erit varia coniectura[39] facienda quo animalia exclu-
121 dantur. quapropter adhibenda medicamina,[40] harum partium
fomentatio ex oleo veteri, et apponenda unctio fellis taurini
aegrotantis umbilico, vel lanae ex ipso tinctae particula. tum
cataplasma ex polline lupini consperso ex decoctione absinthii[41]
aut santonici. admiscendus denique etiam sucus earundem
herbarum.

si vero vehementius oportuerit animalia [alia][42] sauciare, convenit etiam tamquam acriores cibos et propterea aptos, velut in
drymiphagia, dare cepam,[43] allium, quae nunc incocta, nunc
mediocriter cocta, quo minime[44] eorum virtus ⟨pereat⟩,[45] erunt
offerenda. nunc enim urgente lumbricorum exclusione his uti
122 cogimur rebus. facit idem[46] sinapi exuccatum vel adiuncto pani
comestum; item nasturtium cum aceto contritum, sive ut Graeci
vocant cardamum, immisso atque infuso pani; item laser aceto
solutum sive sinapi quo comedenda tinguantur, vel ovo sorbili
admixtus iste liquor detur in ervi modo;[47] item absinthium cum
vino poto datum.

ac si ulceratio fuerit intestinorum, congrua probamus adhibenda pro ulcerum differentia. ac si febres non fuerint neque
alia quaelibet passio lumbricis confuerit, nihil oportet conicere,
sed ex medicaminum varietate eorum interfectionem atque detractionem efficere. sunt enim[48] bestiolae, quae Graeci theridia
123 vocaverunt. sed producenda atque extendenda erit magnitudo
curationis pro accidentium modo. et quoniam aliquando sunt
in ventre constitutae, quod probatur ex aegrotantium querelis
cum locorum sensus[49] tanguntur, aliquando in intestinis, et[50]
necessario quae in ventre sunt celerius afficit medicaminum[51]
cibus ac potus,[52] intestinis vero quae per clysterem fuerint iniecta

---

38 rhinema *A* (*graecis litteris*): rhinen *S*, *fort. retin. cf. CGL III. 538. 6, 557. 5, 620. 46,*
Schmid Mél. Niedermann 121

39 confectura *Rm*
40 *fort. scrib.* medicamina ⟨et⟩
41 *fort.* absinthii ⟨pontici⟩
42 *seclusi:* talia *Rm*
43 cepam ⟨et⟩ *R*

44 minime *Rm*: minima *S*
45 ⟨pereat⟩ *R*: *fort.* ⟨ammittatur⟩
46 *an* item?
47 modum *Rm* (*cf. 105*)
48 enim ⟨nocentes⟩ *R*

of three or four cyathi of water and sprinkle in a spoonful of the shavings (Greek *rhinēma*) of stag's horn. These instructions apply when the patient suffers from a chronic disease (Greek *chronia*), for such a disease requires metasyncrisis and strong, irritant drugs. And if the attack of worms comes during the interval of remission in such a disease, try various methods of driv-

1 ing them out. Thus employ drugs, foment the parts in question with old olive oil, and anoint the umbilicus with ox bile, using a small piece of wool dipped therein. Then apply a plaster made with ground lupines soaked in a decoction of wormwood proper or Santonian wormwood, the juices of the plants also being directly used in the composition of the plaster.

But if it proves necessary to take more drastic measures against these worms, it will be well to give the patient sharp foods, for this type of food will be proper, as in the acrid diet. Thus give him onion and garlic, serving them now uncooked and now slightly cooked, so that as little as possible of their strength is lost. For it is now, when the expulsion of the worms is

2 urgent, that we must use those substances. Mustard juice, which may be eaten with bread, is similarly beneficial; so is nasturtium (or, as the Greeks call it, *cardamon*), rubbed up in vinegar, bread being soaked in the mixture. Silphium juice may also be mixed with vinegar or mustard for the same purpose, and the patient's food dipped in the liquid; or the latter may be mixed with a soft egg and given in the quantity of a vetch seed. A drink of wormwood mixed with wine will also serve the purpose.

Now if the intestines are ulcerated, apply remedies suitable for the particular kind of ulcers. But if there is no fever and if no other disease of any kind occurs along with the worms, do not experiment, but see that the worms are killed off and expelled with a variety of drugs; for these worms are really little animals

3 (Greek *thēridia*). On the other hand, a prolonged and extended treatment may be necessary, depending on the nature of the symptoms. Again, the worms are sometimes found in the stomach, as is indicated by the patient's pains when these sensitive parts are touched; and sometimes they are found in the intestines. Now worms in the stomach are, of course, more quickly reached by food and drink than by any other type of medica-

---

49 sensu *R*   51 *fort.* medicaminibus *erat*: ⟨quam iniecta⟩ medicamina *R*
50 et *om. R*   52 potus ⟨in⟩ *R*

(nam et ex ventre ad intestina haec saepe animalia et ex intestinis ad ventrem refugiunt), erit sanabilius ergo ut, ubi appre-
henderimus esse copiam lumbricorum, usum primo adhibeamus
congrui cibi ac potus, similiter epithematum usum servantes et
124 cataplasmatum, deinde clysterem. oportet igitur potum dari
absinthii pontici decoctionem sive marini aut santonici usque ad
modum duum cyathorum vel trium, et nunc nulla alia admixta
materia, nunc oleo adiuncto vel decoctione lupini aut mixarum[53]
cum cornu cervini serragine, et laser aqua solutum vel aceto et
admixto sinapi aut ovo sorbili transvoratum, item alica in qua
fuerit infusa aloe, sive ipsa transvorata. nec non etiam trochiscus dandus qui appellatur picros, vel illa hiera quae dialoes appellatur, quorum compositiones Responsionum libris de medica-
125 minibus[54] scribentes tradidimus; item cardamum, quod nasturtium vocamus, torridum ac tritum cum aqua vel mulso aut cum
melle in electario datum; item lupini sicci decorticati atque
transvorati cum melle quindecim numero vel viginti. quod si
minime quisquam transvorare valuerit, eorum pollinem[55] conspersum[56] atque tritum quantum tres digiti capere potuerint
aquae bibendum admiscemus, sive mulso aut decoctione mixarum[57] aut electario[58] admixto melle dabimus. item gentianae
sucum in cochlearii modum cum mulso convenit dare atque
horum similibus uti virtutibus, item absinthium cum vino et
castoreum cum mulso. in parvis vero pueris, quo latere possit,[59]
nasturtium frixum sive tritum cum melle atque lacte dabitur
126 potui vel commixtum pani. his igitur rebus erunt cibi ponendi:[60]
pultibus enim atque sorbilibus convenit absinthium concoquere
vel similes herbas. hoc etiam fit[61] sicco fico atque pingui vel palmulis quas patetos appellant, quae concisae atque immissae et
cibo datae mederi valebunt. faciunt praeterea mora cibo data,
quae vulgo celsa Latini vocaverunt, Graeci vero sycamina, item
ex amigdalis amaris sorbilia confecta, quae Graeci rophemata[62]

[53] mixarum *Rm* (my-): noxarum *S*
[54] medicaminibus *Rm*: medicamine *S, Friedel 36*   [55] polline *S*: *corr. Rm*
[56] ⟨aceto⟩ conspersum *Rm*   [57] mixarum *Rm* (my-): noxarum *S*
[58] ⟨pro⟩ electario *R*: *fort. scrib.* ⟨in⟩ electario *ut supra*
[59] possit *R*: possint *S*   [61] fit *Rm*: si *S*
[60] parandi *Rm*   [62] trophemata *S*: *corr. Reinesius 672*

13. Some identify wormwood of the sea (*seriphon*) with Santonian wormwood. Cf.
Diosc. *Mat. med.* iii. 24.

ment; injections by clyster, however, are effective for worms in
the intestines. And these creatures often move from stomach to
intestines and again from intestines to stomach. Therefore,
whenever it is observed that a large number of worms is present,
it will be best to make use, in the first instance, of suitable food
and drink, and at the same time to employ the proper epithems
24 and plasters, and then to prescribe a clyster. Thus have the patient drink a decoction of Pontic wormwood or wormwood of the
sea, or the Santonian variety.[13] As much as two or three cyathi
should be taken, sometimes without the addition of any other
substance, and at other times with the addition of olive oil, a
decoction of lupines, or sebesten with shavings of stag's horn.
Silphium juice mixed with water or vinegar may also be taken,
with mustard, or swallowed down with a soft egg. Aloes, too,
may be taken, either alone or added to spelt groats. Again, the
troche called *picros* ['bitter'] or the so-called 'aloetic hiera' may
be given to the patient. We have set forth the preparation of
these medicines in the section on drugs of our treatise entitled
25 *Answers*. Cardamon (Latin *nasturtium*) may also be heated,
pounded up, and given to the patient in water or mead, or as an
electuary in honey. Or have the patient swallow with honey
fifteen or twenty dry, shelled lupines; but if he cannot swallow
them, rub them down to a powder, and add as much of this powder as three finger-breadths of water will hold. Give the patient
this mixture to drink, or use mead or a decoction of sebestens in
making the mixture; or give the lupines as an electuary with
honey. A spoonful of gentian juice in mead will also be beneficial,
as will other similar drugs; so, too, wormwood with wine, and
castor with mead. In the case of small children, dried or powdered nasturtium should be given with honey and milk as a
drink, or else mixed with their bread; in this way the drug will
126 be concealed. And also prepare the rest of their food with such
drugs; that is, cook wormwood or similar drugs with the soft
and liquid foods. The same may be done[14] with rich dried figs or
the juicy dates called *patētoe;* chopped up and mixed with the
patient's food, they help the treatment. Mulberries (Latin *celsa,*
Greek *sycamina*) are also beneficial when served with food. So,
too, gruels (Greek *rhophēmata*) prepared with bitter almonds

14. The text is uncertain, and it is not clear whether wormwood enters into this
preparation.

vocaverunt, et communiter cuncta quae ventrem deducere valent. hinc denique etiam pinnae aridae vel ustae[63] atque tritae
127 potui sufficientem modum miscuerunt. convenit etiam urtica,
sive sola sive cum aliqua decoctione confecta. nam ob celebrandam curationem vehementer utilia probamus catapotia ex
squilla atque chamelaea confecta. sumpta igitur squilla erit
acriori aceto concoquenda ne fluida fiat, tum terenda diligenter,
ac deinde chamelaea contusa[64] atque creta admiscenda squillae,
quantum res patiuntur, ut ad emplastri veniat qualitatem. tum
facienda catapotia in fabae magnitudinem, et pro viribus aegrotantis danda, ut fortibus octo vel novem, imbecillis sex vel sep-
128 tem, pueris vero tres[65] vel quatuor ex aqua calida. potest etiam
ipsius chamelaeae concisae atque contritae cum mulso quippiam
dari transbibendum, vel cum lenticulae parvo modo sorbendum.
sed pueris obolus unus, maioribus vero oboli duo sunt dandi,
item fortibus tres; perfecta tamen potio drachmae unius continet
modum. utendum praeterea epithemate circa medias partes ex
lupini pollinibus aut melanthio et decoctione absinthii aut bulbo[66] liliorum, aut cerotario cedriae admixtis lupinis tritis aut
absinthio, aut agrestis peponis interioribus, quem[67] Graeci colocyntida vocant, cum melle atque lupinis, aut centaureae vel
aloes partibus duabus et diagridii parte una cum melle et felle
129 taurino. erunt praeterea omnia quae potui ordinavimus danda
etiam per clysterem inicienda, et magis adiuncto vel admixto
oleo plurimo calido et sucis praescriptis, quo plurima mordicatione intestina afficiantur.

ac si lati fuerint lumbrici, erit adhibendus vomitus ex oleo, non
ex radicibus, et alia die clystere utendum, admixta nitri parte vel
salis. danda etiam aqua salsa potui aut glycyrrhizae radicis
decoctio aut similiter incocta glycyrrhiza. alii vero tres drachmas glycyrrhizae cum nitro probaverunt, alii diagridii obolos
tres cum polypodii herbae drachmis duabus, alii ex pinnis medi-
130 camen confectum. sed erit semper tentandum, ubi res patiuntur, ut his utamur medicaminibus quae minime stomachum
afficiant. tum cum sensum acceperint aegrotantes animalium

---

[63] vel ustae *conieci, coll. Th. Prisc. ii. 98, 99*: veluti *S*

[64] contusa *Reinesius 672*: anchusa *S*

[65] tria *Rm*   [66] bulbo *Am*: fulvo *S*: fulvorum *Rm*

[67] interioribus, quem *Rm*: interiora, quae *S, fort. retin.*

and, generally speaking, all substances that can clear the stomach and bowels. Some physicians even add to the drink a suitable
27 amount of feather, dried or burnt and powdered. Nettle is also beneficial and may be used alone or mixed with some decoction. And in our opinion pills made with squill and chamelaea are very helpful in effecting a cure. Take a squill and boil it in strong vinegar, but do not permit it to dissolve. Then pound it down thoroughly and add the chamelaea, triturated and strained, in the amount necessary to bring the mixture to the consistency of a plaster. Then make up pills, each the size of a bean, and prescribe them according to the patient's strength; eight or nine for strong patients, six or seven for weak, and three or four for
28 children, the pills to be taken in hot water. Chamelaea may also be cut up and pounded by itself; this may then be given with mead as a drink or supped up with a little lentil. For children the dose is one obol, for adults two, or even three in the case of strong persons; but the whole drink when prepared should have the weight of a drachm.[15] In addition apply to the middle parts an epithem made with ground lupines, black cumin, a decoction of wormwood, or the bulb of lilies; or a wax plaster made of oil of Syrian cedar, with the addition of ground lupines or wormwood; or the inner parts of wild gourd (Greek *colocynthis*) with honey and lupines; or else a mixture of two parts of centaury or aloes and one part of scammony juice, together with honey and
29 ox bile. In addition, all the substances prescribed above to be taken by mouth should also be injected as clysters, with the addition or admixture of a great deal of warm olive oil and the juices mentioned above. In this way the intestines will be subjected to considerable irritation.

In the case of broad worms prescribe olive oil as a vomitive, but not radishes. On the following day employ a clyster, adding some nitrum or salt. And give the patient salt water to drink, or a decoction of sweetroot, or even the juice of uncooked sweetroot. Some, however, prescribe three drachms of sweetroot with nitrum; others three obols of scammony juice with two drachms
30 of polypody; and still others a drug prepared with feathers. But we should always try, so far as circumstances permit, to use drugs that have little effect on the gullet. Then when a dis-

15. That is, 6 obols. If the interpretation is correct, the purpose of the clause is to indicate the strength of the mixture.

carendorum, ut interpellatione ventris admoneantur, subicienda erit aqua calida quo et loca relaxentur et animalia procedant, ne frigore percussa fugiant. erit praeterea curandum ne frequenter haec animalia renascantur, ut unctione regulari corpora fortificemus, adhibito praeceptore, adhibita etiam recorporatione cyclica, quae fit vomitu radicum et drimyphagia et dropace et sinapismo et paroptesi et horum similibus virtute rebus.

131   IX. DE MOLLIBUS SIVE SUBACTIS, QUOS GRAECI MALTHACOS VOCANT

Molles sive subactos Graeci malthacos vocaverunt, quos[1] quidem esse nullus facile virorum credit. non enim hoc humanos ex natura venit in mores, sed pulso pudore libido etiam indebitas partes obscenis usibus subiugavit, cum nullus cupiditati modus, nulla satietatis[2] spes est, singulis Spartae non sufficiunt suae[3] (nam sic[4] nostri corporis loca divina providentia certis destinavit officiis), tum denique utentes[5] veste atque gressu et aliis femininis rebus quae sunt a passionibus corporis

132 aliena, sed potius corruptae mentis vitia. nam saepe tumentes[6] vel, quod est difficile, verentes quosdam quibus forte deferunt, repente mutati parvo tempore virilitatis quaerunt indicia demonstrare, cuius quia modum nesciunt, rursum nimietate sublati plus quoque quam virtuti convenit faciunt, et maioribus se peccatis involvunt. constat itaque etiam hoc nostro iudicio hos vera sentire. est enim, ut Soranus ait, malignae ac foedissimae mentis passio. nam sicut feminae tribades appellatae, quod utramque venerem exerceant, mulieribus magis quam viris misceri festinant et easdem invidentia paene virili sectantur, et cum passione fuerint desertae seu temporaliter relevatae, †ea quae-

[1] aegros *Barth 1969*

[2] satietatis *R*: satietati *S*

[3] Spartae non sufficiunt suae *Barth 1969*: Sparta non sufficit sua *Reinesius 673*: spartanum sufficiunt sua *S*: *cf. Eurip. Frag. 723 (Nauck)*

[4] sic *A*: si *S*

[5] utentes *conieci*: volentes *S*   [6] timentes *Rm*

---

1. Or reading *aegros* (Barth): 'are sick.'

2. Or if *timentes* (*Rm*) be read: 'often out of fear, etc.'

3. Perhaps 'that these persons know what is right.'

turbance in the abdomen gives the patient the feeling that the worms are about to be passed off, inject a clyster of warm water so that the parts may be relaxed and the worms may issue forth without drawing back by reason of the shock of the cold. In addition, try to prevent the renewed appearance of these worms, and see to it that the body is strengthened by a regimen of anointing under professional direction, and by cyclical metasyncrisis. The latter consists of the vomitive treatment with radishes, the acrid diet, pitch plasters, mustard plasters, intense heat, and other treatments of like nature.

IX. ON EFFEMINATE MEN OR PATHICS (GREEK *MALTHACOE*)

31

PEOPLE find it hard to believe that effeminate men or pathics (Greek *malthacoe*) really exist.[1] The fact is that, though the practices of such persons are unnatural to human beings, lust overcomes modesty and puts to shameful use parts intended for other functions. That is, in the case of certain individuals, there is no limit to their desire and no hope of satisfying it; and they cannot be content with their own lot, the lot which divine providence had marked out for them in assigning definite functions to the parts of the body. They even adopt the dress, walk, and other characteristics of women. Now this condition is different from a bodily disease; it is rather an affliction of a diseased mind.

32 Indeed, often out of passion[2] and in rare cases out of respect for certain persons to whom they are beholden, these pathics suddenly change their character and for a while try to give proof of their virility. But since they are not aware of their limitations, they are again the victims of excesses, subjecting their virility to too great a strain and consequently involving themselves in worse vices. And it is our opinion that these persons suffer no impairment of sensation.[3] For, as Soranus says, this affliction comes from a corrupt and debased mind. Indeed, the victims of this malady may be compared to the women who are called *tribades* because they pursue both kinds of love.[4] These women are more eager to lie with women than with men; in fact, they pursue women with almost masculine jealousy, and when they

4. The reference is probably to heterosexual and homosexual love. *Tribas* is derived from *tribō*, 'rub.'

133 runt aliis obicere quae pati noscuntur iuvamini[7] humilitate[8] duplici sexu confectam,[9]† velut frequenter[10] ebrietate corruptae in novas libidinis formas erumpentes, consuetudine turpi nutritae,[11] sui sexus iniuriis gaudent: sic illi comparatione talium animi passione iactari noscuntur. nam neque ulla curatio corporis depellendae passionis causa recte putatur adhibenda, sed potius animus coercendus qui tanta peccatorum labe vexatur. nemo enim pruriens corpus feminando correxit vel virilis veretri tactu[12] mitigavit, sed communiter querelam sive dolorem alia[13] ex ma-

134 teria toleravit. denique etiam a Clodio historia curationis data ascaridarum esse perspicitur, quos de lumbricis scribentes vermiculos esse docuimus longaonis in partibus natos.

Parmenides libris quos De natura scripsit eventu inquit conceptionis molles aliquando seu subactos homines generari. cuius quia graecum est epigramma, et hoc versibus intimabo. latinos enim ut potui simili modo composui ne linguarum ratio misceretur.

> femina virque simul veneris cum germina miscent
> venis, informans[14] diverso ex sanguine virtus
> temperiem servans bene condita corpora fingit.

135
> nam[15] si virtutes permixto semine pugnent,
> nec faciant unam permixto[16] in corpore, dirae[17]
> nascentem gemino vexabunt semine sexum.

vult enim seminum praeter materias esse virtutes, quae si se

[7] = *adiutorio? an* iuvenum? iuvenibus? in animi?

[8] *fort.* -i *aut* -ae

[9] confecta R: *fort.* -ae

[10] frequenti R

[11] nutritae R: -as S

[12] tractu Rm

[13] tali Rm

[14] venis informans] unius in formam *coniecit Diels, Doxograph.*, *193*: venis conformans *id.*, *Parmenides, 44*

[15] at R

[16] vim mixto Rm: mixtae uno *T. Gomperz, Sitz. Wien. Ak. 134 (1896) II. Abh., p. 14*

[17] *fort. scrib.* Dirae

---

5. Text and meaning are unclear. Perhaps 'in (*or* to overcome) their degradation they seek to blame others for their affliction; then plagued by double sexuality, etc.' But *ea . . . noscuntur* may refer to renewed (heterosexual?) promiscuity.

6. The reference is probably to sodomy (see 134, *init.*), and it seems inadvisable to take *pruriens corpus* more broadly and *feminando* of venery in general.

133 are freed or temporarily relieved of their passion . . .[5] they rush, as if victims of continual intoxication, to new forms of lust, and, sustained by this disgraceful mode of life, they rejoice in the abuse of their sexual powers. So the pathics, like the *tribades*, are victims of an affliction of the mind. For there exists no bodily treatment which can be applied to overcome the disease; it is rather the mind that is affected in these disgraceful vices, and it is consequently the mind that must be controlled. For no man has ever overcome bodily lust by playing the woman's sexual role,[6] or gained relief by contact[7] with a penis. In general, the
134 relief of pain and disease is achieved by other means.[8] Thus the account of a cure as given by Clodius obviously refers to a case of ascarides. The latter, as we showed in our chapter on worms, are small worms arising in the parts of the rectum.

Parmenides in his work *On Nature*[9] indicates that effeminate men or pathics may come into being as a result of a circumstance at conception. Since his account is contained in a Greek poem, I shall also give my version in poetry. For I have done my best to compose Latin verses of the same kind, to avoid the commingling of the two languages:[10]

'When man and woman mingle the seeds of love that spring from their veins, a formative power maintaining proper propor-
135 tions molds well-formed bodies from this diverse blood. For if, when the seed is mingled, the forces contained therein clash and do not fuse into one, then cruelly will they plague with double seed the sex of the offspring.'[11]

Thus Parmenides holds that the seminal fluids are not merely material bodies but possess active principles, and if these fluids

7. According to *Rm* (reading *tractu*) the reference is to masturbation, but this seems irrelevant to the argument.

8. The meaning here is doubtful. Possibly: 'in general any pain or affliction that was relieved must have come from some other source,' i.e., other than unnatural sexual desire. This fits the sequel somewhat better, though it does not accord so well with the text in its present form.

9. Diels, *Frag. Vors.*, Parmenides B18 (cf. A54). Diels retranslates the verses into Greek in his *Parmenides*, p. 44. Against Diels's interpretation of the passage as referring to hermaphroditism see Wilamowitz, *Sappho u. Simonides*, p. 72. Quite apart from the question of Parmenides' intention, it is clear that Caelius (Soranus) understood the passage to be concerned not with the nature of the sexual organs but with sexual perversion.

10. I.e., to avoid the quotation of Greek in a Latin work.

11. Possibly 'the Furies will torment, etc.'

ita miscuerint ut[17a] eiusdem corporis faciant unam,[18] congruam[19] sexui generent voluntatem. si autem permixto semine corporeo virtutes separatae permanserint, utriusque veneris natos adpetentia sequatur.

multi praeterea sectarum principes genuinam dicunt esse passionem et propterea in posteros venire cum semine, non quidem naturam criminantes, quae suae puritatis metas aliis ex animali-

136 bus docet (nam sunt eius specula a sapientibus nuncupata), sed humanum genus, quod ita semel recepta tenuerit vitia, ut nulla possit instauratione purgari, nec ullum novitati liquerit locum, sitque gravior †mentis culpa ut† cum[20] plurimae genuinae seu adventiciae[21] passiones corporibus infractae[22] consenescant, ut podagra, epilepsia, furor, et propterea aetate vergente mitiores procul dubio fiant. omnia etenim vexantia validos effectus dabunt firmitate opposita subiacentium materiarum, quae cum in

137 senibus deficit, passio quoque minuitur, ut fortitudo. sola tamen supradicta quae subactos seu molles efficit viros senescenti corpore gravius invalescit, et infanda magis libidine movet, non quidem sine ratione. in aliis enim aetatibus, adhuc valido corpore et naturalia veneris[23] officia celebrante, gemina luxuriae libido[24] dividitur, animo eorum nunc faciendo nunc patiendo iactato.[25] in his vero qui senectute defecti virili veneris officio caruerint, omnis animi libido in contrariam ducitur appetentiam, et propterea femineam[26] validius venerem poscit. hinc denique coniciunt plurimi etiam pueros hac passione iactari. similiter enim senibus virili indigent officio, quod in ipsis nondum et[27] illos deseruit.

[17a] ut *Rm*: et *S*

[18] *hic virgulam posuit Diels, post* faciant *edd.*

[19] *fort.* unam, ⟨unam⟩ congruam

[20] ⟨senescentibus⟩ mentis culpa, cum *R*: *fort.* senescentibus, cum *vel* senescenti corpore, cum

[21] seu adventiciae] *fort. del.*: *an* seu ⟨non⟩ adventiciae *vel* non adventiciae?

[22] infarctae *Rm*

[23] veneris *Rm*: ventris *S*: viri *Rm*

[24] libido ⟨non⟩ *R*

[25] animorum nunc faciendo, nunc facie iactata *S*: animo nunc patiendo nunc faciendo iactato *Am*

[26] femina *S*: *fort.* femininam (*an* feminam?)

[27] *fort.* ⟨est⟩ et (*sic fere Rm*): est *Barth 1096*

mingle in such a way as to form a unified force in the body, they
will thereby produce a desire appropriate to the sex of the individual. But if, despite the mingling of the seminal matter, the
active principles fail to merge, a desire for both forms of love
will harass the offspring.

On the other hand, many leaders of the other sects hold that
the condition which we are discussing is an inherited disease,
that is to say, is passed on from generation to generation by way
of the seed.[12] For this they do not blame nature, since the latter
shows us its strict purity by the example of the brute animals,
136 whom philosophers call 'nature's mirrors.' These physicians
place the blame rather on the human race, because, having once
incurred the defects, it retains them and cannot rid itself of them
by any kind of renovation, and leaves no opportunity for a fresh
start . . .[13] though other diseases, whether heriditary or adventi-
tious, in the great majority of cases become weaker as the body
grows older; this is true, for example, of podagra, epilepsy, and
mania, which unquestionably become milder in the patient's
declining years. The fact is that whatever irritates will produce
its strongest effect when the underlying matter offers strong
opposition; but, since such opposition fades in the case of old
137 people, disease, like strength, is also blunted. But the affliction
under discussion, which produces effeminate men or pathics, is
the only one that becomes stronger as the body grows older. It
causes a hideous and ever increasing lust. And there is good reason why this takes place. For in other years when the body is
still strong and can perform the normal functions of love, the
sexual desire [of these persons] assumes a dual aspect, in which
the soul is excited sometimes while playing a passive role and
sometimes while playing an active role. But in the case of old
men who have lost their virile powers, all their sexual desire is
turned in the opposite direction and consequently exerts a
stronger demand for the feminine role in love. In fact, many infer that this is the reason why boys too are victims of this affliction. For, like old men, they do not possess virile powers; that is,
they have not yet attained those powers which have already
deserted the aged.

12. Cf. *Chr.* v. 29.

13. The text is uncertain, but the point may have been that the affliction under
discussion becomes even worse as the person grows older.

LIBER QUINTUS

I   ## I. DE ISCHIADICIS ET PSOEADICIS

A PARTIBUS quae dolore vexantur hae passiones nomina
sumpserunt. nam vertebrorum ⟨ossa, quorum⟩ summitas iliorum[1] initio terminatur, Graeci ischia vocaverunt. item musculos clunium sub spinae finem ex interioribus
atque exterioribus adhaerentes psoeas vocaverunt.

generantur istae passiones nunc ex manifestis, nunc ex occultis causis, ut est perfrictio profunda vel terrena cubatio aut casus
vel repentinus percussus aut iugis atque immodicus usus vene-
2 reus aut quilibet longissimi temporis morbus, item vehemens
abductio vel raptus in exercitio factus aut longissimi temporis
haemorrhoidarum fluor retentus[2] vel insueta humi fossio aut
cuiusdam ponderis levandi ex inferioribus[3] conatio.

fit praeterea in omnibus aetatibus, sed frequentius in mediis.
sequitur ischiadicos dolor ⟨vertebri vel⟩[4] vertebrorum, quam
passionem multi duplicem ischiada vocaverunt, attestante gravedine et difficili motu contra solitum morem, et quibusdam cum
levi torpore ac formicatione, quibusdam cum vehementi atque
3 pungenti et fervido dolore, et ad sensum patientis tamquam ser-
pentis convolutus motus, aliquando etiam cum febribus ut neque
in lecto suam conventionem ferre valeant aegrotantes; et primo
in vertebro, dehinc partis suae penetrans loca usque ad mediam
natem ac superius ad inguen, vel ad ancalen perveniens atque
suram, dehinc etiam talum et pedis summitatem.

tum cum passio tardaverit, cessante nutrimento cruris totius
tenuitas fiet, quam Graeci atrophian vocant, incipiens a clunibus
sive ab inferioribus locis, attestante debilitate et saepe conductis
partibus brevitate cruris, aut ultra naturam longitudine passionis distensione suffecta ut in paralysin veniat, aut ipsius ver-

---

[1] vertebrorum summitas ipsorum *S*: *corr. Schmid 42, coll. Isid. Orig. iv. 7. 29*

[2] fluoris tentus *S*: *corr. Rm*

[3] inferioribus *Rm*: interioribus *S*

[4] *supplevi* (*cf.* renis aut renum, *52*)

BOOK V

I. SCIATICA AND PSOITIS

CIATICA and psoitis derive their names from the parts affected. For the Greek word *ischia* signifies the hip bones,
whose ends are situated at the extremity of the flanks;
and the word *psoae* refers to the loin muscles, both interior and
exterior, attached at the end of the spine.

These diseases arise either from observable or from hidden
causes, e.g., a severe cold, lying on the ground, a fall, a sudden
blow, continual and excessive venery, or any disease prolonged
2 over a period of time; also a violent pulling or strain in the
course of exercise, a long-protracted stoppage of the flow from
hemorrhoids, digging in the ground when the person is not used
to such activity, or the exertion of lifting a weight from below.

These diseases occur in all ages, but more frequently among
the middle-aged. In sciatica there is pain in one or both hips; in
the latter case many call the disease 'double sciatica.' There is
also a feeling of heaviness and unusual difficulty in moving
about; in some cases a slight numbness and a creeping irritation
of the skin, sometimes with a severe pricking and burning pain
3 which gives the patient the sensation of a creeping animal's tor-
tuous motion. Sometimes there is fever, and the patient is unable to remain composed in bed.[1] The pain begins in the hip and
then moves through the affected side; it reaches the middle of
the gluteal region and the upper inguinal region, or passes to the
bend of the knee and the calf, and then even to the ankle and
the extremity of the foot.

Later, when the disease becomes chronic, the whole leg becomes thin with the loss of nourishment (Greek *atrophia*). This
attenuation begins at the haunches or at the lower parts. It is
accompanied by weakness in the leg and by a shortening thereof
because of a contraction of the parts; or else the prolonged illness
brings about an abnormal distention of the leg so that it is virtually paralyzed, or the parts about the hip itself become hard

1. *Conventio* may possibly mean 'position,' but one may justly suspect the text at
this point.

4 tebri duratae partes extantiores fiant. constringitur praeterea
saepe ac retinetur ventris officium, aut cum plurimo dolore perficitur ob tensionem atque spiritus retenti percussum. et in
itineris gressu,⁵ quibus forte permittitur, [ut]⁶ initia motus im-
pediuntur,⁷ fervore partium attestante; ac⁸ si perseverans fuerit
motus facilior fiet. tum rursus subsidunt vel intenti resistunt
repente, tamquam fuerant necdum gressu tentato. tunc magis
vehementem dolorem sentiunt. et ambulant quidam capitibus
digitorum gradientes, alii extenti quidem sed sinuatis clunibus
ut neque se pronos inclinare valeant, alii contracti atque con-
5 ducti, qui peius omnibus habere noscuntur, siquidem passio ap-
prehenderit etiam spinae musculos et propterea duritia quadam
haec invasisse videatur loca.

  patitur autem principaliter membrana quae ossa circumtegit,
quam Graeci periosteon vocant, item musculorum capita vel
summitates. denique augmento passionis intercreatus humor et
frequenti dolore corruptus in saniem transiens partes aliquas
collectionibus afficit.

  sed quoniam plurima supradictorum sequentur etiam eas quae
matricis vexatione afficiuntur, et magis cum eius fuerit inclinatio
facta, quam parenclisin⁹ vocant, facienda est discretio pas-
6 sionum: et primo quod matrice patiente in eadem potius causae
inveniantur atque ex ipsa initium sumant; psoeadici vero clunium dolore afficiuntur et tardo motu, ut se retinente¹⁰ dolore
nec inclinare valeant ac difficilius et dolentius subrigant. plurimis igitur dolor cito conquiescit, aliquibus vero perseverat, partes durescunt atque conducuntur. his denique usque ad paene
cutem unicus sequetur gressus. si itaque exteriores musculi
fuerint in passione constituti, etiam tactu tentati dolescunt, interiores autem ex interioribus dolorem accipiunt, tamquam in
7 nephriticis contingit. quos propterea denique similes discernimus, siquidem alia multa eisdem propria concurrant quae de
ipsis scribentes memorabimus.¹¹ psoeadicis autem atque ischia-

⁵ pressu *edd.*

⁶ *seclusi*

⁷ impediantur *edd.*

⁸ at *Rm*

⁹ paraclisin *edd.*

¹⁰ renitente *edd.*

¹¹ memoravimus *edd.*

4 and swollen. Again, the functioning of the bowels is often impeded or suppressed or is accomplished only with the greatest difficulty because of the tension of the parts and the impact from the holding-back of the breath. And even in the case of one who is able to walk, the first steps are difficult and there is a burning sensation in the parts; but if the motion is continued, it becomes easier. But then all of a sudden the patient has to sit down again, or he remains standing tensely, just as he was before he tried to walk; and then he feels even more severe pain. Some walk on tiptoe, others with body erect but with back so arched that they are unable to bend forward; still others have their bodies drawn

5 and bent [forward]. The latter are the worst afflicted of all, for in their case the disease has attacked the muscles of the spine and, as a consequence, has evidently caused a stiffening of these parts.

The parts chiefly affected are the membrane which incloses the bones (Greek *periosteon*), and the heads or extremities of the muscles. In addition, during the increasing phase of the disease a fluid forms internally; this decomposes at repeated attacks and turns into sanies, forming abscesses in various parts.

Since many of the aforementioned symptoms are also present in affections of the womb, especially in cases of flexion (Greek

6 *parenclisis*), we must distinguish the diseases. Now in the first place, in diseases of the womb the malady has its origin in that organ and is primarily to be found there. In psoitis, on the other hand, there is pain in the loins and the patient's movements are impeded, so much so that because of the pain it is impossible for him to bend forward, and he can rise to his feet only with difficulty and distress. Now in most cases this intense pain passes quickly, but sometimes it persists, and the parts become hard and contracted. In these latter cases there is a single, continuous progression until practically the skin itself is affected. Thus, if the exterior muscles are affected, they are painful even to the touch; but if the interior muscles are affected, the pain is in-

7 curred from within, as in cases of nephritis. Hence nephritis is similar in this respect to the diseases under discussion. But we may distinguish them, for there are many other symptoms characteristic of nephritis, as we shall show in our discussion of that disease.[2] Again, in psoitis and sciatica, the diseases with whose

2. 54–58, below.

dicis, quorum nunc curationem scribimus, dolor efficitur nunc
iugis, nunc deficiens, ordinatus aut inordinatus, ac longis vel
parvis intervallis recurrens, ac puris[12] limpidis lenimentorum
variatus spatiis aut mediocres reliquias servans.

　　utilem inquit Hippocrates ischiadicis dysenteriam, habet enim
imitationis quiddam recorporationis faciundae, quamquam
plurima vexatione corpus afficere videatur; item haemorrhoidas
8 vel varices, ut alii dicunt, laxamenti causa. sunt autem difficiles
curatione magis qui plurimo tempore fuerint passione vexati, et
multis atque variis accidentibus[13] signis affecti.

　　in ordine itaque curationis haec erunt intuenda, ut cum recens
fuerit passio, vel veterata sed in superpositionis tempore constituta, iacere faciamus aegrotantem mollioribus stramentis calido in loco, adhibita abstinentia et requie usque ad primam diatriton. tunc lanis mollibus ac limpidis oleo calido dulci praetinctis dolentia loca contegenda. adhibenda etiam fomentatio
iugis ex oleo dulci calido, item vaporationum commutatio, sicut
in multis docuimus scribentes, et phlebotomia tempore consueto
atque ex brachio dolenti parti contrario[14] vel plurimum dolenti
9 comparatione alterius. ac si aequalis in utraque fuerit parte
dolor, ex eo in quo fuerit facilior vena erit detractio facienda. si
neque hoc occurrerit, ex sinistro brachio adiutorium adhibendum, siquidem minus officiis domini necessaria pars esse videatur, nisi forte sinistri, hoc est scaei, fuerint aegrotantes.

　　tum tertia die adhibenda perunctio ex oleo dulci atque calido;
dehinc ora lavanda; cibus dandus nutribilis calidus tener, tamquam stricturae conveniens, et potui aqua calida usque ad declinationis tempus. servanda etiam cibi alterna dierum oblatio.
10 tunc cessante dolore resumptio adhibenda; perseverante vero,
aliae[15] diatriti tempore adhibenda iniectio ex decoctione faenigraeci seminis aut lini aut hibisci, quam Graeci althaean vocant,
quo pariter fota atque vaporata interiora laxamento consentiant. admiscendum denique oleum calidum, item sucus alicae
vel ptisanae; vel oleum solum aut admixto adipe anserino vel

---

[12] puris ⟨et⟩ R

[13] accidentibus ⟨et⟩ R (cf. Ac. ii. 176)

[14] econtrario S: corr. R

[15] aliae conieci: alia S: alius Rm

treatment we are now concerned, the pain is sometimes constant and sometimes intermittent, recurring either regularly or irregularly and at long or short intervals; and during these intervals of remission the patient may be completely free from symptoms of the disease or may show slight traces.

Hippocrates considers dysentery helpful in cases of sciatica,[3] for dysentery involves a certain element of metasyncrisis, though it does subject the body to considerable distress. According to others, hemorrhoids or varices are helpful because of their
8 loosening effect. The treatment of sciatica is more difficult in the case of patients who have been troubled by the disease for a long time and who show many different symptoms of it.

Now, in arranging the treatment, note the following. If the disease is of recent origin or, if chronic, is in the stage of an attack, have the patient lie on a soft bed in a warm room; withhold food and prescribe rest until the end of the first three-day period. Cover the affected parts with soft scoured wool dipped in warm sweet olive oil. Also foment the parts continuously with warm sweet olive oil, and apply a series of steamings of the kind we have often described. Perform venesection at the customary time, using the arm opposite the painful side or, if both sides are
9 affected, the arm opposite the more painful side. And if both sides are equally painful, withdraw the blood from the arm in which the vein is easier to reach. But if there is no choice in this respect either, operate on the left arm, for this arm is less essential in performing tasks for the master, unless the patient happens to be left-handed (Greek *scaeos*).

Then on the third day anoint the patient with warm sweet olive oil and wash his face. Give him nourishing food that is warm and light and thus suitable for a state of stricture; and give him warm water to drink until the attack declines. Have the patient continue to take food only on alternate days. Then, if
10 the pain abates, use the restorative treatment; but if the pain persists, at the end of the next three-day period prescribe a clyster consisting of a decoction of fenugreek seed, flaxseed, or marsh mallow (Greek *althaea*), so that the inner parts may be both fomented and steamed and thus agreeably relaxed. Then add warm olive oil, spelt water, or pearl barley water to the above; or inject olive oil alone or with an admixture of goose or

3. *Prorrhetic* ii. 8 (IX. 26 Littré).

gallinaceo iniciendum, vel his quicquam simile consolutum. ac si venter fuerit abstentus, erit mulsum iniciendum. tentanda denique et properanda sequentibus diebus facilitas ventris, quo convenit, si hoc minime perficere valuerimus, etiam linozostin herbam nunc solam cibo dare, nunc adiuncta malva, item agres-

11 tem[16] coliculum. sed fugienda praedicimus quaecumque fuerint vehementiora, quantum quidem res admittunt, ut diagridium, helleborum nigrum, chamelaeae semen, quod Graeci coccum cnidium vocant, agaricum, agrestem peponem, quem colocyntida dicunt, singularia vel coniuncta, item hieran[17] quam diascammonias appellant, ne plurima vexatio pro parva commoditate sequatur.

nam[18] post fomenta convenit cataplasmata adhibere quorum confectiones atque species saepe conscripsimus. ac si permanserit dolor, adhibenda scarificatio. hirudines etiam adhibendae,

12 quas Graeci bdellas appellant; hoc quidem secundo vel tertio faciendum si causae poposcerint. tunc vaporatio spongiarum ex aqua calida vel aliqua decoctione laxativa virtute[19] mitigantium materiarum adhibenda, quarum iam saepe species memoravimus. ex ipsis quoque encathismata facienda. item cerotaria dolentibus apponenda partibus ex oleo pingui, vel cyprino aut sicyonio, vel ex radice hibisci confecto, aut irino aut malabatrino, singularibus atque commixtis. ac si duritia emerserit, admiscendum adipem aut medullam cervinam vel bubulam aut melilotum, aut hibisci radicem percoctam[21] in mulsa ac diligenter contritam, aut decoctionem eiusdem hibisci vel faeni-

13 graeci et lini seminis triti in mellis crassitudinem[22] confecti. ac si difficile passionem declinare viderimus, erit embasis adhibenda ex oleo et aqua calidis. tum cum fuerit plurimum minutus dolor, varius offerendus est cibus ex mediae qualitatis materia. adhibendum etiam lavacrum, dehinc lene vinum; tunc malagmata partibus in passione constitutis, ut diachylon vel Mnaseu[23] aut dioxelaeu[24] vel Nileos; item unctiones quae mitiganter emolliant et neque perfrigescere partes permittant; cerotaria quoque limpida aut diasamsucu[25] acopum aut irinum oleum aut samsucinum.

---

[16] agrestem *Rm*: agreste *S*
[17] hiera *S*: *corr.* R (-am)
[18] *fort.* tunc

[19] laxativae virtutis *Rm*
[21] percocta *S*: *corr.* R
[22] crassitudine *S*: *corr.* R

[23] mnaseum *S*
[24] dioxeleum *S*
[25] diasamsucum *S*

chicken fat. Or inject any other solution similar to those mentioned. And if the bowels do not function, use mead as a clyster. On the succeeding days seek to soften the patient's bowels without delay. If this cannot be effected in any other way, it is well to give the patient the mercury plant as food, now alone, and now with the addition of mallow; wild cabbage may also be

11 given. But we urge the avoidance, so far as possible, of any strong substances, such as scammony juice, black hellebore, chamelaea seed (Greek *coccos cnidios*, 'Cnidian berry'),[4] tree fungus, wild gourd (Greek *colocynthis*), either separately or in combination, and also the hiera preparation known as the 'scammony drug.' These drugs bring slight relief at best, but they may instead cause severe distress.

After the fomentations apply those plasters whose nature and composition we have often described. And if the attack persists, employ scarification. Also make use of leeches (Greek *bdellae*),

12 applying them a second or even a third time if the case requires. Then foment the parts with sponges dipped in hot water or in some decoction that is relaxing by reason of its soothing ingredients; we have often referred above to preparations of this kind. Also use these substances for sitz baths. And to the painful parts apply cerates made with a thick oil, such as henna oil, Sicyonian olive oil, oil obtained from the root of the marsh mallow, iris oil, or malabathrum oil, separately or in combination. If a hardening appears, add the fat or marrow of deer or oxen, or else melilot or marsh mallow root cooked in hydromel and thoroughly pounded, or else a decoction of marsh mallow or of triturated fenugreek

13 seed or flaxseed brought to the consistency of honey. And if the disease shows hardly any decline, prescribe a bath in warm olive oil and water. Then, when the attack has been largely overcome, give the patient varied food of the middle class. Also prescribe bathing, then mild wine. In addition, apply emollient plasters to the parts affected by the disease; for this purpose the plaster of juices, Mnaseas' plaster, the plaster of vinegar and olive oil, or Nileus' plaster may be used. Anoint the patient with ointments that will soothe and soften the parts and prevent them from being chilled; employ also clear cerates, or the restorative ointment of marjoram, or iris oil, or oil of marjoram.

4. But cf. *Chr.* iii. 138, where Cnidian berry and chamelaea are not identified.

14   ac si passio fuerit tarditate inveterata et plurimo tempore perseverans et in lenimento constituta, si non²⁶ limpidum viderimus
lenimentum, erit pro modo permanentis doloris curationis facienda moderatio. tunc enim convenit motus quidem, sed fertorio lecto, dehinc cathedra vel sella **²⁷

** tamquam apollophanion aut diaeuphorbiu.²⁸ utile plerique
veteres huic passioni etiam macerinum²⁹ emplastrum memorant,
item icesion, usque ad quinque dies imposita linquentes laudaverunt. convenit recorporationi etiam salis³⁰ igniti vaporatio.
oportet autem saccellum lineum implere sale torrido et apponere
patientibus partibus, tunc superaspergere aquam salsam calidam, et superimponere cauteres latos aut aes³¹ igne repletum
15 congruae latitudinis. sic enim calefacto saccello instillans humor et cum fervore acerrimo decedens atque meatus³² singulos
invadens, quos Graeci poros appellant, lacessendo demutant
recorporativa sine dubio virtute. facit enim tamquam de sinapismo partium ruborem, quem Graeci phoenigmon appellant.
prodest denique etiam ex oleo rubor effectus hoc genere. farina
conspersa atque manibus exercitata quo facilior fiat, erunt partes
in passione constitutae circulatim ambiendae, cuius spatium
16 sive medium oleo replendum. tunc cauteres longi atque igniti
immittendi, qui quidem cutem tangere minime debent. hoc faciendum alterna vice donec oleum calefactum fervorem corpori
tradat. iubendum praeterea aegrotanti ut se immobilem praebeat cum oleum summo fervore caluerit,³³ ne se mutando adurat.
tentandum denique etiam cauteres sine olei motu submittere
atque levare,³⁴ supposita spongia statim ne distillatione cauteris
vicinae partes adurantur. tum cum mediocrem senserit aeger
ustionem, ei vas erit supponendum vel adiungendum, ut se repente inclinando unam faciat olei refusionem ne vicinantia usta
17 pustulentur. alii caccabuli vel vasis fictilis fundum perforantes
labia vel ora pertusurae patientibus locis adfixerunt, supradicto
more farina conspersa circumdantes. sic oleo caccabulum im-

²⁶ non *scripsi*: hoc *edd.* (*quod si retineas, scribendum esse videtur* si hoc limpidum
viderimus lenimentum, ⟨recorporativa curatio adhibenda; si autem turbidum,⟩ erit
pro modo *etc.*, *vel tale quid*

²⁷ *v. Chr. iii. 133, 155 adnn.*

²⁸ diaeuphorbiũ *S*   ³⁰ solis *S: corr. R*

²⁹ macerinos *S: corr. R*   ³¹ aes *conieci*: ex *S*

³² meatus *Rm* (*cf. Orib. Lat., p. 33. 7 Mørland*): artus *S*

³³ caluerit *Rm*: coierit *S*   ³⁴ lavare *S: corr. Rm*

14   Now if the disease becomes chronic and lasts over a long period of time, then, during a remission, unless it is found to be a
complete remission, modify the treatment in accordance with
the degree of pain that persists. And at this time passive exercise is suitable, the patient being carried on a couch and afterward in a sedan chair.

. . . [apply plasters] such as that of Apollophanes or the plaster of spurge. Most of the earlier physicians consider the plaster
of Macer beneficial in this disease; they also refer to a plaster of
Hicesius, and they prescribe that these applications be left on as
long as five days. Hot applications with heated salt also help
along metasyncrisis. Fill a linen bag with hot salt and apply it to
the affected parts. Then pour hot salt water over the bag and
place on top of it broad cauteries or copper of suitable width,
15   thoroughly heated. For in this way the bag will be heated and a
burning hot liquid will drip onto the parts and enter the several
pores[5] (Greek *poroe*); the consequent irritation will alter the
character [of these pores], since the fluid obviously has metasyncritic properties. For, like a mustard plaster, it causes a reddening of the parts (Greek *phoenigmos*). Also beneficial is the irritation produced with olive oil in the following way: Moisten some
flour and soften it by kneading; then place it in a circle around
the parts affected by the disease and fill the central space with
16   olive oil. Next take a long cautery, heat it in fire, and immerse it
in the oil; but do not let it touch the skin. Use a second cautery
in alternation with the first until the heated oil transmits its
warmth to the body. And have the patient keep perfectly still
to avoid burning himself in changing his position when the oil is
very hot. Try also to immerse and withdraw the cautery without causing any motion of the oil; and just as the cautery is
withdrawn, hold a sponge beneath it to prevent the neighboring
parts from being burned by drops of oil from the instrument.
Then when the patient feels a slight burning, place a vessel next
to the oil pool so that the latter may be drained all at once by a
swift bending on the patient's part; this will prevent the burn-
17   ing and blistering of the neighboring parts. Some physicians
make use of a small earthen pot. They make a hole in the base,
fix the lips or mouth of this opening over the affected parts,
place moistened flour around the parts, as described above, and
then fill the vessel with oil; they carry out the rest of the pro-

5. Or 'joints,' if *artus* (*S*) be retained. But this would hardly fit *poroe*.

pleverunt, cetera supradicto ordine gerentes. alii usque ad ustionem vaporibus igneis usi sunt. alii diversis generibus pustulationem locorum faciendam probaverunt, vel extemplo escharas
patientibus ingesserunt partibus, aliquando solo sinapi cataplasmantes quo superficies cutis pustulescat.[35] item sinapi admiscentes glebae calcis aequis ponderibus et sulphuris partem
atque simul conterentes, parvo oleo et aqua admixta, linteolo
18 illita, prostrato alio linteolo tenui eidem parti quam curamus
superimponemus illitum, quo sensim atque per triplicem materiam transiens vis medicaminis pustulationem faciat loci.
item non aliter etiam ex cinere salicis haec facere poterimus.
eius enim corticem inurentes atque ex eius cinere pulvisculum
facientes, in umbra siccari sinimus. tunc locis praeulceratis ad-
ponimus superdistillantes liquefactam calcem, quam vulgo cola-
tam vocant, sed paulatim. cum enim fuerint humectati pulvis-
culi cutis superficiem pustulabunt: quod si quisquam plurimum
perseveraverit, etiam altiora inusta putrescunt et, ut Graeci
appellant, escharam faciunt.
19 alii denique ex radice herbae quam struthium vocant loca ul-
cerari praecipiunt. usta etenim radix, concepta flamma, cuti
apposita pustulationem necessario facit. sed alii hanc ustionem
tamquam imbecillem reprobantes cauteribus aiunt faciendam,
quos quidem primo tepidos probant apponendos donec cutis
pustuletur, tunc igneos. sed his omnibus interiecto spatio trium
digitorum loca dicunt inurenda, et esse cauteres semper aduncos
in modum gamma literae.
sed alii hanc appositionem metuentes ancistris ex utraque
parte cutem praetendunt, et inter ea[36] cauteres imponunt, ne
20 ulla ustione nervi tangantur. alii ligneos fungos inferius[37] ac
superius angustos formantes patientibus apponunt locis, quos
summitate accensos sinunt concremari donec cinerescant atque

[35] pustulescant S: corr. R
[36] ea Rm: eos S
[37] inferius Rm: interius S

---

6. The abrupt change of subject may mean either (1) that the Methodists here
adopt a treatment that had been used by others or (2) that Soranus is quoting directly
from the works of another author and that Caelius, as often in such cases, keeps the
first person.

cedure in the manner indicated above. Others use hot steam to the point of burning. Still others prescribe measures to cause the skin to blister in various ways at the affected parts; or they quickly produce scabs in these parts. Sometimes they use a plain mustard plaster to cause blistering at the surface of the skin. Again, we[6] mix equal weights of mustard and quicklime and add a part of sulphur, rubbing up all the ingredients together, adding a little olive oil and water, and smearing the preparation on a

18 linen cloth. First, however, we lay another thin linen cloth over the part being treated, and then place over that cloth the cloth containing the preparation. In this way the strength of the drug can only gradually penetrate the substantial covering and cause blistering in the area. It is also possible to produce the same effect with willow ashes. Thus, burn the bark of this tree and powder the ashes, allowing them to dry in the shade. Then scarify the parts and apply the ashes, letting lime in liquid solution (Latin *colata*, 'filtered') fall drop by drop upon the parts. But use only a little liquid at one time, for when the ashes are moistened they cause the surface of the skin to blister, and if one prolongs this treatment, he will burn the deeper parts, too, and cause them to rot away, forming a scab (Greek *eschara*).

19 Some physicians use the root of the plant called *struthion* ['soapwort'] as a means of causing the skin to blister, holding that when the root embraces the flame and is burnt, its application to the skin must produce a blistering irritation. But others reject this method of burning the skin as ineffectual, and hold that cauteries should be used. First, they prescribe the application of warm cauteries until the skin is blistered, and they follow this with fiery hot cauteries. And they hold that in all cases the points of application of the cauteries should be at intervals of three digits, and that the cauteries should be curved in the form of the letter gamma.

Others, however, distrust this method of using cauteries; they first stretch the skin on both sides with hooks, applying the cauteries between these hooks. Their purpose is to avoid subjecting

20 the sinews[7] to any burning. Some take woody fungi and cut them down from above and below to narrow proportions; they then place them over the affected parts, and permit them to take fire

7. I.e., the sensitive fibers beneath the skin. The term *nervi*, as frequently, seems to include loosely the fibers of nerves, muscles, and tendons.

sponte decidant. est enim haec ustio leni penetratione moderata.

item alii linteolum aqua tingentes partibus resimplicatum[38] apponunt. tunc tabulam tiliarem[39] apponentes, struthium herbam concidunt in breves particulas,[39a] ac deinde ferramento igneo singulas partes oleo tingentes accensas imponunt tabulae scilicet tiliari,[40] hoc secundo vel tertio facientes per intervalla donec materia carbonescat atque pustulas cutis efficiat.

21 item alii, ex quibus sunt Demetrii sectatores, eius partis quae patitur manum inter pollicem et demonstrativum digitum, quem Graeci lichanon sive dicticon,[41] iuxta inferiorem articulum involutis inurunt cauteribus, quos quidem nunc nudae cuti apponunt, nunc praemisso linteolo oleo tinctos. modum autem ustionis constituunt cum in alia manu, hoc est quae sit contraria parti patienti, sudor emergens apparuerit. tum post supradictas ustiones imperant ulcera reservata[42] in saniem provocari. alii

22 denique statim lana sucida eadem contexerunt loca; alii marrubii coma contrita cum sale vel oliva nigra aut sesamo infuso sive nucibus, tum tertia die lenticula multa atque mulso decocta, donec ulceris cadat eschara. tunc oenomeli aiunt imponendum, vel ea quae valeant lacessendo puris exitum provocare. item florem aeris cum nigro helleboro apponunt. et quidem aliqui relevantur intervenientis recorporationis causa; sed quoniam istiusmodi ustionibus plurima vexatio coniuncta est, erit melius aliis adiutoriis mederi.

ausi sunt praeterea quidam etiam venerem adhibere in his qui non ex usu venereo ischiadici facti videntur, quo magis vexata nervositas geminet causam.

23 item alii cantelenas adhibendas probaverunt, ut etiam Philistionis frater idem memorat libro XXII De adiutoriis, scribens quendam fistulatorem loca dolentia decantasse, quae cum saltum sumerent palpitando discusso dolore mitescerent. alii

---

[38] reduplicatum *Rm, sed cf. Chr. iii. 134, Cael. Aur. Gyn. ii. 7, 86, 88*

[39] tabulae tiliari *S: corr. Rm*

[39a] perticulas *edd.*

[40] tiliari *Rm*: tiliae *S*

[41] dicticon ⟨appellant⟩ *R*

[42] reserata *Rm*

---

8. Cf. *Chr.* i. 116 n.

9. Cf. Theophrastus Frag. 87 (Wimmer) = Aulus Gellius iv. 13. 1–2. See *Chr.* i. 175–76, 178.

on top and to burn until they are reduced to ashes and fall off by themselves. Now cauterization by this method is less violent because of the gradualness of the penetration.

Others, again, dip a linen cloth in water, spread it out, and place it on the affected parts. They then place a flat piece of linden wood over the parts. Now they cut up some soapwort into small pieces, dip them in olive oil, and kindle them with a fiery hot iron. Then they place these pieces one by one over the covering, i.e., the linden tablet. This is repeated a second or third time at intervals until the wood is reduced to charcoal and the skin is blistered.

21   Others, including the followers of Demetrius, cauterize the hand on the side affected; they burn it between the thumb and the forefinger (Greek *lichanos* or *deicticos*) alongside the lower joint. For this purpose they use covered cauteries; sometimes they apply these to the unprotected skin, but at other times they first cover the skin with linen dipped in olive oil. They terminate the burning as soon as sweat appears on the other hand, that is, the one opposite the side affected. Then after this cauterization they keep the wounds open and cause them to exude sanies.

22   Some at once cover these parts with unscoured wool, others with a preparation of horehound tops rubbed up with salt, black olives, sesame juice, or nuts. Then on the third day they freely use a decoction of lentils in mead until the scab falls off. After this they prescribe an application of honey wine or any other preparation that will by its irritant action induce the flow of pus; they also apply chalcanthum[8] mixed with black hellebore. And such a treatment, to be sure, relieves many patients by reason of a metasyncrisis which takes place. But, since cauterizations of this kind cause the patient considerable distress, it will be better to use other treatments.

Again, some physicians even go so far as to prescribe venery in those cases of sciatica which do not appear to have been caused by venery. But such a treatment upsets the system of nerves and sinews even more, and only aggravates the disease.

23   Other physicians prescribe music,[9] as the brother of Philistion tells us in Book XXII of his work *On Remedies*. He writes that a certain piper would play his instrument over the affected parts and that these would begin to throb and palpitate, banishing the pain and bringing relief. And some hold that it was Pythag-

denique hoc adiutorii genus Pithagoram memorant invenisse. sed Sorani iudicio videntur hi mentis vanitate iactari qui modulis et cantilena passionis robur excludi posse crediderunt.

item plurimi ex talo atque ancala eiusdem partis quae fuerit passione possessa venam dividentes sanguinem detraxerunt. sed magis partes impletae gravantur, cum repente vacuata loca in semet materiae fluxum invitant.

24   nobilium vero principum Hippocrates libro quo De locis conscripsit cucurbitam iubet sine scarificatione apponi. utitur etiam ferventibus medicaminibus potis, quae si essent vere congrua passioni, minime tamen ad excludendam vetustatem valere crederentur.

Diocles libro quo De passionibus atque causis et curationibus scripsit, item secundo libro De curationibus, regulam dixit siccam et frigidam et nutribilem aegris convenire, cum humida at-
25 que calida prodesse huic passioni demonstraverimus. utitur etiam urinalibus medicamentis, quae diuretica appellavit, et probat conditum bibendum, quod plerique Latini[43] mulsum vocant. utitur etiam cibo e visceribus asinorum, et clysteribus sanguinem provocantibus, et vino nunc albo, nunc nigro, neque ordinis neque temporum neque congruae qualitatis memor.

item Themison secundo libro Tardarum passionum in quibusdam peccare perspicitur, phlebotomans talum vel ancalen, atque lanis sucidis cum oleo et aceto et sale statim patientia contegens loca, articulos astringens et intestina per clysterem exul-
26 cerans et os ipsum quod ischion Graeci vocant. ante haec omnia et equitare imperat aegrotantes, quo magis ob vehementiam motus partium faciat vexationem. item alternis sinapizat diebus, quod est immoderatum. et in omnibus ulcerationem cutis existimat faciendam, qua plurima congrua prohibentur adiutoria adhiberi, cum partes ulceratae apposita tolerare non possint.

---

[43] latine *Kalbfleisch* (*v. Wellmann, Diocles Frag. 77*)

---

10. *On Places in Man* 22 (VI. 314 Littré).

11. I.e., to prevent future attacks.

12. For *conditum* and *mulsum* see Isid. *Orig.* xx. 3. 9, 10. *Mulsum* is regularly used by Caelius to translate Greek *melicraton* ('diluted honey,' 'mead').

oras who discovered this kind of treatment. But in the opinion of Soranus anyone who believes that a severe disease can be banished by music and song is the victim of a silly delusion.

Again, many physicians withdraw blood by venesection at the ankle and the bend of the knee on the same side as that affected by the disease. But the parts in question only become more congested and weighed down, for on suddenly being emptied they draw a flow of matter to themselves.

24   Among the famous physicians, Hippocrates in his book *On Places*[10] employs cupping without scarification. He also prescribes the drinking of hot drugs. But even if these measures were really suitable in [an attack of] this disease, they would still, in our opinion, prove quite inadequate to overcome the disease in its chronic form.[11]

Diocles in his book *On Diseases and Their Causes and Treatment* as well as in Book II of his *Treatments* declares that a dry, cold, and nourishing diet is suitable for the patients, though we have shown that moisture and warmth are beneficial in this dis-
25 ease. Diocles also prescribes drugs to promote urination (Greek *diurētica*); and he recommends the taking of the mixed drink commonly called *mulsum* in Latin.[12] He uses food prepared from the viscera of asses and employs clysters to induce the flow of blood. And he prescribes white wine at certain times and dark wine at other times, but indicates neither the precise order in which they are to be taken nor the precise times nor what type of wine is suitable.

Themison, too, in Book II of his *Chronic Diseases* is clearly in error on certain points. Thus he performs venesection at the ankle or the bend of the knee and immediately covers the affected parts with unscoured wool together with olive oil, vinegar, and salt. But in so doing he constricts the joints; and by administering clysters he damages the intestines and the hip joint
26 itself (Greek *ischion*). Indeed, before all these treatments he has the patient do some riding; but the vigorous motion in riding only adds to the irritation of the parts. Again, he applies mustard plasters every other day, which is excessive. And in all cases he prescribes that the skin be irritated to the point of ulceration; but he thereby makes impossible the use of many beneficial remedies, since the skin when ulcerated cannot endure the application of these remedies.

Thessalus vero vaporationem faciendam improbe recusavit: est enim recorporativae virtutis. neque initio recte constrictiva probat adhibenda: etenim ischiadica passio vehementi atque difficili strictura confecta perspicitur.

27 II. DE ARTICULORUM PASSIONE, QUAM GRAECI ARTHRITIN VOCANT, ET DE PEDUM DOLORE, QUEM PODAGRAM APPELLANT

UTRAQUE passio a parte corporis quae patitur nomen accepit: altera communiter ab articulis omnibus, altera specialiter a pedibus. sed podagram Graeci etiam ab impedimento vel retentione pedum aiunt nominatam, vel a ferali dolore, siquidem omne quod immite fuerit abusive agreste vocamus.

earum denique passionum discretio promptissima atque manifesta esse perspicitur. nam podagra pedum tantummodo dolor est; arthritis vero etiam cunctorum articulorum sive multorum,
28 et aliquando a pedibus sumens dolor exordium ceteros articulos implicavit, aliquando in aliis incipiens pedes invasit. nam quidam medici arthriticam passionem genus vocant, podagricam vero speciem. etenim podagra etiam arthritis[1] recte nuncupatur, siquidem sit in articulis dolor, quamquam in pedibus constitutus. arthritis vero non ilico podagra dici potest, siquidem genua vel manus tenens gonagra aut chiragra, vel tenontagra dicatur,[2] si maiores tenuerit nervos. sed de his nominibus quae locorum causa discreta videntur, unius tamen esse virtutis intelligantur,[3] in curationibus certandum non est.
29 sunt enim harum passionum antecedentes causae variae, ut vinolentia, frigus profundum, cruditatio, libido venerea, labor immodicus, vel repentina desertio solitae exercitationis in ante actum[4] morem, aut rursum non ex infantia sed secunda et sera aetate affecta, cum mollibus nervis atque insuetis fuerit illata quassatio, item percussio antecedens ex palaestrae[5] forti exercitio.

[1] podagra etiam arthritis *scripsi*: quod Graecis hamartritis *S*: podagra Graecis arthritis *Rm*

[2] dicatur *scripsi*: dici potest *S*: dicitur *R* (*post* chiragra)

[3] intelliguntur *R*

[4] actem *S*: corr. *R*

[5] palaestrae *scripsi*: palaestra *S*: palaestra ⟨vel⟩ *Rm*

And Thessalus errs in rejecting the use of steaming, for steaming has a metasyncritic effect. He is also wrong in prescribing astringent measures at the commencement of the disease. For sciatica obviously involves a strong state of stricture, which is not easily overcome.

7 II. DISEASE OF THE JOINTS (GREEK *ARTHRITIS*) AND OF THE FEET (GREEK *PODAGRA*)

EACH of these diseases derives its name from the part of the body that is affected, the former from all the joints generally, the latter from the feet in particular. Now the Greeks say that *podagra* gets its name from the trapping or seizure of the feet,[1] or else as a 'wild' disease, since we metaphorically apply the term 'wild' (*agreste*) to everything that is unsubdued.

The distinction between the two diseases is, of course, very clear and obvious. For podagra is a disease only of the feet, while arthritis is a disease of all the joints or of several of them. 8 Arthritis sometimes begins at the feet and later involves other joints; while sometimes it begins in other joints and later attacks the feet. Thus some physicians call arthritis the general class and podagra a species of the class. And, indeed, podagra is properly considered a form of arthritis, for it is an affection of the joints, but with special reference to the feet. On the other hand, arthritis cannot simply be identified with podagra, for arthritis may affect the knees or the hands, and in these cases is called either *gonagra* or *cheiragra;* or it may affect the large sinews [of the neck], in which case it is called *tenontagra*. But in a discussion of treatments we need not argue about these names; indeed, though the diseases referred to are differentiated according to place, clearly they are all of the same general type.

9 These diseases have various antecedent causes, e.g., excessive drinking of wine, extreme cold, indigestion, immoderate sexual lust, excessive physical exertion, the sudden abandonment of exercise to which the individual had been long accustomed, or, again, the taking-up of exercise not in early years but subsequently and even late in life, with consequent shock to weak sinews unused to the strain, and, finally, any previous injury received in wrestling or other violent exercise.

1. Greek *agra*, 'hunting'; *agreō*, 'seize.'

frequentat autem in viris magis atque mediis aetatibus, difficile vero in mulieribus atque in eunuchis et pueris et iuvenibus fieri invenitur. videtur praeterea plurimis antiquis medicis etiam genuino cursu in posteros migrare cum semine, et propterea succedentes invadere, de qua re principaliter Responsionum docuimus libris. item per aliquas probatur frequentare regiones, ut Cariam et Alexandriam Aegypti vicinam;[6] nec non temporibus certis nasci, item magis asperari videtur, ut primo verno, secundo autumno, tertio hieme, aestate vero difficile.

sequitur autem passione articulari tentatos torpor atque formicatio eorum articulorum qui tanguntur, et difficilis flexio atque rursum extentio, item gravedo et vacandi dulcedo, et ad parvum motum vehemens labor, atque dormientibus sensus quidam resonantium articulorum. et cum de somno surrexerint veluti saltu earundem partium afficiuntur. tum horror vel rigor atque tremor sine ulla manifesta ratione partium sequentur.

dehinc cum passio se extollere coeperit, in podagricis dolor alterius pedis aut utriusque cum punctionibus nascetur, incipiens a vestigio aut plantae cavitate vel saepius a maiore digito, attestante torpore et gravedine et difficili motu, cum horrore rigido atque inaequali per membra, et aliquando plurimo fervore, aliquando frigore, ut alii refrigerantia, alii calida desiderent aegrotantes. et propterea quidam alteram calidam, alteram frigidam podagram putaverunt nuncupandam.

item initio, ut saepe contigit, similis color patientium atque sanarum videtur partium attestante aequalitate, nullo emergente tumore. dehinc inflatio partium fiet cum rubore; quapropter relevatio altiorum saepe sequetur. tum peiorante passione arthritica sufficitur passio, cum in unum omnium cogitur articulorum consensus, et facile ex articulo in articulum venit

[6] *fort.* ⟨et⟩ Aegypti viciniam

---

2. Cf. Corp. Hipp. *Aphorisms* vi. 28–30.

3. 'Near Egypt,' according to the text. Perhaps an alteration in the text is required: 'Alexandria and the neighboring parts of Egypt.'

This type of disease is most commonly found among men of middle age; it is least common among females, eunuchs, boys, and young men.[2] Again, many physicians of the past have believed that the disease was inherited and that it passed successively from generation to generation with the seed. We have given special attention to this question in our work entitled *Answers*. The disease seems to occur commonly in certain regions, e.g., Caria, and Alexandria in Egypt.[3] It also seems that cases originate and become exacerbated at certain seasons of the year more frequently than at others, i.e., principally in the spring, then in autumn, thirdly in winter, and least often in summer.

Those who are on the verge of an attack of disease of the joints experience numbness and a creeping irritation at the affected joints, together with difficulty in bending and again in straightening out the members in question. There is a feeling of heaviness and a desire to rest, severe distress resulting even from slight movement. The patient's sleep is troubled by a sensation of creaking joints, and when he awakes from sleep he experiences a sort of throbbing in these same parts, together with a stiffening or rigor and a trembling of the parts without any obvious reason.

Then in cases of podagra, when the disease begins to emerge, a piercing pain develops in one or both feet. This pain begins in the hollow of the sole of the foot or even more commonly in the big toe, and is accompanied by numbness, heaviness, difficulty in movement, and a stiffening of various parts. In some cases there is a feeling of intense heat, in others of intense cold. Thus some patients need cool remedies, others hot. And for this reason some physicians have held the opinion that one type of podagra should be called 'hot' podagra and the other 'cold.'

At the beginning of the disease it often happens that the affected parts appear of the same color as the corresponding sound parts and maintain their symmetry with the latter. That is, no swelling appears at first. But later the parts become red and swollen, and the deeper parts are often, in consequence, relieved. Then as the disease becomes worse, a general arthritic condition develops, the affection of all the joints being concentrated upon one at a time, so that the pain passes successively from joint to joint and does not abate until it has entered every

dolor nec desinens priusquam cunctos invaserit nodos. saepe
denique prioris articuli dolore declinante secundus invaditur,
atque eodem similiter mitescente tertius sumit exordium, con-
sentiente etiam vesica atque spinae maioribus nervis, quos tenontas appellant, et in stomacho etiam nausea vel vomitu iactantur aegrotantes. tunc articuli tumentes inflantur ac deinde
durescunt et solidati saxeam faciunt qualitatem. tum etiam ni-
33 griores efficiuntur atque contorti, ut in obliquas partes digiti
vertantur aut reflexi supinentur aut vicinis adfixi incumbant, et
aliquando humore purulento vel mucilento collecto aut viscoso
generent poros, quos nos transitus[7] dicere poterimus.[8] dehinc
etiam lapides sufficiant,[9] qui quidem articulos solvant et cutem
distendant atque erumpentes promineant, et chirurgia detrahantur aut exilientes cyathisco[10] ferramento[11] tollantur, quod
nos laureolum dicere poterimus, et rursum renascantur. tum
crura[12] dolentium partium cessante nutrimento tenuata lan-
guescunt et arida efficiuntur. erunt praeterea aegrotantes parvis ex causis mobiles atque iracundi, siquidem motum vel actum
non sine querela accipiant.

34 principaliter autem haec passio constituitur in nervis vel
eorum colligationibus; tum cetera morbo consentiunt atque con-
tiguos vel superpositos lacertos et maiores nervos pati demonstrant. est praeterea passio non facilis curatione et aliquando
magnitudine insanabilis, non ut plerique putant natura.[13] causae autem difficillimae curationis, vel ut saepe contingit impossibilis, manifestae atque plurimae reperiuntur. est enim passio in
nervis constituta qui sint natura densissimi et inter articulorum
nodos constituti, quorum angustia comprimuntur et ad omnem
motum asperantur; magis in pedibus, hi enim plurimas conliga-
tiones nodorum naturaliter habent, et totum corpus sustinendo
35 laborant.[14] praeterea haec passio initio parvitatis causa negli-
gitur et contempta convalescit, quippe cum a multis minime

[7] tophos *Rm*

[8] *fort.* generetur poros quem nos tofum dicere poterimus

[9] sufficiuntur *Rm: fort.* sufficiantur

[10] cyathisco *Reinesius 673:* cyathis quo *S*

[11] ferramenti *S: corr. R*

[12] membra *R*

[13] naturae *S: corr. Rm*

[14] laborat *S: corr. Rm*

single one of them. Thus it often happens that as the pain in one joint is subsiding, a second is attacked, and as the pain in the latter similarly abates, it begins in a third. There is also concomitant pain in the bladder and in the great sinews of the back (Greek *tenontes*); and the patient is affected by nausea and vomiting. The joints then become inflamed and swollen, and later harden and solidify, assuming a stony character. They then also

33 take on a darker color and become twisted. Thus the toes and fingers are either turned sideways, or bent over backwards, or rest immovably upon their neighbors. Sometimes a purulent, slimy, or sticky fluid gathers, producing channels (Latin *transitus*, 'passages');[4] then stones develop that dislocate the joints and distend the skin, and then burst through and jut out. These are removed surgically, or, upon appearing, are merely lifted out with a spoon-shaped instrument (Greek *cyathiscus*, which we may translate by the Latin *laureolum*), though later they grow again. In addition, the limbs containing the affected joints become weak, attenuated, and dry. And the patients are upset and irritated by little things, for they cannot perform any movement or action without pain.

34 While the disease is centered chiefly in the fibers[5] and sinews, the pressure of concomitant pains elsewhere is an indication that adjoining muscles as well as the major tendons[6] are also affected. And this disease is not easy to treat; in fact, it is sometimes incurable by reason of its extent, though not, as is generally held, by reason of its nature. And there are many obvious reasons why the cure is quite difficult and frequently impossible. For one thing, the disease centers in those cords that are naturally thickest and are situated between joints in the various members. The narrowness of the joints constricts these cords, and every movement aggravates the irritation. This is particularly true of the feet, for they naturally have a large number of connecting sinews at the joints, and have the burden of supporting the weight of

35 the whole body. Again, this disease is often neglected at first as something unimportant, and while thus ignored it gathers

4. If *transitus* be the correct reading, we have here a confusion between *pŏros* ('passage') and *pōros* ('chalkstone'), whether due to a faulty text of Soranus or a misunderstanding on Caelius' part. It is tempting to correct the text, but the type of confusion here represented is not impossible.

5. The term may here include nerve, tendon, and muscle fibers.

6. I.e., of the back and shoulders.

credatur emergere. alii denique digiti luxati, aliqui pedis ver-
sionem, aliqui cuiusdam rei calcatae vel offensae duritiam aut
fervorem queruntur. tum necessitate coacti, augmenti temporibus in confessionem veniunt aegrotantes. ob hoc igitur passio
perseverare atque corpora possidere meditatur; non autem minus etiam longorum lenimentorum causa, quibus recessisse putatur, cum sanos aegrotantes fingendo promittit, adiuvante
etiam intemperantia, qua cum saepe concipi passio perspicitur,
manere posse non dubitatur.

36   **[15] quod dicam diatrito. si venter officium non agnoverit,
clyster adhibendus simplex. atque ita totius passionis statu
accepto ut inflata vel tumentia loca videantur, scarificatio adhibenda, et ubi permiserint partes cucurbita figenda vel hirudines
admovendae. est autem omnium levior praeter cucurbitam
scarificatio, siquidem nulla quassatio partium fiet,[16] quae necessario cucurbitae coniuncta est. item hirudinum morsibus consensus adiungitur, et propterea, ut supra dictum est, simplex
scarificatio[17] lenius[18] probatur. adhibenda etiam vaporatio
spongiarum, tum aquae calidae fomentatio, vel aqua et oleo, aut
37 decoctionis faenigraeci aut lini seminis vel hibisci; item cataplasma mitigativum, quod iamdudum minime posse adhibere
videbatur, siquidem tumentia pondere gravari non debeant.[19]
sit igitur panis diligentius emollitus solus aut admixta radice
argallici, quod Graeci symphyton vocant, vel hibisci decocta vel
cuiusquam similis virtutis quorum probavimus adhibendas vaporationes.

tum cum firma declinatio fuerit constituta, adhibenda lavacra
atque varius cibus et aqua potu danda. et propter passionis ne-
quitiam adhibenda etiam cerotaria ex oleo dulci vel cyprino, aut
ex adipe confectum medicamen, quod Graeci diasteaton vocant;
tunc malagma diachylon vel Mnaseu[20] aut quod appellant dia-
38 teleos vel dioxelaeu[21] vel diathalasses. tum[22] paulatim fortifican-
dum corpus deambulatione liberis calciamento pedibus, et cum
cautione adversantium rerum, ut ne quid nimis, maxime vini

[15] *lacunam indicavit Sm*
[16] fiat *Helmreich 185*: fit *R*
[17] scarificatio *Rm*: conflatio *S*: *an* curatio (*cf. 38*) *vel* detractio?
[18] lenior *Rm*   [20] mnaseū *S*
[19] *fort.* deberent   [21] dioxeleon *S* (-eum *R*)
[22] diathalasses. tum *Friedel 27*: diathalassestum *edd.*

strength. In fact, in many cases the patients are not aware of its development. Thus they complain of hardness or a burning sensation, ascribing it to the dislocation of a toe, or to the wrenching of a foot, or to the fact that they have stepped on or stumbled over some object; but during attacks they come perforce to realize the true state of affairs. These, then, are the reasons why this disease is supposed to have so persistent a hold upon the body. No less important, however, is the fact that the intervals between attacks are long, and it is therefore erroneously supposed that the disease is over and the patient cured.[7] Moreover, the intemperance, which seems in many cases to have given rise to the disease, may doubtless remain with the patient.

6   . . . on the third day. If the bowels do not function, use a simple clyster. And at the peak of the whole disease, when the affected parts appear swollen and inflamed, employ scarification, and, if the parts can endure it, apply cupping or leeches. The use of scarification without cupping is the mildest procedure, since it causes no such disturbance of the parts as is always involved when cupping is employed. And, since the bite of leeches also produces concomitant pain, simple scarification is a milder procedure. Also apply heat with sponges, and foment with hot water, olive oil and water, or a decoction of fenugreek seed,

37 flaxseeed, or marsh mallow. And now a soothing plaster may be employed. (This was previously not possible, because it was necessary to avoid burdening the inflamed parts with the weight.) For the plaster employ thoroughly softened bread, either alone or with the addition of boiled comfrey root (Greek *symphyton*), or marsh mallow root, or any similar substance among those recommended for use in steaming.

Then, when the decline of the disease is fully corroborated, prescribe baths and give the patient varied food to eat, and water to drink. And because of the stubborn character of the disease employ cerates made with sweet olive oil or henna oil, or the drug prepared with fat (Greek *diasteatōn*). Then, too, employ the emollient plaster of juices, or that of Mnaseas, or the so-called 'plaster of fenugreek,' or of vinegar and olive oil, or of

38 sea water. Then have the patient strengthen his body by walking without shoes and by avoiding anything which might be harmful, that is to say, excesses of any kind, particularly of wine,

7. The text is uncertain here, but the general meaning seems clear.

aut indigestionis aut veneris. arthriticis vero convenit etiam digitis ceram emolliendam dare, vel manipulos tenendos, quos palaestritae alteres appellant, tum movendos, cereos vel ligneos, primo cum parvo plumbo interfuso, tum pro modo profectus graviores.

et intardante[23] passione superpositionis tempore supradicta servanda simplicitas curationis. in lenimento vero adhibenda fortificatio, tum recorporatio. sit igitur primo gestatio pro modo virium, tum deambulatio molli stramine coaequato solo, adiecto

39 vocis exercitio cum corporis unctione. etenim vacatio crassificat corpora; adeo etiam et[24] in his qui ex aliis forte plurimo tempore iacuerint causis, hac ratione articuli commoveantur, cum nervi non exerciti invalidiores[25] efficiuntur.[26] adhibenda etiam lavacra per intervalla dierum, et varius cibus ex mediae materiae qualitate, vinum parvum lene et semper post cibum, tum dropax simplex atque compositus, paroptesis ex igni vel ex sole atque pellibus fervefactis et ex arena littoris, tum aspergines, quas Graeci sympasmata vocant, ex nitro et adarce et euphorbio et saepe memoratis speciebus, tum unguenta et acopa ex squilla

40 confecta et agresti cucumere, item euphorbio et adarce. dehinc malagma adhibendum, ut est quod appellant diahalon aut diadaphnidon aut diadarces aut diastactes conias vel quicquam similium. item rubor cutis ex sinapi faciendus, quem Graeci phoenigmon appellant; item drimyphagia et cyclorum regula et radicum vomitus et hellebori et embasis facienda, sicut de ischiadicis scribentes memoravimus; vel fomentatio ex decoctione artemisiae herbae aut marinae ferventis aquae, dehinc natatio fervens vel frigida. item usus adhibendus aquarum naturalium calidarum, tum frigidarum, ut sunt in Italia quae appellatae

41 sunt albulae vel cotiliae. et omnium supradictorum affectanda repetitio. dabit enim curatio aliis integram sanitatem, aliis raram doloris admonitionem, ne iugi superpositione vexentur. veterum quidam annalia medicamina potanda probaverunt,

[23] in tardante *edd.*

[24] ut *Rm*

[25] validiores *S*: *corr. Rm*

[26] efficiantur *Rm*

---

8. Cf. 12–13, above.

indigestion, and venery. In cases of arthritis it is well to give the patient wax to knead with the fingers, or weights, which athletes call *haltēres*, to hold in the hands and afterward to swing. These wax or wooden weights should at first have only a little lead inserted; later, as the patient improves, they should be made heavier.

If the disease becomes chronic, then during periods of exacerbation adhere to the simple treatment described above. And in the intervals of remission strengthen the body and then apply metasyncritic treatments. Thus first prescribe passive exercise with due regard to the patient's strength, and then prescribe walking on ground strewn evenly with soft straw, and, in addi-
39 tion, vocal exercise and anointing of the body. For lack of exercise makes bodies thick; and, in fact, even in other diseases, when a patient has been sick a long while, the joints are affected for the reason that the sinews have become weakened through lack of exercise. Also prescribe baths at intervals of some days, and give the patient varied food of the middle class, and only a little mild wine, in all cases after the food. In addition, use pitch plasters, simple and composite, and apply intense heat, using fire or the heat of the sun, together with hot skins or hot beach sand. Also employ dusting powders (Greek *sympasmata*) of nitrum, adarce, spurge, and other substances to which we have often referred; and, in addition, ointments and restorative lini-
40 ments made with squill, wild cucumber, spurge, and adarce. And apply an emollient plaster, such as the so-called 'plaster of salts,' the bayberry plaster, or those plasters made with adarce, lye, and the like. Again, use mustard to irritate the skin to redness (Greek *phoenigmos*). And prescribe the acrid diet, the cyclic regimen, the use of radishes and hellebore to induce vomiting, and baths such as we described in the chapter on sciatica.[8] Or foment the body with a decoction of wormwood or hot sea water; and then have the patient swim in hot or cold water. Also prescribe the use of natural springs, both hot and cold, e.g., the Albulan
41 or Cutilian springs in Italy. And keep repeating these prescriptions, for the treatment will in some cases bring about a complete restoration of health, and in others it will help to make the recurrence of an attack infrequent and thus save the patient from the pain of continual attacks.

Some of the ancient physicians have the patient take such

ut est quod appellant diacentaurion, item diascordeon,[26a] bibendum anno continuo iudicantes in his qui non plurimo tempore
fuerint passione vitiati, hoc est intra quinquennii tempus constitutis,[27] adicientes quod bibi debeat medicamen praedigesto
corpore et omnino nullo obstaculo impedito; sin minus, reprae-
sentandum numerum dierum, quo integer compleatur annus,
42 quamquam longo tempore porrectus. secundum nos autem,
iuxta Sorani iudicium, est metuenda diuturna medicaminis
sumptio, cum neque soliti cibi iuges, atque iidem utiles, recte
probentur. sic denique legimus quosdam veteres memorasse ex
iugi medicamine poto in celeres vel acutas venisse passiones, et
alios apoplectos, alios pleureticos, alios peripleumonicos inter-
isse, item quosdam continua difficultate spirationis affectos,
quam Graeci dyspnoean vocant. hi vero qui se isto medicamine
profecisse testantur non advertunt servatae digestionis causa id
fuisse permissum, quippe cum ceterarum rerum excessus declinando, quidam servaverint sanitatem, cum interrumpere me-
43 tuerint sumptionem medicaminis sui, et propterea his intentionibus occupati alias sibi nesciverint profuisse rationes.

item alii ustionem nodorum faciendam probant, quam nos
reprobamus siquidem consensus faciat tumorem. item alii
transeundum ex aliis in alia probant ungenta et cataplasmata,
nunc specie, nunc genere differentia, donec aegrotantes releventur, siquidem alia pro aliis corporibus videantur convenire, et
propterea doloris mitigatio sequetur. ordinaverunt denique
etiam contrarias virtute materias, laxativas simul atque constrictivas et recorporativas, ut Mnaseu[28] malagma vel diachy-
44 lon; item e contrariis vehementius constringentia, ut diaiteon et
cyzicenum[29] et erasistration[30] emplastrum; item ex panici polline
et lini semine cataplasma, et ex coliculo agresti vel herba eri-
geronte et stratiote[31] et mandragora et alterco et lenticula et
citri medio vel peponis, et origani vel thymi aut uvae lupinae aut

[26a] *fort. scrib.* diacentauriu, item diascordiu

[27] temporis constituti *S: corr. Rm*

[28] mnaseum *S*

[29] cyzicenem *S: corr. Rm*

[30] erasistrion *S: corr. Rm* (-ium)

[31] stratiote *Rm*: bramite *S*

---

9. Daily, as the sequel seems to indicate.

10. Presumably 365 doses.

11. Cf. 50, below.

drugs as the so-called 'centaury drug' or the 'scordium drug'
over a period of a year; they prescribe the potion continually[9]
for a year in cases where the patient has not had the disease for
a very long time, say for less than five years. And they require
that the drug be taken only when there has been complete digestion and the body is entirely free from obstruction; whenever
these conditions are not present, they postpone the treatment
and thus require an additional number of days to complete a
full year's cycle of doses.[10] They follow this procedure regardless
42 of the length of time required for the treatment. But we hold
with Soranus that the taking of a drug over a long period of time
is to be avoided. (And, in fact, even in the case of food, it is
wrong to prescribe any one kind continually, no matter how
common and beneficial it may be.) Thus ancient physicians
record cases of swift or acute diseases arising from the continual
drinking of a drug, the patients dying of apoplexy, pleurisy,
pneumonia, or an unrelieved difficulty of breathing (Greek
dyspnoea). Now those who claim to have had success with this
treatment do not realize that success was possible only because
the digestion was carefully watched. That is, in some cases,
though the patient continues to take his drug without interrup-
43 tion, he preserves his health by avoiding all other excesses. But
his thoughts are primarily of the drug, and he therefore fails to
realize that it was the rest of the regimen that proved beneficial.

Again, some physicians prescribe the use of the cautery at the
joints. But we disapprove of this procedure, since the accompanying pain produces inflammation. And some keep changing
the ointments and plasters, varying now the general classes and
now the individual kinds, until the patient finds relief; the argument is that different remedies are found to be beneficial for different bodies, causing the pain to abate. And they even prescribe
drugs that have opposite qualities, using at one and the same
time relaxing, astringent, and metasyncritic preparations. Thus
they employ Mnaseas' plaster and the plaster of juices; and
again, on the contrary, those plasters that are extremely astrin-
44 gent, such as the plaster of willows, the Cyzican plaster, and
that of Erasistratus;[11] also a plaster made with panic-grass flour
and flaxseed, or with wild cabbage, groundsel, water lettuce,
mandragora, henbane, lentil, the center of a citron or a melon,
the green foliage of marjoram, thyme, strychnos, purslane, beet,

portulacae aut betae aut mali punici foliis viridibus, vel eius
caduco, quod Latini ambulacium[32] vocant, decocto cum aceto;
aut[33] ruta agresti cum aceto, singulari vel cum simplici alica,[34]
aut aceti sedimine cum apio; aut vitis folia[35] cum simplici pulento; vel ex herbi polline aut fabae vel hordei aut lolii aut lupini
cum faece vini vel aceti; vel ex fico decocto cum aqua et vino,[36]
45 contrito donec mellis sumat crassitudinem, ex quo detractis durioribus partibus imperant coquenda rursus residua; item ex
papaveris caliculis,[37] quos Graeci codias[38] vocant, vel eorum
foliis, et malis cydoniis et punicis in vino decoctis, et bulbis cum
melle; vel alterci radice[39] cum storace vel iaquintio,[40] et marrubii.[41] item calce melli concocta[42] et opio, storaci et amygdalis
amaris cum cyprino oleo et aceto iugiter coctis partes ungendas
docent.

　　ex dissimilibus rebus sine ullo ordine materias admoventes,
insanabiliter simul atque indocte descensum ab aliis in alias
species faciendum iubent donec, ut aestimant, iudicia[43] reperi-
antur, siquidem sit pro corporibus alius ex alia specie liberatus.
46 et est haec experimenti tentatio, quam Graeci schediasticen
piran vocant, quae non destinata passionibus adhibeat adiutoria,
sed probanda. fit praeterea ut accessiones tempora percurrant
et sua sponte levigentur, atque ita occurrens declinatio vel paulo
proximius lenimentum eventum curationis afferat. quod si forte
vere profuisse putaretur declinationi adhibitum, rursum initiis
noxium necessario comprobatur, siquidem non suo tempore
videatur admotum. alios igitur ex aliis relevatos rebus existimant; sed hoc temporum fieri causa respondere debemus, quae
47 corpora urgentius obtinere necesse est. conveniunt enim initiis[44] mediocriter constringentia, augmentis vero atque statui
mitigantia vel laxantia, declinationibus emollientia, lenimentis
fortificantia atque recorporativa. frigida vero vel coercentia,

---

[32] fort. scrib. ampullacium (cf. Chr. iv. 52)

[33] fort. aut ⟨ex⟩

[34] simplici alica] simila aut alica Rm

[35] fort. foliis vel ⟨ex⟩ foliis

[36] vino ⟨et⟩ R

[37] caliculis scripsi (= caly-): coliculis S

[38] codias Rm: cocias S

[39] radicem S: corr. Rm

[40] fort. iaquinto (= hyacintho)

[41] fort. marrubio

[42] concoctum S: corr. R

[43] fort. utilia vel sim.

[44] initiis Rm: in istis S

or pomegranate. And they also use the flower of the latter (Latin *ampullacium*) boiled down in vinegar; or wild rue and vinegar, either alone or mixed merely with groats, or with parsley and sediment of vinegar; or vine leaves mixed with pearl barley alone; or flour of bitter vetch, beans, barley, darnel, or lupines, and the dregs of wine or vinegar. Again, they make a plaster out of a fig boiled down with water and wine and pounded until it 45 attains the consistency of honey, the harder parts being removed and the remainder again boiled down. They also use poppy heads (Greek *cōdeiae*) or foliage, quinces and pomegranates boiled down in wine, bulbs mixed with honey, henbane root mixed with storax, or hyacinth, or horehound root similarly prepared. And they prescribe the anointing of the parts with quicklime cooked with honey, and with poppy juice, storax, and bitter almonds cooked long and steadily in henna oil and vinegar.

Thus these physicians use the most diverse substances, prescribing them without any fixed order. They would have us proceed from one medicine to another until, in their opinion, there is a favorable turn;[12] for they hold that one patient is relieved by one drug and another by another, depending on the body in each 46 case. But this procedure is merely one of trial and error (Greek *schediasticē peira*, 'casual trial'); it is a procedure in which remedies are adduced, not because they are known to be suitable for a particular disease, but merely as a trial. Moreover, the fact is that attacks run their course and are spontaneously relieved; that is, the decline appears, and soon afterward a period of remission, with consequent relief to the patient. But let us suppose that a drug administered during the decline of the attack is actually found to be beneficial. It follows that if this same drug is used at the beginning of the attack, it will be found harmful, for in that case it is applied at the wrong time. Now those physicians conclude that different drugs bring relief in different cases. Our answer, however, is that the element of time, which always has a strong effect upon the body, is actually the controlling factor. 47 Thus the following types of drug are beneficial: at the beginning of an attack, mildly astringent preparations; during the increasing phase of the attack and at its peak, soothing and relaxing drugs; during the decline, emollients; in periods of remission, restorative and metasyncritic preparations. Now the addition

12. Or if *utilia* be read: 'until helpful remedies are found.'

quae apocrustica[45] vocant, etiam igne sacro vexatis admixta congrua efficiuntur. sed aiunt aliqui nunc quoque tamquam laxativa incensos [nunc][46] frigerantia relevare: fervori etenim ex tumore venienti admota contactu[47] tepefacta conveniunt, et tunc temperata mitigant, tamquam aquae ferventi admixta frigida. sed est hoc falsa conclusione collectum, quam Graeci sophisma vocaverunt. oportebat enim, quantum ad hanc ut

48 putant rationem, omni tumori frigidas convenire materias. igitur secundum passiones ac tempora nos discretas aptamus.

alii vero acopum ex rana rubea in podagricis admirantur; alii marini vituli adipe[48] pedes unxerunt, ex eius tergo calciamenta facientes; alii viventem beluam oleo coxerunt; alii lupum, et specialiter unctionis genus hoc convenire probaverunt. multa enim ficta fide[49] sine ratione creduntur, cum forte passio non fuerit insidiosa et cum in corpore[50] tardaverit, non in uno atque eodem tempore[51] perseverans.

item plurimi vomitum post cibum laudaverunt, secundo vel tertio per menses singulos adhibendum, siquidem et materiam[52] redarguat et indigestos esse non sinat, non advertentes quod

49 magis vexabilis approbetur, cum hoc adhibito gingivae putrescant, dentes moveantur, oculi confundantur, et totum impleatur caput, stomachus quoque graviter afficiatur, et propterea omnes consentiant nervi. est igitur conveniens magis parva cibatio, atque initium ex abstinentia ciborum sumendum curationis.

multi autem medicinae scriptores purgativis et acrioribus pollent clysteribus et urinalibus medicamentis, quae diuretica vocaverunt. sed oportet cavere stomachi vexationem, quae varietate facile medicaminum fiet; item vesicam quae sit nervosae qualitatis provocare, tradit enim necessario universo corpori vexationem per sibi cognatam nervorum qualitatem.

[45] apocroustica *Rm*: agrostica *S*   [49] fide *om. R*

[46] *om. R*   [50] in corpore *Rm*: corpus *S*

[47] contactu *Rm*: eius factu *S*   [51] tempore *fort. del.*

[48] adipe *Rm*: alii *S*   [52] materia *A*

13. Or if *nunc* (*S*) be retained: 'that these substances also bring relief in cases of burning inflammation, sometimes by exerting a relaxing effect, and sometimes a cooling effect.'

14. Or '[surplus] matter.'

of cold substances and repellent substances (Greek *apocrustica*) is beneficial in cases of erysipelas. But there are some who say that cold substances will also have a relaxing effect in cases of arthritis and will relieve the inflammation.[13] They adduce the fact that, when burning heat occurs through inflammation, the direct application of lukewarm preparations is beneficial, and the use of the proper mixture, e.g., of cold water with hot, has a soothing effect. But this is a specious argument (Greek *sophisma*); for, according to this reasoning, cold substances would be

48 beneficial in every case of inflammation. But [in our sect] we employ different drugs according to the particular disease and the element of time.

Now in cases of podagra some physicians prescribe a restorative ointment made from bramble toads; others anoint the patient's feet with the fat of a seal, and make slippers from the animal's skin. Others boil a hyena alive in oil, and still others do the same with a wolf, holding that this kind of ointment in particular is beneficial. For many remedies win adherents on specious grounds and without good reason in cases that are not immediately dangerous, that is to say, in chronic cases, when the disease persists and is not limited to a single time.

Again, many physicians have the patient vomit after his meal, prescribing this treatment twice or three times a month, on the ground that it removes food[14] and prevents indigestion. But these physicians do not realize that they are recommending a

49 remedy which is more troublesome [than mere indigestion], for its use causes rotting of the gums, loosening of the teeth, and distortion of the vision; moreover, the whole head is congested, the esophagus is severely shaken, and as a consequence all the nerves and sinews are sympathetically affected. It is therefore a better procedure to reduce the patient's food; in fact, the treatment should begin with a complete withholding of food.

Many writers on medicine offer an abundance of purgatives, sharp clysters, and drugs that induce urination (Greek *diurētica*). But one should avoid agitation of the esophagus, a condition which will easily be produced by such a variety of drugs; and one should avoid stimulating the bladder, for this organ has an abundance of fibers, and by reason of this fibrous character necessarily transmits to the whole body any agitation which it suffers.

50   specialiter autem veterum pertransiendo errores, vanum puto
atque prolixum quod de podagricis scripserunt, et propterea
fastidiosum maxime cum sufficiat communis materiarum me-
moratio suprascripta, tacitis dominis qui nunc dicentur: Diocles
libris quos De passionibus atque causis et curationibus scripsit,
Praxagoras tertio libro De morbis, Erasistratus libro quo De
podagra scripsit, prohibens tamen purgativa adhiberi, quae
catartica vocaverunt, malagma vero Ptolemaeo regi promittens
cuius scripturam non edidit, quamquam quidam sibi visum
51   Erasistrati nominent medicamen; item Herophili sectatores
multi, atque Asclepiades libris Ad Erasistratum scriptis, et Heraclides Tarentinus, et Themison secundo libro Tardarum passionum aliqua ut methodicus, aliqua ut non methodicus decurrens,[53] phlebotomat enim ex pedibus et vinum[54] approbat et
cataplasmatum qualitates confundit, non discernens constrictivis laxativa. quibus respondere quid oportet, cum vinolentia
nervos amputet, phlebotomia patientes impleat partes? Thessalus autem secundo libro Regulari imperfecte quidem sed consequenter methodicis intentionibus curationem ordinavit.

52   III. DE RENALI PASSIONE, QUAM[1] GRAECI
NEPHRITIN APPELLANT

RENALIS passio a patientibus partibus nomen accepit: est
autem intellecta passio tarda renis aut renum. passio inquam tarda, siquidem cum insidenti atque perseveranti querela
renalem intelligamus passionem, et non ex novello atque recenti
tumore, sicuti neque cuiusquam ossium coxae, ni fuerit perseverans, ischiada intelligere poterimus. item adiecimus 'renis
aut renum,' siquidem nunc alterum, nunc utrosque teneat renes
tumentes ac duratos et in saniem saepe venientes et ulceratos et
53   humore fluentes. igitur de cunctis purulentationibus vel vomi-

[53] decurrens *scripsi*: decurrerit *S*: decurrit *R*
[54] vinum *Reinesius 674* (*coll.* vinolentia *infra*): nihil *S*
[1] quem *S*: *corr.* R

---

15. Perhaps *sibi visum* means 'approved of it.'

1. 91 ff., below.

50   And in examining in particular the errors of the ancient physicians, I find what they wrote on the subject of podagra long-winded and empty. This is especially annoying because it would have sufficed merely to mention such remedies as are described above. Yet the following leaders among physicians are silent about these remedies: Diocles in his work *On Diseases and Their Causes and Treatment*, Praxagoras in Book III of his work *On Diseases*, and Erasistratus in his book *On Podagra*. Erasistratus did, to be sure, bar the use of purgative drugs, called *cathartica* in Greek, and he prescribed a plaster for King Ptolemy without publishing a description of the drug, though some who saw it[15]

51   called it 'Erasistratus' remedy.' Also silent on the proper remedies for podagra are the many followers of Herophilus, Asclepiades in his treatise *Against Erasistratus*, and Heraclides of Tarentum. Themison, too, in Book II of his *Chronic Diseases* has a summary which, though partly Methodist, is not wholly so; for he performs venesection at the feet, recommends wine, and prescribes plasters of conflicting qualities, failing to discriminate between the relaxing and the astringent. What further need is there to refute such prescriptions, when we know that the drinking of much wine impairs the functioning of nerves and sinews, and venesection causes congestion in the affected parts? Thessalus, however, in Book II of his work *On Regimen*, describes a treatment which, though incomplete, is in harmony with Methodist principles.

52   III. DISEASE OF THE KIDNEYS
                    (GREEK *NEPHRITIS*)

THE kidney disease takes its name from the parts affected, for it is a chronic disease of one or both kidneys. I say 'chronic' since we recognize the kidney disease on the basis of a deep-seated and long-continued complaint, and not from an inflammation of recent origin. (In the same way pain in a hip bone cannot be considered to be sciatica unless the condition persists.) And in our definition we speak of one or both kidneys because the disease sometimes affects only one, and sometimes both, causing them to be inflamed, hard, and often sanious, ulcerated, and festering.

53   tering. Later on, we shall consider purulence of all kinds and abscesses in general;[1] at present, however, we shall limit the dis-

cis communiter secundo dicemus; nunc de ceteris supra memoratis scribemus, et primo de tumore.

antecedentes itaque causae quae renalem faciunt passionem, aliae ⟨occultae, aliae⟩[2] manifestae, ut perfrictio, indigestio, percussus, casus vehemens super clunes, acres cibi plurimi contra consuetudinem, libido venerea vehemens, vel urinalia frequentata medicamina, aut venena quae specialiter ipsas afficiant partes, ut sunt ex cantharidis confecta.

54   afficiuntur autem hac passione iuvenibus magis grandiores[3] atque senes, et viris mulieres, et habitudine plenis teneriores,[4] siquidem sit in his gravior. et generaliter curatio difficilis ob angustiam locorum quae passione vexantur, et ob acrimoniam urinae quae insuete aliquando renibus immorata in vesicam transit.

sequitur autem patientes, cum adhuc levis fuerit tumor, dolor levis, et magis cum proni fuerint inclinati, secundum clunes,[5] circa ilia alterius aut utriusque partis,[6] et priorum in clunibus

55   nodorum. cum autem tumor vehementescere coeperit, dolor etiam plurimus fiet cum gravedine et fervore clunium omnium atque iliorum et pubetenus vel umbilico, cum consensu usque ad vesicam tendente[7] ob tumorem urinalium viarum, quas Graeci ureticos poros appellant, quae quidem a renibus usque ad vesicam sunt porrectae, attestante urina tenui et aquata et ita subalbida ut colaturae liquidae colorem fingat, quam Graeci charopon vocant, et primo parva, dehinc plurima aut coacervatim effusa, quae nullam faciat relevationem: peiorante tu-

56   more, in faeculentum colorem veniens, cum iam nimia tensione tenuissimae venulae fuerint ruptae, item in vini transiens qualitatem viscosae crassificationis causa, tum oleosam[8] veluti adipis qualitatem simulans, cum renum fluorem[9] pinguis acceperit.[10] dehinc per incrementa etiam febres accedunt, cum consensu iecoris ut quidam etiam fellis colorem sumant, attestante ventris abstinentia cum tormento et ructatione, inflatione cogente.

57   tum hebetudo sequetur et articulorum frigus et vomitus. et

[2] addidi, coll. Chr. v. 1
[3] grandiores Rm: graviores S
[4] tensiores S: corr. Schmid RPh 153: tenuiores Rm (sed cf. 100, 101)
[5] clunes ⟨et⟩ R
[6] partes edd.
[7] tendentem S: corr. R
[8] oleosam scripsi: oleosum S: oleosa R
[9] fluorem scripsi: fluor edd.
[10] acciderit Rm: accesserit Almeloveen

cussion to the other aspects of the kidney disease that were just mentioned, and particularly to inflammation.

Now of the antecedent causes of this disease some are observable, others hidden. These causes include, for example, a severe cold, indigestion, a hard blow or a fall on the loins, the eating of acrid foods in large quantity, contrary to the patient's habit, immoderate sexual excitement, the repeated use of diuretics or of those poisons that have a particular effect upon the kidneys, e.g., those obtained from beetles.

54   Persons along in years and old people are more apt to be affected by this disease than are young, also women rather than men, and thin people rather than corpulent, the disease being more severe in these cases.[2] In general, the treatment is difficult because of the narrowness of the parts affected by the disease and the acrid character of the urine, which sometimes remains an abnormally long time in the kidneys before passing into the bladder.

When the inflammation is still slight, the patient feels a mild pain, particularly when he bends forward; this pain occurs in the loins, in one or both flanks, and in the joints at the ends of
55 the loins. But, as the inflammation grows more intense, the pain also becomes severe and is accompanied by a feeling of heaviness and a burning sensation throughout the lumbar, iliac, lower abdominal, and umbilical parts, the concomitant pain extending even to the bladder by reason of the inflammation of the urinary passages (Greek *poroe urēticoe*), which extend from the kidneys to the bladder. Again, the urine is thin, watery, and so pale that it takes on the appearance of pure filtered fluid (Greek *charopos*, 'glassy'). At first there is only a little urine, but later a copious amount pours forth all at once, though this brings the patient no relief. As the inflammation grows worse, the urine takes on a
56 muddy appearance, the very narrow blood vessels bursting under the extreme tension. Then the urine becomes thick and sticky and assumes a winelike quality; later on it becomes oily and has a fatty appearance, for it receives a flow of fat from the kidneys. And as the attack progresses, fever appears and the liver is affected. Thus in some cases jaundice appears, the bowels do not function, and the presence of gas gives rise to cramps and
57 belching. The limbs become numb and cold and there is vomit-

2. I.e., among thin people; and perhaps also among old people and women.

tardante passione, corporis tenuitas nimia adeo ut quidam un-
cati permaneant et semper proni ambulare cogantur, nec umquam se erigere possint. est praeterea signum declinationis supradictorum in contraria mutatio, ut urina aquata in crassitudinem veniens, crassior vero vel viscosa in tenuitatem, item
quae paulatim atque cum mordicatione ferri solebat, sine labore
adveniens, et si plurima, mediocris effecta; et ad summum
omnia cum naturae solita vel similia fuerint visa.

58   aiunt aliqui eos qui ex casu vel percussu aut vehementi libidine fuerint **[11]

**[12] tormenta irruisse videantur; colicos vero maior interior
vel ventri vicinarum partium dolor sequatur atque inde sumat
exordium, consentientibus vel compatientibus clunibus. item
renali vitio extemplo difficultas urinae coniuncta sit; colicis vero
per consensum atque secundo concurrat. haec est similium passionum discretio.

accidunt haec item similia etiam in urinalibus viis vitio constituto, ex renibus quae usque ad vesicam ducunt, quibus eadem
quae supra diximus recte concurrunt, sed dolor vel eius sensus
erit inter renes et intestina et vesicae fundum, nulla inflatione
59 vel extantia in externis renum partibus prominente. haec est
omnis atque perfecta significatio.

sed oportet sanguinis mictu adfectos similiter curari tamquam
sanguinem spuentes. alios vero qui ceteris fuerint passionibus
adfecti, sicut de vesica scribentes demonstrabimus, pro suis concursibus vel accidentibus, quae Graeci symptomata vocant, par-
tita curari ratione. non enim sola generalis sed etiam specialis
eorundem convenit adiutoriorum curatio, solum differens quod

[11] *lacunam statui: post* visa (*supra*) *lac. statuit* R

[12] *fort. suppl.* .... (item colici similes sunt nephriticis, sed discernuntur siquidem nephriticis exordium a clunibus sumpsisse et ad interiores partes) tormenta irruisse videantur *etc. sed cf. Esc.*, *p. 63B* (*ed. 1544*)

---

3. The passage dealing with the differential diagnosis of nephritis is almost entirely
lost. The lost part may have begun somewhat as follows: 'Disease of the colon and nephritis are similar, but are to be differentiated by the fact that in nephritis the pains
are found to pass from the loins to the inner parts. But in disease of the colon, etc.'

4. I.e., whether due to *solutio, strictura,* or *status mixtus.*

ing. And when the disease is chronic, the body becomes quite
thin, and, indeed, some patients are permanently crippled and
always have to walk bent over, being unable to straighten up.
Now a change to the contrary in any of the symptoms mentioned is an indication of the decline of the attack, e.g., watery
urine becoming thick, or urine that is too thick and sticky becoming thinner, or a change from scanty and painful urination
to that which is free from pain, or a change from an excessive to
a moderate amount, in short, the reappearance of completely
normal and natural conditions.

58   Some say that those who [incurred the disease] through a fall
or a blow or by reason of intense sexual lust. . .

...[3] But in the disease of the colon there is greater internal
pain, i.e., within the abdomen and neighboring parts, and, in
fact, the pain originates there, while the pains in the loins are
only secondary and sympathetic. Again, painful urination is,
from the beginning, an essential feature of the kidney disease;
but in the disease of the colon painful urination is a secondary
and sympathetic affection. So much for the differential diagnosis of the kidney disease.

Again, a like situation occurs when the seat of the affection is
in the urinary ducts leading from the kidneys to the bladder.
Precisely the same symptoms as we described above occur in
these cases, but the pain, or at least the sensation of it, occurs
between the kidneys and the intestines, on the one hand, and
the fundus of the bladder on the other. Moreover, there is no
59 puffiness or swelling in the external regions of the kidneys. With
this we complete our account of the symptoms of the kidney
disease.

As for the treatment, those cases in which blood is passed with
urine must be dealt with in the same way as cases of the spitting
of blood. But the other cases, in which the patients are affected
by other kinds of disease, as we shall describe them in the chapter on the bladder, must be treated in various ways, depending
on the particular combination of symptoms (Latin *accidentia*,
Greek *symptōmata*). For not only must the treatment be based
on the genus of the disease,[4] but even when the proper remedies
are determined, they must be correctly administered in accordance with the special form of the disease. And in the diseases
under consideration there is a difference in the method of apply-

ea quae localia sunt adiutoria in his qui renalibus laborant vitiis magis clunibus adhibeantur, illis vero qui vesicae pectini vel pubetenus, quod Graeci ⟨etron vocant, vel circa veretri initium, quod Graeci⟩[13] perineon[14] vocant.

60   IV. DE TARDIS VESICAE PASSIONIBUS

IN VESICA speciales plurimae passiones eveniunt: tumor, collectio, ulcus, durities, pitiriasis,[1] item psoriasis, quam scabiem vel scabrum appellamus, capillatio, debilitas, paralysis, calculatio, quam lithiasin vocant, sanguinis fluor sive effusio, quam haemorrhagian appellant, mictus tarditas aut difficultas, aut in toto guttae aquatiles, quas hydatidas vocant.

sed ne porrecta longitudine fastidiosa curatio videatur, una praeceptione omnia apprehendere festinandum. de paralysi
61 igitur superius docuimus cum de ea specialiter diceremus; de collectionibus vero et ulceribus secundo dicemus, cum de singulis corporis partibus communem trademus curationem.

[1a]tumente igitur vesica, sequitur dolor secundum pectinem atque veretri radicem et ilia et clunes, et magis initio ac fine urinae reddendae; tum fervor incendiosus, item pulsus et extantia partis in passione constitutae, cum iugi ac frequenti urinae reddendae desiderio. et repentina cessatio ac rursum egestio fiet cum dolore intolerabili per singulos mictus, ut extenti aegrotantes etiam ventum per podicem reddant, aut ipse podex praecadens excludatur; et praeterea aegrotantibus supinus[2] exitus urinae
62 facilior. quidam denique necessitate coacti, defixo capite sublevatis[2a] pedibus sese locaverunt, ut lapis angusta deserens loca atque vesicae ambitum[3] repetens, mictus tribuat facultatem. mulieres denique etiam digitis immissis in muliebrem sinum sibi-

---

[13] *supplevi, coll., e.g., 68*   [14] perineon *R*: peritoneon *S* (*cf. 65, 68, 79*)
[1] phthiriasis *edd.*

[1a] *lacunam aliquo loco ante* quidam denique (*62 in.*) *statuendam existimat Schmid RPh 154*

[2] supinis *Almeloveen*
[2a] sublevatis *Almeloveen, coll. 68*: super latus *S*: *cf.* relevatione, *72*
[3] ambitum *scripsi, coll. 65*: aditum *edd.*

---

1. The term refers to branlike particles in the urine (cf. 64), just as psoriasis and trichiasis refer to scaly and hairlike concretions, respectively.

1a. *Chr.* ii. 12.

ing local remedies. Thus, in the kidney disease these remedies are applied to the loins, while in the diseases of the bladder they are applied to the pubic or the lower abdominal region (Greek *ētron*) or the region where the genital organs begin (Greek *perineon*).

60   IV. CHRONIC DISEASES OF THE BLADDER

THERE are many special diseases of the bladder, viz., inflammation, abscess, ulceration, hardening, pityriasis,[1] psoriasis (Latin *scabies* or *scabrum*), trichiasis, weakness, paralysis, gravel (Greek *lithiasis*), flow or discharge of blood (Greek *haemorrhagia*), slowness or pain in urination, or urination entirely in drops (Greek *hydatides*).

But, to avoid making the description of the treatment seem long-winded and unsatisfactory, we must try to include all the essential features in a single brief account. In fact, we have already discussed paralysis of the bladder in the special chapter on

61 paralysis.[1a] And we shall later discuss abscess and ulceration of the bladder[2] in the course of a general account of these lesions as they occur in the several parts of the body.

Now in cases of inflammation of the bladder[3] there is pain in the pubic region, at the base of the sexual organ, in the groin, and in the loins, particularly at the beginning and end of urination. There is also a burning sensation and a throbbing and swelling of the diseased organ, with repeated and frequent desire to urinate. Urination is interrupted by sudden stoppages, and during each discharge there is unbearable pain. As a consequence the patient must lie down and stretch out; he passes wind through the anus, or the anus itself descends and is thrust out. While thus lying on his back, the patient is able to pass urine

62 more easily. And indeed in some cases he must perforce take a position with head down and feet raised up in order to get the stone away from the narrow parts and toward the broadly curved parts of the bladder; in this way he will facilitate urination. And women patients even insert their fingers into the va-

2. E.g., 124.

3. We must either assume that inflammation due to stone is being described, or else assume (with Schmid) a lacuna somewhere in 61. If a portion of the text is, in fact, lost, it presumably contained descriptions of other diseases of the bladder mentioned in 60.

met ipsae hortatione quadam lapidem provocando dimiserunt.
pueris autem magis prominens veretrum fiet.   saepe etiam extantia quaedam aegrotantibus occurrit, si suo digitum iniecerint
podici. in ipsa praeterea urina sedimina inveniuntur, aliquando
crassiora et calida,[4] aliquando arenosa et saxosa. item quibusdam asper lapis aut sanguinolentus excluditur et saniosus.

63   sed quoniam signa communia sequentur ulceribus vesicae atque lapidibus generatis et his qui gelato sanguine impediti mictus difficultate afficiuntur, confirmabitur apprehensio lapidis
generati adhibita melotide, cuius rationem atque usum Responsionum libris chirurgiam scribentes plenissime tradidimus, in
quibus etiam auferendi lapides opus docuimus. nunc enim correctionem demonstramus cuiusdam in corpore morbi, quo vesica
lapidum generatione vexatur, et non ut alium masculum appelle-
mus lapidem, alium feminam, ut quidam levium medicorum,
non adhibita recorporativa curatione cum solius auferendae
alienitatis intentione medici capiantur; sed quodam corporis
vitio,[5] cuius plurimae sunt differentiae.

64   est praeterea urinae reddendae impedimentum, quod Graeci
stranguriam vocant, mictus officium retardatum; difficultas
autem, quam iidem dysuriam appellant, quae id adiuncto dolore ingesserit; impossibilitas autem, quam ischurian[6] vocant,
perfecta eius officii negatio. sed haec tria accidentia, quae
Graeci symptomata vocaverunt, nunc stricturae sunt appendicia, cum tumor vesicam tenuerit sive durities aut paralysis vel
tensio, ut quidam volentes urinam usu solito ac naturali deponere, obstantibus causis longo tempore continentes officii dilatione vexantur; aliquando alienitatis obtrusione vesicae impedito meatu, ut lapidis aut arenae aut capillorum aut squamularum cantabri similium vel quocumque sedimine crassiore.

65 fluor autem sanguinis per vesicam, quem Graeci haemorrhagian

---

[4] olida *Almeloveen, coll. Corp. Hipp. Aph. iv. 81, Cels. ii. 7. 12*: pallida *Rm:fort.* albida
vel turbida *vel* capillosa (*cf. 64, 67*)

[5] sed quodam corporis vitio *transposui*: habent edd. *post* medicorum *supra*

[6] ischurian *Rm*: urian *S*

---

4. As it is passed? Perhaps 'ill-smelling,' following Almeloveen's conjecture.

gina and themselves remove the stone by gradually working it forward. In the case of boys the penis becomes enlarged. And sometimes the swelling can be felt if the patient inserts his finger into the anus. Again, a precipitation is found in the urine, sometimes thick and hot,[4] and sometimes sandy or stony; in some cases a rough stone, which may be bloody or sanious, is actually passed.

63   But, since the same symptoms occur in ulcerated bladder, stone of the bladder, and in cases of difficulty of urination due to the impediment of a blood clot, the suspicion that a stone has formed in the bladder will have to be corroborated by the use of a probe. We have given a very full account of this instrument and its use in the section on surgery of our work entitled *Answers*, and have also in that work described the procedure of removing bladder stones. Here, however, we are concerned with the correction of a bodily disease in which the bladder is affected by the production of stone. We do not bother to call one type of stone male, another female, as do certain inferior physicians, who do not employ any metasyncritic treatment,[5] and who are concerned merely with the removal of the foreign body. Our interest, on the other hand, is in the disease of the body; and, in fact, there are many different forms of this disease.

64   Now there may occur impeded urination (Greek *stranguria*), i.e., a slowing-down of urination; also difficult urination (Greek *dysuria*), in which the function is performed with pain; finally the inability to urinate (Greek *ischuria*), i.e., the complete suppression of the function. These three conditions are symptoms (Greek *symptōmata*, Latin *accidentia*) of disease. They may be concomitants of a state of stricture in cases of inflammation, hardness, paralysis, or distention of the bladder. Such distention is the case, for instance, when a person has a normal and natural desire to urinate but for one reason or another is prevented from so doing and holds back for a long time; the delay in performing the function causes irritation. Again, these conditions [strangury, dysuria, or ischuria] may be due to the blocking of the opening of the bladder by some foreign body such as stone, gravel, hair, branlike particles, or any thick sediment whatever.

65 Again, flow of blood (Greek *haemorrhagia*) in the bladder is in-

5. I.e., such as would eliminate the cause of the production of stone and obviate recurrences.

vocant, est[7] manifestus cum acervatim[8] per urinae meatum sanguis excluditur. sed quoniam non solo ex ambitu vesicae fluor iste fiet, sed etiam ex collo vel mictualibus viis coacervatus[9] sanguis excluditur, aliquando etiam de renibus, erit locorum discretio facienda. nam renibus patientibus dolor in clunibus demonstratur. vesicae autem ambitu patiente, sub umbilico vel pubetenus apparet dolor, et saepe urinae commixtus sanguis excluditur. item collo vesicae patiente, circa veretri initium,

66 quod Graeci perineon[10] vocant, dolor sentitur. mictuali autem via patiente, ipsam veretri radicem dolor afficit, attestante sanguinis puritate, cum iugi ac non intercapedinata emissione, etiamsi digitis loca quae iuxta sessionem veretri sunt presserimus, quo in loco est ultima mictualis via, quam ut supra diximus uretran[11] Graeci vocaverunt. nam si ex aliis locis sanguis feratur, digitorum impressione magis abstinetur, cum supradictis locis, hoc est perineo[12] vel podici vicinis, renititur impressio. tunc ex vesicae collo impedimento repressus feretur, ex superioribus vero abstinetur. aliorum autem medicorum signa de his discretionibus conscripta Responsionum libris chirurgiam scribentes elogiavimus.

67   sunt autem vesicae vitia vel passiones generaliter curatione difficiles. est enim natura nervosa, et altioribus insita locis atque celata, et quae corporis superflua sustineat acriora.

    sed ne rationem variare videamur, erit demonstrandum quoniam fluori sive solutioni vesicae, quam Graeci rheumatismon vocant, sunt adscribenda plurima quae specie discrepare videntur, ut plurimus mictus cum arenoso vel capilloso sedimine, item sanguinis fluor. stricturae autem adscribendus tumor est atque durities vel saxea duritas, quam Graeci scirrhosin vocant.

68 horum duplicem generaliter in superpositionibus curationem demonstramus.

    fluente igitur vesica, hoc est solutionem patiente, locandus aeger frigido mediocriter in loco, adhibita requie cum abstinen-

---

[7] vocant, est *Rm*: vocantes *S*
[8] *fort. scrib.* cum coacervatim, *sed cf. Ac. iii. 164*
[9] viis coacervatus *scripsi*: visco acervatus *S*: viis ureteribus *Rm*
[10] peritoneon *S*: *corr. R*
[11] uraeam *S*: *fort. scrib.* uretan. *cf. 87, 93*
[12] perineo *R*: peritoneo *S*

---

6. I.e., depending on whether *solutio* or *strictura* is involved.

dicated by the passage of a mass of blood through the urinary canal. But, since this mass of blood may come not only from the curved part of the bladder but also from the neck of the bladder or the urinary canal, and sometimes even from the kidneys, we must distinguish the cases according to the part primarily affected. Thus when the kidneys are the seat of the affection, pain is felt in the loins; when the curved part of the bladder is affected, the pain is below the umbilicus in the lower abdominal region, and the urine is often mixed with blood; when the affection is in the neck of the bladder, pain is felt in the region where

66 the [external] genital organs begin (Greek *perineon*). Finally, when the urinary canal is the part affected, pain seizes the base of the genitals, and pure blood is emitted in a steady flow. Now this flow is not interrupted even if one constricts with one's fingers the parts around the base of the genitals, where a terminus of the urinary canal is located. (The Greek word for this canal is *urēthra*, as we have already remarked.) But if the source of the flow of blood is some part other than the urethra, the flow will be substantially checked by pressure of the fingers at the aforesaid places, viz., the perineal or the anal region. That is, any flow originating in the neck of the bladder will be retarded by this pressure, and any flow originating at a higher point will be completely suppressed. In the surgical books of our treatise entitled *Answers* we have described the different types of case as they are given by various physicians.

67 Diseases of the bladder are, in general, difficult to cure. For the organ is fibrous by nature, is situated and, in fact, concealed deep in the body, and contains acrid waste matter of the body.

Now, in keeping with our principles, we must first point out that many conditions differing outwardly from one another are to be ascribed to a state of flow or looseness in the bladder (Greek *rheumatismos*); among these conditions are copious urination with sandy or hairlike sediment, and also discharge of blood. On the other hand, inflammation of the bladder and induration or stony hardness (Greek *scirrhōsis*) are conditions

68 which must be attributed to a state of stricture. And so there are, in general, two types of treatment for these attacks.[6]

Thus, when there is a fluid state, i.e., when the bladder is affected by a condition of looseness, place the patient in a moderately cool room, prescribe rest, withhold food from him, and

tia et articulorum tenaci ligatione. et si sanguinis fuerit fluor, clunibus prominentius sublevatis, et officio mictus admonente, quantum datur, imperandum aegro ut neque id retento faciat spiritu, neque vi quadam vel conatu excludi cogat aliena. apponenda etiam spongia nova aceto tincta secundum clunes vel umbilicum ac pubetenus, quod Graeci etron appellant, usque ad veretri initium, quod iidem perineon[13] vocant, addita tenaci

69 cum amplexu ligatione; tum epithemata iisdem locis atque cucurbita constrictiva. potus dandus frigidus, parvus cibus. species de sanguinis fluore et sputo scribentes docuimus; similiter etiam quae praebibenda conscripsimus, eiusdem scilicet qualitatis. et sessionem ex vino vehementiori confectam,[14] quam encathisma vocant, in qua sint praecoctae murtae bacculae cum rosis, vel in pusca aut aceto facta decoctio herbae talliae vel[15] rubi aut mali punici corticis et horum similium, vel per ferramentum quod Graeci cathetera vocant iniectio facienda[16] quae similiter medendo constringat,[17] acaciae, hypocystidis aut plan-

70 taginis suco,[18] vel polygonii herbae aut intybi vel puscae frigidae, singularis aut adiuncta thuris drachma una cum aequali pondere hypocystidis vel gallae cum nigro vino, vel talliae herbae aqua caelesti concoctae. quae cum fuerit expressa et abiecta, erit aqua coquenda donec ad mellis veniat crassitudinem. mulieribus vero etiam pessaria adhibenda quae ad fluorem matricis Responsionum conscripsimus libris, muliebria vitia curantes.

est autem curatione ac correctione facilis[19] eruptione factus vel osculatione[20] sanguinis fluor vel percussu aut saltu confectus:

71 etenim influxio abstinetur et rupta conglutinantur. difficilis vero correctione ex putredine effectus fluor, retento enim sanguine vel abstento ulcus permanebit. est praeterea ex putredine sanguis ater et male redolens atque purulentus ex ulcere praefecto, et dolore antecedente qui putredinis causa advenisse

---

[13] peritoneon S: corr. R

[14] sessio ex vino vehementiori confecta Rm

[15] vel fort. secl. (cf. βάτου θαλίας, Sor. Gyn., p. 119. 32)

[16] facienda ⟨eorum⟩ Rm: secunda S

[17] constringant edd.

[18] succi Rm

[19] correctior ac facilis S: corr. Rm

[20] osculatione Rm (cf. Chr. ii. 121 ff.): oscitatione S

have his limbs tightly bound. In cases where blood is discharged
have him lie with his buttocks raised quite high. Whenever he
feels a desire to urinate, instruct him so far as possible to hold
his breath and avoid performing this act, and in no case to use
force or intensive effort to pass off the waste matter. Apply fresh
sponges dipped in vinegar to the loins and to the umbilical and
the lower abdominal region (Greek *ētron*), as far down as the beginning of the genitals (Greek *perineon*), bandaging the parts
69 tightly. Then apply epithems to the same parts and also astringent cupping; and give the patient cold drink and little food.
Use the same kind of food as we indicated above in the chapter
on hemorrhage and the spitting of blood. The same applies to
what the patient drinks, i.e., use substances of the same type.
Also prescribe a sitz bath (Greek *encathisma*) of strong wine containing cooked myrtle berries and roses, or a decoction of bramble foliage, pomegranate rind, and the like, in diluted or undiluted vinegar. Or, using the instrument called *cathetēr* by the
Greeks, make an injection that, along with its astringent action,
will have a curative effect, e.g., the juice of acacia, hypocist,
70 plantain, knotgrass, or endive, or else a cold mixture of vinegar
and water, alone or with the addition of a drachm of frankincense, and an equal weight of the juice of hypocist or oak gall
with dark wine, or of [bramble] foliage cooked in rain water.
That is, these substances are discarded after their juice is extracted, and the water is then boiled off until the juice attains
the consistency of honey. And in the case of women use vaginal
suppositories of the kind we described in discussing flow of the
uterus in the section on women's diseases of our treatise entitled
Answers.

When the flow of blood takes place by the bursting of a vessel
or by anastomosis, being caused by a blow or violent jumping,
it is easier to treat successfully. For the flow is checked, and the
71 ruptured parts are joined together in healing. But when the flow
is caused by a rotting-away of the parts, the treatment is difficult. For, though the flow of blood may be checked or suppressed, the ulceration will remain. Again, the flow that is discharged in such cases of disintegration is dark, foul-smelling,
and contains pus from the previously existing ulceration; moreover, pain is present even before [the discharge of the blood],
and is evidently due to the disintegration of the parts. But when

videatur. in eruptione autem flavus, et non antecedentibus supradictis, sed excussu vel saltu aut percussu effectus.

 solent praeterea, sicut in podice vel feminarum sinu aut matricis collo, etiam in vesica haemorrhoides generari, quae fluo-
72 rem sanguinis praestent quibusdam intervallis variatum. quod
oportet apprehendere prudentem, cum non coacervata primo
fuerit effusio, sed augmentis quibusdam promota, interiectis defectionibus, ac saepe retento sanguine doloris pubetenus admonitione attestante,²¹ cum tensione inguinum et gravedine
clunium vel renum consensu, et cum sanguis eruperit, supradictorum relevatione²² sequente, siquidem aliquando inflatae ac
tumentes haemorrhoides difficultatem vel abstinentiam faciant
mictus, quam Graeci dysurian vocant vel ischuriam.²³ haec
sunt quae de his necessario dicenda credidimus.

 declinante autem passione, convenit adhibere cerotaria ex
murtino vel viridi oleo et alumine, cibum varium dare atque
vinum, ac deinde lavacrum adhibere.

73 ac si strictura fuerit ventris vel vesicae, convenit iacere aegrotantem loco mediocriter calido atque lucido, adhibita abstinentia usque ad tertium diem cum requie. item locis in dolore constitutis manuum calidarum cum blando amplexu vaporatio adhibenda, vel pubetenus ac veretri initio et clunibus calida lin-
teamina; aut vascula ex aqua calida, vel saccelli ex pollinibus
calidis, aut vesicae oleo calido plenae admovendae. ac si vehemens fuerit dolor, phlebotomia adhibenda. et partes in passione constitutae lanis limpidis oleo calido ac dulci infusis contegendae; ex eo etiam totum corpus ungendum; tum ora fo-
74 venda. adhibenda etiam encathismata ex aqua calida, vel aqua
et oleo, aut decoctione laxativa ex his quae saepe memoravimus.
tunc cibus dandus sorbilis, et potui aqua calida, moderatione
dominante. et usque ad declinationem passionis intervallis
dierum nutrimenta offerenda. ac si dolor minime cessaverit,
convenit usus cataplasmatis laxativi et cucurbitae appositio
levis, quam Graeci cuphen appellant, cum adiecta scarificatione
et vaporatione spongiarum aqua calida expressarum. ac si

---

²¹ attestante *Rm*: cessante *S*: vexante *Reinesius*: *fort.* testante
²² relevatione *Rm*: relatione *S*: relaxatione *Reinesius*   ²³ ischuriam *Rm*: uriam *S*

the discharge is due to the breaking of a vessel, the blood is bright-colored, and the antecedent conditions just described are absent, the hemorrhage being caused by violent shaking or jumping or by a blow.

Now, just as varices may form in the anus, the vagina, and the neck of the womb, so they may form in the bladder and 72 be a source for the discharge of blood at certain intervals. The observant physician will recognize such a case, since the discharge is not copious at first, but keeps growing larger, though it is interrupted from time to time; and while the flow is thus suppressed there is often a sensation of pain in the lower abdominal region along with tenderness in the groin, a feeling of heaviness in the loins, and sympathetic pain in the kidneys. Now when the blood is discharged, the conditions just mentioned are relieved; in fact, it is when the varices are gorged and swollen that they may cause painful urination (Greek *dysuria*) or suppression of urination (Greek *ischuria*). So much for these cases.

When the disease declines, apply cerates made with myrtle oil or green olive oil and alum, give the patient varied food and wine, and then prescribe bathing.

73   But if the condition in the abdomen[7] or bladder is one of stricture, have the patient lie in a moderately warm and light room, withhold food until the end of the three-day period, and prescribe rest. Heat the painful parts by gently caressing them with warm hands; or apply warm linen cloths to the lower abdominal region, the perineum, and the loins. For this purpose vessels of hot water, bags of heated flour, or skins filled with hot olive oil may also be used. If the attack is severe, perform venesection; and cover the parts affected by the disease with scoured wool dipped in warm, sweet olive oil. Also anoint the whole body 74 with this oil; then apply fomentations to the face. And prescribe sitz baths of hot water, water and olive oil, or a relaxing decoction made of the substances we have often referred to. Give the patient gruel to eat and warm water to drink, in moderation; have him take nourishment every other day until the decline of the attack. If, however, the attack does not abate, it will prove beneficial to use a relaxing poultice, and to apply cupping that is mild (Greek *cuphos*), but with scarification, and also to steam the parts with sponges wrung out of hot water. If the bowels do

7. The reference may be merely to costiveness of the bowels.

venter retentus fuerit, clyster convenit simplex, et secundo cucurbita clunibus adhibenda ac pubetenus praerasis[24] capillis.
75 tunc hirudinum appositio, quas sanguisugas vocant, atque embasis adhibenda ex calida et oleo. sic enim laxatis tensionibus
non solum dolores solventur vesicae, sed etiam consequens urinae difficultas vel abstinentia. cavendus praeterea usus urinalium medicaminum, quae diuretica Graeci vocant: sunt enim
quae vesicam provocant[25] et propterea tumores faciant[26] commoveri.

ac si minutis doloribus urinae ⟨non iam⟩ fuerit[27] retentio vel in
toto conquieverit dolor, tamquam factis superpositionibus re-
petant lenimenta, adhibenda fortificatio per variam gestationem
et vocis exercitium, unctionibus quoque ac defricationibus admotis quae superiora corporis magis exerceant, interiecto lava-
76 cro et vario cibo ac vino. et iuxta methodicum modum adiec-
tiones cyclicae ac detractiones faciendae. tum ad recorporativa
atque vehementia redeundum adiutoria, ut ex resina vel dropace
ac paroptesi et solis torrore vel arena ignita et appositione cucurbitae forti raptu atque tractu quodam circumductae ⟨et⟩ remotae[28] corpora roboremus, morborum pulsa segnitie, adhibito
usu asperginum, quae sympasmata Graeci vocaverunt. tunc
malagmatum atque acoporum lacessentium usus adhibendus,
adiecto etiam sinapismo et fricatione partium quae passione
afficiuntur. tum encathismatibus utendum ex aqua marina vel
salsa calida, et magis his qui mordicatione quadam locorum in
77 iisdem passionibus tanguntur. tum cataclysmo utendum cuius
nominis vim praescriptis libris saepius latinavimus.[29] ita natatio adhibenda aquarum sua virtute medentium, quibus magis
erit in solutionibus utendum. eligendae sunt namque specialiter quae aluminis habeant qualitatem, ut sunt in Italia albulae
appellatae et nepesinae et cotiliae et auguriae. his vero qui
lapidibus vel scabro vesicae afficiuntur erunt eligendae aquae
salsae, vel quae nitri habeant qualitatem, ut apud Aenariam[30]

[24] praeraris *S*: *corr. Rm*
[25] *fort.* provocent
[26] faciunt *R*
[27] ⟨non iam⟩ fuerit *scripsi*: cessaverit *Rm*: *fort. scrib.* fuerit ⟨soluta⟩ *vel sim.*
[28] circumductae ⟨et⟩ remotae *conieci* (*cf. Chr. ii. 31*): circunducto remota *edd.*
[29] latinizavimus *Rm* (*cf. Ac. ii. 8*)
[30] Tenariam *S*: *corr. Rm*

not function, inject a simple clyster, and use cupping for a second time; apply the cups to the loins and to the pubes, first shav-
75 ing off the hair. Then apply leeches or bloodsuckers, as they are
called; and prescribe bathing in hot water and olive oil. For
these measures will relax the state of stricture, and as a consequence not only will the pains of the bladder abate, but the attendant difficulty or suppression of urination will also clear up.
But avoid the use of the drugs that promote urination (Greek
diurētica); for they irritate the bladder and thus give rise to
inflammation.

Now if the pains are reduced and urination is no longer suppressed, or if the affection has entirely abated and with the end
of the attack there ensues what may be considered a period of
remission, then strengthen the patient's body with varied passive exercise and vocal exercise. Also employ anointing and
massage to exercise in particular the upper parts of the body;
have the patient bathe in the intervals between these treat-
76 ments, and give him varied food and wine. And, in accordance
with Methodist principles, make the required cyclical additions
and subtractions. Then pass to the drastic metasyncritic remedies, strengthening the patient's body with resin or pitch plasters and applications of intense heat, e.g., sun-bathing and the
use of heated sand. Also apply cups having a strong action: draw
them around circularly and remove them with a pull. These
measures will help to dispel the disease in its chronic state, as
will also the use of dusting powders (Greek *sympasmata*). Furthermore, apply strong emollient plasters and restorative ointments as well as mustard plasters; and massage the affected
parts. Again, prescribe sitz baths of hot sea water or salt water,
especially in cases of these diseases in which sharp pains are
77 present in the parts. And use the shower bath (Greek *cataclysmos*, which we have often translated into Latin in previous sections[8]). Also prescribe swimming in waters that have curative
properties, employing this measure chiefly in cases involving a
state of looseness. In such cases choose especially those waters
that contain alum, e.g., the so-called Albulan, Nepesine, Cutilian, and Augurian springs in Italy. But in cases of bladder
stone or scabies, choose waters containing salt or nitrum, e.g.,

8. I.e., *aquarum illisio*, sometimes with the addition of *superne, e supernis,* or *super-
cadentium* (cf. *Chr.* i. 42, 46, 99; ii. 70; iii. 10; iv. 1, 103).

insulam, quae potandae atque lavacro adhibendae sunt. tum residuus adhibendus est cyclus et acriora medicamina | potanda, ut ex radice lapati[31] et capparis et strutii[32] vel polii[33] herbae,

78 itemque panacis et horum similium, et lithotomia[34] in his[35] qui maiorem generaverint lapidem. item in omnibus ellebori[36] adhibendus est usus si passiones supra dictae permanserint. tum navigatio atque peregrinatio et earum varietas adpetenda.

erit praeterea longo tempore ut cetera quaeque nimia venus praecavenda. his enim qui ob vesicae paralysin[37] propter officium suscitandum[38] usum venerium[39] probaverunt, consentiendum non est: trahit enim secum totius corporis vexationem. ob quam causam[40] erit reprobanda[41] etiam ferularum tenerarum vel tabellarum usque ad ruborem cutis ab his probata percussio,

79 itemque ustionibus scarae faciendae[42] pubetenus atque clunibus et circa initium veretri circulatim, quod Graeci ⟨perineon vocant⟩.

⟨V. DE DIABETE⟩

⟨VI. DE SEMINIS LAPSU, QUEM GRAECI GONORRIAN VOCANT⟩[1]

**ri debilitate adficiens.[2] sunt praeterea aquosa semina quae excluduntur, et magis cum se pronos fecerint aegrotantes vel celeri ambulaverint gressu. inruit autem corporibus cum fuerint longa[3] debilitate vexata aut inmodico usu venerio adfecta. sed est accipienda curatio ex his quae ⟨de⟩[4] vesica sanguinem[5]

| inc. L fol. 129r (vid. p. xxi, supra). cf. Ilberg, 'Vorläufiges,' et Schmid 16n., quorum lectiones affero.

---

31 lapathi S   32 strutium L: corr. S (-thii)
33 poliae L: corr. S
34 lithotomiam L: corr. S
35 hiis S, iis R, ut solent (alia exempla non afferam)
36 ellevori L: hellebori S
37 paralysi L: corr. S
38 suscitandum scripsi: sciscitandum L: solicitandum Rm
39 venereum S, ut solet (alia exempla non afferam)
40 causa L: corr. S
41 reprobanda Rm: probanda LS: fort. prohibenda Ilberg
42 ustionibus scarae faciendae Kind, Phil. Woch. 59 (1939), 375 ff.: ustionib. scarefaciendae L: ustio et scarificatio faciendae S

the springs on the island of Aenaria; these springs should be used for both drinking and bathing. Then employ the rest of the metasyncritic cycle, having the patient drink acrid drugs, e.g., those made from dock root, caper, soapwort, hulwort, allheal, 78 and the like. Prescribe lithotomy in cases where a large stone has been formed. And in all cases where the diseases under discussion permit, use hellebore. Finally, prescribe varied sea trips and foreign travel.

The patient should avoid venery and every other form of excess for a long time. For we cannot agree with those who recommend venery in cases of paralysis of the bladder as a means of getting the bladder to resume its function; in fact, the proposed remedy agitates the whole body. On the same account we reject other remedies recommended by these physicians, e.g., beating the body with pliant whips or flat boards until the skin is red; 79 also scarring the flesh by cauteries at the lower abdominal region and the loins and in a circle about the region where the genital organs begin (Greek *perineon*).

V. DIABETES[1]

VI. DISCHARGE OF SEMEN
(GREEK *GONORRHOEA*)

... causing weakness. In addition [to the diseases mentioned], there is also the discharge of watery semen, especially when the patient has been bending forward or walking at a quick pace. Bodies affected by long-continued weakness or subjected to the strain of excessive venery are particularly susceptible to this disease. The treatment is the same as that which we gave for

1. The Table of Contents of the first edition (and hence presumably of the manuscript; cf. also 81, below) indicates that chapters on diabetes and gonorrhea belong here. The chapter on diabetes is wholly lost; but if Kind's suggested transposition, which I adopt, is sound, a small fragment of the chapter on gonorrhea is preserved (cf. *Phil. Woch.*, LIX [1939], 375 ff.).

---

[1] *quae sint supplenda docet tabula capitum apud S, p. 118 (ubi* gonorrhoean *S, ut solet*)

[2] quod Graeci ..ri debilitate adficiens *(ante* ri *versu ineunte duae litterae detritae)* L: quod Graeci ⟨perineon (peritoneon *S, ut solet; cf. 59*) vocant⟩ debilitate afficiens *R*: quod Graeci ⟨perineon vocant, pa⟩ri debilitate adficiens *Fuchs, Phil. Woch. 46 (1926) 825: lacunam post* Graeci ⟨perineon vocant⟩ *statuit Ilberg: finem capitis IV post* ⟨perineon vocant⟩ *statuit Kind (loc. cit.),* —ri debilitate adficiens *ad cap. VI transponendo, quem sequor*

[3] longa fuerint *S*   [4] ⟨de⟩ *R*: ⟨e⟩ *S*   [5] sanguinum L: *corr. S*

fluente memoravimus, item ex his quae in lenimentis passionum fortificandi corporis causa ac demutandi[6] saepissime probavimus. est enim haec passio seminalium viarum paralysis.

80   VII. DE SOMNO VENERIO, QUEM GRAECI
              ONYROGMON[1] APPELLANT

PER somnos inanibus visis adfecti aegrotantes seminis lapsu vexantur.[2] nomen autem sumsit[3] ab accidenti, siquidem effectum venerium provocando perficiat. sed generaliter neque ilico[4] passio est neque accidens passionis, quod Graeci sintoma[5] vocant, sed est consequens visis, quam[6] Graeci fantasian[7] vocaverunt, per somnum aegrotantes adficiens ob desiderium veneriae[8] voluptatis, vel iugem atque continuam libidinem, sive[9] contrario longam usus dilationem vel continentiam. sed hoc frequentius accidens ⟨in⟩[10] passionem[11] saepe | deveniet, itemque alterius passionis aliquando antecedens[12] fiet, ut epylemsiae,[13] furoris,[14] quem[15] Graeci manian[16] vocant,[17] cuiusquam similis morbi, quoniam vexationem ostendere probatur atque praemovi[18] corpus sive praetangi accessione ventura.

item aliquando antecedens causa supra dictae passionis, quam[19] seminis appellamus lapsum, fuisse[20] probatur, a qua discernitur siquidem illa passio etiam per diem vigilantibus aegris fluere faciat semen, nulla fantasia in usum venerium provocante, somnus autem venerius eo solo tempore quo dormiunt aegrotantes inanibus visis concubitum fingat. aliqui etiam aiunt oniropolesin ab onirogmo[21] discerni, siquidem oniropolesis illa sit quae per somnum concubitum fingat cum operantium

---

    | inc. L fol. 129v

---

    [6] demutandis L*S*: *corr. R*

    [1] onirogonon *S*, *ut solet* (*alia exempla non afferam*)

    [2] vexatur L: *corr. S*

    [3] sumsit *S*, *ut solet* (*alia exempla non afferam*)

    [4] ilio L: *corr. S* (-ll-)

    [5] symptoma *S*, *ut solet*   [9] sive ⟨e⟩ *S* (*sed cf. Chr. i. 64, 87*)

    [6] quam *S*: qua L   [10] ⟨in⟩ *S*

    [7] pantasia L: *corr. S* (ph-)   [11] passione L: *corr. S*

    [8] veneria L: *corr. S* (-eae)   [12] accedens L: *corr. S*

    [13] epilepsiae *S*, *ut solet* (*alia exempla non afferam*)

    [14] ⟨vel⟩ furoris *Ilberg, coll. 83*

81

82

hemorrhage of the bladder;[1] employ, in addition, the measures for strengthening the body and the metasyncritic measures we have often recommended for use during the intervals of remission in chronic diseases. For the disease involves a paralysis of the seminal ducts.[2]

80   VII. NOCTURNAL EMISSION
                      (GREEK *ONEIRŌGMOS*)

NOCTURNAL emission is the discharge of semen in the course of a dream. The name [*oneirōgmos*] is derived from this symptom, for the dream [*oneiron*] provides the venereal stimulation which gives rise to the emission. But, in general, nocturnal emission at the outset is not a disease or even a concomitant (Greek *symptōma*) of disease; it is essentially a consequence of what the person sees (Greek *phantasia*) while he sleeps, and results from a longing for sexual enjoyment, that is to say, from constant and uninterrupted sexual desire, or, on the other hand,

81   from continence or a long interruption of sexual activity. But this condition may often become a disease, or may be the forerunner of another disease such as epilepsy, insanity (Greek *mania*), or the like. For [in these other diseases] the body suffers agitation and is shaken and affected even before the arrival of the attack.

Nocturnal emission is sometimes an antecedent cause of gonorrhea (Latin *seminis lapsus*, 'discharge of semen'), which we have discussed above. But there is the following distinction between them. Gonorrhea produces a flow of semen even during the day, while the patient is awake and there is no vision that stimulates him sexually; nocturnal emission, however, takes place only while the patient is asleep and is the sequel to a

82   dream in which he imagines he is copulating. Now some say that a distinction should be made between *oneiropolēsis* and *oneirōgmos*. They use the former term to refer to dreaming about coitus,

1. 68–72.
2. Cf. *Chr.* ii. 13.

---

15 quam *S*   18 praemoveri *S*
16 mantam L: *corr. S*   19 quam *S*: qua L
17 vocant ⟨aut⟩ *S*   20 fuisse *S*: suis se L
21 onirogmon L: *corr. Ilberg*: onirogono *S, ut solet*

sensu sed sine seminis iactu, onirogmos vero usque ad defectum
deducat[22] seminis lapsum. sed Milesius nihil inquit supra dicta
differre: unum etenim[23] atque eundem fluorem dicit esse seminalium viarum. sed quod, inquit, nunc exclusio perficitur seminis, nunc inpeditur, quamquam visa per somnum eadem[24]
fingantur, ob alias inquit inruentes fieri causas. sed non est
plurima discretionis[25] intentio adhibenda, quippe cum neque
necessaria conprobetur.

83   eos igitur, qui ratione futurae accessionis epylemsiae vel
furoris aut cuiusquam alterius morbi commoventur,[26] ex his
quae suis sunt passionibus tribuenda mitigamus. eos vero qui
specialiter hoc vitio adficiuntur, tamquam parva gonorria[27]
affectos curamus. supra dictorum enim augmentum in istam[28]
cadere passionem facit aegrotantes fluentium seminalium viarum vel paralysi vitiatarum[29] causa. quapropter convenit primo
aegrotanti[30] ab intentione veneria visa mentis avertere, quae
Graeci phantasmata vocaverunt, atque aliorsum[31] applicare,[32]
84 intentionibus externis admotis, siquidem facile quae[33] vigilantes
accipiunt somnorum visis ad activa congruis[34] motibus exerceant aegrotantes, et propterea corpus seminis discussione
vexetur.

| tum stramenta[35] duriora atque frigerantia procuranda.
iubendi etiam supra latus iacere cum se somno dederint, †et
ante se,† vel subponenda tenuis ac producta lammina plumbea
clunibus; vel spongiae circumdandae pusca frigida infusae, vel
inicienda loca[36] rebus frigidae virtutis ex anterioribus, ut balaustio vel acacia aut ypoquistida[37] vel psyllio herba, quae sunt sin-
85 gularia vel cum palmulis adhibenda. cibus etiam constrictivus
dandus vel densabilis et frigidus, ut de sanguinis[38] fluore conscripsimus. poto quoque frigido nutriendi vel constrictivis non

---

| inc. L fol. 130r

---

[22] deductum L: corr. Ilberg: deducit S
[23] etenim Ilberg: est enim L
[24] eandem L: corr. S
[25] discretionis Schmid 108: discretio nisi L
[26] commovetur L: corr. S
[27] gonorrian L: corr. S (-rrhoe-, ut solet)
[28] istam S: stam L
[29] vitiatum L: corr. S
[30] aegrotantis Rm: -es Ilberg

[31] aliiorsum L: corr. S
[32] aplicare L: corr. S
[33] facile quae S: facileq: L

the dreamer having the sensation of performance without the actual ejaculation of semen; they hold that *oneirōgmos*, on the other hand, involves a complete discharge of semen. But Milesius holds that there is no essential difference, the flow within the seminal ducts being the same in both cases; he attributes to other supervening causes the fact that the ejaculation of semen is accomplished in the one case and blocked in the other, despite the formation of the same dream images in both cases. But we need not make any great effort to distinguish the terms, for such a distinction is not really essential.[1]

83   In all cases where nocturnal emission is a prelude to a coming attack of epilepsy, insanity, or any other disease, the treatment must employ the measures appropriate to that particular disease. But when the patient is suffering specifically from nocturnal emission, treat the case like a minor case of gonorrhea. For the aggravation of the symptoms may cause the patient to lapse into gonorrhea by reason of the fluid state of the seminal ducts or paralysis thereof. And so it is first necessary to turn the patient's mental images (Greek *phantasmata*) away from preoccupation with sex, and to direct his thoughts along other
84   lines by providing external interests. For the patient's sensations in waking life readily give rise to dream images in which the movements resemble actuality.[2] There is consequent agitation of the body with the churning-about of the semen.

Provide the patient with a hard, cold bed, and have him lie on his side when he goes to sleep. . . .[3] Place a long, thin lead plate under his loins, or put sponges soaked in cold vinegar water around them. Or inject[4] into the urethra juices of a cold nature, e.g., wild pomegranate flower, acacia, hypocist, or psyllium,
85   using them plain or with dates. Prescribe cold food that is binding or astringent, i.e., food of the kind we described in the chap-

---

1. I.e., to the treatment.   2. The text is quite uncertain.

3. *Et ante se* has been interpreted to mean 'or prone.' But the text and meaning are uncertain.

4. It may be that the reference is not to an injection but to an external application; *ex anterioribus* may mean 'substances previously mentioned.'

---

34 ad activa congruis *coni. Ilberg*: ad activa cum is L: *fort.* adactis (*vel* adacta) vacuis

35 stramen L: *corr. S*

36 inicienda loca *Ilberg*: initiendo doloca L: inijciendo loca *S*

37 hypocistide *S*

38 sanguinibus L: *corr. S*

quidem curiose confectis constringendi. tum adhibenda fortificatio ex communi resumtione, et facienda consuetudo frigidi lavacri, quod Graeci psycrolusian[39] appellant; loca etiam in passione constituta forti inpressione fricanda. sunt enim haec sufficientia constrictionis[40] faciundae.

aliqui vero convenire dixerunt etiam mictus dilationem tendere, ne frequenti officio causa refricetur, sed[41] conpleta vesica se

86 somno aegrotantes dare, quo neque in altum somnum venire sinantur et intercessu frequenti excitentur, quo visa veneriae voluptatis quae somno finguntur amittant, et extenta[42] vesica seminales vias sibi vicinas conprimendo semen retineat.[43] alii maiorem[44] digitum ligandum atque constringendum forti filo[45] vel lino iusserunt, quo dolore interveniente altior arceatur somnus et neque animorum visa[46] in veneriam voluptatem[47] solvantur.

sed erunt haec utraque a nobis excludenda. vexant enim vigiliae aegrotantem, et ultra modum urinae retentio difficultatem mictus[48] saepe refecit,[49] ut alterius passionis inlatae causa videatur, ut supra docuimus.

87 ## VIII. DE DEBILITATE SEMINALIUM VIARUM

MILESIUS debilitate[1] fieri dixit seminalium viarum vel sequi in usu venerio pro semine sanguinis emissionem. sed hoc commune est etiam his qui in osculo vesicae, quam uretan[2] vocant, ulcus habuerint. et est harum | manifesta discretio. in his enim qui ulcus hab ⟨uerint, cum mictum fecerint san⟩[3]guis fluet adtestante mordicatione et dolore et aliquando egestione

88 corpusculorum, quae efelcidas[4] Graeci vocaverunt. in his autem

---

| inc. L fol. 130v

[39] psichrolusian *S, ut solet*

[40] constrictioni *R*

[41] sed *S*: set L: et *R*

[42] extenti L: *corr. ed. Aldina (1547)*

[43] retineant L: *corr. Ilberg*

[44] maiore L: *corr. S*

[45] filo *S*: vita L

[46] visi L: *corr. S*

[47] voluntatem L: *corr. S (cf. 135)*

[48] ictus L: *corr. S*

[49] efficit *Rm*

[1] debilitatem L: *corr. R*

[2] urethran *Rm*

[3] ⟨ ⟩ *S: litterae nunc paene evanidae in* L

[4] quefelcidas L: quae ephelcydas *S*

ter on hemorrhage;[5] and let the patient's drink also be cold and astringent, but not elaborately compounded. Further, employ the usual measures to strengthen the body, have the patient take a cold bath regularly (Greek *psychrolusia*), and prescribe massage with strong pressure for the parts specially affected. These treatments should suffice as astringent measures.

But some physicians have also held that the patient should keep postponing urination, on the theory that the frequent performance of this function would aggravate the case. They order 86 him to go to sleep with a full bladder, so that he will be unable to fall into a deep sleep but will be awakened at frequent intervals. They reason that in this way dreams involving sexual delight will be dissipated; and, further, that if the bladder is distended, it will exert pressure on the adjoining seminal ducts and thus hold back the flow of semen. And some physicians recommend that one of the patient's big toes[6] be bound up tightly with a strong thread, say of linen; they hold that the pain which arises will prevent deep sleep, and that the patient's imagination will not find its outlet in sexual dreams.

But we reject both these procedures. For lack of adequate sleep only harms the patient, and the holding-back of urine too long generally brings about difficulty in urination. That is to say, the retention becomes the cause of another disease, as we have indicated above.[7]

87   VIII. WEAKNESS OF THE SEMINAL DUCTS

MILESIUS says that the ejaculation of blood instead of semen in the course of coitus takes place as a consequence of weakness of the seminal ducts. But this same symptom is also present in cases of ulceration of the mouth of the bladder (Greek *urēthra*). There is, however, an obvious means of distinguishing between the two conditions. Thus in the cases of ulceration, blood will also be discharged whenever urine is passed, and there will be sharp pain and tenderness, and sometimes bits of scabby 88 matter (Greek *ephelcides*) will be discharged. On the other hand, in cases of weakness of the seminal ducts, it is only at the time

5. *Chr.* ii. 174–82.

6. Perhaps 'thumbs.'   7. 64.

qui debilitate seminalium viarum[5] adficiuntur, solo tempore
veneris exercendae sanguis excluditur adtestante iucunditate;
nullis corpusculis et, cum mictum faciunt, nulla mordicatione
vexantur.[6]

sed etiam nunc curatio ex supra dictis accipienda ubi[7] vesicam
fluentem sanguinem[8] curari conscripsimus: constrictione enim
atque densitate fluentia retinentur. tunc resumtio adhibenda
ac deinde recorporatio, ut[9] saepe memoravimus.

89

IX. DE PRIAPISMO[1]

SINE ullo dolore vel consensu tentigo[2] veretri fiet et appellatur
priapismos. sed vocabulum sumsit ab[3] similitudine Pria-
porum, quod[4] ita formentur[5] ut recto[6] veretro fingantur. huius
autem passionis meminit Demetrius Apameus[7] libro Signorum.
ait enim ⟨quod viderit⟩[8] senem[9] in semet manu operantem nec
quicquam[10] potuisse peragere; tensionem autem fuisse veretri
nimiam[11] cum parvo dolore ut cornum[12] putaretur, et ita perseverasse multis mensibus; nullo quoque adiutorio medicinali
90 cessisse,[13] at[14] tarde atque longo tempore requievisse.[15] quo fiet
ut a satyriasi[16] discernatur priapismus, siquidem illa celer sit et
non tardet in corpore. fiet[17] sane cum contractu nervorum et
stimuloso desiderio veneriae voluptatis. nam[18] intellegitur
priapismus paralysis esse seminalium viarum atque aliorum nervorum ad veretri partes ducentium, quorum contractu aegrotantes[19] adficiuntur. sed etiam nunc curatio sumenda est ex his
quae de vesicae strictura longo tempore tardante conscripsimus.

[5] viarum S: utarum L

[6] vexante R

[7] ubi S: qui L

[8] sanguine S (sed cf., e.g., 79)

[9] ut S: et L

[1] priapismon L: corr. S

[2] tentigo Rm: vertigo L

[3] ab Ilberg: alii L: a S

[4] qui Rm

[5] formantur Rm

[6] retro L: corr. S

[7] appameus L: corr. S

[8] suppl. Ilberg, coll. Ac. iii. 179

[9] senem Rm: semen

[10] quiquam L: corr. S

[11] nimiam S: enim iam L

[12] cornu S. cf. Ac. iii. 179

of coitus that blood is discharged; there is no loss of pleasure and no bits of matter are passed, and urine is passed without any sharp pain.

The treatment of these cases should be based on the treatment described above for cases of bleeding from the bladder.[1] First the flow is checked by binding and astringent measures; then the body is strengthened, and finally metasyncritic measures are employed, as we have often described them.

89

IX. PRIAPISM

PROLONGED tension of the genitals without any pain or sensation is called 'priapism.'[1] The term is derived from a comparison with representations of Priapus, who is depicted with erect penis. Demetrius of Apamea mentions this disease in his book *On Signs*. He says that he saw an old man try unsuccessfully to relieve the tension by masturbating; so powerful was the erection, though with little sensation, that the organ might have been thought to be of horn.[2] He tells us that the condition persisted for many months and did not yield to any medical rem-
90 edy, but after a long period of time was finally relieved. Hence the distinction between satyriasis and priapism, for the former disease is acute and does not remain in the body for a long time; it involves not merely the contraction of sinews but also a goading desire for sexual gratification. Priapism, on the other hand, is a paralysis of the seminal ducts and of other sinews leading to various parts of the sexual organ; the disease consists in the contraction of these sinews. As for the treatment of priapism, here, too, we must refer to our previous discussion of chronic and persistent stricture of the bladder.[3]

1. Cf. 68–72.

1. Cf. the chapter on satyriasis, *Ac*. iii. 175.   2. Cf. *Ac*. iii. 179.   3. 73.

[13] cessasse *S* (*sed cf. Ac. iii. 179*)

[14] at *Almeloveen*: ad L: ac *S* (*cf.* sed *Ac. iii. 179; p. xxiv supra*)

[15] quievisse L: *suppl. Ilberg, coll. Ac. iii. 179*

[16] satyriasis L: *corr. S*

[17] *sed* fiat *Ac. iii. 179*

[18] at *Rm*

[19] egrotantas (?) L: *corr. S*

91

X. DE VOMICIS SIVE INTERNIS COL-
LECTIONIBUS, QUAS[1] GRAECI
EMPYEMATA VOCANT

PLENA igitur de his tradenda est ratio. haec enim sunt quae in occultis nata | collectiones nuncupantur, ut in splanchnis ac membrana quae latera cingit vel in pulmone aut discrimine thoracis ac ventris, quod Graeci diaphragma vocant, item stomacho vel ventre, iecore, liene, intestinis, renibus, vesica aut mictuali via vel matrice aut peritoneo.[2] sed de his quae in matrice generantur libris quos De muliebribus vitiis conscripsimus Responsionum docuimus. de ceteris vero nunc dicemus.

92 harum igitur aliae solo medicamine curantur atque medicinali delectu gubernante usum chirurgiae non exigunt, siquidem sint occultis in locis et plurimis superpositis membris, et sit impossibile atque illicitum plurimas incidere partes ne sanguinis pomposus[3] fluor periculum faciat aegrotanti, ut sunt quae in pulmone generantur, vel diaphragmate intrinsecus vel in ipsa[4] altiore[5] altitudine, aut in stomacho superius scilicet a diaphragmate, vel in ventris sessione aut intestinis, excepto fine longaonis, item in posterioribus vesicae vel in renibus.

93 alia[6] vero accedente chirurgia curantur, quoties ad exteriora corporis collectionum liquores[7] erumpendo feruntur, vel magis ab altioribus recedunt, ut in hypozygo[8] membrana vel diaphragmate forinsecus atque stomachi fundo et ventre[9] circa eius superiorem altitudinem, item iecore et liene et longaone ad eius exteriora atque sphincteri[10] vicina, et vesicae in anterioribus vel sub umbilico pubetenus, quod Graeci etron appellant, item in vesicae collo vel in prima eius parte, quam Graeci uretan[11] vocant, et in peritoneo.[12]

| expl. L fol. 130v

[1] quos L: *corr. S*
[2] perineo *R*
[3] copiosus *Rm*
[4] *fort.* ipsius
[5] altiore *conieci, coll.* superiorem, *93:* alteriore *S:* ulteriore *Rm*
[6] aliae *Rm, ut supra, 91*
[7] liquorē *S: corr. Rm*
[8] *fort. scrib.* hypezocote
[9] ventre *Rm:* ventris *S*
[10] sphincteri *Rm:* sphinteri *S*
[11] urethran *Rm. cf. 87*
[12] perineo *R*

91 ## X. INTERNAL ABSCESSES OR GATHERINGS
(GREEK *EMPYĒMATA*)

WE MUST now give a complete account of these abscesses. They are the so-called 'gatherings' that develop in the concealed parts of the body, e.g., in the inner organs, the membrane lining the sides, the lung, the membrane that divides the chest from the abdomen (Greek *diaphragma*), the esophagus, stomach, liver, spleen, intestines, kidneys, bladder, urinary canal, uterus, and peritoneum. We have already discussed cases of abscess of the uterus in the section on women's diseases in our treatise entitled *Answers*. We shall here discuss the other kinds of internal abscess.

Now some of these accumulations are treated by medicine alone, the course of the treatment being determined by a proper
92 choice of medicine. These cases do not call for surgery, since the accumulations lie in parts deeply hidden under numerous structures, and it would be impossible and improper to cut into so many parts; for the loss of so much blood would endanger the patient's life. Examples of abscesses of this kind are those which develop in the lung, or in the inner part of the diaphragm,[4] i.e., where its arch is higher, or in the esophagus, i.e., above the diaphragm, or in the base of the stomach, in the intestines with the exception of the end of the rectum, in the posterior parts of the bladder, or in the kidneys.

But other cases of internal abscess are treated surgically. These are the cases in which the accumulated fluids, when they break out, move away from the inner and toward the outer parts
93 of the body,[5] e.g., abscess in the pleura, the outer part of the diaphragm, the lower part of the esophagus, the upper surface of the stomach, the liver, the spleen, the parts of the rectum near the surface of the body, i.e., near the sphincter, the anterior parts of the bladder, the parts below the umbilicus, i.e., the lower abdominal region (Greek *ētron*), the neck of the bladder or the part thereof which is farthest front (Greek *urēthra*), and, finally, the peritoneum.

4. I.e., farther away from the surface of the body. But the interpretation is doubtful. Perhaps: 'on the inner (under?) surface of the diaphragm, particularly where its arch is higher.' Cf. also 93, 97, 104.

5. I.e., nearer the surface of the body. But perhaps the meaning is 'outer (or upper?) surface of the diaphragm.' Cf. 92.

communiter autem omnis vomica vel collectio antecedente tumore nimio generatur. denique empyici,[13] quos nos vomicosos
appellamus, alii ex pleuretico morbo alii ex pleumonico in supra-
94 dictam passionem devenerunt, sequentibus signis, nunc communibus cuiusdam partis in vomicam venientis, nunc specialibus
pro singulis corporis locis. sed ne longa haec[14] oratione aestime-
mus[15] omnium communia simul ordinanda probamus; tum singulatim specialia designantes etiam una[16] adiungemus.

omnibus igitur collectionibus generatis, vel cum tumor in
liquorem[17] vertitur, sequitur febricula vehemens, inordinata, et
saepe cum rigore et torpore frigido vel iniquitate[18] corporis,
tunc loci fervor incendiosus, gravedo, tensio, et exceptis quae in
pulmone fiunt, saepe stimulans dolor et pulsuosus, tum celer
pulsus atque humilis et saepe sudor, magis capitis atque col-
95 lorum. dehinc perfecta purulentatione rigor corporis atque
tremor circumscribetur, et febrium recedit inquietudo ac dolorum.

sed specialiter ac proprie in communibus,[19] si in membrana
quae latera circumtegit, hypozygos[20] appellata, fuerit generata
collectio, difficultas spirationis sequetur, quam dyspnoean vocaverunt, et difficilis iacendi potestas supra contrarium patienti
latus, hoc est quod causa non tangitur, cum sensu quodam in-
terno veluti pendentium membrorum.[21] et saepe commotu corporis[22] quasi sonus auditur velut inclusi atque collisi humoris:
nam[23] Graeci hydatismon appellant. sequitur etiam displicentia post acceptum cibum, quam Graeci dysarescesin[24] vocant,
96 et plurima tensio medii lateris, aut verrucosa[25] inflatio impressioni digitorum cedens ac resurgens.

in pulmone vero emergente vomica, spirandi plurima difficultas sequetur aegrotantes, tussis vehemens, vox obtusa vel rauca

---

[13] empyicis S: corr. R

[14] haec Rm: hac S

[15] extimemus S: fort. scrib. existimemus

[16] etiam una scripsi: etiā munia S: etiam ⟨com⟩munia Rm: fort. scrib. etiam ⟨ad com⟩munia vel etiam ⟨com⟩munibus

[17] liquore S: corr. Rm

[18] inquietudine Rm: inquietate Almeloveen: cf. inaequalitate, 140 et gr. ἀνωμαλία

[19] in communibus] praeter communia Rm

[20] fort. scrib. hypezocos

[21] membranarum Rm

In general, every internal abscess or gathering develops as a consequence of a severe inflammation. Now cases of abscess (Latin *vomica*) arise sometimes from pleurisy and sometimes
94 from pneumonia. The symptoms are in part those general symptoms that occur when any organ is affected by such an abscess; but there are also special symptoms depending on the precise part of the body affected. But for the sake of brevity we shall first list together the symptoms common to all cases; then, indicating the special symptoms in the several cases, we shall also add these as a group.[6]

Thus in all cases where an abscess develops, i.e., when the inflammation turns to pus, there is intense and irregular fever, often accompanied by stiffness, numbness, chills, and general bodily discomfort; further, there is burning heat, heaviness, and tension in the part affectĕd, and, except in cases of abscess of the lung, there often occurs a piercing, throbbing pain. The pulse is rapid and submerged; and there is often sweating, especially
95 at the head and neck. When the formation of pus has been completed, the bodily stiffness and trembling subside, and the restlessness due to fever and pain is lessened.

But in addition to these general symptoms, if the abscess occurs in particular in the pleural membrane (Greek *hypozygos*), there are certain characteristic symptoms, viz., shortness of breath (Greek *dyspnoea*), difficulty in lying on the side opposite the affected side, i.e., on the side not touched by the disease, and a feeling within the body as if the parts were hanging down. Often when the body is shaken, a sound may be heard like that of fluid splashing about in a container, a sound which the Greeks called *hydatismos*. Also there is distress (Greek *dysarestēsis*)
96 after the taking of food, and considerable tension in the midlateral region. Again, a pointed swelling may appear, which recedes when pressure of the fingers is applied, and then returns.

If the abscess develops in the lung, the patient experiences considerable difficulty in breathing, and there is violent coughing. The voice is thick and harsh, the breath is of foul odor, and

6. Or reading *etiam* ⟨*ad com*⟩*munia*, 'append them to the list of general symptoms.'

---

[22] commotu corporis *R*: cōmotus corporis *S*: *fort.* cum motu corporis *vel* commoto corpore
[23] quem *Almeloveen* (*cf. 106*)   [24] *fort. scrib.* dysarestesin
[25] verrucosa *Rm*: verri- *S*: ventosa *Haller*

et odoris tetri spiratio, thoracis gravedo et adductio superiorum ad inferiora, item gravatio atque tensio supinatis aegrotantibus et relevatio sedentibus; denique se ipsi sustollunt ad partes lecti superiores, quo levatius habeant caput. sequitur etiam cavitas oculorum, genarum rubor et albedo sub lingua venarum. et si eruptio tardaverit, inflatio quoque articulorum sequetur, vultus pallor et macies ora deformans.

97 item in diaphragmate emergente vomica, dolor supra praecordia sequitur penetrans per latera utraque usque ad posteriora, et aliquando inflatio vel tensio iuxta finem pectoris vel sub extremis costis atque ossibus ultimis, perseverans usque ad alia.[26] et si collectio forinsecus fuerit, sonitus aliquando humoris inclusi sequetur, tunc tussicula et in spirationibus difficultas plurima ac respiratio longa, et forinsecus spiritu attracto dolor. quod numquam sequetur eos qui pulmonis vomica vexantur: etenim pleumonici hauriendo magis spiritum relevantur.

98 in stomacho autem emergente vomica, ructationes tetrae atque difficultas spirationis sed minor aegrotantes sequetur, et aliquando tussicula parva[27] sine ullo humoris[28] excreatu, tunc torpor frigidus articulorum, animi defectio, sudor in summitate cutis, pulsus parvus et corruptio sumpti cibi atque acidae ructationes et nausea et aliquando vomitus, siccitas linguae vel asperitas, sitis, transvoratio difficilis, plurima vel parva pro collectionis magnitudine.

quod si fuerit in superioribus stomachi, donec cibus transvoretur pressuram sentient aegrotantes, post effectum[29] vero relevantur.[30]
99 ac si in inferioribus, erit facilis transvoratio ac deinde dolida cibi perceptio sequetur, cum ad destinata pervenerint quae sumantur, dolore ex anterioribus partibus in ore ventris attestante, cum inflatione vel extantia quae impressioni[31] digitorum cedat ac resurgat. si vero in superioribus fuerit collectio, nulla videbitur prompta inflatio vel extantia, sed dolor atque

[26] ilia *Rm*

[27] parvo *S*: *corr. Rm*

[28] tumoris *S*: *corr. Rm*

[29] effectum *conieci*: effectus *edd.*

[30] relevantur *Rm, fort. recte*

[31] impressioni *scripsi, coll. 96, 99 fin.*: impressione *edd.*

the chest heavy; there is a sensation that the upper parts are
being pulled downward. Patients lying on their backs have a
feeling of heaviness and tension, and are relieved when they sit
up. Thus they lift themselves to the upper end of the bed in
order to hold the head higher. Eyes are sunken, cheeks flushed,
and the veins under the tongue white. Moreover, if the bursting
of the abscess is long delayed, the limbs become swollen, and
the face grows pallid and so emaciated that the features are
deformed.

97   If the abscess develops on the diaphragm, there is pain in the
upper abdominal region, the pain passing through both sides to
the posterior parts; in some cases there is swelling or distention
near the edge of the thorax, i.e., at the ends of the ribs, especially the lowest ribs, and extending to the others. And if the
abscess is in the outer part of the diaphragm,[7] the sound of
pent-up fluid is sometimes audible; there is coughing, breathing
is very labored and slow, and inspiration, in particular, is painful. This last symptom is never found in cases of abscess of
the lung, for in those cases the pain abates when the patient
breathes in.

98   When abscess occurs in the esophagus, there is malodorous
belching, and the patient's breathing is labored, but only to a
small degree; sometimes there is a slight cough without any
coughing-up of fluid matter. Other symptoms are cold numbness
of the extremities, fainting, sweat on the surface of the skin,
small pulse, the spoiling of food that is eaten, acrid belching,
nausea and sometimes vomiting, dryness or roughness of the
tongue, thirst, and more or less difficulty in swallowing, depending on the size of the abscess.

     Now if the accumulation is in the upper part of the esophagus,
the patient feels distress in eating, until the food is swallowed
99 down, but thereafter he feels relieved. On the other hand, if the
lower part of the esophagus is affected, swallowing is easy, but
the subsequent stages of the ingestion of food are painful; that
is to say, when the food comes to the stomach there is pain at
the upper orifice of that organ toward the anterior surface of
the body. Also there is a swelling or bulging that yields to the
pressure of the fingers and then reappears. No such swelling or
bulging is visible, however, if the abscess is in the upper part of

7. Cf. 92, 93.

gravedo inter scapulas vel ex posterioribus cervicis partibus sentietur.

ac si in ventre fuerit collectio, et magis in eius ambitu, erit inflatio inferius a diaphragmate, quod discrimen appellamus, circa medium praecordiorum sinistrorsus flexa et impressioni digi-
100 torum cedens ac resurgens, attestante fastidio, nausea, siti post cibi sumptionem, cum ructationibus acidis atque sumptorum corruptione et aliquando liquidis per ventrem egestionibus.

ac si in aliquo intestinorum fuerit collectio, erit extantia vel inflatio vomicae secundum eius positionem.[32] in pyloro denique constituta, in ultima parte ventris sub dextro latere atque ilio vel sub iecore. sin vero in nestide fuerit collectio, erit in sinistra parte extantia supradicta atque inflatio veluti sub liene. aliis etiam intestinis tenerioribus[33] collectione vitiatis, inter umbilici atque pectinis regionem supradicta reperiuntur. ac si in colo fuerit collectio, secundum ilium dextrum circa umbilicum usque ad sinistra loca, antecedentibus his quae sunt solita colicos
101 afficere, supradicta reperiuntur. item in longaone collectione suffecta, clunium dolor sequetur cum difficultate mictus et abstinentia ventris et aliquando egestione muculenta vel sanguinolenta. inflatio autem vel extantia erit in superficie occulta, sed immissis per podicem digitis sentietur, et ad inferiora venientibus liquidis commixta stercora putria egerantur,[34] adeo ut plerumque lateat utrum ex pyloro vel nestide aut tenerioribus[35] intestinis haec ferri videantur. sed erunt purulenta separatiora a stercore atque discreta cum ex colo referuntur aut ex longaone.
102 item in iecore vomica constituta, inflatio vel extantia et pulsuosa sequetur aegrotantes appositio, et tangentibus nobis sana principaliter occurrunt, et circa confinium interaneorum, quae ut supra diximus Graeci splanchna vocant, circumscripta collectio sentietur; cum numquam tantum latens atque ita submersa in peritoneo collectio comprobetur, neque ita circumscripta ac decisa videatur, sed paulatim deficiens suos fines sanis

[32] *post* pyloro *interpunx. edd.*

[33] tenerioribus *Almeloveen* (*p. 705*), *coll. 101*: tensioribus *S*: tenuioribus *Rm*

[34] egeruntur *R*

[35] tenuioribus *Rm*

---

8. Possibly 'or in the shoulder blades.' But *vel* may here denote equivalence: 'i.e., in the back, below the neck.'

the esophagus, but there is a feeling of pain and heaviness between the shoulder blades or in the back of the neck.[8]

If the accumulation occurs in the stomach, and particularly on its round surface, there is a swelling below the diaphragm (Latin *discrimen*) at about the middle of the precordial region and turned leftward; this swelling yields to pressure of the fingers and then returns. Additional symptoms are loss of appetite, nausea, thirst after the taking of food, acrid belching, spoiling of the food that is eaten, and sometimes the passing of fluid discharges by way of the bowels.

Again, if the abscess is located in some portion of the intestines, there will be a swelling or bulging according to the location of the accumulation. Thus in abscess of the pylorus the swelling will occur at the extremity of the stomach, i.e., on the right side and flank, below the liver. But in abscess of the jejunum the swelling and bulging will occur on the left side, i.e., under the spleen. Again, if the accumulation is located in the small intestines the swelling is found between the umbilical and the pubic regions. In abscess of the colon, however, it is found along the right flank and around the umbilicus and extends as far as the parts on the left; there are also the antecedent symptoms that usually affect those suffering from disease of the colon. Finally, in abscess of the rectum there is pain in the loins, urination is difficult, the functioning of the bowels is impeded, and there is sometimes a discharge of mucus or blood. No swelling or bulging is visible on the surface, but, if the fingers are inserted into the anus, the swelling can be felt. In these cases putrid fecal matter is discharged, mixed with whatever fluids pass to the lower bowels. And, in fact, it is generally hard to tell whether these fluids come from the pylorus, jejunum, or small intestines. On the other hand, purulent fluids that come from the colon or the rectum are likely to be separated and free from fecal matter.

In abscess of the liver there is a swelling or bulging accompanied by throbbing. On palpating the patient we find that, while healthy tissues predominate, a well-defined gathering of matter can be felt in the vicinity of the internal organs (Greek *splanchna*, as aforesaid). On the other hand, an abscess in the peritoneum is never so completely hidden or concealed as this and, again, never so well defined and delimited. That is, a peri-

partibus iungat, ut non deiecta atque decisa videatur.[36] haec
est vomicarum omnium specialis significatio.

sed earum eruptiones aliquae ad thoracis inania fiunt, aliquae
inter regionem peritonei et intestinorum, aliquae ad stomachum
103 vel ventrem, ut liquida atque purulenta evomantur, aliquae ad
pulmonem sive arteriam maiorem vel rumam, quam Graeci
bronchon appellant, quo liquida et purulenta etussiantur,[37]
aliquae ad intestina vel eorum spatia, quo per podicem liquida
excludantur vel purulenta, aliquae ad matricem, quo per muliebrem sinum profundantur, aliquae ad renes vel mictuales vias
ac vesicam, quo per mictum ferantur, aliquae ad cor, ut Erasistratus ait.

sed harum omnium eruptionum plerique alias rationabiles
dicunt,[38] aliquas irrationabiles. sed rationabiles aiunt, ut ad
104 stomachum vel ventrem[39] venientes per os excludi, ad pulmonem
vero per arteriam maiorem, item ad intestina vel ventrem per[40]
podicem ferri, ad renes vero vel vesicam per mictuales vias, item
ad matricem per muliebre veretrum. irrationabiles autem dicunt eas quae in diaphragmate vel hypozygo membrana aut
iecore et liene generatae rumpuntur, ⟨si⟩[41] per arteriam maiorem
vel stomachum aut vesicam aut matricem excludi credantur,[42]
cum nullae sint ab his partibus quae collectione affectae sunt
naturales viae ad supradicta loca ducentes. alii vero etiam in
his se repertos quaedam vascula demonstrant, anatomica ra-
105 tione adprehensa, quae ad haec penetrant loca. alii aiunt vias
esse latentes, quas logotheoretas appellant, per quas liquida[43]
vel purulenta quadam exudatione ferantur. sed non oportet de
his plurimum disputare: sufficit enim ad disciplinam significationis faciundae manifesta comprobare.

item aliqui etiam in singula loca ex aliis factam susceptionem
puris, quam metalepsin vocaverunt, signis explicare conati sunt,

[36] videantur S: corr. R

[37] fort. scrib. extussiantur (cf. Ac. ii. 97)

[38] dicuntur S: corr. R

[39] vel ventrum fort. secl.

[40] per scripsi: vel edd.

[41] supplevi: ⟨et⟩ R

[42] creduntur Rm

[43] liquida conieci, coll. 103: limpida edd.

toneal abscess tapers off very gradually, the diseased and healthy tissues merging so that the abscess is not at all well defined and delimited. So much for the special symptoms of abscess in the different parts of the body.

Now some of these gatherings, on bursting, discharge into the cavity of the chest; some into the space between the peritoneum and the intestines; some into the esophagus or the
103   stomach, the purulent fluid matter being vomited up; some into the lung or the trachea (Latin *ruma*, Greek *bronchos*), the purulent fluid matter being coughed up; some into the intestinal tract, the purulent fluid matter being passed through the anus; some into the uterus, this matter being discharged through the vagina; some into the kidneys or the urinary canals and the bladder, the matter being discharged with the urine; and some, according to Erasistratus, into the heart.

But with regard to the bursting [and discharge] of these abscesses, most authors divide the cases into two kinds, rational and irrational. They call 'rational' such cases as those in which the purulent matter flows into the esophagus or stomach and is
104   discharged through the mouth, or flows into the lung and is discharged through the windpipe, or flows into the intestines or bowels and is discharged through the anus, or flows into the kidneys or bladder and is discharged through the urinary canal, or flows into the uterus and is discharged through the vagina. But if an abscess develops in the diaphragm, pleura, liver, or spleen, and then bursts and is thought to be discharged by way of the windpipe, esophagus, bladder, or uterus, these authors call the case 'irrational'; for they hold that there are no natural channels leading from the part in which the gathering develops to the part where it is discharged. But others claim even in these cases to have found by anatomical procedures vessels con-
105   necting the parts in question. And still others declare that there are pores which are unseen (Greek *logotheōrētoe*)[9] and that through them the purulent fluid matter seeps in some way and is discharged. But we need not argue at length about these opinions, since it is sufficient, for the purpose of giving an account of the symptoms, to consider only what is visible.

Some seek to connect the passing of pus from one part to another (Greek *metalēpsis*) with certain symptoms; they point

9. I.e., apprehended only by the intellect.

quae quidem non necessaria sed frequentia probaverunt. etenim ad arteriam maiorem sive gutturis cannam, quam Graeci
bronchon appellant, facta eruptio spirationis ingerit difficul-
106 tatem et tussiculam; ad stomachum vero, nauseam atque fastidium et eversionem vel vomitum ingerit aegrotanti; item ad
intestina vel ventrem, tormentum facit partium cum inflatione
ac ventositate; ad vesicam vero, delectationem facit frequenter
urinae reddendae; ad inania autem thoracis atque inter peritoneon membranam et vitalia interna, nulla sunt antecedentia
eruptionis signa. sed utramque factam intelligimus. nam[44] pro
aegrotantium motu vel conversione iacendi sonus quidam efficitur velut inclusi humoris, quem Graeci hydatismon vocaverunt.
praestantius[45] autem si inter peritoneon atque intestina id evenerit; sequetur etiam[46] prominentia partium hydropem fingens
107 cum mordicationibus ac doloribus repentinis. sed si ⟨ad⟩ inania[47] fuerit ruptio thoracis facta, superiorum partium a discrimine, quod Graeci diaphragma vocant, cum difficultate spirationis ac tussicula[48] querela sequetur. sin vero in regionem[48a] quae
intestinis atque peritoneo interiacet fuerit facta, inferiorum partium querela sequetur cum intestinorum tormento. novitate
enim repentinae effusionis acriorum humorum atque corrupti
puris edacitate, ea quae naturali habitu custodita manebant[49]
vitalia vehementissime vexabuntur.[50]

108 praeterea repentina atque coacervata[51] ruptio fit, aliquando
paulatim, tenuatis primo vomicae tegminibus ut praeliquatum
atque parvum liquorem mittant. quod apprehendimus cum
tussicula desiverit esse sicca, atque sputa pollui admixtione
puris viderimus, vel in egestionibus ventris quicquam saniosi
liquoris fuerit repertum, vel in egestionibus urinae sedimina
purulenta fuerint inventa.

sed post supradictas eruptiones, si omnis fuerit facta liquoris
effusio febres ilico solvuntur atque loci prominentia reflatur et

---

[44] nam *Rm*: sed *S*

[45] praestantior *Rm*

[46] *fort.* enim

[47] ⟨ad⟩ inania *scripsi, coll. 106 et* ad inanitatem, *112*: inanis *S*

[48] tussiculae *edd.*

[48a] regione *S*: *corr. R*   [50] vexabuntur *scripsi*: vexabantur *S*

[49] manebunt *S*: *corr. R*   [51] aliquando *add. R*

out, however, that these symptoms are not always present but frequently so. Thus, if an abscess begins to suppurate into the trachea or windpipe (Greek *bronchos*), coughing and difficulty
106 of breathing [generally] result; if into the esophagus, the patient suffers nausea, loss of appetite, gagging, or vomiting; if into the stomach[10] and intestines, cramps, swelling, and gas develop in these parts; if into the bladder, a frequent desire to urinate results. But when an abscess begins to suppurate into the chest cavity, or between the peritoneum and the contained viscera, there are no antecedent symptoms. We are able, however, to ascertain the occurrence of both these cases after the completion of suppuration. For a sound like that of water splashing in a container (Greek *hydatismos*) may be heard when the patient moves or changes his position, and this sound is more clearly heard in the cases where the flow of pus has been between the peritoneum and the intestines. Also in the latter case there is an abdominal swelling that simulates dropsy, with cramps and
107 sudden pains. Again, when the flow has been into the cavity of the chest, there is pain in the parts above the dividing membrane (Greek *diaphragma*), difficulty in breathing, and a cough. But when the flow has been into the space between the intestines and the peritoneum, there is pain in the parts below the diaphragm and also intestinal cramps. For, because of the corrosive action of putrid pus, the sudden and unnatural flow of the acrid liquid severely injures these vital organs, which had normally been well protected.
108 Again, the effusion of pus is [generally] sudden and accomplished all at once, though sometimes it is gradual. In the latter case the covering of the abscess is first dissolved and a small quantity of thin fluid seeps out. This we may recognize when the patient's coughing[11] ceases to be dry and we see the sputa mixed with pus, or if we find any sanious fluid in discharges of the bowels, or purulent matter in the urine.

Now after the breaking-up of an internal abscess, if there has been a complete discharge of all the fluid, the fever is broken up immediately, the swelling subsides, and the feeling of heaviness

10. *Ventrem* may here be merely a synonym for *intestina*, 'bowels.' Cf. 103–4.

11. I.e., in cases of abscess where a cough had been present. But it may be that this paragraph, perhaps with some textual alteration, should be considered as still forming part of the previous discussion of the symptoms of suppuration into the chest cavity or between the peritoneum and the intestines.

gravedo circumscribitur. sin vero ex parte fuerit effusa collectio, quod fiet debilitate aegrotantis aut crassitudine liquidorum,
109 aut non in fundo vomicae[52] osculatione suffecta sed e lateribus
aut supernis partibus, paulatim limpida invenientur.[53] sed erit
approbanda significatio non in fundo factae ruptionis, cum inter
aliquos dies repleta vomica sine eruptione[54] tensionem rursum
atque gravedinem cum febre moverit aegrotanti. tunc post
effusionem superflui liquoris omnia levigantur; ac similiter per
intervalla dierum eaedem difficultates repraesentantur.[55]

communiter autem omnium eruptionum tutior est comparatione ceterarum illa quae in vesicam venerit atque mictuales
vias. etenim naturaliter creduntur hae partes iugem acrimo-
110 niam liquidorum excipere ac reddere, quapropter neque nunc ulla
novitate facile vexari posse videntur, cum in se aliena atque
acriora susceperint quae eruptione vomicae descendunt; dehinc
quod naturali urinae[56] commixta purulenta, quae collectione[57]
corrupta videntur, obtusa mitescunt; ultimo quod neque coacervatam sed paulatim redditam ac requiescentem sumant egestionem, urinae per exitum tractam.[58]

item facilitate secunda est quae ad intestina ruperit. haec
enim quoque creduntur transitum stercorum sustinere, sed a
prima[59] minus tuta iudicatur, siquidem possit coacervatae effusionis causa per podicem aegrotanti defectionem facere et propterea mortem.

111   tertia est quae ad matricem ruperit, et magis in his quae iam
naturali lege purgantur. didicerunt enim loca materiae [et][60]
transitum sustinere. minus quidem a prioribus tuta est, siquidem neque ex initio nativitatis, neque per dies singulos naturalem meatum ipsae sustineant partes, neque ita acria ferre consueverint liquorum, siquidem nihil in se sanguis habeat morda-
cissimae qualitatis.

omnium tamen periculosior iudicatur, ut Erasistratus ait,

---

[52] vomica S: corr. Rm

[53] limpida invenientur scripsi: liquidam inventurum S: ⟨exeuntia⟩ liquida inveniuntur Rm

[54] sine eruptione conieci: sive eruptio edd. (an sive collectio?)

[55] eadem d. repraesentantur Rm: easdem d. repraesentet S

[56] fort. urina   [57] collatione S: corr. Rm

[58] tractam scripsi: tractum S: ⟨et⟩ tractum R

[59] a prima scripsi: ad primā S: quam prima Rm   [60] om. R

passes. But if the accumulation is only partially discharged (which may happen by reason of the patient's weakness, or the thickness of the fluids, or because the abscess does not open all the way from the bottom, but only from the sides or the upper parts), the abatement will be gradual.[12] The indication that an abscess has failed to open completely is that after a few days the discharge stops and the abscess fills up again and brings renewed tension, heaviness, and fever to the patient; then after another discharge of excess fluid all the symptoms again abate, only to return as before, and the process keeps recurring at intervals of several days.

In general, the discharge of the pus into the bladder and the urinary canal is safer than all the other types of discharge that may occur. For these are the parts that even in health are supposed to receive a continual flow of pungent fluids and to discharge them; and so it does not seem likely that they will be injured by having suddenly to receive the influx of acrid foreign matter that reaches them after the breaking-up of the abscess. Again, the purulent matter that becomes putrid in the abscess loses some of its pungency by being mixed with the patient's normal urine. And, finally, this purulent matter is not discharged from the body all at once, but flows out gradually and at intervals, carried through the same opening as the urine.

Next [to the discharge of an abscess into the bladder,] the discharge into the intestines is the most favorable type of case; for the intestines are also supposed to afford a passage for the feces. But discharge into the intestines is not so safe as discharge into the bladder, for the pouring of so much matter at once through the anus may cause the patient to faint and thus may even bring about death.

The third most favorable case is discharge into the uterus, especially in women who menstruate; for then the parts are accustomed to furnish a passage for fluid matter. But this case is not so safe as the two previously mentioned. For the parts in question do not afford a natural channel of flow from birth, nor do they so function every day. And they are not used to enduring such pungent fluids, since blood does not possess any very acrid qualities.

But the most dangerous case, as Erasistratus tells us, is that

12. This seems to be the meaning, but the text is uncertain.

quae ad cor fuerit facta. eius secunda quae ad arteriam gutturis, quam Graeci bronchum appellant; et eius repentina magis atque
112 coacervata ab ea quae paulatim fuerit effusa, siquidem defectiones[61] ingerat aegrotanti atque difficultatem spirationis et tussiculam et praefocationem, cum neque naturalibus liquidis ulla consuetudo per ipsam partem transeundi videatur. tertia quae ad stomachum fuerit facta, siquidem praefocationem minus ingerat, minus quidem a supradicta, appetitum quoque cibi extinguat, et propterea fame aegrotantes afficiendo debilitet. item post hanc secunda est quae ad inanitatem thoracis fuerit facta, siquidem circumfundatur pulmoni humor corruptus atque cordi. ultima est quae inter regionem peritonei et intestinorum venerit,
113 siquidem circumfundatur humor iecori et lieni et ventri atque intestinis, quae cum fuerint vexata ingerant periculum.

communiter autem sive universim dicendo, quod Graeci catholicon vocant, omnium vomicarum vel eorum qui his afficiuntur salutarem intelligimus ductum fore, si post eruptionem factam febres cessaverint, et magis extemplo vel eadem die, siti quoque recedente atque perfecto appetitu cibi, ventris quoque officio parva atque congesta reddente, ipsius etiam puris albido[63] atque eodem colore apparente, et cum lenitate ac sine dolore suarum egestionum; et si per superna egeritur, sine vehementi
114 tussicula neque coacervatim sed per partes excluduntur liquida. pessimas[64] autem aut difficillimas[65] aut, ut saepe contingit, interfectivas esse iudicamus eas[66] quibus post eruptionem febres annexae perseveraverint, attestante siti cum fastidio cibi et ventris fluore vel ipsius puris felloso vel livido colore, coacervatis egestionibus cum[67] vehementi tussicula viribus depurgatis. haec est vomicarum significatio.

sed oportet ob earum generationem fugiendam congruam tumoribus adhibere curationem. horum enim augmenta collectiones faciunt generari, ut saepe in pleureticis vel peripleumoni-

[61] *an* defectionem?

[63] albedo *S*: albedine *Rm*

[64] pessima *edd.*

[65] difficulter *S*: difficillima *Rm*

[66] interfectiva ferri iudicamus eis *edd.*

[67] ⟨aut⟩ cum *R*

in which the pus flows to the heart, and the next most dangerous case is that in which the flow is to the windpipe (Greek *bronchos*). In the latter case the sudden discharge of all the pus at

112 once is more dangerous than a gradual discharge; for it may cause fainting, difficulty in breathing, coughing, and choking, since normally fluids do not pass through the windpipe. Third in point of danger is the case in which the pus is discharged into the esophagus. For this occurrence is less apt to cause choking— at any rate, less than when the discharge is into the windpipe— but it also destroys the patient's appetite for food, thus bringing about weakness through lack of food. The next most dangerous case is the discharge of pus into the chest cavity, for then a putrid fluid pours round the lung and heart. And the last among the dangerous cases is that in which the discharge is between

113 the peritoneum and the intestines; for the fluid pours round the liver, spleen, stomach, and intestines, and any injury to these organs involves danger.

Generally or universally speaking (Greek *catholicon*), we may expect a favorable outcome for all abscesses, i.e., for the patients, if after the breaking-up of the gathering the fever terminates, especially if it terminates quickly, say on the same day; if the patient's thirst also abates, and his appetite for food returns to normal; if the bowel movements are small and compact, and the color of the pus white and unchanging; and, finally, if the discharges of fluid are accomplished without pain, and, in the case of upward discharges, without violent coughing, and

114 not all at once but in parts. But we hold that the worst and most difficult cases, cases in which the outcome is often fatal, are those in which the fever connected with the disease persists after the breaking-up of the abscess, as does the patient's thirst and his lack of appetite. In these cases there is a flux of the bowels, the pus discharged is yellowish or livid, and the patient's strength is exhausted by the copious discharges and by violent coughing. So much for the symptomatology of internal abscesses.[13]

But, to prevent the development of an internal abscess, suitable treatment must be applied to the inflammations. For abscesses develop from the spread of inflammation, and this often takes place in cases of pleurisy, pneumonia, and similar diseases.

13. Including, of course, prognosis (= *significatio praescia, Chr.* iv. 112).

cis[68] vel similibus morbis, quibus ita formavimus curationes ut
minime sinantur initia fieri vomicarum.

115   at vero si iam perfectam vomicam viderimus, et humore[69] corrupto in toto aut ex parte tumoris caruerit nomine, oportebit
similibus adhuc perseverare adiutoriis, ut cataplasmatibus ex
polline tritici vel seminis lini aut faenigraeci vel hordeacii confectis, vel ex aqua mulsa aut hibisci decoctione, cuius etiam radix erit conterenda addita vaporatione spongiarum. vel si in
inferioribus corporis partibus fuerit collectio, encathismatibus
quoque iugibus erit utendum ex aqua et oleo calido ac decoctione cuiusquam ex his quae cataplasmatibus congrua[70] supra
116 diximus. ante cibum praeterea olei calidi quicquam poto dandum, dehinc etiam mulsi mediocriter cocti; tunc sorbilis offerendus est cibus atque calidus. est enim improprium ex parte adhuc manente tumore quicquam acrius adhibere, quo magis labor
aegrotantibus geminetur, scilicet tumore asperato, unde maiores
collectiones efficiuntur.

   pausante igitur tumore omni ex parte et nondum erupta collectione, oportet eius adiuvari[70a] celeritatem, ut primum praescriptis[71] cataplasmatibus ficum faciamus admisceri cum hibisco; tum resinam terebinthinam[72] adiuncto usu malagmatum
117 quae congrua Responsionum docuimus libris, ut est Mnaseu,[73]
item ex tribus resinis, quod Graeci diatrion retinon vocant, tum
etiam diagalbanes vel melinen, vel quam appellant Serapionos,[74]
aut ⟨dia⟩dictamnu[75] vel quicquam simili permistione[76] conscriptum. cibo autem dandus sucus ptisanae cum melle, item
porri capitati vel atriplex, quam Graeci andraphasin vocant,
itemque urticam. iubendi praeterea aegrotantes magis supra
latus iacere, si in superioribus a diaphragmate partibus collectio
fuerit generata. cavenda etenim supina iacendi positio, siquidem extenta arteria angustetur, quo et magna difficultas spirationis fiat et minima liquidorum exclusio perficiatur.

118   sed si his adhibitis collectionis non provenerit eruptio, oportebit vehementioribus eam provocare ne humor inclusus plurima

---

[68] *formas* pleurit- *et* peripneumon- *solas praebet G in Cel. pass. libris*   [69] *fort.* tumore
(*aut mox* humoris *pro* tumoris)   [70] cataplasmatibus congrua quae *S: transp. R*

[70a] *sed* adiuvare *Cass. Fel., p. 36. 4 (Rose)*

[71] perscriptis *S: corr. Schmid RPh 155*   [74] Serapionis *R*

[72] resina terebinthina *S: corr. R (cf. 121)*   [75] diadictamnum *Rm:* dictamnū *S*

[73] mnaseū *S*   [76] permistione *Friedel 35:* promissione *S*

Our treatment of these diseases has been so designed as to prevent abscesses from beginning to develop.

115   But even if we find a fully developed abscess, the fluid having wholly or partly decomposed[14] so that the term 'inflammation' is no longer really applicable, still continue to use the same remedies, e.g., poultices made with flour of wheat, flaxseed, fenugreek seed, or barley, together with hydromel or a decoction of marsh mallow. Triturated marsh mallow root may also be used, along with applications of heat by means of sponges. And if the gathering is located in the lower parts of the body, also prescribe the regular use of sitz baths. The latter should consist of olive oil mixed with water and a decoction of any of the sub-

116   stances mentioned above as suitable for poultices. And, before giving the patient food, have him drink some warm olive oil and then some mead moderately cooked; after that give him a warm gruel. So long as even a part of the inflammation persists, it is wrong to employ any sharp substance; for the patient's distress is increased when the inflammation is irritated, and, as a result, a greater accumulation of pus develops.

But if the inflammation has ceased completely and the gathering has not yet broken up, the bursting must be accelerated. For this purpose first add fig and marsh mallow to the poultices described above. Then employ resin of the terebinth tree in conjunction with suitable emollient plasters, as described in our

117   treatise entitled *Answers*, e.g., Mnaseas' plaster, that made with three resins (Greek *dia triōn rētinōn*), the allheal plaster, a yellow plaster such as that of Serapion, the dittany plaster, or any other plaster similarly compounded. For food give the patient pearl barley gruel with honey, and also scallions or orach (Greek *andraphasis*), and nettles. And if the pus has accumulated in the parts above the diaphragm, have the patient lie chiefly on his side. He should avoid lying on his back, since the windpipe is then narrow and elongated, a circumstance that causes great difficulty in breathing and reduces the discharge of fluid matter to a minimum.

118   But if, despite these measures, the gathering still does not break up, it will be necessary to use stronger measures to induce the bursting, so that the fluid may not be pent up for too long a time and do widespread damage to the neighboring parts. And

14. I.e., turned to pus.

tardando membra corrumpat. quapropter praepotandi sunt
aegri decoctione fici vel hyssopi ac rutae et origani et tragorigani
et thymi vel satureiae aut absinthii vel centaureae aut marrubii
aut semine radicum aut sinapi aut nasturtii cum melle, quorum
aliqua etiam viridia erunt mandenda. item medicamen quod
appellatur dia trion pipereon potu dandum vel diascordeon[77] aut
zopirium. multi tamen etiam hieram dandam probaverunt, et
119 magis illam quae appellatur diacolocyntidos. adiuvat quoque
eruptionis celeritatem sternutatio adhibita, et aliquibus etiam
excreatus quidam hinnibilis iugiter affectatus. ac si neque ita
eruptio fuerit consecuta, erit ieiunus, vel dato poto aut radicibus
comestis, vomitus adhibendus. aliqui vero in his quae superioribus a diaphragmate partibus vexantur fumationes adhibuerunt,
tardante eruptione, hyssopum vel thymum aut origanum in-
cendentes vel sulphur; et sandaraca aut aloe vel storace imposi-
tis igni aegros hiscere iusserunt, et raptu quodam potili nidorem
transvorare, tunc dandum vel tymiama[78] probant per diem bis
vel ter: similare[79] enim inquiunt[80] curationis genus chirurgiae.
120 sed vehementer caput gravat implendo.

ac si in intestinis fuerit collectio, erunt per clysterem inicienda
ea quae praebibenda nuper ordinavimus.

tum eruptione facta speculandum utrum per partes atque disposito[81] liquida excludantur, an vero coacervata aut omnino
difficulter et paulatim. sed si partim et nullis obstantibus excludi viderimus, erit a cibo abstinendus aegrotus, viribus permittentibus. tum alia die adhibita corporis unctione praepotandus his quae supra memoravimus; cibis quoque adiuvare collectionem quo omnia liquida detrahantur, dato mulso vel solo
melle bibendo[82] cum resina terebinthina aut butyro non veteri.
121 tum sorbilem dabimus sucum ex alica vel ptisana melle admixto,
item porros coctos cum oleo atque garo et ptisana, tum etiam

[77] *fort. scrib.* diascordiu

[78] dandum vel tymiama *scripsi:* dandum vel tymminum *S:* adhibendum hoc thymi-
ama *Rm: fort.* dandum mel t(h)yminum

[79] simile *R*

[80] inquiunt ⟨hoc⟩ *R*

[81] disposito *scripsi, coll.* indisposito *Ac. i. 51:* deposito *S*

[82] bibendo *transp. R post* mulso

so, first, have the patient drink a decoction of fig, hyssop, rue, marjoram, goat's marjoram, thyme, savory, wormwood, centaury, or horehound, or a preparation of radish, mustard, or nasturtium seed with honey; the greens of some of these plants should also be eaten. And have the patient drink the so-called 'drug of three peppers,' the scordium drug, or Zopyrus' drug. Many physicians recommend a hiera drug, especially the so-
119 called 'hiera of colocynth.'[15] The bursting is also accelerated by the use of sternutatories, and in some cases by vigorous and continual hawking. If even after such measures there is still no breakup, induce vomiting when the patient's stomach is empty, giving him an emetic to drink or radishes to eat. In cases where an abscess located above the diaphragm is slow to break up, some physicians make use of fumes. They burn hyssop, thyme, marjoram, or sulphur; or they place sandarac, aloes, or storax over a fire and have the patient open his mouth wide and draw in the vapors as if drinking them down. Then they add incense, and they use the treatment twice or three times a day. They
120 declare that it resembles surgery;[16] but the fact is that it causes severe congestion and heaviness of the head.

If the abscess is located in the intestines, inject by clyster such substances as we have prescribed above[17] for drinking.

Now when the bursting takes place, ascertain whether the fluid matter is being discharged part by part and in an orderly manner, or all at one time, or only a little at a time and very infrequently. If the discharge takes place part by part without obstacle, keep the patient from food, his strength permitting. Then on the following day anoint his body and let him drink any of the preparations we have mentioned above. Also help along the discharge of the abscess with suitable foods, so that all the fluid matter will be withdrawn. Thus have the patient take a drink of mead or plain honey with resin of the terebinth
121 tree or butter that is not old. Then give him a porridge of spelt groats or pearl barley with an admixture of honey; also cooked scallions with olive oil, fish sauce, and pearl barley, or a mixture

15. Of the six *hierae* described by Paul of Aegina (vii. 8), all but one contain colocynth as an ingredient.

16. Presumably because it brings about the complete removal of the abscess, as if by a knife.

17. 118.

ex tritico ptisanam confectam[83] aut cum protropo vino aut scybelitico,[84] item lac cum mulso. et si eruptio liquidorum ad mictuales vias pervenerit, erunt adiungenda supradictis etiam mictualia medicamina quae urinam provocent, a Graecis diuretica appellata, ut asparagi, olus atrum,[85] lactucae nunc coctae nunc incoctae, item radices et sorbilia lacte quoque confecta. sin vero ad intestina eruptio pervenerit quo per podicem exitum habeat, cum supradictis communiter erunt adhibenda quae ventris officium non densent neque plurimum laxent. quapropter
122 mictualibus prohibitis,[85a] cibo ordinabimus[86] malvam dandam, betas, cauliculos, cucurbitas.

sed si coacervatim ac nimis liquida ferri viderimus, erit abstinentia recusanda. dandum mulsum poto sufficienter decoctum, et plurima sitis aegrotantibus indicenda.[87] dandus praeterea cibus | qui ventris teneat officium, ut orizae sucus[88] sorbilis aut lenticulae, item pisces duri corporis, quos sclerosarchus[89] Graeci vocaverunt, et volantum sicciora, et poto aqua imbrialis offerenda, quam[90] vulgo cisterninam[91] vocant, calida; item medicamina[92] quae ad humectam tussiculam[93] conscripta sunt, tum vinum mediocriter asperum.[94]

123 sin vero difficulter atque paulatim liquida fuerint exclusa, erit inquirenda causa, utrumne ob debilitatem aegrotantis id evenerit, quo minime valeat excludere aliena, an vero ob crassitiem[95] liquidorum vel ob eruptionem ⟨aut⟩[96] in lateribus factam vel ⟨in supernis partibus, non⟩[97] in fundo collectionis. etenim si ob debilitatem aegrotantis id adverterimus fieri, erunt sublevandae vires per resumtionem; si autem ob crassitudinem[98] liquidorum, tenuantia[99] adhibenda atque praepotanda quae supra memora-

---

| inc. L fol. 136r

[83] ptisana confecta S: corr. R (cf. 116)

[84] scybelitico Reinesius 675: squillitico S

[85] atriũ S: corr. R

[85a] prohibiti S: corr. R

[86] ordinavimus S: -amus R

[92] medicamina S: evanuerunt ultimae 4 litterae in mg. L

[93] tussicula L: corr. S

[94] asperum S: primae duae litterae evanidae L

[87] indigenda edd.

[88] oryzae succus S, ut solet

[89] sclerosarcos S

[90] qua L: corr. S

[91] cisternina L: corr. S

[95] crassitiem S: crassi tum L: fort. crassitudinem Ilberg, coll. crassitudinem infra, etiam Ac. i. 121, Chr. ii. 205, v. 57, 109

of pearl barley and wheat.[18] Wine of the first flow or Scybelan wine[19] may also be used; so, too, milk with mead. If after the bursting of the abscess the fluid matter reaches the urinary canal, add to the above prescriptions such preparations as will induce urination (Greek *diurētica*), e.g., asparagus, alexanders, lettuce cooked or uncooked, radishes, and porridges, the latter prepared also with milk. If, however, the pus reaches the intestines, whence it has an outlet through the anus, prescribe, in addition to the foods mentioned above, such foods as will prevent costiveness and at the same time will not relax the bowels

122 excessively. Thus, while forbidding the use of diuretics, prescribe as food mallows, beets, cabbage, and cucumbers.

If, however, the fluids are found to be discharged in excessive amounts at one time, do not withhold food from the patient.[20] Let him drink only mead that is well boiled down, and let him develop considerable thirst.[21] In addition, give him such food as will retard movements of the bowels, e.g., a rice or lentil soup, fish with hard flesh (Greek *sclērosarcoe*), and the drier meat of birds. And have him drink hot rain water, commonly called in Latin *cisternina* ('cistern water'), and the remedies that have been prescribed against moist cough;[22] then a moderately tart wine.

123 But if only a little pus is discharged at long intervals, investigate whether the patient's failure to discharge this foreign matter satisfactorily is due to his own weakness, or to the thickness of the fluids, or to the circumstance that the bursting of the accumulation of pus took place from the sides or top rather than from the bottom. If the patient's weakness is found to be the cause, repair his strength through restorative treatment. But if the thickness of the fluids is the cause, prescribe remedies that will make them thinner. Thus have the patient drink the preparations mentioned above;[23] and, in addition, give him elec-

---

18. Or perhaps merely 'a gruel made with wheat.'
19. Or 'wine of squills' if the reading of *S* be retained.
20. Cf. 120.   22. *Chr.* ii. 116.
21. The text and meaning are uncertain.   23. 118.

---

96 ⟨aut⟩ *Ilberg*: ⟨non⟩ *S*: *lacunam trium litterarum nunc habet* L
97 *suppl. Ilberg* (*sim. Rm*), *coll. 109*
98 *crassitudine* L: *corr. S*
99 *tenuantia S*: *tenuentia* L (*form. vulg.?* cf. *tardentia, 124*)

124 vimus, adiectis quoque similibus electariis, ut sunt ex melle, resina vel lini semine cum melle confecta ac nucleo pineo[100] vel strobilis[101] et urticae semine. praebibendum senape[102] cum parvo pipere longo; tunc ellebori[103] adhibemus purgationem.

ac si ex vomicis ulcera tardantia[104] perseveraverint, ea quae supra ⟨a⟩[105] diafragmate[106] fuerunt, quod discrimen appellavimus, ita curabimus[107] ut est ⟨de⟩[108] ptysicis[109] scriptum, in stomaco[110] vero vel ventre[111] ut de quiliacis,[112] item in intestinis ut de disintericis;[113] in renibus vero ac vesica vel mictualibus viis potis medicaminibus atque clystere iniectis vel per cathetera[114] inmissis[115] utemur. etenim ⟨si⟩[116] sordida apparuerint ulcera,
125 lacte atque melle potamus semine cucumeris praefuso[117] aut mulso aut pinguibus palmulis cum passo aut nucleis cum amigdalis[118] et amilo.[119] similia etiam per cathetera inmittenda, ut tetrafarmacum[120] medicamen diligenter[121] solutum. sin vero limpida fuerint ulcera, erint[122] encathismata[123] adhibenda, quibus praecocta fuerint aliqua constringentia, atque extrinsecus apponenda emplastra quae cicatricem facere valeant, a Graecis epulotica appellata. poto[124] dandum lac cum amylo et cucumeris semine, cum | decoctione finicobalani[125] aut papaveris frixi[126] atque contriti[127] cum vino protropo et amigdalis[128] vel decoc-
126 tione[129] malae cydoniae,[129a] sorbarum[130] et palmularum thebaicarum vel suco[131] mali punici vel his quae in farmaceuticon[132] Responsionum tradidimus libris, ex quibus est quod appellatur Ariu et Menecratus[133] et ex tracanto[134] atque amylo et lyciriza.[135] utendum etiam aquis sua virtute medentibus, quas supra memoravimus, itemque his quae in Aenaria[136] insula et Teanitarum[137]

| inc. L fol. 136v

[100] nunc lupyneo L: corr. S   [101] strobylis S   [102] sinapi S

[103] ellebori Ilberg: ellevori L: hellebori S

[104] tardantia S: tardentia L (form. vulg.? cf. 123)   [105] ⟨a⟩ Ilberg, coll. 119

[106] diaphragma S   [107] curavimus L: corr. S   [108] de S: evanidum in L

[109] phthisicis S   [110] stomacho S   [111] ventrem L: corr. S

[112] coeliacis S   [113] dysentericis S

[114] cathetera A: catethera LS (sic iterum infra)   [115] inmissa L: corr. A (ed. 1722)

[116] si S: detritum in L   [117] praeinfuso Schmid RPh 43   [118] amygdalis S

[119] amylo S   [120] tetrapharmacum S   [121] diligenter ⟨lacte⟩ R

[122] erunt S   [123] encathismata S: enchatis . . . a evanidis 3 litteris L

124 tuaries of the same kind, e.g., those made of honey, resin or flaxseed with honey, pine kernels or cones, and nettle seed. Also have him drink a preparation of mustard with a small quantity of long pepper; then administer the hellebore purge.

If the ulceration resulting from the abscess persists for a long time, proceed as follows. If the abscess was above the diaphragm, which we have called *discrimen*,[24] use the treatment described in the chapter on phthisis;[25] if it was located in the esophagus or stomach, proceed as in the coeliac disease; if in the intestines, proceed as in cases of dysentery; if in the kidneys, bladder, or urinary canal, use potions as well as preparations injected by clyster or catheter. And if the ulceration seems to be unclean, have the patient drink milk and honey to which

125 the juice of cucumber seed has been added, or mead, or raisin wine containing juicy dates or pine kernels, almonds, and starch. Also use a catheter to introduce substances of similar properties, e.g., the 'four drug' preparation, well dissolved. But if the ulceration is clean, prescribe sitz baths containing some astringent decoctions; also apply externally such plasters as are able to promote cicatrization (Greek *epulōtica*). Let the patient drink milk containing starch and cucumber seed, or a decoction of dates or dried and powdered poppy with wine of the first flow

126 and almonds, or a decoction of quince, sorb apples, and Theban dates, or pomegranate juice, or the preparations we have described in the section on drugs of our treatise entitled *Answers*. Among these preparations are the so-called 'drug of Arius' and that of Menecrates, and a remedy made of tragacanth, starch, and sweetroot. Also employ waters having curative properties; to those mentioned above[26] we may add the waters on the island of Aenaria and those in the region of Teanum. In

---

24. Cf., e.g., 91.   25. *Chr.* ii. 202 ff.   26. E.g., 77.

---

[124] potui *S*

[125] finico valani L: phoenicobalani *S*

[126] fixi L: *corr. Rm*

[127] constricti L: *corr. Rm*

[128] amygdali *S*

[129] decoctione vel L: *transp. Ilberg*

[129a] mali cydonii *S*

[130] sorborum *R*

[131] succo *S, ut solet*

[132] Farmaceuticon *Friedel 36* (Ph-): farmaceutico L*S* (ph-)

[133] ariu et menecratus L: carui et oenocraton *S*

[134] trachanto *S*

[135] glycyrrhiza *S*

[136] Aenaria *Rm*: aria L

[137] teanitorum L (Th- *S*): *corr. Rm*

provincia esse perhibentur, ceterarum[138] quoque resumtivarum materiarum usum adhibentes,[139] ut nutribiliorum sucorum.[140]

ubi vero inter stentina[141] et peritoneum[142] eruptio fuerit facta, sive ex ioecore[143] sive ex aliqua veniens[144] collectio[145] parte, 127 quaesitum est quomodo puris detractio fieri possit: utrumne per tenues vias vesicae veniens atque in intestina acceptum videatur[146] et propterea per urinam vel per ventris officium excludi possit, an vero sectis inguinum locis detrahi facilius videatur, quod quidem Erasistratus demonstravit. sed apparet nunc chyrurgia[147] exitum puris faciendum, incisa secundum inguen peritoneo[148] membrana, quo corruptis liquoribus prolapsio inferioribus apertis[149] praebeatur. tunc congrua adhibenda curatio. etenim incisa peritoneos[150] membrana in cicatricem facile 128 conducitur, et sine ullo periculo aegrotantis sanitas datur, ut est coniciendum ex ydropum[151] paracentesi[152] atque chyrurgia ramicis, quam Graeci enterocelen vocant. neque inpossibile putandum, etiam si quid remanserit[153] facta detractione chyrurgiae,[154] per superficiem cutis ac tenuis[155] vias et per intestinorum cavitatem sudari, quippe cum etiam in ydropibus circumfusus humor intestinis saepe fuerit exsiccatus,[156] quibusdam per vesicam, feminis[157] per matricem.

sed omnibus communiter fortitudinem convenit per nutrimenta praestare. facile enim correctio[158] partium depulsa passione fiet, cum corpus[159] fuerit naturali fortitudine possessum. |

| expl. L fol. 136v

[138] caeterarum S, *ut solet*
[139] usum adhibendo R: usus adhibendus *Ilberg*
[140] sucorum *scripsi*: sucus L: succos S
[141] intestina S
[142] peritoneum S: perineum L
[143] iecore S (*cf. Ilberg, Berl. Ak. Sitz. 1922, p. 283*)
[144] veniat R
[145] collectio *scripsi*: collectionis LS
[146] videamur L: *corr.* S
[147] chirurgia S, *ut solet (alia exempla non afferam)*
[148] peritonei S
[149] aperte S
[150] peritonei S
[151] hydropum S, *ut solet (alia exempla non afferam)*
[152] paracentesin L: *corr.* S
[153] remanserint L: *corr.* S

addition, prescribe other restorative substances, e.g., nutritious juices.

Now when an abscess discharges into the space between the intestines and the peritoneum, whether the gathering was origi-
127 nally located in the liver or some other part, the question arises how the withdrawal of the pus may be best effected. Does it seem best to wait for the pus to pass through the narrow channels connected with the bladder, or enter the intestines, and thus be passed off during urination or movement of the bowels? Or, on the other hand, does withdrawal by an incision in the inguinal region, as described by Erasistratus, seem more feasible? In this type of case we believe surgery is the better method for withdrawing the pus. An incision of the peritoneum should be made in the inguinal region, giving egress to the putrid fluids through the opening below. Then apply suitable treatments. In this way the cut made in the peritoneum can easily be brought to cicatrization and the patient restored to health with-
128 out any risk, as we may infer from our experience with tapping in dropsy, and surgery in intestinal hernia (Greek *enterocēlē*). And it is not to be thought impossible that whatever pus remains, after the bulk has been withdrawn surgically, should be exuded through the surface of the skin, the thin pores, and the region of the intestines.[27] For in cases of dropsy, too, a large mass of fluid is often drained off through the intestines, and in some cases through the bladder, and in women through the uterus.

But in all cases without exception build up the patient's strength by proper nourishment; for, after the disease is overcome, the affected parts will easily be restored to health when the body is possessed of its normal strength.[28]

27. The Latin seems to refer exclusively to sweat; but in view of the sequel it may be that Soranus was referring to the urinary channels and the intestinal tract.

28. Or retaining *corruptio* with the addition of *non* (Ilberg): 'for though the disease is overcome, the affected parts will easily deteriorate unless the body is possessed of its normal strength.'

154 *fort.* chyrurgica *Ilberg*
155 tenues *S* (*cf. 127 in.*)
156 exiccatus *S*
157 foeminis *S, ut solet*
158 correctio *Am. cf. Chr. i. 64; v. 140*: corruptio L*S*
159 non̄ *add. Ilberg* (corruptio *retento*)

129   ## XI. DE SUPERFLUA CARNE, QUAM GRAECI POLYSARCIAN VOCANT

Accidunt corporibus superflua carnis incrementa, quae Graeci ob nimietatem polysarcian vocaverunt. sed est hoc passionis genus contrarium nutrimento cessante,[1] siquidem cessans nutrimentum tabida faciat corpora; idem ultra naturae modum vehementius elatum plurimam faciat carnem generari, ex qua corpora gravata premantur. praeterea hoc quoque speciem accipimus cachexiae siquidem indecens difficultas patientes afficiat. nam sequitur nimia ac superflua multitudo carnis,

130 quae in pinguem prominentiam erigatur, cum tardo motu atque gravatione et debilitate et ex parvo gressu anhelatione ac sudore, ut suo se corpore praefocari sentiant aegrotantes, quo neque levia ferre valeant vestimenta.

multi igitur medicorum atque aliptarum salutaribus praeceptis adiungendam diligentiam detrahendae carnis putaverunt, intuentes coenoteta, quam epidosin vel euexian vocant, hoc est

131 habitudinis augmentum. sed hoc a Sorano repulsum. nos igitur solam ⟨bonam⟩[2] habitudinem intelligimus quae fuerit cum modica carne fortitudo, et servanda magis quam repellenda. polysarcian[3] vero, quam nunc passionem dicimus, recte cachexian nuncupamus quae multis accidentibus denuntiet periculum. etenim quae sequentur[4] animalia nutrimento dedita vel custodia reservata, ut flato[5] atque extento et prominenti corpore videantur, haec eadem cuncta patientes sequentur, similiter accidentia[6] corporibus ulceratis quibus vana[7] caro concrescit vel eorum[8] labiis quae fuerit[9] acie circumcisa renascatur.[9a]

132   sed istius passionis duplex traditur differentia curationis: alia quae cohibeat fieri plurimum corporis nutrimentum, quae quidem ponitur in gestatione celeri et cibis non multum nutribilibus ac moderatis, ne plura corpus quam insumit accipiat; alia quae

---

[1] cessanti *Rm, fort. recte*

[2] *add. R*

[3] polysarcia *edd.*

[4] sequetur *S*: sequuntur *Rm*

[5] inflato *Rm*: elato *Triller Clinotechnia 254*

[6] *fort.* accident in

[7] *fort.* nova

[8] *fort.* cum   [9] fuerint *Rm*   [9a] renascantur *S*: renascitur *Rm*

129   XI. OBESITY (GREEK *POLYSARCIA*)

BODIES may keep acquiring additional flesh beyond what is
needed; and it is because of the superfluous nature of these
accessions that the Greeks call the condition *polysarcia*.[1] This
disease is in its nature the opposite of atrophy. For the latter
involves a wasting-away of the body; but an extreme and unnatural trophic increase causes the development of excessive
flesh, which oppresses the body and weighs it down. Now we
consider polysarcia a form of cachexia, for the patient suffers
from an unsightly affliction. He has an abnormal and excessive
130 amount of flesh, which bulges out in full prominence; his movements are sluggish, and there is a feeling of heaviness and weakness. A little walking causes shortness of breath and sweating,
so much so that the patient feels suffocated by his own body and
cannot endure even light clothing.

Now many physicians and trainers believe that the treatment for reduction of flesh is an adjunct of the rules of hygiene.
They consider the common characteristic of the condition under
discussion to be what they call *epidosis* ['increase'] or *euexia*
['good habit of body'; 'embonpoint'], that is to say, increase in
131 corpulence. But this view is rejected by Soranus. And [in agreement with Soranus] we hold that there is only one kind of good
habit of body, namely, that in which there is strength with a
moderate amount of flesh; and that this is a condition to preserve rather than alter. And we properly consider polysarcia,
the disease under discussion, to be a form of cachexia with many
symptoms indicative of danger. Thus the patients show the
very same characteristics as animals that are specially selected
for fattening and are kept in the feeding stall, so that their bodies
become large and bulky and puffed up. The case is similar to
what happens when a body sustains a wound and superfluous
flesh develops, or when flesh cut from the lips by a knife grows
again.[2]

132   The treatment of this disease takes two forms. One form of
treatment seeks to restrain the excessive nourishment of the
body. It relies on vigorous passive exercise, and employs, in
limited amounts, foods that do not give much nourishment; in

1. *Sarx*, 'flesh.'
2. The text is uncertain.

cyclica regula atque operosa recorporatione formetur demutandi corporis causa. sed ut docilis sermo ac manifesta tradatur praeceptio, partium[10] erit memoranda curatio.

convenit igitur corpus exercere gestatione plurima ac perseveranti, animalium iugo vel curriculi motu et equitatione ac navicula; item lectione et vocis exercitio vehementi vel meditatione modulationis agonisticae et celeri gressu quo magis labor surarum fiat; item cursu atque sicca fricatione manibus puris vel aspero linteamine et arenae aspergine; tum volutatione[11] in palaestra varia, quam Graeci †celadian† atque coricomachian vocaverunt, quae sunt specialiter ab ipsius artis praeceptoribus imperanda, tum hoplomachia, hoc est armorum ficta conflictione,[12] item alienis[13] laboribus exercitio, hoc est colluctantium vel coexercentium, quam Graeci heterocopian[14] vel trachelismon vocant, atque longo vel raptorio machinamento, quod macron sparton vocaverunt, item italica sphaera et luctatione celeri, et dura atque multa vel sicca fricatione. etenim oleo labentibus manibus fortitudo solvetur exercitii. convenit etiam sole corpora torrere, quod Graeci heliosin vocant; tum paroptesi ex flamma vel carbonibus et siccis vaporationibus provocatur sudor. et nunc ferventia lavacra quae plurimum detrahant, nunc frigida quae corpus in densitatem cogant: denique psychrolutarum corpora densa ac veluti testea sentiuntur. convenit etiam arenae littorariae adhibendus fervor, tum natatio[15] maritima vel aquarum naturali virtute medentium; et in lavacris sudore perfecto asperginem salis adhibere, qua saepe condita caro ani-

133

134

135

---

[10] *an* particulatim?

[11] volutatio *S*: *corr. R*

[12] confrixio *S*: flictione *Rm*

[13] alternis *Rm*

[14] haterocopian *S*: hecaterocopian *Rm*   [15] natatio *R*: natatione *S*

this way the body's growth will not exceed its actual intake. The other form of treatment employs the cyclical regimen and drastic metasyncritic measures for the purpose of altering the state of the body. But in order that our meaning may be understood and our instructions clear, we shall set forth our treatment of the parts.

The body should be given continual passive exercise. For this purpose the movement of a small carriage drawn by a team of 133 animals is suitable; so also is riding on a horse or sailing. In addition, prescribe reading aloud; vigorous vocal exercise of the sort employed in practicing for contests in poetry and song; swift walking in order to exercise the calves of the legs; running; dry massage with bare hands or with a rough linen cloth, the body being sprinkled with sand; various types of vigorous exercise in the palaestra, including those called by the Greeks . . .[3] and *cōrycomachia*,[4] which in particular are prescribed by gymnastic trainers; *hoplomachia*, i.e., a mock battle with heavy armor;[5] physical training in which two participants are engaged, say wrestling or other forms of exercise for two (Greek *heterocopia*, 'exercise for two,' and *trachēlismos*, 'neck holds in wrestling'); exercise with the long traction device (Greek *macron* 134 *sparton*, 'long rope'); use of the Italian ball; swift wrestling; and vigorous and prolonged massage of the body, the massage to be dry, since it loses its vigor if the hands of the masseur become slippery with oil. Further, it is beneficial to bake the body in the sun (Greek *hēliōsis*); also to apply intense heat, using flames, hot coals, and dry steaming, in order to induce perspiration. Prescribe some hot baths, for these are very effective in reducing flesh, and also some cold baths, for these condense the body; in fact, the bodies of persons who bathe in cold water are found to be hard and like shells. In addition, let the patient bake 135 his body with the hot sand of the beach. Also prescribe swimming in the sea or in waters that have natural curative properties. And in the hot baths, after sweating is completed, have the

3. The reading is uncertain. If *celadian* ($<\kappa\dot{\epsilon}\lambda\alpha\delta$os), the reference would be to a sort of contest in shouting (so Vietmeier, p. 27). But some word derived from $\kappa\epsilon\rho\alpha\tau\dot{\iota}\zeta\epsilon\iota\nu$ or $\kappa\epsilon\lambda\eta\tau\dot{\iota}\zeta\epsilon\iota\nu$, referring to a kind of hockey or riding contest, respectively, may be involved here.

4. The term includes 'punching the bag' and performing various other exercises with a filled leather bag that is suspended. See Antyllus in Oribasius *Coll. Med.* vi. 33.

5. On this exercise see *ibid.* vi. 36.

malium ciborum voluptati[16] sicca servatur atque densior, nec collecta marcescit. tum fricamentum adhibendum, quod Graeci zegma[17] vocant, ex nitro tuso atque in pulverem redacto.

et post lavacrum longa cibi dilatio vel potus: tunc enim appetitio maxima[18] marcescit et eius acies temporis obtunditur dilatione, cum etiam digestionis parata protervitas detracto fomite languescit. erit praeterea potus semper ante cibum prohibendus, vel in toto parvus dandus, et magis cum cibi sumuntur.

136 etenim immisso liquore plurimo fluidantur accepta atque caro mollitur et digestione facile solidiora propriantur.[19] sed si plurimum quisquam sitierit, ⟨vinum⟩[20] parvum dabimus mediocriter asperum. pulmentum vero alicam, amylum, lac, nucleos, cerebrum, ova, pisces autem teneros vel pinguia quaeque reprobamus. panem dabimus frigidum fermentatum autopyrum: est enim minus nutriens, et magis si fuerit veteratus. specialiter autem siccus probandus est cibus. item pulmento danda sunt olera et pisces durioris naturae vel avium sicciora vel agrestium,

137 ut leporis, capreae, porcina ex deposito, hoc est longo tempore sale siccata. convenit praeterea unum cibum sumere, et post sumptionem plurimum vigilare, in requie quidem, quo multa corpus exhalatione insumatur vigilando. additur enim plurimum somno; denique dormientium corpus validius[21] fiet. potus dandus frigidus, et perseverante carnis multitudine erunt initia cycli adsumenda, nunc ab omni abstinentia, nunc a parvo cibo et aqua, nunc augmenta[22] ordine regulari. item a ieiuno vomitu sumendum est initium, vel ex radicibus; tunc ad drimyphagian veniendum ac mediae qualitatis materiam, tunc volantum atque

138 agrestium. quae quidem erunt celeranda per dies minoris brevi-

[16] voluptati *Rm*: voluntati *S* (*cf. 86*)

[17] *fort. scrib.* zmema (-ima) *aut* smegma (-igma)

[18] maxima *Rm*: minima *S*

[19] *fort.* appropriantur *Triller Clinotechnia 127*

[20] *add. R*

[21] uvidius *Rm*

[22] augenda *Rm*: *fort.* augendo

patient's body sprinkled with salt. (In fact, the flesh of animals is often treated in this way and then preserved dry until needed for food; it becomes hard and compact and does not decompose.) Then rub the patient's body with a cleansing preparation (Greek *smēgma*) of nitrum ground down and reduced to a powder.

After the bath, withhold food and drink for a long time. For then even the strongest appetite[6] is weakened and its keenness is blunted by the delay in giving food, since at first the digestion is all ready for action, but becomes languid when the tinder is withheld. Never permit the patient to drink before he takes food; let him drink only a little all together, and least of all while

136 food is being taken. For when a considerable amount of fluid is imbibed, the food that has been eaten is dissolved, the flesh is rendered soft; and solid foods are more readily assimilated by digestion. But if a patient is very thirsty, let him have a little moderately tart wine. Do not give him such foods as spelt groats, starch, milk, pine kernels, brains, eggs, tender fish, or any fatty foods.[7] Let him eat cold, leavened, whole-wheat bread, this being less nourishing, especially if it is stale. And give him dry food in particular; as a main dish give him vegetables, tough fish, the drier varieties of fowl or of game animals like

137 hare and roe, or preserved pork, i.e., salted pork that has been dried for a long time. It is best for the patient to take only one food and, after eating, to stay up a long while, even if resting, so that as he remains awake his body may be used up by continual exhalation. For the body undergoes considerable increase in sleep: thus, when a person sleeps his body becomes more robust. Let the patient have only cold drink; and if the obesity persists, institute the cyclical treatment, first withholding food altogether, then permitting a little food and water, and then making the increases according to the regular procedure. Also begin vomitive treatment, having the patient vomit when the stomach is empty; radishes may be used for this purpose. Then employ successively the diet of acrid foods, foods of the middle

138 class, fowl, and game animals. Do not prolong these diets, but

6. Or reading *minima* (*S*): 'the appetite is reduced to a minimum' or, possibly, 'even the smallest appetite is [further] weakened.'

7. Or, with a different punctuation, 'give him spelt groats ... eggs; but avoid tender fish, etc.' This seems a less probable interpretation because of *item pulmento danda*, below.

tatis, quo urgentius initia repetantur. et in oleribus erunt urinalia providenda, ut asparagus, pastinaca, apium, feniculus,
daucus, porri capitati, et horum similia. sic enim communia servantes corpus valebimus demutare, accidentium quoque coniec-
turam facientes, quo elimatio carnis atque diductio procedat.

aliqui medici phlebotomiam probant atque purgativa medicamina, quae catartica appellant, et clysterem, et post lavacrum
ilico venerem adhibendam ante cibum, atque ipsa die parvum
139 nutrimentum, poto aquam dandam; item vomitum post vespertinum cibum.²³ alii quoque veluti passioni contrariam corporis
expansionem ex thalamo fieri probaverunt, et appellant anti-
palon; itemque nocturni roris auram ante solis ortum bibendam.

sed horum deliratio manifestis proditur rebus. nam phlebotomia vires depurgatae vexantur, et corpora pannescunt,²⁴ nam
Graeci racosin vocant; item purgativis medicaminibus et²⁵ clysteribus, cum supradictis etiam liquida corrumpantur,²⁶ quo
malus²⁷ habitus corporis fiat, nam Graeci cachexian vocant.
venereus vero usus effeminat membra atque fortitudinem tollit.
140 item aliquibus bis in die ordinatum lavacrum et somnum²⁸ prius
quam cibus sumatur, quod quidam voluerunt. crassificat enim
somnus, non tenuat corpora. item vomitus post cibum: vires
enim tollunt, et quamquam corpori detrahant carnem, implent
tamen necessario caput atque sensuales vias vexant et gingivas
in putredinem mittunt atque os odore foedant²⁹ tetro,³⁰ stomachum limant et ipsum hominem sibimet faciunt displicere, nam
Graeci dysarescesin³¹ vocant, cum inaequalitate febrium vicina.
est et improprium atque prava ratione aestimatum ob corrup-
141 tionem³² parvorum³³ maiores corporis³⁴ vexationes inferre. sed
si forte ciborum³⁵ fuerit excessa moderatio, tunc erit vomitus

---

²³ cibum *conieci, coll. 140, 141*: vinum *edd.*

²⁴ pannescunt *Reinesius, coll. Ac. i. 86 (cf. Kühn 54)*: pallescunt *S*: flaccescunt *Rm*

²⁵ et *scripsi, coll. 138*: ex *edd.*

²⁶ corrumpuntur *R*

²⁷ quo malus *Rm*: cum alius *S*

²⁸ *fort.* somnus

²⁹ foetant *S*: *corr. Rm*

³⁰ tetro *Reinesius 675*: retro *S*   ³³ *fort.* parvarum

³¹ *fort. scrib.* dysarestesin   ³⁴ corpori *R*

³² *an* correctionem? *cf. Chr. i. 64; v. 128*   ³⁵ ciborum *Rm*: vinorum *S. cf. 139, 140*

employ them only for a few days, so that the cycles may be begun again and again at frequent intervals. Among the vegetables given to the patient include those with diuretic properties, e.g., asparagus, parsnip, parsley, fennel, wild carrot, scallions, and the like. In this way, by keeping in mind the general characteristics of the disease, we shall be able to promote metasyncrisis. But pay attention to the symptoms, too, and continue the reduction and thinning of the flesh.

Some physicians prescribe venesection, purgative drugs (*cathartica*), and the use of the clyster. Furthermore, they prescribe coitus immediately after a bath and before the patient takes food, and on that day they give only a little to eat and only 139 water to drink. And they induce vomiting after the evening meal. Again, other physicians prescribe stretching of the body after coitus, believing that this measure will serve as a counteragent (Greek *antipalos*) to the disease; and they order the patient to inhale the dewy night air just before dawn.

But the folly of all these physicians becomes clear when we consider the obvious facts. For venesection depletes and does injury to the bodily strength, and also causes a wrinkling of the body (Greek *rhacōsis*). Likewise purgative drugs and clysters have the same effect, causing, as they do, decomposition of the bodily fluids, so that an abnormal bodily condition results (Greek *cachexia*). Again, coitus weakens the parts of the body 140 and reduces the general strength. The same is true of the prescription of bathing twice a day and sleep before eating, as recommended by certain physicians in some cases. For sleep causes a thickening rather than a thinning of the body. Vomiting after eating [is also harmful], for the patient's strength is thereby impaired. And though the treatment reduces the amount of flesh on the body, still it always brings about congestion in the head, injures the sensory channels, causes rotting of the gums, affects the mouth with a foul odor, abrades the esophagus, and brings about in the patient a state of malaise (Greek *dysarestēsis*) and an indisposition like that found in cases of fever. Moreover, it is illogical and wrong to subject the body to great injury 141 to prevent the decomposition of a little food.[8] But if, as it happens, the patient has actually eaten an immoderate amount of food, vomiting should then be prescribed; for the weighing-down

8. Or reading *correctionem*: 'while seeking to remedy small defects.'

adhibendus: eius enim vexatione maior est immodicae sumptionis gravatio.

item prae ceteris vehemens, et maior quam ut oportet, animi officiis sive curis adplicatio. videmus ob has causas etiam studentium corpora fieri tenuiora limatione quadam animi iugium cogitationum atque disputationum; eorum vero qui segni ac pigro ductu vitam trahunt solidiora atque pleniora fieri corpora ob contrariam rationem.

his de superflua carne conscriptis, omnium tardarum passionum curationes explicavimus, intentione ⟨non⟩ [36] neglecta.

[36] *addidi* (*aliter fort.* perfecta *pro* neglecta)

of the body by excessive eating is more serious than the agitation caused by the remedy.

But it is most important in this disease to get the patient to apply himself intensively, indeed more so than is necessary, to mental concerns and problems. In fact, it is because of this type of application that studious persons generally have thin bodies, for they are continually sharpening their minds with thought and discussion. And for the opposite reason those who lead a lazy and inactive life generally have fuller and fatter bodies.

With this chapter on obesity we conclude our account of the treatment of all the chronic diseases, thus carrying out our purpose.

ADDITIONS AND CORRECTIONS

Page 160, line 4.—The reading *Philippum* should probably be retained, on the strength of Galen XVI. 684 and XVIIA. 640. In that case Philippus' error may consist in claiming priority either for the name *catochē* or for the recognition of the true nature of the disease. If *Chrysippum* be read, the reference is probably to the Asclepiadean, whose error would be in ascribing the term *catochē* to his sect, when Asclepiades himself used *cataleipsis*.

Page 375, line 24.—*Read* Charidemus.

Page 388, line 15, and page 476, line 7.—M. Wellmann is probably right in conjecturing that Soranus' text originally had *Lysimachus* rather than the otherwise unknown *Salimachus* or *Silimachus*. See *RE*, *s.v.* 'Lysimacho's,' 39.

Page 687, line 5.—The reference is to *De morbis* i. 14 (VI. 164 Littré).

Page 734, last line.—For *fico*, which gives an unsatisfactory sense, perhaps *foco* should be read.

INDEXES

INDEX OF NAMES

The date appended to a name marks the period when the person flourished. In accordance with the system employed by George Sarton in his *Introduction to the History of Science*, "I-2" indicates the second half of the first century after Christ; "III-1, B.C.," the first half of the third century before Christ; etc.

INDEX OF SUBJECTS

The list of chapters before each treatise gives a good indication of the contents of Caelius' work. In seeking out a particular item, it should be kept in mind that the order of discussion (though not the scope) within each disease is substantially the same (see p. xii).

The following Index is, of necessity, selective. An index which gave every occurrence of 'food,' 'fever,' or 'pain,' to cite but a few examples, would hardly be of sufficient use to the general reader to justify its bulk. Again, only relatively few of the foods, drugs, and substances mentioned by Caelius are included here. A complete index (Greek, Latin, and English) of these and of anatomical and other medical terms would be desirable, to complete the work begun by Karl Vietmeier; but it was not feasible to include this material in the present volume.